HANDBOOK OF PHYSIOLOGY

SECTION 1: The Nervous System, VOLUME III, PART 1

HANDBOOK OF PHYSIOLOGY

A critical, comprehensive presentation

of physiological knowledge and concepts

SECTION 1: The Nervous System

Formerly SECTION 1: Neurophysiology

VOLUME III.

Sensory Processes, Part 1

Section Editors: JOHN M. BROOKHART
VERNON B. MOUNTCASTLE

Volume Editor: IAN DARIAN-SMITH

Executive Editor: STEPHEN R. GEIGER

American Physiological Society, BETHESDA, MARYLAND, 1984

Library of Congress Catalog Card Number 78-315957

International Standard Book Number 0-683-01108-1

Printed in the United States of America by Waverly Press, Inc., Baltimore, Maryland 21202

Distributed by The Williams & Wilkins Company, Baltimore, Maryland 21202

Preface

This volume on *Sensory Processes* aims to provide a comprehensive, balanced account of current knowledge of the neural mechanisms that enable us to sense the world around us. Of course, no two views of what is important in the mass of observation and conjecture on these sensory processes will be the same. It is expected, however, that most readers seeking information and insight into particular sensory events in mammals, and especially in primates, will find what they are looking for in this volume. Rightly, there is some overlap in the scope of *Sensory Processes* and the two previous volumes of the *Handbook—Cellular Biology of Neurons*, edited by Eric R. Kandel, and *Motor Control*, edited by Vernon B. Brooks. Necessarily in a many-authored volume of manageable size, some aspects of sensory function have been only partially considered in each of several different sections rather than within a single cohesive chapter; fortunately, coverage of this type is infrequent in this volume.

Excepting Jung's chapter on the historical and philosophical perspectives of sensory research, the chapters in this volume are mainly concerned with advances in knowledge made over the twenty years since the publication in 1959 and 1960 of the first edition of the *Handbook* volumes on the nervous system, a notable scientific landmark. I clearly remember being astonished and delighted by three chapters relevant to my particular research interests as a young postdoctoral fellow. These were J. A. B. Gray's account of receptor function, Rose and Mountcastle's chapter on the somatic senses, and Hans Lucas Teuber's chapter on perception. All three chapters can still be read with profit: each, in intellectual terms, was well ahead of current thinking in 1960, and each contains important and relevant comment and speculation. To a postdoctoral fellow working in a laboratory intensely concerned with synaptic transmission and its detail, Teuber's chapter was probably the most disturbing of the three. At that time few sensory physiologists, while trying hard to record impulses from single neurons on the central nervous system of the deeply anesthetized cat, dared to avert the eyes from the face of the oscilloscope to look at the animal's or human subject's everyday sensory behavior. Fortunately, that bias has substantially changed in the intervening years, as is seen in the pages that follow. It is hoped that these pages will have some of the impact that was achieved by the earlier *Handbook* volumes on the nervous system.

The plan of this volume is straightforward. The first chapter by Jung gives historical perspective to what follows: its subjects range across Western culture and span more than two millennia, including the thirteenth century Emperor Frederick II's instructions for imprinting the hunting falcon, as well as the philosophical concepts of Kant and others that have shaped much of the experimental study of sensory processes from the seventeenth century to the present. Chapters 2, 3, and 4, by Hochberg, by Galanter, and by Stebbins, Brown, and Petersen, are concerned with the substance and measure of sensory behavior in both man and experimental animals. The goal of this section of the volume is to direct the reader to a detailed and quantitative consideration of sensory behavior whenever particular neural processes that relate to this behavior are being considered.

In chapter 5 on the thalamocortical complex and in chapter 6 on the brain stem reticular formation Jones and Scheibel, respectively, consider the structural organization of two of the more complex regions of the mammalian central nervous system that have, among their other functions, an important role in the sensing of the world around us.

Most of the remaining sections of the volume, which together form its greater part, present a systematic survey of our current knowledge of the neural bases of vision, hearing, somatic sensation, and the chemical senses. In each of these sections the emphasis on sensory performance and its correlation with neural events is sustained.

Investigations of the neural mechanisms of vision have flourished in the last 20 years and have been the focus of inquiry in many laboratories. Yellott, Wandell, and Cornsweet discuss in detail the formation of the retinal image and some of the retinal factors that determine visual acuity, color vision, and adaptation to changes in ambient illumination. In considering retinal function Dowling and Dubin emphasize its synaptic organization and neuronal circuitry. Bishop examines the transmission of visual information within the retinostriate system, systematically comparing the responses of distinctive neuron types at successive levels within this system in the cat and monkey. In their chapter De Valois and Jacobs review the neural processing of information about the spectral content of a visual stimulus and how these responses are modified by other features, such as intensity of the visual stimulus. Schiller's chapter complements these reviews, particularly that of Bishop, by considering the role of the superior colliculus in vision. Finally, Mitchell and Timney examine the postnatal development of visual perception and the mediating neuronal mechanisms and explore how this may be shaped by various types of visual deprivation.

In their extensive chapter introducing the section on hearing Green and Wier focus on auditory perception. They assess the different theories of space, pitch, and loudness perception, but in particular they consider the capacities of a subject to detect and discriminate the features of acoustic stimuli. Signal detection theory, previously developed by Green and Swets, substantially shapes their presentation of auditory perception. Dallos reviews the mechanisms of the outer and middle ear and particularly the inner ear in an analysis of the recent elegant studies of transduction processes in the organ of Corti and the mechanoelectric environment in which these processes occur. All the information about the auditory world that a subject can use must be represented in the activity in the fiber populations of the auditory nerves; Kiang examines the representation of this information in the responses of single auditory nerve fibers and in populations of these fibers. The concluding chapter on hearing deals with the central processing of acoustic information. Aitkin, Irvine, and Webster systematically examine those populations of neurons that signal this information from the cochlear nuclei to the neocortex.

A fascinating, unique reflection of the development of knowledge of sensory processes over the past 20 years comes from comparing the chapters on touch and kinesthesis in the first edition of this *Handbook* with those in the present volume. Mountcastle wrote the earlier chapter with Rose in 1958–59 and also wrote the matching chapter in this volume. In 1959 there was still an immense gap between observations on sensory behavior and experimental studies of the determinant events in the central nervous system. The latter were all done in anesthetized animals, and the earliest studies of single-neuron responses in the thalamus and postcentral gyrus of the cerebral cortex were just being reported. It was evident from these latter studies of Mountcastle that we would soon obtain new insight into the central processing of sensory information, and of course this was to become the signature of the 1960s. The next technically important step, the recording of unitary activity in the monkey's cerebral cortex while the animal performed a specific sensorimotor task, was developed by Evarts (1966–67), and this set investigators in a new direction. Combining this procedure with increasing attention in the laboratory to the measurement of the monkey's performance, and to changes in the behavioral state of the animal, has opened up fresh problems that could not have been seriously considered for study in 1960. Finally, the powerful new neuroanatomical techniques for tracing pathways, for analyzing synaptic organization, and for defining regional metabolic activity already provide a flood of new data that have yet to be assimilated into our thinking about sensory processes. Perl's chapter on pain illustrates with clarity the great value of combining these new methods in the study of a field that in the past proved so intractable.

The chapter by Goldberg and Fernandez and the chapter by Young concern the perception of the body in space and some underlying mechanisms. Then two aspects of the chemical senses have been selected for detailed review: McBurney considers the psychophysics of taste and olfaction, and Norgren examines the central processing of information about the taste of a substance. This survey of sensory processes is completed by a chapter on the functional asymmetry of the human cerebrum, written by Trevarthen.

One critical problem, yet to be resolved, is the analysis of the transmission of sensory information by populations of neurons responding to a common stimulus. Correlating the responses of single neurons with behavioral events is a truly major advance, but alone it can convey only part of the story of sensory processing. Full specification of the activity of populations of sensory neurons in responding to a common input is the major immediate challenge in this field.

In editing the present volume I have learned much neuroscience and much about neuroscientists. It would have been difficult indeed to have brought together a more dedicated, enthusiastic, and patient group of contributors than the authors of the chapters in this volume. There were frustrations for every contributor: tolerating a carping volume editor's comment and enduring the many delays that have occurred were the more irritating of these. I am convinced, however, that the final scholarly product has more than compensated for these frustrations and delays, and I trust the reader will find this to be so.

I am most grateful for the continued guidance and support that the Section Editors, John M. Brookhart and Vernon B. Mountcastle, provided over the several years of preparation of this volume.

IAN DARIAN-SMITH
Volume Editor

Contents

Sensory research in historical perspective: some philosophical foundations of perception

R I C H A R D   J U N G | *Albert-Ludwigs-Universität, Freiburg, West Germany*

CHAPTER CONTENTS

Das Wissen versteht sich in seiner Geschichte.
K. Jaspers (201)

THIS CHAPTER PRESENTS a description of some of the origins and philosophical foundations of the sensory sciences and traces their historical development. It may be useful for the sensory physiologist to know something about the theoretical bases in history and philosophy in order to better understand present-day concepts. Sensory science cannot ignore its past. The historical roots can only be understood with some reference to the cultural tradition and the zeitgeist. Hence, in addition to philosophy, some preconditions of research in culture and religion must be mentioned.

In antiquity and during the Middle Ages remarkable theoretical concepts about perception were proposed, but experimental control was lacking and the interrelationship with philosophy and religious symbolism made the problems too complex for scientific verification. With the rise of science after the Renaissance, systematic observations, measurements, and mathematical solutions led to a focusing on special research problems. Scientists learned to pose restricted questions about sensory mechanisms that were soluble by observation and experiment. This corresponds to a methodological reduction in effective research that is different from philosophical reductionism. However, methodological restriction of research procedures does not mean that the sensory scientist must be a specialist. On the contrary, the problems of specialized research should be enlarged by general theories and viewed in their context with results obtained by other methods. Hence, different approaches such as subjective sensory experiences must be compared with objective recordings of sensory mechanisms. Historical perspectives of perceptual research may help to find these connections in the diversity of the sensory sciences.

In this chapter, I expect to show that correlations

among various research procedures may compensate for the necessary methodological restrictions in specific areas of sensory research.

SENSORY SCIENCE AND PHILOSOPHY

In the course of more than two thousand years innumerable philosophical concepts have been developed to explain perception and sensory functions; only a few of them can be discussed here. Many philosophies will not appeal to the sensory physiologist, and some may even appear absurd to him when they contradict the results of the sensory sciences. Pure speculations and unclear abstractions and extreme concepts, such as radical idealism and solipsism (with its denial of the existence of the real world), may be passed in silence. This does not imply, however, that philosophical thought is useless for scientists. On the contrary it appears necessary to know some of the historical roots and general philosophical concepts from which modern science has developed and to discuss theories of perception that may compensate for the esoteric isolation of specialist research.

Perception and Theory

Perception is based upon anticipatory attention and the integration of many sensory mechanisms, and it represents their final synthesis. This integration is experienced subjectively as a percept. The integrative processes of perception cannot be understood without theories. The notion of sensory physiology as a science collecting many barren facts about sensory mechanisms is unsatisfactory and incorrect. In a world of progressive specialization and immense accumulation of information on sensory functions there is a need for theory and for problem-centered research. Theoretical concepts allow a synthesis of hypotheses and facts and have their place in physiology as in all sciences. Every physiologist must use his reasoning powers to plan good experiments. For this purpose he must think, use philosophical speculation, and know some general and a priori principles before he can solve his special problem. This of course, does not mean that he has to create general theories about the mind-body problem in perception. I am sorry to disagree with my old friend Eccles when I say that the mind-body question can remain unanswered in our branch of science. It may even be unanswerable for the neuroscientist; and yet philosophical reflection can help him to find a suitable theory for his research problem. Even when problems appear to be aporias (i.e., insoluble problems) it is still worthwhile to speculate about them and to build hypotheses for future experiments. So Popper and Eccles's concept (310) of *The Self and Its Brain*—even if one does not accept their mind-body dualism—may be useful in raising questions that can be answered by appropriate perceptual research. It

may also help in questioning other assumptions that have been taken for granted by naive sensory physiologists and positivistic philosophers.

In the following pages I discuss those philosophical concepts that I have personally found useful for research in perception. Among these are Kant's synthesis of empirical and rational knowledge and Nicolai Hartmann's level concepts of the world and the sciences. In admitting this bias I fully appreciate that others may prefer different philosophical positions. Every scientist should select what is useful for his work and find his own pragmatic way to combine theory and experiment.

Perceptual Research and History

In the historical sections of this chapter I concentrate on ancient philosophy and on the sixteenth to the eighteenth centuries, the time when the basic concepts of modern science were developed. I am deliberately brief and selective in discussing the nineteenth century for the following reason: Boring's (52) monograph, which appeared in 1942, gives an excellent survey of the history of sensory physiology and its cultural background from 1800 to 1920 that cannot be surpassed by modern authors. So the English reader must use this classic book for orientation on the predominantly German literature that founded sensory physiology, psychophysics, and psychology during the last century. I restrict my sections on recent perceptual research to comment on some points of this period that were somewhat neglected in Boring's book and on relations to modern objective sensory physiology.

In this chapter I use the term *perception* in a general sense to include "sensations" and to represent both conscious and behavioral responses to sensory stimuli. Hence I avoid the classic distinction between perception (*Wahrnehmung*) and sensation (*Empfindung*) that has been traditional in German sensory physiology since the time of Helmholtz (164) and von Kries (234). It was doubted by Gestalt psychologists but still adopted by Boring (52). Modern physiology has also cast doubt on the existence of "elementary" or "simple" sensations, since complex neuronal processing begins in the retina and inner ear, at least for vision and audition. So even records obtained from visual or auditory nerves cannot be regarded as equivalents of primary sensory messages. "Simple sensations" are hypothetical abstractions for which neither physiological nor psychological equivalents are known. All sensory messages received by the central nervous system are highly elaborated neuronal processes and are still more so after the first stages of cerebral processing. Hence the existence of elementary sensations postulated by ancient authors and later by Wundt (380) is uncertain. Leibniz's (243) *petites perceptions* include preconscious sensory processing, and his term *apperception* for higher perceptual events has scarcely been used in recent times.

HISTORICAL ROOTS. A short retrospect of the history of perceptual sciences from antiquity to modern times shows some characteristic aspects of the different cultural periods. The classical Greeks attempted general explanations of perception embedded in philosophical systems and related to cosmological views. In the late Roman time a chaos of many competing philosophies and religions was superseded by the Christian church and transformed into a conformist dogmatic attitude. During the dark centuries and the Middle Ages research was motivated by religion and the Christian church's ideological striving for divine grace, as shown in the writings on optics by ecclesiastic authors. During the Renaissance new philosophical concepts of world order and harmony arose. They motivated research in gradually supplementing the Christian principles of the Middle Ages. Specialization began in the selection of methods and procedures. This resulted in a restriction of inquiry to soluble problems. In the seventeenth century, however, the main advances originated not for sensory specialists but from universal scientists such as Kepler, Galileo, Descartes, and Newton. Their concepts again stimulated detailed research in specific fields. During the eighteenth and nineteenth centuries new research procedures with the use of modern techniques and experimental quantification caused a split into different sciences, each conducted by specialists. This increasing specialization could only partly be supplemented by theoretical concepts that yielded synthetic views. Like science, philosophy itself had a long path to tread in order to become independent of Church ideology and theological doctrines. But this autonomy turned academic philosophy in a wrong direction. During the nineteenth century and the beginning of this century philosophy lost contact with the natural sciences. The homemade philosophies of some scientists were not sufficient in quality to combat the philosophical segregation that avoided discussions with natural scientists and hindered research continuity with science. Only few modern philosophers such as Nicolai Hartmann and Karl Popper had enough knowledge of the biological and physical sciences to build up their philosophy in close relation to modern science.

Perception and Preparation for Action

Since antiquity the interrelation of perception, cognition, and action has been considered important, but physiology has yet to explain the underlying mechanisms. Some biocybernetic models such as von Holst's reafference principle (186, 188) have not yet found a physiological correlate, and other hypothetical concepts still wait for experimental verification or are too general, as with Claude Bernard's concept of human endeavor. He said in his general physiology (43) that human beings have the faculty of foreseeing and acting in the environment: *prévoir et agir* are the behavioral characteristics of human activity in life and science.

Bernard's concepts have some relation to those theories of perception that accentuate the intentional anticipation and modeling functions of perceptual processes as a preparation for active behavior. These are described in the last part of this chapter, but a brief discussion of abstraction and attention in perceptually guided action may be given as an introduction.

SENSORY SIGNALS, INTEGRATION, AND ABSTRACTION. Perception is built up from many sensory messages, including multisensory convergence and association. It is related to sensorimotor coordination and to intentional motor acts; the latter is most evident in vision and eye movements. This complex integration occurs in both attentive behavior and cognitive processing; in human beings it is essential for perception and recognition at higher levels such as speech, reading, and writing. Perception is a synthesis of sensory information processing and an abstraction from the real world. The neurosciences have cleared many details of the mechanisms of sensory processing but have taught us very little about perceptual integration and the coordination of perception and action. Only a few data of multisensory neuronal convergence (210), cross-modal integration in behavior (256), and cognition by action (160, 161) are known. On the other hand, philosophy and psychology have, for more than 2,000 years, accumulated many theories about perceptual conditions a priori (i.e., by innate functions of mind and brain) and a posteriori (i.e., by experience and by learning from sensory information). These are preserved in cultural tradition of the humanities and show somewhat neglected analogues with the biological sciences. The philosophical intention of Kant to synthetize innate order and experienced perception, and to demonstrate the limits of perceptual knowledge of the real world as phenomena, may have some parallels in physiology (207). Many physiologists have recognized that the senses deliver only some signs of reality: Helmholtz (164) called them *Zeichen der Aussenwelt* and Pavlov (297) used the term *signale*. In 1943 Kenneth Craik (74) formulated a precybernetic concept of perception and cognition: the brain produces a model of the real world. In 1947 Adrian (6) wrote that man produces "a small-scale model of external reality and of its own possible actions." Mountcastle (286) said in 1975: "Sensation is an abstraction not a replication of the real world." To understand perception and action we must add that an abstracted world model leads to the anticipation of percepts and intended actions.

PERCEPTION, ATTENTION, AND ACTION. Percepts are not merely passive imprints of sensory stimulation on brain activity but arise also from an active search for sensory information. This involves a complex of physiological regulation, exploratory behavior, and psychological set. The interrelations of sensation, attention, expectation, and action are essential processes to understand conscious perception in both physiology and psychology. Since these processes of sensorimotor coordination and willed acts are related to perception by many philosophies from antiquity to modern times, the characteristics of the anticipatory act that prepares perception and action are discussed later with some historical sources (see PERCEPTION AND ACTION, p. 57). Knowing the role of attention, anticipation, judgment, or action that is involved in human percepts, one may understand some historical trends of perceptual research and philosophies of perception and knowledge, which include will and action. The essentials of Kant's concept that perception is made possible by our own mental apparatus, and the ordering of sensory signals in time and space, can be better understood when we accept the active participation of brain structures as preconditions of perceptual processing. Mountcastle's recent work on neuronal mechanisms of directed attention in monkeys (286) and my own experiments on visual attention and eye movements in man (86, 208) demonstrate some neurophysiological correlations of perceptual abstraction and attentive action.

In these pages some historical surveys are referred to, but I have avoided a bibliography of secondary sources that would be more expertly made by historians of science. I have thought it better to cite the results of some of the great innovators of the seventeenth, eighteenth, and nineteenth centuries from their original work rather than give a pedantic enumeration of many names and dates. A few anecdotal additions may characterize the historical context. I omit anatomical studies and mention only a few morphological findings in instances where these are significant in relation to perception and behavior. I expect thus to explain some of the origins and influences that have been instrumental in forming the scientific tradition on which the perceptual sciences are based. Where possible, the most important sources are quoted from the original editions or, for Greek authors, from good Latin, English, or German translations.

GREEK SCIENCE AND ANTIQUITY

Western science and philosophy has its origin in the classical Greek civilization of the fifth and fourth centuries B.C. In a historical chapter on the development of the sensory sciences, therefore, these roots of modern thinking in antiquity must be considered. For details the treatises on the history of philosophy (373, 385) and of science (76) may be consulted, along with other books on the subject for the general reader (319).

Early Greek Philosophy and the Origin of Science

GREEK SCIENCE AND CULTURE. Philosophy, science, and art had much closer relations in ancient Greece than in our modern civilization. An important scientific and artistic evolution began around 500 B.C. when the cities of the Mediterranean coasts from Asia Minor to Sicily and Southern Italy were a multicentered community of Greek language and culture. In the fifth century B.C. the great philosophers in the Ionian cities developed their systematized concepts of the world that replaced the old mythological cosmologies. Simultaneous innovations appeared in the arts, as for example the new forms of tragedy founded in Athens by Aeschylus, who introduced a second actor with dialogues into the theatre in 465 B.C. At the same time Greek sculpture changed its rigid archaic style from strong frontal or profile aspects toward postures in counterpoise and expression of movement. These simultaneous changes in different aspects of the Greek culture certainly were not fortuitous but evolved from common sources, and in turn new fields of philosophy, science, and art developed from them.

The cultural innovations of the fifth century, facilitated after the short Greek triumph and the victories over the Persian invasions of 490–480 B.C., were followed by four centuries of cultural development, in spite of the disastrous effects of civil war between the Greek cities. After the defeat of Athens by Sparta this spiritual movement continued during the Hellenistic period between 330 and 200 B.C. The great political success of Alexander's conquest of the Persian empire and the penetration of Hellenistic culture into Egypt and India were followed by political decline. Greek science, however, continued to progress even after the Roman conquest of Greece and then to dominate Roman science.

PRE-SOCRATIC SCIENTISTS. The early Greek philosophers of the sixth and fifth centuries, usually called *pre-Socratic*, lived in the Ionian cities of Asia minor. Most of them were more notable for cosmological, astronomical, and physical concepts than for their sensory science, but Democritus, who deserves the more detailed report that follows, was the exception. The earliest, Thales of Miletus (flourishing around 600 B.C.), became famous by his prediction of the solar eclipse dated 587 B.C. and taught that water was the original substance from which all matter and life developed. Among the later pre-Socratic philosophers, Pythagoras, Heraclitus, and Empedocles developed concepts that were important for science.

Pythagoras appears to be one of the most interesting of these early philosophers. A native of Samos who flourished around 530 B.C. in Croton, he combined the qualities of a good mathematician and a religious mystic. A similar coexistence of exact science and mysticism is apparent in the character of Empedocles and later can be found in medieval authors and post-Renaissance scientists such as Kepler and Newton. The strange teaching of the Pythagorean sect mixed precise explanations of the mathematical basis of tones and music with a belief in transmigration of the soul and other incredible superstitions that need not be described here. In my opinion, the most important idea of Pythagoras—besides his mathematical discoveries—is his concept that the same logical and mathematical principles apply both to the analysis of material nature and to the mind. This point has not been sufficiently stressed in the histories of philosophy. The same general rules apply for quantification in physics, physiology, and psychology. So Galileo's exact physical measurement has a forerunner in Pythagoras; the Pythagorean statements that the same laws govern knowledge and reality preceded by 2,500 years those similar modern concepts of the philosophy of science developed by Nicolai Hartmann and Karl Popper in our century.

The other great pre-Socratic figure, Heraclitus of Ephesus, taught that unity results from diversity and that opposites may combine in strife ("war the father of all things"). Hence a dialectic synthesis of different theses is possible. This concept of a developing and continuously changing world was modified by Empedocles for the emotional antagonism of strife and love, and it reappears in the nineteenth century in Fichte's and Hegel's principles of philosophy: the synthesis of thesis and antithesis. Heraclitus's opposite forces, combined to produce motion, may be considered as an embryonic idea of the antagonist functions in motor and sensory physiology that were developed after the Renaissance. One can compare them to Sherrington's principle of reciprocal innervation of agonists and antagonists in locomotion (328) that had been conceived in principle by Descartes in the seventeenth century (see Fig. 10), and to Hering's *Gegenfarben* concept in vision (172, 174), already foreseen by Leonardo about 1500 (see COLOR AND VISUAL CONTRAST, p. 21).

An interesting pre-Darwinian idea of the survival of the fittest was taught by Empedocles, who flourished about 440 B.C. in Sicily and put his philosophy in a poetic form. Nevertheless, this hypothesis was not taken up seriously as a condition for biological evolution until the last century. More influential were his ideas of Chance and Necessity and Strife and Love as antagonist principles of mixtures of four elements in a changing world.

I refrain from mentioning the pantheism of Anaxagoras and the Eleatic school with their generalization and simplification of the variety of nature. None of these interesting and often exciting theories were followed up by experimental or observational verification, at least not in perceptual research and biological sciences. As Russell (319) remarks in his clear but sometimes simplifying manner, "There was no very sharp distinction, in ancient times, between empirical observation and logical argument." From Pythagoras onward to Plato the Greeks used exact mathematical proofs in geometry and applied them to astronomy, but never to the sciences of life and rarely to practical technology. Archimedes (287–212 B.C.), who made quantitative physical and engineering experiments, was quite exceptional.

Hippocratic Medicine and Democritian Materialism

During the second half of the fifth century B.C. Greek medicine and science and philosophy developed to a height of achievement that was paralleled by classical art. The most important trends were the realistic medicine of Hippocrates, the materialism of Democritus, and the Socratic school in Athens. The first two offer more for physiological applications than the latter.

HIPPOCRATIC CONCEPT OF THE BRAIN. Hippocrates (ca. 460–ca. 380 B.C.), the most famous medical author of antiquity, lived on the island Kos; he was mainly interested in practical medicine, including epilepsy, which he asserted to be a cerebral disease. His notions of brain function are more akin to modern concepts than those of any other Greek scientist. Nevertheless, his writings, which are preserved in the *Corpus Hippocraticum* (180), had surprisingly little influence on the concepts of the main scientific schools in the Greek cities.

Describing the sensations and emotional symptoms such as fear experienced by patients during the epileptic aura, Hippocrates postulated that these originate in the brain. Of course, he did not yet attempt a brain localization of sensory functions such as Hughlings Jackson in the nineteenth century and Foerster and Penfield in this century achieved by comparing the epileptic aura and the site of the associated focal brain lesion. Hippocrates said only that pain can sometimes be felt on one side or the other of the head, and he related this to the two cerebral hemispheres, without mentioning contralateral projections. He apparently was referring to the hemicranial attacks of migraine. In stressing the natural cause of epilepsy as a cerebral disease he rejected the belief in its divine origin as a sacred disease.

Some quotations may give an impression of his statements: He says that "eye, ears, tongue, hands, and feet act in accordance with the discernment of the brain." From this he argues against the localization of thought and emotion in the heart and claimed that the brain is the "interpreter of consciousness." He asserts: "Pleasures, joys, laughter, and jests as well as sorrows, pain, griefs, and tears originate in the brain." "Through the brain we think, see, hear, and distinguish the ugly from the beautiful, the bad from the good, the pleasant from the unpleasant." As symptoms of a diseased brain he mentions: "Dread and fear ... sleeplessness ... anxieties, and acts that are contrary to habit .... These things that we suffer all come from the brain, when it is not healthy."

All these remarkable insights were written by Hippocrates in the fifth century B.C. as a contemporary of Socrates and Plato. But the scientists and philosophers in the fourth century B.C., such as Aristotle and his schools, developed different theories on brain function without regard to Hippocrates' writings.

DEMOCRITIAN ATOMISM AND SENSORY FUNCTIONS. Democritus flourished around 430–420 B.C. in Abdera, Thrace, after having traveled widely in Egypt and the East. His views of nature are surprisingly modern, being most akin to nineteenth century concepts in the natural sciences, and are of great interest to physiologists. In his magnum opus of Greek philosophy Zeller (385) ranks Democritus more highly than the other Greek philosophers of this or earlier periods for his wealth of knowledge, sharp intellect, and logical thinking.

Democritus's famous theory of moving atoms as the basic matter of the world and his postulate that qualitative knowledge should be defined and controlled in quantitative terms are his most noteworthy general principles. His axiom that both chance and necessity are the bases of evolution has been used recently by Monod (282) for his biological philosophy.

Unfortunately, Democritus's writings are known to us only indirectly by their titles, contents, and fragments through the reports of Aristotle and others. Nearly all of the 298 authentic fragments of Democritus quoted by different authors (Diels Nos. 1–298 in ref. 87) concern general rules of life and conduct. They give little information about his concepts of sensory functions, so that the following sketch of his teachings is based on indirect sources, such as the references made by historians of philosophy to many ancient authors' descriptions of Democritus's concepts.

Only the titles and chapter headings of Democritus's books were preserved (see ref. 87, vol. I, p. 357–358). Among these the *Physica* is the most interesting book for physiologists. In it he first propounds his atomic theory and describes the micro- and macrocosmos and then in special chapters treats the patterns of nature, the human body, mind, and perception through the *eidola*. Only four of the verbal quotations preserved from this book [Diels Nos. 7–9 and 11 (87) and also one from an unknown source] concern sensory function and knowledge. In these Democritus said, "The senses do not show real things indubitably [Diels No. 8 (87)], but only selected perceptual small images of them, modified by our concepts." (*doxis*, ref. 87, No. 7) He also stated (No. 11) that the five senses must first be refined in order to become "genuine knowledge." Nevertheless, it remains uncertain from this fragment whether Democritus meant that this process of searching (*zetein*) for more accurate and reliable knowledge is in fact the central processing of the sensory signals, or only the final conscious judgment of the mind itself. The latter appears more probable, since he called sensation (*aisthesis*) confused or obscure (*skotios*), and called thought (*dianoia*) genuine (*gnesios*).

To explain perception in general he said that many small images (*eidola*) from the external world are received through the senses and are processed and integrated in thinking. Ideas were for Democritus—in contrast to Plato—perceptual gestalten or schemes, which originate from empirical percepts. From this he derived theories about the real world that he regarded as being independent of perception and that should be explored by scientific methods to investigate atomic movements.

Democritus explained vision and light rays as movements of the air that travel from the object to the eye, and not in the opposite direction as ocular emanation to the object seen, as conceived by Plato. According to Democritus the different modalities and qualities of sensation not only result from transformation in the sense organs, but are also, at least in the case of colors, determined by the atomic structure of the stimuli. Democritus distinguished four simple colors, among them white and black. It remains uncertain whether he also had a general concept of opponent spectral colors. He explained white and black by opposite properties of bright and dark objects, but no theory of spectral colors is to be found among the preserved fragments of his writings.

Democritus stated that we do not perceive constant remote stimuli but only the changing conditions of the external world that affect the sense organs or act directly on the body, and that all these processes are atomic movements. Sensory stimuli are perceived according to the actual state of our body and the responses of the sense organs. In another reported statement Democritus said that sensory percepts are conventions and do not correspond exactly to real things. However, Democritus stressed his opinion that the mind is dependent on perception. In an imaginary dialogue he lets the senses reproach the mind: "Poor reason [*phren*], you draw all evidence from our sensory messages and yet you assume to be superior to us, but your victory will lead to your defeat." [Diels (87) No. 125.]

Democritus developed a materialistic concept of the world based on the mechanics of atoms. He enlarged his atomic theory to construct mechanical models of the living and inorganic world, but we do not know enough of his work to understand how he defined and distinguished organic and inorganic structures. He taught that only causal connections without final purpose exist in the real world of inanimate structures and living organisms. Stressing the causality of interaction, he developed a strong determinism. Hence, his psychology left little chance for free will. He taught that all percepts and thoughts are secondary and can be explained, like all matter, by primary physical events: the mind consists of atoms. That which appears intellectually as qualitative relations can be reduced in physical terms to quantitative states. However, his reductionism still recognized psychic contents as phenomena and ideas. According to Aristotle's report Democritus taught to *diasozein ta phainomena* (to discern perceptive phenomena) and to define the phenomenal world as dependent on an ordered physical world. Thought is the means by which the true causes of real things and mental events are realized to be form and movements of atoms.

In spite of his materialism Democritus distinguished two kinds of experienced reality, the perceived phenomena and the thought rationalities. He said that a perceiving individual recognizes single and special objects, but a thinking man determines general knowledge at a higher level, so that his conclusions may also be valid for others. In this thought concept Democritus was less opposed to his contemporary Socrates and the subsequent system of Plato than the later atomists.

Democritus did not reject the world of the senses in favor of a spiritual world of thought, as did Plato, but he tried to investigate the material basis of sensory and rational knowledge. It appears that he influenced Aristotle to direct his attention to nature and reality.

For Democritus the real world is composed of moving atoms that are also responsible for sensations and small images (*eidola*) of real things. The atoms are not perceived as such by the senses, and the sense organs also consist of atoms and are moved by them. With these basic concepts he had less mistrust of sensory information than all earlier Greek philosophers and the members of Plato's Athenian school; nonetheless he also postulated sensory processing of the eidola by reason. He had an empiricist's concept of sensory information that is processed in the mind. Because of his recognition of reason, Democritus cannot be classified as a pure materialist but as an early sensualistic empiricist—i.e., a man who derives human knowledge from sensory experience.

Democritus's concept of sensory functions has some link with modern physiology. He conceived a theory of the senses that may be regarded as a precursor of Johannes Müller's law of specific sense energy, published 2,300 years later. Democritus taught that the various sensory modalities are determined by special functions of the sense organs and that their sensory messages are not a simple function of stimulus quality. He was as far from having a naive belief that sensory information gives a true image of the world as from having an idealist's doubt of reality.

POST-DEMOCRITIAN MATERIALISM AND EPICUREANISM. During and after the Hellenistic period, when Greek culture expanded with Alexander's success in 333 B.C., its philosophy and science became dominant in the Western world and Democritian ideas gained great influence in Athens and Rome. The Greek and Roman atomists developed further the concept of a materialistic world of moving atoms founded by Leucippus and Democritus. Epicurus (341–270 B.C.) came from Samos to Athens and lived there in a garden for 37 years, teaching his disciples the pleasure of a harmonious simple life found in friendship. His books are not preserved, but the Latin version of his teaching by Lucretius (259) gives a good survey. Although Epicurus did not recognize his dependence on Democritus, he gave clear and systematic formulations of his ideas and enlarged their validity into a sphere of ethics. As far as we know Democritus gave only general rules of behavior and made few ethical conclusions based on his atomic theory, but the fame of Epicurus and his school rests on this application to human life. During late Roman antiquity Epicureanism became the most influential philosophy in opposition to Stoicism. (See EPICUREAN ATOMISM IN ROME, p. 9, and STOICISM, p. 10.)

Aristotle and the School of Athens

SOCRATIC AND PLATONIC CONCEPTS. Socrates (469–399 B.C.) taught in the streets and in the market place of Athens or privately, but he did not write books. So Plato (306) wrote down his opinions in the form of dialogues. From these and other reports Socrates appears as an influential teacher of a group of Athenian intellectuals, as a rationalist who overrated the force of intellectual knowledge and insight on drive and emotions. He objected to the teaching of the sophist Protagoras, namely, that knowledge is only acquired by perception and that man is the measure of all things; but in Plato's dialogue *Theaetetus* (306) Socrates admitted that human knowledge stems from sensory information and stressed the role of memory and reflection, which he regarded as more important for knowledge than the senses.

Plato (428–348 B.C.) lived in Athens and founded its Academy, after a sojourn in Syracuse during which he had failed in an attempt to convert the tyrant Dionysius to his state theory. His influence on Greek, Latin, and Renaissance philosophy was strong and long lasting. Although recognizing some functions of the brain, he assigned psychic functions and their location to various parts of the body. According to this theory drives originated in the diaphragm, emotion in the heart, and thought in the brain. The soul was believed to be immortal and rather independent of the body, as in the Christian dogma. Although he compared the soul to the eye, Plato preferred the world of ideas to the realm of sensory perception (306, 373).

In his famous parable of the cave he demonstrates that those lacking a philosophy have the fire behind them and see only moving shadows. The ideal philosopher may see the full daylight, but all others perceive no more than the shadow of reality. Plato, as well as Socrates (to whom he ascribed most of his opinions), was apparently not greatly interested in sensory functions, even devaluing information of the senses. Plato's world of thought, including geometry, was in fact created by rejection of the world of the senses (306). Hence, Plato's contribution to sensory physiology was unimportant in contrast to his great and lasting influence on philosophy. In spite of his mathematical interests in geometry, his concepts of optics and acoustics were rather general and vague. With regard to vision he inaugurated the unfortunate idea, taken up by Aristotle and others, that rays were emitted by the eye toward the objects seen. He taught that colors originate from attraction of the eye's emission by special particles of the objects. Although he said that sound was caused by motion of air particles, he was unable to explain how this motion could be received by the ear. Plato interpreted sense modalities as being due to inherent qualities of the external objects rather than to the information transduction of the sense organs themselves. This was a retrogression from Democritus, who already had developed clear concepts about the specificity of sensory modalities and their quantitative relations to external stimuli. Both Democritus and Plato doubted the reliability of sensory information, but for different reasons: with realistic reserve in the Democritian school, and with idealistic self-confidence in the Platonic tradition that emphasized the autonomy of the soul.

ARISTOTELIAN PHILOSOPHY AND PSYCHOLOGY. Aristotle (384–322 B.C.) the great polyhistor of antiquity, wrote many books on biology, psychology, and philosophy that also contain his concepts of sensory functions. With his astonishing universality in all fields of human knowledge he synthetized and summarized the Greek sciences of the fourth century B.C. After he had been the tutor of the young Alexander at the Macedonian court of Philip II, he succeeded Plato at the Athenian Academy in 343 B.C. and then founded his own school, the Lyceum, in Athens.

All his statements are written clearly, with the essential points formulated in short sentences. His terminology remained valid in Greek and Latin for two thousand years. Even for the modern scientist it is still a pleasure to read Aristotle's beautiful and succinct writings (16). One can readily understand why Arab and Western philosophers were fascinated by his books, as well as why he was so highly esteemed and why he was considered to be the main scientific authority during the Middle Ages, at a time when relatively few new observations were being made.

However, some of Aristotle's concepts are too clear and simple to be true, and he made some grave errors in physiology. Some of these false teachings, such as his concept of circulation and brain function, were believed for many centuries and were corrected quite late. A neurophysiologist has difficulty in forgiving him his wrong concept of the brain, declared to be a cooling device for the blood, and his localization of psychic functions in the heart (16). One should be less severe in criticizing his and Plato's concept of vision as a reflection of luminous rays sent out by the eyes to the viewed objects, since this depicts rather well the active function of visual attention and eye movements in vision. Aristotle and the medieval scientists, although having a dualist concept of mind and body, often combined psychological and physiological functions in description and explanation.

ARISTOTLE'S VIEWS OF THE SENSES. In the second book of De anima (Peri psychen) Aristotle characterized the five senses (vision, hearing, olfaction, taste, and touch, each in a special chapter), the functions common to all senses, and the principles of perception and cognition. In chapters 2 and 11 he said that the tactual senses are not uniform and that they signal several qualities such as sensations of pressure, temperature, movement. All these chapters are nearer to sensory physiology than the physiological and psychological concepts described in the books on animals and metaphysics. Aristotle's concepts of opposite sensations within the various sensory modalities are of special interest for the modern reader. He said that opponent qualities can be perceived through all senses—for example, white and black through vision, and warmth and cold through the tactual sense. He added other opponent qualities such as sweet and bitter, dry and moist—sensations we would not classify as strictly opponent. The general functions of all senses are called secondary or common (koine aisthesious). This concept is the origin of the "common sense" of later authors.

In perception Aristotle stressed the active role of the organism in selecting those percepts that are important for orientation, for the organism's needs, and for survival. He distinguished sensation (aesthesis) and recognition (gnosis) and also recognized emotional factors in perception. He even developed some pre-Hartmannian concepts of the role of causality and finality at different levels of the world in relation to their specific laws. He said that living organisms not only are the product of lower physiochemical processes but are recognizable in goal-directed action and have their own laws of finality, which are not to be found at the lower levels that have causal relations. He ascribed a greater role to teleology and to purposive action in biology, postulating an entelechy in all living organisms. This was used as an argument by the vitalists, who ascribed finality to biological processes, in opposition to materialist physicochemical explanations of life. Some Aristotelian principles survived the refutation of his concepts of the functions of the brain and the eyes during the seventeenth and eighteenth centuries. They can be useful for the concepts of perception and action (see Fig. 18A).

Aristotle collected a remarkable number of important biological observations during his life span of 60 years. His writings remained the main source of physiological knowledge during the Middle Ages and until the sixteenth century, when a new human anatomy was founded by Vesalius (352) in 1543–1555, and after 1600, when exact physiological concepts of circulation were developed by Harvey (see HARVEY'S DISCOVERIES AND SENSORY PHYSIOLOGY, p. 28). The great weakness of Aristotle's concepts of perception was his location of sensation and psychic functions in the heart as depicted by scholastic scientists 1,500 years later with the sensorium commune (Fig. 1). Aristotle's cardiocentric hypothesis of sensation was probably motivated by his appreciation of the emotional background of perception.

The physiologically absurd notion of the brain cooling the blood could only be defended as a psychological metaphor for the interaction of emotional and rational processes: according to the Greeks, and to popular belief down the centuries, the heart was the seat of the emotions. So the notion that the emotions carried

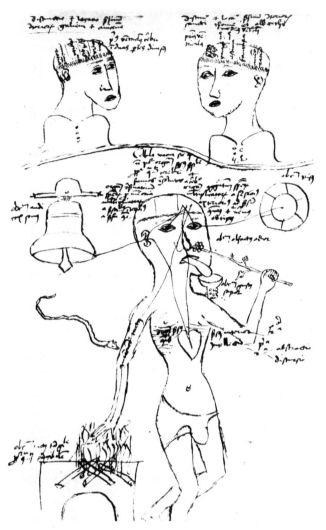

FIG. 1. Aristotelian and medieval concept of five senses projecting to the heart and the sensorium commune, made around 1500. An unknown English scholar added this pen drawing to the sensory chapter of G. de Hardewyck's book of 1496 on Aristotle. *Lower part:* stimuli of five senses (acoustic, visual, olfactory, gustatory, and somatosensory for heat and pain). Sense organs project by lines to heart as seat of the soul (according to Aristotle's scheme), either directly or after coordination in "sensus communis" in the anterior part of head. *Upper part:* two heads with a fancy cerebral location of labeled division of four and five brain compartments; *left,* Galen's and Avicenna's "sensus communis," "phantasia," "cogitativa," and "memorativa"; *right:* Albertus Magnus's similar concept of five faculties: "sensus communis," "imaginativa," "estimativa," "phantasia," and "memorativa." (From the Library of the Wellcome Institute for the History of Medicine, London, by courtesy of the Trustees.)

by the heated blood would be cooled down by the brain's unemotional chilling thoughts may have helped to maintain Aristotle's wrong concept of the brain as a blood-cooling machine until the late Middle Ages.

Aristotle's concept of intentional preparation of voluntary action and its relation to sensory anticipation and control is discussed in PERCEPTION AND ACTION, p. 57.

Roman Science and Late Antiquity

Roman philosophy was dependent on Greek tradition and mediated it through the large Hellenistic libraries, the greatest being in Alexandria, Egypt, which entered the Roman domain after being conquered by Julius Caesar in 47 B.C. The Romans were more interested in politics and practical organization than in theory and philosophy. So the Roman state, in spite of civil war and palace revolutions, survived for nearly 1,000 years, whereas the Greek culture flourishing from the fifth to the third century B.C. ended in political catastrophe—self-destruction by warring Greek cities and the culminating blow of the Roman conquest. Latin gradually supplemented Greek as the world language in the Roman empire. The Latin terms *virtus* (self-discipline), *res publica* (state organization of citizens), *labor* (hard work), *ordo* (social order), *justitia* (justice by law) were key words that characterized the Roman civilization better than its philosophy and art or the Greek ideal *kalokagathia* (beauty and goodness). So the Latin language acted as a bridge connecting the classical tradition through late antiquity to the Middle Ages after Germanic tribes and Christian fanatics had destroyed essential parts of the Greco-Roman pagan culture. Over this Latin bridge Greek philosophy survived in Western culture from the fifth to the seventeenth century.

Cicero, the influential Roman philosopher and statesman who lived from 106–43 B.C., while preferring the Greek language for philosophical discussions, wrote his books interpreting and extending Greek philosophy in a clear Latin that remained a model for classical philologists for the next 2,000 years.

EPICUREAN ATOMISM IN ROME. Titus Lucretius Carus (98–55 B.C.) made a rhymed Latin synthesis of the Epicurean concepts of nature, *De rerum natura* (259). Even a modern scientist can find pleasure in reading this work, which was edited posthumously by Cicero. Besides the atomist concept one will find in this poetic book many analogies with biology and psychology and one of the first descriptions of landscape. In the field of vision Lucretius described perspective foreshortening of spatial percepts to the form of a cone (Book 4 of ref. 259). Lucretius (259) stressed the importance of sensory information: "ab sensibus esse creatam notitiam veri" (the senses teach us the cognition of the true world).

The atomist concepts of antiquity created by Democritus and systematized by Epicurus were based on everyday observations and experiences and remained pure hypotheses without any attempt at experimental or mathematical proofs. Classical atomism of Greek and Roman science is not directly comparable with the nineteenth century atomic and molecular theories such as the periodic system of Mendeleev or the molecular structural concept of Couper and Kekulé or with modern physicochemistry. The Greek atomists postulated the atoms to be indivisible in the original verbal sense. Factually their theories remained speculative postulates and had no consequences for scientific research or for technical applications. So the world of atoms remained unexplored for 2,300 years after Democritus's concept until the atomic weights, the valences, and the periodic system were discovered during the last century.

STOICISM. The Stoa originated in Greece and Syria during the third century B.C. and developed from a materialist and cynical attitude to post-Socratic ethics and a condemnation of passions. The Stoic philosophers who hero-worshipped Socrates were mainly interested in ethical rules of virtue, and their view of nature tended towards pantheism. Although Zeno, the founder of the school, had defended the reliability of sense information, most Stoics were rather skeptical of perception by the senses, considering it to be uncertain. Some Stoics, however, made interesting psychological observations and did have a clear concept of the selective process of perception. I mention only the emperor-philosopher Marcus Aurelius (A.D. 121-180), whose sentence about the active role of attention in selecting among the multitude of passive sensory messages was cited by Mountcastle (286).

During the first three centuries A.D., when the Epicurean and Stoic schools flourished in the Roman Empire, science was represented by encyclopedic writers such as Pliny the Elder (*Natural History*, A.D. 77). The most important Roman scientist of lasting influence was Galen, who was a Greek by birth.

GALENIC MEDICINE. Galen (A.D. 129-200) lived in Pergamon, Alexandria, and Rome, where he became court physician of the philosophical emperor Marcus Aurelius. He collated the knowledge of anatomy, physiology, and practical medicine of his time in many books (123). As an experimentalist and empiricist he discovered important new anatomical and physiological facts and saw their functional correlations; his character, however, was described as arrogant and boastful. Galen recognized the brain as an organ governing perceptive, motor, and psychic faculties. He had a better knowledge of the functions and projections of sense organs than Aristotle: he considered the eye to be a receptor of light and not an emitter of previsual rays reflected from the viewed object. Some errors and misinterpretations, such as his mistaken concept of the heart functions and blood circulation, were handed down, however, and were widely accepted until the sixteenth century.

Galen demonstrated sensory pathways and cerebral function by experiments: by cutting the spinal connections of the brain and pressing on the brain (and, as he thought, its ventricles), he observed that movements and sensory responses of animals were abolished, whereas pressure on the heart even in a man caused no loss of sensation and consciousness. Thus, Galen explicitly contradicted Aristotle and postulated that afferent nerves lead to the brain. His brain anatomy, which included the hypothalamic infundibulum, the pineal and pituitary bodies, the fornix, and the cerebellar vermis, contained the best description for many centuries. Unfortunately, besides his misleading statements about blood circulation, his concept of cerebral blood supply by several arteries overlooked the circle of Willis at the base of the brain where the carotid and vertebral arteries converge. Instead of this arterial circle he postulated a vascular plexus, derived from his autopsies in lower mammals, the *rete mirabile*. This, however, was a minor error in view of his correct concept of the anatomical pathways of sensation. He taught that all somatosensory nerves project to the brain by the spinal cord and that the cranial nerves from the higher sense organs converge in the brain stem. For sensory physiology it is interesting that Galen distinguished sensory, or "weak," nerves leading from the body to the spinal cord, and motor, or "strong," nerves leading from the spinal cord to the muscles, although he did not distinguish the anterior and posterior roots. In his experiments he discovered that respiration stopped and death occurred after cutting the high spinal cord in the occipital region.

Long-Term Influence of Greco-Roman Science

GREEK, ROMAN, MEDIEVAL, AND MODERN SCIENCE. Most of the important concepts of scientific knowledge and philosophy that were to shape Western thought until the Renaissance were already developed in ancient Greece between 500 and 300 B.C.

Science and philosophy in the Roman Empire was dependent on these Greek sources during the next 500 years. Medieval Christian theology also followed the Greco-Roman spirit a further thousand years until the Renaissance. During the Middle Ages a latent Greek tradition mainly drawn from Aristotle survived in the writing of Arabic authors and the Christian scholastic schools (see ARAB CONTRIBUTIONS TO MEDIEVAL SCIENCE, p. 12). In the fifteenth and sixteenth centuries the classical sciences were revived again, due to the humanistic interest in the original Greek texts. This renewal of ancient Greek and Roman traditions was facilitated by the exodus of Byzantine scientists before and after the Turkish capture and destruction of Constantinople in 1453.

Clearly, scientific work in classical Greece, including mathematics as founded by Euclid, differed in many aspects from modern scientific research. Systematic experiments played a much less important role, the procedure usually consisting of speculation following a few basic factual observations. The conclusions reached from empirical observation were generalized into philosophical systems that endeavored to explain too much, so that the early pre-Socratic scientists made systems for the whole of nature. Specialists in natural science appeared rather late in the school of Aristotle. More specialized research developed among

Alexandrian scientists after large libraries were founded and more factual knowledge and literature became available. These libraries were destroyed in the Dark Ages following the great migrations, and very few complete works of Greek scientists were handed down to posterity. Among those that endured, however, were Aristotle's writings, mostly translated from the Greek into Arabic and Latin. These remained the main source of medieval knowledge of Greek science.

MEDIEVAL SCIENCE AND SENSORY STUDIES

Characteristics of Medieval Research

During the Middle Ages the Christian faith was the greatest formative influence on Western science and philosophy. As a result, in medieval thought the perception and description of the real world were neglected in favor of concepts of a divine world and a heavenly future. The attitude toward nature and research from the fourth and the twelfth centuries was therefore entirely different from that of modern times, the medieval scientists using moral equivalents and religious symbolism in order to relate nature to theology.

After the traditions of antiquity had vanished, the Augustinian philosophy of the Christian church dominated Western science for the next millenium. From the seventh century onward Mohammedanism influenced Arab scientists in a similar way. There were remarkable periods, however, in which some early Renaissance tendencies to revive Greco-Roman science and art can be seen. These include the Carolingian and the Romanesque periods and, after the contact with Arab culture during the Crusades, the pre-Renaissance in Sicily and Southern Italy brought about by the Frederician court. These were short-lived periods, soon countermanded by the Church to integrate them into the fixed patterns of medieval Christendom. Only the last pre-Renaissance period of the thirteenth century produced a rise of scientific activity comparable to modern research. The influence of this period on perceptual research is therefore described in some detail.

Medieval science influenced by antique and Christian influences may be characterized by its lack of quantification and the prevailing use of symbols.

LACK OF QUANTITATIVE EXPERIMENTATION. In antiquity and the Middle Ages the attitude of many scientists toward facts and measurement was one of neglect or even of contempt for experimental verification. In ancient Greece this was due to the prejudice of the educated against the manual labor essential for experimenting, any such work being left to banausic practitioners in handicraft. In the medieval period it arose from the preference for religion over worldly affairs. Although the knowledge of logic and of essen-

tial philosophical principles during the Middle Ages was concise and often superior to that of modern scientists, medieval science was more interested in divine enlightenment than in sensory information. Early Christian researchers in optics during the Middle Ages, for example, preferred dogmatic statements to experiments and taught their pupils: If the dogma cannot be verified in reality, the worse for the real world. Hence ideological prejudice and not scientific incapacity hindered the experimental sciences. In the time period that followed from the Renaissance to the end of the eighteenth century self-made experiments and measurements became a recognized attitude for scientists, but mathematical constructions were often preferred and ideological interests still provided a powerful motivation for research, as shown by the work of Kepler and Newton.

SYMBOLISM VERSUS SCIENCE. Exact scientific thought during the Middle Ages was hindered not only by the restrictions of the theology but also by a general tendency toward the use of symbolism. A nonscientific symbolic trend of literature had already begun during late antiquity in the pre-Christian Greek circles of Alexandria with the animal book *Physiologus*. This bestiary contained neither physiology nor zoology; rather, it described uncritical narratives of symbolic animal life and became very popular during the early Middle Ages. Such animals were symbols, not objects of science. This symbolism is characteristic of medieval science, art, and religion.

AUGUSTINIAN FOUNDATION OF CHRISTIAN PHILOSOPHY. St. Augustine (354–430) laid the main philosophical foundations of the early Christian church. Although he made no essential contributions to perception and sensory functions, his work must be mentioned here for three reasons: first, his profound influence on Christian philosophy for more than 1,000 years; second, his concept of time; and third, his symbolism of divine illumination that later initiated an interest in optics in some scholastic scientists.

Augustine lived in the last decades of the Christianized Roman Empire during which the Germanic invasions caused its downfall; the first sack of Rome by the Western Goths occurred in 410 when he was bishop of Hippo in northern Africa. Augustine was not a friend of science except for his belief in the truth of arithmetic. He accepted very little from Aristotle and it is uncertain whether he ever read Plato. He wrote in Latin and apparently had some bias against the Greek language. His main source was Plotinus and the neo-Platonist school of the Latin West. So he brought only the late-Roman conceptions into the Christian church and excluded earlier Greek philosophies and sciences—from Democritus to the Epicurean and Stoic schools.

Augustine's relativistic theory of time is interesting for psychology and physiology. It demonstrates his subjective evaluation of experience and also his concept of human existence proved by thought, a pre-Cartesian form of the *Cogito, ergo sum.* His time concept begins with the experience that we know only the present of reality, whereas the past is given by memory and the future by expectation. The latter two are facts only in representation, so that three represented times exist: "A present of things past, a present of things present, and a present of things future," as Russell (319) has translated Augustine's teaching. How Augustine combines these subjective concepts with God's eternity is another story.

Augustine's fanatical orthodoxy is partly responsible for the Christian denial of the real world and the Church's attitude against science in the Dark and Middle Ages. He taught that this wicked world is of no interest to a good Christian and can only be accepted as a symbol for God, the sole authority. The only compensation I can find for the adverse influence of Augustine on objective science may be his unintentional stimulation of optic research by his symbolism of light. Augustine's analogy of natural light as divine illumination and the logic of God was the motivation for those ecclesiastical studies of light and vision during the twelfth and thirteenth centuries that resulted in the work of Grosseteste, Peckham, and Dietrich of Freiberg (see DIETRICH'S OPTICAL EXPERIMENTS, p. 15, and Fig. 3). To describe the main achievements of Augustine by which Christian ethics reached a higher moral level than that of the decaying late antiquity is beyond the scope of this chapter.

Arab Scientists and Greek Tradition

ARAB CONTRIBUTIONS TO MEDIEVAL SCIENCE. From the ninth to the eleventh centuries the Greek tradition was accepted only selectively by the Church in the Christian countries of Western Europe. During this period Arab scientists made more complete translations of Aristotelian writings, and these in turn influenced medieval science through contact with the Mohammedan culture in Spain. In addition to the preservation of Greek science the achievements of Arab scientists were mainly in the fields of astronomy, practical medicine, and mathematics. Some original contributions to optics made by Arab scientists, such as Alchindus and Alhazen, were inverted and parabolic mirrors and the camera obscura, which became known among Arab circles that were located mainly in Spain. Prominent Spanish Jews, such as Maimonides, left Cordova for Egypt and wrote their medical treatises in Arabic. After Toledo was captured by the Spaniards in 1085, Arab scientific achievements became known in Christian countries.

Some Arab scientists had a long-lasting influence on Western culture, not only by their commentaries on Aristotle. Paradoxically, the Arab tradition of Avicenna and Averroës was kept from the twelfth to the fifteenth century by Christian scientists, i.e., longer than in the Arabic countries themselves, where it was interrupted by religious zeal in the twelfth century.

SENSORY FUNCTIONS AND OPTICS. Alhazen (ca. 965–1039) made important contributions to optics, but these were mainly physical observations of straight light emission and refraction. They have some indirect interest for visual physiology, because by using his pinhole camera as an eye model he recognized a similar mechanism in the eye, in contrast to the Platonic concept that the eyes emit light toward the objects seen. However, Alhazen thought the lens and not the retina to be the light receptor (76).

Avicenna (ibn-Sina 980–1037) in Persia relied on Aristotelian science and Galenic medicine and added some empirical knowledge to it. His philosophy was mainly empiricist and his medical practice more empirical than traditional. To explain sensory functions he considered the five senses as the main source of sensory information and said that thought caused a generalization of sensory experience in perception. Perception was considered to occur in a general sensorium commune similar to the Greco-Latin and later concepts (see SENSORY INTEGRATION AND SENSORIUM COMMUNE, this page). This "common sense" was considered to be an integrating faculty of the human brain that had similar peripheral sensory mechanisms in animals.

Averroës (ibn-Rushd 1126–1198), living in Spain at the court of the Omayad caliphs, taught a rationalistic philosophy of panpsychism. He was the first to consider the retina and not the lens as receptor structure of the eye; this concept was proved and recognized only 500 years later by Kepler and others, along with recognition of the inverted retinal image (see VISUAL PROJECTIONS, p. 29). Accepting the sensorium commune, he postulated that the intellect is essentially the same in all human beings and that this common spirit manifests itself in different individuals. His works were translated into Latin by Michael Scotus, the friend and court philosopher of Frederick II of Hohenstaufen. Later, Averroës's teaching, called Averroism, had an important influence on the scholastics of Paris University. It was opposed, however, by Thomas Aquinas and orthodox theologians, since Averroës had taught that philosophy and religion can be separated. So the Averroists could defend the coexistence of apparently different opinions in philosophy and religion, as also did Duns Scotus (see CONCEPTS OF PERCEPTION AND KNOWLEDGE AMONG THOMISTS AND SCOTISTS, p. 17). To reduce theological opposition Averroës made the clever statement that religion may contain philosophical truth in a different allegorical form. How far he accepted sensory experience as a contribution to the intellect, in the sense of Avicenna, is uncertain.

Medieval Concepts of the Senses

SENSORY INTEGRATION AND SENSORIUM COMMUNE. The sensory functions were considered for many centuries as being limited to the five senses: olfaction, vision, audition, taste, and "feeling" (including all somatosensory modalities). Only at the end of the nineteenth century, when Blix (50) and Goldscheider (128) demonstrated differently localized sensory spots of four different modalities at the skin, were the mechanisms of touch, pain, and hot and cold sensations distinguished and the proprioceptive modalities of the vestibular, muscle, and joint receptors added.

In antiquity the sensorium commune, the concept of the location of multisensory convergence, was derived from the perceptive integration of various sensory modalities in subjective experience. The anatomical and physiological mechanisms of this integration of sensory information were unknown, however, until modern neuronal recordings demonstrated neuronal convergence of different senses in many structures, including the basal ganglia, the brain stem reticular formation, and the cerebral cortex (210).

There exist several schematic drawings of the sensory inputs and the sensorium commune from medieval and Renaissance times, some probably derived from older lost manuscripts of Greco-Roman or Arabic origin. They show the pathways of the five senses converging on the heart (the Aristotelian version) or the brain (the Galenic teaching). Thus Greek authors had already realized that these different sensations must be integrated for perception in a sensorium commune, be it in the heart or in the brain or in both.

The drawing by a fifteenth-century scholar reproduced in Figure 1 gives a good illustration of the Aristotelian and medieval concept of sensory convergence at the heart and in the brain. Specific sensory excitation is depicted by typical stimuli: tones from a clock for the ear, light for the eyes, warmth from a fire for the hand, pain from the bite of a snake for the arm, odor from a flower for the nose, taste from a bowl for the tongue. The lines from the sense organs show two loci of convergence—one at the sensorium commune, and from there to the heart another that also receives direct input to the heart from the ear and the nose.

During and after the sixteenth century the sensorium commune was mostly localized in the brain. Many authors believed that the cerebral ventricles were the seat of this common sense and of higher mental functions such as phantasy, thought, and memory. In the seventeenth century Descartes proposed the speculative and often-ridiculed localization of conscious perception in the pineal body as seat of the soul (Figs. 8, 9). From the late Middle Ages until the end of the eighteenth century the cerebral location of sensory convergence was confused due to the false concept that the sensorium commune and other psychic functions were localized in the cerebral ventricles instead of in the brain tissue. Hence the numerous fanciful drawings and woodcuts, published in the sixteenth and seventeenth centuries and showing a location of mental faculties in three brain ventricles, are of little value for modern science. Those interested in these schemes will find many examples collected from the Middle Ages to modern times in Clarke and Dewhurst's (71) profusely illustrated book.

The Sciences in the Thirteenth Century

The thirteenth century saw the height of medieval culture in art and literature, the songs of the later troubadours and the minnesingers, the flowering of Gothic architecture and sculpture. A Greco-Roman pre-Renaissance began in Southern Italy, where Nicola Pisano, the renewer of classical sculpture, received his first stimuli in the Sicilian court school of sculpture founded by Emperor Frederick II.

Philosophy flourished in the scholastic institutions in Paris and Cologne, with Albertus Magnus (ca. 1200–1280) incorporating Greek scientific ideas obtained from Arabic translations. In Italy Thomas Aquinas, and in England Roger Bacon and Duns Scotus, taught a reconciliation of Aristotelian science and theology. Apart from these ecclesiastical achievements an entirely different worldly civilization, striving for a revival of the Roman empire, was created in Sicily from 1220 to 1250 by the emperor Frederick II.

SENSORY STUDIES IN ANIMALS. During the Middle Ages most concepts of sensory functions were influenced by theological and philosophical teaching or were used as supplements of practical medicine. Several theologians, mainly of the northern scholastic institutions, wrote books on nature and biology—for example, Albertus Magnus's famous treatise *De animalibus*. However, nearly all these studies—with the notable exception of those of Frederick II—compile data from the classical and medieval literature, mainly from Aristotle, and contain relatively few original observations.

The most detailed quasi-experimental studies of animal behavior, the influence of sensory stimuli and of avian anatomy, were made by Frederick II between 1210 and 1240. They were described in his manuscript on bird life and the training of falcons, which deals with visual learning and deprivation (115, 372). It was written, as said in the introduction, after 30 years of bird watching and falconry with training and hunting. The falcons were imprinted to man, using deprivation by lid suture followed by special training, as shown in Figure 2.

It seems that the Scottish court astrologer Michael Scotus (whom Dante relegated to the Fourth Circle of Hell because of his "sorcery") contributed to the early part of these studies before his death in 1235, since the book is dedicated to "M.S." (115, 372).

THE COURT OF FREDERICK II AND SCIENCE. In Sicily and southern Italy the court of Frederick II (1194–1250), grandson of Frederick Barbarossa of Hohenstaufen, combined the classical Greek tradition with Arabic, Byzantine, Italian, German, and even southern French troubadour influences. Frederick at the age of 18 became German King in 1212 and Holy Roman Emperor in 1220, after growing up in Palermo following the early death of his father Henry VI in 1197. He learned six languages, spoke and wrote Arabic as fluently as Italian, German, Latin, and Greek, and

FIG. 2. Emperor Frederick II's method of visual learning conditioning of falcons after visual deprivation, written ca. A.D. 1240. During a period of visual exclusion by lid suture the falcon is accustomed to the voice and touch of the falconer. After this period of visual deprivation the falconer trains the seeing falcon for hunting in a series of stages. *A*: some weeks after opening the lids the falcon is tied to a bar by a long line and quieted by feeding, the attendant keeping his face averted. Then the falcon is accustomed to the man wearing a hat. *B*: after this imprinting to a human being the falcon learns to sit on a leather glove and is trained to remain there with and without a hood covering the eyes. *C*: unrest is quieted by feeding with averted face and by caressing. This procedure is repeated until the falcon remains on the gloved left fist of the falconer. *D*: conditioned falcon keeps sitting on the falconer's glove, first while walking, then while riding. Frederick's original illustrated manuscript was lost during the siege of Parma in 1248, but several copies were preserved, the best being that of his son King Manfred. These figures are taken from a good facsimile of Manfred's manuscript. (Colored miniatures in Vatican library Codex Ms. Pal. lat. 1071. fol. 92y, 106r, 89r, 108r.)

tried later to reconcile the best traditions of these different cultures at his court (73). From his youth he excelled in an ability to see the essentials in a complex situation. Burckhardt (66) characterized him as "the first modern man on a throne." He was quick to recognize the character and the talents of men and selected the most gifted for high office, such as Piero della Vigna, who was promoted as a young man to protonotary of the kingdom, and later high court justice. Frederick wrote poetry in Italian and found new verse forms, but literary historians have not yet decided whether it was Frederick himself or his chancellor Piero who invented the sonnet. With Piero he introduced effective financial controls and bureaucratic order in state life and government.

In his last years, from 1246 to 1251 after the Parma defeat, he became a lonely man; his fierce struggle with the popes reached its climax, his son Enzio was captured, and many of his old friends left him. Frederick recognized the Church solely as a spiritual force

and opposed its mundane power. After he had been excommunicated by the popes several times he was denounced by Innocent IV as the Antichrist. His legendary fortune declined and the cultural splendor of his court diminished; he died suddenly in 1251. During the following years his sons were killed in battles or died in prison, and his grandson Conradin was beheaded publicly in Naples.

In the nineteenth century Frederick's role in history and science was rediscovered by German and Italian historians. After the main documents were published in the nineteenth century, Haskins' work (153) in America and Kantorowicz's book (218) in Germany made Frederick's achievements widely known, though they possibly overrated them.

Frederick II as a scientist. Being a bird-watcher from his youth, Frederick developed a keen interest in the natural sciences. As emperor he continued and systematized these studies and carried on a voluminous correspondence about many basic problems of physiology and biology with prominent contemporary scientists of many nations, especially with famous Arab scholars. Insofar as the increasingly difficult struggle with the papacy and the North Italian cities left him time, he studied birds, experimented with training falcons, and wrote his famous book on birdlife and falcon hunting, the first systematic ornithological work (115). The falcons were visually deprived only after they had visual experience as nestlings with their parents and the early critical period had passed when lasting visual damage might develop. So the late imprinting to man was first made without visual cues. It is not clear why Frederick used the long visual deprivation by lid suturing for the falcon training even after he himself had introduced the falcon cap for exclusion of vision (Fig. 2C). He acquired the cap from the Muslim courts during his crusade to Palestine in 1228 and improved it by air holes.

In all his studies, as well as in their psychological and political applications, he observed his motto (115) to investigate and recognize the world as it is, by observation and experiment: "manifestare ea quae sunt sicut sunt" (to demonstrate and verify things as and where they really are). This and his proud dictum that truth can only be accepted when it "is proved by nature or by the force of reason" were in opposition to the teaching of his time, which relied on books and religious traditions as taught by church and university authorities.

Besides his realism two basic concepts distinguished Frederick's views on nature and biology from the prevalent teleologic thinking of his time, which saw purpose and God's will in all life: 1) a recognition of cause and effect in biological structure and function, and 2) a recognition that the learning process can shape and change instinctive behavior. He used his second principle of learning for two applications: 1) the changing of behavior by experience and training, and 2) the prevalence of visual learning. Of course these were simplifications partly originating from his own experience and personality. He apparently overrated learning when he expected it to cause a change of nature. He stressed the experience that falcons can learn to catch different types of prey and to release them to the hunter, which of course they would not do by instinct (115). He prescribed rules for the training to modify instinctive responses by imprinting a different behavior and tried to apply these principles to the human being with his greater capacity for learning. He expected to change human behavior in society and to become himself an *immutator mundi*, a "reformer of the world" (73), as he was called in his time. As with all reformers, he underestimated the human indolence and conservatism that lead to natural resistance against changes in society.

Optics and Vision

The studies of optics in the Middle Ages had religious motivations, initiated by St Augustine's analogy of light with the grace of God and the illumination of human intelligence by divine inspiration (see AUGUSTINIAN FOUNDATION OF CHRISTIAN PHILOSOPHY, p. 11). They also tried to give an explanation of the rainbow, mentioned in the Bible as a token of God to Noah and his offspring. The ecclesiastical authors writing on vision and optics hoped to prove their symbolic analogies by mathematics. Hence, the theory of rectilinear propagation of light and its change by refraction was developed along with some concepts regarding binocular vision in England by the tradition from Grosseteste to Bacon and Peckham (76).

OPTICAL STUDIES IN ENGLAND. Robert Grosseteste (ca. 1168–1253), the teacher of Roger Bacon, was interested in optics and tried to explain the laws of reflection and refraction of the lens. He developed some concepts of wavelike properties of visual rays and sounds but was apparently more interested in explaining the rainbow than the eye. He said light and sound move in straight lines. Although he postulated experimental proof he made no decisive experiments. If he had experimented only once or twice in optics he would have disproved his own laws of refraction. So Combie's assertion (77) that the "origin of experimental science" dates back to Grosseteste has to be taken *cum grano salis*!

The book on optics of John Peckham (ca. 1230–1294) contains an interesting early diagram of binocular vision (Fig. 9 of ref. 307) that to my knowledge is the first picture of binocular convergence with concepts of crossovers behind the eyes. Peckham's manuscript *Perspectiva* was written in the thirteenth century during his last term as Archbishop of Canterbury, and it is preserved at Oxford. Although it repeats the erroneous Arabic concept that the visual image is received and concentrated on the lens, Peckham postulated that a convergence of the two images of both eyes must take place somewhere in the brain. So he was a somewhat naive medieval forerunner of Newton's concept of optic nerve decussation (see NEWTONIAN VIEWS ON OPTICS AND VISION, p. 31). Of course his view of the mechanisms of this convergence had no anatomical and physiological bases, so he depicted it as an optical crossing of straight light rays. Further, Peckham, in agreement with the traditional view, localized the sensorium commune in the most anterior ventricle of the brain, a speculation often repeated until the fifteenth century and also depicted in Leonardo's writings.

DIETRICH'S OPTICAL EXPERIMENTS. In spite of Roger Bacon's postulate regarding the use of experimentation and induction, the English scholars mostly dispensed with experiments. If they had made them they might have disproved some of their theories, as Crombie (76) remarks. In Germany, however, remarkably exact experiments in optics were made independently in Peckham's time by a Saxon churchman, Dietrich of Freiberg (Theodoricus Teutonicus de Vriberg d. 1310).

He attempted to provide a better explanation of the rainbow by studying light refraction. His manuscript *De iride et radialibus impressionibus* preserved in the Basel University Library contains sketches of these interesting experiments (Fig. 3). Dietrich was the first to give an adequate explanation of the rainbow spectrum by double refraction and reflection in raindrops. He made some pre-Newtonian experiments on color by refraction with crystals, glass vessels, and flasks shown in Figure 3. From these he derived his theory of the rainbow, which surpassed that of Grosseteste and Bacon, although he assumed too low a value for the angle between the sun, the rainbow, and the observer's eye, whereas Bacon had given a more correct value of this angle (76).

AUDITION AND MUSIC. In contrast to vision, medieval science contributed relatively little to auditory perception except some theory of music and harmony. This is surprising, since music and singing were used in the Christian church as early as the fourth and fifth centuries. Augustine's musical motion of the soul and Boethius's *musica humana* and *musica mundana* have led to Gregorian music, polyphony, developments of musical instruments, notes for worldly and ecclesiastical use, and organ playing since the ninth century. A wealth of musical symbolism was often depicted in the visual arts. It originated in the ancient traditions of Pythagoras and the music of the spheres and influenced the mystics of the thirteenth and fourteenth centuries and the latest medieval representations of the dance of death, and it is well described by Meyer-Baer (279).

Scholasticism and Science

The scholastic schoolmen of the Franciscan and Dominican Minorite orders made important contri-

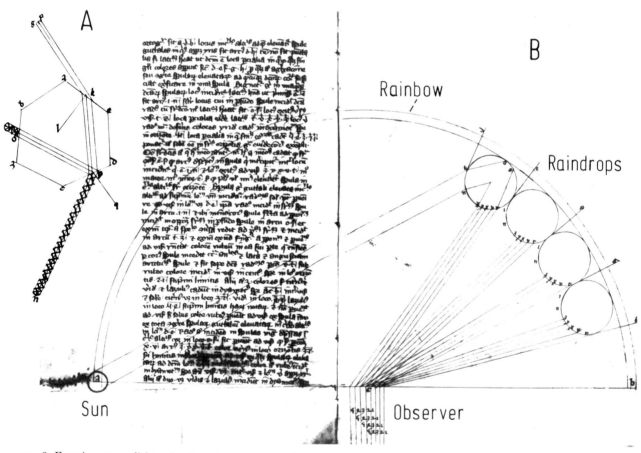

FIG. 3. Experiments on light refraction, *A*, and theory of the rainbow, *B*, drawn by Dietrich (Theodoricus) of Freiberg around 1300. To explain the rainbow colors Dietrich studied the spectral refraction of light in glass models of raindrops. *A*: refraction study with hexagonal crystals and vessels filled with water showed spectral colors: he found that red is nearest, blue farthest, from original angle of the light rays, and yellow and green lie between them. White light beam enters vessel, refracting at *k*, is partly reflected at inner wall, passing out at left; partly refracted again, it leaves vessel downward in *q*. *B*: Scheme of the rainbow originating from sun, *a*, by double spectral refraction and reflection in 4 raindrops (*right*). Observer, *c*, sees red light from upper drop and yellow, green, and blue from other drops in order of the rainbow. Divergence of doubly refracted colored light is drawn incorrectly in the parallel lines for each color. (From Dietrich's manuscript in the University Library, Basel, reproduced with kind permission of the Library.)

butions to philosophy and science in the thirteenth century. However, the founders of these orders, St. Francis (1181–1226), a poetic spirit who advocated poverty, and St. Dominicus (1170–1221), a practical organizer, had not the slightest interest in science and were even hostile toward research. In their original form these two Minorite orders battled against secular science and heretical sects. They became the main allies of the papacy against lay heretics like Frederick II and religious heretical sects such as the Albigensian movement in southern France. The Albigensians were cruelly suppressed by the Dominicans in collaboration with the French king. At the same time, however, the northern ecclesiastical schools and universities were invaded by Franciscan and Dominican monks of another type, who were primarily interested in philosophy and science. In England, Germany, and France these Minorite monks took the place of the old Benedictine and Augustinian fathers. The most prominent figures among the Dominicans were Albertus Magnus and Thomas Aquinas, and among the Franciscans, Roger Bacon and Duns Scotus.

ALBERTUS MAGNUS'S NATURAL HISTORY STUDIES. Albertus, Count of Bollstädt (ca. 1200–1280), taught at the ecclesiastical university of Cologne, where Thomas Aquinas became his disciple. Albertus as the most eminent Dominican scholar in Germany became interested in all fields of biology and was the universal spirit of his century. He had remarkable insight into ontogenetic and phylogenetic evolution. As the earliest pre-Darwinian he mentioned the principle of natural selection and demonstrated it by man's cultivation of plants and breeding of animals. Albertus's physiological knowledge was rather limited, however, and his interests were mainly confined to morphology and embryology. Although he postulated that the natural sciences should be empirical and that experiments should be used instead of relying on literary traditions, he himself did not experiment and made only some optical and botanical observations. Besides these remarks on light refraction and the rainbow, his many books on animals, human anatomy, women, reproduction, embryology, and botany contain few observations related to sensory physiology. Although Albertus cites "dicta falconariorum Federici imperatoris," it remains uncertain whether he had read one of Frederick's manuscripts, since he visited Italy in 1223 before Frederick's falcon book (115) was written.

CONCEPTS OF PERCEPTION AND KNOWLEDGE AMONG THOMISTS AND SCOTISTS. The Dominican and Franciscan scholastics were divided into two main schools founded by St. Thomas of Aquinas and Duns Scotus. Thomas Aquinas (1224–1274), descendant of a noble family of the Frederician court in Sicily, became a Dominican against the strong advice of his relatives. He was a pupil of Albertus Magnus in Cologne and established a synthesis of Christian theology and Aristotelian philosophy that survived for 700 years in Catholic philosophy. Although he had less interest in

natural science than Albertus, he fully recognized the importance of sensory information for human knowledge. In discussing divine truth in *De veritate*, Thomas made a remarkable statement about the sensory source of intelligence that was cited later as a scholastic source of sensualistic philosophy. "Nihil est in intellectu, quod non sit prius in sensu" (nothing is in our intellect which has not been previously in the senses). In his main work *Summa theologiae* Thomas quoted Aristotle's teaching about the sensory principle of cognition as follows: "Principium nostrae cognitionis est a sensu" (our knowledge originates from the senses). In this book Thomas coined the term *tabula rasa* to characterize the human mind as entirely dependent on sensory information. However, his somewhat rationalistic theology concentrated on the soul and valued religious concepts higher than worldly percepts. In his doctrine all events depended on divine providence, although he conceded that God's power had some limits. In spite of some opposition in other scholastic circles the Thomist doctrines became the official Church philosophy.

Whereas Thomas was canonized in due course, two English Franciscans of the late thirteenth century, Roger Bacon and Duns Scotus, did not accept all of Thomas's doctrines and had some trouble with church officials.

Roger Bacon (ca. 1214–1294), teaching at Oxford, accepted the Averroist distinction of intellect and soul. He appreciated mathematics, showed a theoretical interest in mechanical problems, and proposed experimental methods in science. For this he was later hailed by historians of science as an early experimentalist and prophet of engineering. Like most medieval scientists, however, his appreciation of experiments and empirical knowledge remained a theoretical postulate. It is difficult to say what he contributed to sensory physiology besides some experiments on light refraction and yet another theory of the rainbow. He did not follow his own advice to use experimental methods for research: in 1266 when he proposed convex spectacles to correct hypermetropic sight he made no measurement nor practical application, the spectacles being invented by Italian friars 20 years later. Bacon made some interesting technical prophecies of inventions such as motor cars, flying machines, and submarine vessels, but this was pure science fiction. Bacon had neither the engineering techniques nor practical intentions to build such models himself (76).

Duns Scotus (1270–1308) also lived in Oxford, in Paris, and, during his last year, in Cologne, where he died at the age of 38. He had a brilliant mind but was involved in some theological quarrels. He initiated the Scotist school of scholastics. Most orthodox churchmen rejected his opinions as heretical, however, and restrained him in Paris. Duns said that intellectual action is predominant in perception. He was a realist, however, and made an early pre-Kantian synthesis of rational and empirical knowledge in his explanation of evidence: Knowledge of things may evolve either from essential principles or by sensory experience or by action. He differentiated theology as a practical and philosophy as a theoretical science (373). He said that philosophical knowledge may be independent of theological dogma, and that knowledge (*ratio*) and faith (*fides*) are different. This apparently made him suspect to the general of the Franciscan order, because scientific knowledge could always be made an excuse for differing from dogma. Some Scotists followed the Averroic tradition, that a knowledge can be right *secundo ratione*, i.e., in science, although it might be wrong *secundo fide*, i.e., in theology.

Raimundus Lullus (1232–1316), a Franciscan tertiary from Mallorca, wrote many books in Latin, Catalan, and Arabic, some with a poetical flavor, in the attempt to lead different religions and cultures to mutual understanding. His famous *ars magna*, the "great art" of combination, is a method of ascent by way of combinations of sensory experience and rational knowledge to the contemplation of God. It also involves a descent, returning to human sensory knowledge in the effort to communicate the intellectual vision to other men. In this connection he proposed language as a "sixth sense" in addition to the classical five senses.

In the fourteenth century William of Occam (ca. 1290–1349) continued the trend toward science and the investigation of the real world, saying that perception contains only signs but not images of reality (373). His nominalism criticized general principles as conventional names and opposed the scholastic belief in the primacy of universals. During his adventurous life, which led him from Oxford to Avignon and Munich and to papal excommunication, Occam taught that observations of the real world are the primary sources of knowledge, while universals are mere names, and that general conceptions are secondary depending on the perception of individual things. This latter concept might have led to empirical research independent of metaphysics. Verifiable sensory investigations were not attempted by Occam and his nominalist school, however, and sensory research began only 200 years later. Still later, sensory empiricism was introduced into philosophy by Locke.

SENSORY SCIENCE IN FIFTEENTH AND SIXTEENTH CENTURIES

Seeing Nature Through the Eye of Renaissance Man

During the fifteenth century artists became interested in the depiction of nature, and scientists in its investigation. In the last decades of that century landscape drawing and painting were created by Leonardo and Dürer. This trend in the arts toward nature began with theoretical and practical studies of perspective.

PICTORIAL PERSPECTIVE. In 1400 to 1430 several Florentine architects and painters began to use geometrical line drawings for visual perspective to represent pictorial space. In 1435 the architect, philosopher, and poet Leon Battista Alberti (1404–1472) summarized these attempts and his own experiments, which used a box, a peephole, and a checkerboard to represent pictorial space. The simple statement, not known to the Greeks, that parallel lines meet at infinity, made the convergence of perspective lines at a point of the horizon (*punto centrico*) understandable (Fig. 4). Alberti's manuscript *Della pittura* became very popular among painters and sculptors and was printed later in several editions, such as in the Appendix to Leonardo (245). The Florentine painters were impressed by the pictorial application of clear geometrical laws governing vision after Alberti had demonstrated their construction by the visual pyramid or cone formed by the visual angle. A section of the cone of vision corresponds to the picture plane (see Durer's scheme, Fig. 5). The diminishing apparent sizes of distant objects are explained by the convergence of their parallel edges to a virtual point on the horizon (Fig. 4B). After 1470 Piero della Francesca joined the mathematician Luca Pacioli in producing a perfect geometrical construction of linear perspectives, which was only partially published together with Leonardo da Vinci's illustrations in 1494.

The emotional fascination with problems of perspective construction of space among Renaissance artists, and the novelty of their solution by means of linear projection in two-dimensional pictures, is difficult to understand for us who daily see photographs in which perspective is an inherent factor. The geometrical constructs, hailed by Uccello and other artists as *dolce prospettiva*, continued to be used for two centuries until Kepler (219) in 1604 showed the relationship of perspective to conic sections and the method of drawing ellipses and hyperbola by pins and strings. (197).

Linear perspective and Dürer's textbook. After Alberti, Pacioli, and Leonardo had proposed linear constructs of perspective views, Dürer in 1525 wrote a popular textbook (91) illustrating the practice of perspective drawing for artists (Fig. 5). This German painter and engraver Albrecht Dürer (1471–1528), who was 19 years younger than Leonardo, concentrated on practical methods describing simple techniques of perspective drawing and painting. During his second journey to Venice in 1506 he visited Pacioli in Bologna to ask him about the geometric laws of perspective, but he apparently had difficulties in understanding the mathematics. Leonardo had already used a glass window for drawing perspective lines, and Dürer improved this method. Whereas Leonardo's results remained hidden in his diaries, Dürer published his work in 1525 in a book that was reprinted in four German and five Latin editions. As a result, Dürer's work became more widely known than Leonardo's. It was an illustrated textbook for practicing artists. The glass window and strings used for simple representations of perspective foreshortening are shown in Dürer's sketch and wood-

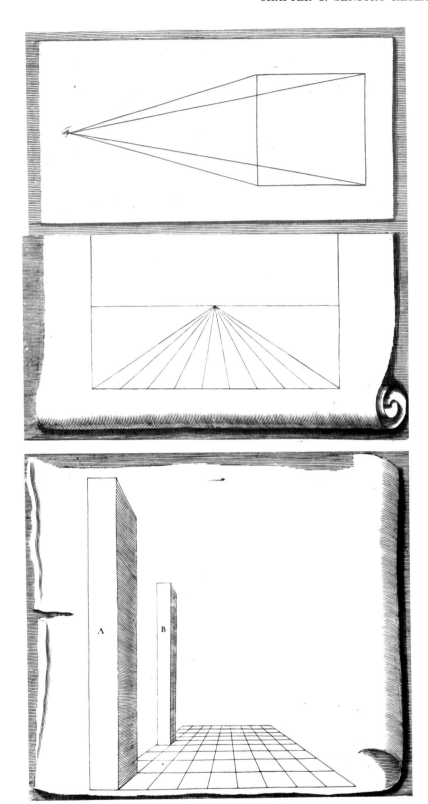

FIG. 4. Alberti's illustrations of visual pyramid, perspective convergence of parallel lines, and foreshortening of horizontal and vertical patterns. *Top*: visual angle of eye looking to a quadrangle forms a pyramid; length and width of base increase linearly with distance. *Middle*: parallel lines on a plane converge to a central point (punto centrico) at horizon. *Bottom*: quadratic pattern on floor and two columns (A and B) show the same perspective convergence. Text says, "linea giacente, 9 bracchia. A, B pilastri o muri di 10 bracchia" (Floor lines of 9 ells and columns of 10 ells). [From Alberti about 1430, in printed 1652 edition of Leonardo (245), p. 5, 17, 27.]

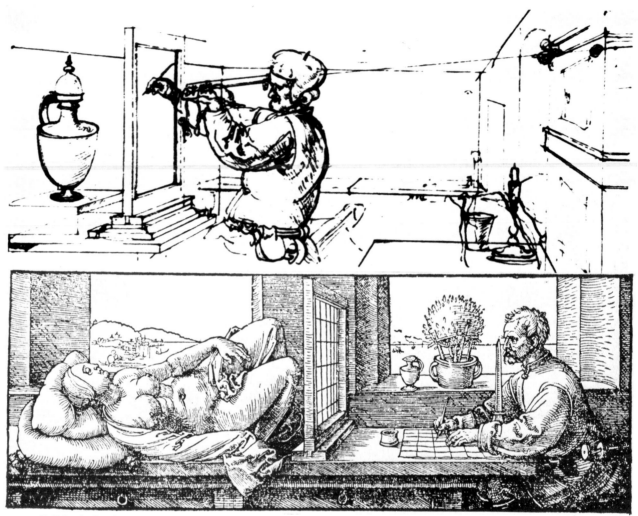

FIG. 5. Dürer's sketch and woodcut of perspective reproduction with help of squared glass window grid. (made around 1524). *Top*: draftsman marks main object contours on glass window, where they are seen with perspective foreshortening. In addition he uses a string for measuring distances and for demonstrating direction of visual pyramid from eye to objects seen. *Bottom*: draftsman copies foreshortened contours of a woman on paper from projection of glass window that has same squared network as the paper. Pointed bar marks eye position and window distance. [*Top*: pen drawing in Landesbibliothek, Dresden. Reproduced with kind permission of the Library. *Bottom*: woodcut from Dürer (91), 3rd ed.]

cut (Fig. 5A, B). Dürer's work on geometrical body proportions as models of beauty was also anticipated by Leonardo and Pacioli. He proposed rules for depicting the ideal human bodily form using circular and cubistic simplifications of body structures. This, however, does not concern us here.

Views of nature and landscape by artists and scientists. It is probably not fortuitous that during the Renaissance, at a time when landscape painting was being created in Europe, similar ideas and studies of nature were proposed by many different scientists and artists.

In the decades around 1500 landscape painting was beginning in Europe. The first examples are Leonardo's pen drawing of the Arno valley in 1473 and Dürer's landscape aquarelles made during his Italian journey in 1494-1495. These were followed in 1510-1520 by Altdorfer, who made the earliest oil painting showing a pure landscape without human figures.

It is significant that the earliest preserved landscape drawing is by Leonardo, whose universal mind and broad interest embraced art, anatomy, physiology, engineering, and many problems of science. His observations on visual contrast were another important contribution to sensory science and deserve a detailed description.

Physiological Concepts of Leonardo da Vinci

Leonardo da Vinci (1452-1519) added to his exact anatomical studies of the human body a number of new observations on vision and spinal cord function, which are of great physiological interest. All these observations, however, although well documented and illustrated by pen drawings (Fig. 6), were kept hidden in his diaries, written in the mirror script of a left-hander (Fig. 7), and were not published until hundreds of years later (246). They therefore had much less influence on the scientific community of the period than the voluminous books published by his humanist and medical contemporaries, who rushed into print with less original thoughts and investigations. Leonardo's lonely personality shaped the style of these observations and experiments of a self-made scientist and was the reason for the defective communication of this genius with his contemporaries.

COLOR AND VISUAL CONTRAST. Leonardo was the first author who described clearly the laws of visual contrast and their effects in color vision. As a primary order he distinguished six basic colors by adding black and white to the chromatic qualities of yellow and blue and red and green. In his diaries he wrote, around 1490:

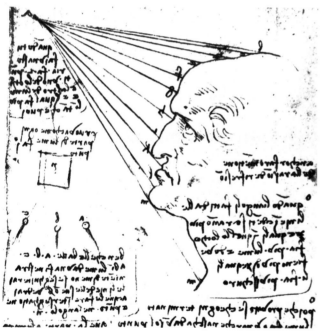

FIG. 6. Leonardo's drawing of dependence of illumination on angle of reflecting surface. The light rays *b–m* from source *a* meet different parts of face, with maximal luminance in rectangular projection (*g, h,* "equal angles"). Leonardo's mirror script reads in MacCurdy's translation: "Since it is proved that every light with fixed boundaries emanates or appears to emanate from a single point, that part illuminated by it will have those portions in highest light upon which the line of radiance falls, between two equal angles, as is shown above in the lines a–g, also in a–h, and similarly in a–l; and that portion of the illuminated part will be less luminous upon which the line of incidence strikes at two more unequal angles, as may be seen in b, c and d; and in this way you will also be able to discern the parts deprived of light, as may be seen at m and k." [(246); Pen on paper. From Leonardo manuscript in Royal Library of Windsor Castle. Reproduced with permission. Copyright reserved.]

There are six simple colors. The first is white although philosophers do not accept white and black as colors, since the first is the cause of colors and the other their occlusion. However, since painters cannot renounce either of them we add them to the other colors and say: white should be the first of the simple colors, yellow the second, green and third, blue the fourth, red the fifth, and black the sixth. (Codex Vaticanus No. 1270; see ref. 246.)

For practical use in painting he studied the contrast effects of opposed pairs of colors and distinguished three pairs of basic contrasting stimuli each with two opposed colors (like Hering's *Gegenfarben*) and called these pairs *color retto contrario*: To green-red and yellow-blue he added white-black as a third pair, although they usually are not considered as colors.

In Leonardo's textbook of painting (245) published in 1651, more than a century after his death, all these concepts are clearly described and show remarkable analogies with modern visual physiology. In chapter 63 the simultaneous contrast effects are demonstrated by observations on relative brightness and darkness and of opposite colors: When one sees black beside white, blue beside yellow, and green beside red, these opposite colors appear stronger. Among visual contrasts of dark and bright areas he distinguished two kinds of contrasting effects for planes and borders: *1)* areal contrast (Hering contrast, ref. 33) and *2)* border contrast (Mach contrast). Leonardo described the first as stronger whiteness or blackness of areas surrounded by dark or bright areas, respectively. The second was characterized as border enhancement between bright and dark areas (245).

PUPILLARY FUNCTIONS AND SPACE PERCEPTION. Leonardo conceived clearly the functions of the pupil as a regulating device and observed binocular stereopsis and its enhancement by light and shadow. His way of thought and his quick grasp of the essentials in visual functions are demonstrated by the following quotations from his diaries:

The pupil of the eye changes to as many different sizes as there are differences in the degrees of brightness and obscurity of the objects which present themselves before it: In this case nature has provided for the visual faculty when it has been irritated by excessive light by contracting the pupil of the eye, and by enlarging this pupil after the manner of the mouth of a purse when it has had to endure varying degrees of darkness. And here nature works as one who having too much light in his habitation blocks up the window half way or more or less according to the necessity, and who when the night comes throws open the whole of this window in order to see better within this habitation. Nature is here establishing a continual equilibrium, perpetually adjusting an equalising by making the pupil dilate or contract in proportion to the aforesaid obscurity or brightness which continually presents itself before it. (MacCurdy's translation, ref. 246.)

Stereopsis and spatial effects of luminance are characterized briefly:

Things seen with both eyes will seem rounder than those seen with one eye. . . . Things seen between light and shadow will appear to have the highest relief.

PERSPECTIVE AND REFRACTION. Like all Renaissance artists, Leonardo was interested in problems of perspective. After the geometrical constructs were solved by others, he enlarged linear perspective by adding air perspective and color perspective in the perception of distant objects. In the *Trattato* (245) he described the effect of the atmosphere and of fog on colors as contributing the perspective effects or *prospettiva de colori* (ref. 245, chapt. 64) and taught the use of hazed contours for air perspective in painting *prospettiva aerea* (ref. 245, chapt. 65).

Leonardo anticipated Dürer's method of perspective drawing on a glass window (Fig. 5) as a cross section of the visual pyramid:

Perspective is nothing else than the seeing of an object behind a sheet of glass, smooth and quite transparent on the surface of which all the things may be marked that are behind the glass; these things approach the point of the eye in pyramids, and these pyramids are cut by the said glass. [Ms A.1 Institut de France (246).]

To supplement perspective Leonardo studied the angle between light rays and surface determining the relative brightness and darkness of light reflection of the body. Figure 6 illustrates this and "Cap. 632" (chapter 632) of the Codex Vaticanus explains the angular dependency of luminance (this text differs from the *Trattato* and a similar figure of Cap. 287).

Unfortunately Leonardo's views on optics of the eye were not so precise as one would expect. In his drawings he located the lens in the middle of the eyeball, and his view of the projection of visual messages to the brain is influenced by the ancient concept of the sensorium commune and their relations to three brain ventricles.

Leonardo conceived an improvement of lens refraction by glass apposition to the cornea. Although the optical system in this picture is incorrect, Duke-Elder and Wybar (90) have considered Leonardo's drawing to be the first proposal for a contact lens; it consisted of a ball of thin glass filled with water. A better artificial corneal lens was conceived much later by the French mathematician de La Hire in 1648, but it was not implemented until the end of the nineteenth century.

Leonardo's general concept of sensory integration is more traditional in accepting the sensus communis. He added to this old notion the functions of sensory information processing at successive levels: *1*) separate process, *2*) multimodal perception, *3*) judgment, and *4*) memory. At the highest level of memory, knowledge is stored for recognition.

The common sense is that which judges the things given to it by the other senses. . . . And these senses are moved by objects, and these objects send their images to the five senses by which they are transferred to the organ of

perception (imprensiva) and from this to the common sense; and from thence being judged they are transmitted to the memory, in which according to their potency they are retained more or less distinctly. (246).

SPINAL CORD FUNCTIONS. Whereas most of Leonardo's own research was anatomical, he made some important physiological experiments in the decapitated frog: after observing reflex movements of the spinal frog he demonstrated the disappearance of these sensory responses after destruction of the spinal cord as an experimentum crucis. This is illustrated in his *Quaderni* conserved in Windsor Castle Library (Fig. 7).

Only a few of Leonardo's findings became known by personal communication, and his main achievements were ignored by scientists during the next centuries, since they were hidden in his notebooks. His concepts about color and contrast vision were first published by Dufresne in 1651 in France 123 years after his death

FIG. 7. Leonardo da Vinci's note and sketch of his experiments with frog spinal cord (about 1500). Leonardo drew the spinal cord in the vertebral canal with vertebrate bodies. He wrote in mirror script on the cord "generative power" and described on left and right sides the experiment of cord destruction. English translation of the essential result of abolishing reflex action: "The frog instantly dies when its spinal cord is perforated. Although it lived before without head, without heart, or any entrails of intestines or skin. It thus seems that here lies the fundamental of motion and of life." (From Leonardo manuscript in Royal Library of Windsor Castle. Reproduced with permission. Copyright reserved.)

(245) and illustrated by engravings made after Poussin's drawings. This "textbook on painting" was mainly read by painters and rarely by physicists or physicians. The physiological importance of Leonardo's observations was recognized rather late in the mid-nineteenth century by Helmholtz (164) and by others.

RISE OF SCIENCE AFTER THE RENAISSANCE

Modern science had its origin in the basic discoveries of the sixteenth and seventeenth centuries made by Copernicus, Kepler, Galileo, and Newton in astronomy and physics. Although this work is only indirectly related to physiology, it must be discussed here along with the biological hypotheses of Descartes, since all these concepts became relevant to visual research and neurophysiology.

After Copernicus had discovered the heliocentric concept, which was published in 1543 and became the basis of astronomy, Kepler and Galileo laid the foundations of exact mathematical astronomy and physics in 1600 to 1630. These and some basic observations on biology were taken up by Descartes between 1630 and 1650. After 1680 Newton, Leibniz, and others initiated modern science by developing mathematical criteria for research in optics and mechanics. One hundred fifty years later, during the nineteenth century, new experimental methods for the verification of theoretical concepts were developed in biology and psychology. Simultaneously, general theories were formulated as a framework in which to order the wealth of accumulating experimental facts. Examples of such theories whose influence has lasted from the nineteenth century to the present day are the periodic system, the molecular compounds in chemistry, and the theory of the evolutionary origin of species in biology.

The origins of modern science can only be understood when the physical discoveries made from 1550 to 1700 and their philosophical roots are known. Advances in sensory physiology were often secondary deductions made from optics and acoustics, or they were elicited by philosophical concepts relating to perception and knowledge. Among these Descartes's machine theory of the organism and Locke's empiricism had a profound influence on physiology. Hence we must refer to these sciences and philosophies in order to understand the condition of sensory research in the sixteenth to eighteenth centuries.

Heliocentric Theory and Physics

COPERNICAN HYPOTHESIS. Nicolaus Copernicus (1473–1543) transformed man's image of the world by introducing the heliocentric concept and disproving the Ptolemaic geocentric theory of astronomy, which had reigned since antiquity. After studying Greek, law, and philosophy at the universities of Krakow, Bologna, and Padua, Copernicus became prebendary canon of the church in Frauenburg (in East Prussia). There he carried out astute observations and calculations in his observation tower. He created a new theory of the solar system proving mathematically that all planets, including the earth, revolved around the sun. According to his hypothesis the planets revolved in perfect circles. These circles, however, did not explain all observed planetarian movements, and Copernicus had also to make use of the complicated epicycles that were a most difficult complication of the old Ptolemaic system.

Copernicus's theory was published in Nürnberg in the year of his death (1543) from the copy made by his pupil Rheticus. This book established the principle of the heliocentric theory but did not give an adequate mathematical explanation of the many anomalies of circular movements. The difficulties of the epicycles remained unsolved for more than five decades until Kepler presented a simple solution by his elliptic concept.

KEPLER'S CONTRIBUTIONS. The German astronomer Johannes Kepler (1571–1630) worked during his most productive years in Prague at the court observatory of the emperor Rudolph II. He solved all the major problems of the heliocentric hypothesis in an ingenious way in three simple mathematical laws of planetary motion published in 1609 and 1619 (220): 1) Planets move in elliptical orbits and the sun is located in one focus. 2) A planet sweeps over equal sectorial areas in equal time at various distances from the sun. 3) The square of the period of each planet for orbiting the sun is proportional to the cube of its average distance from the sun.

These mathematical equations, reflecting Kepler's genius, became the first natural laws formulated in precise mathematical terms. Kepler's laws at once explained all astronomical observations and definitely excluded the epicycles. They left open only the cause of the revolving movement, until the concept of gravitation was added 70 years later by Newton (293).

For the sensory physiologist Kepler is interesting not only for his mathematical rigor in explaining the laws of optics and planetary motion but also for his discovery of the eye's dioptrics: his works on the function of the lens and the projection of the retinal image were published in 1604 and 1611, respectively. This work developed as a biological application of his experience with the telescope and other astronomical instruments and is described in VISUAL PROJECTIONS, p. 29. Kepler used geometrical optics to demonstrate mathematically that the lens must project on the retina an inverse image of the visual surround. Later the reversed image of the retina was clearly demonstrated on the ox's eye, after removal of the sclera, by the German Jesuit Christoph Scheiner in 1619, and it was illustrated by Descartes in 1637 (see JESUIT SCIENTISTS AND OPTICAL STUDIES, p. 30 and Fig. 11).

GALILEIAN PHYSICS AND EXPERIMENTAL QUANTIFICATION. Galileo (1564–1624), the Italian physicist working in Pisa, Padua, and Florence, made important new astronomical discoveries by improving the telescope, and with his quantitative measurements he founded experimental physics. He was a contemporary of Kepler, but their scientific correspondence from 1597 onward was somewhat unilateral and interrupted by long pauses, since Galileo often "forgot" to answer the letters of the somewhat younger Kepler. Galileo accepted Kepler's laws as a proof of the heliocentric theory but hesitated to publish his confirmatory observations in face of increasing pressure from the papacy. By making better telescopes Galileo discovered many new facts of planetary astronomy, such as the existence of the satellites of Jupiter and the phases of Venus. He also provided further proof of the Copernican-Keplerian theories and made basic contributions to optics that were important also for visual physiology. He introduced exact measurements and experimental quantification into science. Galileo's main discoveries concerned physics and included the notion of acceleration and the mathematical laws of motion and of falling bodies. These laws were more important for motor action than for sensory physiology, but Galileo's general concept of quantification, introduced as a scientific principle, was fundamental for all physical and biological sciences. This also had a great influence on physiology, as shown by Harvey's work, although it remains uncertain whether Harvey knew Galileo during his student days in Padua.

Galileo's conflict with the papacy when the Counter-Reformation was at its height in Italy resulted in his public denial of his heliocentric concepts. This resulted in the popular anecdote that after his famous trial Galileo made the aside "Eppur si muove" (and yet it moves) i.e., that the earth continues to move despite inquisitional objections.

Galileo's importance for science lies in his mechanical philosophy of nature and his strictly empirical methollogy. This is a consequence of his mathematical rigor in formulating the physical laws, his clear thought, and his ability to make simple experiments to obtain distinct quantified data.

Although he was mainly interested in physics and astronomy, not in physiology and biology, Galileo made some remarks on perception in his book *De coelo*. The following quotation from Crombie's translation (76) characterizes Galileo's concept of sensory perception in his own words:

> I hold that there exists nothing in external bodies for exciting in us tastes, odors and sounds other than sizes, shapes, numbers, and slow or swift motions; and I conclude that if the ears, tongue and nose were removed, shape, number and motion would remain but there would be no odors, tastes or sounds, which apart from living beings I believe to be nothing but names.

MATHEMATICAL FOUNDATIONS OF SCIENCE. During the seventeenth century progress in mathematics enabled scientists to elaborate their results with mathematical rigor. This was applied first in astronomy and physics before quantitative methods were used in physiology. The applications of logarithms (founded by Napier in 1614) and of differential and integral calculus (developed independently by Newton and Leibniz in the last decade of that century) were not used in the biological sciences until much later.

BACON'S INDUCTIVE RESEARCH POSTULATES. Francis Bacon of Verulam (1561–1626) was often praised as founder of the inductive method in science. However, on reading his books that claimed to inaugurate a new science, one is disappointed. Bacon propagated induction, facts, and experiments. But every scientist who reads his observations can immediately see that these inductive conclusions and explanations of facts stem not from an experimenting scientist but from a speculating writer who composes his science at the writing desk.

The two famous books of Bacon (18) contain very few exact observations, no important basic facts, and no quantitative measurements. The book on nature (1627) is full of rather trifling enumerations of "spirits" and naive descriptions of "experiments" denounced rightly by Liebig in 1863 (250) as erroneous and even as frauds.

Cartesian Machine Theory of the Body

Rene Descartes (1596–1650) had already decided in his early youth to reform philosophy by calling into doubt earlier conceptions. Being a good mathematician and sharp observer, he linked his philosophy with original studies in optics and geometry. From this he proceeded to a rigid dualism of body and soul, using the principles of extension (*extensio*) for all physical things, and thought (*cogitatio*) for the mind or soul (*anima*). The physical things included both the body and the brain of man and animals. He derived by rational deduction his concept of mechanical interaction between brain and body, which is important for physiologists.

DESCARTES'S PHILOSOPHY OF SCIENCE. As a young man Descartes served as a soldier in Germany for the first part of the Thirty Years' War. During the winter pause of 1619–1620 he found time to develop his philosophy by mere thought, relaxing in a well-heated room and trying to find the criteria of truth in the sciences: "Je demeurais tout le jour enfermé seul dans un poêle ou j'avais tout le loisir de m'entretenir de mes pensées," as he said in his first book *Discours de la méthode*, written in French and later translated into Latin. He wrote down these ideas at the age of 23 and published them in 1637 together with *Dioptrique, Météores*, and *Géométrie* (81), the results of his physical research pursued during the decade following his military service. These latter books contain several new mathematical and physical observations well summarized by Crombie (76) and others. Some biophysical results of his dioptric studies are discussed later with Figure 11 and the nerve mechanisms.

Descartes was a difficult person, and his intolerant

and exclusive character, full of mistrust of others, prevented open discussions and critical opinions that could correct his original ideas. So he became somewhat extravagant in making easy hypotheses and conjectures for explaining many facts and observations. In his *Principia philosophiae* he tried to explain nearly everything in the earth and the heavens, extending his hypotheses from the flame of a candle to the sun, to magnetism, and to planetary movement. Most of these explanations were pure speculation.

HYPOTHESIS, FICTION, AND EXPLANATION. In Descartes's opinion theories and hypotheses could be fictions used to explain the nature of things. He said that these ad hoc hypotheses could be useful for leading to explanations and positive results even if the theories were false. So Descartes favored a conventional and pragmatic use of his many theories. He said:

> I wish that my writings should be used simply as an hypothesis, which is perhaps far removed from the truth; but that having been done, I believe that it will be well done if everything deduced from it agrees completely with the observations. For if this happens it will be no less useful in practice than if it were true, because we can use it in just the same way to set out the natural causes to produce the effects we want.

The Cartesian optimism in finding true explanations by rational thought and early hypotheses provoked the criticism of Newton (see NEWTON ON HYPOTHESIS, DEDUCTION, AND INDUCTION, p. 32). Crombie (78) has

compared to modern positivist conceptions the Cartesian use of theories to be confirmed or falsified.

Descartes's famous statement of the existence of human consciousness derived from the experience of thought—*Cogito, ergo sum*—was considered by other philosophers to be a mere syllogism. Nevertheless, it remains a clear expression of Descartes's tendency to a rational subjectivism. In considering the psychology of perception Descartes was rather brief. He compared perception and knowledge stored in memory to impressions of wax "inspected by the mind" and thus recognized (83). In his book on passions, *Les Passions de l'âme*, appearing in 1649 he distinguished between perception and imagination. He said that bodily sensations are caused by peripheral nerves and their conduction of nerve impulses (*esprits animaux*) to the brain, whereas imagination originates by similar excitation in the brain itself (82).

MACHINE CONCEPT OF THE BODY AND PHYSIOLOGY. Descartes's importance to sensory physiology lies in his concept of the body as a machine and his predictions of neurophysiological mechanisms demonstrated in some of his pictures (Figs. 8–11).

Descartes's machine theory of the organism, although it was a philosophical concept developed to prove that the soul created by God is different from the body, helped physiological research of brain function to become independent of philosophy and theology. In contrast to Galileo, who was content in solving

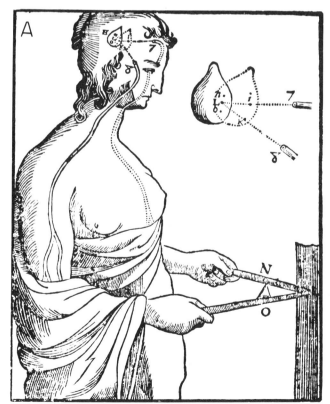

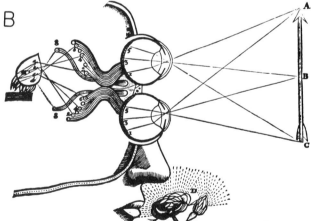

FIG. 8. Descartes's schemes of multisensory perception. *A*: visual and somatosensory control. Under visual control two bars *N* and *O* are directed by hands to a target *B*. This movement elicits afferent "animal spirits" of nerves to brain and pineal body *H*. The pineal is supposed to bend for receiving and sending impulses from and to eyes, *7*, and arms, *8*. *B*: bisensory interaction of vision and olfaction, and visual attention. Nerve impulses from both eyes via optic nerves converge in brain from *2*, *4*, and *6* to the pineal. There visual attention is aroused and causes an efferent flow (*abc*) facilitating visual input from the arrow (*ABC*). This suppresses olfactory afference from flower *D* via olfactory nerves *8* having less access to the pineal (*dotted lines*). [From Descartes (83a).]

A

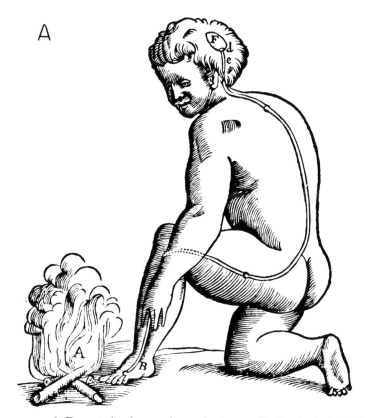

B

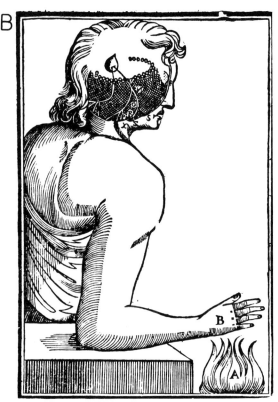

FIG. 9. Descartes's schemes of sensorimotor coordination in the brain show cerebral mechanisms of reflex movements (A) and voluntary and emotional action (B) elicited by sensation of warmth. A: cerebral mechanisms of reflex movements. Heat of fire A stimulates reflex withdrawal of foot B and defense movements of hand. This is effected by afferent and efferent impulses ("animal spirits") of nerves, conducted along filament CC to and from brain after convergence at pineal gland F. Descartes's text reads in English: "If the fire A is close to the foot B, the small parts of this fire, which move, as you know, very rapidly, have the power to move along with them the part of the skin of this foot which they touch; and by this means, pulling the small filament CC, which you see attached to it, they open at the same time the entrance of the pore de, where this small filament ends, just as, by pulling one of the ends of a cord, you cause a bell attached to the other end to ring at the same time." B: voluntary and emotional action elicited by sensation of warmth. Burning heat of a fire causes different cerebral responses of attraction or avoidance, sent by pineal body into different nerve channels. When hand B is cold it is extended voluntarily toward fire A for warmth. If fire burns hand the strong sensation of pain, conducted by more animal spirits in nerves to the brain, causes efferent impulses in cranial nerves oprs and an outburst of crying and tears. Descartes's general conclusion for sensory projections to the brain is this: "There are many small filaments similar to CC; they all begin to separate from one another at the inner surface of the brain, from whence they originate, and going from there to disperse throughout the rest of the body they serve as the organs for the sense of touch." [From Descartes (83a).]

restricted problems with mathematical rigor and experimental simplicity, Descartes generalized most of his observations without using quantitative experiments. He extended his interests to many fields of physics, physiology, and psychology and pursued his hypotheses systematically to their ultimate conclusions.

The main trouble with Descartes's book for the modern reader is his erroneous concept that the pineal body is the coordinating central organ in the brain, where all sensory channels converge to be transmitted to the soul. Hence Descartes postulated that sensory messages, motor commands, and even many reflex actions are integrated by the pineal body (Figs. 8, 9) as the only unpaired cerebral structure. This unfortu-

nate hypothesis could have been refuted by experiments and anatomical control of nonexisting sensory pathways to the pineal gland. However, in spite of his false generalizations and free speculations, Descartes made so many right and astonishing predictions in his posthumous work *De homine* (83) that these must be discussed in extenso. This book offered the first systematic neurophysiology of sensory and sensorimotor coordination, and yet its sources were only deductive inferences derived from simple observations and a few anatomical facts, without any physiological experiments. It shows what a sharp thinker can attain when he systematizes observations and facts and constructs a logical system of functions, but it also shows how he can err when he abstains from experimental control.

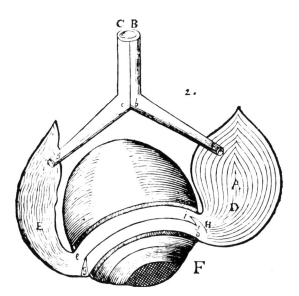

FIG. 10. Descartes's concept of reciprocal innervation of two antagonistic eye muscles. Tube *CB* represents a nerve branching at *CB* to innervate the two antagonistic ocular muscles *E* and *AD*. Muscle *AD* is contracting after receiving more impulses (esprits animaux) than relaxing muscle *E* and moves eye to side *F*. In addition to centrifugal nerve impulses Descartes discussed a nonexisting peripheral interaction between the two antagonists by valves in sclera; these allow impulses to flow from *e* to *i*, but not in opposite direction, because valve *g* is closed. [From Descartes (83a).]

De homine (83) was printed posthumously (in Latin in 1662, in French in 1664) and the figures were made by Dutch and French artists after Descartes's drawings. It remains uncertain how far Descartes checked these pictures. They depict his concept in a clear and lucid way, however, and therefore are used to illustrate his neurophysiological ideas here. Figures 8, 9, and 10 are reproduced from the first French edition (83a).

CARTESIAN PRINCIPLES OF SENSATION AND ACTION. Descartes inaugurated four concepts that became essential for perceptual research and neurophysiology:

1. Nerve impulses (*esprits animaux* or *spiritus animales*) originate in the sense organs and convey their messages via the nerves to the brain and, in turn, conduct excitation from the central nervous system to the effector organs (Figs. 8–10).

2. Multisensory convergence in the brain and evaluation of different sensory messages by attention is essential for perception and action (Fig. 8).

3. Sensorimotor coordination and reflex mechanisms function by conduction of afferent and efferent messages to and from the central nervous system where they are integrated (Fig. 9).

4. Reciprocal innervation of antagonistic muscles causes movement (Fig. 10).

While Sherrington (328) greatly developed the concept of reciprocal innervation, he fully recognised Descartes as the originator of this principle. Of course, Sherrington refuted the Cartesian hypothesis of peripheral cross-connections between agonist and antagonist muscles, which located reciprocity "in the mus-

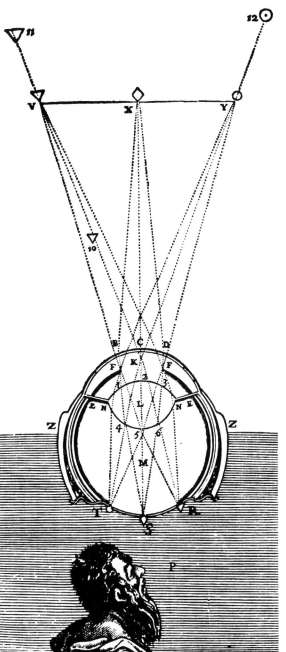

FIG. 11. Descartes's picture of inverted retinal image. It is observed after removal of posterior part of sclera as in Scheiner's experiment on ox's eye. The observer at P sees inverted image TSR of the outer object VXY projected through cornea BCD and lens 1–6 to retina. [From Descartes (81).]

cle, not in the nerve centers themselves." Another picture of Descartes's book reproduced in Figure 10 corresponds better with modern neurophysiological concepts of reciprocal inhibition, since Descartes says that the animal spirits are directed from the central nervous system into different channels and that the contracting agonist receives more nerve impulses than the relaxed antagonist.

Two other concepts of Descartes concerning brain

action, which I have depicted in a recent paper (208), are more important for psychology and psychophysics than for neurophysiology, since their neural mechanisms are not yet demonstrated clearly enough in modern science: 1) the patterned structure of memory, and 2) the restriction of sensory channels during sleep, contrasted with wider sensory information during wakefulness.

Descartes's machine theory was modified by several authors to avoid placing the soul in the pineal body. The necessity to explain purposive behavior in animals without an immortal soul, and the difficulties arising from the Christian soul concept, led Willis in 1672 to the postulation of an *anima brutorum* (372a). In contrast to the immortal soul of man, Willis's mortal or brutish soul was common to man and animals and consisted of two parts: one was in the blood for metabolic functions such as nourishment and heat production, while the other was in the nervous system for the regulation of perception, action, and sleep. In this book Willis also described the cochlea as the receptor organ of hearing (327a).

Systematic Physiology, Evolution, and Behavior

The advances of the biological sciences from the seventeenth to the nineteenth centuries are based on the idea that the functional mechanisms underlying living organisms can be investigated by physical and chemical methods. This methodological reductionism differs radically from the medieval attitude with its primary attention to the human soul and its neglect of corporal mechanisms. Descartes's mechanistic model of the body paved the way for physiology, as shown in Figures 8–11. These were mostly qualitative, not quantitative, investigations. Galileo's quantification principle was first used in physics and much later in physiology and biology. The latter disciplines were not yet ripe for quantitative measurements, but they did develop some system concepts. These and mechanistic principles laid the foundations of modern biological research.

KEPLERIAN AND CARTESIAN CONCEPTS OF BODY MECHANICS AS PRECONDITIONS OF PHYSIOLOGY. Kepler's notions of the living eye as an optical apparatus and of the stellar world as a clockwork were important theoretical advances toward modern science. They were followed by the Cartesian concept of the *machine animale* that made it possible to investigate single physiological mechanisms. Descartes's dualistic separation of body and soul showed a machinelike body that can be investigated independently from psychic phenomena. So he got rid of the medieval symbolisms of body functions. His hypothesis that the body functions as an engine was the initial key to success of all subsequent physiological discoveries. Crombie has demonstrated convincingly that from then onward, physiological questions of sensory functions could be separated from psychological problems of perception

and knowledge (78). This and Galileo's quantification in mechanical physics allowed the scientist to restrict his investigation to concise questions and to discover partial mechanisms and specific sense cues. Thus the scientists of the seventeenth century transformed into special and solvable questions the general approach of the medieval authors, who had often contaminated rather confused philosophical problems by tingeing them with theological symbolism for their investigations of optics, vision, and divine enlightenment.

The concept of physiological systems cooperating in function but occupying different parts of the body began with Harvey's studies of circulation and movements in the seventeenth century and was followed 100 years later by Haller's general physiology and Buffon's behavioral descriptions. System concepts were applied to sensory physiology much later, when in the nineteenth century J. Müller, Helmholtz, and Hering developed their theories of the visual, auditory, and other sensory systems (see JOHANNES MÜLLER, p. 46; HERMANN L. F. HELMOLTZ, p. 47; EWALD HERING, p. 47).

HARVEY'S DISCOVERIES AND SENSORY PHYSIOLOGY. William Harvey (1578–1658), professor of anatomy in London and court physician of Charles I, was the most original experimental physiologist of the seventeenth century. Harvey's writings and his discovery of the mechanisms of blood circulation in 1618–1628 not only were important for cardiac physiology but also contained ideas relating to autoregulation in the organism. Harvey's importance for sensorimotor function and autoregulation—now called biocybernetics—has only been appreciated in the past fifteen years, due to the studies of Mrs. Whitteridge (368) and W. von Brunn (65). Harvey's manuscript on animal movement "De motu locali animalium," which remained unpublished, describes the central nervous system as regulator of body functions and coordinator of perception and motility. His treatise on the movement of the heart and the blood (152) made him famous and was frequently reprinted in the eighteenth century.

Harvey is usually considered a pure experimentalist, but besides being a good observer and experimenter he had excellent abilities for abstraction and theory, although he drew some erroneous conclusions from investigations about animal generation. The following quotation from Barlow characterizes Harvey's personality: "He was a keen and accurate observer and an enthusiastic naturalist, and he had a mind reflective as to the causes and relations of things, fertile in recognizing resemblances, and, above all, ready in making working hypotheses and in devising experiments which would more or less verify those hypotheses." (65, 221).

HALLER'S PHYSIOLOGY. Albrecht von Haller (1708–1777), the most famous physiologist of the eighteenth century, developed his concept of irritability and sensibility in his monumental eight-volume treatise *Elementa physiologiae corporis humanae* (139). His experiments on nerve conduction were limited and his neural theory was incomplete, but we must remember that his investigations took place forty years before Galvani's electrical nerve stimulation. The nerves were considered to be "tools for perception and motion." He distinguished between two kinds of sensory (*sensibilis*) and motor (*irritabilis*) nerves, without recognizing the sensory conduction of the anterior and posterior spinal roots. His methods of nerve stimulation (mechanical, thermic, and chemical) were rather crude. Although he knew of electricity, he did not use electrical stimuli and rejected electrical conduction because of the essential difference of nerves and isolated metal wires.

Haller declared the brain to be the seat of mental functions and defended a realistic concept of brain activity as a coordinator of many somatic functions. In his treatise (139) and his shorter book on physiology (140) he repeatedly said that behavior and movements can be independent of the mind and of voluntary action in the "body machine and its splendid construction in animals and man." He noted that unilateral lesions in the brain resulted in contralateral disturbances of movement and sensation, and that excitation of the cerebral penduncles caused contralateral movements, but he did not discuss the reason why homolateral effects can also be observed. All higher functions were treated as "internal senses" and an elaboration of the classical five "external senses." The fifth modality (*tactus*) included warmth, cold, pain, tickling, and even hunger, thirst, and lust. The limits of the internal senses and the mental functions remained unclear. So Haller was careful to leave open for further discussion the issue of the higher brain functions. Among these cerebral functions he considered the rather modern concept of a representative model of the world in the brain, but he said that it is not known how this can be obtained. Dreams and the images appearing at the onset of sleep were considered abnormal functions of the internal sense. Haller taught a solid brain anatomy and did not accept special brain localizations besides the contralateral motor and sensory projections of the cerebral hemispheres.

In reading his publications I came to the conclusion that one should not label Haller a principal antilocalist, as Polyak (307) did. Haller just described what was known at his time, and this was limited to some relations of the cerebral cortex to contralateral motor functions. He was careful not to speculate too much on functional localization in the brain and not to ascribe too much of the regulation of functions to the mind, as most of his contemporaries did. He repeatedly said that many movements are involuntary and automatically controlled, or they occur even contrary to voluntary tendencies. Among these he listed autonomous actions of the heart, the bowels, and even penile erection. His concept of nerve conduction, however, was rather general: he spoke of the "incredible velocity of nerve impulses," which is understandable 100 years before Helmholtz (162) measured the conduction velocity of animal and human nerves (see ELECTROPHYSIOLOGY AND NERVE CONDUCTION, p. 44).

VISION RESEARCH FROM KEPLER TO NEWTON

THE RETINAL IMAGE AND THE OPTIC NERVES. Following 2,000 years of misinterpretation, between 1604 and 1738 the optic projection of the retinal image and the cerebral projections of the optic nerves were elucidated in a series of steps by Kepler, Scheiner, Descartes, Newton, and J. Taylor. The long history of the erroneous concepts of the eye's dioptrics was described by Polyak in 1957 (307) with many illustrations. The Platonic misconception of rays sent out by the eye and the misunderstanding of the position and function of the lens are two examples of false ideas influencing scientific tradition for more than a millenium (SOCRATIC AND PLATONIC CONCEPTS, p. 7). Even during the Renaissance such astute observers as Leonardo and Vesalius continued to depict the lens in the central part of the eye and did not recognize the retina as the receptor structure. It was not until 1583 and 1603 that Felix Platter (1536–1614), the anatomist of Basel, drew the lens in the anterior part of the eye (although still inexact in one detail, in that it did not touch the iris), and stated that the retina received the image of the outer world. In 1604 and 1611 Kepler, referring to Platter's anatomy, gave an exact optical explanation of the projection of the retinal image through the cornea and the lens (see KEPLER'S CONTRIBUTIONS, p. 23). After an earlier observation of the Italian Maurolico remained unnoticed, the retinal projection was demonstrated by experiments on the ox's eye first made by the Jesuit Scheiner in 1619 and depicted by Descartes in 1637 (Fig. 11). Descartes's posthumous book *De homine* (1662) shows cerebral projections of both eyes via the optic nerves to the pineal body (Fig. 8*B*), but he did not recognize the crossing of optic nerve fibers in the chiasma: this was conceived later by Newton in 1704, and depicted by Taylor in 1738 (see Fig. 13*A*).

Kepler's Dioptrics

VISUAL PROJECTIONS. A sidetrack from Kepler's major achievements in astronomy were his geometrical studies of optic projections on the retina of the eye. Although Kepler believed in a sort of world harmony he formulated his mathematicomechanical approach succinctly for both stellar movements and the human eye. He said in his astronomy in 1619,

> My goal is to show that the heavenly machine is not a kind of divine living being but similar to a clockwork. (219).

The retinal image inversion was clearly described by him in 1611 as follows:

> Vision is brought about by a picture of the thing seen, being formed on the white concave surface of the retina. That which is to the right outside is depicted on the left on the retina, that to the left on the right, that above below, and that below above.... Green is depicted green, and in general things are depicted by whatever color they have. [Crombie's translation (76) from the original in Latin (219).]

Kepler was the first scientist who discussed the optic nerve decussation, although he did not yet propose a precise partial crossing of the nasal half-fields as Newton did 100 years later. Kepler even confused the issue by proposing antidromic impulses from the left and right brain to both eyes crossing in the optic nerves. He also proposed the necessity of lens accommodation, but the exact observation of light reflection during accommodation was made by Scheiner.

In his first geometrical analysis of optics in 1604 Kepler had left the physiological questions open— "to be solved by natural philosophers." When he returned to this problem in the *Dioptrice* in 1611 (219) he used the afterimages as a proof of the action of light on the retinal substance. He assumed that sensations might be "representative images" conducted through nervous pathways to the brain. Anticipating Descartes's later concept of the esprits animaux traveling via the nerves to the brain, Kepler mentioned the possibility of a wavelike conduction in the optic nerves. In his *Dioptrice*, which treats physiological optics in 141 paragraphs containing definitions, axioms, problems, and propositions, he first discussed both an afferent and an efferent conduction in the optic nerves between the eyes and the brain centers. Then he said that the retinal image could be transmitted through the optic nerves like waves spreading in water. It is still a long way from these Keplerian *undes* or *spiritus visivi* (waves of vision) and the Cartesian *spiritus animales* (animal spirits of nerves) to modern concepts of propagated nerve action potentials. Objective electrophysiology of nerve conduction began only 200 years later, after Galvani's discoveries had paved the way for Dubois-Reymond's and Helmholtz's recordings of electric potentials from nerves and muscles (see ELECTROPHYSIOLOGY AND NERVE CONDUCTION, p. 44).

KEPLER'S WORLD PICTURE. Physical principles are to be found in Kepler's books among symbolic interpretations of the world similar to medieval concepts. A scientist reading Kepler's book on "World Harmony" (220) in search of his physical and mathematical results may wonder why he has to go through many poetic and religious predications. And yet Kepler's desire to find general rules for harmonies in the sensory and stellar worlds was a genuine part of his *Weltbild*; he was striving to define the place of man in nature. A similar desire, more clearly separated from his scientific papers, sparked up three centuries later

in Sherrington's remarks on life in nature and on the values of man (329).

It is interesting that the sober Galileo, who accentuated measurement and quantification, missed the eliptic course of the planets, whereas the more speculative and symbolically minded Kepler discovered it in his striving with verifications and complex mathematics. However, if Kepler's *Harmonices mundi* were published in modern times, it would be judged to be a confused mixture of scientific, metaphysical, and religious ideas held together by Neoplatonic mysticism and Christian piety, among which Kepler's third law is hidden somewhere. As Crombie (76) said, it is "an almost unintelligible matrix into which gems of science somehow got embedded." Kepler's *Dioptrice* (219), his most important work for the sensory physiologist, is very differently written in the clear style of a modern scientific publication. It treats the optics of the eye, its anomalies, and their compensation by glasses, using clearly stated mathematical methods and figures without any additional speculation or mysticism.

Kepler believed that the anatomical structure of the eye, as well as the mechanics of the universe, can be revealed by mathematical laws. His *Harmonices mundi* (220), however, contains not only a clear comparison of the clockworklike planetary movements but also symbolic discourses on such topics as geometric solids, acoustic harmonies, God's creation, and (in chapter 3) an appraisal of Pythagoras's number symbolism. Thus late Renaissance science was influenced not only by the Christian religion but also by the ancient Greek geometric mythology of the Pythagorean school.

The transition from medieval to modern science was not a sudden break or revolution but a slow process of conceptual development. Ancient beliefs in the soul were, however, maintained for three centuries. As explained above, even Descartes's mechanical theory of the body postulated a cerebral seat of the soul to keep the organism functioning. A hundred years later Newton defended divine creation and in his later years developed religious and mystical ideas.

Other Visual Studies

JESUIT SCIENTISTS AND OPTICAL STUDIES. In the time of Kepler and Galileo the Jesuit order was increasing its influence at all levels of Western society. The founder of the order, Ignatius of Loyola, a militant organizer with some psychological intuition, was not interested in research, and some of his followers were even involved in the inquisition against scientists. Nevertheless, there were other Jesuits who became successful researchers.

Two Jesuit priests of German origin, Christoph Scheiner (1579–1650) and Athanasius Kircher (1601–1680), should be mentioned for their discoveries in optics. Scheiner discovered the sun spots, experimented with animals' eyes, and observed the human eye to discover the functions of the lens and pupil. In 1619, by removing the sclera of the ox's eye (see Descartes's illustration of this experiment in Fig. 11), he proved Kepler's theory of the projection of the retinal image through refraction of the lens. Scheiner further discovered the process of accommodation in the human lens, postulated by Kepler in 1611 (219) after observing light reflections within the living human eye.

Kircher constructed the magic lantern for slide projection. Both avoided the touchy problems of heliocentric theories after these were listed as forbidden on the Index of the Church.

From Kepler onward came the disappearance of the medieval prejudice against the inverted image by lens refraction that had troubled investigators of optics for five centuries from Alhazen to Leonardo. Now it became possible to ask definitive and answerable questions of physiological optics, and to make testable propositions for sensory physiology. So Kepler's dioptrics stimulated Scheiner's experiments to demonstrate the retinal image in the ox's eye and to observe the accommodation of the lens in the living human eye. Furthermore, new scientific procedures, specifically adapted to the particular problems being studied, led to methodical advances in sensory physiology; these were separated from the complex philosophy of human knowledge and the soul, with their theological implications, that had so complicated medieval science.

When the scientists of the seventeenth century began to ask different kinds of questions about body mechanisms not related to mystical and religious universals in philosophy, and when they began to use quantitative measurements, the way was free for a modern kind of science.

Newton's Work on Optics and Vision

NEWTONIAN PHYSICS. Isaak Newton (1642–1727), born in the year of Galileo's death, worked in Trinity College of Cambridge University, where he pursued his work on astronomy, mechanics, and optics with ingenious theories and with great success. Newton's work was soon recognized, and it profoundly influenced eighteenth century science and philosophy in Europe and America.

Newton's law of universal gravitation, discovered in 1666, elucidated the effects made by the attraction between the sun and the planets on their revolution that could be expressed in simple and exact mathematical terms. The attraction between the sun and a planet was proportional to their masses and inversely proportional to the square of the distance between them. This relationship at once explained Kepler's laws. Newton was a pious Protestant and hence reserved some functions for God, including the primary moving force for planetary revolution. He postulated that divine creation was necessary only for the initiation of the solar system, which once set into motion, would move according to Kepler's laws and to the gravitational forces conceived by himself.

NEWTONIAN VIEWS ON OPTICS AND VISION. Newton's work on the analysis and theory of light and colors induced him to think further on visual perception and the processing of sensory information. Besides his studies of the spectral colors and of physiological optics, he described afterimages following moving light stimuli and retinal phosphenes during mechanical pressure on the eyeball, and he postulated the crossing of fibers in the optic chiasma.

Figure 12 shows Newton's sketch of his spectral experiments on light and color. The first English version of Newton's book *Optics* (294) appeared in 1704 and laid the foundation for all subsequent work on color vision. By showing that all spectral colors can be extracted from white light and that they appear in a definite rainbow order after spectral dispersion, he inaugurated an important new era in physical optics. One hundred years later Thomas Young (384) provided a physiological supplement explaining color vision with his three-color theory (1802), and a further fifty years later Helmholtz introduced the systematic analysis of the mixing of colors and developed ideas of the three retinal receptor types responding to color (164). Although in his emission theory of light Newton did not consider light to be a wave process, he admitted that there might be different periodic states of light emission. At the present state of knowledge these could be compared to different frequencies first discussed in Huygens's wave theory of light, which explains the physical base of color by different wave lengths in the spectrum.

It is usually overlooked that Newton, in addition to making his well-known discovery of spectral colors, was also the first to discuss the partial crossing of the optic nerve fibers in the chiasma and to appreciate its functional significance. The chiasmal crossing had been misconceived by Descartes (81), who pictured the chiasma without crossing fibers in his attempt to explain central visual projections by convergence to the pineal body (Fig. 8). Newton gives no anatomical details or picture of the decussation, but later authors depicted his postulate of crossing fibers. In 1738 the ophthalmologist Taylor in his French treatise on the human eye and its diseases, which was translated into German in 1750 (343), reproduced a clear scheme of the partial decussation in man (Fig. 13A), an approximation of present-day concepts. In 1775 J. Harris in his *Treatise of Optics* (141) showed a similar drawing with the binocular convergence in the brain (Fig. 13B).

Newton postulated the partial crossing in a rather long but clear sentence as follows:

Qu. 15. Are not the Species of Objects seen with both Eyes united where the optick Nerves meet before they come into the Brain, the Fibres on the right side of both Nerves uniting there, and after union going thence into

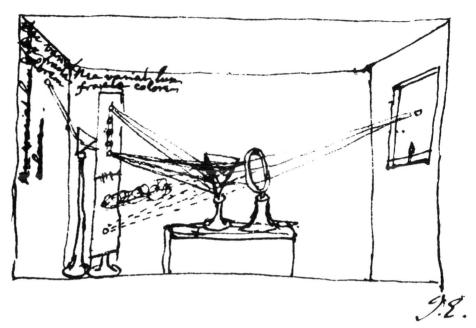

FIG. 12. Newton's sketch of his prismatic experiments made around 1700. This original design, preserved among other "non-optic" writings of Newton, shows how rays of white sunlight from the window hole are refracted by a prism into their spectral colors and are projected to a perforated screen at left. Lowest spectral color is projected further, beyond a screen hole and through a second prism to left side of wall, excluding the other spectral components that were projected above. Newton's Latin script says twice: "Nec variat lux fracta colorem" (the refracted light does not change its color). (Drawing at Bodleian Library, Oxford. Reproduced with kind permission of the Library and New College, Oxford.)

the Brain in the Nerve which is on the right side of the Head, and the Fibres on the left side of both Nerves uniting in the same place, and after union going into the Brain in the Nerve which is on the left side of the Head, and these two Nerves meeting in the Brain in such a manner that their Fibres make but one entire Species or Picture, half of which on the right side of the Sensorium comes from the right side of both Eyes through the right side of both optick Nerves to the place where the Nerves meet, and from thence on the right side of the Head into the Brain, and the other half on the left side of the Sensorium comes in like manner from the left side of both Eyes. (294).

In the next sentences he discusses whether animals with lateral position of the eyes have different or no crossing of optic nerves. (Although Dr. D. T. Whiteside, an expert on Newtonian scripts, helped me in searching, I was unable to find Newton's sketch of the partial optic nerve decussation among his manuscripts preserved in the University Libraries of Cambridge and Oxford. It may have existed in the eighteenth century as a model of Harris' picture shown in Figure Fig. 13B and could still exist, hidden in a private collection.)

It is remarkable that the optic nerve decussation remained a hypothesis for about 150 years until direct anatomical evidence and clinical applications for visual field disturbances in man were obtained in the second half of the nineteenth century, when Gudden

(136) studied the optic chiasma and neurologists observed the hemianopsias.

Newton made no essentially new propositions to explain the action of the sense organs for nervous conduction besides the chiasma-decussation hypothesis. He said in *General Scholium* and *Opticks* that all sensations are excited by vibrations and "propagated along the solid filaments of the nerves, from the outward organs of sense to the brain and from the brain into the muscles." This adds nothing to Descartes's earlier concepts depicted in Figure 8. Newton was careful not to postulate too much about nerve functions, since he lacked experience outside the field of vision. He said that we need more experiments to determinate the laws of nervous conduction. For this he discussed an "electric and elastic spirit," which he compared to gravity and electricity.

NEWTON ON HYPOTHESIS, DEDUCTION, AND INDUCTION. Newton, whose theories of vision are of special interest for the sensory physiologist, expressed caution in making hypotheses, in contrast to Descartes's and Huygens's readiness to propose generalizations. The gravitation concept was a most fruitful hypothetical deduction, and yet Newton criticized deductive science; in 1604 (294) he spoke against hypothetical deduction:

As in Mathematicks, so in Nature Philosophy, the Inves-

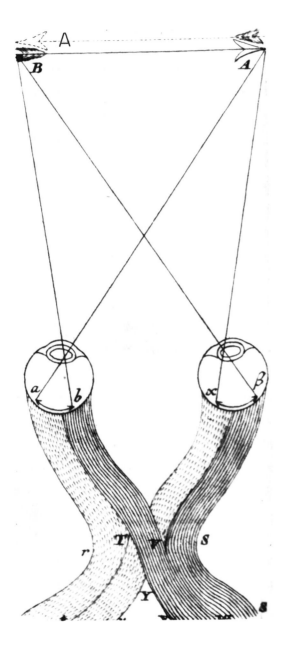

FIG. 13. Newton's postulate of partial decussation of optic nerves in the chiasma as illustrated in the eighteenth century by Taylor (1738) and Harris (1775). *A*: Taylor's figure of optic chiasma depicts crossing over of nasal parts of the retina to explain single vision in two half-fields of both eyes without reference to Newton; images of the object (arrows *BA*) are projected to retinas of both eyes (*a–b* in left eye and α–β in right eye). From chiasma onward the right parts of both retinas (*continuous lines*) project to right (*XWS*), and left parts (*dashed lines*) to left optic tract (*rtu*). *B*: Harris's figure of binocular convergence to illustrate Newton's concept of central projection of corresponding parts of retina when eyes converge on line *PS*. After crossing of nasal parts of the retina the corresponding retinal areas *T* and *X* and *V* and *Y* are drawn to unite in *FGH* so that binocular convergence occurs in brain and is projected to a hypothetical central area *abcd*. [*A*: from Taylor (343). *B*: from Harris (141).]

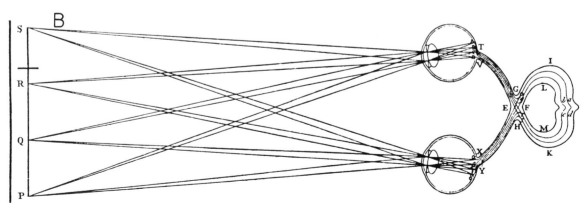

tigation of difficult Things by the Method of Analysis, ought ever to precede the Method of Composition. This Analysis consists in making Conclusions from them by Induction, and admitting of no Objections against the Conclusions, but such as are taken from Experiments, or other certain Truths. For Hypotheses are not to be regarded in experimental Philosophy. And although the arguing from Experiments and Observations by Induction be not Demonstration of general Conclusion; yet is is the best way of arguing which the Nature of Things admits of, and may be looked upon as so much the stronger, by how much the Induction is more general.

However, a few lines later he admits synthesis:

This is the Method of Analysis: And the Synthesis consists in assuming the Causes Discover'd, and established as Principles, and by them explaining the Phenomena proceeding from them, and providing the Explanations.

Again in contrast to Descartes, who pretended to recognize the qualities, causes, and principles of many events, Newton was careful to deduce only those explanations that were inferred from measurements and quantitative analysis of the observed phenomena. He wrote in *Opticks* (294), Query 31:

To tell us that every Species of Things is endow'd with an occult specified Quality by which it acts and produces its manifest Effects, is to tell us nothing: But to derive two or three general Principles of Motion from Phenomena, and afterward to tell us how the Properties and Actions of all corporeal Things follow from those manifest Principles, would be a very great step in Philosophy, though the Causes of those Principles were not yet discover'd.

The sequence—*1*) observation of phenomena, *2*) measurement of effects, *3*) analysis, and *4*) synthesis in principle and a mathematical formula—appeared to Newton to be a general rule for scientific progress by inductive methods, as proposed by Galileo and Bacon. Of course, Newton also used deductive methods, proceeding from theory to experiment, but considered them exceptions. From that time deduction became less respectable until Boltzmann, Planck, and Einstein developed theoretical physics in the nineteenth and twentieth centuries.

Newton's famous and often-quoted sentence *Hypotheses non fingo* (I do not invent hypotheses) in the final *scholium generale* of the *Principia* is here only used for gravitation (293), but later it became an argument of inductivists against theories and deductive methods in science. But this sentence does not mean that Newton makes no hypotheses; it says only that he is against science fiction and does not accept fantastic and ill-founded hypotheses. The Latin word *fingere* means not only "build up" or "think" but also "dream" or "corrupt"; briefly, it is the source of "fiction." Newton distinguished these fictive hypotheses from axioms. Before the second edition of the *Principia* appeared in 1713 he wrote to Cotes:

... as in Geometry the word Hypothesis is not taken in so large a sense as to include the Axioms and Postulates,

so in Experimental Philosophy it is not to be taken in so large a sense as to include the first Principles or Axioms which I call the laws of motion. These principles are deduced from Phenomena and made general by Induction: which is the highest evidence that a Proposition can have in this philosophy. And the word Hypothesis is here used by me to signify only such a Phenomena as is not a Phenomenon nor deduced from any phenomena but assumed or supposed without any experimental proof. (76).

So Newton distinguished assumed hypotheses and deduced principal postulates, but passed in silence the other scientific approach (which he himself used also in *Optics*): namely, to make the experiment after a conceived theory and to plan it according to a precise hypothesis that could be proved or shown to be false by the experiment.

Hence it would be absurd to believe that the author of the most successful quantitative hypothesis for stellar movements is against theories in science, when he warns against making unfounded hypotheses and premature deductions: "hypotheses seu metaphysicae, seu physicae, seu qualitatum occultarum." (293).

Even now, 300 years after Newton, we do not yet know the nature of gravitation, how it is caused, or how it is transmitted, but we can measure it and use it in mathematical formulas, and this is sufficient for science. Other examples of Newton's hypothetical deductions are his astonishing predictions in vision, such as the partial crossing of the optic nerves. This was a purely deductive hypothesis without any empirical experiment or anatomical verification. So in spite of his repeated appraisal of inductive methods, Newton's work shows the best applications of theoretical deduction and is an early illustration of Popper's statement in 1935 (308) that empirical sciences are systems of theories.

The modern sensory physiologist appreciates mainly the clear discourse of Kepler on the eye's dioptrics and Newton's results on color and visual functions. But he must realize that these are only selections of their works that may not represent the true intention of the authors. The sensory and physical research of these prominent scientists was also motivated by rather mystical and religious ideas.

EMPIRICISM AND RATIONALISM IN SEVENTEENTH AND EIGHTEENTH CENTURIES

Sensualist Empiricism and Materialism

HOBBES'S EMPIRICISM. The English philosopher Thomas Hobbes (1586–1679) was a contemporary of Galileo, Kepler, Descartes, and the young Newton. His long lifespan enabled him to see all their scientific advances. Hobbes visited Galileo in Florence and criticized Descartes, collecting his scientific observations for a synthesis of physiology and philosophy and carrying on discussions and correspondence with him until the annoyed Descartes stopped it. Hobbes founded philosophical empiricism by deriving thought and imagination from sensory experience. He was an original and vigorous man with many contradictory traits and political tendencies that he later suppressed during the period of Cromwell's protectorate. Although he formulated a theory of the Commonwealth he was a monarchist. Despite stressing the ruthlessness of man ("homo homini lupus"), he recognized individuality. While admitting that the variety of human beings have very different instincts and inclinations, he was a determinist, denying free will. He said that in reality sensations are motion, but at the same time he was a sensualist. Furthermore, he was a nominalist, devaluating general terms and throwing doubt on the conceptual knowledge obtained through the senses.

Hobbes's physiological ideas concentrated on motion, overrating its role immensely. He used his motion concept also for perception in confounding stimulus conditions and sensory experience. He said rightly that sensations are caused by external movements of things—such as mechanical pressure, sound waves, light reflection—but not by the stable objects themselves. Hobbes's materialistic concept of man declared bodily motions the source of human drive and knowledge.

So far as one knows, this original and somewhat arrogant philosopher, who was interested in all fields of human knowledge, made not a single experiment to prove his motion theory of sensation. Hobbes's general philosophical influence as founder of empiricism and social theory was greater than his importance to the history of natural science and sensory functions, to which he contributed less than his followers Locke and Hume.

LOCKE'S WHITE PAPER. The most interesting figure for sensory physiology among the British philosophers of the seventeenth century is John Locke (1632–1704). After studying medicine in Oxford he became interested in many fields of research and politics, lived for some time in Paris and Holland during the Restoration, and published his main work, *An Essay Concerning Human Understanding* (251), in 1690 on his return in England. This book founded the sensualist teaching of the *tabula rasa* of the mind into which sensory information is fed, its "white paper" being inscribed from birth with empirical experience received from the senses. Thus Locke revived the old Aristotelian and scholastic teaching that human knowledge originates in the senses. He avoided, however, mentioning these ancient sources of sensory philosophy such as Thomas Aquinas's concept of the tabula rasa.

Although Locke recognized reflection as well as sensation, he maintained that all ideas are acquired by experience. His concepts were in sharp contrast to those of Leibniz, who also divided his interests between philosophy and politics but postulated "inborn ideas" and taught that perception needs a rational order to become clear and distinct. Locke was also

successful in his political endeavors after the Glorious Revolution of 1688. His influence furthered the empiricist movement, which had been less clearly conceived by Hobbes. It was stated more fully by Locke and further elaborated by Hume.

In contrast to Hume, who later elaborated his concepts, Locke was not a sharp reasoner, preferring probability to certainty, and believing in practical reason and sensory information. With his emphasis on perception as the sole source of knowledge he rejected all a priori or deductive arguments.

Some citations from his writings may illustrate Locke's (251) concepts.

> [Perception is] the *first* step and movement towards knowledge and the inlet of all . . . . Knowledge is the perception of the agreement or disagreement of two ideas. . . . Let us then suppose the mind to be, as we say, white paper, void of all characters, without any ideas; how comes it to be furnished? Whence comes it by that vast store, which the busy and boundless fancy of man has painted on it with an almost endless variety? Whence has it all the materials of reason and knowledge? To this I answer in one word, from experience: in that all our knowledge is founded, and from that it ultimately derives itself. . . . The grounds of probability are two: conformity with our own experience, or the testimony of other's experience.

Locke had much common sense but his general logical conclusions were not always convincing. He was often right in concrete details, but his general concepts and abstractions commonly ended in inconsistencies. His dislike of metaphysics made him careless in logic and blind to the a priori logic in mathematics. As is common among innovators, in pressing his views he overstated some of his concepts. These exaggerations then caused logical difficulties, e.g., when he denied all innate principles. Hence, his postulates of empirical knowledge and learning from the senses cannot be generalized or maintained as principles, and they often appear paradoxical in their consequences.

In postulating that the mind is a white paper and that nothing other than perception works on it, Locke had difficulties in ascribing some functions to thought. So he said that perception is assisted by thought, a concept not very different from that of his adversary Leibniz. Thus he admitted an "internal sense" that produces the percept from primary sensation. For human self-consciousness he even accepted intuition.

As a sensualist and empiricist Locke asserted that the mind has no content prior to sensory information, and that all ideas come from experience. Of course, Locke could not deny that we think. So he accepted the role of thought and Descartes's *Cogito, ergo sum*. While admitting that man is certain about his own existence, he gave no convincing explanation of how this certitude could develop by sensory experience. How Locke's internal sense is related to the sense organs and how reflections produced ideas remains unclear.

It is not surprising that more sophisticated philosophers who preferred logical thought to simple statements refused to accept Locke's philosophy and to discuss it seriously, calling his main assertions either truisms or illogical inferences. So they dismissed his empiricism as common sense naiveté and lay philosophy. Locke's concepts did, however, give rise to the main streams of British empiricist and sensualist philosophies and were supported by stronger, logical arguments by Hume, who influenced Kant. They were also taken up in France, where the main figures were Voltaire (who ridiculed Leibniz) and the materialist *philosophes* of the Parisian circles.

THE FRENCH MATERIALISTS AND SENSUALISTS. Locke, Newton, and Hume influenced the French philosophers, encyclopedists, and writers of the eighteenth century who adopted empiricist concepts. This was facilitated by personal contact, since both Locke and Hume lived for some time in Paris. Literature, science, and philosophy were related more closely in France than in England and Germany. Voltaire wrote a book on Newton's concepts and another on Locke's philosophy. Several French materialists developed Descartes's machine theory of the organism but did not accept his dualism and his theological conclusions. They dispensed with the soul by adopting the British sensualist concept of the perceptual origin of knowledge and by relating mental functions to the brain. The main driving forces of human behavior were explained by emotion and desire, the simplest being hunger and sex and the more complex being cultural and spiritual requirements.

J. Offroy de La Mettrie (1709–1751) became the leading satiric spirit of the French materialists. His most famous book, *L'Homme machine* (240) in 1748, and his elegant style and esprit were highly esteemed by the Prussian king Frederick II (1712–1786), who also was a materialist philosopher. He called La Mettrie to Berlin as a member of his newly founded Academy, where several French scientists found more freedom than in France after the public burning of La Mettrie's first book *Histoire naturelle de l'âme* (1745).

According to La Mettrie's *L'Homme machine* man consists of matter that, nonetheless, is a perceiving organism by virtue of its brain; this model contrasts with Descartes's *machine animale*, which is also matter and a nervous mechanism but needs the soul (residing as a sort of ghost in the pineal gland) for perception. It is less well known that La Mettrie also demonstrated the biological limits of materialism in another book, *Les Animaux plus que machines* in 1750 (240a).

A positivistic sensualism was defended by Bonnot de Condillac (1715–1780) in his *Traité des sensations* (1754) with some reserve concerning materialism. In saying that all human knowledge consists of sensations and in recognizing no innate faculties he dropped Locke's reflection and introduced instead a *langue des calculs* based on learned logic and mathematics. He said that our reason can only make use of sensory signals (*signes*), but admitted analyzing and combining processes: *décompositions des phénomènes* and *compositions des idées*. Hence he could not exclude thought in the processing of sensory information. During the second half of the eighteenth century many scientists felt a need for a compromise between the sensualist and rationalist philosophies. This synthesis was attempted by Kant (see *Kantian Synthesis of Perception and Thought*, p. 39).

Leibnizian Rationalism

Gottfried Wilhelm Leibniz (1646–1716) was a philosopher with universal interests and a mathematician who even in early youth demonstrated great originality of thought. Through a large correspondence and discussions with contemporary philosophers such as Spinoza, Locke, Clarke, and others he ensured that his concepts were widely known. Simultaneously with but independently of Newton, he invented the differential and integral calculus in 1684. Among other scientific achievements I mention only the construction of a calculating machine (1710) and, as a stroke of genius, the invention of the binary number system conceived and written in manuscript in 1679 (Fig. 14) and published in 1705 (242). This dual code received a belated appreciation and universal application with the development of modern computers.

Despite his very different concepts Leibniz had a high esteem for Locke's achievements and avoided irreverent comments. Locke was less careful and liked to make fun of some of Leibniz's ideas. Leibniz discussed Locke's book, chapter by chapter, in his *Nouveaux essais* (243), and the two imaginary persons in his work who dispute about Locke's concepts may partly be derived from life and the personal contrasts between the two philosophers, softened by correspondence with their common friends, Lady Masham and Clarke in London. Deploring the death of Locke, to whom he had intended to send the final version, Leibniz delayed the publication of the *Nouveaux essais* so that they were not printed until 1765, 52 years after his death (243). This posthumous book, written in French, contains Leibniz's main systematic philosophy, which before this time had been dispersed during four decades in some popular books or in fragments and letters written during his busy life in Mainz and Hanover. The strength of his philosophy is logical consistency.

PERCEPTION AND APPERCEPTION IN LEIBNIZIAN PHILOSOPHY. Leibniz distinguished two kinds of sensory information, called *perception* and *apperception*. Perceptions, or *petites perceptions*, are defined as elementary material delivered by the senses and appearing as somewhat confused sensory experience that also could remain unconscious. In contrast, apperception is con-

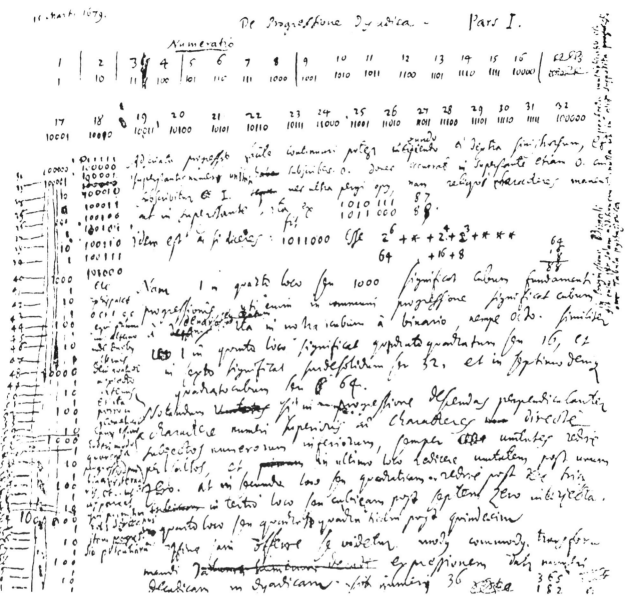

FIG. 14. G. W. Leibniz's manuscript of the binary number theory, written on March 15, 1679. Latin text explains the principle to use the two signs 1 and 0 for all numbers. Upper part of page shows his scheme of dual number systems, which he called "Progressio dyadica," as written in title at *top*. Sequence of upper lines 1–32 is continued in left vertical column to reach number 100 in lowest part (not reproduced). Leibniz submitted this dual system to the Paris Academy in 1703, where it was published in 1705 (242). Practical application of this principle had to wait for electronic computers, which had less difficulty in using the long number sequences than a hand-writing mathematician. (Reproduced with kind permission of the Leibniz-Archiv, Niedersächsiche Landesbibliothek, Hannover.)

scious, clear, and distinct and is obtained by intellectual effort as rational knowledge. Furthermore, Leibniz distinguished two kinds of primary truth: *vérité éternelle* (the rationally conceived knowledge that is common to the human intellect and valid for all human beings) and *vérité de fait* (the knowledge acquired empirically and individually with limited general validity). The latter consists of a multitude of different empirical statements disclosed by research and common sense as factual truth (243).

Although Leibniz made some concessions to the sensory empiricist in allowing the concept of factual truth acquired by the senses, he maintained that the primary condition of human knowledge is the intellect. So he added to the old scholastic sentence *Nihil est in intellectu quod non fuerit in sensu* the important addition *nisi intellectus ipse* (Nothing is in our knowledge which has not come from our senses, except the intellect itself). Leibniz founded mathematical logic (319, 320).

The rationalist philosophy of Leibniz, which introduced the Age of Enlightenment, influenced mainly the German universities. It was systematized by Christian Wolf (1679–1754), who taught mathematics and philosophy in Marburg and Halle. In France and England, however, the empiricist and sensualist philosophies dominated and were propagated in literature by Voltaire and Diderot. Parallel trends were the materialistic conceptions promoted in France and in Berlin, and Berkeley's sensualistic idealism in Great Britain.

Berkeley's Concept of Space and Hume's Associationism

BERKELEY'S SUBJECTIVISM AND VISUAL SPACE. In his early writings George Berkeley (1685–1753) published some interesting theories related to visual and tactile perception and its role in our concept of space. He also discussed the possible role of eye movements and convergence in space perception. Berkeley wrote well but attempted no experimental verification of his sensory theories. His arguments are entertaining to read but do not always convince, as when he denies reality independent of the mind and accepts objects as existing only in the act of subjective perception: "Whatever is immediately perceived is an idea, and can any idea exist out of the mind?"

Berkeley turned from his analysis of sensory functions to an extreme idealism in which he appears to have confused percept and object, but he recognized an empiricist conception of space perception. His teaching that tactile information completes the visual sense influenced the investigation of sensory interaction and integration. He said that our concept of distance and space is acquired empirically, that is, from experience. This contrasts with Kant's later view of space and time as a priori categories. I think the best way to convey Berkeley's opinion on vision and touch is by quoting the following points from his book *Essay Towards a New Theory of Vision* (41):

> 1. My design is (a) to shew the manner wherein we perceive by Sight the Distance, Magnitude, and Situation of objects; also (b) to consider the difference there is betwixt the ideas of Sight and Touch, and whether there be any idea common to both senses.
> 2. It is, I think, agreed by all that Distance, of itself, and immediately, cannot be seen. . . .
> 3. I find it also acknowledged that the estimate we make of the distance of objects considerably remote is rather an act of judgement grounded on experience than of sense. . . .
> 4. But, when an object is placed at so near a distance as that the interval between the eyes bears any sensible proportion to it, the opinion of speculative men is, that the two optic axes (the fancy that we see only with one eye at once being exploded), concurring at the object, do

there make an angle, by means of which, according as it is greater or lesser, the object is perceived to be nearer or farther off. . . .

> 13. Since therefore those angles and lines are not themselves perceived by sight, it follows, from sect. 10, that the mind does not by them judge of the distance of objects. . . .
> 20. From all which it follows, that the judgment we make of the distance of an object viewed with both eyes is entirely the result of experience. . . .
> 45. In these and the like instances, the truth of the matter, I find, stands thus:—Having of a long time experienced certain ideas perceivable by *touch*—as distance, tangible figure, and solidity—to have been connected with certain ideas of sight, I do, upon perceiving these ideas of sight, forthwith conclude that tangible ideas are, . . . what he sees only *suggests* to his understanding that, after having passed a certain distance, *to be measured by the motion of his body, which is perceivable by touch*, he shall come to perceive such and such tangible ideas, which have been usually connected with such and such visible ideas.

Berkeley's statement in points 2 and 3 that distances cannot be seen immediately was made at a time when stereopsy was not yet known. After Wheatestone's demonstration of depth perception by retinal disparity in 1839 (367) the visual component of spatial perception naturally became more important, and Berkeley's tactile hypothesis lost much of its value. It remains true, however, that some learning mechanisms are involved in distance perception.

The subtitle of Collier's book of 1713, *Demonstration of the Non-existence or Impossibility of an External World*, which deals with the consequences of Berkeley's *Essay*, points to the absurdities of his general theory. The modern reader and especially the sensory physiologist cannot help feeling that the young Berkeley was trying to provoke contradiction and discussion by adding these far-reaching postulates when he published his important new ideas on vision and touch. After Berkeley later became a bishop he was glad to link his postulate of the nonexistence of matter with the existence of God, who could always perceive the real world, thus allowing it some reality ("The visible world is the language of God"). To propose God as a substitute reality in order to postulate the existence of the objective world may appear surprising to a present-day scientist. I confess to having some difficulty in understanding Berkeley's mixture of sensory perception and theology, but I would accept it as a motivation for his philosophy. I prefer Kant's clear refutation of all philosophical proofs of God's existence (which, however, he did not deny) and his sober statement that we perceive only the phenomena of external things but not the things themselves (213), and that man's perceptive apparatus controls his knowledge of the external world (214).

HUME'S CRITICISM OF RATIONALISM AND CAUSALITY. David Hume (1711–1776), the great Scottish philosopher, developed Locke's empiricism with greater consequence and without the obvious inconsistencies of Locke's philosophy. His clear and sharp reasoning was already apparent in his first work *Treatise on Human Nature* (193). It was written at the early age of 28 and published in 1739–1740 but was little read. So he modified its main philosophical part in the *Philosophical Essays Concerning Human Understanding* of 1748, and again in the definitive version *An Enquiry Concerning Human Understanding* of 1758 (194). These books found more resonance both at home and abroad; they influenced continental philosophers, such as the encyclopedists and Condillac in France, and Kant in Germany. Hume's critical empiricism endeavored to show the achievements and the limits of human perception and knowledge. Hume distinguished between sensory impressions and ideas but said that "ideas are derived from impressions." He appreciated some positive performances of mental association in the analysis of causal relationships, thus becoming the first association psychologist. He had a very sceptical attitude toward causality and said that the temporal sequence is the only criterion we have, so that *post hoc* is perceived and *propter hoc* is only indirectly inferred and cannot be proved. His denial of causation appears to be the main difficulty for physiological applications of his philosophy. The reduction to a plain temporal sequence of events also dissolves into uncertainty the information processing of sensory systems. In his first book Hume described the human self as a mere agglomeration of impressions and concepts; he left out this passage in the later editions, to avoid objections of theologians who missed the idea of the soul. He remained skeptical toward religious dogmas, but he admitted some "belief" and paid some lip service to religion. In contrast to Descartes and Leibniz he did not try to prove God's existence. It appears difficult for a sensory physiologist to accept Hume's broad concept of impressions that includes perceptions, emotions, and desires, as separate from ideas. Although we appreciate that percepts may contain feeling and desire, Hume's definition of ideas as "less lively perceptions" is not very convincing; Hume's objections against general principles and speculative constructions of cause and effects may have more appeal for physiologists, for he said, "In that case his enquiry wou'd be much better employ'd in examining the effects than the causes of his principle." (194).

To emphasize Hume's influence one should mention two outcomes of his philosophy—first, Kant's dictum that on reading the *Enquiry* he awakened from his dogmatic slumber (214); and second, the effects of the moral theses of Hume stressing the role of sympathy in social organization. This stimulated his friend Adam Smith, the founder of scientific economics and sociology, to write his important book *Inquiry into the Nature and Causes of the Wealth of Nations*, which appeared in 1776, the year of Hume's death.

Hume's criticism stimulated Kant to strive for a synthesis of perception and knowledge that remained an open question in all empiricist philosophies. The sensory regulations could be explained better by proving an a priori order of reason as a precondition of perception than by the chance associations proposed by Hume that would result in an agglomeration of time-related events.

Kantian Synthesis of Perception and Thought

Immanuel Kant (1724–1804) is probably the most fascinating philosophical figure of the eighteenth century. He combined original thought in philosophy with a profound knowledge of the essentials in natural science. During his long life he tried to resolve the problems of sensory information and thought into its intrinsic precondition, i.e., the interrelation of experience a posteriori and reasoning a priori. Thus Kant's philosophy integrated the empiricist postulates of Hume and the rationalist teachings of Leibniz with the principles of experimental science. As a young man Kant was deeply impressed by the rise of science in the seventeenth century, which, as he said, "shed a new light on our view of nature" (213).

KANT'S CONCEPTS OF SCIENCE. During his early years, when he became magister of philosophy, mathematics, and physics at the university of Königsberg in 1755, Kant wrote a book on the cosmology of the solar system: *Naturgeschichte und Theorie des Himmels* (212). In this he tried to prove the mechanical origin of planetary motion "after Newton's principles." He proposed that planets originate from a revolving *Urnebel* that condensed into solid matter. His arguments were of course rather speculative, and it was not until 40 years later that Laplace gave a more solid mathematical foundation of this theory in his *Mécanique céleste* (1796) and his *Système du monde* (1799–1825).

Kant's original ideas about a mechanical origin of the stellar world led him to important astronomical predictions, as shown by the following translation of the contents of the first part of his theory of the heavens (212):

> Sketch of a general systematic order among the fixed stars derived from the phenomena of the milky way. Discovery of many such galactic systems which are visible in the distant heavens forming elliptic nebular figures .... Conclusions: A probable hypothesis that planets exist beyond Saturn derived from the law that the eccentricity of planets increases with their distance from the sun.

Kant published the concept that spiral nebulas are distant galaxies six years before the astronomer Lambert conceived a similar hypothesis. The prediction of distant planets was made by Kant 26 years before Herschel discovered the planet Uranus in 1781. In 1758 Kant published a pre-Einsteinian idea of the relativity of movement and interpreted the stationary state as infinitely small motion (217).

Kant remained interested in the results of natural

science and followed new discoveries until his late years. Even at the age of 75 he assisted in the electrophysiological demonstrations of nerve stimulation by Ritter, who elaborated on the discoveries of Galvani, and became impressed by this new aspect of nerve conduction (1).

Kantian philosophy and science. In his famous introduction to the second edition of the *Critique of Pure Reason* Kant postulated that the philosopher should experiment with thought just as the scientist experiments with real things (213). He then limited this postulate by explaining the differences between a *Gedankenexperiment* and the natural sciences. On the first page of his book he stated that all our knowledge begins with sensory experience but that philosophy cannot, as the empiricists have postulated, be limited to sensory information alone. He distinguished pure and empirical knowledge and said that although knowledge begins with sensory experience, it does not consist only of experience, since the mind has a synthetizing faculty of judgment that is a precondition of perception.

In 1783 in his *Prolegomena* (214) Kant gave a brief introduction to "scientific metaphysics," in which he argued against some detractors of his *Critique of Pure Reason*. This short book is written in a lively style and is still pleasurable to read; it is in this he said that Hume's writings had interrupted his dogmatic slumber and made him see the essential role of sensory information for thought and knowledge. Kant argued that Hume's criticisms of metaphysics provided the original spark for developing a new scientific philosophy but that Hume himself missed the opportunity to do so.

Kant explained that Hume's principle of cause and effect is too narrow and that deductive demonstrations can also be made without inductive experience, "which appeared impossible to my sharp-witted predecessor." Kant recognized aprioristic truth in pure mathematics and reproached Hume for his neglect of mathematics. Then he criticized rationalist philosophers and joked over their "cheap metaphysics." He compared their pseudophilosophy to the easily collected foam floating on the surface of the deep sea of science, whereas the real origins of knowledge and the bases of the natural laws must be searched for in the depths with laborious care (214).

The *Prolegomena* defend empirical knowledge, but these parts are usually neglected by philosophers who appreciate only Kant's transcendental idealism, for which Kant proposed the term *critical idealism*. His concept is characterized as follows: "Alles Erkenntnis von Dingen aus bloss reinem Verstand oder reiner Vernunft ist nichts als blosser Schein, und nur in der Erfahrung ist Wahrheit" (214) (All knowledge of things obtained from pure intellect or pure reason is nothing but mere illusion; only experience yields truth).

Kant's most important book for the scientist besides his work on the philosophy of nature (215) is his *Kritik*

der Urteilskraft (216), imperfectly translated as *Critique of Judgement*. Unfortunately, only the aesthetic parts of this book were considered by philosophers; those on natural science usually were neglected. Another English translation giving the title as *Critique of Aesthetic Judgement* shows this limited reception of the book. Those parts on nature treat the limitations of natural science: Kant said that scientists cannot investigate the totality of conditions of life and that they should try to explain all events of nature, even the most purposeful (*zweckmässigste Ereignisse*), in mechanistic terms so far as possible (216). Kant's postulate of mechanical explanations of nature corresponds to a methodological but not to an ontological reductionism (see METHODOLOGICAL REDUCTION AND CONSCIOUS INFORMATION, p. 65). He limited his apparently materialistic statement about mechanisms by saying in the second part of his long sentence that the nature of our reason forces us to suppose purposeful relations in the mechanisms of living organisms. Kant adds, however, that we cannot hope to fully understand the growing of a simple blade of grass in purely mechanical terms.

Kant's *Metaphysical Foundations of Natural Science* (215), appearing in 1786, emphasized the importance of mathematics and physics, calling them the only exact sciences. He stated bluntly: "Research in nature [*Naturlehre*] contains only as much essential science [*eigentliche Wissenschaft*] as it allows mathematical application." Hence, Kant recognized as true science only those branches that allow quantification and mathematical treatment, and he expressed doubts about the exactness of chemistry and of biological and psychological sciences. He called chemistry a *scientific art* and biology *empirical knowledge*. One may understand this bias for mathematics and his doubts whether chemistry and biology can be exact sciences when one thinks of the state of chemistry at that time, before the periodic system and the atomic weights became known. Eighty years before Fechner's psychophysics, Kant doubted also that quantification of sensory information was possible. He said that perception and thought function on one-dimensional time scales and that time is a given category of our mind.

PERCEPTION, THOUGHT, AND RECOGNITION. According to Kant only the close interaction of sensory information, thought, and memory produces knowledge. Since reason cannot perceive without the senses and sensory signals cannot be understood without reason, he proposed that associative mechanisms drawn from memory, reproduced as intuitions, and synthetized by imagination result in recognition.

Kant's views of perception and recognition were summarized in the first edition of the *Critique of Pure Reason* (1781; deleted in the 2nd edition of 1787) as follows:

There are three subjective sources of knowledge upon which rests the possibility of experience in general and of knowledge of its objects—sense, imagination and apperception. Each of these can be viewed as empirical, namely, in its application to given appearances. But all of them are likewise a priori elements or foundations, which make this empirical employment itself possible. Sense represents appearances empirically in perception, imagination in association (and reproduction), apperception in the empirical consciousness of the identity of the reproduced representations with the appearances whereby they were given, that is, in recognition. (213).

For present-day sensory physiology Kant's empirical realism and transcendental idealism are still important concepts for an understanding of the acquired content and innate structure of the senses. When he said that our psychic apparatus orders the world in space and time as experienced by our senses, he was right in principle, but he overrated his a priori concept of time and space. This was opposed by Helmholtz (164), who taught the dependence of space perception on empirical experience, and later by William James (199), both of whom denied the a priori category of space.

Some practical parallels of the philosophical synthesis of Kant relating perceptual and rational knowledge with sensory research may be mentioned. The physiologist should investigate the organism's responses to sensory stimuli as a sensualist studies perception and should in addition analyze the central mechanisms of information processing and their integrated functions as a rationalist analyzes intellectual performance (207). One may conclude that the investigation of mental processes (including perception) and of brain function (including central sensory processing), in spite of methodical differences, should be combined to stimulate each other. To my knowledge such pragmatic matching of philosophy and science was rarely stated in the old literature until Nicolai Hartmann (147) in the 1930s applied his level concept to the hierarchy of sciences and said that thought and reality are governed by the same principles. Max Hartmann (146) used these principles in his philosophy of nature (146), and K. Lorenz in 1943 (256) also compared Kant's philosophy with behavioral research.

KANT'S A PRIORI CONCEPTS AND CEREBRAL ORDER. In summarizing some parallels of Kant's philosophy and sensory physiology the following statements can be made for the inborn and acquired components of perception and the apriorism of cerebral order.

Innate structures and functions of the sensory systems are considered as a priori conditions that are modified by experience in perception. This pragmatic application of Kant's a priori concept to neurobiology is of course a simplification of his philosophy at a lower level, but it agrees with similar ideas of Lorenz (256) for instinctive behavior. It can be maintained, although Kant's postulate that space and time are pure a priori categories was rejected by Helmholtz (164) and others, who showed that space concepts develop after empirical experience. However, our ability to perceive outer structures in space and time is rendered possible by the intrinsic order of the sensory systems and the brain. So Kant's main concept, that our mental apparatus orders the world as experienced by our senses in space and time, is still valid. Furthermore, perceptive experience a posteriori and reasoning a priori are also combined into an intricate synthesis with this opposite sequence. Hence in perception and neurobiology a priori knowledge and instincts are combined with a posteriori experiences in two ways: knowledge becomes primarily possible through the structural and functional order of the neural systems and is verified (or eventually falsified) secondarily by sensory experience and learning.

Kant's dictum "Gedanken ohne Inhalt sind leer. Anschauungen ohne Begriffe sind blind" (213) may be adapted for perception and understanding as follows: sensory input without abstract labeling is blind, and formal abstraction without empirical verification is empty.

The preperceptive and structural order of the sensory systems is innate and is modified by sensory input to obtain the acquired contents of consciousness. The active search of the organism for certain biologically significant sensory patterns may be compared to a perceptual theory of the organism selecting the relevant from the multitude of irrelevant sensory data.

Similar procedures are also used in science, and this agrees with Popper's (308) emphasis on the primacy of deduction and the importance of theory in the natural sciences, as in his succinct statement: "The empirical sciences are systems of theories."

The sensory scientist encounters two groups of a priori categories: first, the subjective, which renders possible his own sensory experience; and second, the objective order of structures and functions of the sense organs and their cerebral projections that perform sensory processing. The first influence his perception and thought, the second guarantee the physiological mechanisms of information processing. Their correlations are imperfectly known, but many parallels of sensory mechanisms and perceptive experiences demonstrate that they exist. Hence, objective neurophysiological and subjective perceptual (psychophysical) research can and should be combined (207). Of course, this correlation of results of these different methods giving complementary concepts must be made critically to avoid premature conclusions, uncontrolled equivocation, and naive speculations. Much further work is necessary before we can attain a true synthesis of primary (a priori) sensory functions and secondary (a posteriori) perceptions. Modern methods of neuronal and behavioral studies in waking performing monkeys (103, 286) and of psychophysical research in conscious man (208) promise that these combined ways of research will be fruitful in the future. The question What can sensory physiologists learn from Kant? may be answered by a pragmatic application of Kant's apriorism and synthetic concepts to neurobiology. After proposing this idea for vision (207) I generalize it to all sensory performance as follows: Innate structures and functions of the sensory systems are considered as a priori conditions that are modified by experience, and learning a posteriori.

This also avoids the antagonisms of the empiricism-nativism conflict. By the innate order of sensory and cerebral structures of the perceiving organism, perception and learning can be understood as performances of the same neurobiological structures, the higher sensory centers of the brain.

THE NINETEENTH CENTURY AND MODERN PERCEPTUAL RESEARCH

Rise of Sensory Sciences

From 1800 onward important contributions to sensory physiology appeared in the literature, beginning with investigations of the visual system. The history of the sensory sciences during the nineteenth century is fully described in Boring's monograph (52). Some original papers were reprinted or translated, and parts are available in English (113, 176). For the sake of brevity, I merely list the trends and discoveries, giving names of leading scientists with a few essential dates and key words. Only some special trends and their philosophies that are related to modern research are treated in more detail.

VISUAL PHYSIOLOGY. Research in vision was inaugurated in 1802 by Thomas Young (1773–1829) with his three-color concept (384), which was derived from subjective visual observations and which postulated three groups of retinal receptors, each selectively responding to red, green, and blue light. Helmholtz, whose achievements are described in HERMANN L. F. HELMHOLTZ, p. 47, elaborated this theory in 1852 and depicted it in 1860 (164) as shown in Fig. 15A. The Young-Helmholtz theory has continued to command interest in the field of color vision, as is apparent from the chapters by Hochberg, by Yellott, Wandell, and Cornsweet, and by De Valois and Jacobs in this volume of the *Handbook*. Johannes Purkinje (or Purkyne, 1787–1869) described many visual phenomena in his dissertation of 1819 (311): phosphenes resulting from mechanical and electrical stimuli of the retina, spontaneous movements in the *Eigengrau*, two kinds of afterimages (*Nachbilder* and *Blendungsbilder*), and the images of retinal vessels by transretinal illumination. In 1825 a second book described the short-wave spectral shift of brightness in the dark, later called the Purkinje phenomenon. In 1826 Johannes Müller (see JOHANNES MÜLLER, p. 46) published his book on comparative visual physiology in which he stated his law of specific energy of the senses.

In 1838 Wheatstone (1802–1875) demonstrated retinal disparity to be the basis of stereoscopic vision (367). Further studies of binocular vision by Brewster,

Dove, and Panum developed the concepts of the horopter (first proposed by Aguilonius in 1613) and of retinal parallax. M. E. Chevreul in 1838 studied color contrast. These and other contributions on vision were published between 1820 and 1860. From 1860 onward the fundamental books of H. Helmholtz (164), G. Fechner (105), and E. Hering (170) appeared, and Ernst Mach, Wilhelm Wundt, Hermann Aubert, and Ernst W. Brücke followed with important new contributions to subjective visual physiology. The work of the first five scientists is described with some detail later in this section. In 1865 the Swedish physiologist Alarik F. Holmgren (1831–1897) discovered the electroretinogram, and Willy Kühne (1837–1900), succeeding Helmholtz as professor in Heidelberg, described visual purple (the pigment rhodopsin) in 1877 (237, 238) after its bleaching had been demonstrated by F. Boll in 1876. The two kinds of retinal receptors—cones and rods—were discovered by Max Schultze (1825–1874), who related cones to color vision and rods to night vision. This discovery was later elaborated in the duplicity theory of vision by Johannes von Kries (1853–1928), who joined Helmholtz's laboratory in Berlin and became professor of physiology at Freiburg University in 1882.

The next 30 years brought mainly an expansion of the original discoveries of the nineteenth century in psychophysics. The rise of objective visual physiology began with Adrian's recordings from the optic nerve in 1927. Hartline's work from 1932 onward initiated neuronal recordings and correlations with visual perception, described in NEURONAL MECHANISMS OF VISION, p. 57.

HEARING: COCHLEAR AND CENTRAL NEURAL FUNCTIONS. The history of research on audition in the nineteenth century is well described in Boring's chapters (52) on the psychophysics of tone and on auditory perception and auditory theory. Hence, I mention only two early contributions, not alluded to in his book. Between 1840 and 1845 Ohm (296) and Seebeck (325) made some basic experiments and introduced the Fourier analysis of acoustic stimuli. Their work inaugurated the quantitative analysis of auditory perception and human speech. Ohm showed that complex acoustic stimulus patterns including speech could be represented by the sum of many sinusoidal tones, and Seebeck found that complex sounds having a periodicity were heard subjectively with periods not present in the objective Fourier analysis of the reproduced tones. This proved that the ear is not a long-term frequency analyzer but is able to analyze sounds from a few cycles. Helmholtz's work on the perception of tones and the physiological basis of music theory (165) followed in 1870 and became a classic for auditory perception. Research of cochlear functions during the last 100 years culminated in the contributions of Georg von Békésy (31, 32), whose experiments from 1928 onward proved that the basilar membrane shows a

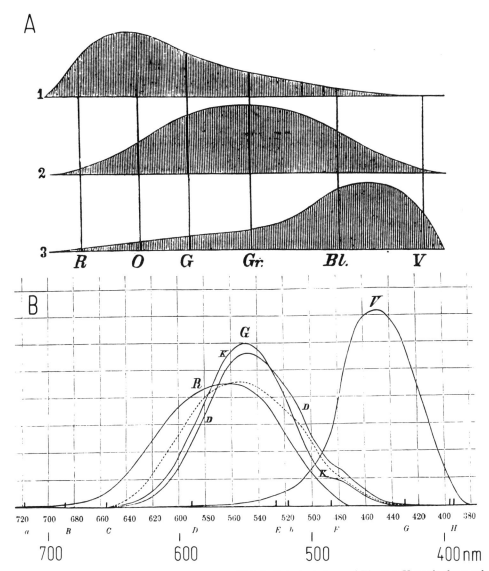

FIG. 15. Helmholtz's depictions of Thomas Young's three-color concept compared with his own spectral sensitivity curves. *A*: for Young's theory of three receptor elements Helmholtz postulated in 1850 relatively broad spectral absorption curves showing 3 maxima—in orange, in green, and in blue-violet, respectively. *B*: Helmholtz used König's and Dieterici's psychophysical data of their normal trichromatic eyes to obtain sensitivity curves of three elementary color sensations. Red curve *R* is shifted toward short-wave side with a maximum at 560 nm, green curve *G* has a maximum at 550 nm, and violet *V* at 450 nm. This corresponds approximately to modern objective measurements of receptor absorptions (570, 540, 450 nm). Some individual differences are marked *K* for König and *D* for Dieterici. [From Helmholtz (164), 2nd ed.]

longitudinal *Wanderwelle* (traveling wave) instead of Helmholtz's local resonance; von Békésy received the Nobel prize for his work. The analysis of auditory information processing in the brain was initiated from 1935 onward by Kornmüller's and Bremer's (56, 232) recordings of acoustically evoked potentials in the cortex and Rose's (316) neuronal recordings from the medial geniculate nucleus. The important contributions of electrophysiology of the cochlea, the acoustic nerve, and the central pathways of audition during the last four decades cannot be discussed here and are treated in the chapters by Dallos and by Aitkin, Irvine, and Webster in this volume of the *Handbook*.

THE VESTIBULAR ORGAN. The last sense organ discovered during the long history of sensory research was the vestibular apparatus, the decisive experiments being made between 1873 and 1927. Although Flourens (111) had already proposed a relation of the semicircular canals with postural regulation in 1825, the current belief remained that they had acoustic functions. In 1873–1875 Ernst Mach, Josef Breuer, and A. Crum

Brown nearly simultaneously discovered that the labyrinth receptors signal head acceleration—circular for the canals, and linear (including g, the gravitational acceleration) for the otoliths. Mach's work on vestibular function concentrated on psychophysical experiments (362). Twenty years later the otologist R. Bárány (19) developed his caloric method for stimulating a single vestibular canal in man. In 1927 Steinhausen (334) gave the final direct proof of the mechanism of cupula deflection in the canal during head rotation in fish. This explains how the cupula receptors can integrate acceleration over time and the vestibular nerve fibers can signal this integration, i.e., the final velocity, to the vestibular nucleus.

From 1911 to 1924 the pharmacologist Rudolf Magnus (1873–1927) used reflexes for the investigation of brain stem responses elicited by vestibular afferents and clarified the multisensory coordination of vestibular and neck receptors in body posture, distinguishing *Haltungsreflexe* (tonic postural reflex) and *Stellreflexe* (righting reflex). His work with de Kleyn and other co-workers was summarized in his famous monograph *Körperstellung* in 1924 (272). In 1925–1928 the Spaniard Rafael Lorente de Nó (253), the last pupil of Ramón y Cajal, pioneered the vestibulooculomotor mechanisms in German and Swedish laboratories. He continued his early work on vestibuloocular reflexes in the United States with electrophysiological recordings. In 1935 he published the first indirect measurement of synaptic transmission delay at eye muscle motoneurons (254) and in 1938 proposed interneuronal circuits of vestibuloocular transmission in the reticular formation (255). His work laid the foundations of modern research on brain stem control of eye movements and nystagmus, elaborated by J. Szentágothai (341) and many others.

ELECTROPHYSIOLOGY AND NERVE CONDUCTION. The rise of electrophysiology in the second half of the nineteenth century made only few contributions to the sensory sciences. For 60 years after Galvani's discovery (125) and Humboldt's demonstration (195) of the resting potentials between the cut muscle and its surface (now known as the membrane potential) electrophysiology concentrated on the nerve muscle preparation and motor functions. The bioelectric contributions to sensory physiology during the nineteenth century were restricted to the discovery of the electroretinogram by Holmgren in 1865 (185) and rather uncertain descriptions of sensory potentials of the cerebral cortex (70). For the development of electrophysiology I refer to Brazier's article (55) and mention but few data.

Modern electrophysiology was initiated from 1840 onward by Carlo Matteucci (1811–1868), professor of physics in Pisa (274, 283), and Emil Dubois-Reymond (1818–1896), who was a pupil of Johannes Müller and co-worker of Helmholtz and was professor of physiology in Berlin over a period of four decades (78).

Helmholtz (162) in 1850 introduced the measurements of the velocity of nerve conduction and extended it to human motor nerves (166) in 1867. Similar recordings from sensory nerve action potentials were obtained only much later in the 1920s, when the cathode oscillograph and amplifiers were available and Erlanger and Gasser made their systematic studies of nerve action potentials and described the relation between conduction velocity and fiber diameter (102).

CUTANEOUS SENSATION. Skin sensation remained a neglected field until about 1880 despite early allusions: Aristotle in 330 B.C. had remarked that the sense of touch contains different qualities; E. Weber in 1834–1846 proposed receptive fields of sensory nerve endings; and anatomists in the nineteenth century described various kinds of cutaneous receptors—but functional correlates were lacking. The specificity and location of cutaneous modalities were recognized only after M. Blix (50) discovered the warm and cold spots in 1882 and gave a clear description in 1884. In 1884 and 1885 A. Goldscheider (128, 129) described specific spots of the skin causing sensations of touch, warmth, and cold: *Druckpunkte*, *Kältepunkte*, and *Wärmepunkte*. He also added *Schmerzpunkte* for pain but maintained that pain is a nonspecific quality arising after high-intensity stimulation of different receptors. The latter view together with the frequency of warm spots was opposed by Max von Frey (1852–1932), who in 1894 introduced exact quantification of the stimuli and discovered the pain spots (116, 117). In systematic investigations he differentiated the four modalities of the cutaneous senses by local stimulation, using *Reizhaare* after 1895 and *Stachelborsten* since 1914. Von Frey (118, 119) distinguished specific spots of skin sensation signaling touch (*Drucksinn*), warmth, cold, and pain, and he explained the paradoxical sensations occurring with biting cold and burning heat by coexcitation of cold and pain spots neighboring the warmth spots. He also proposed correlations with certain receptors in and below the skin forming mechanoreceptors, thermoreceptors, and nociceptors (119). However, the anatomical identification of modality-specific receptors, successfully accomplished for vision, audition, vestibular muscle, and taste receptors in the nineteenth century, was still lacking for the skin. This identification remained difficult even after Adrian (2–4), Zotterman (386, 387), and many others had recorded the impulses of specific nerve fibers and elaborated on the physiological characteristics of somatosensory receptor functions, their specificities, and adaptation properties (see *Adrian's Achievements*, p. 53).

EXNER'S NEURONAL MODELS OF ATTENTION AND EMOTION. The Austrian physiologist Siegmund Exner (1846–1926) made important contributions to sensory physiology and general neurophysiology. He was the first to investigate chromatic adaptation in 1868 and to measure the time intervals for apparent movement in 1875, preceding Wertheimer's work by four decades. He founded the concepts of facilitation and inhibition in the central nervous system, words that were translated from the German *Bahnung* and *Hemmung*. Exner enlarged the reflex concept, giving it a functional meaning for sensorimotor control. He defined the *Sensomobilität* as the faculty to move, which is controlled and guided by sensory messages. In his monograph (104) appearing in 1894 Exner wrote the first neurophysiology of the central nervous system and proposed neuronal circuits for locomotion, attention, and emotion.

Exner's neuronal circuits envisaged a neurophysiological explanation of attention and emotion. They were the first neuronal concepts of the regulation of perception by centrifugal impulses impinging upon interneurons activated by sensory afferents. Sigmund Freud, who proposed cerebral correlates of drive and emotion, also constructed neuronal diagrams of emotional mechanisms but did not publish them when Exner's book appeared. Exner's diagrams are of historical value as early applications of the neuron concept to higher brain functions (206).

REFLEX PHYSIOLOGY. During the nineteenth century sensory responses of the central nervous system were investigated mainly by reflexes. The concept of the reflex, although theoretically known since Descartes, was clarified for spinal cord functions when Charles Bell (1774–1842) and F. Magendie (1783–1855) proved between 1811 and 1827 that the dorsal roots were afferent and the ventral roots efferent. The spinal reflex arc was considered as the simplest input-output mechanism of the cerebrospinal system. The significance of reflex action for central nervous function became widely accepted also for human beings when neurologists showed its diagnostic usefulness. The human tendon reflexes and their use in clinical neurology were described simultaneously and independently by W. Erb (100) and C. Westphal (366) in 1875, about half a century after Marshall Hall and F. Magendie (137, 271) had demonstrated the basic mechanisms of reflexes in animal experiments. Another four decades passed before Paul Hoffmann (183, 184) established from 1910 onward the monosynaptic transmission of the stretch reflexes in man. He called them *Eigenreflexe* because their excitation was sent back to the same muscle from which the stretch stimulation originated. C. S. Sherrington's physiology of the spinal cord (75, 328) and R. Magnus's work on the vestibular regulations of body posture (272) were based on the reflex principle, although both made some reservations and did not accept the reflex as the elementary nervous mechanism. Sherrington (329) maintained that reflexes are modifiable release reactions and their isolation from other neural functions is artificial. A. Bethe (44) emphasized the plasticity of spinal reflexes. From 1900 onward J. P. Pavlov (297) extended the reflex concept broadly to cerebral learning by his *conditioned reflexes*. However, during the last century E. Pflüger (301), a physiologist, and J. Dewey (85), a philosopher, had protested against the undue emphasis on reflexes in discussing the complex interaction of sensation, behavior, and reflex function.

SHERRINGTON'S DUALISM AND VISUAL PERCEPTION. The long research life of Charles Scott Sherrington (1857–1952), the grand old man and founder of modern neurophysiology, was very productive in ideas and pupils but yielded less-important new discoveries than the work of Adrian. Sherrington had many excellent students such as Eccles, Denny-Brown, Fulton, Penfield, Granit, and many others, who spread basic and applied neurophysiology throughout the world. Sherrington's contributions to the basic mechanisms of nervous action and his philosophy of evolutionary pantheism are well described in two biographies (96, 132). In 1906 Sherrington's classic book *The Integrative Action of the Nervous System* (328) founded the experimental physiology of the spinal cord and differentiated sensory functions by the distinction of proprioceptive, exteroceptive, nociceptive, and enteroceptive systems. In vision he described psychophysical experiments on monocular and binocular flicker fusion. Sherrington's late book *Man on His Nature* (329), which he wrote as emeritus, recognized the mind as an autonomous entity in perception, "concerned with the aim not the act," and stressed a duality of mind and matter that nature treats as a unity.

Sherrington's dualism is of interest for sensory physiology, as some quotations on "vision subbrains" will demonstrate. He said (329) that each eye may have a separate sensorium on which mental processes are built up to full perceptual levels that "would amount physiologically to a visual subbrain" or to "two such subbrains, one for the right eye and one for the left eye." This Sherringtonian concept is of some actual interest in view of the clearly separate monocular structures in the primary visual cortex demonstrated by Hubel and Wiesel (191). "It is as though the right-eye and left-eye perceptions are elaborated singly and then psychically combined to one. Contemporaneity of action rather than structural union seems to provide their mental collaboration. Matter and energy seem granular in structure, and so does 'life', but not so mind." (329).

Sherrington stressed the unity and singularity of conscious experience in perception in contrast to the multiple structures of the senses and the brain. Popper and Eccles (310) further elaborated this Sherringtonian dualism (see THE THREE WORLDS OF POPPER AND ECCLES, p. 65).

CONTRIBUTIONS OF NEUROLOGY. The principle of cortical localization guided the research of higher cerebral functions during the nineteenth century. It was started by Gall's (124) speculative phrenology, opposed by Flourens (110, 111), extended by studies of hemispheric dominance for speech in man (59, 363), and more precisely defined by animal experiments of Fritsch and Hitzig (121) and Ferrier (106). Following Hughlings Jackson's studies of focal epilepsy and of integration and dissolution of different levels of the cerebrum (198), other neurologists contributed to sensory physiology in this century by studying peripheral and cerebral lesions. Henry Head (1861–1940), after working with Hering in Prague, demonstrated the human dermatomes of sensory roots by studying referred pain and zoster in the period 1893–1900. He made his important experiment on nerve division in 1903 and published the results in 1908 with Rivers (315). Head distinguished the protopathic and the epicritic systems of somatic sensation, investigating their inhibitory interrelation and different rate of regeneration. He developed with Holmes the notion of sensory disinhibition to explain central pain (157). Head's notable contributions are available in his collected papers (156). Otfried Foerster (1873–1941) enlarged Sherrington's and Head's investigations of segmental innervation of the skin (113) and clarified some aspects of sensorimotor coordination, its disturbance, and its compensation after loss of sensory control (112). His studies of electrical stimulations of the human cerebral cortex are summarized in a handbook article (114) and were followed by Wilder Penfield's extensive work on cortical stimulation in neurosurgery (298, 299). These studies of sensory and sensorimotor areas of the cortex in human beings and animals, as well as J. F. Fulton's excisions of cortical areas in monkeys and later recordings of evoked potentials (see EVOKED POTENTIALS, p. 56), were based upon and correlated with the cytoarchitectonic and myeloarchitectonic maps of the human and primate cortex made by K. Brodmann (62) and C. and O. Vogt (354, 356) between 1900 and 1919.

Six Founders of Sensory Physiology

This short survey of the nineteenth century avoids biographical details but serves to characterize briefly the work and philosophy of six men who created the field of sensory physiology at German universities and elaborated its basic concepts: Müller, Weber, Fechner, Helmholtz, Hering, and Mach.

Contrasting with the early pioneers Young and Purkinje, and with those of the following generation such as Wheatstone, Holmgren, Ohm, and Seebeck, who discovered special sensory mechanisms, these six scientists in addition to their fundamental discoveries also propounded general theories of sensory function and perception. Experimental physiology in other fields was developed at about the same time in France and Germany by Claude Bernard (1813–1878) and Carl Ludwig (1816–1895).

JOHANNES MÜLLER. Johannes Müller (1801–1858), called the father of German physiology, developed a clear concept of sensory function in his monograph on vision in man and animals (291) and gave a comprehensive survey in his textbook (292). Müller is important not only for his original concepts but more so as teacher and founder of a most successful research school. Müller's laboratory was the cradle of the most famous German neurophysiologists of the last century: Du Bois-Reymond, Helmholtz, and Brücke were his pupils, and other more anatomically minded scientists such as Max Schultze (who discovered rods and cones in the eyes of nocturnal and diurnal animals), Schwann, Virchow, Henle, Remak, and Haeckel all came from his laboratory. Müller's early and most productive research years were spent in Bonn, where he wrote his books between the ages of 24 and 33 and founded a chair of physiology. He spent the following two decades as professor of physiology in Berlin. Despite phases of depression during these years he inspired original young scholars to attack all fields of physiology before they were later sent to the new chairs of physiology at German universities. He also developed biophysical and biochemical trends of research as opposed to the nonexperimental speculative generalizations of the previous generation. Müller himself was still influenced by romantic natural philosophy and endeavored to produce a synthesis of physiology with morphology and psychology on a Kantian philosophical basis.

Müller's principle of the specificity of nerve messages was first proposed in 1825 (291) and elaborated with eight arguments in his *Handbuch* (292) of 1838. The unusual term *specific energy*, which referred to sensory specificity, meant that peripheral and central messages from a particular sense organ elicited specific sensations, which depended on which sense organ was excited and not on the kind of stimulations used. He said that all sense organs produce specific sensations peculiar to them and that these can be elicited by quite different stimuli; for example, visual sensations in the eye may be caused by light or by mechanical, electrical, or chemical stimuli. Müller left open whether the sensory specificity was peripheral or central in origin—i.e, caused by specific afferent nerve fibers or by special terminations in the brain. He had a clear concept of the interrelation of vision and eye movements and developed Vieth's horopter concept proposed in 1817 (353) that was enlarged by Hering and Helmholtz 40 years later.

ERNST H. WEBER. E. H. Weber (1795–1878) belonged to the same generation as J. Müller and became professor of anatomy and physiology at Leipzig University at the age of 26. In 1834 he investigated the cutaneous senses and introduced quantification into sensory physiology by measuring just noticeable differences and thresholds (359). He found an exact relation between relative increases of stimulus magnitude and just perceptible changes in the intensity of a sensation. This was enlarged in 1860 by Fechner (105) into the logarithmic psychophysical law. Weber's compass test provided data on tactile spatial acuity (two-point discrimination) for different parts of the body surface, on which his concept of sensory circles (*Tastkreise*) was based. Thus he introduced the concept of receptive fields into physiology. Although Weber's general distinction between *Drucksinn*, *Ortssinn*, and *Raumsinn* was not accepted by others, his investigations of cutaneous sensation led to Hering's reciprocal concept of cold and warm sensation, to von Frey's sensory spots (117), and still later, to Head's systems of epicritic, protopathic, and deep sensibility (156). Aside from his contributions to cutaneous sensation, Weber's most important achievements in physiology were the discovery of vagal inhibition of the heart, made in 1854 with his brother Eduard (360), and the foundation of the physical principles of circulation and hemodynamics.

GUSTAV THEODOR FECHNER. Gustav Fechner (1801–1887) founded psychophysics, but his philosophy may appear strange to physiologists. Born 20 years before Helmholtz, he belonged to an early nineteenth century generation that grew up with romantic natural philosophy. After studying medicine and science he became professor of physics at Leipzig in 1834, but he refocused onto philosophy and sensory sciences after six years of illness. His tendency toward a somewhat mystical pantheism may be explained by the romantic influence. Fechner's monistic philosophy and pantheism avoided dogmatic formulations, however, and appeared more often in his early publications that preceded the *Psychophysik* (1860). In this important monograph (105) Fechner created experimental quantitative sensory psychophysics with his general mathematical formulation of Weber's law as the logarithmic function of the relation of stimulus and sensation. Further, he introduced statistics of the *mittlere Fehler* (averaged error) in measuring just noticeable differences in sensation. This would correspond in modern langauge to a standard deviation.

In vision Fechner discovered the lack of binocular brightness summation, since called the Fechner paradox. His visual experiments were interrupted after he burned his fovea by high-intensity light. Fechner, in contrast to the sober experimentalist Weber, searched for general laws in science and for philosophical applications of experiments. His psychophysical theory, although challenged by other sensory scientists, inaugurated one of the most important new lines of perceptual research (see WEBER'S DIFFERENTIAL AND FECHNER'S LOGARITHMIC FUNCTION, p. 49).

HERMANN L. F. HELMHOLTZ. H. L. F. Helmholtz (1821–1894), a pupil of Johannes Müller, was the leading scientist of the last century in both physiology and physics. His achievements in these two fields of research are so well known that I mention only some early and outstanding contributions. He began his research work as a student of medicine in Johannes Müller's laboratory. The mark of genius was already apparent in his first publications: the dissertation on the connection of axon and nerve cell in 1842, the principle of energy conservation in 1847, the first measurement of nerve impulse velocity in 1850 (162), the invention of the ophthalmoscope in 1851 (163), and the resonance theory of hearing in 1863. The last was conceived as an anatomical and physiological synthesis of Ohm's frequency analysis of acoustics of the human ear. Helmholtz became professor of physiology at the age of 28 in Königsberg, then moved to Bonn and Heidelberg; he was called to Berlin as professor of physics in 1871. Many of his contributions to sensory physiology are described in his two monumental works: *Handbuch der physiologischen Optik*, written in 1851–1866 (164), and *Die Lehre von den Tonempfindungen*, appearing in 1863 (165). Both had several editions, the second and third of the *Optik* appearing posthumously in 1896 and 1909, edited by his pupils; it was translated into English in 1924. Helmholtz modified Young's three-color concept for three kinds of retinal receptors and demonstrated their function by psychophysical experiments and color mixing (Fig. 15). Although he accepted some Kantian ideas, Helmholtz emphasized that space perception is acquired by sensory experience, thereby founding the empiricist school of sensory physiology. To become free from the burden of teaching as professor of physics he transferred to a new research institute, the Physikalisch-Technische Reichsanstalt, in 1888. There he continued his research on electricity and electrochemistry and stimulated von Kries's and König's experiments in visual physiology. He was knighted by the German Emperor in 1882; hence the *von* before his name was a late addition. Helmholtz had few friends and pupils, talked little, and did not like long discussions or stylistic elegance. A great thinker and experimenter, he preferred to work alone.

Helmholtz's work represented an ideal synthesis of theory and experiment. He consistently applied his experimental skill to significant basic problems, using simple constructs of models and logical theories. During the 50 years of his active life he made fundamental contributions to the physiology of nerve conduction, of vision, and of audition, in addition to his theoretical achievements in thermodynamics and electricity. Helmholtz's research goal was to understand nature, "die Natur zu begreifen," as he wrote in 1847.

EWALD HERING. Ewald Hering (1834–1918) is known mainly for his work in visual physiology, although he made many important discoveries in general neurophysiology (nerve afterpotentials, artificial synapse of injured nerves, reciprocal warm and cold sensation, adaptation, and self-regulation of respiration). Hering succeeded Purkinje to the chair in physiology at Prague in 1870 and in 1895 moved to the chair in Leipzig to succeed Carl Ludwig. His first papers of 1861–1864, on the spatial order of the visual field and retinal disparity in stereopsy (170), were followed by his articles on eye movements and attention (173) and on his theory of visual contrast (172). Hering's opponent-color concept was a basic contribution to visual physiology. His six *Gegenfarben* (white-black, yellow-blue, and red-green) included brightness and darkness, declaring black to be a nonchromatic color. His theory explained all contrast vision by retinal interaction, thus foreshadowing Hartline's discovery of on- and off-center neurons of lateral inhibition and Kuffler's surround inhibition. Throughout his long life, Hering unfortunately maintained and defended his early and somewhat difficult metabolic terminology of *Sehsubstanzen*, using anabolic and catabolic functions to describe opponent colors. This photochemical interpretation hindered the acceptance of his otherwise clear and pertinent contrast theory (172, 174).

Hering's bitter struggle with Helmholtz, fought over three decades along the front of nativists opposing empiricists, created a personal antagonism of their schools. Refuting Helmholtz's psychological interpretation of contrast, Hering postulated physiological mechanisms of reciprocal and lateral inhibition in the retina and explained simultaneous contrast by retinal inhibition. In contrast to Helmholtz and his often somewhat difficult style in which he explained his otherwise clear thought, Hering had the capacity for elegant formulation and intuitive clarification. He invented impressive metaphors to elucidate the mechanism of visual contrast coding and to demonstrate the difference between stimulus luminance and the sensation of brightness: coal in sunlight has a higher physical luminance than white paper in a dimly lit room, yet the coal always is seen as black and the paper as white, both in the strongest sunlight and in twilight. Hering's contrast concepts—besides influencing Sherrington's ideas of reciprocal innervation—paved the way for objective sensory physiology. His postulate of physiological contrast mechanisms with retinal inhibition was verified 80 years later by the neuronal recordings of Kuffler (236) and Baumgartner (26–28). Besides retinal interaction, Hering also assumed central processing of contrast coding in cerebral visual structures (174). Hering's concept of areal brightness contrast, differing from Mach's border contrast, was revived by von Békésy (33) in 1968.

Hering's work was a peculiar mixture of basic experimentation, clear perceptual observations, and theoretical systematization. Although starting from phenomenological aspects of perception and using descriptive terms for his experiments, his concept of reciprocal systems in vision and temperature sensations became a general theory guiding further research. If one discards Hering's pet hypothesis of dissimilation and assimilation, one can see that his main concept of reciprocal inhibition of brightness and darkness information and of the two opponent pairs of chromatic qualities corresponds well with modern results of neuronal recordings (28, 205, 207).

ERNST MACH. Ernst Mach (1838–1916), a physicist interested from his youth in the sensory sciences, described in 1865 his fundamental experiments on border contrast (261) later known as Mach bands. Mach spent most of his productive years in the universities of Prague and Vienna. The revival of Machian ideas on visual contrast and their objective correlates in modern neuronal physiology are well described in a monograph by Ratliff (313). I have always admired Mach's ability to see the essential in a few basic observations and to prove it by simple experiments. I was disappointed, however, by his philosophy as documented in his later books (263, 264).

Mach's views of perception and his psychophysical concepts are summarized in his book on the analysis of sensation (263), which appeared in several editions from 1886 to 1922. During these years he advocated a peculiar antimetaphysical form of research positivism that denied essential differences of the physical and the mental and overrated the sensations as "elements." This is expressed briefly in the following quotation: "Nature is composed of sensations; the thing is an abstraction the name of a symbol; the world is not composed of 'things' as its elements but of sensations; the world consists ... of colors, sounds, ... temperatures, pressures, spaces, tunes etc." (263).

Of course, Mach also recognized complex qualities of sensations and the invariance of perceptions. However, his enumeration of incompatible terms describing different qualities of the senses and their relation to nature makes it difficult to accept his philosophy and his tendency to classify even time and space among the sensations. In his youth Mach had read Kant's *Prolegomena* and was impressed by the empirical bases of his philosophy. Later, his admiration changed into a sceptical attitude toward reality and *das Ding an sich*. With some justification Mach warned against arbitrary, one-sided theories. The warning, however, developed into a basic scepticism of such fundamental concepts as those of the atom and molecule and an overestimation of perceptual contents.

Mach's basic discoveries—the contrast concept (261), the investigation of vestibular functions, and visuovestibular and oculomotor interaction in space perception (262)—remain as important contributions to sensory physiology, even if one does not accept his philosophy of sensory positivism and empiriocriticism. Mach's philosophy influenced the Vienna school of logical positivism founded by Schlick (322) and Carnap (68); that is, however, beyond the scope of this chapter. I mention only von Hayek's book on the sensory order (154) as a late outcome of the Vienna school that is interesting for sensory physiologists.

Psychophysics and Scaling of Sensations

PSYCHOPHYSICS PAST AND PRESENT. Quantitative measurements of sensory perceptions, now called psychophysics, began in the eighteenth century with Bouguer (53) in vision, were revived by E. H. Weber (359) in 1834 and 1846 for somatosensory qualities, and were generalized by Fechner (105) in 1860 with a mathematical formula that elicited long and undecided discussions about the general validity of his logarithmic law. In 1959 Stevens proposed his power function that has influenced psychophysical research and scaling experiments during the last two decades (335). The power law was first conceived by Plateau in 1872 (320), 87 years before Stevens.

EARLY QUANTIFICATION. Paul Bouguer (1698–1758), a French physicist who contributed to the development of photometry, made the first studies of quantitative visual stimulation using different light intensities. His measurements of the differential threshold of brightness, occurring with 1/64 change of illumination magnitude, were published in 1760 in a book appearing posthumously (53). This pre-Weberian notion of just noticeable differences was forgotten by sensory scientists for about 100 years until Fechner introduced psychophysics and integrated Weber's work.

PSYCHOPHYSICAL AND PSYCHOCHEMICAL PHILOSOPHIES. Some speculations using analogies with mathematical and chemical formulas were developed before Fechner. The German philosopher J. F. Herbart (1776–1841), who occupied Kant's chair in Königsberg, propagated a synthesis of mathematical, philosophical, and empirical methods in psychology. He invented a system of mental mathematics in 1824 and 1825 (168) and postulated mental forces in analogy with physical forces. He said that these forces either can be fused or can act as antagonists, being mutually exclusive by inhibition. Herbart was the first philosopher who traced a clear concept of inhibition regulating perception, thought, and emotion—long before inhibitory mechanisms were investigated by physiologists (324).

Herbart postulated that the strength of inhibition is a function of time with a temporal decay. In the 220 mathematical pages of his first volume Herbart produced a multitude of more or less complicated formulas without a single empirical verification. He said that percepts and intuitions penetrate into consciousness after building up a sum of mutual inhibition, S. In order to develop ordered percepts S must be reduced as a function of time (t) to σ. The rate of change of inhibition $d\sigma/dt$ is proportional to what remains to be inhibited; i.e., the difference between S and σ

$$\text{S} - \sigma = \text{const}\,\frac{d\sigma}{dt} \quad \text{or integrated} \quad t = \log\frac{\text{const}}{\text{S} - \sigma}$$

Herbart was an intuitive associationist and postulated mental self-regulation. Unfortunately his *Erfahrung* used only subjective experience but not psychophysical experiments. He influenced German philosophy of the nineteenth century and the new psychologies of Wundt and Freud in coining some terms that became popular in psychoanalysis, such as *Verdrängung*. Wolman (376) has recently given in English a concise survey of Herbart's philosophy.

John Stuart Mill (1806–1873) proposed a mental chemistry to explain the complex interrelations and alterations of psychic functions (280). He supposed that quantitative changes become qualitative and new contexts arise from elementary thought, in analogy to elements and compound molecules: As the physical, chemical, and biological qualities of water cannot be derived from its atomic constituents hydrogen and oxygen, certain ideas arising from different percepts can have different qualities. This concept is, of course, only a nice metaphor and says nothing about the real mechanisms of mental functions and perception.

WEBER'S DIFFERENTIAL AND FECHNER'S LOGARITHMIC FUNCTION. Ernst H. Weber, whose work was described in ERNST H. WEBER, p. 46, found in his quantitative studies of cutaneous sensation and scaling of weights (359) from 1834 onward that relative increments of stimulus intensity corresponded to constant increments in perceived intensity. Mathematically, these differential thresholds of just noticeable differences (JND) of the stimulus intensity I would correspond to a constant k

$$\Delta I/I = k \quad \text{or} \quad \text{JND} = k\Delta I/I$$

In generalizing Weber's observations of just noticeable differences G. Th. Fechner in 1860 (105) postulated a general logarithmic law of perceptual intensity that he thought valuable for different sensory modalities with various constants. Fechner's law of sensory response magnitude S related to the logarithm of stimulus intensity I multiplied with a constant k is $S = k \cdot \log I$. This formula was used by Adrian, Zotterman, and Matthews to describe the impulse of discharge of single stretch receptors (11, 276) and by Hartline and Graham (145) to describe visual receptor discharge. However, many exceptions to this proposed logarithmic relationship have been observed, both for sensory behavior and for the underlying neural events.

VISUAL POWER FUNCTION OF PLATEAU. Joseph A. F. Plateau (1801–1883), known for his invention of the stroboscope and his spiral, around 1850 established the law of contrast constancy at different illuminations, also called the law of equal sense distances. In 1872, as a blind man continuing to work in visual research, he proposed a pre-Stevensian concept of the power law of sensory intensities (305) derived from visual experiments with his friend Duprez. Corrected to the same abbreviations as the Weber-Fechner equations, i.e., I = stimulus intensity and S = sensation magnitude, his formula was $S = k \cdot I^c$.

STEVENS'S POWER LAW AND MAGNITUDE SCALING. Plateau's formula was generalized and applied to other sensory modalities by S. S. Stevens during the 1950s [(335, 336) and see the chapter by Galanter in this *Handbook*]. The exponent and constant vary in different sensory modalities. The main advance of Steven's studies, besides the generalization of Plateau's power function and its special exponential numbers for different modalities, was his method of ratio scaling in numerical estimations. Stevens's magnitude scaling yields relevant results, even for complex processes such as motion perception (86). It stimulated modern psychophysics (98) and neurophysiology (288, 362).

Logarithmic and power functions are compatible with various physiological processes. Since Stevens's scaling method estimates the final perceptual elaboration of sensory information, one cannot expect that all previous stages of receptor and neuronal function obey the same power law. Linear, logarithmic, or power functions may be valid at different levels, and the exponent and constant may vary at different stages of information processing. In a study of retinal receptive fields Fischer and Freund (107) demonstrated that Fechner's logarithmic function and Stevens's power function may be derived from the same physiological mechanisms, and that both correlate with Ricco's law of spatial summation.

Psychology of Sensory Research

LOCAL SIGNS AND TOPOGRAPHIC PROJECTIONS OF THE SENSES. Rudolph Hermann Lotze (1817–1881) combined a mechanistic system of sensory functions with a teleological concept of the mind. In his *Physiology of the Mind* (1852) he introduced the concept of localization into sensory physiology, creating the term *Lokalzeichen*. He postulated that all sensory messages signal the localization of their excitation rather independently of quality and intensity (258). His concept of local perception was proposed as a theory without experiments, but it influenced all following research on cerebral localization and the topographical projections of the sense organs to the brain. Hering's work on retinal points related to stereopsy (170, 175) and later retinocortical mappings were based on this concept, and so were the projections of the somatosensory and the auditory afferents to the cortex. These primary projection areas were defined by their anatomical connections (109, 136, 354) and investigated by stimulation and ablation in human beings (114, 299), by strychninization of cortical areas (92), and finally, after 1932, by electrophysiological criteria of evoked potentials (see EVOKED POTENTIALS, p. 56).

BIRTH OF EXPERIMENTAL PSYCHOLOGY. Wilhelm Wundt (1832–1920), a pupil of Johannes Müller and Helmholtz, created experimental psychology in the nineteenth century. His first work concerned visual perception and binocular coordination (379), which was completed before he founded the first Institute of Psychology in Leipzig, at the same university in which Fechner and later Hering taught. During four decades he developed his institute in Leipzig to become the cradle of experimental psychology, its influence spreading to America through Wundt's pupils. His textbook of psychology (380), first published in 1874, had six editions. Wundt's concepts are rooted in the associationist tradition of Hume and J. S. Mill and recognize elementary sensations that have two attributes—quality and intensity. Perceptions are integrated from sensations by association. In reviving the Leibnizian apperception (*Wahrnehmung*) in contrast to sensation (*Empfindung*) he maintained that percepts are built up from identifiable elements, which are conscious realities and not artifacts resulting from the experimental methods used. After about 1900 this concept was opposed by the Gestalt psychologists and Würzburg school of Külpe, Ach, and Selz, who denied elementary sensations. Wundt, however, also emphasized creative synthesis (*schöpferische Synthese*) despite his elementarism and taught the principle of the "heteronomy of purpose" to explain the unforeseen consequences of purposeful planning. Wundt did not accept the positivist trend of Mach and his school. In his later years he regarded emotion and will as basic mental functions.

AMERICAN PSYCHOLOGY. Wundt's American counterpart was William James (1842–1910), who also began in physiology and after his study in Germany and France founded the first American psychological laboratory at Harvard University in 1872. James regarded himself as a radical empiricist and propagated a pluralistic pragmatism until in his later years he concentrated on volitional and emotional processes and religious psychology.

James claimed his psychology to be positivistic and pragmatic in considering mental events as objects. He relied mainly on subjective experience and introspection. His own words (199) are, "Introspective observation is what we have to rely on first and foremost and always."

The behaviorists objected to these statements but had to use a rather complicated language to explain simple psychological observations. Introspection is also transmitted by language, and this complication led to philosophical semantics and the logical positivism of Wittgenstein, who claimed that thoughts are facts [(374, 375), see PHILOSOPHY AND PERCEPTION, p. 52].

I am deliberately brief in considering radical behaviorism, the stimulus-response (SR) models of organisms, and similar psychologies of conditioned reflexes; these ignore perception and subjective experience. When they consider the organism as a black box, both physiological mechanisms and introspection remain excluded. Before J. B. Watson's behaviorism became widely accepted, E. L. Thorndike (1874–1949) inaugurated experimental studies of animal learning by stimulus-response observation. E. C. Tolman (1886–1959) taught that behavior also includes meaning and can be important for perception.

Among twentieth century American psychologists who followed James the most interesting for perceptual research are Titchener, Dodge, Stratton, and McDougall (a Scot who went to Harvard in 1920). E. B. Titchener (1867–1927), a pupil of Wundt, proposed a context theory of perception and emphasized the meaning of perception. R. Dodge introduced eye movement recordings with Erdmann in 1898 (101) and made detailed studies of optokinetic nystagmus during the next three decades.

George M. Stratton (1865–1957) was the most original of the second generation of American psychologists. His experiments on vision following reversal of the retinal image (337) and his eye movement recordings (338) are two very important contributions to visual research. The first proved the role of visual learning in space perception. The second demonstrated the prevalence of visual versus oculomotor mechanisms in form perception. The reversal experiments showed a remarkable behavioral adaptation and restoration after the change of retinal image projections. They were the classic source of all later work on the influence of prismatic distortions of retinal images and visual habituation, such as the investigations of Held and Hein (160, 161) and I. Kohler (224).

The somewhat eccentric William McDougall (1871–1938) emphasized the integrative functions and the organization of consciousness and defended introspection. Defining instincts as "congenital perceptual systems," he correlated them with emotions and psychophysical energy (265), foreshadowing Lorenz's theory of instincts (256).

CONDITIONING AND BEHAVIOR RESEARCH. The Russian physiologist Ivan P. Pavlov (1849–1936) developed the behavioral investigations of learning by his conditioning experiments in dogs; he systematized his concept of conditioned reflexes while working more than three decades with many students. His basic method is the association of combined sensory stimuli with feeding, to which American behaviorists added instrumental and operant conditioning. John B. Watson (1878–1958) may be said to have founded the behaviorist school of American psychology. He strongly criticized the use of introspection in the study of perception. This was a sharp break with the psychology of Wundt and James and with those using psychophysical methods. Watson's behaviorism, marshaled in 1913 as a "purely objective experimental branch of natural science" (358) developed in parallel with Pavlov's doctrine of conditioned reflexes (297). Both excluded introspection as unscientific and were not interested in conscious perception. They believed in an objective behavioral science, and Watson envisaged a "prediction and control of behavior" (358). The

American behaviorist school mainly studied human subjects, the Pavlovian school mainly dogs. Pavlov later developed a concept of two signaling systems: the first sensory information system consists of afferent signals for unconditioned and conditioned reflexes; the second signaling system corresponds to language, uses verbal signal abstraction, and is specific to human beings (297). Both Pavlovists and behaviorists restricted their work to input-output studies of sensory stimuli.

ANIMAL BEHAVIOR AND ETHOLOGY. In 1917 the German gestalt psychologist W. Köhler (225) began behavioral studies in chimpanzees, demonstrating their ability to use tools and to perceive complex situations for adequate responses. These studies in apes and higher monkeys were developed further by R. M. Yerkes (382) in the United States. The Russian behaviorist N. Kohts (228) studied sensorimotor learning in apes and monkeys in 1928. His pictures and movies showed complex performances such as unlocking guided by sensory signals, but they also showed the limits of planned behavior in chimpanzees when remote goals, complex visual cues, and future planning were needed. The German zoologist von Uexküll (351) strove for a synthesis of perception and behavior in distinguishing the *Umwelt*, the "special milieu," the *Merkwelt*, the "perceptual compound," and the *Wirkwelt*, the "field of action" of individual animals.

During the 1930s a new movement of behavioral sciences, using nonmammalian animals, was started by zoologists such as K. von Frisch (120), K. Lorenz (256, 257), N. Tinbergen (348), E. von Holst (186, 188), and H. W. Thorpe (347). These ethologists were more interested in sensory physiology and perceptual science than the American behaviorists. The recent development of ethology cannot, however, be treated in this historical chapter.

RECENT THEORIES OF PERCEPTION. I cannot discuss the immense psychological literature of the twentieth century, but I mention only three currents of perceptual research. First, the German Gestalt psychologists, who stressed preformed qualities and organized wholes, were represented mainly by Max Wertheimer (364, 365); Wolfgang Köhler (226, 227); Kurt Koffka (223); Kurt Lewin (247), who emigrated to America; and Wolfgang Metzger (278). They may be considered as psychological followers of Kant's principle that primary structures determine perception and cognition. K. Lewin's topological psychology (247) developed this further. Second, the Franco-Swiss school of Jean Piaget (303) studied perceptual development and maturation. Third, some American schools of sensory psychologists—F. H. Allport (13), R. Arnheim (15), and J. S. Bruner (63, 64)—emphasized cognition and personality structure; D. O. Hebb (158) and C. L. Hull, behavior and learning; and F. Attneave (17), the use of information theory and redundancy for explaining sensory structure and organization. James J. Gibson

(126, 127) rightly stressed the role of attention and the sensorimotor aspects of perception, e.g., in vision the importance of eye movements and fixation sequences. J. Gibson (127) and R. Held (160, 161) have studied attention and sensorimotor components of perception.

Philosophies and Perceptual Research

PHILOSOPHY AND PERCEPTION. During the nineteenth century German philosophy was divided by the antagonism of idealists and materialists. In England and France the empiricist and positivist schools dominated.

Idealistic philosophers in Germany contributed only a few general principles to the perceptual sciences. Some of these, such as Fichte's and Hegel's scheme of thesis, antithesis, and synthesis, had more relation to the processing of information in thought than to perceptual processing proper. The Hegelian dialectic was reversed by K. Marx and F. Engels into their dialectic materialism. Other materialists of the younger Hegelian school such as L. Feuerbach and L. Büchner postulated that perception results from nervous mechanisms, but they did not contribute to sensory research. Among Kant's followers Herbart's mathematical speculations about mental mechanisms foreshadowed Fechner's psychophysics (see PSYCHOPHYSICAL AND PSYCHOCHEMICAL PHILOSOPHIES, p. 49).

Positivist philosophies propagated the practical use of philosophy and science and denied the usefulness of metaphysics. Comte (1798–1857), the French founder of positivism, had somewhat romantic views of the *pouvoir spirituel* in science. His philosophy and the later pragmatic movements, such as dialectic materialism, monism, pragmatism, and Dewey's instrumentalism, had little influence on perceptual research, with the exception of Mach's work (see ERNST MACH, p. 48). The empirical psychology of Franz Brentano (1838–1917) opposed the positivists and stressed intentionality in perception (57). This prepared Husserl's phenomenology and the existentialist philosophies of Heidegger (159), Jaspers (201), and Merleau-Ponty (217). Their reduction of cognition to the inner world broke most connections between perceptual research and philosophy. Similarly, Henri Bergsons's elegant writings, his *élan vital* and perception of change and simultaneity, did not contribute much to the perceptual sciences. The logical positivism of Ludwig Wittgenstein (1889–1951)—starting from mathematical logics such as that founded by G. Frege, D. Hilbert, H. Poincaré, and Bertrand Russell (320)—had little application in perceptual research. Wittgenstein's teaching influenced British epistemology, but his posthumous book, published in 1953 (375), questioned some of his own principles of the *Tractatus* (374) and reduced semantics to language games. In contrast to these rather disappointing results of modern philosophy, the ideas of N. Hartmann and K. Popper allow more substantial applications to sensory science. In

the border field of philosophy and psychology Jean Piaget's concepts of perceptual maturation (302–304) created a synthesis of sensorimotor coordination and perception that combined innate and acquired knowledge.

EMPIRICISM AND NATIVISM REVISITED. The scientific battle that was fought out a hundred years ago between the nativists and empiricists of visual physiology had its philosophical roots in the seventeenth and eighteenth centuries. Descartes and Leibniz had postulated innate ideas, whereas the empiricist concepts of sensory physiologists originate in Locke's and Hume's principles of the association of perceptual knowledge. Among modern neurophysiologists, who appreciate sensory data as the main source of knowledge and behavior, Mountcastle (286) cites Locke as his philosophical ancestor. Others such as Hubel, who are more interested in the morphological and functional order than in learned functions, might regard Descartes or Leibniz as their philosophical forebears. Those who believe in intricate cooperation between sensory experience and the neuronal order, as does the author of this chapter, regard Kant's philosophy as the most useful basis (207, 208), although his categories of time and space cannot be considered as aprioristic notions, since Helmholtz (164) and James (199) denied the a priori concept of space perception without visual experience. The physiologist who looks from a distance at the old and new battles between the nativist and empiricist concepts of visual physiology may find it surprising that they are often discussed dogmatically as exclusive alternatives, instead of as a natural interrelation of both innate order and learning. Such a synopsis of preformed rational and acquired empirical knowledge would correspond also to Hartmann's and Popper's philosophies of science (see LIMITED DOWNWARD INFLUENCE OF PERCEPTION AND ACTION, p. 64, and THE THREE WORLDS OF POPPER AND ECCLES, p. 65).

INNATE AND ACQUIRED CONTENTS OF PERCEPTION. In 1826 Johannes Müller's theory of specific nerve energy (291) provided the physiological foundation for a nativistic order of all sensory projections to the brain. From 1861 onward Hering and his students defended the nativisitic concept of an innate order of retinal points and their cerebral connections as the explanation for binocular depth perception and contrast vision (170–175). Simultaneously, Helmholtz (164) and his school proposed acquired visual knowledge and judgment (*Wahrnehmungsurteile*) as the empiricist explanation of space perception and contrast vision. This theory was right for space perception but wrong for contrast vision. After this struggle was over the impression was left that each concept could be right for certain sensory functions but not for others, and that both innate and acquired mechanisms were interdependent, as proposed by Kant (213–216). It appears evident that empirically acquired visual learning must have an innate basis in the ordered structures of preformed neural connections to achieve a cerebral performance of perception (207).

NEURONAL CORRELATES OF NATIVISM AND EMPIRICISM. During the past ten years discussions similar to those conducted in the nineteenth century between nativists and empiricists have arisen between different groups of experimental visual physiologists: on the one hand the research team of Hubel and Wiesel and on the other the groups of Barlow, and of Spinelli, with their co-workers. Wiesel and Hubel (370, 371) found that the receptive-field organization of orientation-selective neurons is innate and already exists in visually inexperienced kittens. In contrast, Barlow, Blakemore, Hirsch, and Pettigrew (21, 49, 181, 300), and Spinelli concluded from their experiments that environmental factors may be more important than innate factors of specific maturation. The two series of observations are not mutually exclusive, however, since Hubel and Wiesel have shown that early visual exposure is necessary for the maturation and maintenance of certain orientation-selective neurons during a susceptible phase of early life (191, 371). Hubel's and Wiesel's later experiments and anatomical demonstrations of special monocular and binocular projections and cell columns in the visual cortex of monkeys have shown a surprisingly fine and complex architectonic order that develops innately. In their own words the primary visual cortex is "genetically programmed" and develops in the monkey during "the first 6 weeks, whether or not the animal has visual experience" (191, 192). It appears evident that the acquired mechanisms of visual learning also use this complex apparatus and that perfect visual performance can only be achieved after some perceptual experience. Even if these structures are mainly innate and genetically fixed patterns, they must be set in action for depth perception and other visual performances by using empirical data, i.e., by learning.

SENSORY DEPRIVATION, CRITICAL PERIODS, AND LEARNING. All visual deprivation studies, inaugurated by Hubel and Wiesel (191, 192, 370, 371), have demonstrated a critical period after birth during which experience of pattern vision is necessary for the development and functioning of higher visual mechanisms such as binocular coordination and stereopsis. Without such exercise of binocular pattern vision certain neuronal structures and coordinations show atrophy and mostly irreversible damage of innate, genetically programmed connections (191, 371) similar to amblyopia in the human being. In later life, after the critical period, higher mental and language functions also need continuous exercise, as the negative effects of intellectual deprivation during war conditions, captivity, or imprisonment demonstrate. Hence, the shaping and reshaping of perception by experience, the so-called plasticity of the behaving organism, is perceptual learning. Unfortunately, until now physiological

and anatomical correlates of such effects concern mostly the negative aspects of perceptual learning through deprivation experiments. Positive learning experiments are scarce and time consuming, and neuronal correlations are lacking in mammals. Some promising experiments have been made in molluscs (211). The cerebral correlates of perception are not a white paper, as Locke postulated, but inborn ordered structures of the brain. The structural order of the sensory systems can explain innate mechanisms of sensory information processing as postulated by the nativists, and learned functions of the brain permit a perceptual synthesis as postulated by the empiricists. All acts of perception require both innate order and empirically acquired sensory learning that lead to recognition by contributing prior information drawn from memory stores (207).

OBJECTIVE SENSORY PHYSIOLOGY
AND NEURONAL RECORDINGS

Adrian's Achievements

In 1926 Edgar Douglas Adrian (1889–1977) introduced the technique of recording action potentials from single somatosensory nerve fibers evoked by adequate stimulation of their receptor terminals (2), thus inaugurating objective sensory physiology. Within a few years his work established the mode of action of the sense organs and their information transmission. Adrian's results also had general implications for the mechanisms of the nervous system: they were the first demonstration of frequency-modulated spikes of nerve fibers, generated according to the all-or-none principle, and they provided strong physiological support for the neuron theory. He later investigated the central projections of sensory systems in the brain (6). It is appropriate to say here that Lord Adrian's accomplishments and his friendly counsel have influenced my own research over a period of four decades.

AFFERENT NERVES. In 1926 Adrian and Zotterman's records from various afferent nerves (10, 11) established the basic features of receptor mechanisms: the rhythmic discharge of sensory fibers, their functional specificity, their adaptation and receptive fields. In 1928 in his important survey in these pioneer studies on the bases of sensation, Adrian and his co-workers (3, 4) demonstrated objective correlates of different modalities of cutaneous sensation in animals, which corresponded to von Frey's work (118, 119) on specific receptor spots of touch, cold, and warmth in the human skin (see CUTANEOUS SENSATION, p. 44). In 1960 these analogues of animal experiments and human sensation were found to have direct physiological proof through human nerve fiber recordings made rather late in the experiments of Hensel and Boman (167). Zotterman's correlations of pain and tickling (386, 387) were followed by his recordings from human gustatory nerves responding to quantified stimuli (51).

Adrian's schemes of the relation between stimulus, sensory message, and sensation and of receptor adaptation are still, 50 years after their publication (3, 4), the best depictions of these functions, and they have become classic textbook illustrations. Figure 16 shows Adrian's personal sketches of his results made for lectures.

In 1929 Adrian extended his work to the discharges of motoneurons. After Liddell and Sherrington (249) in 1925 had proposed the term *motor unit* for the complex of motoneuron and its innervated muscle fibers, Adrian and Bronk (7) recorded the first single motor unit discharges from human muscles. This led to the prediction that "two qualitatively different processes can occur in the synapses to account for the inhibitory and the excitatory effect" (7). These two kinds of synaptic membrane polarization were discov-

ered 24 years later by John C. Eccles and his co-workers (60, 61, 93, 94) by intracellular recordings from spinal motor nerve cells. Eccles called them *excitatory* and *inhibitory postsynaptic potentials* (*EPSP* and *IPSP*).

SYNAPTIC EFFECTS OF SENSORY DISCHARGES. Eccles's recordings of postsynaptic potentials at the motoneuron membrane extended Adrian's recordings of axonal discharge to the nerve cell and allowed a precise investigation of the central action of afferent impulses. In the period from 1939 to 1945 Adrian's pupil Alan Hodgkin paved the way for the recording from nerve cell membranes: together with A. F. Huxley he penetrated with relatively coarse electrodes into the giant axons of the squid, a marine mollusc, and obtained the first direct measurements of neuronal membrane po-

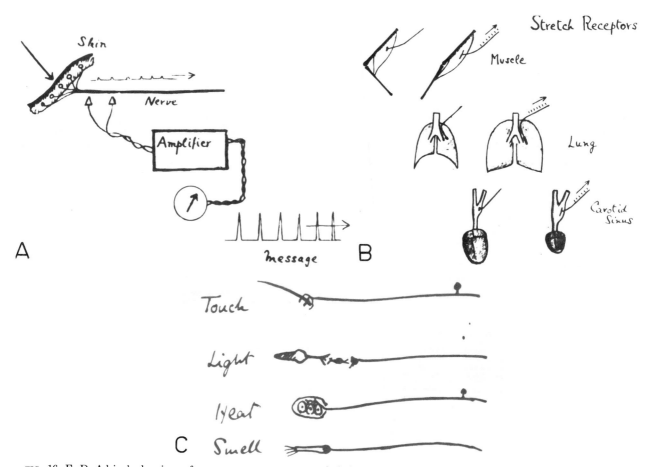

FIG. 16. E. D. Adrian's drawings of sensory nerve messages and their recording. *A*: cutaneous sensation. ↘, Stimulus touching skin elicits rhythmic action potentials in nerve fiber. These messages are picked up from electrodes and magnified by an amplifier for recording instrument, ⊘. *B*: stretch receptors from muscle, lung, and carotid sinus are excited by muscle-lengthening lung extension and carotid sinus dilatation, respectively. *C*: afferent neurons signaling touch, light, heat, and smell, and their processing of the receptor excitation: afferent fiber is connected with a hair touch receptor; optic nerve fiber is activated from a cone over two synapses; thermoreceptor activating a posterior root fiber and olfactory receptor with its primary fiber send their messages to central nervous system directly or after various synaptic transformations. (Original drawings made by Lord Adrian about 1927, reproduced with the kind permission of Dr. Richard Adrian.)

tentials from an axon (182). The development of finer microelectrodes in 1951 to 1953 made it possible for Eccles and his co-workers to penetrate into the living mammalian motoneuron soma in the spinal cord of the cat (61). At the motoneuron membrane Eccles recorded the excitatory postsynaptic potentials elicited as monosynaptic reflexes by electrical stimulation of muscle spindle afferents and showed that inhibitory postsynaptic potentials are produced by interneurons (93, 94).

The investigation of proprioceptive impulses conducted from muscle spindles to the spinal cord was also initiated by Adrian and Zotterman (12). It was pursued in Adrian's laboratory by his co-worker Bryan Matthews. In the first of two basic papers Matthews proved that the receptor discharge increases with the logarithm of stimulus intensity (276); in the second he demonstrated the spindle response during active muscle contraction (275). These experiments laid the foundation of all modern work on proprioceptive feedback and alpha-gamma interaction in sensorimotor regulation.

SENSORY IMPULSES AND PERCEPTION. In 1928 Adrian (3, 4) summarized his ideas of the perceptual correlates of receptor function and afferent nerve impulses in a classic diagram that was reproduced in many textbooks. His informative depiction showing the relation between stimulus, sensory message, and sensation demonstrated that the intensity of sensation parallels the frequency of afferent nerve discharge: "The rise and decline of the sensation is a fairly close copy of the rise and decline of the excitatory process in the receptor. The quality of the sensation seems to depend on the path which the impulse must travel, for apart from this there is little to distinguish the message from different receptors." (4).

Besides stating these principles, Adrian was rather cautious to deduce general implications on perception from his work. In his own words, he did it "timidly" because "the whole problem of the connection between the brain and the mind is as puzzling to the physiologist as it is to the philosopher" (4). He expected a "drastic revision of our systems of knowledge" to "explain how a pattern of nervous impulses can cause a thought, or show that the two events are really the same thing looked at from a different point of view."

Sensory Afference and Brain Potentials

EARLY CONTRIBUTIONS. The British physiologist Richard Caton (1842–1926) had seen the first visual evoked potentials of the cortex in 1877 (67) but was not able to record them. Similar observations on stimulus-evoked and spontaneous cortical electrical activity were published in 1890 and 1892, by Beck and Cybulski (29, 30), working at the Polish-Austrian University of Krakow, but they were ignored by physiologists. Ten years later Einthoven's string galvanometer allowed better recordings of weak bioelectric currents. This instrument was used by Hans Berger (1873–1941), a German neuropsychiatrist working in Jena, to record brain potentials of the exposed dog's cortex in 1902–1910 and from the human skull in 1924–1928. After his unpublished animal experiments had shown rather doubtful effects of sensory stimuli Berger resumed brain wave recordings 14 years later from trephined humans and in 1929 published his first paper on human brain potentials (37), for which he proposed the term *Elektrenkephalogramm (EEG)*. The spread of brain waves over the skull and skin was investigated by Tönnies (350).

SENSORY AROUSAL AND THE HUMAN ELECTROENCEPHALOGRAM. During his early EEG studies, before sensory evoked potentials and event-related slow brain potentials became known, Berger observed a diffuse general effect of sensory stimuli related to attention and arousal in EEG records of man, and he published this in 1930 (38). His early records from 1925 to 1929, which were made before the first publication, already showed a prolonged disappearance of rhythmic α-waves and a flattened EEG pattern after stimuli of very different modalities as well as during mental effort. As a general explanation Berger proposed that flattening of the EEG is related to attention (38, 39). Adrian (8) and others interpreted the flattened EEG pattern as desynchronization.

Berger's EEG curves, recorded without amplifiers by a mirror galvanometer, are shown in Figure 17; A and B are skull recordings from normal subjects that were presented in the 1930 paper (38); D and E are unpublished direct recordings from the human brain, obtained in the same year in a patient with a brain tumor. The latter recordings were planned by Berger to prove the origin of the EEG in the cerebral cortex and to explore the possibilities of brain tumor localization by electrophysiological methods. There was no time for a systematic study of sensory effects, and Berger gave only three stimuli, one acoustic and two tactile, as noted in his protocol preserved in the Berger-Archiv at Freiburg. He could not see an immediate evoked response in the parietal cortex of the trephined patient. Some flattening of the EEG occurred later, however, and for a longer time, when the patient expected a new stimulus (record E in Fig. 17).

These records are historical documents of the first directly recorded human brain potentials, led simultaneously from the cortex and white matter, from which Berger reproduced only a short strip in 1931 (39). All earlier records of Berger were indirect EEG derivations—partly from the scalp above the dura of trephined regions where the bone was removed, partly from occipitofrontal leads with the skull intact. Most of these EEG records showed clearly the global flattening as an unspecific sensory response (Fig. 17A) and a periodic waxing and waning of α-waves, which

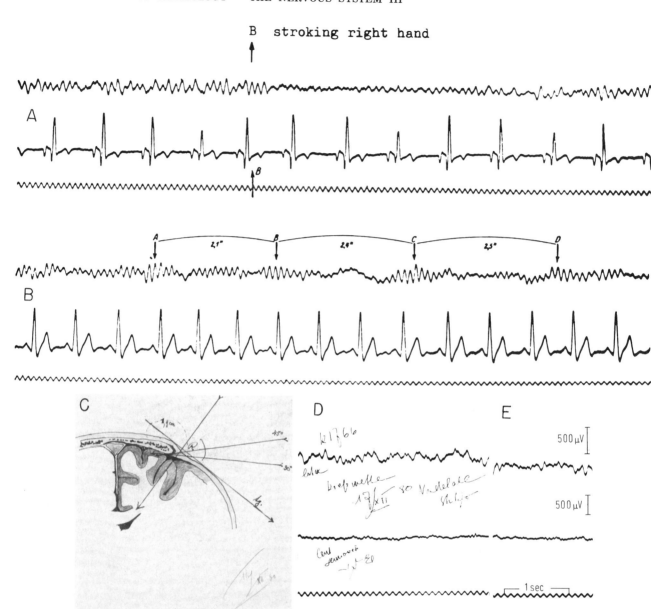

FIG. 17. Hans Berger's early 1929 and 1930 recordings of desynchronization of electroencephalogram (EEG) in man by sensory stimuli and attention. *A, B*: scalp recordings show blocking of α-waves and EEG flattening caused by sensory stimuli, A, and during periodic alterations of attention, B, with EEG (middle records) and time 50/s (lowest records). Subjects: healthy men aged 30 (*A*) and 34 years (*B*). *C, D, E*: Berger's unpublished first direct recordings from human brain in 1930: *C*: Berger's drawing shows how the coated silver needle pairs were inserted in the parietal cortex and 4 cm below in the white matter during a diagnostic cerebral puncture in 20-yr-old man with brain tumor. *D, E*: simultaneous records demonstrate origin of EEG waves in cortex, the white matter having less electrical activity. On *D* Berger wrote "Cortex, Centr. semiovale," and after name and date, "Nadelabl.", in shorthand: "Augen geschlossen; eingeführte El." (needle recording; eyes shut, electrodes inserted). *E*: during expectation of a second sensory stimulus the EEG flattened. [*A, B*: from Berger (38). *C, D, E*: records K 1766, 1768 Dec. 17, 1930, from the Freiburg Berger-Archives.]

Berger thought to correspond with spontaneous fluctuations of attention (Fig. 17*B*). This flattening of the EEG following sensory arousal or eye opening was later called α-*blocking* or *EEG arousal* and was interpreted in 1949 by Moruzzi and Magoun (284) as an ascending activation of the cerebral cortex from the midbrain reticular formation.

EVOKED POTENTIALS. Modality-specific and localized sensory evoked potentials from cortical areas were first recorded in 1931–1932 by Bartley, Bishop, and Newman (22, 23) from the visual cortex of dogs and rabbits and by Fischer (108) and by Kornmüller and Tönnies (231, 233) from the visual and auditory cortex of rabbits. The recording of somatosensory evoked potentials in cats and monkeys was initiated by Gerard in 1936 and by Bard in 1937. Systematic mapping of cortical projections of the visual field by Talbot and Marshall (342) followed in 1941 and the localization of cutaneous sensation in the somatosensory cortex by Adrian (5, 6) and Woolsey et al. (377). Modern methods of computer averaging facilitated the research on sensory evoked potentials also in man, but this is not the place to describe these recent developments. MacKay and Jeffreys (270) summarized some relations of visual evoked potentials with perception in 1973. Computer analyses yielded other results of importance for sensorimotor action by demonstrating slow brain waves related to expectation of sensory stimuli during conditioning, to the preparation of motor action, and to accompanying goal-directed movements (see STIMULUS EXPECTATION, READINESS, AND AIMED MOVEMENTS, p. 60).

Cerebral Neuronal Mechanisms

NEURONAL RESPONSES IN BRAIN. The neuronal components of evoked potentials in the cortical receiving areas were analyzed from 1952 onward. Twelve years before, Adrian and Moruzzi (10) in 1939 had already recorded efferent impulses of the motor cortex from pyramidal axons. The intracortical processing of afferent messages was then investigated in the cat by several research groups simultaneously and independently, the first publications appearing in 1952 and 1953: our group described five different responses of visual cortex neurons to diffuse illumination (24, 203, 209); Li and Jasper (248) and Amassian (14) recorded neuronal discharges in the somatosensory cortex; Rose and Galambos (316) described neuronal responses to acoustic stimuli in the medial geniculate nucleus; and Rose and Mountcastle (317) studied the somatosensory responses in thalamic neurons. Mountcastle (285) in 1957 discovered the columnar order of different modalities and their receptive fields in the sensory cortex. The best correlations of neuronal activity and perception were found in the visual systems mainly for brightness and darkness information, contrast vision, and afterimages (205, 207).

NEURONAL MECHANISMS OF VISION. A new era of objective visual physiology was initiated in the 1930s. After Adrian and R. Matthews (9) in 1927 described mass recordings from the vertebrate optic nerve, H. Keffer Hartline recorded the first single-fiber discharges of visual neurons—in 1932 from the compound eye of the invertebrate *Limulus* and from 1935 onward in the frog's retina (142, 143). Hartline's work inaugurated an important development of visual neuron physiology that continued over three decades. From 1939 onward Granit made systematic neuronal recordings from the mammalian retina (130, 131). Hartline's discovery of lateral inhibition in *Limulus*, made in 1949 (144), was followed by Kuffler's clarification of the receptive-field organization (236) in the cat's retina

in 1953. Hartline pursued the *Limulus* experiments systematically, with Ratliff explaining contrast mechanisms (144, 313). From 1952 onward our Freiburg group, with G. Baumgartner, O. Creutzfeldt, O. J. Grüsser, and H. Kornhuber and others, inaugurated the neuronal physiology of the visual cortex (24–28, 203, 205–210). The work of P. O. Bishop (47) and others extended the analysis of visual processes to the lateral geniculate. In 1959 to 1962 Hubel and Wiesel discovered the orientation specificity and columnar organization in the cat's striate cortex (189, 190). A dual concept of two neuronal systems, on-center neurons signaling brightness and off-center neurons signaling darkness (205–207), was derived from Kuffler's receptive-field organization and Baumgartner's experiments of contrast stimulation of retinal, geniculate, and visual cortex neurons (25–27). During the last decade visual neuronal physiology concentrated on the monkey's visual cortex (192, 371); the main results are described in the chapters by De Valois and Jacobs and by Schiller in this *Handbook*.

PERCEPTION AND ACTION

Following this review of the history and philosophy of sensory research I wish to discuss a neglected field in physiology: the relation of perception to attention, anticipation, and decision. These are old problems of philosophy. Aristotle first discussed the intentional preparation for action 2,000 years ago (16), and Kant in 1781 (213) proposed *Anticipationen der Wahrnehmung* (anticipations of perception). Nineteenth century physiology brought the first measurable data for simple sensorimotor functions by reflex recordings. Nevertheless, even Pavlov's conditioned reflexes could not explain the programming mechanisms of the higher cortical processes of perception and action. Only during the last decade have neurophysiologists recorded some objective cerebral correlates of the processes that precede conditioned and voluntary action.

These problems are now being attacked from several sides. Psychological investigations of "set" in human beings, combined behavioral and neuronal analyses in monkeys, and the electrophysiological recordings of human voluntary activity may lead to some new insights into the coordination of intention, perception, and action—briefly, the preprogramming processes for these behavioral phenomena. Modern communication sciences have proposed quasi-mathematical models of information flow for these programs.

Intentional Preperception and Anticipation

Cybernetic scientists asserted rightly the continuous control of sensorimotor action (369) and the role of information in programming, but they neglected the primary intentional impetus of the organism. In contrast to the computer, the living organism actively searches for adequate sensory patterns, such as the innate releaser mechanisms of Lorenz (256, 257). A satisfying concept of perception therefore must pay attention to these processes in the interaction of the organism and its environment. They have physiological, behavioral, and psychological aspects and can be depicted in cybernetic models of the brain.

ATTENTIVE ADJUSTMENT. In 1890 William James postulated an anticipatory preperception by sensory adjustment during attention, to facilitate perception and action. After mentioning the neglect of the phenomenon of attention by English empiricists and associationists, he pointed out that attentive adjustment to sensory messages with ideational labeling prepares perception (199). These psychological concepts were related later to physiology and cybernetics.

RELEVANCE CONTROL AND MATCHING. In 1941 W. R. Hess (177) discussed some proprioceptive mechanisms of attentive adjustment for movement control and proposed a precybernetic matching concept. There followed cybernetic feedback models of N. Wiener (369) and von Holst and Mittelstaedt (186-188). These were applied to motion control by Hess (179) and to perception by MacKay (268, 269) and many others. The attentive search for significant sensory patterns and their anticipatory control are functions of a perceptual process that selects the relevant from a multitude of irrelevant sensory data (199, 208). Action has informational requirements similar to perception, and both need matching and "evaluation" (267–269). Comparing the functions of the brain and of modern computers illustrates that the nervous system may perform logical operations that cannot be explained in terms of reflex action.

MEANING AND ACTION IN PERCEPTION. Physiological as well as psychological experience demonstrates two characteristics of sensory perception: 1) Sensory stimuli are effective in animals and human beings mainly for their meaning to the recipient, and less because of their intensity, quality, or modality; 2) the organism learns from perception mainly during action, on the basis of emotional and instinctive motivation. Both involve an anticipation of the sensory stimulus. This is apparent from such different research fields as Pavlov's conditioned reactions (297) as well as from Piaget's psychological observations (302, 303). If we assume that a dog in a conditioning experiment perceives something, his perception will be directed to the meaning of the stimulus, i.e., the anticipation of food. Hence, a psychological description that the sound signal means food and that the dog's salivation starts in anticipation of food may be more suitable for perceptual research than to say that the sound elicits conditioned reflexes before feeding.

Modern physiology and psychology also agree that the organism learns by activity, motivation, and programming. The psychologists Piaget (302) and Held

(160); the biologists Lorenz (256), Weiss (361), and Tinbergen (348); the physiologists Hess (177–179), Eccles (95), and Granit (132); and the neurologists Droogleever Fortuyn (88) and I (206, 207) may be quoted as supporting this proposition.

PREPROGRAMMING IN PERCEPTION AND ACTION. When we direct our attention to perceive or to seize an object, we look at it. By directing the gaze toward the anticipated object we use directed attention and perform a preparatory act of anticipation of a future goal. There is objective evidence that the brain is involved in this anticipatory programming. During preperceptive expectation, readiness, and control of voluntary action, bilateral cortical potential shifts have been recorded in man (see Fig. 19 and *Cerebral Correlates of Intention in Man*, p. 60), and neuronal correlates have been found in performing monkeys (286). Hence, the anticipation of sensory stimuli and of voluntary action not only is a philosophical problem but also concerns the physiologist.

ANTICIPATION AND PURPOSE. The first attempts to solve the problems of anticipation of action were made by Aristotle in the third century B.C. In the book of *Metaphysics* (16) he postulated for voluntary action a preparatory purposeful foresight, called *noesis*, which is directed toward an imagined and intentional aim, called *eidos*. After anticipating this eidos the organism realizes the intended action. To explain these processes in time, Aristotle used the word movement (*kinesis*) for both the intention and the realization. In 1951 Nicolai Hartmann (151) made a simple diagram of the Aristotelian concept (Fig. 18A). This diagram already contains, in essence, a synthesis of rational and empirical conditions of knowledge, will, and action, when we translate *noesis* as *Vorstellungswahl* or "selection of intuition." It shows that man can act with finality (purpose) at the mental level and with causality at the physical level.

A second diagram by Hartmann (Fig. 18B) demonstrates by the arrows a seemingly paradoxical reversal of time in anticipation and purposeful action: The conscious mind prepares the willed movement by purpose (*Zweckbestimmung*), and the planned anticipation presupposes the end envisaged before selection of the means. The decision to act follows the goal presupposition and the motivated selection of the means. All these preparations are modified by perceptual cues and precede the action. I have enlarged this scheme in Figure 18C for some mental and neural correlates of intentional percepts and acts that are guided by envisaged preconcepts. The German term *Vorstellung* (imperfectly translated by "idea" or "imaging" or "intuition") contains also an implicit temporal anticipation of Brentano's intention as a preperceptive act (57). These philosophical concepts can be applied in principle to subject-object interaction during goal-directed and programmed behavior. Some cerebral correlates are shown in Figure 19.

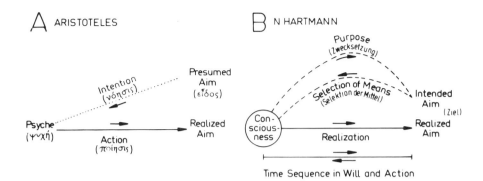

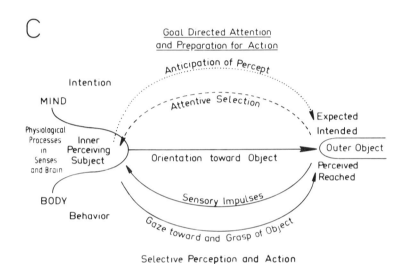

FIG. 18. Diagrams of intentional perception, aimed action, and directive attention. Schemes demonstrate anticipating preparation of perception and action in inner world and sensorimotor processes of behavior in outer world. *A*: Time relations of anticipating purpose, intention, and action as conceived by Aristotle. Aristotle described in the "Metaphysics" the cooperation of human knowledge and action by anticipation (*noesis*) of a foreseen aim (*eidos*) which acts in reverse in determining the action (*poiesis*) toward a goal. *B*: time relations of anticipating purpose, intention, and action, by scheme of N. Hartmann. Hartmann uses arrows to depict the peculiar time relations in the anticipating preparation of goal-directed action. Willed intention must precede selection of means for the ends and this selection also precedes realization. Time scale of purpose (*Zwecksetzung*) and selection (*Mittelwahl*) shows opposite directions: purpose projects to future, and selection paradoxically acts against time flow as shown by *arrows* and time abscissa. This seemingly paradoxical inversion of time by preconceived future is present also in perceptual attention using internal world models given by sensory experience to search for and perceive the intended objects. *C*: psychophysical scheme of attentive perception, anticipation, and action. Interactions between perceiving subject and intended object are schematized for three active processes of expectation, attention, and orientation, and for passive afferent messages from sense organs to brain. Above the *middle horizontal line* are shown anticipatory processes of directive attention in the mind; below are shown physiological correlates of attentive orientation and perception in body and brain. *Upper* processes are psychic; *lower* are neurophysiological and behavioral functions. For vision the attentive and orientating processes include eye movements. [*B*: adapted from Hartmann (151).]

INTENTION, ATTENTION, AND ACTION. The philosophical schemes of voluntary action (Fig. 18*A* and *B*) can be enlarged to cover attentive perception and the intentional preparation of a goal-directed movement, the *Bewegungsentwurf* or "action program" of Wundt and his school (380). Figure 18*C* summarizes some psychological and physiological functions of intention, directed attention, and orientation involved in the grasping of an object. It demonstrates that an attentive subject anticipates the percept, orients himself toward

the selected object, and prepares information processing of sensory and motor impulses in the brain—all before actual perception and action. The final action of motor command that responds to the perceived meaning by seizing the object must have some time delay. Hence, the time sequence of Figure 18*C* is more complex for the anticipating preparation, the resulting perception, and the goal-directed action of reaching than in Figure 18*B*. The depicted separation of psychic processes occurring in the mind (above mid-line) from their neurophysiological and behavioral correlates in the body and outer space (below mid-line) is of course artificial, and the time abscissa is not exactly corresponding for both.

The scheme of five processes of subject-object interaction represented in Figure 18C may look rather complicated but is of course an abstract simplification. The concrete information processing of different sense messages in the brain that occurs in an everyday percept and simple reaction involves so many complex pathways and cerebral structures that this figure is certainly much simpler than the astonishing cerebral performances of directed attention and anticipated perception.

These anticipatory activities are guided by perception of von Uexküll's *Umwelt* and by willed spontaneity that arises in the organism to act in its *Wirkwelt* (351). Both are prepared by a genetically determined structural and functional order of the brain. Ethological research in animals has given rise to an analogue of innate anticipation in behavior since Lorenz in 1943 (256) conceived his *angeborenes Schema*, the "innate releasing mechanism." In the same year Craik (74) discussed an internal model of the external world as an aid to the planning of action.

CEREBRAL MODELS FOR RECOGNITION AND THOUGHT. During the eighteenth century the physiologist A. von Haller proposed an internal model, in the brain, of the world around us to explain recognition and aimed action (139–140). In 1946 Adrian (6) assumed that human thought operates with a cerebral machinery that, using memory stores and percepts, produces a working model of reality. The role of a preconceived image of the environment for orientation is emphasized by Beritoff (40) and is recognized indirectly even by extremely reflex-minded scientists of the Pavlovian school when they use the stimulus-conditioned reflex concept to explain behavioral orientation. For human action we have depicted some interplay between intention, object, perception, and behavior in Figure 18C. Figure 19A and B show the similarities of cortical correlates of intention prior to action both for stimulus-dependent and for free spontaneous movement programming in the human being.

METAPHORS AND MODELS OF CONSCIOUS PERCEPTION AND ATTENTION. Attention and consciousness select certain percepts and mental contents from sensory information and memory. Both may be compared to a spotlight that sheds light on perceived and memorized details arising from the dark unconscious field of the inner and outer world (204, 206, 208). According to this metaphor consciousness will have at any given moment only few data in a focus of attention, and this content changes within various time periods of the daily stream of conscious life. The amount of actual conscious information is estimated to be 16–20 bits per second as demonstrated in the information flow models of Küpfmüller and of Steinbuch and Franck

(239, 333). Küpfmüller's diagram also depicts the processing of perception and action in the brain and the conscious selection of the essential information to act. It shows how psychological reduction by selection of the conscious percept contrasts with the large amount of information processing in the brain. The latter consists of neuronal activity enabling perception and recognition by the addition of memory information. Küpfmüller's model is reproduced and its application to the processes of reading and writing is discussed with some philosophical parallels in another paper (208).

ANTICIPATION IN MAN AND ANIMALS. Philosophers tend to assume that the anticipation of the future as it relates to planned endeavor occurs only in the human mind, but biologists have also found similar anticipations in goal-directed actions of animals (133, 177, 178, 256). Even crude instinctive actions and drives of animals that pursue certain goals in mating, hunting, or escaping are related to an active search of anticipated percepts. For example, a hunting cat waiting before (and looking at) a mouse hole very probably anticipates the prey and may envisage a mouse image when it prepares its catching leap before the mouse leaves the hole.

CEREBRAL CORRELATES. To demonstrate how these schemes are related to neurophysiology I mention some physiological correlates of directed visual attention, recently described in performing monkeys—by Mountcastle for neurons in parietal cortex (260, 286) and by Wurtz for neurons of the tectum (381). Mountcastle has found that the activation of fixation and tracking neurons in the parietal area 7 occurred only when the monkey was motivated to direct its attention to a particular object, but not in similar eye movements occurring without signs of attention and motivation (260). Other cortical neurons in areas 5 and 7 were related to command operations of reaching within extrapersonal space (286), a function represented in the lowest line of Figure 18C. Furthermore, recordings of slow cortical potential shifts during goal-directed action in man demonstrate some correlates of intention also in the human brain (Fig. 19).

Cerebral Correlates of Intention in Man

STIMULUS EXPECTATION, READINESS, AND AIMED MOVEMENTS. Recordings of human brain potentials have shown similar physiological correlates of intention in conditioning experiments, which occur before voluntary movements, and also during goal-directed movements. I designate these three conditions of negative cortical potential shifts by the letters A, B, and C. A, stimulus-evoked expectation before a motor response is triggered by a second conditioned sensory stimulus; B, readiness for and preparation of a brief voluntary action; and C, control of monitored goal-directed movements toward a target.

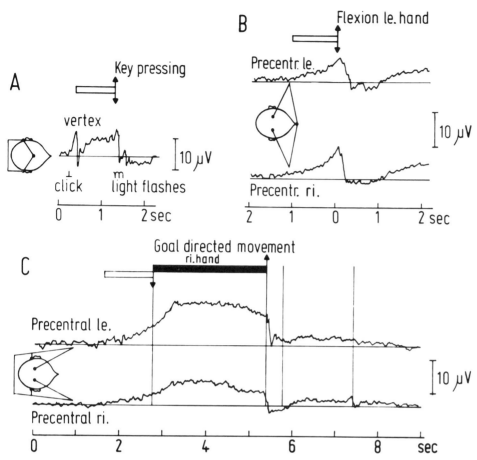

FIG. 19. Slow negative cortical potentials in man, correlated with intention to act (*A, B*) and to reach a target (*C*). Potential shifts (□ before action, ■ during action) are maximal at vertex and show higher amplitudes over motor cortex contralateral to moving limb. Motion is marked by arrows (↕ for brief movements; ↱ for longer movements). *A*: expectation wave or contingent negative variation (CNV) of Walter and co-workers is dependent on sensory stimuli during conditioning. It is elicited by a first stimulus (here auditory and conditional), increases during expectancy of second stimulus (visual and imperative), and is terminated by a positive shift when conditioned action (key-pressing) starts. *B*: readiness potential (Bereitschaftspotential □ of Kornhuber and co-workers) precedes voluntary movements during intention to act and ends with a positive shift when brief movement (left-hand flexion) begins. *C*: goal-directed movement potential [*Zielbewegungspotential* (■) of Grünewald and co-workers] increases premotion negativity (□) during monitored movement for seconds until target is reached and a positive shift occurs. An intentional act with directed attention is common condition of these negative potential shifts. Maximal negativity appears in *A B* before brief movements and in *C* during goal-directed movements. [*A*: adapted from Walter (357); *B*: adapted from Kornhuber and Deecke (230); *C*: adapted from Grünwald-Zuberbier, G. Grünwald, and Jung (135).]

During these three events, surface negative slow potential shifts occur over the parietal, precentral, and frontal cortex in the human being. Figure 19 shows examples of similar brain potentials in these three intentional conditions of preparing and monitoring willed movements. Action *A* is induced by sensory stimuli, *B* is decided freely, and *C* is induced by free decision but controlled by sensory feedback.

The stimulus-evoked potential *A* was called contingent negative variation (CNV), or expectancy wave, by Walter and co-workers (357). The second potential *B* preceding free voluntary movements was named *Bereitschaftspotential*, or "readiness potential," by Kornhuber and co-workers (230). The last potential

shift *C*, which continues during the monitored movement until the goal is reached, was called *Zielbewegungspotential* (135), "goal-directed movement potential," by our group. The common feature of all these long-lasting negative potentials (shown in Fig. 19) is their gradual early rise prior to the movement, as well as the sudden end with reversal to electropositivity when the movement begins in *A* and *B*, or when the goal is reached after longer monitored movements in *C*.

INTENTION AND ATTENTION. The psychological correlate of each of these three events—the preparation for action in cases *A* and *B* or the pursuit of a goal in case C—is an intentional process that induces and controls action and involves attention. Even when the action is triggered by a sensory stimulus in A it is preceded by the intention to act. All these intended actions are attentive and purposive. Although a sensory-evoked expectation of the second stimulus that elicits the motor response in the conditioning experiments (A) is different from a free decision to act (B), there are essential similarities. Both prepare action and correspond to an intention to act. In A, during attentive expectation of the second stimulus, which triggers a conditioned, intended action, the attention is directed primarily to the outer world of the senses and secondarily to the intended movement. In B, before the freely decided movement, attention is internal and directed only toward the inner world of decision. The triggered action (A) differs from free action (B) mainly in its temporal determination by the sensory stimulus. Also during monitored action (C) the perceptual and voluntary guided process of goal fixation and reaching is related to intention and attention. Hence, all these surface-negative cortical potentials may be considered as cerebral correlates of the intentional decision processes of willed action. Of course, the neuronal correlates of these potentials are unknown. The surface negativity of the precentral and parietal cortex that shows larger amplitudes at the hemisphere contralateral to the moving limb (134, 135, 230) is a sign of cortical activity during the initiation and control of movements.

The psychological correlates of slow-potential shifts may be summarized as follows. The negative shift correlates with the strength and duration of the intention to act. The positive shift corresponds to the experienced accomplishment of action and the end of the willed effort and is increased by feedback signals (134).

GENERAL DISCUSSION

Contrasting Concepts and Their Complementary Role

Some concepts of perception, central to both philosophical and physiological analyses, have been discussed since antiquity, often being considered mutually exclusive. These include the following: *1)* Acquired sensory vs. innate rational knowledge. *2)* Monistic vs. dualistic theories of mind-body relations. *3)* Mechanistic vs. mental concepts of perceptual functions. *4)* Objective vs. subjective methods of sensory research.

History as well as present-day science shows us that these are not exclusive antitheses but, rather, they are complementary. By recognizing this we can see how each viewpoint plays a necessary part in an integrated science of perception, although the different methods used by each side may not be strictly comparable.

Some historical examples may illustrate my thesis of the complementary character and coexistence of these seemingly opposing concepts.

INNATE AND ACQUIRED KNOWLEDGE. For the antitheses of empirical knowledge acquired by the senses and rational knowledge innately preformed in the intellect, various solutions have been proposed since 400 B.C., when Plato postulated preformed ideas whereas Democritus presumed acquired sensory percepts. An important controversy over this thesis and antithesis was fought out around A.D. 1700 when Locke and Leibniz discussed a possible synthesis, with Lady Masham as mediator, a debate that ended without agreement. The rationalist pretensions and the empiricist simplifications were adjusted by Kant in his critical synthesis of empirical and a priori knowledge. It became apparent that both claims had some substance, since one philosophy had neglected essential points discovered by the other. For perceptual research innate structures and functions of sensory systems are preconditions of acquired sensory experience in perception.

MONISM AND DUALISM. The dualist theory of the mind-body relation began in antiquity with the Socratic-Platonic soul and dominated medieval science. Most ancient authors favored an interaction of mind and matter. The main emphasis was laid on the soul in the Middle Ages by Christian philosophers, whereas modern scientists have concentrated on body mechanisms ever since Descartes proposed his machine theory. Popper and Eccles have recently presented a new defense of interactionism (310). The parallelist position, advocated by Leibniz in terms of a "pre-established harmony" and illustrated by Geulincx by two independent clocks indicating the same time, was modified in the last century by Wundt (380) and by G. E. Müller with his psychophysical axioms (289). However, it appeals less to the neurobiologist who sees that mental events are readily influenced by crude physical and chemical stimuli such as electrical stimulation and drugs that act on the brain. Fechner (105) tried to combine both monism and dualism by declaring mind and matter as different aspects of the same world but remained a dualist in his epistemology. The concept of isomorphism put forward by Lotze (258) and Köhler (227) points in the same direction. After reviewing these innumerable variations of mind-body theories, however, we can safely conclude that for the work of a pragmatic physiologist the issue of monism versus dualism is irrelevant.

MECHANISMS AND MEANING. Mechanistic explanations of perception were first proposed about 400 B.C. by Democritus. His theory of *eidola* postulated small images of external objects transmitted by atomic movements to the sense organs and from these to sensation. It was opposed to Plato's and Aristotle's visual emission theory and was further developed by

Epicurus, but it was abandoned during the Middle Ages. Descartes's mechanical theory of nerve impulses conducted from the senses to the brain and thence to the soul inaugurated independent research into sensory and body mechanisms in the seventeenth century. The materialists of the eighteenth and nineteenth centuries further developed mechanistic concepts of sensation and extended them to reductionist explanations that were opposed by vitalists. Even radical materialists like La Mettrie expressed some reservations, saying that man and animals are "more than a machine" (240). Neurophysiological modifications of mechanistic theories of perception invoking neuronal "feature detectors" have been defended by present-day neurobiologists. Against this, active participation of psychic experience has been emphasized by philosophers and neurologists who stressed the meaning and purpose of perception and action.

Information theory and computer sciences have been used by some to support mechanistic reductionism in explaining psychic events; MacKay and others have raised objections against such simplistic "nothing buttery" (266, 267, 268). Here, as with the brain-mind problem, a neutral attitude may be the best pragmatic position for the physiologist. In sensory research it has proved useful and necessary to study both physiological mechanisms and mental experience and to correlate psychophysical results with physiological recordings of afferent impulses and their information processing (205, 207).

OBJECTIVE AND SUBJECTIVE SENSORY RESEARCH. Objective and subjective sensory investigations are essentially different in their methods and results: the recordings of the first reveal partial mechanisms, the experiences of the second, complete percepts. In spite of methodological contrasts, both can stimulate and supplement each other. For 2,000 years sensory functions were investigated by purely subjective observations of perceptual experience, later enlarged by psychophysical estimations. During the last 50 years the rise of objective sensory physiology, triggered by Adrian, has clarified the neuronal mechanisms of all sensory modalities. In accumulating an impressive amount of data on sensory messages and their processing, the need for synthesis with the data of perception has become more pressing (202). The correlations of physiology, behavior, and psychophysics have shown how both methods, the subjective and objective, can be used in parallel for perceptual research. I have so often repeated this postulate in relation to vision (205, 207) that it may suffice to say that the complementary function of psychophysical and physiological observations is no less valuable for other sense modalities and for sensory research in general (208).

A separation of physiological mechanisms and perceptual experience had been necessary in past history to start independent physiological research. But later,

when neurophysiology attempted to elucidate higher cerebral mechanisms, it became evident that this rigid separation of subjective and objective sensory research should be supplemented by correlation of neurophysiology and psychophysics.

The pure specialist concentrating on a narrow field of research may well not see the wood for the trees. He may also miss the tree when he analyzes the leaves. Thus one can say that single neuronal recordings from sensory systems cannot show full correlates of perceptual phenomena. They can, however, demonstrate certain relations that make sense also for perception, when use is made of carefully selected and regularly responding types of afferent neurons that were recorded under special stimulus conditions as samples of neuronal populations of similar function. When these are correlated with simple sensory phenomena or typical responses of the living organism, neuronal activity may correspond to some perceptual phenomena and can be interpreted as partial objective equivalents of subjective sensation, as we have demonstrated in vision research (205, 207). The hierarchical concept of stratified levels of the world (and the sciences) lets us better understand the necessity of both specialization and correlation of different methods in research.

Level Concepts and Perceptual Research

THE HARTMANNIAN LEVEL CONCEPT. The German philosopher Nicolai Hartmann (1882–1950) developed his philosophy of science during the 1930s and correlated it with the biologist Max Hartmann (146). Nicolai Hartmann opposed the three current German philosophies, the system-constructing, the phenomenological, and the existential schools. From his publications (147–151) I summarize some of his main concepts in relation to neurophysiology and perception as follows:

Hartmann's *Schichtenlehre* (the hierarchical conception of stratified levels of the world, reaching from the inorganic to the highest mental and cultural strata) is summarized in a schematic diagram (Fig. 20) along with the relations of these strata to sensory research. This was modified from a similar scheme for the neurosciences and medicine (206). The left column shows Hartmann's four levels—inorganic, biological, psychic, and cultural; the middle column, the corresponding classes of science; and the right column, the methods of sensory research in their relation to the main sciences. The lines converging to the right demonstrate the integration of research.

Hartmann's general concept states that each level has its specific laws and that the upper levels depend on the lower. According to these laws of level dependency (*Dependenzgesetze*) the higher mental and social levels can only exist on the bases of intact functions and structures of the lower. These lower levels are, in principle, independent of the higher levels, although a

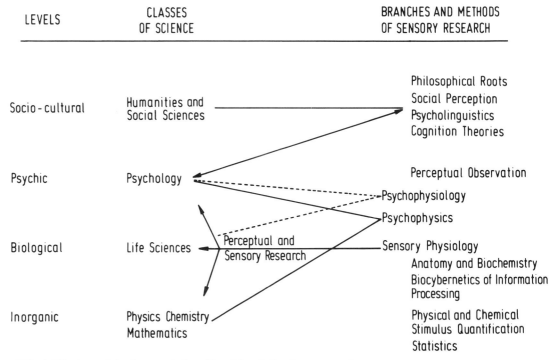

| LEVELS | CLASSES OF SCIENCE | BRANCHES AND METHODS OF SENSORY RESEARCH |

FIG. 20. Diagram of Nicolai Hartmann's level concept of world and its relation to sensory sciences demonstrates structural stratification in four levels (inorganic, biological, psychic, and cultural) on left and shows the related hierarchical order of four classes of science. Sensory research concerns mainly the three lower levels, specialist studies being limited to one level and correlative sciences connecting several levels. Psychophysical research compares physical stimuli at inorganic level with mental experience at psychic level. Recordings of sensory messages belong to biological level. Psychophysiology relates afferent information processing by the brain to percepts. Gulf between organic and psychic strata is bridged by correlating perception at psychic level with sensory messages at biological, and physical stimuli at inorganic level. Each stratum depends on basic functions of all subjacent levels but has its specific new laws. These special laws increase in complexity and differentiation for higher levels, although natural laws of lower are also valid in all upper levels (as indicated by *arrows*). [Adapted from Jung (206).]

person can exercise some mental influence on physical, chemical, and biological mechanisms by knowing their rules and building machines according to the laws of physics and technology.

LIMITED DOWNWARD INFLUENCE OF PERCEPTION AND ACTION. How the human will can influence the lower physical and biological strata cannot be explained by physiology. Neither Descartes's machine theory (see *Cartesian Machine Theory of the Body*, p. 24) nor Popper and Eccles's self or "world 2" (310) explain the mechanism of mind-brain interaction for voluntary movement. We must, however, assume a downward action for attentive perception and for voluntary action that directs the sensorimotor mechanisms toward a goal. My comparison to a car driver who starts and drives his automobile, but lets the automatic devices of the engine self-regulate and control the generating and locomotive mechanisms, also has its limits. Some conditions of downward action may be made clear by MacKay's comparison to a Board of Directors in business (267). The directors determine overall goals but let the lower levels of management regulate details of the productive pro-

cesses. By analogy, voluntary action uses the physiological regulations of the nerve and muscle machine to direct progress toward goals that are set by mental decisions. In other words, human intention and will must respect the physiological regulations and forces to obtain certain effects of perception and action. Willed perception and action cannot act contrary to the rules of the lower levels but must submit to their causal laws. The will can only choose within the limits of causality governing the biological and physiochemical processes of the body and the outer world. Hartmann (149) has put this succinctly for the human will: "Sein Herrschen beruht auf seinem Gehorchen" (man can rule over nature only when he respects the natural laws and, obeying them, uses natural forces for doing so). Claude Bernard (42, 43) recognized similar limits for biological regulations: the organism can direct some of the vital mechanisms to an end that can be reached eventually although not necessarily by purely causal relations. This can be achieved by purpose in occluding certain undesired directions and facilitating others. When there are several possibilities of action the supervising level of the will can select the appropriate one, as when a man diverts a river by constructing a dam to hinder the flow in one direction and enhance it in the desired direction. By analogy, Hartmann claims that willed action and free choice are compatible with rigid causal determination; i.e., free will at the higher level can coexist with biological and physical necessity at the lower level (148, 149, 151).

THE THREE WORLDS OF POPPER AND ECCLES. In 1972 Karl Popper (309) proposed another hierarchical concept of three worlds to denominate the evolution of matter and human knowledge: *1*) the physical, *2*) the conscious, *3*) the cultural world. This order was elaborated by Eccles (95) and in a monograph by Popper and Eccles (310) in relation to cerebral functions. Briefly, these worlds have the following characteristics: World 1 is the objective outer world of factual physical and chemical events and includes brain mechanisms. World 2 is the subjective self of human individuals, the inner mental world—i.e., the mind, which corresponds in older terminology to the soul. World 3 is the cultural world created by man and stored in the individual human memory as world 3b.

Although Descartes's sharp dualistic distinction of the soul and the body mechanisms was met with skepticism by the majority of scientists, Sherrington defended similar dualistic concepts (329). Most modern scientists have tended to monistic or isomorphic concepts of mind and body or have accepted Fechner's thesis of the two aspects (105). In contrast, Popper and Eccles relate Descartes's concept of a mechanical world to their world 1 and the Cartesian soul to their world 2, designating the soul as the self.

Each level of the world requires special and adequate methods in research. To understand perception, however, sensory processes, when investigated by special objective methods, must be compared to subjective experience. Thus, special analysis should find a synthesis through the coordination of several branches of perceptual research (Fig. 20).

Reductionism—Ontological vs. Methodological

LIMITATIONS OF METHODS. On the one hand philosophers have protested with some right against ontological reductionism and oversimplification of brain-mind problems. On the other hand one must realize that all scientists have to choose a conceptual level at which they can obtain precise experimental conditions and ask answerable questions. This corresponds to a reduction in methods. Every true scientist therefore is also a methodological reductionist when he selects his methods to obtain measurable results. When we relate sensation to neuronal activity we transcend primary physiology, and we implicitly accept methodological reduction without being an ontological reductionist. Philosophical minds may be more easily convinced of necessary methodological reductionism upon demonstration of an analogue in the limits of their own conscious perception.

Just as consciousness reduces the amount of sensory information in actual perception, so every scientist must restrict his questions and methods to manageable propositions. Thus he cannot expect more than limited answers. This corresponds to Kant's principle of the necessary limitation of human knowledge: he insisted that in principle neither science nor philosophy can obtain complete information on the real world (216).

Kant held that the scientist should strive for mechanistic explanations of all events in nature, even those that appear as purposive (216). Not only are perception and knowledge restricted by a priori limitations of reason in the individual scientist, but there exist also methodological restrictions on scientific knowledge in general. This does not prevent scientists from recognizing moral and human values beyond their special research fields. The methodological reduction practiced in science must not be confused with the general reductionism that holds that mind is "nothing but" a manifestation of matter.

RESEARCH ANALYSIS AND THEORETICAL SYNTHESIS. Scientists should be both methodological reductionists in analytic research and intuitive theorists who use systematic thought in recognizing coherence and order. Of course, the individual scientist may give preference to one of these procedures of research, but complete neglect of the other is dangerous. History warns against the prevalence of speculative trends of holistic world conceptions and generalizations.

In perception research the need for synthesis by correlation of neuronal analysis with subjective experience and behavioral observations is more evident than in other fields of physiology. So Hering's advice to sensory physiologists is still valid (175). Comparing the senses to a clock, the internal clockwork being the neuronal mechanisms and the hands of the clock indicating the sensory perceptions as time, he said that sensory physiologists must look at the sensations on the dial that indicates the time, when the internal clockwork cannot be examined directly. Vice versa, the "physiological" mechanisms of the springs and cogwheels are the basic mechanisms of the "perceptual" indications on the dial. Physiologists must investigate the neural mechanisms of sensory processing as watchmakers must know the internal clockwork (205, 207).

METHODOLOGICAL REDUCTION AND CONSCIOUS INFORMATION. An analogous reduction, as in science, occurs also in mental events and can be quantified for the information reduction of consciousness: the immense amount of information flow from the sense organs that enters the central nervous system is reduced for conscious perception from about 10^8 to 16–20 bits/s (239, 333). When MacKay (266, 267) compared the selection of significant data in perception and action with the control of higher agencies in business and politics, he also excluded detailed information of special insignificant facts that can be regulated at lower levels from the higher "metaorganizing" activity of consciousness.

SUMMARY

In antiquity and during the Middle Ages perception was considered to be a function of the soul and, except for attention from a few materialist philosophers, sensory mechanisms were neglected. Plato's idealist philosophy decried sensory experience as unreliable, and rationalist philosophers devalued the senses. Conversely, with the rise of science in the seventeenth century the importance of sensory information per se became overstated by Locke and other empiricist philosophers, until Kant proposed a synthesis of empiricism and rationalism. Experimental sensory physiology was created during the nineteenth century through the development of quantitative physical and psychophysical research methods. Finally, in this century, objective recordings of sensory messages, initiated by Adrian, elucidated some of the peripheral and central mechanisms of the senses. It has been the purpose of this chapter to demonstrate the convergence and integration of these seemingly opposed philosophical and physiological research trends in the sensory sciences.

Retrospect and Prospect

This rather long chapter on the history and philosophy of perceptual research may be concluded with four general statements.

1. Many ideas on the functions of the senses were proposed in the early philosophies of ancient authors, but their effective application first began in the sixteenth and seventeenth centuries, when general philosophical speculations were reduced to simple concepts of body mechanisms and precise questions could be answered by experiments. Experimental proof of sensory theories often followed the original ideas after delays of decades or even centuries.

2. Philosophical concepts and theories may help to prevent too-narrow specialization by revealing new aspects and contexts of perception and cognition. Similarly, subjective and objective sensory physiology supplement and stimulate each other. Even nonscientific religious ideas and inadequate theories may produce strong motivations for successful experimental research.

3. Experimental and methodological advances have disclosed some physiological mechanisms of sensory information. These special investigations are necessarily restricted by their methods and limited in specific sense modalities. Despite such limitations they may attain general relevance through correlation with perceptual experience. Just as percepts contain additional information not present in the sensory message but drawn from memory stores during recognition, so the range of perceptual research itself can be enlarged by both the discovery of new facts and their theoretical synopsis with existing knowledge.

4. The historical aspects of sensory research demonstrate not only the interaction of philosophical constructs and empirical observations but also the relative inefficiency of isolated theories without application and experimental verification.

The history of science shows how each advance leads also to the recognition of fresh, unsolved problems. The challenge of sensory research to find the physiological correlates of the complexities of perceptual experience seems likely to remain for an indefinite future.

I am grateful to Prof. D. MacKay (Keele, Staffordshire, England), Prof. H. Leibowitz (University Park, PA), and Dr. D. T. Whiteside (Cambridge, England) for text revisions, and to various libraries for permission to reproduce figures. Sincere thanks for efficient secretarial help are extended to S. Brinkman, Ch. Rodemer, U. Römmelt, K. Schetter, and B. Schramm.

REFERENCES

1. ADICKES, E. Kant als Naturwissenschaftler. *Kantstudien* 29: 70–97, 1924.
2. ADRIAN, E. D. The impulses produced by sensory nerve endings. Part 1. *J. Physiol. London* 61: 49–72, 1926.
3. ADRIAN, E. D. *The Basis of Sensation. The Action of the Sense Organs.* London: Christophers, 1928.
4. ADRIAN, E. D. Die Untersuchung der Sinnesorgane mit Hilfe elektrophysiologischer Methoden. *Ergeb. Physiol. Biol. Chem. Exp. Pharmakol.* 26: 501–530, 1924.
5. ADRIAN, E. D. Afferent discharges to the cerebral cortex from peripheral sense organs. *J. Physiol. London* 100: 159–191, 1941.
6. ADRIAN, E. D. *The Physical Background of Perception.* Oxford, England: Clarendon, 1947.
7. ADRIAN, E. D., AND D. W. BRONK. The discharge of impulses in motor nerve fibres. Part 2. The frequency of discharge in reflex and voluntary contraction. *J. Physiol. London* 67: 119–151, 1929.
8. ADRIAN, E. D., AND B. H. C. MATTHEWS. The Berger rhythm. Potential changes from the occipital lobes in man. *Brain* 57: 356–385, 1934.
9. ADRIAN, E. D., AND R. MATTHEWS. The action of light on the eye. Part 1. The discharge of impulses in the optic nerve and its relation to the electric changes in the retina. *J. Physiol. London* 63: 378–414, 1927.
10. ADRIAN, E. D., AND G. MORUZZI. Impulses in the pyramidal tract. *J. Physiol. London* 97: 153–199, 1939.
11. ADRIAN, E. D., AND Y. ZOTTERMAN. The impulses produced by sensory nerve endings. Part 2. The response of a single endorgan. *J. Physiol. London* 61: 151–171, 1926.
12. ADRIAN, E. D., AND Y. ZOTTERMAN. The impulses produced by sensory nerve endings. Part 3. *J. Physiol. London* 61: 465–483, 1926.
13. ALLPORT, F. H. *Theories of Perception and Concept of Structure.* New York: Wiley, 1955.
14. AMASSIAN, V. E. Evoked single cortical unit activity in the somatic sensory areas. *Electroencephalogr. Clin. Neurophysiol.* 5: 415–438, 1953.
15. ARNHEIM, R. *Visual Thinking.* Berkeley: Univ. of California Press, 1969.
16. ARISTOTLE. *The Works of Aristotle* (transl. by W. D. Ross), edited by J. A. Smith. Oxford, England: Clarendon, 1908–1952, vol. 1–12.

17. ATTNEAVE, F. *Applications of Information Theory to Psychology.* New York: Holt, 1959.
18. BACON, F. *Instauratio magna. I. Novum organum scientiarum.* London: 1620. *II. Sylva sylvarum.* London: 1627. (New impression edited by J. Spedding, R. C. Ellis, and D. D. Heath. London: 1858.)
19. BÁRÁNY, R. *Physiologie und Pathologie (Funktionsprüfung) des Bogengang-Apparates beim Menschen. Klinische Studien.* Wien: Deuticke, 1907.
20. BARLOW, H. B. Single units and sensation: a neuron doctrine for perceptual psychology. *Perception* 1: 371–394, 1972.
21. BARLOW, H. B. Visual experience and cortical development. *Nature* 258: 199–204, 1975.
22. BARTLEY, S. H., AND G. H. BISHOP. Factors determining the form of the electrical response from the optic cortex in the rabbit. *Am. J. Physiol.* 103: 173–184, 1933.
23. BARTLEY, S. H., AND E. B. NEWMAN. Studies of the dog's cortex. *Am. J. Physiol.* 99: 1–8, 1931.
24. BAUMGARTEN, R. VON, AND R. JUNG. Microelectrode studies on the visual cortex. *Rev. Neurol.* 87: 151–155, 1952.
25. BAUMGARTNER, G. Indirekte Grössenbestimmung der rezeptiven Felder der Retina beim Menschen mittels der Hermannschen Gittertäuschung. *Pfluegers Arch. Gesamte Physiol. Menschen Tiere* 272: 21–22, 1960.
26. BAUMGARTNER, G. Kontrastlichteffekte an retinalen Ganglienzellen: Ableitungen vom Tractus opticus der Katze. In: *Neurophysiologie und Psychophysik des visuellen Systems,* edited by R. Jung and H. H. Kornhuber. Berlin: Springer-Verlag, 1961, p. 45–55.
27. BAUMGARTNER, G. Die Reaktionen der Neurone des zentralen visuellen Systems der Katze in simultanen Helligkeitskontrast. In: *Neurophysiologie und Psychophysik des visuellen Systems,* edited by R. Jung and H. H. Kornhuber. Berlin: Springer-Verlag, 1961, p. 296–311.
28. BAUMGARTNER, G., AND P. HAKAS. Reaktionen einzelner Opticusneurone und corticaler Nervenzellen der Katze im Hell-Dunkel-Grenzfeld (Simultankontrast). *Pfluegers Arch. Gesamte. Physiol. Menschen Tiere* 270: 29, 1959.
29. BECK, A. Die Ströme der Nervenzentren. *Zentralbl. Physiol.* 4: 572–573, 1890–1891.
30. BECK, A., AND N. CYBULSKI. Weitere Untersuchungen über die elektrischen Erscheinungen in der Hirnrinde der Affen und Hunde. *Zentralbl. Physiol.* 6: 1–6, 1892.
31. BÉKÉSY, G. VON. Über die Schwingungen der Schneckentrennwand beim Präparat und Ohrenmodell. *Akust. Z.* 7: 173–186, 1942.
32. BÉKÉSY, G. VON. *Sensory Inhibition.* Princeton, NJ: Princeton Univ. Press, 1967.
33. BÉKÉSY, G. VON. Mach- and Hering-type lateral inhibition in vision. *Vision Res.* 8: 1483–1499, 1968.
34. BELL, C. *Idea of a New Anatomy of the Brain: Submitted for the Observation of His Friends.* London: Strahan and Preston, 1811. (Reproduced in: *Selected Readings in the History of Physiology,* edited by F. Fulton. Springfield, IL: Thomas, 1930, p. 273–279.)
35. BELL, C. On the nervous circle which connects the voluntary muscles with the brain. *Philos. Trans. R. Soc. London Ser. B* 2: 172, 1826.
36. BENN, A. W. *The Greek Philosophers.* London, 1882–1883, 2 vol.
37. BERGER, H. Über das Elektrenkephalogramm des Menschen. *Arch. Psychiatr. Nervenkr.* 87: 527–570, 1929.
38. BERGER, H. Über das Elektrenkephalogramm des Menschen. 2. Mitteilung. *J. Psychol. Neurol. Leipzig* 40: 160–179, 1930.
39. BERGER, H. Über das Elektrenkephalogramm des Menschen. 3. Mitteilung. *Arch. Psychiatr. Nervenkr.* 94: 16–60, 1931.
40. BERITOFF, J. S. (BERITASHVILI). *Neural Mechanisms of Higher Vertebrate Behavior* (Engl. transl). Boston, MA: Little, Brown, 1965.
41. BERKELEY, G. *Essay Towards a New Theory of Vision. Theory of Vision Vindicated.* Dublin: Aaron Rhames, 1709. [Reprint: *Selections from Berkeley* (6th ed.), edited by A. D. Fraser. Oxford, England: Clarendon, 1910.]
42. BERNARD, C. *Leçons sur la physiologie et la pathologie du système nerveux.* Paris: Baillière, 1858, vol. 1 and 2.
43. BERNARD, C. *Leçons sur les phénomènes de la vie commune aux animaux et aux végétaux. Cours de physiologie générale du muséum d'histoire naturelle.* Paris: Baillière, 1878/1879, vols. I and II.
44. BETHE, A. Plastizität und Zentrenlehre. In: *Handbuch der Physiologie,* edited by A. Bethe, G. von Bergmann, G. Embden, and A. Ellinger. Berlin: Springer-Verlag, 1931, vol. 15, p. 1175–1220.
45. BETHE, A., G. VON BERGMANN, G. EMBDEN, AND A. ELLINGER (editors). *Handbuch der Normalen und Pathologischen Physiologie. Receptionsorgane I: Tangoreceptoren. Thermoreceptoren. Chemoreceptoren. Phonoreceptoren. Statoreceptoren.* Berlin: Springer-Verlag, 1926, vol. 11.
46. BETHE, A., G. VON BERGMANN, G. EMBDEN, AND A. ELLINGER (editors). In: *Handbuch der Normalen und Pathologischen Physiologie. Receptionsorgane II: Photoreceptoren* (1. Teil, 1929). *Receptionsorgane II: Photoreceptoren* (2. Teil, 1931). Berlin: Springer-Verlag, 1929–1931, vol. 12.
47. BISHOP, P. O. Synaptic transmission. An analysis of the electrical activity of the lateral geniculate nucleus of the cat after optic nerve stimulation. *Proc. R. Soc. London Ser. B* 141: 362–392, 1953.
48. BLAKEMORE, C. *Mechanics of the Mind.* London: Cambridge Univ. Press, 1977.
49. BLAKEMORE, C., AND R. C. VAN SLUYTERS. Innate and environmental factors in the development of the kitten's visual cortex. *J. Physiol. London* 248: 663–716, 1975.
50. BLIX, M. Experimentelle Beiträge zur Lösung der Frage über die specifische Energie der Hautnerven. *Z. Biol. Munich* 20: 141–156, 1884.
51. BORG, G., L. DIAMANT, AND Y. ZOTTERMAN. The relation between neural and perceptual intensity: a comparative study on the neural and psychophysical response to taste stimuli. *J. Physiol. London* 192: 13–20, 1967.
52. BORING, E. G. *Sensation and Perception in the History of Experimental Psychology.* New York: Appleton-Century Crofts, 1942.
53. BOUGUER, M. *Traité d'optique sur la gradation de la lumière, ouvrage posthume.* Paris: H.-L. Guérin, 1760.
54. BOUTROUX, E. *De la contingence des lois de la nature* (2nd ed.). Paris: F. Alcan, 1898. (1st ed. 1874.)
55. BRAZIER, M. A. B. The historical development of neurophysiology. In: *Handbook of Physiology, Neurophysiology,* edited by J. Field and H. W. Magoun. Washington, DC: Am. Physiol. Soc., 1959, sect. 1, vol. I, chapt. 1, p. 1–58.
56. BREMER, F., AND R. S. DOW. The cerebral acoustic area of the cat: a combined oscillographic and cytoarchitectonic study. *J. Neurophysiol.* 2: 308–318, 1939.
57. BRENTANO, F. Vom sinnlichen und noetischen Bewußtsein. In: *Psychologie. Wahrnehmung, Empfindung, Begriff,* edited by O. Kraus. Leipzig: F. Meiner, 1929, part 1.
58. BRINDLEY, G. S. Sensory effects of the electrical stimulation of the visual and paravisual cortex in man. In: *Handbook of Sensory Physiology. Central Processing of Visual Information,* edited by R. Jung. Berlin: Springer-Verlag, 1973, vol. 7, pt. 3B, p. 583–594.
59. BROCA, P. Remarques sur le siège de la faculté de langage articulé suivi d'une observation d' aphémie. *Bull. Soc. Anat. Paris Ser.* 2, 6: 330–357, 1861.
60. BROCK, L. G., J. S. COOMBS, AND J. C. ECCLES. Action potentials of motoneurones with intracellular electrode. *Proc. Univ. Otago Med. Sch.* 29: 14–15, 1951.
61. BROCK, L. G., J. S. COOMBS, AND C. ECCLES. The recording of potentials from motoneurones with an intracellular electrode. *J. Physiol. London* 117: 431–460, 1952.
62. BRODMANN, K. *Vergleichende Lokalisationslehre der Großhirnrinde in ihren Prinzipien dargestellt auf Grund des Zellenbaues.* Leipzig: Barth, 1909.
63. BRUNER, J. S. On perceptual readiness. *Psychol. Rev.* 64: 123–152, 1957.

64. BRUNER, J. S., AND L. POSTMAN. Perception, cognition and behavior. *J. Pers.* 18: 14–31, 1949.

65. BRUNN, W. L. VON. *Kreislauffunktion in William Harvey's Schriften.* Berlin: Springer-Verlag, 1967.

66. BURCKHARDT, C. *Die Kultur der Renaissance in Italien* (12th ed.). Leipzig: A. Kröner, 1919. (1st ed. 1860.)

67. CANNON, W. B. *Bodily Changes in Pain, Hunger, Fear and Rage.* New York: Appleton, 1915.

68. CARNAP R. *Der logische Aufbau der Welt.* Berlin: Weltkreis, 1928.

69. CARTERETTE, E. C., AND M. P. FRIEDMAN (editors). *Handbook of Perception. Historical and Philosophical Roots of Perception.* New York: Academic, 1974, vol. 1.

70. CATON, R. Researches on electrical phenomena of cerebral grey matter. *Trans. Ninth Int. Med. Congr.* 3: 246–249, 1887.

71. CLARKE, E., AND K. DEWHURST. *An Illustrated History of Brain Function.* Berkeley: Univ. of California Press, 1972.

72. CLARKE, E., AND C. D. O'MALLEY. *The Human Brain and Spinal Cord: A Historical Study Illustrated by Writings from Antiquity to the Twentieth Century.* Berkeley: Univ. of California Press, 1968.

73. CLEVE, TH.C. VAN. *The Emperor Frederic Second of Hohenstaufen. Immutator Mundi.* Oxford, England: Clarendon, 1972.

74. CRAIK, K. J. W. *The Nature of Explanation.* Cambridge, England: Cambridge Univ. Press, 1943.

75. CREED, R. S., D. E. DENNY-BROWN, J. C. ECCLES, E. G. T. LIDDELL, AND C. S. SHERRINGTON. *Reflex Activity of the Spinal Cord.* Oxford, England: Clarendon, 1932.

76. CROMBIE, A. C. *From Augustine to Galileo.* Vol. I, *Science in the Middle Ages: V-XIII Centuries.* Vol. II, *Science in the later Middle Ages and early Modern Times: XIII–XVII Centuries.* London: Heineman, 1952.

77. CROMBIE, A. C. *Robert Grosseteste and the Origins of Experimental Science, 1100-1700.* Oxford, England: Clarendon, 1953, vol. 9, p. 369S.

78. CROMBIE, A. C. Early concepts of the senses and the mind. In: *Perception: Mechanisms and Models,* edited by R. Held and W. Richards. San Francisco, CA: Freeman, 1972, p. 8–16.

79. DEMOCRITUS OF ABDERA. Demokritos. In: *Die Fragmente der Vorsokratiker* (grieschisch und deutsch, 2nd ed.), by H. Diels. Berlin: Weidmannische Buchhandlung, 1906/1907, no. 55, p. 350–450.

80. DENNY-BROWN, D. On the nature of postural reflexes. *Proc. R. Soc. London Ser. B* 104: 252–301, 1929.

81. DESCARTES, R. *Discours de la methode pour bien conduire sa raison et chercher la vérité dans les sciences, plus la dioptrique, les météores et la géométrie qui sont des essais de cete méthode.* Leiden: Jan Maire, 1637.

82. DESCARTES, R. *Les Passions de l'âme.* Paris: Le Gras, 1649. (Reprint in *Oeuvres,* Paris: Vrin, 1956/1957, vol. 11, p. 301–497.)

83. DESCARTES, R. *Renati Descartes tractatus de homine et de formatione foetus,* edited by F. Schuyl. Leiden: Offic. Hackiani, 1662.

83a. DESCARTES, R. *L'Homme de Renée Descartes et un traité de la formation du foetus du mesme autheur,* edited by L. de la Forge. Paris: Le Gras, 1664.

84. DESCARTES, R. *Oeuvres de Descartes publiées par C. Adam et P. Tannery.* Paris: Vrin, 1956/1957, 13 vol.

85. DEWEY, J. The reflex arc concepts in psychology. *Psychol. Rev.* 3: 357–370, 1896.

86. DICHGANS, J., AND R. JUNG. Attention, eye movements and motion detection: facilitation and selection in optokinetic nystagmus and railway nystagmus. In: *Attention in Neurophysiology,* edited by C. R. Evans and T. B. Mulholland. London: Butterworth, 1969, p. 348–375.

87. DIELS, H. *Die Fragmente der Vorsokratiker* (griechisch und deutsch. 2nd ed.). Berlin: Weidmannische Buchhandlung, 1906/1907, 2 vol.

88. DROOGLEEVER FORTUYN, J. A contribution of "Cognitive Neurology." In: *Eighth Int. Congr. Cybernetics, Namur, Belgium, 1976,* p. 919–925.

89. DU BOIS-REYMOND, E. *Untersuchungen über thierische Electricität.* Berlin: Reimer, 1848, vol. 1; 1849, vol. 2.

90. DUKE-ELDER, S., AND K. C. WYBAR. The anatomy of the visual system. Sect. 1: Historical development. In: *System of Ophthalmology,* edited by S. Duke-Elder. London: Kimpton, 1961, vol. 2, p. 1–72.

91. DÜRER, A. *Underweysung der Messung mit dem Zirckel uñ Richtscheyt in Linien, Ebnen unnd Gantzen Corporen.* Nürnberg: 1525. (3rd ed. Nürnberg: H. Formschneyder, 1538.)

92. DUSSER DE BARENNE, J. G. Experimental researches on sensory localization in the cerebral cortex. *Q. J. Exp. Physiol.* 9: 355–390, 1916.

93. ECCLES, J. C. *The Neurophysiological Basis of Mind: Principles of Neurophysiology.* Oxford, England: Clarendon, 1953.

94. ECCLES, J. C. *The Physiology of Nerve Cells.* Baltimore, MD: Johns Hopkins Univ. Press, 1957.

95. ECCLES, J. C. *Facing Reality. Philosophical Adventures by a Brain Scientist.* Berlin: Springer-Verlag, 1970.

96. ECCLES, J. C., AND J. J. GIBSON. *Sherrington: His Life and Thought.* Berlin: Springer-Verlag, 1979.

97. ECCLES, J. C., AND C. S. SHERRINGTON. Studies on the flexor reflex. VI. Inhibition. *Proc. R. Soc. London Ser. B* 109: 91–113, 1931.

98. EKMAN, G. Psychophysik und psychologische Methoden. In: *Lehrbuch der Experimentellen Psychologie* (2nd ed.), by R. Meili and H. Rohracher. Bern: Huber, 1968, p. 19–56.

99. EPICURUS. In: *Epicurus. The Extant Remains*; and in: *The Greek atomists and Epicurus,* edited by C. Bailey. Oxford, England: Clarendon, 1926, 1928.

100. ERB, W. Über Sehnenreflexe bei Gesunden und Rückenmarkskranken. *Arch. Psychiatr. Nervenkr.* 5: 792–802, 1875.

101. ERDMANN, B., AND R. DODGE. *Psychologische Untersuchungen über das Lesen auf experimenteller Grundlage.* Halle, Germany: Niemeyer, 1898.

102. ERLANGER, J., AND H. S. GASSER. *Electrical Signs of Nervous Activity.* Philadelphia: Univ. of Pennsylvania Press, 1937.

103. EVARTS, E. V., AND J. TANJI. Gaiting of motor cortex reflexes by prior instruction. *Brain Res.* 71: 479–494, 1974.

104. EXNER, S. *Entwurf zu einer physiologischen Erklärung der psychischen Erscheinungen.* Leipzig: Deuticke, 1894.

105. FECHNER, G. T. *Elemente der Psychophysik.* Leipzig: Breitkopf & Härtel, 1860, 2 vols. (*Elements of Psychophysics,* transl. by H. E. Adler. New York: Holt, Reinhart, 1966.)

106. FERRIER, D. *The Function of the Brain.* London: Smith, Elder, 1876.

107. FISCHER, B., AND H. J. FREUND. Eine mathematische Formulierung für Reiz-Reaktionsbeziehungen retinaler Ganglienzellen. *Kybernetik* 7: 160–166, 1970.

108. FISCHER, M. H. Elekrobiologische Erscheinungen an der Hirnrinde. *Pfluegers Arch. Gesamte Physiol. Menschen Tiere* 230: 161–178, 1932.

109. FLECHSIG, P. *Anatomie des menschlichen Gehirns und Rückenmarks auf myelogenetischer Grundlage.* Leipzig: Thieme, 1920.

110. FLOURENS, P. *Recherches expérimentales sur les propriétés et les fonctions du système nerveux dans les animaux vertébrés.* Paris: Crevot, 1824.

111. FLOURENS, P. *Experiences sur le système nerveux.* Paris: Crevot, 1825.

112. FOERSTER, O. *Die Physiologie und Pathologie der Koordination.* Jena, Germany: Fischer, 1902.

113. FOERSTER, O. The dermatomes of man. *Brain:* 56: 1–39, 1933.

114. FOERSTER, O. Sensible corticale Felder. In: *Handbuch der Neurologie,* edited by O. Bumke and O. Foerster. Berlin: Springer-Verlag, 1936, vol. 6, p. 358–448.

115. FREDERICUS II OF HOHENSTAUFEN. *De arte venandi cum avibus* (facsim. vol. XVI). Graz, Austria: Graz Akademie, 1969, vol. 31. (*The Art of Falconry. Frederick II of Hohenstaufen,* edited by C. A. Wood and F. M. Fyfe. Stanford, CA: Stanford Univ. Press, 1943.)

116. FREY, M. VON. Beiträge zur Physiologie des Schmerzsinns.

Ber. Verh. Saeschs. Akad. Wiss. Leipzig Math. Naturw. Kl. 46: 185–196, 1894.

117. FREY, M. VON. Untersuchungen über die Sinnesfunctionen der menschlichen Haut. 1. Abhandl.: Druckempfindung und Schmerz. *Abh. Math. Phys. Kl. Koenigl. Saechs. Ges. Wiss.* 23: 171–266, 1896.

118. FREY, M. VON. Physiologie der Sinnesorgane der menschlichen Haut. I. Der Temperatursinn. *Ergeb. Physiol. Biol. Chem. Exp. Pharmacol.* 9: 351–368, 1910. II. Der Drucksinn. *Ergeb. Physiol. Biol. Chem. Exp. Pharmacol.* 13: 96–124, 1913.

119. FREY, M. VON. Die Tangoreceptoren des Menschen. In: *Handbuch der Normalen und Pathologischen Physiologie*, edited by A. Bethe, G. von Bergmann, G. Embden, and A. Ellinger. Berlin: Springer-Verlag, 1926, vol. 11, p. 94–130.

120. FRISCH, K. VON. Der Farbensinn und Formensinn der Biene. *Zool. Jahrb. Abt. Zool. Physiol. Tiere* 35: 1–188, 1914.

121. FRITSCH, G. T., AND E. HITZIG. Über die elektrische Erregbarkeit des Großhirns. *Arch. Anat. Physiol. Wiss. Med.*, p. 300–332, 1870. (Engl. transl. in *Neurosurgical Classics* by H. Wilkins. XII, *J. Neurosurg.* 20: 904–916, 1963.)

122. FULTON, F. (editor). *Selected Readings in the History of Physiology.* Springfield, IL: Thomas, 1930. (2nd ed. enlarged, edited by F. Fulton and L. G. Wilson. Springfield, IL: Thomas, 1966).

123. GALEN. *Claudiu Galenu Hapanta. Claudii Galeni opera omnia*, edited by C. G. Kühn. Leipzig: 1821–1833, vol. I–XX.

124. GALL, F. J., AND J. C. SPURZHEIM. *Anatomie et physiologie du système nerveux en général, et du cerveau en particulier . . . .* Paris: Schoell, 1810–1819, 4 vol.

125. GALVANI, L. De viribus electricitatis in motu musculari. *Commentarius de Bononiensi Scientiarum et Artium Instituto atque Academia* 7: 363–418, 1791. (Reprint: *Memorie et esperimenti*, edited by L. Galvani. Bologna, Italy: Capelli, 1937.)

126. GIBSON, J. J. *The Perception of the Visual World.* Boston, MA: Houghton, 1950.

127. GIBSON, J. J. *The Senses Considered as Perceptual Systems.* Boston, MA: Houghton, 1966.

128. GOLDSCHEIDER, A. Über Wärme-, Kälte- und Druckpunkte. *Verhandl. Physiol. Ges. Berlin* 1884–1885. Neue Tatsachen über die Hautsinnesnerven. *Arch. Anat. Physiol. Physiol. Abt. Suppl.* 1–110, 1885.

129. GOLDSCHEIDER, A. *Gesammelte Abhandlungen I. Physiologie der Hautnerven.* Leipzig: Barth, 1898. (Contains ref. 128.)

130. GRANIT, R. *Sensory Mechanisms of the Retina with an Appendix on Electroretinography.* London: Oxford Univ. Press, 1947.

131. GRANIT, R. *Receptors and Sensory Perception.* New Haven, CT: Yale Univ. Press, 1955.

132. GRANIT, R. *Charles Scott Sherrington. An Appraisal.* London: Nelson, 1966.

133. GRANIT, R. *The Purposive Brain.* Cambridge, MA: MIT Press, 1977.

134. GRÜNEWALD-ZUBERBIER, E., AND G. GRÜNEWALD. Goal-directed movement potentials of human cerebral cortex. *Exp. Brain Res.* 33: 135–138, 1978.

135. GRÜNEWALD-ZUBERBIER, E., G. GRÜNEWALD, AND R. JUNG. Slow potentials of the human precentral and parietal cortex during goal-directed movements (Zielbewegungspotentiale). *J. Physiol. London* 284: 181P–182P, 1978.

136. GUDDEN, B. VON. Ueber die Kreuzung der Fasern im chiasma nervorum opticum. *Albrecht von Graefes Arch. Ophthalmol.* 20: 249–268, 1874.

137. HALL, M. On the reflex function of the medulla oblongata and medulla spinalis. *Philos. Trans. R. Soc. London* 123: 635–665, 1833.

138. HALLER, A. VON. De partibus corporis humani sensibilibus et irritabilibus. *Comment. Soc. Reg. Sci. Göttingen* 2: 114–158, 1753.

139. HALLER, A. VON. *Elementa physiologiae corporis humani.* Lausanne: Sumptibus Marci-Michael, Bousquet & Sociorum. Berne: Sumptibus Societatis Typographicae, 1757–1766, 8 vol.

140. HALLER, A. VON. *Grundriß der Physiologie für Vorlesungen.*

(Nach der 4. lateinischen Ausgabe übersetzt von K. F. Uden.) Berlin: 1784. (Nach der 4. lateinischen Ausgabe aufs Neue übersetzt und mit Anmerkungen versehen durch Sömmering und Meckel.) Berlin: Haude & Spener, 1788.

141. HARRIS, J. *Treatise of Optics.* London: B. White, 1775.

142. HARTLINE, H. K. Impulses in single optic nerve fibres of the vertebrate retina. (Abstract). *Am J. Physiol.* 113: 59–60, 1935.

143. HARTLINE, H. K. The response of single optic nerve fibers of the vertebrate eye to illumination of the retina. *Am. J. Physiol.* 121: 400–415, 1938.

144. HARTLINE, H. K. Inhibition of activity of visual receptors by illuminating nearby retinal areas in the *Limulus* eye. *Federation Proc.* 8: 69, 1949.

145. HARTLINE, H. K., AND C. H. GRAHAM. Nerve impulses from single receptors in the eye. *J. Cell. Comp. Physiol.* 1: 277–295, 1932.

146. HARTMANN, M. *Philosophie der Naturwissenschaften.* Berlin: Springer-Verlag, 1937.

147. HARTMANN, N. *Philosophische Grundlagen der Biologie.* Göttingen, Germany: Van den Hoeck, 1912.

148. HARTMANN, N. *Systematische Selbstdarstellung.* Berlin: Junker & Dünnhaupt, 1933.

149. HARTMANN, N. *Der Aufbau der realen Welt. Grundriß der allgemeinen Kategorienlehre.* Berlin: de Gruyter, 1940.

150. HARTMANN, N. *Philosophie der Natur; Abriß der speziellen Kategorienlehre.* Berlin: de Gruyter, 1950.

151. HARTMANN, N. *Teleologisches Denken.* Berlin: de Gruyter, 1951.

152. HARVEY, W. *Exercitatio anatomica de motu cordis et sanguinis in animalibus.* Frankfurt am Main: G. Pfitzeri, 1628. (Engl. transl. by G. T. Whitteridge. Oxford, England: Blackwell, 1976.)

153. HASKINS, C. H. *De Arte Venandi cum Avibus of Frederic II of Hohenstaufen. Studies in the History of Medieval Science.* Cambridge, MA: Harvard Univ. Press, 1927.

154. HAYEK, F. A. *The Sensory Order.* London: Routledge and Kegan Paul, 1952.

155. HAYMAKER, W. (editor). *The Founders of Neurology.* Springfield, IL: Thomas, 1953.

156. HEAD, H. *Studies in Neurology.* London: Frowde, Hodder & Stoughton, 1920, 2 vol.

157. HEAD, H., AND G. HOLMES. Sensory disturbances from cerebral lesions. *Brain:* 102–254, 1911.

158. HEBB, D. O. *Organization of Behavior.* New York: Wiley, 1949.

159. HEIDEGGER, M. Sein und Zeit. *Jahrb. Philos. Phänomenol. Forsch.* 8: 1–438, 1927.

160. HELD, R. Two models of processing spatially distributed visual stimulation. In: *The Neurosciences*, edited by F. O. Schmitt. New York: Rockefeller Univ. Press, 1970, p. 317–324.

161. HELD, R., AND A. HEIN. Movement-produced stimulation in the development of visually guided behavior. *J. Comp. Physiol. Psychol.* 56: 872–876, 1963.

162. HELMHOLTZ, H. Messungen über den zeitlichen Verlauf der Zuckung animalischer Muskeln und die Fortpflanzungsgeschwindigkeit der Reizung der Nerven. *Arch. Anat. Physiol. Wiss. Med.* 276–364, 1850.

163. HELMHOLTZ, H. *Beschreibung eines Augenspiegels zur Untersuchung der Netzhaut im lebenden Auge.* Berlin: A. Förstner, 1851.

164. HELMHOLTZ, H. *Handbuch der Physiologischen Optik.* 1859–1867; 2nd ed. edited by A. König. Hamburg: Voss, 1896; 3rd ed. edited by Gullstrand et al., 1909–1911. (Transl. and edited by J. P. C. Southall. New York: Optical Soc. Am., 1924–1925. Reprinted New York: Dover, 1962.)

165. HELMHOLTZ, H. *Die Lehre von den Tonempfindungen als physiologische Grundlage für die Theorie der Musik.* Braunschweig, Germany: Vieweg, 1863. (*On the Sensation of Tone*, transl. by A. J. Ellis. 2nd English ed., 1885.)

166. HELMHOLTZ, H. (AND N. BAXT). Mittheilung betreffend Versuche über Fortpflanzungsgeschwindigkeit der Reizung in den motorischen Nerven des Menschen, welche Herr N. Baxt aus

Petersburg im Physiologischen Laboratorium zu Heidelberg ausgeführt hat. *Monatsber. Akad. Wiss. Berlin* 228-234, 1867.

167. HENSEL, H., AND K. BOMAN. Afferent impulses in cutaneous sensory nerves in human subjects. *J. Neurophysiol.* 23: 564-578, 1960.

168. HERBART, J. F. *Psychologie als Wissenschaft, neugegründet auf Erfahrung, Metaphysik und Mathematik.* Königsberg: W. Unzer, 1824/1825, 2 vol. (*A Textbook in Psychology, an Attempt to Found the Science of Psychology on Experience, Metaphysics and Mathematics,* transl. by M. K. Smith. New York: Appleton, 1891.)

169. HERDER, J. G. *Ideen zur Philosophie der Geschichte der Menschheit.* Leipzig: Hartknoch, 1785, vol. 1.

170. HERING, E. *Die Lehre vom binocularen Sehen.* Leipzig: Engelmann, 1868.

171. HERING, E. Über das Gedächtnis als eine allgemeine Funktion der organisierten Materie. 1870. In: *Fünf Reden von E. Hering.* Leipzig: Engelmann, 1921.

172. HERING, E. *Zur Lehre vom Lichtsinne.* Wien: Gerold & Söhne, 1878.

173. HERING, E. Der Raumsinn und die Bewegungen der Augen. In: *Handbuch der Physiologie,* edited by L. Hermann. Leipzig: Vogel, 1879, vol. 3, p. 343-601.

174. HERING, E. Grundzüge der Lehre vom Lichtsinn. In: *Handbuch der Gesamten Augenheilkunde,* edited by A. Graefe, Th. Saemisch, and C. Hess. Leipzig: Engelmann, 1905; 2nd ed. 1907, vol. 3/1, p. 1-294. (*Outline of a Theory of the Lightsense,* transl. by L. M. Hurvich and D. Jameson. Cambridge, MA.: Harvard Univ. Press, 1964).

175. HERING, E. *Wissenschaftliche Abhandlungen.* Leipzig: Thieme, 1931, vol. 1 and 2.

176. HERRNSTEIN, R. J., AND E. G. BORING (editors). *A Source Book in the History of Psychology.* Cambridge, MA: Harvard Univ. Press, 1965.

177. HESS, W. R. Die Motorik als Organisationsproblem. *Biol. Zentralbl.* 61: 545-572, 1941.

178. HESS, W. R. *Das Zwischenhirn. Syndrome, Lokalisationen, Funktionen.* Basel: Schwabe, 1949.

179. HESS, W. R. Cerebrale Organisation somatomotorischer Leistungen. I. Physikalische Vorbemerkungen und Analyse konkreter Beispiele. *Arch. Psychiatr. Nervenkr. & Z. Gesamte Neurol. Psychiatr.* 207: 33-44, 1965.

180. HIPPOCRATES. *The Genuine Works of Hippocrates* (transl. by F. Adams). London: Sydenham Soc., 1849, 2 vol.

181. HIRSCH, H. V. B., AND D. N. SPINELLI. Modification of the distribution of receptive field orientation in cats by selective visual exposure during development. *Exp. Brain Res.* 13: 509-527, 1971.

182. HODGKIN, A. L., AND A. F. HUXLEY. Resting and action potentials in single nerve fibres. *J. Physiol. London* 104: 176-195, 1945.

183. HOFFMANN, P. Beiträge zur Kenntnis der menschlichen Reflexe mit besonderer Berücksichtigung der elektrischen Erscheinungen. *Arch. Anat. Physiol. Physiol. Leipzig* 223-246, 1910.

184. HOFFMANN, P. *Die Eigenreflexe (Sehnenreflexe) menschlicher Muskeln.* Berlin: Springer-Verlag, 1922.

185. HOLMGREN, F. Method att objectivera effecten av ljusintryck pa retina. *Upsala Laekarefoeren. Foerh.* 1: 177-191, 1865-1866.

186. HOLST, E. VON. Zentralnervensystem und Peripherie in ihrem gegenseitigen Verhältnis. *Klin. Wochschr.* 29: 97-105, 1951.

187. HOLST, E. VON. Aktive Leistungen der menschlichen Gesichtswahrnehmung. *Stud. Gen.* 10: 231-243, 1957.

188. HOLST, E. VON, AND H. MITTELSTAEDT. Das Reafferenzprinzip. Wechselwirkung zwischen Zentralnervensystem und Peripherie. *Naturwissenschaften* 37: 464-476, 1950.

189. HUBEL, D. H., AND T. N. WIESEL. Receptive fields of single neurones in the cat's striate cortex. *J. Physiol. London* 148: 574-591, 1959.

190. HUBEL, D. H., AND T. N. WIESEL. Receptive fields, binocular interaction and functional architecture in the cat's visual cortex. *J. Physiol. London* 160: 106-154, 1962.

191. HUBEL, D. H., AND T. N. WIESEL. The period of susceptibility to the physiological effects of unilateral eye closure in kittens. *J. Physiol. London* 206: 419-436, 1970.

192. HUBEL, D. H., AND T. N. WIESEL. Functional architecture of macaque monkey visual cortex. *Proc. R. Soc. London Ser. B* 198: 1-59, 1977.

193. HUME, D. *Treatise on Human Nature: Being an Attempt to Introduce the Experimental Method of Reasoning into Moral Subjects.* Reprint of corrected parts of 1777 edition, edited by L. A. Selby-Bigge and P. H. Nidditch. Oxford, England: Clarendon, 1975.

194. HUME, D. *An Enquiry Concerning Human Understanding.* (First ed. 1748 titled *Philosophical Essays Concerning Human Understanding.*) Reprint of posthumous edition 1777, edited by L. A. Selby-Bigge and P. H. Nidditch. Oxford, England: Clarendon, 1975.

195. HUMBOLDT, F. A. VON. *Versuche über die gereizte Muskel- und Nervenfaser nebst Vermutungen über den chemischen Process des Lebens in der Thier- und Pflanzenwelt.* Berlin: Rottmann, 1797, 2 vol.

196. HUSSERL, E. Ideen zu einer reinen Phänomenologie und phänomeno-logischen Philosophie. *Jahrb. Phänomenol. Philos. Forsch.* 1: 1-360, 1913.

197. IVINS, W. M., JR. *Art and Geometry. A Study in Space Intuitions.* Cambridge, MA: Harvard Univ. Press, 1946.

198. JACKSON, J. H. *Selected Writings of John Hughlings Jackson,* edited by J. Taylor. London: Hodder & Stoughton, 1931, 2 vol.

199. JAMES, W. *The Principles of Psychology.* New York: Holt, 1890.

200. JASPERS, K. *Allgemeine Psychopathologie.* Berlin: Springer-Verlag, 1913.

201. JASPERS, K. *Philosophie. I. Philosophische Weltorientierung.* Berlin: Springer-Verlag, 1956.

202. JUNG, R. Allgemeine Neurophysiologie: Die Tätigkeit des Nervensystems. In: *Handbuch der Inneren Medizin,* (4th ed.) edited by G. von Bergmann, W. Frey, and W. Schwiegk. Berlin: Springer-Verlag, 1953, vol. 5/1, p. 1-181.

203. JUNG, R. Neuronal discharge. *Electroencephalogr. Clin. Neurophysiol. Suppl.* 4: 57-71, 1953.

204. JUNG, R. Correlation of bioelectrical and autonomic phenomena with alterations of consciousness and arousal in man. In: *Brain Mechanisms and Consciousness. Symposium,* edited by J. F. Delafresnay, E. D. Adrian, F. Bremer, and H. H. Jasper. Oxford, England: Blackwell, 1954, p. 310-344.

205. JUNG, R. Korrelationen von Neuronentätigkeit und Sehen. In: *Neurophysiologie und Psychophysik des visuellen Systems,* edited by R. Jung and H. H. Kornhuber. Berlin: Springer-Verlag, 1961, p. 410-435.

206. JUNG, R. Neurophysiologie und Psychiatrie. In: *Psychiatrie der Gegenwart,* edited by H. W. Gruhle, R. Jung, W. Mayer-Gross, and M. Müller. Berlin: Springer-Verlag, 1967, vol. 1, pt. 1A, p. 325-928.

207. JUNG, R. Visual perception and neurophysiology. In: *Handbook of Sensory Physiology. Central Processing of Visual Information,* edited by R. Jung. Berlin: Springer-Verlag, 1973, vol. 7, pt. 3A, p. 1-152.

208. JUNG, R. Perception, consciousness and visual attention. In: *Cerebral Correlates of Conscious Experience,* edited by P. Buser and A. Rougeul-Buser. Amsterdam: Elsevier, 1978, vol. 359, p. 15-36.

209. JUNG, R., R. VON BAUMGARTEN, AND G. BAUMGARTNER. Mikroableitungen von einzelnen Nervenzellen im optischen Cortex der Katze: Die lichtaktivierten B-Neurone. *Arch. Psychiatr. Nervenkr. + Z. Gesamte Neurol. Psychiatr.* 189: 521-539, 1952.

210. JUNG, R., H. KORNHUBER, AND J. S. DA FONSECA. Multisensory convergence on cortical neurons. Neuronal effects of visual, acoustic and vestibular stimuli in the superior convolutions of the cat's cortex. In: *Progress in Brain Research. Brain Mechanisms: Specific and Unspecific Mechanisms of Sensory*

Motor Integration, edited by G. Moruzzi, A. Fessard, and H. H. Jasper. Amsterdam: Elsevier, 1964, vol. 1, p. 207–240.

211. KANDEL, E. R. *Cellular Basis of Behavior. An Introduction to Behavioral Neurobiology.* San Francisco, CA: Freeman, 1976.

212. KANT, I. *Allgemeine Naturgeschichte und Theorie des Himmels oder Versuch von der Verfassung und dem mechanischen Ursprunge des ganzen Weltgebäudes nach Newtonischen Grundsätzen abgehandelt.* 1755. (Reprint in *Gesammelte Schriften.* Berlin: Reimer, 1910–1917, vol. 1, p. 215–368.)

213. KANT, I. *Critik der reinen Vernunft.* 1781; 2nd ed. Riga: Hartknoch, 1783. (*Critique of Pure Reason*, transl. by M. K. Smith. London: Macmillan, 1929.)

214. KANT, I. *Prolegomena zu einer künftigen Metaphysik, die als Wissenschaft wird auftreten können.* Riga: Hartknoch, 1783.

215. KANT, I. *Metaphysische Anfangsgründe der Naturwissenschaft.* Riga: Hartknoch, 1786.

216. KANT, I. *Critik der Urtheilskraft.* Berlin: Lagarde and Friederich, 1790.

217. KANT, I. *Gesammelte Schriften.* Berlin: Reimer, 1910–1917, 8 vol.

218. KANTOROWICZ, E. *Kaiser Friedrich II.* Düsseldorf, Germany: G. Bondi, 1927; Ergänzungsb. 1931; 4th ed., 1936.

219. KEPLER, J. *Dioptrice.* Augsburg, Germany: Frank, 1611. In: *Gesammelte Werke*, edited by W. von Dyck and M. Caspar. München: Beck, 1937–1963, vol. 4.

220. KEPLER, J. *Harmonices Mundi.* Linz, Austria: Tampach, Plancus, 1619. In: *Gesammelte Werke*, edited by W. von Dyck and M. Caspar. München: Beck, 1937–1963, vol. 6.

221. KEYNES, G. *The Life of William Harvey.* Oxford, England: Clarendon, 1964.

222. KLUEVER H. *Behavior Mechanism of Monkeys.* Chicago, IL: Univ. of Chicago Press, 1964.

223. KOFFKA, K. *Principles of Gestalt Psychology*, edited by M. R. Harrower. New York: Harcourt, 1935.

224. KOHLER, I. Über Aufbau und Wandlungen der Wahrnehmungswelt: insbesondere über "bedingte Empfindungen." *Sitzungsber. Oesterr. Akad. Wiss. Philos. Hist. Kl.* 227(1): 1–118, 1951. (Engl. transl. with additions: *The Formation and Transformation of the Perceptual World.* New York: Intl. Univs. Press, 1964.)

225. KÖHLER, W. *Intelligenzprüfungen an Anthropoiden.* I. Berlin: Königl. Akademie Wissenschaften, 1917.

226. KÖHLER, W. *Die physischen Gestalten in Ruhe und im stationären Zustand.* Braunschweig, Germany: Vieweg, 1920.

227. KÖHLER, W. *Gestalt Psychology.* New York: Liveright, 1947.

228. KOHTS, N. *Infant Ape and Human Child (Instincts, Emotions, Play, Habits).* Moscow: Darwin Museum, 1935.

229. KORNHUBER, H. H. Neural control of input into long term memory: Limbic system and amnestic syndrome in man. In: *Memory and Transfer of Information*, edited by H. P. Zippel. New York: Plenum, 1971.

230. KORNHUBER, H. H., AND L. DEECKE. Hirnpotentialänderungen bei Willkürbewegungen und passiven Bewegungen des Menschen: Bereitschaftspotential und reafferente Potentiale. *Pfluegers Arch. Gesamte Physiol. Menschen Tiere* 284: 1–17, 1965.

231. KORNMÜLLER, A. E. Architektonische Lokalisation bioelektrischer Erscheinungen auf der Großhirnrinde. I. Mitt.: Untersuchungen am Kaninchen bei Augenbelichtung. *J. Psychol. Neurol. Leipzig* 44: 447–459, 1932.

232. KORNMÜLLER, A. E. Die bioelektrischen Erscheinungen architektonischer Felder der Großhirnrinde. *Biol. Rev. Biol. Proc. Cambridge Philos. Soc.* 10: 383–426, 1935.

233. KORNMÜLLER, A. E., AND J. F. TÖNNIES. Registrierung der spezifischen Aktionsströme eines architektonischen Feldes der Großhirnrinde vom uneröffneten Schädel. *Psychiatr. Neurol. Wochenschr.* 34: 581, 1932.

234. KRIES, J. VON. *Allgemeine Sinnesphysiologie.* Leipzig: Vogel, 1923.

235. KRIES, J. VON. *Immanuel Kant und seine Bedeutung für die Naturforschung der Gegenwart.* Berlin: Springer-Verlag, 1924.

236. KUFFLER, S. W. Discharge patterns and functional organization of mammalian retina. *J. Neurophysiol.* 16: 37–68, 1953.

237. KÜHNE, W. Über den Sehpurpur. *Untersuch. Physiol. Inst. Univ. Heidelberg* 1: 15–103, 1877.

238. KÜHNE, W. Chemische Vorgänge in der Netzhaut. In: *Handbuch der Physiologie. Sinnesorgane*, edited by L. Hermann. Leipzig: Vogel, 1879, vol. 3, pt. 1, p. 235–342.

239. KÜPFMÜLLER, K. Grundlagen der Informationstheorie und der Kybernetik. In: *Physiologie des Menschen. Allgemeine Neurophysiologie*, edited by O. H. Gauer, K. Kramer, and R. Jung. Berlin: Urban & Schwarzenberg, 1971, vol. 10, p. 195–231.

240. LA METTRIE, J. O. DE. *L'Homme machine.* Leiden, 1748. (*L'Homme machine.* Critical ed., with introductory monograph and notes, transl. by A. Vartanian. Princeton, NJ: Princeton Univ. Press, 1960.)

240a. LA METTRIE, J. O. DE. *Les Animaux plus que machines.* 1750.

241. LANGE, F. A. Geschichte des Materialismus und Kritik seiner Bedeutung in der Gegenwart (3rd ed.). Iserlohn, Germany: Baedeker, 1876, 2 vols. (*The History of Materialism*, transl. by E. C. Thomas. London: Routledge & Kegan Paul, 1925.)

242. LEIBNITZ, [G. W.]. Explication de l'arithmétique binaire, qui se sert des seuls caractères 0 et 1 . . .. In: *Histoire de l'Academie Royale des Sciences, année 1703.* Paris: Boudot, 1705, p. 85–89.

243. LEIBNIZ, G. W. VON. Nouveaux essais sur l'entendement humain. In: *Oeuvres philosophiques de feu Mr. de Leibniz*, edited by R. E. Raspe. Amsterdam: Schreuder, 1765, vol. 2, pt. 1, 2. (Reprint: *Philosophische Schriften. Nouveaux essais*, by G. W. Leibniz. Berlin: Akademie-Verlag, 1962, vol. 6.)

244. LEIBNIZ, G. W. VON. *Die Philosophischen Schriften*, edited by C. J. Gerhardt. Berlin: 1875–1890. (Reprint: Hildesheim, Germany: Olms, 1965.)

245. LEONARDO DA VINCI. *Trattato della pittura di Lionardo da Vinci*, novamente dato in luce, con la vita dell'istesso autore, scritta da Raffaelle du Fresne. Paris: Langlois, 1651. (Traktat von der Malerei. In: *Quellenschrift der Kunstgeschichte und Kunsttechnik des Mittelalters und der Renaissance*, transl. by H. Ludwig. Wien: Braumüller, 1882; nach Codex Vaticanus Urbinas no. 1270.)

246. LEONARDO DA VINCI. *The Notebooks of Leonardo da Vinci*, edited by E. MacCurdy. London: Reprint Soc., 1954, 2 vol.

247. LEWIN, K. *Principles of Topological Psychology.* New York: McGraw-Hill, 1936.

248. LI, C., AND H. H. JASPER. Microelectrode studies of the electrical activity of the cerebral cortex in the cat. *J. Physiol. London* 121: 117–140, 1953.

249. LIDDELL, E. G. T., AND C. S. SHERRINGTON. Recruitment and some other features of reflex inhibition. *Proc. R. Soc. London Ser. B* 97: 488–518, 1925.

250. LIEBIG, J. VON. Francis Bacon von Verulam und die Methode der Naturforschung. 1863. Induction and Deduction. 1865. In: *Reden und Abhandlungen.* Leipzig: 1874, p. 220–254, 296–309.

251. LOCKE, J. *Essay Concerning Human Understanding.* London: Holt, 1690. (Reprint edited by A. C. Fraser. Oxford, England: Clarendon, 1894, 2 vol.)

252. LOEWI, O. Über humorale Übertragbarkeit der Herznervenwirkung. 1. Mitt. *Pflüegers Arch. Gesamte Physiol. Menschen Tiere* 189: 239–242, 1921.

253. LORENTE DE NÓ, R. Ausgewählte Kapitel aus der vergleichenden Physiologie des Labyrinthes. Die Augenmuskelreflexe beim Kaninchen und ihre Grundlagen. *Ergeb. Physiol. Biol. Chem. Exp. Pharmakol.* 32: 73–242, 1931.

254. LORENTE DE NÓ, R. The synaptic delay of the motoneurones. *Am. J. Physiol.* 111: 272–282, 1935.

255. LORENTE DE NÖ, R. Analysis of the activity of the chains of internuncial neurons. *J. Neurophysiol.* 1: 207–244, 1938.

256. LORENZ, K. Die angeborenen Formen möglicher Erfahrung. *Z. Tierpsychol.* 5: 235–409, 1943.

257. LORENZ, K. The comparative method in studying innate behavior patterns. *Symp. Soc. Exp. Biol.* 4: 220–268, 1950.

258. LOTZE, R. H. *Medicinische Psychologie (oder Physiologie der Seele).* Leipzig: Weidmann, 1852.

259. LUCRETIUS (TITUS LUCRETIUS CARUS). *De rerum natura,* transl. and edited by C. Bailey. Oxford, England: Clarendon, 1947, vol 1.

260. LYNCH, J. C., V. B. MOUNTCASTLE, W. H. TALBOT, AND T. C. T. YIN. Parietal lobe mechanisms for directed visual attention. *J. Neurophysiol.* 40: 362–389, 1977.

261. MACH, E. Über die Wirkung der räumlichen Verteilung des Lichtreizes auf die Netzhaut. *Sitzungsber. Kaiserl. Akad. Wiss., Wien Math. Naturw. Kl.* 52(2): 303–322, 1865.

262. MACH, E. *Grundlinien der Lehre von den Bewegungsempfindungen.* Leipzig: Engelmann, 1875.

263. MACH, E. *Beiträge zur Analyse der Empfindungen.* Jena, Germany: Fischer, 1886. (Engl. transl.: *Contributions to the Analyses of the Sensations,* transl. by C. M. Williams. Chicago, IL: Open Court Publ., 1897.) *Die Analyse der Empfindungen und das Verhältnis des Physischen zum Psychischen* (2nd ed.) Jena, Germany: Fischer, 1900.

264. MACH, E. *Erkenntnis und Irrtum.* 1905. 5th ed. Leipzig: A. Barth, 1926.

265. MAC DOUGALL, W. *Physiological Psychology.* London: Dent, 1921.

266. MACKAY, D. M. On the logical indeterminacy of a free choice. *Mind:* 69: 31–40, 1960.

267. MACKAY, D. M. Cerebral organization and conscious control of action. In: *Brain and Conscious Experience,* edited by J. C. Eccles. Berlin: Springer-Verlag, 1966, p. 442–445.

268. MACKAY, D. M. Perception and brain function. In: *The Neurosciences, Second Study Program,* edited by F. O. Schmitt. New York: Rockefeller Univ. Press, 1970, p. 303–316.

269. MACKAY, D. M. Visual stability and voluntary eye movements. In: *Handbook of Sensory Physiology.* Central Processing of Visual Information, edited by R. Jung. Berlin: Springer-Verlag, 1973, vol. 7, pt. 3, p. 307–331.

270. MACKAY, D. M., AND D. A. JEFFREYS. Visually evoked potentials and visual perception in man. In: *Handbook of Sensory Physiology. Central Processing of Visual Information,* edited by R. Jung. Berlin: Springer-Verlag, 1973, vol. 7, pt. 3A, p. 647–678.

271. MAGENDIE, F. J. Expériences sur les fonctions des racines des nerfs qui naissent de la moelle épinière. *J. Physiol. Exp. Pathol.* 2: 366–371, 1822. (Transl. by A. Walker in: *Documents and Dates of Modern Discoveries in the Nervous System.* London: Churchill, 1839.)

272. MAGNUS, R. *Körperstellung. Experimentell-physiologische Untersuchungen über die einzelnen bei der Körperstellung in Tätigkeit tretenden Reflexe, über ihr Zusammenwirken und ihre Störungen.* Berlin: Springer-Verlag, 1924.

273. MATTEUCCI, C. *Essai sur les phénomènes électriques des animaux.* Paris: Carillian-Goeury & Dalmot, 1840.

274. MATTEUCCI, C. *Traités des phénomènes électro-physiologiques des animaux.* Paris: Fortin & Masson, 1844.

275. MATTHEWS, B. H. C. The response of a muscle spindle during active contraction of a muscle. *J. Physiol. London* 72: 153–174, 1931.

276. MATTHEWS, B. H. C. The response of a single endorgan. *J. Physiol. London* 71: 64–110, 1931.

277. MERLEAU-PONTY, M. *Phénoménologie de la perception.* Paris: Gallimard, 1945.

278. METZGER, W. *Gesetze des Sehens.* Frankfurt am Main: Kramer, 1936.

279. MEYER-BAER, K. *Music of the Spheres and Dance of Death. Studies in Musical Iconology.* Princeton, NJ: Princeton Univ. Press, 1970.

280. MILL, J. S. *A System of Logic.* London, 1843. (8th ed., New York: Longmans, Green, 1872.)

281. MONAKOW, C. VON. *Die Lokalisation im Großhirn und der Abbau der Funktion durch kortikale Herde.* Wiesbaden, Germany: Bergmann, 1914.

282. MONOD, J. *Le Hasard et la nécessité.* Paris: Seuil, 1970.

283. MORUZZI, G. *L'Opera elettrofisiologica di Carlo Matteucci. Physis rivista internazionale di storia della scienza,* edited by L. S. Olschki. Florence: 1964, vol. 6, fasc. 2.

284. MORUZZI, G., AND H. W. MAGOUN. Brain stem reticular formation and activation of the EEG. *Electroencephalogr. Clin. Neurophysiol.* 1: 455–473, 1949.

285. MOUNTCASTLE, V. B. Modality and topographic properties of single neurons of cat's somatic sensory cortex. *J. Neurophysiol.* 20: 408–434, 1957.

286. MOUNTCASTLE, V. B. The view from within: pathways to the study of perception. *Johns Hopkins Med. J.* 136: 109–131, 1975.

287. MOUNTCASTLE, V. B. An organizing principle for cerebral function: the unit module and the distributed system. In: *The Mindful Brain,* edited by G. M. Edelman and V. B. Mountcastle. Cambridge, MA: MIT Press, 1978, p. 7–50.

288. MOUNTCASTLE, V. B., G. G. POGGLIO, AND G. WERNER. The relation of thalamic cell response to peripheral stimuli varied over an intensive continuum. *J. Neurophysiol.* 26: 807–834, 1963.

289. MÜLLER, G. E. Zur Psychophysik der Gesichtsempfindungen. *Z. Psychol. Z. Physiol. Sennesorg.* 10: 1–82, 321–413; 14: 1–76, 161–196; 1896/1897.

290. MÜLLER, G. E. Zur Analyse der Gedächtnistätigkeit und des Vorstellungsverlaufes. In: *Z. Psychol. Ergänzungsbände.* Leipzig: J. A. Barth, 1911–1917, 3 vol.

291. MÜLLER, J. *Zur vergleichenden Physiologie des Gesichtssinnes des Menschen und der Thiere, nebst einem Versuch über die Bewegungen der Augen und den menschlichen Blick.* Leipzig: Knobloch, 1826.

292. MÜLLER, J. *Handbuch der Physiologie des Menschen für Vorlesungen* (2nd ed.). Coblenz, Germany: Hölscher, 1838.

293. NEWTON, I. *Philosophiae naturalis principia mathematica.* London: 1687. (2nd ed. with *Scholium generale,* 1713.)

294. NEWTON, I. *Opticks: Or a Treatise of the Reflexions, Refractions, Inflexions and Colours of Light. Also Two Treatises of the Species and Magnitude of Curvilinear Figures.* London: S. Smith & B. Walford, 1704. (Repr. of the 1730 ed., the last corrected by the author. New York: McGraw-Hill, 1931; New York: Dover, 1952.)

295. NEWTON, I. *Opera quae extant omnia,* edited by S. Horsley. London: Nichols, 1779–1785, 5 vol.

296. OHM, G. S. Über die Definition des Tones, nebst darangeknüpfter Theorie der Sirene und ähnlicher tonbildender Vorrichtungen. *Ann. Phys. Chem.* 59: 513–565, 1843.

297. PAWLOW, I. P. *Sämtliche Werke* [of I. P. Pavlov]. Berlin: Akademie Verlag, 1954, vol. 1–6.

298. PENFIELD, W. The role of the temporal cortex in recall of past experience and interpretation of the present. In: *Neurological Basis of Behavior,* edited by G. E. W. Wolstenholme and C. M. O'Connor. London: Churchill, 1958.

299. PENFIELD, W., AND T. RASMUSSEN. *The Cerebral Cortex of Man.* New York: Macmillan, 1950.

300. PETTIGREW, J. D. The effect of visual experience on the development of stimulus specificity by kitten cortical neurones. *J. Physiol. London* 237: 49–74, 1974.

301. PFLÜGER, E. F. N. *Die sensorischen Funktionen des Rückenmarks der Wirbelthiere nebst einer neuen Lehre über die Leitungsgesetze der Reflexionen.* Berlin: Hirschwald, 1853.

302. PIAGET, J. *La construction du réel chez l'enfant.* Paris: Delachaux et Niestlé, 1937.

303. PIAGET, J., AND B. INHELDER. *L'Image mentale chez l'enfant.* Paris: Presse Universitaire de France, 1966.

304. PIAGET, J., AND VINH-BANG. Comparaison des mouvements oculaires et des centrations du regard chez l'enfant et chez l'adulte. *Arch. Psychol. Geneva* 38: 167–200, 1961.

305. PLATEAU, J. A. F. Sur la mesure des sensations physiques, et sur la loi qui lie l'intensité de ces sensations à l'intensité de la cause excitante. *Bull. Acad. R. Sci. Lett. Beaux-Arts Belgique Bruxelles* 33: 376–385, 1872.

306. PLATO. *The Dialogues of Plato* (transl. by B. Jowett, II, 3rd ed.). Oxford, England: Clarendon, 1892.

307. POLYAK, S. *The Vertebrate Visual System.* Chicago, IL: Univ. of Chicago Press, 1957.

308. POPPER, K. R. *Logik der Forschung.* Wien: Springer-Verlag, 1935. (Engl. ed., *The Logic of Scientific Discovery.* London: Hutchinson, 1959.

309. POPPER, K. R. *Objective Knowledge: An Evolutionary Approach.* Oxford, England: Clarendon, 1972.

310. POPPER, K. R., AND J. C. ECCLES. *The Self and its Brain.* London: Springer-Verlag, 1977.

311. PURKINJE, J. E. *Beiträge zur Kenntniss des Sehens in subjectiver Hinsicht.* Prague: Calve, 1819.

312. RAND, B. (editor). *The Classical Psychologists ... From Anaxagoras to Wundt.* 1912. (Repr., Gloucester, MA: P. Smith, 1966.)

313. RATLIFF, F. *Mach Bands: Quantitative Studies on Neural Networks in the Retina.* San Francisco, CA: Holden-Day, 1965.

314. RICCO, A. Relazione fra il minimo angolo visuale e l'intensita luminosa. *Mem. R. Accad. Sci. Lett. Arti Modena.* 17: 47–160, 1877.

315. RIVERS, W. H. R., AND H. HEAD. A human experiment in nerve division. *Brain* 31: 323–450, 1908.

316. ROSE, J. E., AND R. GALAMBOS. Microelectrode studies on medial geniculate body of cat. I. Thalamic region activated by click stimuli. *J. Neurophysiol.* 15: 343–357, 1952.

317. ROSE, J. E., AND V. E. MOUNTCASTLE. Activity of single neurons in the tactile thalamic region of the cat in response to a transient peripheral stimulus. *Bull. Johns Hopkins Hosp.* 94: 238–282, 1954.

318. ROTHSCHUH, K. E. *Geschichte der Physiologie.* Berlin: Springer-Verlag, 1953.

319. RUSSELL, B. *History of Western Philosophy and its Connection with Political and Social Circumstances from the Earliest Times to the Present Day.* London: Allen and Unwin, 1961.

320. RUSSELL, B., AND A. N. WHITEHEAD. *Principia mathematica* (2nd ed.) Oxford, England: Oxford Univ. Press, 1925–1927, 2 vol.

321. SCHEINER, CH. *Oculus hoc est: fundamentum opticum ....* Oenoponti (Innsbruck): D. Agricolam, 1619.

322. SCHLICK, M. *Allgemeine Erkenntnislehre* (2nd ed.) Berlin: Springer-Verlag, 1925.

323. SCHRÖDINGER, E. *Mind and Matter.* London: Cambridge Univ. Press, 1958.

324. SECHENOV, I. M. *Physiologische Studien über die Hemmungsmechanismen für die Reflextätigkeit des Rückenmarkes im Gehirne des Frosches.* Berlin: Hirschwald, 1863. (Reprint in: *Biographical Sketch and Essays,* by I. M. Sechenov, New York: Arno, 1973.)

325. SEEBECK, A. Beobachtungen über einige Bedingungen der Entstehung von Tönen. *Ann. Phys. Chem.* 53: 417–436, 1841.

326. SEEBECK, A. Über die Definition des Tones. *Ann. Phys. Chem.* 63: 353–368, 1844.

327. SHANNON, C. E., AND W. WEAVER. *The Mathematical Theory of Communication.* Urbana: Univ. of Illinois Press, 1949.

328. SHERRINGTON, C. S. *Integrative Action of the Nervous System.* New Haven, CT: Yale Univ. Press, 1906; 2nd ed., New Haven, CT: Yale Univ. Press, 1947.

329. SHERRINGTON, C. S. *Man on His Nature. The Gifford Lectures, 1937, 1938.* New York: Macmillan, 1941; Cambridge, England: Cambridge Univ. Press, 1941.

330. SPERRY, R. W. Neural basis of the spontaneous optokinetic response produced by visual inversion. *J. Comp. Physiol. Psychol.* 43: 482–489, 1950.

331. STEGMÜLLER, W. *Wissenschaftliche Erklärung und Begründung.* Berlin: Springer-Verlag, 1969.

332. STEGMÜLLER, W. *Hauptströmungen der Gegenwartsphilosophie* (5th ed.). Stuttgart, West Germany: Kröner, 1975, 2 vol.

333. STEINBUCH, K., AND M. FRANK. Nichtdigitale Lernmatrizen als Perzeptoren. *Kybernetik* 1: 117–124, 1961.

334. STEINHAUSEN, W. Über Sichtbarmachung und Funktionsprüfung der Cupula terminalis in den Bogengangsampullen des

Labyrinthes. *Pfluegers Arch. Gesamte Physiol. Menschen Tiere* 217: 747–755, 1927.

335. STEVENS, S. S. The psychophysics of sensory function. In: *Sensory Communication,* edited by W. A. Rosenblith. Cambridge, MA: MIT Press, 1961.

336. STEVENS, S. S. Sensory power functions and neural events. In: *Handbook of Sensory Physiology. Principles of Receptory Physiology,* edited by W. R. Loewenstein. Berlin: Springer-Verlag, 1971, vol. 1, p. 226–242.

337. STRATTON, G. M. Vision without inversion of the retinal image. *Psychol. Rev.* 4: 341–360, 463–481, 1897.

338. STRATTON, G. M. Eye movements and the aisthesis of visual form. *Philos. Stud. Leipzig* 20: 336–359, 1902.

339. SVAETICHIN, G. The cone action potential. *Acta Physiol. Scand. Suppl.* 106: 565–610, 1953.

340. SVAETICHIN, G. Spectral response curves from single cones. *Acta Phsyiol. Scand. Suppl.* 134: 17–46, 1956.

341. SZENTÁGOTHAI, J. *Die Rolle der einzelnen Labyrinthrezeptoren bei der Orientation von Augen und Kopf im Raume.* Budapest: Akademie-Verlag, 1952.

342. TALBOT, S. A., AND W. H. MARSHALL. Physiological studies on neural mechanisms of visual localization and discrimination. *Am. J. Ophthalmol.* 24: 1255–1263, 1941.

343. TAYLOR, J. *Le mécanisme ou le nouveau traité d'anatomie du globe de l'oeil.* Paris: M. E. David, 1738. (German transl.: Mechanismus oder neue Abhandlung von der künstlichen Zusammensetzung des menschlichen Auges. Frankfurt am Main: Stoks and Schilling, 1750.)

344. TER BRAAK, J. W. G. Untersuchungen über optokinetischen Nystagmus. *Arch. Néerl. Physiol.* 21: 309–376, 1936.

345. TEUBER, H.-L. Perception. In: *Handbook of Physiology. Neurophysiology,* edited by J. Field and M. W. Magoun. Washington, DC: Am. Physiol. Soc., 1960, sect. 1, vol. III, chapt. 65, p. 1595–1668.

346. THEODORICUS TEUTONICUS DE VRIBERG. De Iride et Radialibus Impressionibus. Manuscr. Univ. Bibliothek, Basel. (Some figures are reproduced in ref. 76.)

347. THORPE, W. H. *Learning and Instinct in Animals.* London: Methuen, 1956.

348. TINBERGEN, N. *The Study of Instinct.* Oxford, England: Oxford Univ. Press, 1951.

349. TITCHENER, E. B. *A Text-Book of Psychology.* New York: MacMillan, 1910.

350. TÖNNIES, J. F. Die Ableitung bioelektrischer Effekte vom uneröffneten Schädel. Physikalische Behandlung des Problems. *J. Psychol. Neurol.* 45: 154–171, 1933.

351. UEXKÜLL, J., VON. *Theoretische Biologie* (2nd ed.). Berlin: Springer-Verlag, 1928.

352. VESALIUS, A. De humani corporis fabrica libri septem. Basel: Oporinus, 1543. Transl. by C. Singer of Bk VII: *Vesalius on the human brain.* London: Oxford Univ. Press, 1952 (based partly on edition of 1555).

353. VIETH, G. U. A. Ueber die Richtung der Augen. *Ann. Physiol.* 58: 233–255, 1818.

354. VOGT, C., AND O. VOGT. Allgemeine Ergebnisse unserer Hirnforschung. *J. Psychol. Neurol.* 25: 273–462, 1919.

355. VOGT, O. Psychologie, Neurophysiologie und Neuroanatomie. *J. Psychol. Neurol. Leipzig* 1: 1–3, 1902/1903.

356. VOGT, O., AND C. VOGT. Zur anatomischen Gliederung des Cortex cerebri. *J. Psychol. Neurol. Leipzig* 2: 160–180, 1903.

357. WALTER, W. G. Slow potential waves in the human brain associated with expectancy, attention and decision. *Arch. Psychiatr. Nervenkr. + Z. Gesamte Neurol. Psychiatr.* 206: 309–322, 1964/65.

358. WATSON, J. B. Psychology as the behaviorist views it. *Psychol. Rev.* 20: 158–177, 1913.

359. WEBER, E. H. Der Tastsinn und das Gemeingefühl. In: *Handwörterbuch der Physiologie,* edited by R. Wagner. Braunschweig, Germany: Vieweg, 1846, vol. 3, pt. 2, p. 481–588. (Transl. by H. E. Ross and D. J. Murray: *Weber: The Sense of Touch.* London: Academic, 1978.)

360. WEBER, E. F. W., AND E. H. WEBER. Expériences qui prouvent

que les nerfs vagues, stimulés par l'appareil de rotation galvanometrique, peuvent retarder et même arrêter le mouvement du coeur. *Arch. Anat. Gén. Physiol. Suppl. to Arch. Gén. Méd.*) 4th ser. 1: 12–13, 1846.

361. WEISS, P. A. Life, order and understanding. A theme in three variations. *Graduate J. Suppl.* 8: 1–157, 1970.

362. WERNER, G., AND V. B. MOUNTCASTLE. Neural activity in mechanoreceptive cutaneous afferents: stimulus-response relations, Weber functions, and information transmission. *J. Neurophysiol.* 28: 359–397, 1965.

363. WERNICKE, C. *Der aphasische Symptomenkomplex: Eine psychologische Studie auf anatomischer Basis.* Breslau, Germany: Cohn & Weigert, 1874.

364. WERTHEIMER, M. Experimentelle Studien über das Sehen von Bewegung. *Z. Psychol.* 61: 161–265, 1912.

365. WERTHEIMER, M. Untersuchungen zur Lehre von der Gestalt. II. *Psychol. Forsch.* 4: 301–350, 1923.

366. WESTPHAL, C. Über einige Bewegungserscheinungen an gelähmten Gliedern. *Arch. Psychiar. Nervenkr.* 5: 803–841, 1875.

367. WHEATSTONE, C. Contributions to the physiology of vision. I. On some remarkable and hitherto unobserved, phenomena of binocular vision. *Philos. Trans. R. Soc. London* 128: 371–394, 1838.

368. WHITTERIDGE, G. *William Harvey's de motu locali animalum.* 1627. (Latin text and Engl. transl., Cambridge, England: Cambridge Univ. Press, 1959.)

369. WIENER, N. *Cybernetics, or Control and Communication in the Animal and the Machine.* New York: Wiley, 1948.

370. WIESEL, T. N., AND D. H. HUBEL. Single-cell responses in striate cortex of kittens deprived of vision in one eye. *J. Neurophysiol.* 26: 1003–1017, 1963.

371. WIESEL, T. N., AND D. H. HUBEL. Ordered arrangement of orientation columns in monkeys lacking visual experience. *J. Comp. Neurol.* 158: 307–318, 1974.

372. WILLEMSEN, C. A. (editor). *Kaiser Friedrich II. Über die Kunst mit Vögeln zu jagen.* Frankfurt am Main: Insel, 1964, 3 vol.

372a. WILLIS, TH. *De anima brutorum.* Oxford, England: R. Davis, 1672.

373. WINDELBAND, W. *Lehrbuch der Geschichte der Philosophie.* 1891. (13th ed., Tübingen, Germany: Mohr, 1935.)

374. WITTGENSTEIN, L. *Tractatus logico-philosophicus.* Wien: 1921.

375. WITTGENSTEIN, L. *Philosophical Investigation* (transl. by G. E. M. Anscombe). Oxford, England: Blackwell, 1953.

376. WOLMAN, B. B. (editor). *Historical Roots of Contemporary Psychology.* New York: Harper & Row, 1968.

377. WOOLSEY, C. N., W. H. MARSHALL, AND P. BARD. Representation of cutaneous tactile sensibility in the cerebral cortex of the monkey as indicated by evoked potentials. *Bull. Johns Hopkins Hosp.* 70: 399, 1942.

378. WORDEN, F. G., J. P. SWAZEY, AND G. ADELMAN (editors). *The Neurosciences: Paths of Discovery.* Cambridge, MA: MIT Press, 1975.

379. WUNDT, W. *Theorie der Sinneswahrnehmung.* Leipzig: Winter, 1862.

380. WUNDT, W. *Grundzüge der physiologischen Psychologie* (5th ed). Leipzig: Engelmann, 1902, 1903, 3 vol. (English transl. of 3rd ed. by E. B. Titchener. London: Macmillan, 1896, 2 vol.)

381. WURTZ, R. H., AND C. W. MOHLER. Organization of monkey superior colliculus: enhanced visual response of superficial layer cells. *J. Neurophysiol.* 39: 745–765, 1976.

382. YERKES, R. M., AND A. W. YERKES. *The Great Apes: A Study of Anthropoid Life.* New Haven, CT: Yale Univ. Press, 1929.

383. YOUNG, R. M. *Mind, Brain and Adaptation in the Nineteenth Century. Cerebral Localization and its Biological Context from Gall to Ferrier.* Oxford, England: Clarendon, 1970.

384. YOUNG, T. On the theory of light and colours. *Philos. Trans. R. Soc. London* 92: 18–21, 1802.

385. ZELLER, E. *Die Philosophie der Griechen in ihrer historischen Entwicklung* (5th ed.). Leipzig: Fues, 1891/1892, 3 parts in 6 vol. (New ed. Aalen, Germany: Scientia, 1971.)

386. ZOTTERMAN, Y. Studies in the peripheral nervous mechanism of pain. *Acta. Med. Scand.* 80: 1–64, 1933.

387. ZOTTERMAN, Y. Touch, pain and tickling: an electrophysiological investigation on cutaneous sensory nerves. *J. Physiol. London* 95: 1–28, 1939.

Among the innumerable items of secondary literature only some histories of philosophy and science are mentioned that can introduce the main ideas (36, 76, 318, 319, 373, 376, 385); recent histories of brain research have been included that contain useful bibliographies (72, 383) or illustrations (48, 71). For treatment of the Middle Ages and post-Renaissance, Crombie's two volumes (76), and for general neurophysiology Brazier's handbook article (55), are the most useful guides. Some excerpts from important sources are found as English translations (see refs. 122, 176, and 312), and brief review articles of the philosophical roots are in reference 69. For biographies see reference 155, and for autobiographical notes of modern neuroscientists see reference 378. The important original publications of sensory physiology appearing between 1800 and 1920 are listed and described in Boring's monograph (52) and reviewed in Bethe's handbook (45, 46).

CHAPTER 2

Perception

J U L I A N H O C H B E R G | *Department of Psychology, Columbia University, New York City*

THE STUDY OF PERCEPTION stands at the boundary between physical and physiological sciences, on the one hand, and the more cognitive and social aspects of psychology, on the other. The premises and programs of this area of inquiry have been shaped by relatively few major theories. Some of the theories, but not all, have been explicitly concerned with the attempt to incorporate knowledge or speculation about physiological mechanisms into an account of how we perceive the world of objects and events. By far the most influential of these, the classic theory in the form developed by Hermann von Helmholtz, serves as the framework of this chapter for three reasons: *1)* the relationship between sensory processes and perceptual experience was made explicit in that theory in a way that is helpful in understanding more modern approaches; *2)* the classic theory of perception (but not all of Helmholtz's proposals concerning sensory mechanisms) today remains a popular position, if no longer the overwhelmingly dominant one; *3)* most of the traditional research problems were undertaken, and all of the subsequent approaches were formulated, within the context of the classic theory.

FIRST PRINCIPLES OF STUDY OF PERCEPTION

Any science needs provision for analysis into some smaller set of elements than the set of observations to be explained; it needs combining principles (or synthetic rules) that will enable any actual instance to be accounted for in terms of the analytic elements. Here are considered primarily the principles of analysis through which perceptual explanations have been used in an attempt to analyze the world of perception—i.e., those having the greatest relevance to questions of sensory physiology; the synthetic rules are considered only where they are needed to assess the attempts at analysis.

Even a cursory examination of the appearances of objects and scenes in the world reveals that they have many properties in terms of which they can be described. These properties are functions of the nature of the perceiver as well as of the objects being perceived; they are fewer than the things to be perceived, and both physical and physiological bases can be found for them. The simplest analytic system was based on these facts. This system—the classic system of analysis of perception—serves as a point of departure for all contemporary treatment, whether merely revisionist in its intention or radical in its rejection of the classic picture.

Classic System and Its Background

The study of perception, and indeed its definition in psychology, was shaped by two intertwined sources: the philosophers who sought to dissect all of our ideas about the world into the various combinations of a finite set of simple sensory ideas, or sensations; and the physiologists who sought to discover the physical processes by which complete chains of cause and effect might be traced between the physical events that confront an organism and the physical response that it makes to those events. The early confluence of these two lines of inquiry may be most profitably examined in Helmholtz's efforts to formulate a unified theory of sensation and perception. Before any discussion of Helmholtz's proposals, a brief reminder of the philosophical and physiological backgrounds is in order, to establish his origins and intentions, because without that background Helmholtz himself is often misunderstood about issues that are of contemporary and not merely antiquarian importance.

The line of philosophers (see the chapter by Jung in this *Handbook*) that runs from the British empiricists (Hobbes, Locke, Berkeley, Hume), through the associationists, to James Mill and John Stuart Mill developed what I henceforth call the *classic theory* of perception: All of our knowledge and thought about the world rests on ideas that have come through our senses (i.e., the position is empiricist as opposed to nativist), so it is important to understand how ideas are gained through the senses. Raw sensory data are the simplest indivisible experiences—red, cold, sweet. More complex ideas have been thought to consist of packets of the simple ideas that have become associated with each other because they have occurred together frequently in the individual's experience with the world. The simplest ideas, when occasioned by outer events in the world, are sensations; when they appear in memory because they have been evoked by some other idea with which they are associated, they are fainter copies, or images. A percept, then, consists of a set of sensations occasioned by the stimulation of the sense organs plus the cluster of images that are supplied by the individual's memory of previous clusters of sensations. By reflection (introspection) the philosopher could therefore examine each critical idea—causation, justice, duty—to determine its sensory components and therefore the experiences on which it was based.

From this viewpoint, simple sensations and their memory images constitute the units of which all mind consists; the sensations provide elements of analysis, and the principles of association provide the synthetic rules by which those elements combine to form all the objects and events we can perceive or imagine. The principles of association, formulated by Aristotle (4), are, at least at first glance, capable of being used in an objective and quantitative way. For example, the law of frequency or the law of recency (namely, that other things being equal, the strength of an association between two ideas will be some direct function of the number of times the two have been paired and some inverse function of the time elapsed since the two have been paired, respectively) are in principle open to operational test and application. Regardless of the philosophical inquiry, therefore, if the elements of analysis and the combining laws are themselves valid, the scientific study of the mind in general (i.e., psychology), and of our experiences of the world in particular (i.e., perception), is possible. Originally entirely speculative and qualitative, the enterprise soon became experimental and quantitative: How many different color sensations can we distinguish? What is the precise form of the relationship between associative strength (as measured by the probability of correct recall) and frequency of repetition? Some of the methods used in perceptual research are mentioned later in the chapter; note here, however, that the pursuit of this enterprise does not require any knowledge of sensory physiology. It is true that from its inception with Hobbes in 1651 (108) and Hartley in 1749 (see ref. 87), speculations were offered about the physiological bases of sensations, images, and associations, but such thought was not central to the psychological theory or to subsequent psychological research. That remains true of much in perceptual psychology today; neither Gibson nor Brunswik (theorists discussed at some length later in this chapter) nor much of the work on artificial intelligence (which is only referred to in this chapter) is at all concerned with either real or speculative physiological mechanisms, although they may indeed offer some guidance to physiological inquiry.

Nevertheless much of our perceptual knowledge and theory bear the stamp of physiological fact and fancy and derive from the second line of thought that probably starts with Descartes (1650, ref. 44) and Hobbes (1651, ref. 108). Since antiquity there has been fascination with mechanical automata, usually clockwork dolls, that performed apparently purposive humanlike actions—e.g., writing letters, playing musical instruments—and the attempt to explicate physical cause and effect between the physical events in the world that stimulate living organisms to action and the organisms' final physical responses to those events can be traced to ancient Greece. The modern picture starts with Descartes's view of animals (and of human beings, too, save in the intervention of a soul, which may have been a matter of personal caution as much as theoretical commitment), in which three parts of the nervous system are distinguished. The afferent (sensory) nerves, when excited by the physical energies emitted or reflected by objects, in turn excite the complex pathways of the central nervous system, which in their turn excite the efferent (motor) nerves that finally set some group of muscles into overt action. The specialization of afferent and efferent nerves was duly confirmed in the early 19th century by Bell (13) and Magendie (147); and further specialization of sensory nerves to stimulation by one or another kind of physical energy, which was systematically argued in 1838 by Johannes Müller (156), made plausible the attempt to work through the chain of events from stimulation to behavior. That attempt remains the aim of some physiologists and behavioral scientists interested in sensory process and discriminative behaviors (cf. Graham, refs. 73, 74).

Note that the study of perceptual experience is no more necessary in principle to the attempt to trace the biophysical events from stimulation to response than the study of sensory physiology is necessary to the study of perceptual experience. Attempts have been made with varying degrees of vigor, therefore, to pursue purely physical analyses. Most often the only judgment by the subject that will be taken as acceptable evidence in the physiological enterprise is whether two stimuli are detectably different in a single detectable way—e.g., whether a small circular field is perfectly homogeneous or is divided into two detectably different regions (cf. Brindley, ref. 27). Boynton and Onley (24) have argued that such judgments have no privileged status; and we will, in fact, see that other and more descriptive approaches to the study of perceptual experience (of how things appear) have had important effects on the theory and research of sensory physiologists as well as on the work of perceptual psychologists. In any case, however, the history of sensory and perceptual research, together with the problems that history has bequeathed to us, was shaped mainly by men and women whose intention it was to consider perceptual and physiological research as part of a single inquiry.

In 1651, Hobbes reasoned in his book *Human Nature* (108) that whenever the optic nerve is set into action, whether by internal or external means, a sensation of light is experienced, inasmuch as the organism has no way to detect that the nerve's action is not due to its usual cause, i.e., light. Other writers (Bell, ref. 13; Young, ref. 210) made similar points in similar ways. In 1838, Müller (156) formulated in detail the law of specific nerve energies: Each kind of sensory experience is the result of the excitation of a specific kind of sensory nerve, regardless of how that nerve becomes excited. The specialization of the sense organs is such that normally a particular physical event in the world is the effective cause of each such excitation and, hence, of each sensory experience. Although the first step in putting this doctrine to use was to show in a plausible way how the characteristics of objects and events in the world are transduced into specific neural events, this doctrine was not merely a statement about behavior or even about the effects of stimulation on neural tissue: It was also a statement about perceptual experience as well, and the strength

of Müller's argument rested on its ability to account for otherwise unaccountable aspects of our perceptions of the world by taking into account the characteristics of the sense organs.

This principle offers a first step in the analysis of consciousness into the major kinds or modalities of experience—sight, hearing, touch, taste, smell. It barely scratches the surface, of course. Within each of the modalities are innumerable differences in sensory and perceptual experiences to be accounted for. Müller's student, Helmholtz, took the next step.

Helmholtz Theory of Sensation and Perception: Brief Introduction

Helmholtz undertook to develop a systematic account of the specific nerve energies (more correctly, the specific fiber energies) within each modality, corresponding to each sensation we can distinguish, and to account for all of our possible percepts and thoughts in terms of their origins in the elementary sensations. That is, Helmholtz identified the elementary ideas or sensations of the British associationists with the actions of individual sensory nerves, assuming that the connections are intact between the sensory nerves and the brain. With this theory the foundations of a science of mind would be firmly established within a unified theory of science. Elementary sensation would be accounted for in terms of the receptors and their specific nerve energies, and the perceptions of objects and events would be accounted for by those sensations plus the memories of the previous sensations that have become associated with them through the organism's experiences with the correlated packets of stimuli that are offered by the physical structure of the world. It is this broad and deep attempt, undertaken and almost fully developed only one scientific generation after the formulation of the law of specific nerve energies, that makes Helmholtz's approach important to us and that raised most of the problems with which contemporary perception psychologists are concerned.

Before looking at these issues in more detail, let us see in broad strokes what Helmholtz's theory was and what it was not. First, we consider what it was.

Our perceptions of the physical world are based on elementary sensations. Such sensations are normally experienced when their corresponding receptor neurons and sensory nerves are excited and in turn excite the sensory area in the brain to which they project. Anything that excites the brain in the same way that some sensory nerve does will produce the same sensations as that nerve's action. Perceptions of objects, of their distances, etc., are based on the clusters of sensations that have been received by the organism as a result of its active explorations in the world; e.g., the perspective views generated by an observer moving around a table represents such a simultaneous and sequential cluster of sensations. Given such a set of sensations, what we perceive is that object or event that would most likely have produced those sensations under normal conditions. There is thus a problem-solving or inferential aspect to perception: we fit perceptions to the sensations that occasion them, through a process of unconscious inference that takes into account both the sensations received at any moment and what we have learned about the world. For example, given the retinal image of some object, we take into account both the extent of the retinal image and the perceived distance of the object in order to arrive at a perception of the object's physical size. The process is well practiced, automatic, and unconscious. The sensations on which it is based are also in effect unconscious. In general, we perceive objects and are not aware of the simple fundamental sensations of which they are composed.

This very compact presentation of Helmholtz's development of the classic theory is expanded in an examination of why its various components were proposed, why they were rejected, and why some of them have now regained currency. Before that, some things that are not true of Helmholtz's theory must be considered.

1. Sensations do not consciously precede perception, nor are they normally discernible components of it. The perception of objects and their properties is direct and immediate, as far as conscious adult experience is concerned. Sensations have a place only in the scientist's analysis of the processes that underlie perception.

2. Helmholtz (like Müller before him) was not saying merely that for every sensory experience there is some corresponding event in the nervous system. He was saying that the specific nerve energies that serve to analyze the stimulus pattern by responding to some particular aspect of it also thereby provide the elements of sensory experience (albeit unnoticeable ones) on which perception is based.

3. Although the position is a remarkably consistent one considering how broad and deep it is and how early in history it was proposed, it is neither monolithic nor formally analytic—not monolithic, in the sense that we can abandon some features of it without endangering others; not formally analytic, in the sense that although the classic theory was set up (well before Helmholtz adapted it) with analytic units, synthetic rules, and the firm intention of developing a rigorous science, few attempts at such rigor have been made. (The notable few, in recent years, have been by Hayek, ref. 91 and by Taylor, ref. 186, and in the work on artificial intelligence or pattern recognition that is only mentioned in this chapter.) Although the terms were used in this analytic sense by James Mill (152) and E. B. Titchener (190), attempts to make these units and rules rigorous would be premature, because each component of the classic theory of sensation and perception has been subject to serious objections that have

not yet been successfully met and that in some cases clearly cannot be met.

THE SEPARATE SENSES AND THEIR SENSITIVITIES—SPECIFIC NERVE ENERGIES

The most obvious separation of the different kinds of perceptual attributes is that between the different senses: we can readily find everyday situations that separate sight, hearing, and touch and that demonstrate the differential sensitivities of our separate organs to photic energy, sound-pressure waves, and deformation of the skin, respectively. Other sense experiences are somewhat less easy to separate (e.g., taste and smell). Moreover, most of what we normally think of as being perception via a single modality normally entails the use of information from other modalities as well. Thus the visual perception of space is intimately dependent on the use of information about the movements and positions of eyes, head, and neck; perception of speech is obviously assisted by the sight of the speaker. Nevertheless there is great diagnostic, heuristic, and explanatory value to the concept underlying the law of specific nerve energies, and it serves as an introduction to the task of perceptual explanation. For each modality three parallel analyses are required.

Physical Analysis

Vision, hearing, and touch-kinesthesis are the major senses that inform us about the world. For vision the stimulus is, of course, photic energy. For hearing the adequate stimulus is sound pressure waves. For touch and kinesthesis, the adequate stimuli are deformations of the skin and motion of the joints, respectively. Note that these are not properties of an object—e.g., the reflectance of an object (whether it reflects much or little photic energy), which is what is called a distal stimulus characteristic, or distal variable. Instead, we are discussing the stimulating energy that impinges on the sense organ—the proximal stimulus distribution.

The science that relates the proximal to the distal stimulus is physics, of course—in the case of the visual stimulus, the physics of the propagation of the optical spectrum of electromagnetic radiation.

The minimum amount of energy that will have a detectable sensory effect is its threshold, and the procedures for measuring thresholds are the well-developed psychophysical methods and their modern descendants (designed to assess the perceiver's sensory sensitivity separately from his readiness to judge one way or another; these are discussed in the chapters by Galanter and by Stebbins, Brown, and Petersen in this *Handbook*).

In general, the physical stimuli for sight, sound, and touch are relatively independent in their effects. There are minor interaction effects on thresholds (174), but they do not suffice to challenge in any serious way the law of specific nerve energies in the broad sense in which it is being discussed here.

Note that there is a gross psychophysical correspondence—for a part of the electromagnetic scale, an experience of light. That is, of course, why that spectral energy is singled out for consideration as a stimulus. Photic energy is, however, neither necessary nor sufficient for the experience of light. That is where the law of specific nerve energies comes in: it introduces a set of physiological elements that not only partially bridge the gap between the physics and the psychology but explain why the physical stimulation is neither necessary nor sufficient for the psychological experience.

Physiological Analysis

The sensory elements for this gross distinction between modalities are the parts of the sensory nervous system, from receptor organs to corresponding projection areas in the cerebral cortex, that on the one hand are responsive to the known adequate physical stimuli and on the other are associated with the experience, and that mediate between the two. Thus photic energy may impinge on the viewer, but if his sensory system is nonfunctional anywhere between the photoreceptors and the sensory cortex, he has no experience of light. When photic energy is above its normal threshold but fails to produce an experience of light, the attendant circumstances are obviously significant in diagnosis of abnormalities in the sensory nervous system and brain.

Even with perfectly normal neural structure, stimulation can fail to elicit a sensory response: for example, a homogeneous field of light (*Ganzfeld*) of some clearly perceptible hue will, after a few moments' viewing, first lose its colored appearance and then (at least for some subjects) fail to make any visual impression at all (see Cohen, ref. 39, and Hochberg et al., ref. 119). Closely related to this finding is the fading from view of a variegated field, with stationary objects and contours, if image-stabilization techniques are used to cancel the optical effects of small movements of the eye (Riggs et al., ref. 168). The eye movements normally provide a change of retinal stimulation at each boundary between regions of different luminance in the retinal image. What both the Ganzfeld and stabilization show is that processes of cumulative adaptation make the sensory system unresponsive to continued stimulation and primarily responsive to change, a fact known for a century (Helmholtz, ref. 103; Mach, ref. 146). Depending on the state of adaptation of the sensory system, photic stimulation may be insufficient for the perception of light. The change in psychophysical correspondence that results from adaptation in the normal observer can be expressed in terms of the history of stimulation to which the sense organ has been exposed, so that no mention of physiology is needed. The picture of the relationship between stimulation and response becomes conceptually simpler and more satisfying, however, if a hypothesis is introduced about sensory adaptation in the receptor processes, and if that hypothesis also accounts for other complexities and gaps in the psychophysical correspondence. It is still more satisfying if this purely speculative hypothesis about physiological process can be supported by physical measures of neural activity and explained in terms of biochemical events.

Just as photic energy is not sufficient to produce the experience of light, neither is it necessary to sensory experience. With no photic stimulation at all, anything that elicits the same neural activity in the cerebral cortex does in fact produce the experience of light: pressure or electrical stimulation of the retina in the eye, or electrical stimulation of the intervening nervous structures or of the cortex itself, will produce the experience of light (Brindley and Lewin, ref. 28; Dobelle et al., ref. 45; Penfield and Roberts, ref. 162). Between the object in the world and the subject's experience of it there thus extends a causal chain, which we can for the present extend no further than selected regions of the cortex (e.g., we cannot trace the causal chain through to the verbal motor behavior by which the subject's experience may become known to us).

Although they stand at the end of the causal chain, it is clear that the sensory experiences are the criteria on which the links in that chain are tested: we study that section of the electromagnetic spectrum that we have reason to believe is the normal physical occasion for the experience of light, and we study the part of the bodily tissue that is responsive to photic energy under the same conditions in which we experience light.

Such apparent correlations can be misleading. For example, electrical recordings from the auditory nerve, matching the frequencies of the pressure waves within the approximate range in which the cat discriminates sounds, seemed like a prime candidate for the physiological correlate of auditory sensation and for support for a particular theory of hearing (the frequency theory, described briefly in *Audition: Helmholtz Theory*, p. 82; cf. Wever and Bray, ref. 204). It was subsequently found to be a microphonic effect arising in the cochlea, of unknown relationship to the sensory process, and not the activity of the auditory nerve fibers themselves (see the chapter by Dallos in this *Handbook*; see also Stevens and Davis, ref. 183). It is unlikely that mistakes of this kind could be made today, because it is now commonplace to record the activities of individual cells and fibers. But it should be borne in mind that responses occur in the sensory organs that are correlated with the physical stimulation without any consequence in either behavior or experience, and that many neural structures are responsive to identifiable stimulus properties, whose responses do contribute to behavior but have no correlate in sensory experience. One example of such structures are the receptors in the oculomotor muscles (see Brindley and Merton, ref. 29). The correlation of physiological responses with some aspect of the proximal physical stimulation does not necessarily mean, therefore, that those responses serve a direct, or even an indirect, perceptual function. This point is particularly important in connection with the physiological structures that appear to respond to complex patterns of stimulation (such as frequency channels and edge detectors), for which the perceptual functions are still unknown or completely speculative. These are discussed in the penultimate section of this chapter.

Perceptual Analysis

In this first stage of perceptual analysis, i.e., analysis into modalities of experience, sensations were divided into five classes corresponding to the traditional five senses. Sensations that belong to different modalities could not, it was held, be compared with each other for similarities or differences, whereas sensations within a modality or class could be compared with each other: for example, two different sensations of the sense of sight can be compared with regard to their intensity and color, but neither of them can be compared with a smell or a sound.

Some reservations about the psychological discreteness and noncomparability of the modalities were mentioned earlier, and the validity of the classification scheme has been questioned over the years, most recently by Gibson (59, 60). In any case, however, five properties are obviously too few to describe the objects and events we can perceive. How we sense distinctions within modalities must be explained. Whatever the difficulties in making distinctions between modalities of experience, they are trivial when compared to the difficulty of finding satisfactory criteria for distinguishing fundamental units of experience (i.e., sensations) within each modality.

The basic attempt at analyzing experience and sensory processes within each modality was made by Helmholtz. What is surprising is not that the attempt was wrong in many particulars, but rather that it has held up as well as it has, and that it has in fact regained strength in recent years in relation to opposing theories of perception.

ANALYTIC ELEMENTS WITHIN MODALITIES

The analytic elements for vision, for oculomotor proprioception (part of the kinesthetic sense), and for audition, as they have emerged from the inquiries of sensory physiologists and psychophysicists in the later nineteenth and the twentieth centuries, and as they have been modified by recent research, are considered in this section. [General treatments of sensory processes in the context of perceptual psychology are to be found in Haber and Hershenson (82), Hochberg (116), Kaufman (133, 134), and Kling and Riggs (136).]

Vision: Classic Analysis

In vision the elementary physical variables are those of wavelength, intensity, and direction (or location) of each point of photic energy in the two-dimensional array of proximal stimulation that confronts the eye (the optic array). That is, any scene whatsoever—any arrangement of objects in space—can be replaced by a set of points, each of which has the same spectral distribution of photic energy as its corresponding point in the optic array that would be produced by the scene itself. In fact, however, the optic array of photic energy that is presented to the eye by any scene is not at all necessary to the experience of that scene. Subject to certain constraints, very different wavelengths may be used. Although the photic energy at each point in the scene itself may consist of any part or parts of the continuous spectrum that extends between the infrared and the ultraviolet wavelengths, it can be replaced by a mixture of only three suitably chosen wavelengths at suitably chosen intensities. For more precise statements of this relationship, see the chapters by Yellott, Wandell, and Cornsweet and by De Valois and Jacobs in this *Handbook*.) Color television is a reasonably straightforward application of this fact.

Mixtures of three wavelengths can be used to match or duplicate the appearance of any other wavelength or wavelengths; this is, as Newton (159) noted, a perceptual and not a physical fact. It suggested to Thomas Young (210) in 1802 that at each point on the retina are three independent photoreceptors, each sensitive to a broad part of the spectrum but having different spectral sensitivity curves. Closely related versions of this theory were adopted by Clerk Maxwell (149) and by Helmholtz (101), the latter taking Young's proposal as an instance of specific nerve energies within a modality. The elementary sensations in the Young-Helmholtz theory were appearances of red, green, and violet hues that resulted from the activity of receptors with peak sensitivities to photic energy of 650 nm, 540 nm, or 450 nm, respectively. (For discussion of modern research on the actual spectral absorption curves of cone pigments, see Boynton, ref. 20, and the chapter by De Valois and Jacobs in this *Handbook*). From these elementary color sensations, it was thought, all other visual sensations were produced by mixture. For example, a spot of photic energy of wavelength 580 nm looks identical to a mixture of lights of 650 nm and 540 nm because light of 580 nm stimulates the red cone and the green cone equally and produces the same mixture of red and green sensations as does a combination of lights of 650 nm and 540 nm.

This raises a point that lies at the heart of Helmholtz's theory, one we encounter repeatedly: as Young (210), James Mill (152), John Stuart Mill (153), Maxwell (149), and Helmholtz (101) all noted, we cannot discern the simple sensations that compose a complex or compound mixture. Introspection simply will not serve to reveal the elementary experiences in their mixtures (Maxwell, ref. 149). The point is so evident—when one considers how unlike a mixture of red and green the color yellow appears to be, or how unlike a mixture of red, green, and violet hues a pure white appears to be—that it is often taken to be Helmholtz's theory that each color experience is an equally simple sensation, specific to a particular pattern of activity of the three receptors. It is true that Helmholtz's usage of terms may sometimes encourage that interpretation, but I believe that here, as elsewhere, Helmholtz does indeed posit an elementary or fundamental experience corresponding to each individual receptor's response and normally unavailable to self-observation; indeed, he explains (104) that we cannot detect the individual colors in their compounds, because there is no action the viewer can take that will separate them (cf. ILLUSIONS, p. 84). This point is important to an understanding of the classic theory of perception and several of its more recent descendants and opponents, and we see later why Helmholtz bothered to introduce the notion of fundamental experiences even though the perceiver cannot normally observe that he is having those experiences.

In any case, these hypothetical elements of experience were given their operational meaning by a great deal of psychophysical research on color mixing and on acuity. In the first research on color mixing, which was directed to determining and refining the functions by which one set of wavelengths matches the appearance of another, a subject compares two patches of light that differ in their spectral distribution while they are varied until the two appear identical. Acuity research is directed to questions such as, How far apart must points be in order to be perceived as separate? This is information that was once thought to reflect the sizes of individual receptors. (See the chapter by Yellott, Wandell, and Cornsweet in this Handbook.)

As to the physiological elements of the visual sense, the Young-Helmholtz theory provides three classes of cones, to which we must add an additional type of receptor, the rods. The rods all share the same spectral sensitivity function and are therefore achromatic in response (i.e., the rod system cannot provide information about the wavelength of the stimulus independently of information about the luminance of the stimulus); they are entirely absent from the central region of the retina (the central fovea), and their density of distribution increases with the distance from the center of the fovea; they are sensitive to low levels of photic energy; and they contribute to the central nervous system only through ganglion cells, each of which collects the input from many receptors. The cones, on the other hand, are most densely packed in the fovea, where many fewer receptors contribute to each ganglion cell; they are distributed with de-creasing densities away from the fovea; they are responsive only to relatively high levels of photic energy; and they do not all share the same spectral sensitivity functions, as we have noted. According to the Young-Helmholtz theory there are just three kinds of cones; these have peak sensitivities at 650, 540, and 450 nm. Further details can be found in Riggs (166) and in Boynton (20).

The rods and cones, considered as the source of visual specific nerve energies, provide a set of analytic elements that account for such fundamental facts of visual sensitivity as the laws of color mixing, the course of dark adaptation (the separate contributions of rods and cones can be discerned in the shape of the function that charts the increase in photic sensitivity with time in the dark), the distribution of acuity and its interaction with the level of photic energy and the state of adaptation of the eye (acuity is highest where cones are most dense and receive sufficient photic energy). Moreover, these elements can account for the full diversity of our visual experience of the objects and events in the world, in the limited sense that we can replace any scene at all by an appropriate array of red-appearing, green-appearing, and violet-appearing points of light. And finally, in addition to a great deal of indirect evidence, there is now direct physiological evidence of three kinds of cones with three different photopigments [Brown and Wald (30) and Marks et al. (148); see also the chapters by Yellott, Wandell, and Cornsweet and by De Valois and Jacobs in this Handbook] having absorption characteristics similar to those required by the Young-Helmholtz theory. Such findings are impressive vindication of speculations based on data on color mixing, but they cannot, of course, tell us that the three receptor types produce the three independent sensations of hue that the theory proposes.

There are in fact severe problems with the notion of red, green, and violet as the sensory elements of visual perception, as is discussed later in this chapter. Before we can work our way up from color sensations to the perception of the visual world, however, we must first consider the nonvisual factors involved in oculomotor behavior.

Oculomotor Kinesthesis

Kinesthesis refers to the discrimination of the positions and movements of parts of the body, and of pressures exerted by those parts. Sensory receptors in joints, muscle-tendons, and the vestibular system of the inner ear, as well as information about the efferent commands that have been sent to the muscles, compose the traditional specific nerve energies for these discriminations [see Howard (122, 123) and the chapter by McBurney in this Handbook]. Kinesthesis is intimately involved in visual perception in several ways, one of which arises in connection with eye movements. The fact that the parafovea and periphery of the eye are capable of detecting only gross features and areas severely limits the commonplace analogies between eye and camera (as noted above, acuity drops off with increasing distance from the center of the fovea). The question is thus raised, How do we see the world through so narrow an instrument?

The muscles associated with the eye change the direction in which it points, allowing the single eye to receive foveal images of different places in the array of light that confronts it. The eye may move to bring some point to the fovea—i.e., to fixate it—by executing ballistic saccades; it may move to keep some moving object stationary on the retina, by means of smooth pursuit movements; or it may move to keep some stationary object's image on the retina despite movements of the head or body, by means of smooth compensatory movements. The two eyes together receive foveal vision from some small region in tridimensional space that is defined by the angle of convergence between their directions. In addition, muscles within the eye change the focal length of the lens (change its accommodation), and other muscles determine the diameter of the iris diaphragm that controls the amount of light entering the eye and also determines the eye's depth of field. [For more detailed discussion of these oculomotor systems, see Alpern (1), Monty and Senders (155), and the chapter by Young in this *Handbook*.]

The physical state of the oculomotor system, taken with a point in the fovea of each eye, therefore makes it possible to analyze (or to specify) any tridimensional or bidimensional spatial scene, by determining for each point in that scene its color, direction, and distance from the viewer. Physiologically, there are two possible sources of information about the movements and dispositions of the muscles and the eyes. First are the receptors embedded in the muscles and tendons of the system. Second are the efferent nerve impulses that are sent to the muscles (what Helmholtz called sensations of innervation). Actual sensations from either source are difficult or impossible to detect, but as long as the information is available at some level of the perceptual system, the specific nerve energies of the retina and of the oculomotor system would appear to be sufficient to analyze any possible spatial arrangement in the visual world.

Before considering the problems that arise in attempting that sensory analysis with real objects and scenes we must note that similar analyses have been undertaken, with varying success, within the other modalities (see the pertinent sections of this *Handbook*). Most research on perception of objects and their properties has been research in vision, however, and Helmholtz's theory of the sensory basis of hearing is considered here only because it will be useful later in the discussion of contemporary research on spatial frequency channels in vision.

Audition: Helmholtz Theory

The physical stimuli for sounds are, of course, trains of pressure changes at the ear that describe simple or complex wave forms over time. A very simple theory of hearing would have each pressure change transduced to nerve impulse and transmitted to the cortex. Individual nerve fibers cannot fire at the rate required by the higher frequencies that we can hear, so theories of this type (frequency theories) must provide for some less direct way of encoding the sound pressure waves. The Wever-Bray (204) phenomenon, mentioned in *Physiological Analysis*, p. 79, was originally taken as support for a frequency theory.

Helmholtz's theory, on the other hand, provided for the parallel sets of physical, psychological, and physiological elements that should be familiar from the previous discussion of vision. Fourier showed in 1822 that any complex wave form or vibration can be specified as the sum of a set of component sine waves of different frequency and phase. It had been known since Galileo that the pitch of a plucked string depends on the frequency with which the string vibrates; Ohm maintained that we in fact hear each component frequency in a complex waveform or chord and that we hear any pitch only if the temporal pattern of the pressure waves contains energy at the corresponding frequency (see the chapter by Green and Wier in this *Handbook*). Helmholtz proposed in 1863 that individual receptor neurons (the hair cells on the basilar membrane of the inner ear) resonate to the component frequencies of the pressure wave that is transmitted through the middle ear, and that the responses of those receptors provide the specific nerve energies for pitch. All possible sounds can be physically replaced or reproduced by a set of pressure waves that differ only in their momentary intensity at each frequency within the auditory range; anything that we hear consists of a mix of auditory sensations that differ only in their momentary pitch and loudness; and the specific nerve energy for each sensation arises in the activity of an individual receptor, which responds most strongly to pressure waves of a particular frequency, the amount of its activity determining the loudness of the pitch sensation it provides. (See the chapters by Green and Wier, by Dallos, and by Kiang in this *Handbook*.)

In this theory other sound qualities reduce to pitch and loudness. For example, the timbre or difference in quality between two instruments playing a note of the same pitch and loudness depends on the different harmonics that accompany the fundamental frequency (which determines the pitch) in each instrument: each pattern of harmonics is perceived as the note's timbre, but the individual sensations of pitch corresponding to each harmonic are very difficult to discern (Helmholtz, ref. 101).

Certain features of this theory have received direct physiological confirmation: it is a place theory, in that different frequencies of stimulation affect hair cells on different parts of the basilar membrane, and von Békésy (12) has in fact shown that the basilar membrane is distorted into different spatial patterns by stimuli of differing frequency (see the chapter by Dallos in this *Handbook*). The hypothesis that experienced pitch is correlated with the response that a specific receptor (or receptor group) makes to a particular frequency has become increasingly untenable, largely because of the problem of the "missing fundamental"—i.e., that the pitch of a tone remains the same when the lowest component is deleted, leaving only the higher harmonic frequencies (cf. Green, ref. 79, and the chapter by Green and Wier in this *Handbook*). Green has concluded that we do not now have a satisfactory theory of pitch and, as we have seen, pitch is the fundamental element of Helmholtz's theory of hearing.

The notion of a sensory analogue to Fourier analysis has been adapted to the search for new elements of sensory analysis in vision, however, and that idea is considered in the next to the last section of this chapter.

ASSESSMENT OF PROGRAM OF SENSORY ANALYSIS

In accounting for perceptual experience the classic units of analysis may be inadequate in two ways: they may fail to include the properties of appearance that must be accounted for, and they may fail to combine in orderly or predictable ways.

1. It is obvious that many more visual properties have not been accounted for than have—e.g., shape, movement, solidity. Helmholtz, like the empiricist philosophers before him, could account for all these properties (and many more) as being compounded from the basic visual sensations already described here plus memories of other sensations provided by past experiences with the objects of the world.

2. The appearance of a patch of light is not predictable from the stimulation on that region alone. It depends as well on the context of stimulation in which it is presented, differing from what the local stimulation alone would lead us to expect in one of three major ways. The appearance of some local region (e.g., its apparent size or its apparent color) may be better predicted by the objective distal property of the object projecting the proximal stimulus to the eye (e.g., by the object's physical size, or by the object's reflectance) than by the proximal stimulation at the retina. These phenomena are called the constancies. In addition, the appearance of the local region may vary from both what the proximal stimulation and the object properties would lead us to expect. These phenomena are usually called the illusions. Finally, the derived properties (e.g., perceived shape, movement) are not predictable from the local stimulation of the receptors involved in each case but depend on the configuration; these are called the Gestalt phenomena or organizational phenomena. Research on these phenomena and on the explanation of such missing properties as depth or motion have provided the bulk of the traditional research in perception.

Missing Properties

According to the classic account, all perceptual properties that are distributed in two- or three-dimensional space, like shape, movement, and distance, are compounds derived from the addition of kinesthetic sensations, or memories of them, to particular packets of visual sensations that have become associated with them through experience with seeing and touching the objects in the world.

SHAPE AND MOVEMENT. By the classic theory, a point's apparent location in two-dimensional space is given by the perceiver's experience with eye movements executed to bring any object from that point to the center of the fovea, i.e., to fixate it (51, 52, 144). The perception of a shape is then the sum of the perceptions of the locations of the points on the single contour that bounds the shape, plus other memories that have become associated with frequently encountered shapes (Wundt, ref. 209): that is, the names of familiar objects and shapes; the consequences of various oculomotor and other behaviors that have become associated with those shapes (e.g., how the shape will change with some change in the perceiver's viewing position); and tastes, touches, etc., that are characteristic of objects having those shapes. The perception of an object's movement is the change in locations perceived over a period of time; it results from movement of the object in the world relative to the viewer's eye, or from movement of the viewer's eye relative to the object.

DEPTH AND DISTANCE. By the classic account, the perception of distance is based on memories of muscular and tactual sensations that are different when the perceiver focuses his eyes on, and touches, objects that lie at different distances from him (14). The perception of depth is in turn based on the differences between perceived distances. By virtue of his experiences with the world, the perceiver has learned that certain shapes and movements (e.g., linear perspective and motion parallax) are associated with particular tactual-kinesthetic sensations, so that in the absence of the latter, memories of previous tactual kinesthetic experience make those shapes and patterns signs for depth—what are now called depth cues.

Note that the empiricist theory of perception will account not only for the perception of space but for the perception of any other properties as well (e.g., smiles, surface textures, gestures), as long as they can ultimately be analyzed into the units that have been discussed in this and previous sections. The missing properties do not, therefore, pose any necessary difficulties for the classic theory at this point in the discussion.

Effects of Context

CONSTANCIES. As the illumination on an object changes, the light it reflects to the eye also changes, but the object's apparent surface color, or perceived reflectance, remains unchanged (color constancy) under many conditions. Objects show size constancy despite changes in retinal image size with different viewing distance, shape constancy despite changes in viewing angle, velocity constancy despite differences in retinal image movement with different viewing distances, and position constancy when the viewer changes his fixation relative to a static object.

In short, our perceptions of the properties of objects are usually more veridical (more in agreement with the distal state of affairs) than we would expect them to be, given the local proximal stimulation and the local sensations corresponding to those properties. A large part of perceptual research has been devoted to the study of the constancies, and that research is surveyed later in this chapter. Helmholtz's explanation of such phenomena was that perceptual learning enables us to discount the changing sensations in order to perceive the unchanging properties of objects—e.g., we take perceived illumination into account in perceiving an object's reflectance; we take perceived distance into account in perceiving an object's size; we take the perceived direction of our gaze into account in perceiving an object's location in space.

ILLUSIONS. For each example of the constancies we can find an illusion, in which the perceived property is like neither the object property nor the sensory stimulation. For example, in simultaneous contrast, the same gray disk looks darker with a white surround than with a black one. In the Müller-Lyer pattern a line's apparent length decreases when diagonal lines are added to its ends at an acute angle and increases when the angle is obtuse. The list of illusions is long, and their relationships to each other are only partially explicated. Recent surveys and discussions of illusions are Coren and Girgus (41), Hochberg (113), and Kaufman (133).

In general, Helmholtz explained the illusions by the same logic that he used in explaining the constancies. We can see why past experience with the world might lead one to see it more veridically than the local sensory stimulation would dictate (i.e., the constancies). It is not immediately evident, however, how experience with the world and with the properties of objects should teach one to perceive them incorrectly. In making clear how Helmholtz explained illusions we make explicit the major features of his theory of perception.

According to Helmholtz we perceive that object or event that would (under normal seeing conditions) produce the same sensations as those we presently receive. Thus contrast arises from the same mechanism (functionally equivalent to taking the illumination into account in order to draw perceptual conclusions about an object's reflectance) that normally produces constancy of lightness. For example, if a surround is lighter than average, the viewer will take the illumination to be greater than average and consequently will conclude that the reflectance of a surface that is producing a sensation of some given brightness is in fact lower than it really is—i.e., the result is the illusion called simultaneous contrast. In the case of the Müller-Lyer illusion, it has recently been argued that the converging lines (arrowheads) are mistaken for the depth cue of linear perspective: for equally long retinal images, the line that is perceived as farther away must also be perceived as larger, and the one that is nearer must be perceived as smaller.

Illusions are produced, then, by the same mechanisms that normally contribute to perceiving the world correctly but are misleading when confronted by uncommon circumstances. This explanation has a great deal of support today [see Day, (42), Gillam (66), Gregory (80), Ittelson and Kilpatrick (128), Kaufman and Rock (135), Leibowitz and Pick (142), and Rock (170)]. Note that knowledge about the true state of affairs does not dispel an illusion, so the acts of "taking into account" of distance, of illumination, and of other properties, are at most inferencelike and are not the inferences of conscious logic. Moreover, if the sensations of brightness that correspond to the photic stimulation of rods and cones, or if sensations that correspond to the length of a stimulated line in the retinal image, are in fact the bases for the inferencelike processes that produce illusions such as contrast and the Müller-Lyer pattern, respectively, the perceiver cannot discern those sensations, just as he cannot discern red and green sensations in the compound color experience of yellow. Inferencelike processes and nonnoticeable sensations are not unique to Helmholtz's theory: they characterize more generally what I have called the classic theory and serve a function in that explanation of perception.

Unconscious Inferences and General Nonnoticeability of Sensations

Stimulation of a receptor that is appropriately connected to the brain—the "organ of consciousness" to Helmholtz (101)—results in a sensation. Specific nerve energies were presumed to be independent of each other. Because proximal stimulus properties reach the sense organs in patterns or structures that are imposed by the nature of objects in the physical world, those structures of sensations become associated as simultaneous and as sequential mental structures. (Although Helmholtz did not dwell on the nature of the associative process, his views are those of the British associationists discussed in *Classic System and Its Background*, p. 76.) As we move around objects and view them from different angles, and as we view them under different illuminations, our sensations change. The object properties are constant, however, and therefore the sensations that would be expected to occur with each change in viewing conditions are a defined set that we learn to expect. For example, the patterns of visual sensations provided by a single view of some familiar object are associated with each other simultaneously; the next view that would occur if the object were rotated is associated sequentially with that first pattern, and the expectation of what sensations would be perceived with any change in viewing condition (e.g., head movement), added to the present moment's sensations, constitutes the perception of the object.

The object we perceive is almost always a response to partial information: e.g., one view, not the full 360° sequence of views of all aspects of an object. The permanent object properties we perceive—i.e., the other sets of sensations that we expect to receive with each change in viewing conditions—result from an inference based on the momentary sensation, according to Helmholtz (101) and J. S. Mill (153). In the case of the constancies the inference is correct, as is usually true; in the case of the illusions the inference is mistaken. The inference in both cases is equally unnoticeable because it is so habitual. Sensations are not noticeable in general because each individual momentary sensation, transient and dependent on each shift in viewpoint, is part of a packet of sensations that is strongly associated with some permanent object or event. Because the sensation is strongly associated with the others in the packet and normally is not separated by some habitual specific action (cf. the discussion of compound colors in *Vision: Classic Analysis*, p. 80), and because the entire packet of sensations is strongly associated with the potential sequence of sensations that defines the permanent object, the separate sensations are not observable. Two questions are immediately raised by this theoretical account.

First, what does it mean to postulate fundamental experiences, if they are not consciously noticeable? To Helmholtz, it meant that the activation of a particular neural event is available for association into a mental structure; that it will serve to trigger an association that has previously been formed; and that under the proper conditions (if it can be separately evoked by some action) it can be experienced. Of course, this means that because the sensations cannot be directly observed in perceptions, other indirect means must be found to test and corroborate, if possible, the theory that posits their existence.

Second, analysis into sensations does nothing whatsoever to help the perception psychologist predict or explain the appearance of the perceptual compounds they comprise (consider the discussion of the appearances of yellow and white in *Vision:Classic Analysis*, p. 80); because of this the Helmholtz theory would be grossly incomplete, even if it were valid: it is precisely the prediction and explanation of appearance that most perception psychologists have taken as their primary task. Ever since the classic theory was first wedded to the law of specific nerve energies, alternative attempts have therefore been made to analyze

perceptual experience in ways that better account for perceptual appearances.

Alternative Units of Analysis

The analysis of visual experience into the simple, independent specific nerve energies of the Young-Helmholtz theory was challenged very early. Certain objections to classic theory, coming from Mach (146) and Hering (105), and later from Gestalt theory, were grounded in phenomenology, the attempt to describe appearances unbiased by any assumptions about the nature of underlying sensations. From that standpoint, the Young-Helmholtz theory certainly fails. Specific nerve energies for the proposed sensations of red, green, and violet may have accounted most simply for the facts of color matching, but not at all for the appearances of the resulting colors: some hues appear to be blends of others, some appear unique, and some blends appear to be excluded, e.g., a reddish green. The description of appearances is viewed with suspicion by many psychologists and physiologists (unsystematic anecdotal observations that cannot be checked for reliability are taken as scientific data by no one), but the perception psychologist must return to them in some form.

On the basis of the appearances of colors Hering (105) proposed three paired-opponent units: a yellow-blue unit, a red-green unit, and a black-white unit. These pairs of hues were to be the basic dimensions or variables of color experience, and each was to be mediated by a physiological unit that could signal more or less of the process underlying one member of its pair, but not both. For example, the red-green unit could signal some degree of red, or of green, but not of both. Unlike the Young-Helmholtz theory, this scheme allows us to predict the appearance of each possible hue from the degree to which each of the opponent pairs is activated by photic stimulation (or by the effects of previous or adjacent stimulation): that is, any mixed hue is clearly describable as a red-yellow, a red-blue, a green-yellow, or a green-blue. The fundamental hues themselves (red, yellow, green, blue) appear to be pure and unmixed, i.e., unique.

This proposal permits the appearance of any mixed color to be predicted in terms of the appearances of its components. Any individual viewer's phenomenological judgments of appearance are quite rightly regarded as a dubious basis for either psychological or physiological theories. Nevertheless there is a great deal of agreement between the ways in which the fundamental color names are used in different cultures [Berlin and Kay (15), Bornstein (19), Trandis et al. (191)], and the agreement in the ways in which subjects in our culture name hues defines a space in which all colors can be located (see Boynton, ref. 22 and Shepard, ref. 180) and in terms of which wavelength discrimination data (i.e., subjects' ability to detect the fact that two adjacent patches of light differ in wavelength) can be predicted: where the distance in a color space changes most rapidly, wavelength discrimination is most acute [see Boynton (21), Boynton and Gordon (23), Smith (181)].

Most directly relevant to the mass of data on color mixing that had been accumulated since Maxwell (149), Hurvich and Jameson (126, 127) devised a psychophysical procedure, based on purity judgments, that enabled them to express the intensities of arousal of each of the assumed opponent processes as functions of stimulating wavelength: for example, at each wavelength in the red part of the spectrum, the strength of the red appearance was measured by the amount of pure green light (the wavelength that the subject judged to be uniquely green) that was needed to make the color appear neither reddish nor greenish; similarly, the strength of the yellow response was measured by the amount of unique blue needed to cancel it. By use of these curves the prediction of color mixtures from simpler elementary colors is meaningful and feasible. All of the previous data on color mixing for which the three-hue Young-Helmholtz theory provided the simplest solution are fitted equally well by the opponent-process (or four-hue) solutions [see Hurvich and Jameson (126, 127) and Judd (131)].

Against the opponent-process theory stood two main obstacles. The first was the law of specific nerve energies as Müller and Helmholtz used it, i.e., that each nerve can signal the presence and degree of a single sensory property, whereas the opponent-process theory requires two properties for each unit. The second obstacle was the evidence, very impressive by now, that the retinal response is mediated by three sets of receptors, much as the Young-Helmholtz theory held. With respect to the first objection, in 1956 Svaetichin (185) reported that direct microelectrode recording from the goldfish retina revealed cells whose response (positive or negative) depended on the wavelength of stimulation, and he pointed out their implications for the opponent-process theory that hitherto had been based only on investigations of appearances. De Valois and his colleagues (44a, 44b) have subsequently shown that the macaque monkey has 1) color discrimination close to that of human beings, and 2) opponent-paired cells that increase or decrease their rates with respect to their base lines of response and perform very much like the units required for Hering's theory. Not only is something very similar to Hering's original proposals vindicated, but we see that the law of specific nerve energies cannot be used as an analytical tool on the principle of "one sensory attribute per physiological unit."

With respect to the evidence that three receptors provide the initial differential response to wavelength, consensus appears to favor a "zone" system (131): three broadband receptors that accord with the Young-Helmholtz theory (see the chapter by De Valois and Jacobs in this *Handbook*) and whose output is reencoded by an opponent-process system. It has

become fashionable lately, especially among sensory psychologists and physiologists, to conclude that the issue between Helmholtz and Hering has been resolved, and that they were both right. If my presentation of the two positions is at all correct, that amiable conclusion is only trivially true.

The Young-Helmholtz theory about the initial receptors is now thought to be essentially valid. But the fact that three photopigments determine initial cone response to wavelength is of no more general significance to perceptual theory than are the limitations imposed by the optics of the eye on the resolution of the retinal image. The general perceptual significance of that theory lay in Helmholtz's belief that each sensory unit could provide only one sensation, and the belief that "raw" sensations cannot in general be observed—in the case of hue, that the simple or fundamental responses cannot be discerned in the compounds. Both of these beliefs, which if true would be central to any perceptual theory, are false if the opponent-process theory is true as a perceptual theory.

The opponent-process theory implies that phenomenal analysis can serve to discern the underlying simple experiences, and that these may correspond to the activities of complex units that encode the input of more than one receptor (i.e., that respond to patterns or combinations of stimulation). These implications are very important today to the future of perceptual theory. They have not yet been explored in any systematic fashion, although we see (cf. *Recent Research on Complex Sensory Analyzers*, p. 93) that there is currently a great deal of research activity on complex units of sensory analysis.

Mach, Hering, and others argued for the importance of lateral connections between receptors, connections that make interaction, rather than independent action, the primary characteristic of the sensory nervous system. These speculations, like those on opponent-process color vision, were originally proposed to account for the viewers' phenomenal experiences, i.e., for the visual appearances of simple patterns and objects. For example, Mach was concerned with the conditions under which a definite edge or contour is perceived in the region of a brightness margin, or transition, between areas of different luminance. The transition need not be sharp for a definite edge or contour to be perceived (and in fact the optical conditions in the eye are such that a perfectly sharp edge cannot be produced in the retinal image, regardless of how abrupt the distal stimulus change may be). As long as the luminance gradient exceeds a given value, a contour will be perceived, suggesting that the differences in luminance between adjacent regions in the retinal image are enhanced: i.e., brighter is brightened or darker is further darkened, or both. These observations suggested in turn the existence of lateral inhibitory processes extending from one region to the next, as did the phenomena of "Mach bands" (illusory bright and dark lines, parallel and adjacent to the margin between regions of different luminance, that appear in the lighter and darker regions, respectively), and as did the local contrast that appears to darken a light region when a still lighter region is placed next to it. In fact, in 1949 Hartline (88) found that the activity of a photoreceptor in the *Limulus*, as measured by direct recording, decreased when an adjacent receptor was stimulated. Von Békésy (11) has shown how simple arrangements of such lateral inhibitory processes into neural units of response, in which each point of stimulation produces a central region of excitatory effect surrounded by an annulus of inhibitory effect, could account for the appearance of contours and for Mach bands. Although such analysis in terms of lateral inhibitory units can explain some phenomenological experiences, like Mach bands and certain aspects of contrast, it fails to explain the appearance of brightness of areas larger than a degree or so [see Fry (54) and Hood and Whiteside (121)]. Mathematical models of various networks of lateral connections and their possible sensory consequences are reviewed by Graham and Ratliff (77, 165). Given such cross-connections, one can hypothesize an endless variety of sensory units that are responsive to entire patterns of stimulation; their characteristics depend on the parameters and the configurations with which the cross-connections are speculatively endowed. (Some of these hypothetical units are considered in *Recent Research on Complex Sensory Analyzers*, p. 93.) Note here that at least some primitive aspects of shape perception (i.e., contours) appear to be direct results of the way the nervous system is "wired," and lightness contrast and constancy may also be partially explained in terms of some of the consequences of retinal organization rather than in terms of perceptual inference.

Hering (105) even proposed that depth perception has an innate, direct component; i.e., that our central nervous systems are innately provided with binocular elements that are sensitive to the spatial distance at which objects lie nearer and farther than the convergence distance for which the two eyes are set. Hering proposed a set of local signs, different in distance sensation in the nasal and temporal halves of each retina, that cancel when corresponding points in the two retinas are stimulated and that sum to either "nearer" or "farther," depending on the direction of the disparity in the eyes' views of any point (cf. Hochberg, ref. 109). Although this particular mechanism is not plausible today, cells in the visual system that are most active when stimulated by a particular degree of binocular disparity provide a possible innate basis for depth responses [see Barlow et al. (8) and the chapter by Bishop in this *Handbook*]. It has not been established that such cells actually contribute to depth discrimination (cf. Kaufman, ref. 133). The point here, however, is that recent physiological research shows the nervous system to be complex enough to support speculation about receptive systems tuned to almost any conceivable feature of stimulation, and those stud-

ies were themselves prefigured by Hering's and Mach's attempts to explain the appearances of objects.

The most consistent attempt to provide a thoroughgoing alternative to the classic theory, based on phenomenological descriptions of the appearances of things and events, was that of Gestalt theory, the central phenomena of which offer at least as much support as refutation for the Helmholtz perceptual theory.

Figure-Ground, Gestalt Transposition, and Laws of Organization

A sketch of the classic explanation of shape perception was given in SHAPE AND MOVEMENT, p. 83. No such definition can predict what shape will be perceived, however, for a reason not yet mentioned. Imagine a contour that bounds a closed area that has some definite shape, e.g., a vase. The area to the other side (or outside) of that contour comprises a quite different shape (e.g., a face to either side of the vase, the two faces looking at each other). This introduces the figure-ground phenomenon described by Rubin (173). To phenomenological (nonanalytic) observation, a figure appears to have definite and recognizable shape, is hard and like a surface; the ground is amorphous, extends behind the figure's apparent edge, and is without definite shape. In general, only one or the other area along any segment of the contour is likely to be "figure." If the factors that make one or the other of the alternative figures are in approximate balance, the two shapes will alternate; if not, one region may remain ground, and its shape may then remain completely unrecognized.

What will be perceived as figure is thus a question prior to that of shape. Using pencil and paper demonstrations, the Gestalt psychologists offered a host of laws about figure-ground organization (137, 202). For example, the law of good continuation (we perceive that figure-ground organization that breaks the fewest continuous lines), and the law of proximity (contours, or lines, that are close together are perceived as bounding the same surface) are particularly strong in static displays. In moving displays, common fate (things that move together are perceptually grouped together) is probably the most powerful factor. Many such laws can be summarized in a minimum principle or simplicity principle: We perceive the simplest object or arrangement that will fit the sensory pattern (137).

To Gestaltists the configuration of the patterned photic energy is itself the stimulus. It is the nervous system's response to that configuration, not the responses of individual receptor cells, that comprises the physiological unit; the experience that corresponds to that internal organization is the psychological unit (cf. Koffka, ref. 137; Wertheimer, ref. 202). A melody played in any key remains the same melody, because the relationship between the tones remains invariant, even though an entirely different set of auditory receptors may be stimulated; when the eye moves, an object's image falls on totally different retinal receptors, but we perceive the same object, nevertheless, because the configuration or form of the stimulation, and therefore the configuration of the directly consequent Gestalt physiological response and corresponding perceptual experience, is invariant.

The Gestalt theory was the most radical and persistent opponent of the classic system. The laws of organization and the minimum principle were in fact the subject of very little objective and quantitative inquiry, although reformulations in terms of information measures (5, 6, 55, 56) looked promising (6, 7, 118). The physiological proposals concerning the global neural processes that might underlie the Gestalt phenomena (139, 140) cannot be taken seriously today.

On the other hand the figure-ground phenomenon and the laws of organization, neither really explained by the Gestalt theory, are readily incorporated in the Helmholtzean explanation of object perception. Consider a viewer who directs his gaze near the edge of some object that stands before a more distant background. Even a slight head rotation will produce a shift in view, or motion parallax, that is likely to occlude points on the background that lie near the edge of the object at which the viewer gazes. The oculomotor behavior needed to change fixation from one point to another on the near object's surface is therefore simpler and more straightforward than that needed to change fixation from a point on the near object to some point on the other side of the edge, i.e., to some point on the background. In making the latter change, ocular accommodations and convergence must change, and the target point is moving relative to the starting point and may even be occluded completely by motion parallax. It is plausible that the perceptual system learns to make assumptions about which side of any contour is a near surface and which a background; the "laws of organization" would thus be cues to what will lie on the same surface and will therefore move together in motion parallax, as contrasted with what lies on different surfaces and moves independently. This argument is developed in Hochberg (113, 115); precursors can be found in Brunswik and Kamiya (31, 32) and Woodworth (208).

Like the illusions, therefore, the figure-ground phenomenon and the laws of organization may be explained as being the result of well-learned perceptual assumptions about objects in space, assumptions that are here misapplied to the perception of lines on paper. Gestalt transposition then is merely another name for object constancy, which we have seen was classically explained as an act of unconscious inference. The Gestalt formulation (that our physiological response to the invariant form is itself invariant regardless of the specific receptors stimulated), which has been retained in more modern versions simply by dropping the physiological references and speaking in terms of the perception of invariants under transformation (36,

62, 63), has been influential in disciplines outside of the study of perception, but the formulation is unjustified in at least two ways:

1. When features of a stimulus pattern (e.g., corners, curves) fall on different receptors, the output of those receptors may be recoded more centrally into receptive fields that respond to the same features, regardless of where they fall within a fairly wide retinal region [Hubel and Wiesel (124, 125)]. This kind of explanation does not imply any holistic response to configuration, and we do not know to what extent such a piecemeal process might account for the actual facts of shape constancy or Gestalt transposition.

2. The invariance of perceptual response to transposed objects is greatly overemphasized, and the generality and degree of object constancy are both often exaggerated in the course of setting up theories of perception based on them [Hochberg (113, 116), Rock (170), Wallach and Austin (198)].

On the other hand Helmholtz's explanations of object perception must now be evaluated on indirect evidence, because they assume that the raw sensations are generally unobservable. Furthermore although those explanations are necessary to save the classic analytic units, the explanations may themselves be valid and the classic units invalid, so that these two questions must be considered separately.

INDIRECT ASSESSMENT OF THEORIES OF SPACE AND OBJECT PERCEPTION

The classic account kept its set of analytic elements small in number by attributing most of the perceived properties of space and objects to the effects of perceptual learning from a structured environment. Three main lines of research have been addressed to this issue.

According to Helmholtz, we perceive those distal events that would most probably have produced our (unnoticeable) sensations, under normal viewing conditions. The basis for that perceptual rule is this: The most likely object will be the one most often encountered in connection with the given pattern of stimulation. Taken together with the ancient idea that the strength of associative learning is some positive function of frequency of association, this reasoning suggested to Brunswik (31) that the strength of a perceptual association must mirror the frequency with which any proximal stimulus pattern is associated with a distal event in the normal environment. For example, in accordance with linear perspective (one of the traditional depth cues; cf. DEPTH AND DISTANCE, p. 83) parallel lines that extend away from the viewer produce lines that converge in the retinal image. By Brunswik's theory, the probability that a viewer will perceive the base of a pair of edges or lines that converge in his retinal image to be nearer to him than the apex of those lines will be proportional to the frequency with which that pattern is in fact produced by parallel lines that extend away from the viewer rather than by lines that are truly converging in the environment. If Brunswik's minor amendment of Helmholtz is correct, and if we know the probability that a cue is associated with some event (i.e., its ecological validity) in the normal ecologically representative environment, we should be able to predict with some known probability of error the normal subject's perceptual response to that cue even if we know nothing at all about his sensations, conscious or otherwise.

Brunswik's program was, of course, to measure in ecologically representative circumstances the ecological validities of various cues. There are problems in setting the criteria for ecological representativeness; even more serious problems are connected with the choice of cues to be measured. The proximal stimulus patterns that fall upon our eyes are correlated in very many ways with the distal state of affairs; i.e., there are many more potential cues, or "informative variables of stimulation" (Gibson, ref. 60) than have yet been studied. What should we choose to measure, and in what combinations?

In an approach that is closely related to Brunswik's, Gibson (61–63) has concentrated on a theoretical search for those features of proximal stimulation that, essentially, are perfectly correlated with the distal properties of objects and events in the world. Amidst the transformations of the proximal stimulation that are received by a moving observer in a changing world, certain relationships remain constant and invariant under the transformations [see Cassirer (36), Gibson (62, 63), and Koffka (137).] Let us consider an early and relatively simple example of Gibson's (60): Given a normally textured ground plane that is extending away from the viewer, the proximal pattern of stimulation, or optic array, will contain a gradient of texture density, as a form of size perspective, that is correlated with the slant of the surface in the field of view. Where an object stands on the ground plane in the distal environment determines where its projection in the optic array intersects the texture density gradient in that array. The point at which the object intersects the texture density gradient is correlated with the object's distance; how much of the texture (i.e., how many textural units) it subtends at that intersection is correlated with the object's size. If the viewer can respond directly to each of these two stimulus variables, the perception of the object's distal size is as direct and immediate as the perception of its distance and is not the result of taking perceived distance into account in a Helmholtzean inference (see *Unconscious Inferences and General Nonnoticeability of Sensations,* p. 84). Gibson's approach is sometimes called, therefore, the direct theory of perception.

The principle applies as well to the stimulation that is obtained by an active, moving observer. As was discussed earlier (*Unconscious Inferences . . .,* p. 84),

Helmholtz had emphasized that as we actively explore the objects in our world by obtaining different views of them, we perceive what Cassirer later called the invariant object undergoing the transformation, and not the constantly changing stimulus pattern. Gibson proposes that we respond directly to the invariant undergoing the transformation, either through sensory prewiring that is sensitive to the characteristic variables of motion parallax provided to a moving observer by surfaces in space, or through a process that consists of learning to attend to those informative variables (57). We can assume that motion parallax would provide the moving observer with ecologically valid information about, for example, the object's sizes, distances, velocities relative to the viewer, in all normal environments [cf. Hay (90), Lee (141), Purdy (164)]. If we could also assume that the viewer is normally sensitive to that stimulus information, Brunswikian ecological surveys and cue measurements would be unnecessary. Ecological optics is the name given to the study of such potentially informative aspects of proximal stimulation that are provided by the normal environment.

It is by now clear that in the nervous system higher order units of sensitivity can indeed be found; these units include the opponent-process units and the lateral inhibitory processes discussed in *Alternative Units of Analysis,* p. 85, others are discussed later in this chapter. The more our sensory systems are directly tuned to variables of stimulation that are correlated with distal object properties, the less remains to be explained in terms of unconscious inference from mental structure. Although Gibson's approach can be reached from "Helmholtz's rule" (see ILLUSIONS, p. 84) that we perceive that object or event that normally would be most likely to a given set of sensory excitations, and although Gibson is similar to Helmholtz in his emphasis on the importance of movement-produced stimulation to the perception of the constant object that underlies the transformations in proximal stimulation resulting from the viewer's movements, Gibson's goal is a very different kind of perceptual theory. For Gibson, local sensations (conscious or otherwise), mental structure, and perceptual inference (unconscious or otherwise) are all superfluous. No serious attempt has yet been made, however, to find sensory mechanisms that respond directly to the Gibsonian variables of stimulation, nor has systematic research been addressed to the question of whether the presumably ubiquitous information in the proximal stimulus can in fact be picked up and used. Moreover, it is also true that there is a fair amount of evidence for the existence of inferencelike processes and mental structure at work in at least some important perceptual phenomena and in several more esoteric ones, as is discussed in the last section of this chapter, so some aspects of Helmholtz's theory will have to be retained regardless of the eventual success of Gibson's program.

Helmholtz's proposals about specific nerve energies

were far too simple, and some of the aspects of perception that were thought to be learned may in fact be innate consequences of sensory structure. These observations do not by themselves invalidate the classic theory in general; that can only be done by research addressed directly to the study of perceptual development and perhaps to the study of perceptual relearning.

DIRECT AND INDIRECT RESEARCH ON NATURE AND NURTURE IN PERCEPTION

Unlearned Responses to Visual and Auditory Information About Space

Centuries after philosophers concluded that a man or animal who had no opportunity to associate visual cues with spatial motor behaviors would be unable to respond appropriately to those visual cues to spatial distance and location (see *Classic System and Its Background*, p. 76), we have clear demonstrations to the contrary [Gibson and Walk (58, 194), Thorndike (189)]. Animals that have been raised in darkness, with no occasion to associate tactual kinesthetic experience with visual depth cues, adjust the force of a jump to the distance to be spanned, guided only by sight (189), and avoid stepping on the "deep" side of a "visual cliff," which consists of a horizontal plate of heavy glass suspended some distance above a patterned surface on one side of a division with an identically patterned surface up against the glass on the other side of the division (58). Similarly, with respect to auditory cues to spatial direction, a newborn human infant, stimulated aurally by finger-snapping to one side or the other after a drugless delivery, turned reliably toward the direction from which the stimulus was sounded [Wertheimer (203)]. At least some minimum amount of sensory response, specific to visual spatial distance and auditory direction, is innately possessed and must be accounted for. A recent review of visually guided spatial behaviors after initial sensory deprivation is given in Rosinski (171) and in Day and McKenzie (43).

There is now a considerable body of positive findings in support of innate responses to visual space. Negative findings in such research, moreover, are difficult to interpret, because there is clear evidence that sensory mechanisms deteriorate with the deprivation that is often integral to experiments in this area [Chow et al. (37); Wiesel and Hubel (205)], and in any case perceptual learning might be necessary to the use of any spatial sensory abilities, even though the latter be innate in themselves.

Sensorimotor Recorrelation and Perceptual Relearning

Another approach to testing the empiricist theory of space and object perception rests on the assumption, made explicitly by Helmholtz (102) and by Held and his colleagues (96, 97), and implicitly by many others, that any perceptual response or ability that is subject to change by relearning must itself be learned and is not innate. In one sense (as it is used by Held), of course, this assumption must be true: whatever is relearned readily must surely have been subject to that relearning during the history of the individual, regardless of whether there was some initial ability to be displayed before any relearning occurred. But with respect to the question of whether any particular set of abilities originally required learning, as all do according to the classic theory, research on relearning must in fact be silent, because Helmholtz's assumption on this point was almost certainly wrong. Visuomotor correlations may be both innate and relearnable. For example, dark-reared chicks, wearing laterally displacing prisms during their first visual experiences, peck appropriately to the side of grain placed before them (107), showing that their perception of visual direction is innate. (Sperry, ref. 182, and von Holst, ref. 120, had shown closely related phenomena with lizards and insects, respectively.) Rossi (172) found that after much practice with such rearranged visuomotor conditions the chicks do learn to peck correctly while wearing the prisms and show the characteristic aftereffect (pecking too far in the opposite direction once the prisms are removed), showing clearly that a sensorimotor correlation, which is known to be innate, can be overcome by learning.

Let us consider separately the results of recorrelation or relearning for shape perception and for depth perception. A great deal of research has been done that is often taken as testing the theory that shape perception rests on the explicit [Wundt (209)] or potential [Festinger and colleagues (51, 52); Lotze (144)] eye movements that must be made to fixate (or hand movements made to touch) each point on the contour. Using prisms, mirrors, and computer-generated visual displays that are contingent on where the viewer is looking, the correlations between where the viewer is looking or pointing and what he sees can be changed, and the effects of practice on various tasks performed under these changed conditions, or after the normal correlations are restored, can be measured. [For partial reviews of the vast amount of such research that has been done, see Harris (84), Hochberg (113), Kaufman (133), and Rock (169).] These experiments cannot tell us, however, whether the changes that occur are *1)* alterations in perceived visual direction and shape [see Festinger et al (51), Kohler (138), Taylor (186)], *2)* changes in the viewer's perception of the position of his eye [Helmholtz (102)] or of the arm with which he points [Harris (84), Hochberg (110), Walls (200)], or *3)* only sensorimotor recorrelations [Held and Bossom (96, 97)] with no changes in either perceived visual or kinesthetic space. Research in which the gross relationships between looking and touching (or moving) are rearranged is almost always unable to tell us which modality, if either, was changed through experience with the changed relationship. Adaptation to prism-induced distortions within the visual field, such as adaptation to the prism-induced curvature of objectively straight lines and movements, would be more convincing evidence of the plasticity of visual space [Hochberg (110)]. To date only one experiment, that of Held and Rekosh (98), has demonstrated such effects under suitably controlled conditions: while wearing the prism, the subject walked around in an environment that contained only randomly spaced disks and no straight lines, so as to avoid the occurrence of a form of purely intravisual adaptation to curvature that is known from the work of Gibson and Radner (59, 64) not to require eye or body movements. A recent finding by Miller and Festinger (154) appears to show directly that eye movement plans or habits do not determine perceived shape: perceived shapes may remain unaffected when subjects relearn the eye movement that will bring some point from peripheral to foveal vision. The experimental procedure was as follows: In order to look from one point to another on a horizontal, curved line (concave upward) while viewing computer-generated displays that are made to vary with the direction of the eye's gaze, it was necessary for the viewer to execute a purely horizontal (straight) eye movement; even after the viewer learned to make straight movements in looking along a curved line, the line's curvature appeared to him unchanged.

The theory that depth and distance perception depend on our having learned how the various visual depth cues (e.g., linear perspective) correlate with the oculomotor behaviors and touching behaviors that are appropriate to different distances is also not supported by the evidence from recorrelation experiments. Wallach and his colleagues (see ref. 197) have demonstrated that the depth that is perceived with oculomotor cues (e.g., the cues of accommodation and convergence) may be altered by pairing those cues with purely visual ones that are so arranged as to indicate a different distance from that indicated by the oculomotor cues (for example, the familiar size of known objects, which is surely itself a learned cue to distance). The relearning that was obtained in these experiments therefore does not support the theory that visual depth is learned by the correlation of depthless visual sensations with the kinesthetic sensations occasioned by oculomotor behavior.

It is difficult to summarize the very large body of research that must be considered relevant to the Helmholtz explanation of space and object perception and to its competitors. Some forms of perceptual relearning do occur, particularly those involving correlation between the sensory modalities, and between sensory information and guided spatial behaviors. Neither those kinds of learning nor the studies on early spatial performance in visually deprived animals invite much confidence in relevant aspects of the classic theory or in its set of nonspatial specific nerve energies.

We have at least as much reason as otherwise to believe that perceived space and movement are originally visual in nature, and that we have specific nerve energies to mediate these properties.

CONTINUING SEARCH FOR UNITS
OF PERCEPTUAL ANALYSIS

To the perception psychologist it seems reasonable to worry first about whether some proposed process of sensory analysis makes perceptual sense before being concerned with whether that process is embodied physiologically in the particular form in which it was envisioned. The receptors of the Young-Helmholtz theory, the opponent-process units, the lateral inhibition that accentuates response to luminance-difference contours, the binocular comparator cells that may be responsive to stereoscopic disparity—these were all proposed because they made perceptual sense, long before they were found in physiological reality.

Indeed, even if our nervous systems lack a particular structure at birth, Hebb (92, 93) pointed out that the required structures could readily be acquired through learning, or through rewiring of the central nervous system. In 1949 Hebb had proposed a perceptual theory with at least two distinctly separate classes of unitary processes, cell assemblies and phase sequences. A cell assembly is a hypothetical network of cells in the brain that begins to respond as a single unit to a pattern of sensory (or more central) stimulation (e.g., an auditory phoneme or a visual corner) that has been very frequently occasioned by the organism's experience with its environment. Cell assemblies thus are plausible but entirely speculative mechanisms in the associative cortex of the brain, which as proposed would respond in a unitary and direct (i.e., noninferential) fashion to those aspects of stimulation that always occur together in a given context.

A phase sequence is a succession of responding cell assemblies that has occurred so frequently in the life of the organism that the activation of one part of the sequence results in intracortical stimulation of the next, and that makes the latter more likely to be fired by its appropriate pattern of sensory stimulation. A stimulus pattern, alone, will generally be insufficient to fire its corresponding cell assembly, unless the latter has also been primed by stimulation from previously fired cell assemblies that have become associated with it in a phase sequence. For example, the phase sequence of a familiar shape like a triangle provides expectancies of the sensory stimulus pattern that each eye movement will provide, facilitating the appropriate cell assembly's response to that pattern and comprising the hypothetical physiological correlate of the perception of that shape.

From the physiological side of the question, the nervous system offers possibilities enough to allow us to consider higher order analytic units of almost any desired complexity. In what follows, therefore, we are not as concerned with physiological verification as with the possible contribution of any proposed set of analytic units to our understanding of perceptual process.

Direct Stimulus Bases for Contrast and Constancy

The central problems of perceptual research arose, as we have seen, because the proposed units of sensory analysis and their corresponding fundamental sensations are inadequate to account directly for the appearances of objects. Additional indirect psychological processes, like unconscious inference, were therefore introduced to bridge the gap between what could be accounted for and what in fact we normally experience. An object's reflectance or lightness, for example, is a relatively permanent quality, but the luminance of the proximal stimulus that it presents to the eye changes with each change in illumination. According to the Helmholtz theory we perceive the coal in the sunlight as darker than the white paper in the shade, even when the former reflects more photic energy to the eye, because the brightness of the sensation produced by that stimulus is not itself noticed but is instead taken, together with our perceptions of illumination falling on the object, to infer the object's reflectance. That is, we perform an unconscious inference, calculating the perceived reflectance, R', from the relationship $R' = L/I'$ where I' is perceived illumination and L is the sensed brightness, which is presumably a direct sensory function of photic intensity.

This kind of explanation—involving unnoticed fundamental sensations, learned structures (e.g., the relationship between R, L, and I), and unconscious inferences—was offered quite generally for the perception of object properties (size, shape, distance), as noted repeatedly in this chapter. What kinds of neural mechanisms, if any, could provide for more direct response to distal object properties, making it unnecessary to invoke these complex and largely speculative psychological phenomena?

Invariances in stimulation that are correlated with invariant object properties and that do not change with each change in viewing conditions are, as Gibson argued (see p. 89), prime candidates for which we should seek to find direct sensory mechanisms and direct perceptual responses. The situation would seem particularly simple in the case of perception of degree of lightness. An object normally reflects some constant proportion of the light that falls upon it. The piece of coal and the white paper on which it rests may each reflect changing luminance to the eye when a cloud shades both of them from the sun, but the ratio of the light that the two reflect remains constant. It has long been realized, therefore, that under normal conditions the viewer's response would vary with the object's reflectance as a permanent quality of the object, regardless of the absolute levels of illumination, if his sensory system were to respond directly to the ratio of the luminances provided to the eye by an object and its background. Lightness constancy (and lightness contrast, too) would both be direct responses to stimulation, obviating Helmholtzean appeals to unconscious inferences and unnoticed sensations alike. This fact was recognized both by Helmholtz (100) and by Hering (105). If we were to look only at the physics of the relationship between distal and proximal stimulation, we would without further ado take this ratio as the direct stimulus for apparent object lightness. It does not appear difficult to imagine or even to find physiological mechanisms that would account for response to the ratios of luminances. Hering had proposed that lateral inhibition would produce such effects (see *Alternative Units of Analysis*, p. 85), and in fact Hood and his colleagues have found action potentials from single optic nerve fibers in the frog that are approximately linearly related to the reflectance of a (moving) target (33). Neither physics nor physiology makes it implausible that we respond directly to objects' reflectances by responding to the ratio of luminances, instead of by drawing unconscious conclusions from unnoticed sensations. The results of psychological study of the matter are in some ways equally encouraging for this view. Thus for a disk and its surround of different luminances, the apparent lightness of the disk remains constant, even though its luminance changes, as long as the ratio of the two luminances is invariant within a certain range of ratios [see Heinemann (94), Hess and Pretori (106), Jameson and Hurvich (129, 130), and Wallach (196)].

Outside of a restricted range of ratios, however, the target's apparent lightness does not remain constant with changing luminance, even though its ratio to surround luminance is kept constant (106, 130), so the picture is not quite as simple as it could be. Theoretically more serious, however, is the fact that by changing the depth cues that indicate whether the target lies flat on a surface and therefore receives the same illumination as that surface, or is inclined in another plane and therefore receives different illumination, the apparent lightness of the target is changed even though the ratios of luminance (and in fact the absolute luminances as well) have remained unaltered. That is, something at least roughly like "taking illumination into account" (see CONSTANCIES, p. 83) has been found with what are essentially constant luminances. Although this set of phenomena, initially noted by Mach (146) and by Helmholtz (100–102), has been confirmed in some cases (9, 10, 49, 65, 72, 117) and not in others (48, 53), it reminds us that even if a direct sensory basis for perceived object reflectance could be firmly established, mental structure and the Helmholtz inferences might still participate in the perceptual process as parallel or supplemental mechanisms.

*Recent Research on Complex
Sensory Analyzers*

The search for visual sensory units that respond directly to the more spatial properties of objects—e.g., to aspects of their two-dimensional shapes and their three-dimensional forms or volumes—has proceeded along several lines, as it clearly must. A great deal of work is currently in progress on several of these fronts, and occasional claims are made to the effect that a particular proposed unit "removes the need for a little man in the head" (which is, in one sense, what Helmholtz's "unconscious inference" amounts to, until that day in which it is specified in less mentalistic terms) by accounting for one perceptual phenomenon or another. In general, however, the search for new sensory units is inspired more by the fact that microelectrode research has shown that complex units do exist (see the chapter by De Valois and Jacobs in this *Handbook*) and that certain perceptual anomalies seem to suggest the existence of new underlying units, than by any clear or systematic view on how a theory of the perception of objects would profit from the findings. The perceptual functions to be served by such units, if they exist, have not in general been spelled out, so it is not yet clear to what extent the success of these ventures would really make the more mentalistic aspects of the classic theory unnecessary. And in any case, as we see in the final pages of this chapter, there are phenomena of form and shape perception that simply cannot be reduced to the response of complex sensory mechanisms or attributed to present stimulation. Some provision must therefore be made for mental structure in the perception of form, shape, and space, no matter how successful the search for mechanisms of direct sensory response to certain aspects of these perceptual properties turns out to be.

SENSORY FATIGUE. The method that has been most used in the behavioral search for units of shape and form perception is based on what appears to be a general phenomenon of sensory fatigue. Subsequent to prolonged stimulation by light of one predominant hue, one sees the complementary hue under many (but not all) conditions and in the absence of any photic stimulation to account for it; furthermore, thresholds for the detection of the original light are raised. Similar negative aftereffects are obtained with other simple sensory qualities, and such effects in general have usually been explained as being due to fatigue or depletion of the sense organs being stimulated. Negative aftereffects of more complex properties can also be obtained; e.g., after prolonged inspection of a line that is concave to the right, a straight line appears concave to the left (Gibson, ref. 59). These aftereffects are often offered as evidence that the response to those properties is as direct and sensory as those to hue or temperature (59, 64, 207). Such aftereffects have been obtained for a very wide variety of single properties, such as slant and curvature [Gib-

son and Radner (59, 64); Köhler and Wallach (140)], direction of movement [Wohlgemuth (207); Sekuler and Ganz (178)], and patterns of a given element size or spatial frequency [Blakemore and his colleagues (16, 18); Pantle and Sekuler (161)]. Spatial frequency refers to the number of elements per degree of visual angle; the phenomenon referred to here is that repetitive patterns, like gratings, look smaller or more densely packed after inspection of a less dense (lower spatial frequency) matrix, and vice versa.

Negative aftereffects have also been found with many pairings of stimulus properties. Thus, McCullough (151) found that after an alternating inspection of a set of stripes of one orientation and hue (e.g., vertical orange on black) and of another set at complementary orientation and hue (e.g., horizontal blue-green on black), the hue aftereffect is contingent on the slant of the test stripes that are viewed; in this example, white on black test stripes look blue-green if they are vertical and look orange if they are horizontal. Similarly, hue aftereffects have been found to be contingent on curvature [Riggs, (166)], and movement [Stromeyer and Mansfield (184)]. Contingent aftereffects of slant and of movement have been found that occur only when the pattern with which adaptation has occurred and that on which the aftereffect is tested are of the same color [see Held and Shattuck (99) for the former and Favreau et al. (50) and Mayhew and Anstis (150) for the latter]. Color aftereffects are contingent on spatial frequency [Teft and Clark (187); Harris (85)], and spatial frequency aftereffects are specific to orientation (Blakemore et al. (17)). Negative aftereffects are found in other modalities as well, and these may also be contingent on the pairing of properties: for example, the perceived size of an object as judged by active touch is contingent on the object's location (to the left or right of the subject) even though the same hand is used for both locations [Walker and Shear (195)].

Explanations and models relating these perceptual phenomena to known and speculative physiological structures abound [cf. Anstis (3), Coltheart (40), Over (160), and Sekuler (177)]. McCullough originally explained her findings in terms of color-sensitive, orientation-specific edge detectors, and they are probably not attributable to simple afterimages [Harris and Gibson (86)]. With such a bewildering variety of phenomena, however, it is not clear how the effects are to be interpreted and whether some or all of them are in fact due to associative learning (85, 138, 157) or to the kind of recalibration or relearning process discussed in connection with prism adaptation.

INTERACTION. A second and closely related set of procedures that has been used to search for new analytic units of perception employs interaction (interference, masking, etc.) between simultaneous or successive stimuli to identify different sensory channels. That is, if one pattern raises the threshold needed to detect another, or lowers its apparent contrast, responses to the two patterns are, it is argued, sharing or competing for a single channel or mechanism. For example, Weisstein and Bisaha (201) have reported that a grating masks a previously presented bar if both have the same fundamental spatial frequency; using a more naturalistic stimulus (a portrait of Lincoln), Harmon and Julesz (83) showed that recognition of the face is impaired more by the addition of spatial frequencies close to those of the features than by the addition of more remote frequencies. Alternatively, when two components of a pattern excite the same channel, the presence of the pattern should be more detectable than either component taken alone (i.e., summation should occur), whereas if they contribute to different channels, the compound pattern should be little if at all more detectable than the most detectable component in the compound. In fact, the contrast thresholds needed to detect whether patterns composed of three superimposed sinusoidal gratings of very different frequencies are present are only slightly lower than the thresholds for the most detectable of the gratings [Graham and Nachmias (76) and Sachs et al. (175)].

The aftereffect paradigm and the various versions of the interaction paradigm have been used to argue for the existence of sensory channels that are specifically sensitive to particular spatial frequencies. For reviews of this proposed unit and for discussions of the compatibility of the diverse assumptions made by its proponents, see Graham (75). It has been suggested that one function these units serve is to provide the visual system with means for performing Fourier analyses on the visual stimulus pattern [Campbell and Robson (34), Enroth-Cugell and Robson (47), and Kabrisky et al. (132)]. The analogy here of course is to Helmholtz's theory of hearing that was discussed briefly in *Audition: Helmholtz Theory*, p. 82. The idea that the visual system encodes and decodes space and spatial patterns in terms of Fourier transforms has been proposed on other grounds as well (3, 16, 68, 132), but it is unlikely that the evidence for spatial frequency channels supports that proposal. Best present estimates of the number of channels and their bandwidths [see Graham and Rogowitz (78) and Harvey and Gervais (89)] are too low and too high, respectively, for anything approaching a true Fourier analysis of the aperiodic, detailed shapes and volumes that we can perceive. Although a few broadband spatial frequency channels might indeed account for the entire gamut of apparent frequencies of the periodic patterns or textures that we can perceive (just as the Young-Helmholtz theory accounted for all wavelength discriminations and color sensations in terms of three broadband receptors), a much larger set of component frequencies would be needed for specifying sharp-edged nonrepeating shapes.

The fact that frequency-sensitive phenomena have been demonstrated does not, of course, necessarily imply that the perceptual system uses frequency sensitivity at all. Whatever can be explained in terms of a frequency channel can also be phrased in terms of a set of receptive fields of a given size [cf. Graham (75) and Thomas (188)], which changes the connotations considerably. That is, the phenomena we have bee.• considering may be adventitious consequences of the distribution of receptive fields and may not be directly in the service of the perception of objects and events. Indeed it is not clear what the existence of frequency channels would imply for a theory of perception of objects and events. The frequency channel model cannot be based on the assumption that the activity of each channel is accompanied by a sensation of the appropriate grating, as Sekuler (177) and Graham (75) point out, so that the significance of these proposed elements depends entirely on some statement and test of their perceptual functions. Attempts are currently being made to spell out systematically the parts that channels having different spatial and temporal responses might play in the perception of movement and patterns [Breitmeyer and Ganz (26) and Sekuler et al. (179)], but these attempts are still tentative and fragmentary.

FRAGMENTATION. The fragmentation method was suggested by the piecemeal fading of the image in the eye when the retinal image is stabilized [see Riggs et al. (168)]. The fragmentation appears to be orderly or lawful, and it has been hoped that the fragments represent units of processing at some level, probably at the level of cell assemblies in Hebb's theoretical system [see CONTINUING SEARCH FOR UNITS OF PERCEPTUAL ANALYSIS, p. 91; Donderi and Kane (46) and Pritchard et al. (163)]. One difficulty with this method is that the fragments may merely reflect conceptual or verbal units that the subject finds easiest to describe, rather than units of visual processing [Schuck and Leahy (176); cf. also Galnzer and Clark (70) for an approach to the analysis of perception based explicitly on this difficulty, and Haber and Hershenson (82) and Hochberg (113) for reviews of this method]. A second and related drawback, contributing to the first, is that the fragmentation is provided by the viewer's perceptual system and is not under the control of the experimenter. In any case, moreover, there is no way in which we can decide whether these fragments serve as perceptual elements in any sense until combining rules of some sort have been formulated and procedures devised to test those rules; neither has yet been done.

SEQUENTIAL PRESENTATION. Instead of attempting to observe the fragmentation of a stabilized retinal image in order to find the joints along which patterns or scenes come apart, we can present shapes and objects piecemeal in sequence, to determine the consequence of fragmenting the objects in different ways and of varying the rate and sequence in which those fragments are presented to the viewer [Hochberg (111, 112), Lichtenstein (143), MacFarland (145)]. For example, when a line drawing of an object is presented as a sequence of slices in which the intersections and corners either appear intact within each slice or are divided between two successive slices, the two-dimensional shape of the stimulus is recognizable as a pattern in both cases, but only the former sequence appears tridimensional (111). Such observations and others (67) support the proposal that the intersections act as unit depth cues that cannot be subdivided without destroying their efficacy and in this sense are unitary stimuli for unitary responses, whereas the overall form of the object is not a unitary response to a unitary configuration. It appears possible in this sense to analyze perceived objects into smaller units.

Generalizations that can be based on such research are limited by the choice of patterns analyzed and therefore depend on the theory that guides such choice. Some thought has been given to compiling elementary intersections for static scene analysis and recognition by computers [Clowes (38) and Guzman (81)], which when specified will determine the arrangement of solid objects in space; a very few studies have been done to determine what kinds of tridimensional intersections will, when rotated in space, look compellingly solid [e.g., Wallach and his colleagues (199)]. Aside from these considerations, no theoretical basis for the search for elements of shapes and objects has, to my knowledge, been formulated.

Both the method of fragmentation and the method of piecemeal sequential presentation are inspired by (but not rigorously derivable from) Hebb's picture of perceptual process (see CONTINUING SEARCH FOR UNITS OF PERCEPTUAL ANALYSIS, p. 91). The latter method, however, has deeper roots and implications: in the method of sequential presentation the entire pattern never falls on the retina at one time. In this respect it resembles the nature of a set of glances in which detailed, foveal vision (see *Vision: Classic Analysis*, p. 80) is directed at different parts of an object or scene. In both cases, when responding to the shape of any object the viewer must draw on the information he has stored from more than one view. This is particularly evident when all of the successive views of the object are presented on the same place in space—i.e., as would occur when successive glimpses of an object are obtained as it moves around behind a small stationary window. Imagine that the corners of a cross are visible in such an aperture, one corner at a time (Fig. 1). For the viewer to recognize that it is a cross and to know which arm he is being shown at any moment, he must place each successive glimpse in the context of a mental structure—a form of visual knowledge that provides the spatial meaning to the temporal sequence. Without such structure one can see only a sequence of corners that appear one after another at the same place; with structure to provide a context, each corner takes its proper place in the spatial relationships that constitute a cross, visualized but never seen. The question of mental structure is critical today in the study of perception: even if new analytic units

and invariances (see CONTINUING SEARCH FOR UNITS OF PERCEPTUAL ANALYSIS p. 91) should be found that can account directly for the perception of most (or even all) of the properties of objects and events in the world under some circumstances (i.e., when all of the information needed for the response is indeed present in stimulation), the heart of the classic theory of perception (i.e., perceptual inference from mental structure) may still be sound.

LIMITS OF DIRECT OR SENSORY ACCOUNTS OF PERCEPTION: MENTAL STRUCTURE AND PERCEPTUAL INFERENCE

With an adult viewer and a normal perceptual situation (in which the proximal stimulus array provides enough information to specify, for example, distal size, distance, illumination, reflectance, slant, shape) we cannot distinguish the alternative perceptual theories from each other. Only when the information present in the stimulus and at the sense organs is insufficient to provide even in theory for a direct response can we seek clear evidence of mental structure.

One kind of evidence for mental structure consists of *completion phenomena*, in which there simply is not enough information present in stimulation to account plausibly for the response obtained, regardless of what one postulates in terms of complex, higher order sensory mechanisms. In the case of piecemeal sequential presentations through a stationary aperture that was just discussed, neither the stimulus pattern presented at any moment, nor the aftereffects of each presentation, nor any efferent record of the direction of gaze (see *Oculomotor Kinesthesis*, p. 81) can explain the perception of the overall shape, because the only information that these can convey is that all of the fragments were presented at the same place in space. Nevertheless, given the opportunity to visualize simple or familiar objects presented in this manner, the adult viewer recognizes the objects and can detect omissions or errors in the sequence [Girgus (69), Hochberg (111, 112), Murphy (158)]. This task is a start at providing measures of the structure of sequential expectations that, to J. S. Mill (153), comprise the "permanent possibilities of sensation" (see *Unconscious Inferences* . . ., p. 84).

The second important kind of evidence for mental structure lies in the coupling of two or more perceptual properties, the phenomenon that Helmholtz most characteristically explained as unconscious inference (see *Unconscious Inferences* . . ., p. 84): e.g., that perceived size varies as a function of perceived distance and that perceived shape varies as a function of perceived slant. It has been argued (see INDIRECT ASSESSMENT OF THEORIES OF SPACE AND OBJECT PERCEPTION, p. 88) that such coupling between properties does not in fact comprise evidence of mental structure; that these properties are perceived or sensed directly, in unitary response to higher order informative vari-

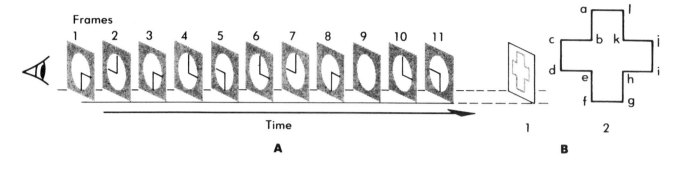

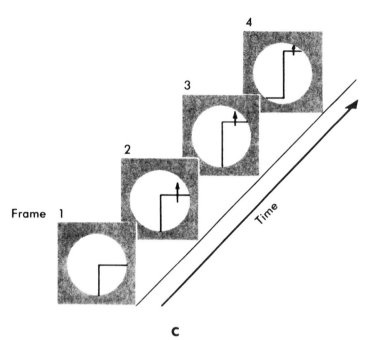

FIG. 1. Temporal completion phenomena and mental structure. A: sequence of right angles projected one after another on the same place on a screen. Sequence is much too long to remember as a set of independent events. B: if the viewer fits successive corners to his schema for a cross, given to him (for example) by a preliminary overall view as shown at *1* followed by a closeup of the corner a, the sequence becomes comprehensible as the succession labeled a, b, c, ... in 2, and the viewer recognizes that the sequence has taken a shortcut from h to k on the cross. C: adults do not require the preliminary overall view if there is sufficient overlap between the steps in the sequence, or if the views of the individual corners are connected by continuous motion (111, 158); children do not respond so well, and the younger they are the more poorly they respond. [From Hochberg (116).]

ables of stimulation; and that they are coupled in the viewer's responses not because one is taken into account in inferring the other but because they vary together in the proximal stimulation presented to the eye. Two kinds of coupling, however, cannot plausibly be explained as parallel responses to stimulus covariation: the coupling that is found in reversible perspective figures and in research on familiar sizes, and the coupling that overcomes contradictory stimulus information and therefore cannot be attributed to the latter.

Coupling Without Stimulus Basis

There is a great deal of evidence that changing the cues to one property can change the perception of other properties, approximately as one would expect from perceptual inference: e.g., with changing binocular cues to distance and slant, perceived size [Heinemann et al. (95)], angular velocity [Wist et al. (206)], and reflectance [Beck (9), Hochberg and Beck (117), Gogel and Mershon (72); and see *Direct Stimulus Bases for Contrast and Constancy*, p. 92] also

change. Because changing the cues necessarily means changing the stimulus conditions, however, the results of such experiments are not conclusive. In the next two classes of experiment, coupled perceptual responses are obtained even though no change in visual stimulation occurs.

Reversible perspective figures are drawings that can readily be perceived as two mutually exclusive spatial arrangements. The fact that two responses can be obtained in response to the same proximal stimulus pattern is not in itself evidence of mental structure, inasmuch as two competing responses can be directly tuned to a single stimulus variable with no intervening processes. What brings mental structure into the issue is that the changes in apparent perspective are also sometimes accompanied by changes in apparent size: e.g., when perspective is reversed in viewing a skeleton cube, the side that looks nearer usually appears smaller (as it should; cf. ILLUSIONS, p. 84); if the cube is made of wire and is physically rotating when the reversal occurs, it appears to change its direction of rotation. Such coupling between perceived properties in reversible perspective objects has been reported on many occasions [see Hochberg (114)], but not jointly measured in an adequate way, so that the reliability and degree of the coupling cannot be assessed.

Other and more experimental evidence to the same point comes from research on familiar size. In the absence of any other depth cues, the known size of an object will determine its apparent distance [Gogel (71), Ittelson and Kilpatrick (128), Wallach (197)]. This phenomenon can only be explained either in terms of perceptual inference from mental structure (i.e., taking the object's known size into account in solving the "size-distance equation") or in terms of an absolute distance response associated with each size of retinal image for each familiar object. These explanations, both perfectly compatible with the classic theory, have not been separately tested. In the final line of evidence that we consider next, only the inferential explanation can apply.

Static Cues vs. Kinetic Stimulus Information

Imagine a trapezoid, upright and facing the viewer (Fig. 2A): its large end, 2, is on the right, its small end, 1, is on the left, and both are equally far from the viewer. Viewed from a few yards, the object appears rectangular, with 2 nearer than 1. If the object is set into continuous rotation around a vertical axis and is viewed from a few feet, it is correctly perceived to be a rotating trapezoid (Fig. 2B). Viewed from a few yards, it appears to oscillate back and forth so that the large end, 2, always appears nearer, and the object appears to remain at least roughly rectangular in shape [Ittelson and Kilpatrick (128); Braunstein and Payne (25)].

In its original form, this demonstration works because of the viewer's perceptual assumption of rectangularity, or because of his assumption that convergence arises only from the static depth cue of linear perspective (see INDIRECT ASSESSMENT OF THEORIES OF SPACE AND OBJECT PERCEPTION, p. 88), which is much the same thing. Such other static depth cues as interposition (the interruption of a far shape by a nearer one) also generate the effect [Canestrari and Farnè (35)]. One aspect of this phenomenon that makes it theoretically important is that the rotating object, whose shape provides an invariant undergoing the transformations in the proximal stimulus array, is not necessarily correctly perceived. This fact makes it clear that the direct theory of perception (i.e., of response to the invariant undergoing transformation; see INDIRECT ASSESSMENT . . ., p. 88) must include explicit consideration of threshold limitations and their consequences; this has not yet been adequately done.

More important than that, however, is the point that this phenomenon necessarily implicates some form of mental structure: shape, distance (or slant), and movement are all coupled in the response to the rotating trapezoidal object, even though in this ex-

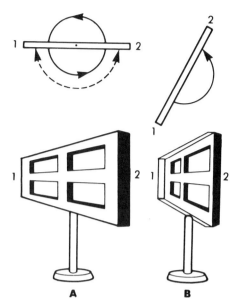

FIG. 2. The rotating trapezoid and perceptual coupling. *A*: the Ames window is a flat trapezoid (often painted to look like a window) that rotates as indicated by the *solid arrows* in the *top view*. When viewed monocularly from a distance of a few yards (2, 128), however, it appears to oscillate rather than rotate, as shown by the *dotted arrows*. A possible explanation for this robust phenomenon is as follows. *B*: even when edge 2 is farther away than edge 1 the static depth cues of linear perspective and relative size make edge 2 look nearer, and oscillatory movement is perceived because that accords with the depth cues and the apparent rectangularity of the trapezoid. Perceived shape and perceived distance (or perceived movement) thus seem to be coupled in a way that is not to be explained by the stimulus information itself, and is consistent with the Helmholtz idea of unconscious inference. [From Hochberg (116).]

ample the coupling cannot possibly be attributed to separate direct responses to covariant stimulus information. Instead the results fit nicely into the Helmholtz theory of the illusions; i.e., if we have taken the shape to be the object that would most normally produce a trapezoidal retinal image (a rectangle slanted to the line of sight), we perceive that motion best fitting that shape to the changing proximal stimulus pattern.

Regardless of how successful the various attempts to provide direct explanations of perceptual properties may eventually be, a body of evidence therefore remains that is more consistent with the core of the classic theory of perception than with any other. Because such evidence can by its nature be demonstrated only in special impoverished circumstances (i.e., those chosen so as to rule out direct response to proximal stimulus information), it cannot now be said whether mental structure contributes to perception under more natural conditions. Mental structure may merely be a trivial byproduct of normal perceptual processes, revealed when the viewer is given unsolvable perceptual problems, or it may be the essential core of the perceptual process, as it is in Helmholtz's theory of perception. Whichever it is, nothing general can be said about perception nor about how our sensory processes contribute to the perception of objects and events until the status and nature of mental structure are clarified.

SUMMARY

The systematic effort to explain our perceptions of the world in terms of real or hypothetical underlying physiological events started in earnest with Helmholtz's attempt to apply Müller's doctrine of specific nerve energies within each modality of experience, by identifying the specialized sensory receptors that provide for fundamental elements of sensory experience. In vision, these were thought to be sensations of red, green, and violet corresponding to the responses of each of the three cones of the Young-Helmholtz theory, plus the achromatic responses of the rods (see the chapter by De Valois and Jacobs in this *Handbook*). This set of sensations omits many other properties of the perceived world—distance, shape, spatial location.

In the classic theory (to which Helmholtz subscribed) and its contemporary variations, such properties are not sensed directly: they are structures of expected and remembered sensations. Such structures are acquired through experience with the structures of the physical world. For example, the far end of a rectangular table is smaller in the retinal image than is the near end, and by being associated with the muscular sensations characteristic of reaching to touch either end, the pattern of convergence in the retinal image becomes what we now call a depth cue, or linear perspective. The physical world is rich in such constraints on stimulation: e.g., the retinal size of an object's image usually varies with the distance indicated by the depth cues that provide its context; the luminance of an object's image usually varies with the cues to the illumination that falls on the object. Through experiences with such structured stimulation we learn to perceive just those objects and events that would most often be the cause of the particular set of sensations we receive.

In this bipartite theory, we must therefore distinguish the sensations from the mental structures that are based on them and that provide in turn the bases of our perceptions. The sensations themselves are not normally noticeable; the appearance of any combination of stimuli cannot be predicted from the appearances of the component stimuli when viewed separately; and the processes of inference, by which the perceptions of objects were thought to be fitted to the sensations, are themselves unconscious. That is, neither the elementary sensations nor the nature and origins of the mental structures on which perceptions are based can be tested by direct appeal to experience.

Indirect research methods are needed therefore to assess and advance this theory, and the bulk of experimental perceptual research has been directed to issues that center around this task. Three groups of phenomena have been particularly important theoretically: *1)* the constancy phenomena, in which objects' unchanging physical properties, such as surface reflection or physical size, are perceived as remaining constant even when the stimulation of the receptors (e.g., by retinal image luminance and retinal image size, respectively) varies greatly as viewpoint and situation change; *2)* the illusions, in which the appearance of physical properties, such as lightnesses or lengths, are very different from both the distal properties and the proximal stimulus measures; and *3)* the phenomena of organization (usually considered in terms of Gestalt theory), in which the appearance of any part is shown to be determined by the configuration of the overall pattern. Each of these topics has been offered as a challenge to the classic theory, and each is at least as well explained by that theory as by any of the competitors.

Since the work of Mach and Hering, sensory mechanisms, other than those implicit in the classic theory, have been proposed that would contribute more directly to perceptual experience, and that would account better for the appearance of objects. These generally are proposals that some aspect of the world we perceive is a direct response to some relatively complex variable of proximal stimulation that varies with some important property of the distal object. For example, if a sensory response is proportional to the ratio of luminances between adjacent regions of the visual field, such as those of an object and its immediate surroundings, that response will also normally be proportional to the object's constant surface reflectance, and it will not be affected by any changes in the overall illumination of the scene that fall equally on the object and its surroundings. In this way the phenomenon of lightness constancy would be explained without recourse to notions about mental structure and unconscious inference. Many such informative variables of stimulation have been noted that are in correspondence with invariant object properties; several sensory mechanisms that could respond directly to such stimulus variables have been proposed; and some physiological structures have actually been found that might serve as mechanisms of perceptual sensitivity in this sense. Although it is now clear that the Helmholtz specific nerve energies were too simple to be taken as units of sensory experience, the part that the more complex mechanisms actually take in object perception is still not known. Moreover, there are several phenomena in which something very much like mental structure is manifested, so some aspects of Helmholtz's bipartite theory of perception remain viable today.

REFERENCES

1. ALPERN, M. Effector mechanisms in vision. In: *Woodworth and Schlosberg's Experimental Psychology* (3rd ed), edited by J. W. Kling and L. A. Riggs. New York: Holt, 1971, p. 369–394.

2. AMES, A. Visual perception and the rotating trapezoidal window. *Psychol. Monogr.* 65: 324, 1951.

3. ANSTIS, S. M. What does perception tell us about visual coding? In: *Handbook of Psychobiology*, edited by M. S. Gazzaniga and C. Blakemore. New York: Academic, 1975.

4. ARISTOTLE. *De memoria et reminiscentia* (transl. by J. I. Beare). In: *The Works of Aristotle*, edited by W. D. Ross. Oxford: Clarendon Press, 1931, vol. 3, chapt. 2. Reprinted in: *A Source Book in the History of Psychology*, edited by R. J. Herrnstein and E. G. Boring. Cambridge, MA: Harvard Univ. Press, 1965.

5. ATTNEAVE, F. Some informational aspects of visual perception. *Psychol. Rev.* 61: 183–193, 1954.

6. ATTNEAVE, F. Symmetry, information and memory for patterns. *Am. J. Psychol.* 68: 209–222, 1955.

7. ATTNEAVE, F. *Applications of Information Theory to Psychology.* New York: Holt, 1959.

8. BARLOW, H., C. BLAKEMORE, AND J. PETTIGREW. The neural mechanism of binocular depth discrimination. *J. Physiol. London* 193: 327–342, 1967.

9. BECK, J. Apparent spatial position and the perception of lightness. *J. Exp. Psychol.* 69: 170–179, 1965.

10. BECK, J. *Surface Color Perception.* Ithaca, NY: Cornell Univ. Press, 1972.

11. BÉKÉSY, G. VON. Neural inhibitory units of eye and skin: quantitative description of contrast phenomena. *J. Opt. Soc. Am.* 50: 1060–1070, 1960.

12. BÉKÉSY, G. VON. The variation of phase along the basilar membrane with sinusoidal variation. *J. Acoust. Soc. Am.* 19: 452–460, 1974.

13. BELL, C. *Idea of a New Anatomy of the Brain: Submitted for the Observation of His Friends.* London: 1811. Reprinted in: *A Source Book in the History of Psychology*, edited by R. J. Herrnstein and E. G. Boring. Cambridge, MA: Harvard Univ. Press, 1965.

14. BERKELEY, G. Essay toward a new theory of vision. [1709]. In: *The Works of George Berkeley Bishop of Cloyne*, edited by A. A. Luce and T. E. Jessop. Toronto: Nelson, 1948, p. 143–239.

15. BERLIN, B., AND P. KAY. *Basic Color Terms: Their Universality and Evolution.* Berkeley: Univ. of California Press, 1969.

16. BLAKEMORE, C., AND F. W. CAMPBELL. On the existence of neurons in the human visual system selectively sensitive to the orientation and size of retinal images. *J. Physiol. London* 203: 237–260, 1969.

17. BLAKEMORE, C., J. NACHMIAS, AND P. SUTTON. Perceived spatial frequency shift: evidence of frequency-selective neurons in the human brain. *J. Physiol. London* 210: 727–750, 1970.

18. BLAKEMORE, C., AND P. SUTTON. Size adaption: a new aftereffect. *Science* 166: 245–247, 1969.

19. BORNSTEIN, M. H. Color vision and color naming: a psychophysiological hypothesis of cultural difference. *Psychol. Bull.* 80: 257–285, 1973.

20. BOYNTON, R. M. Color vision. In: *Woodward and Schlosberg's Experimental Psychology*, edited by J. W. Kling and L. A. Riggs. New York: Holt, 1971, p. 315–368.

21. BOYNTON, R. M. The visual system: environmental information. In: *Handbook of Perception*, edited by E. C. Carterette and M. P. Friedman. New York: Academic, 1974, vol. 1.

22. BOYNTON, R. M. Color, hue and wavelength. In: *Handbook of Perception*, edited by E. C. Carterette and M. P. Friedman. New York: Academic, 1975, vol. 5.

23. BOYNTON, R. M., AND J. GORDON. Bezold-Brücke hue shift measured by color naming technique. *J. Opt. Soc. Am.* 55: 78–86, 1965.

24. BOYNTON, R. M., AND J. W. ONLEY. A critique of the special status assigned by Brindley to "Psychophysical Linking Hypotheses" of "Class A". *Vision Res.* 2: 383–390, 1962.

25. BRAUNSTEIN, M. L., AND J. W. PAYNE. Perspective and the rotating trapezoid. *J. Opt. Soc. Am.* 58: 399–403, 1968.

26. BREITMEYER, B., AND L. GANZ. Implications of sustained and transient channels for theories of visual pattern masking, saccadic suppression, and information processing. *Psychol. Rev.* 60: 181–188, 1953.

27. BRINDLEY, G. S. *Physiology of the Retina and Visual Pathway.* Baltimore, MD: Williams & Wilkins, 1970. (Monogr. Physiol. Soc. Ser.)

28. BRINDLEY, G. S., AND W. LEWIN. The sensation produced by electrical stimulation of the visual cortex. *J. Physiol. London* 196: 479–493, 1968.

29. BRINDLEY, G. S., AND P. A. MERTON. The absence of position sense in the human eye. *J. Physiol. London* 153: 127–130, 1960.

30. BROWN, P. K., AND G. WALD. Visual pigments in single rods and cones of the human retina. *Science* 144: 45–52, 1964.

31. BRUNSWIK, E. *Perception and the Representative Design of Psychological Experiments.* Berkeley: Univ. of California Press, 1956.

32. BRUNSWIK, E., AND J. KAMIYA. Ecological cue-validity of "proximity" and other Gestalt factors. *Am. J. Psychol.* 66: 20–32, 1953.

33. CAMPBELL, A. G., R. HARTWELL, AND D. C. HOOD. Lightness constancy at the level of the frog's optic nerve fiber (Abstract). *Proc. East. Psychol. Assoc.* 49: 47, 1978.

34. CAMPBELL, F. W., AND J. G. ROBSON. Application of Fourier analysis to the visibility of gratings. *J. Physiol. London* 197: 551–566, 1968.

35. CANESTRARI, R., AND M. FARNÉ. Depth cues and apparent oscillatory motion. *Percept. Mot. Skills* 29: 508–510, 1969.

36. CASSIRER, E. The concept of group and the theory of perception. *Philos. Phenom. Res.* 5: 1–35, 1944.

37. CHOW, L. L., A. H. RIESEN, AND F. W. NEWELL. Degeneration of retinal ganglion cells in infant chimpanzees reared in darkness. *J. Comp. Neurol.* 107: 27–42, 1957.

38. CLOWES, M. Transformational grammar and the systematization of pictures. In: *Automatic Interpretation and Classification of Images*, edited by A. Grasselli. New York: Academic, 1969.

39. COHEN, W. Color perception in the chromatic Ganzfeld. *Am. J. Psychol.* 71: 390–394, 1958.

40. COLTHEART, M. Visual feature-analysers and aftereffects of tilt and curvature. *Psychol. Rev.* 78: 114–121, 1971.

41. COREN, S., AND J. S. GIRGUS. *Seeing is Deceiving: The Psychology of Visual Illusions.* Hillsdale, NJ: Erlbaum, 1978.

42. DAY, R. H. Visual spatial illusions: a general explanation. *Science* 175: 1335–1340, 1972.

43. DAY, R. H., AND B. E. MCKENZIE. Constancies in the perceptual world of the infant. In: *Stability and Constancy in Visual Perception: Mechanisms and Processes*, edited by W. Epstein. New York: Wiley, 1977.

44. DESCARTES, RENÉ. Les Passions de l'ame. Amsterdam: 1650. In: *The Philosophical Works of Descartes* (transl. by E. S. Haldane and G. R. T. Rose). Cambridge, England: Cambridge Univ. Press, 1931.

44a. DE VALOIS, R. L. Behavioral and electrophysiological studies of primate vision. In: *Contributions to Sensory Physiology*, edited by W. D. Neff. New York: Academic, 1965, vol. 1.

44b. DE VALOIS, R. L., I. ABRAMOV, AND W. R. MEAD. Single cell analysis of wavelength discrimination of the lateral geniculate nucleus in the macaque. *J. Neurophysiol.* 30: 415–433, 1967.

45. DOBELLE, W. H., M. G. MLADEJOVSKY, AND J. R. EVANS. "Braille" reading by a blind volunteer by visual cortex. *Nature* 259: 111–112, 1976.

46. DONDERI, D. C., AND E. KANE. Perceptual learning produced by common responses to different stimuli. *Can. J. Psychol.* 19: 15–30, 1965.

47. ENROTH-CUGELL, C., AND J. G. ROBSON. The contrast sensitivity of retinal ganglion cells of the cat. *J. Physiol. London* 187: 517–552, 1966.

48. EPSTEIN, W. Phenomenal orientation and perceived achromatic color. *J. Psychol.* 52: 51–53, 1961.

49. EVANS, R. M. *An Introduction to Color.* New York: Wiley, 1948.

50. FAVREAU, O., D. EMERSON, AND M. CORBALLIS. Movement aftereffects contingent on color. *Science* 76: 78–79, 1972.

51. FESTINGER, L., H. ONO, C. A. BURNHAM, AND D. BAMBER. Efference and the conscious experience of perception. *J. Exp. Psychol. Monogr. Suppl.* 637: 1967.

52. FESTINGER, L., C. W. WHITE, AND M. R. ALLYN. Eye movements and decrement in the Müller-Lyer illusion. *Percept. Psychophys.* 3: 376–382, 1968.
53. FLOCK, H. R. Achromatic surface color and the direction of illumination. *Percept. Psychophys.* 9: 187–192, 1971.
54. FRY, G. A. Mechanisms subserving simultaneous brightness contrast. *Am. J. Optom. Arch. Am. Acad. Optom.* 25: 162–178, 1948.
55. GARNER, W. *Uncertainty and Structure as Psychological Concepts.* New York: Wiley, 1962.
56. GARNER, W. Good patterns have few alternatives. *American Sci.* 58: 34–42, 1970.
57. GIBSON, E. J. *Principles of Perceptual Learning and Development.* Englewood Cliffs, NJ: Prentice-Hall, 1969.
58. GIBSON, E. J., AND R. WALK. The "visual cliff." *Sci. Am.* 202: 64–71, 1960.
59. GIBSON, J. J. Adaptation, aftereffect, and contrast in the perception of curved lines. *J. Exp. Psychol.* 16: 1–31, 1933.
60. GIBSON, J. J. *The Perception of the Visual World.* Boston, MA: Houghton, 1950.
61. GIBSON, J. J. Perception as a function of stimulation. In: *Psychology: A Study of Science*, edited by S. Koch. New York: McGraw-Hill, 1959.
62. GIBSON, J. J. *The Senses Considered as Perceptual Systems.* Boston, MA: Houghton, 1966.
63. GIBSON, J. J. On the analysis of the change in the optic array. *Scand. J. Psychol.* 18: 161–163, 1977.
64. GIBSON, J. J., AND M. RADNER. Adaption, aftereffect and contrast in the perception of titled lines: 1. Quantitative studies. *J. Exp. Psychol.* 20: 453–467, 1937.
65. GILCHRIST, A. Perceived lightness depends on perceived spatial arrangement. *Science* 195: 185–187, 1977.
66. GILLAM, B. A depth processing theory of the Poggendorff illusion. *Percept. Psychophys.* 10: 211–216, 1971.
67. GILLAM, B. Perceived common rotary motion of ambiguous stimuli as a criterion for perceptual grouping. *Percept. Psychophys.* 11: 99–101, 1972.
68. GINSBURG, A. Psychological Correlates of a Model of the Human Visual System. Wright-Patterson, Air Force Base, OH: Air Force Inst. Technology, 1971. Master's thesis.
69. GIRGUS, J. S. A developmental study of the effect of eye movement on shape perception in a sequential viewing situation. *J. Exp. Child Psychol.* 22: 386–399, 1976.
70. GLANZER, M., AND W. CLARK. The verbal loop hypothesis: conventional figures. *Am. J. Psychol.* 77: 621–626, 1964.
71. GOGEL, W. C. The effect of familiarity on the perception of size and distance. *Q. J. Exp. Psychol.* 21: 239–247, 1969.
72. GOGEL, W. C., AND D. H. MERSHON. Depth adjacency in simultaneous contrast. *Percept. Psychophys.* 5: 13–17, 1969.
73. GRAHAM, C. H. Visual perception. In: *Handbook of Experimental Psychology*, edited by S. S. Stevens. New York: Wiley, 1951.
74. GRAHAM, C. H. (editor). *Vision and Visual Perception.* New York: Wiley, 1965.
75. GRAHAM, N. Spatial frequency channels in human vision: detecting edges without edge detectors. In: *Visual Coding and Adaptability*, edited by C. Harris. Hillsdale, NJ: Erlbaum, 1980.
76. GRAHAM, N., AND J. NACHMIAS. Detection of grating patterns containing two spatial frequencies; a comparison of single-channel and multiple-channels models. *Vision Res.* 11: 251–259, 1971.
77. GRAHAM, N., AND F. RATLIFF. Quantitative theories of the integrative action of the retina. In: *Contemporary Developments in Mathematical Psychology*, edited by D. Krantz, R. D. Luce, R. C. Atkinson, and P. Suppes. San Francisco, CA: Freeman, 1974, vol. 2.
78. GRAHAM N., AND B. ROGOWITZ. Spatial pooling properties deduced from the detectability of FM and quasi-AM gratings: a reanalysis. *Vision Res.* 16: 1021–1026, 1976.
79. GREEN, D. M. *An Introduction to Hearing.* Hillsdale, NJ: Erlbaum, 1976.
80. GREGORY, R. *The Intelligent Eye.* London: Weidenfeld, 1970.
81. GUZMAN, A. Decomposition of a visual scene into three-dimensional bodies. In: *Automatic Interpretation and Classification of Images*, edited by A. Graselli. New York: Academic, 1969.
82. HABER, R. N. AND M. HERSHENSON. *The Psychology of Visual Perception.* New York: Holt, 1973.
83. HARMON, L. D., AND B. JULESZ. Masking in visual recognition: effects of two-dimensional filtered noise. *Science* 180: 1194–1197, 1973.
84. HARRIS, C. S. Perceptual adaption to inverted, reversed, and displaced vision. *Psychol. Rev.* 72: 419–444, 1965.
85. HARRIS, C. S. Insight or out of sight? Two examples of perceptual plasticity in the human adult. In: *Visual Coding and Adaptability*, edited by C. S. Harris. Hillsdale, NJ: Erlbaum, 1980.
86. HARRIS, C. S., AND A. GIBSON. Is orientation-specific color adaption in human vision due to edge detectors, afterimages, or "dipoles"? *Science* 162: 1056–1057, 1968.
87. HARTLEY, D. *Observations on Man, His Frame, His Duty and His Expectations.* London: Johnson, 1791, vol. 1, p. 1–12, 103–110. Reprinted in: *Readings in the History of Psychology*, edited by W. Dennis. New York: Appleton, 1948.
88. HARTLINE, H. K. Inhibition of activity of visual receptors by illuminating nearby retinal elements in the *Limulus* eye. *Federation Proc.* 8: 69, 1949.
89. HARVEY, L. O., AND M. J. GERVAIS. Fourier analysis and the perceptual similarity of texture (Abstract). *Invest. Ophthalmol. Vis. Sci. Suppl.* 16: 48, 1977.
90. HAY, J. C. Optical motions and space perception: an extension of Gibson's analysis. *Psychol. Rev.* 73: 550–565, 1966.
91. HAYEK, F. A. *The Sensory Order; an Inquiry Into the Foundation of Theoretical Psychology.* Chicago, IL: Univ. of Chicago Press, 1952.
92. HEBB, D. *The Organization of Behavior.* New York: Wiley, 1949.
93. HEBB, D. *A Textbook of Psychology.* Philadelphia, PA: Saunders, 1958.
94. HEINEMANN, E. G. Simultaneous brightness induction as a function of inducing- and test-field luminances. *J. Exp. Psychol.* 50: 89–96, 1955.
95. HEINEMANN, E. G., E. TULVING, AND J. NACHMIAS. The effect of oculomotor adjustments on apparent size. *Am. J. Psychol.* 72: 32–45, 1959.
96. HELD, R. Exposure-history as a factor in maintaining stability of perception and coordination. *J. Nerv. Mental Dis.* 132: 26–32, 1961.
97. HELD, R., AND J. BOSSOM. Neonatal deprivation and adult rearrangement: complementary techniques for analyzing plastic sensory-motor coordinations. *J. Comp. Physiol. Psychol.* 56: 872–876, 1963.
98. HELD, R., AND J. REKOSH. Motor-sensory feedback and the geometry of visual space. *Science* 141: 722–723, 1963.
99. HELD, R., AND S. SHATTUCK. Color- and edge-sensitive channels in the human visual system: Tuning for orientations. *Science* 174: 314–316, 1971.
100. HELMHOLTZ, H. VON. On the relation of optics to painting. In his: *Popular Lectures on Scientific Subjects, 2nd Series* (transl. by E. Atkinson). New York: Appleton, 1901.
101. HELMHOLTZ, H. VON. *Treatise on Physiological Optics* [vol. 2, transl. by J. P. C. Southall from the 3rd (1909–1911) Ger. ed.]. New York: Optical Soc. Am., 1924–1925; reprinted, New York: Dover, 1962.
102. HELMHOLTZ, H. VON. *Treatise on Physiological Optics* [vol. 3, transl. by J. P. C. Southall from the 3rd (1909–1911) Ger. ed.]. New York: Optical Soc. Am., 1924–1925; reprinted, New York: Dover, 1962.
103. HELMHOLTZ, H. VON. *The Facts of Perception.* Berlin: August Hirschwald, 1879. In: *Helmholtz on Perception: Its Physiology and Development*, edited and transl. by R. M. Warren and R. P. Warren. New York: Wiley, 1968.
104. HELMHOLTZ, H. VON. The recent progress of the theory of vision. Lectures delivered in 1867 [transl. by P. H. Pye-

Smith]. In: *Popular Scientific Lectures.* New York: Appleton, 1873. Reprinted in: *Helmholtz on Perception: Its Physiology and Development,* edited by R. M. Warren and R. P. Warren. New York: Wiley, 1968.

105. HERING, E. *Outlines of a Theory of the Light Sense* (transl. by L. M. Hurvich and D. Jameson). Cambridge, MA: Harvard Univ. Press, 1964.

106. HESS, C., AND H. PRETORI. Messende Untersuchungen über die Gesetzmässigkeit des simultanen Helligkeits-Contrastes. *Albrecht von Graefes Arch. Ophthalmol.* 40: 1–27, 1894. (transl. by H. R. Flock and J. H. Tenney in: *Technical Report FLP-1.* Toronto: York Univ., 1969.)

107. HESS, E. H. Space perception in the chick. *Sci. Am.* 195: 71–80, 1956.

108. HOBBES, T. *Human Nature.* 1651, chapt. 2. Reprinted in: *Readings in the History of Psychology,* edited by W. Dennis. New York: Appleton, 1948.

109. HOCHBERG, J. Nativism and empiricism in perception. In: *Psychology in the Making,* edited by L. Postman. New York: Knopf, 1962.

110. HOCHBERG, J. On the importance of movement-produced stimulation in prism-induced after-effects. *Percept. Mot. Skills* 16: 544, 1963.

111. HOCHBERG, J. In the mind's eye. In: *Contemporary Theory and Research in Visual Perception,* edited by R. N. Haber. New York: Holt, 1968.

112. HOCHBERG, J. Attention, organization, and consciousness. In: *Attention: Contemporary Theory and Analysis,* edited by D. I. Mostofsky. New York: Appleton, 1970.

113. HOCHBERG, J. Perception, I. Color and shape. II. Space and movement. In: *Woodworth and Schlosberg's Experimental Psychology* (3rd ed.), edited by J. W. Kling and L. A. Riggs. New York: Holt, 1971, p. 395–550.

114. HOCHBERG, J. Higher-order stimuli and interresponse coupling in the perception of the visual world. In: *Perception: Essays in Honor of James J. Gibson,* edited by R. B. MacLeod and H. L. Pick. Ithaca, NY: Cornell Univ. Press, 1974, p. 17–39.

115. HOCHBERG, J. Organization and the Gestalt tradition. In: *Handbook of Perception,* edited by E. C. Carterette and M. P. Friedman. New York: Academic, 1974, vol. 1.

116. HOCHBERG, J. *Perception* (2nd ed.). Englewood Cliffs, NJ: Prentice-Hall, 1978.

117. HOCHBERG, J., AND J. BECK. Apparent spatial arrangement and perceived brightness. *J. Exp. Psychol.* 47: 263–266, 1954.

118. HOCHBERG, J., AND V. BROOKS. The psychophysics of form: Reversible-perspective drawings of spatial objects. *Am. J. Psychol.* 73: 337–354, 1960.

119. HOCHBERG, J., W. TRIEBEL, AND G. SEAMAN. Color adaption under conditions of homogeneous stimulation (Ganzfeld). *J. Exp. Psychol.* 41: 153–159, 1959.

120. HOLST, E. VON Relations between the central nervous system and the peripheral organs. *Br. J. Animal Behaviour* 2: 89–94, 1954.

121. HOOD, D. C., AND J. A. WHITESIDE. Brightness of ramp stimuli as a function of plateau and gradient widths. *J. Opt. Soc. Am.* 58: 1310–1311, 1968.

122. HOWARD, I. Orientation and motion in space. In: *Handbook of Perception,* edited by E. C. Carterette and M. P. Friedman. New York: Academic, 1973, vol. 3, 291–315.

123. HOWARD, I. The spatial senses. In: *Handbook of Perception,* edited by E. C. Carterette and M. P. Friedman. New York: Academic, 1973, vol. 3.

124. HUBEL, D., AND T. WIESEL. Receptive fields, binocular interaction, and functional architecture in the cat's visual cortex. *J. Physiol. London* 160: 106–154, 1962.

125. HUBEL, D., AND T. WIESEL. Receptive fields and functional architecture of monkey striate cortex. *J. Physiol. London* 195: 215–243, 1968.

126. HURVICH, L., AND D. JAMESON. An opponent-process theory of color vision. *Psychol. Rev.* 64: 384–404, 1957.

127. HURVICH, L., AND D. JAMESON. Opponent processes as a model of neural organization. *Am. Psychol.* 29: 88–102, 1974.

128. ITTELSON, W. R., AND F. KILPATRICK. Experiments in perception. *Sci. Am.* 185: 50–55, 1952.

129. JAMESON, D., AND L. M. HURVICH. Complexities of perceived brightness. *Science* 133: 174–179, 1961.

130. JAMESON, D., AND L. M. HURVICH. Theory of brightness and color contrast in human vision. *Vis. Res.* 4: 135–154, 1964.

131. JUDD, D. B. Basic correlates of the visual stimulus. In: *Handbook of Experimental Psychology,* edited by S. S. Stevens. New York: Wiley, 1951, p. 811–867.

132. KABRISKY, M., T. TALLMAN, C. M. DAY, AND C. M. RADOY. A theory of pattern perception based on human physiology. In: *Contemporary Problems in Perception,* edited by A. T. Welford and L. Houssiadas. London: Interntl. Publications Service, 1970.

133. KAUFMAN, L. *Sight and Mind: An Introduction to Visual Perception.* New York: Oxford, 1974.

134. KAUFMAN, L. *Perception: The World Transformed.* New York: Oxford, 1979.

135. KAUFMAN, L., AND I. ROCK. The moon illusion: I. *Science* 136: 953–961, 1962.

136. KLING, J. W., AND L. A. RIGGS (editors). *Woodworth and Schlosberg's Experimental Psychology* (3rd ed.). New York: Holt, 1971.

137. KOFFKA, K. *Principles of Gestalt Psychology.* New York: Harcourt, 1935.

138. KOHLER, I. The formation and transformation of the perceptual world (transl. by H. Fiss). *Psychol. Issues* 3: 1–173, 1964.

139. KÖHLER, W. *Die physischen Gestalten in Ruhe und im stationären Zustand.* Brunswick: Vieweg, 1920.

140. KÖHLER, W., AND H. WALLACH. Figural after-effects: an investigation of visual processes. *Proc. Am. Philos. Soc.* 88: 269–357, 1944.

141. LEE, D. Visual information during locomotion. In: *Perception: Essays in Honor of J. J. Gibson,* edited by R. B. MacLeod and H. L. Pick. Ithaca, NY: Cornell Univ. Press, 1974.

142. LEIBOWITZ, H. W., AND H. PICK. Cross-cultural and educational aspects of the Ponzo illusion. *Percept. Psychophys.* 12: 403–432, 1972.

143. LICHTENSTEIN, M. Phenomenal simultaneity with irregular timing of components of the visual stimulus. *Percept. Mot. Skills* 12: 47–60, 1961.

144. LOTZE, R. H. *Outlines of Psychology: Dictated Portions of the Lectures,* transl. and edited by G. T. Ladd. Boston, MA: Ginn, 1886.

146. MACH, E. *The Analysis of Sensations and The Relation of the Physical to the Psychical* (transl. by S. Waterlow from 5th Ger. ed., 1886). New York: Dover, 1959.

147. MAGENDIE, F. Expériences sur les fonctions des racines des nerfs rachidiens. *J. Physiol. Exp. Pathol.* 2:276–279, 1822; Expériences sur les fonctions des racines des nerfs qui naissent de la noëlle épinière. *Ibid.* 2: 366–371, 1822. Transl. by M. D. Boring, in: *A Source Book in the History of Psychology,* edited by R. J. Herrnstein, and E. G. Boring. Cambridge, MA: Harvard Univ. Press, 1965.

148. MARKS, W. B., W. H. DOBELLE, AND E. F. MacNICHOL. Visual pigments of single primate cones. *Science* 143: 1181–1183, 1964.

149. MAXWELL, J. C. On colour vision. In: *The Scientific Papers of James Clerk Maxwell,* edited by W. D. Niven. London: Cambridge Univ. Press, 1890.

150. MAYHEW, J. E. W., AND S. M. ANSTIS. Movement aftereffects contingent on color, intensity and pattern. *Percept. Psychophys.* 12: 77–85, 1972.

151. McCULLOUGH, C. Color adaption of edge-detectors in the human visual system. *Science* 149: 1115–1116, 1965.

151a. McFARLAND, J. H. Sequential part presentation: a method of studying visual form perception. *Br. J. Psychol.* 56: 439–446, 1965.

152. MILL, J. S. *Analysis of the Phenomena of the Human Mind.* London: 1829. In: *A Source Book in the History of Psychology,* edited by R. J. Herrnstein and E. G. Boring. Cambridge, MA: Harvard Univ. Press, 1965.

153. MILL, J. S. *An Examination of Sir William Hamilton's Phi-*

losophy. London: 1865. In: *A Source Book in the History of Psychology,* edited by R. J. Herrnstein and E. G. Boring. Cambridge, MA: Harvard Univ. Press, 1965.

154. MILLER, J., AND L. FESTINGER. Impact of oculomotor retraining on the visual perception of curvature. *J. Exp. Psychol. Human Percept. Performance* 3: 187–200, 1977.

155. MONTY, R. A., AND J. W. SENDERS (editors). *Eye Movements and Psychological Processes.* Hillsdale, NJ: Erlbaum, 1976.

156. MÜLLER, J. *Handbuch der Physiologie des Menschen.* Coblenz: 1838, 1840, books V, VI; transl. by W. Baly as *Elements of Physiology,* vol. II, London, 1842. Reprinted in: *A Source Book in the History of Psychology,* edited by R. J. Herrnstein and E. G. Boring. Cambridge, MA: Harvard Univ. Press, 1965.

157. MURCH, G. M., AND J. HIRSH. The McCollough effect created by complimentary afterimages. *Am. J. Psychol.* 85: 241–247, 1972.

158. MURPHY, R. Recognition memory for sequentially presented pictorial and verbal spatial information. *J. Exp. Psychol.* 100: 327–334, 1973.

159. NEWTON, I. *An Hypothesis Explaining the Properties of Light* ..., 1675. In: *History of the Royal Society of London,* by Thomas Birch. London: 1757, vol. 3. Reprinted in: *A Source Book in the History of Psychology,* edited by R. J. Herrnstein and E. G. Boring. Cambridge, MA: Harvard Univ. Press, 1965.

160. OVER, R. Comparison of normalization theory and neural enhancement explanation of negative aftereffects. *Psychol. Bull.* 75: 225–243, 1971.

161. PANTLE, A., AND R. SEKULER. Size-detecting mechanisms in human vision. *Science* 162: 1146–1148, 1968.

162. PENFIELD, W., AND L. ROBERTS. *Speech and Brain-Mechanisms.* Princeton, NJ: Princeton Univ. Press, 1959.

163. PRITCHARD, R. M., W. HERRON, AND D. O. HEBB. Visual perception approached by the method of stabilizing images. *Can. J. Psychol.* 14: 67–77, 1960.

164. PURDY, W. C. The Hypothesis of Psychophysical Correspondence in Space Perception. Ithaca, NY: dissertation, Cornell Univ. (Ann Arbor, MI: Univ. Microfilms, 1958, no. 58-5594.)

165. RATLIFF, F. On fields of inhibitory influence in a neural network. In: *Neural Networks, Proceedings,* edited by E. R. Caianello. New York: Springer-Verlag, 1968.

166. RIGGS, L. A. Vision. In: *Woodsworth and Schlosberg's Experimental Psychology* (3rd ed), edited by J. W. Kling and L. A. Riggs. New York: Holt, 1971.

167. RIGGS, L. A. Curvature as a feature of pattern vision. *Science* 181: 1070–1072, 1973.

168. RIGGS, L. A., F. RATLIFF, J. CORNSWEET, AND T. CORNSWEET. The disappearance of steadily fixated visual test objects. *J. Opt. Soc. Am.* 43: 493–501, 1953.

169. ROCK, I. *The Nature of Perceptual Adaptation.* New York: Basic Books, 1966.

170. ROCK, I. In defense of unconscious inference. In: *Stability and Constancy in Visual Perception: Mechanisms and Processes,* edited by W. Epstein. New York: Wiley, 1977.

171. ROSINSKY, R. R. *The Development of Visual Perception.* Santa Monica, CA: Goodyear, 1977.

172. ROSSI, P. J. Adaptation and negative aftereffect to lateral optical displacement in newly hatched chicks. *Science* 160: 430–432, 1968.

173. RUBIN, E. *Synsoplevede Figurer.* Copenhagen: Gyldendalske, 1915.

174. RYAN, T. A. Dynamic, physiognomic, and other neglected properties of perceived objects: a new approach to comprehending. *Am. J. Psychol.* 51: 629–650, 1938.

175. SACHS, M. B., J. NACHMIAS, AND J. G. ROBSON. Spatial-frequency channels in human vision. *J. Opt. Soc. Am.* 61: 1176–1186, 1971.

176. SCHUCK, J., AND W. R. LEAHY. A comparison of verbal and non-verbal reports of fragmenting visual images. *Percept. Psychophys.* 1: 191–192, 1966.

177. SEKULER, R. Spatial vision. *Annu. Rev. Psychol.* 25: 215–232, 1974.

178. SEKULER, R., AND L. GANZ. Aftereffect of seen motion with a stabilized retinal image. *Science* 139: 419–420, 1963.

179. SEKULER, R., A. PANTLE, AND E. LEVINSON. Physiological basis of motion perception. In: *Handbook of Sensory Physiology,* edited by R. Held, H. W. Leibowitz, and H. L. Teuber. New York: Springer-Verlag, 1978, vol. 8, p. 67–96.

180. SHEPARD, R. N. The analysis of proximities: multi-dimensional scaling with an unknown distance function. II. *Psychometrika* 27: 125–245, 1962.

181. SMITH, D. P. Derivation of wavelength discrimination data from colour-naming data. *Vision Res.* 11: 739–742, 1971.

182. SPERRY, R. W. Effect of 180 degree rotation of the retinal field on visuomotor coordination. *J. Exp. Zool.* 92: 263–277, 1943.

183. STEVENS, S. S., AND H. DAVIS. *Hearing: Its Psychology and Physiology.* New York: Wiley, 1938.

184. STROMEYER, C. F., AND R. MANSFIELD. Colored aftereffects produced with moving edges. *Percept. Psychophys.* 7: 108–114, 1970.

185. SVAETICHIN, G. Spectral response curves of single cones. *Acta Physiol. Scand.* 39 *Suppl.* 134: 18–46, 1956.

186. TAYLOR, J. G. *The Behavioral Basis of Perception.* New Haven, CT: Yale Univ. Press, 1962.

187. TEFT, L. W., AND F. T. CLARK. The effect of stimulus density on orientation specific aftereffects of color adaptation. *Psychon. Sci.* 11: 265–266, 1968.

188. THOMAS, J. P. Model of the function of receptive fields in human vision. *Psychol. Rev.* 77: 121–134, 1970.

189. THORNDIKE, E. The instinctive reactions of young chicks. *Psychol. Rev.* 6: 282–291, 1899.

190. TITCHENER, E. B. *An Outline of Psychology.* New York: Macmillan, 1896.

191. TRANDIS, H. C., R. S. MALPASS, AND A. R. DAVIDSON. Psychology and culture. *Ann. Rev. Psychol.* 24: 355–378, 1973.

194. WALK, R. D. The study of visual depth and distance perception in animals. In: *Advances in the Study of Behavior,* edited by D. S. Lehrman, R. A. Hinde, and E. Shaw. New York: Academic, 1965, vol. 1.

195. WALKER, J. T., AND K. S. SHEAR. A tactual size aftereffect contingent on hand position. *J. Exp. Psychol.* 103: 668–674, 1974.

196. WALLACH, H. Brightness constancy and the nature of achromatic colors. *J. Exp. Psychol.* 38: 310–324, 1948.

197. WALLACH, H. *Hans Wallach on Perception.* New York: Quadrangle, 1976.

198. WALLACH, H., AND P. AUSTIN. Recognition and the localization of visual traces. *Am. J. Psychol.* 67: 338–340, 1954.

199. WALLACH, H., D. N. O'CONNELL, AND U. NEISSER. The memory effect of visual perception of three-dimensional form. *J. Exp. Psychol.* 45: 360–368, 1953.

200. WALLS, G. L. The problem of visual direction. *Am. J. Optom. Arch. Am. Acad. Optom.* 28: 55–83, 1951.

201. WEISSTEIN, N., AND J. BISAHA. Gratings mask bars and bars mask gratings: visual frequency response to aperiodic stimuli. *Science* 176: 1047–1049, 1972.

202. WERTHEIMER, MAX. Untersuchungen zur Lehre von der Gestalt: II. *Psychol. Forsch.* 4: 301–350, 1923.

203. WERTHEIMER, MICHAEL. Psychomotor coordination of auditory and visual space at birth. *Science* 134: 1692, 1961.

204. WEVER, E. G., AND C. W. BRAY. Action currents in the auditory nerve in response to acoustic stimulation. *Proc. Natl. Acad. Sci. USA* 16: 344–350, 1930.

205. WIESEL, T. N., AND D. N. HUBEL. Effects of visual deprivation on morphology and physiology of cells in the cat's lateral geniculate body. *J. Neurophysiol.* 26: 978–993, 1963.

206. WIST, E., H. DIENES, J. DICHGANS, AND T. BRANDT. Perceived distance and the speed of self-motion: linear versus angular velocity? *Percept. Psychophys.* 17: 549–554, 1975.

207. WOHLGEMUTH, A. On the aftereffect of seen movement. *Br. J. Psychol. Monogr. Suppl.* 1: 1911.

208. WOODWORTH, R. S. *Experimental Psychology.* New York: Holt, 1938.

209. WUNDT, W. *Outlines of Psychology* (transl. by C. H. Judd). New York: G. E. Steelhert and Co., 1907.

210. YOUNG, T. On the theory of light and colours. *Philos. Trans. R. Soc. London* 18–21, 1802.

CHAPTER 3

Detection and discrimination of environmental change

EUGENE GALANTER | *Department of Psychology, Columbia University, New York City*

CHAPTER CONTENTS

AS A BIOLOGICAL SYSTEM, human sensibility represents the evolutionary development of sensory mechanisms that enhance and sustain biological survival. This system exhibits a strong interplay between the internal states of the organism and the environmental events that impinge on the receptors. It derives meaning (i.e., relevance for action) from the psychological side. The interaction between this end-organ stimulation and these internal organizational structures is most naturally interpretable in terms of concepts such as *goal* and *purpose*. These teleological concepts, prescientific as they are, explain as well as describe the nature of the behavioral interactions between humans and their environment.

An ontological dualism emerges easily from such a conceptual base. This dualism can be justified by its descriptive efficiency; but scientific reductionism and its psychic counterpart, behaviorism, which has preempted the dualistic position, generate "engineering" solutions to the vexing problems of survival and procreation. Although these antagonistic positions each have a claim to rational support, behaviorism is the current favorite. Whereas dualism closely matches one's phenomenal experience, monistic materialism represents an adaptation to the world as represented by physical stimulations and therefore serves to predict and control such externalities.

The physical environment represented as a psychological system can be examined on two levels. First, we may construe certain structural features of the environment as imposing the Kantian imperatives of space and time on our mental processes. In addition to these fundamental categories of experience, there are other perceptually represented coherences induced by various environmental states. These physical contingencies generate a psychological interpretation of the external world. They constitute what psychologists often describe as the learning mechanisms by which appropriate adjustments of behavior conform to the limitations of freedom imposed by the environment.

These psychological mechanisms have, for the dualist, both imaginative and physical components. Thus from the dualists' position, the solution to many psychological problems may be accomplished either by psychologically reshuffling the conceptual and associative organization of one's internal state or by physical, chemical, and mechanical alterations of the states of nature. One way or another, whether dualist or not, we may generate in our actions the conditions required for the satisfaction of our physical and psychic needs. From this double point of view we can interpret the physical environment as an informational system rubbing against the psychological organism via its biological interface. The extraction of information from the environment constitutes the solution to the psychological problems of survival and to the enrichment of the mental apparatus for its own sake.

PERCEPTUAL PROCESSES

Guidance of action depends on knowledge of the ways of the world. An understanding of the world is contingent on the organization of sensory information into perceptual entities that preserve certain invariant properties of the physical environment through time and space. These perceptual invariants give information about the connection of two aspects of human mental nature and the external environment. The first of these—the cognitive aspect of the human psychological structure—is related to the veridical analysis of the object properties of the environment in which one maneuvers. The second concerns the affective structure of the human mind and its role in the preservation and continuation of ongoing activities.

We may distinguish in a rough-and-ready way between two features of environmental stimulation that are normally locked to the cognitive and emotional perceptual modes. On one hand, the perception of form and structure, the shape and appearance of objects, and tunes of melodies, and the cadences of speech all represent the central physical bases for cognitive activity. These environmental features are a kind of "frequency" modulation of the "carrier signal" of physical events. On the other hand, changes in the signal amplitude of the carrier—amplitude-modulated information—are normally associated with emotional response and the dynamics of autonomous biological functions. Thus we may expect to observe emotional responses to changes in the physical dynamics of impinging energy (a useful feature for a biological system designed to survive in a universe where danger often presents itself in the form of large sweeps in the amplitude of environmental events).

The primitive biological representation of such dynamic amplitude effects are clearly seen in the startle reflex. Indeed it is likely that the decoding of the cognitive components of the perceptual input—the "frequency-modulation (FM) demodulation"—only begins to function when amplitude stability in a given perceptual field is obtained. We can observe the interference of amplitude instabilities on cognitive functioning (e.g., in the effects of glare, distance changes, noise, or random amplitude variations in perceptual information). One might suppose that within normal ranges, stimulus dynamics add to form and content. This may be true within a closed perceptual field; however, such a view presumes an analytical theory that, though robust, has consistently failed to explain most of the interesting perceptual phenomena. We do not sacrifice much by giving up stimulus dynamics as a source of sensory form; we stand to gain a new conceptual scheme by characterizing these events as the drivers of affect.

We conclude from these considerations that the study of frequency-modulated characteristics of the physical environment provides the basis for cognitive control over behavior, which we term *perception*. Changes in environmental amplitude serve best the transmission of signals that generate either quiescent or galvanizing effects on the organismic state. It has turned out that although the nature of perception as a basis for cognition and action constitutes the most interesting and imperative means to advance our understanding of human nature, the technical and experimental development of methods for assessing signal energy dynamics represents the most advanced technical aspects of psychological research. Consequently psychologists, like all other scientists who search where the light is best, have attended in great-

est detail and with greatest precision to the detection and discrimination of amplitude change. These are the areas that are most amenable to the experimental methods and techniques of laboratory research. Because of their intrinsically one-dimensional structure, logical and mathematical models to explain and analyze the data from these experiments have been relatively simple to formulate. Consequently we attend in this chapter to the nether side of the perceptual world—primarily the amplitude-modulated side—and leave for other chapters in this *Handbook* the characterization of the perceptual mechanisms of form, structure, and content.

The study of the effects of environmental change on psychic states has proceeded from the plausible assumption that if we induce a physical change in the presence of a responsive organism, then the organism can report behaviorally whether the change is detectable or not and can possibly also report the sign and magnitude of the change. These assumptions are at the heart of Fechnerian psychophysics. They have given us the experimental data for constructing models of the sensory systems and their neurological substructure (3). The experiments relate physical energy characteristics and sense modalities to realize the doctrine of specific nerve energies. The apparent purpose of these psychophysical experiments is to extract from humans (and other animals) the capacities and limitations of the sensory systems as defined on the physical continua by behavioral loci. Thus the notion of absolute and differential thresholds or limens partitions the physical continuum into detectable and indetectable segments; in the detectable region it also represents psychic-system resolution vis-à-vis a physical parameter.

These efforts that delimit the sensory functioning of the organism constitute a technology for mapping the postulated mosaic of elements on which the perceptual process operates. Indeed there is good reason to believe that the elegance of these experimental techniques has supported the underlying conceptual theory in the face of evidence that such mosaic theories of perception are inadequate to explain large sets of human perceptual functioning (2). However, if the theories for which psychophysics is performed are themselves inadequate, what is the reason for the psychophysical research? One answer is that the ability of psychophysical data to elucidate the nature of sensory dynamics may also help to uncover the nature of affective or emotional response. Consequently, although psychophysics and its various data may not be of central importance in understanding cognitive aspects of perception, these methods may help us answer important social and practical problems in areas far removed from the original sensory models for which they were designed. Before we enlarge upon these notions, however, let us examine recent psychophysical methods and procedures.

MODERN PSYCHOPHYSICS

One of the more pervasive and subtle problems of experimental psychology is how to interpret the verbal responses of people who make judgments in psychophysical experiments. We presume that they tell us something about the impact of environmental stimuli. From the time of Fechner (7), in 1860, and for 75 years thereafter, such responses were construed as directly representative of the observer's state of mind. In these early cases the interpretation seemed plausible insofar as the respondent was asked merely to report the presence or absence of some event or whether one event was greater or less than another. These phenomenal reports were occasionally challenged by the experimental introduction of false or misleading stimuli designed to "trip-up" the observer if he failed to understand the instructions or was actually dissembling. These catch-trial procedures were primarily defensive, though: they helped the experimenter select data worth further analysis.

The use of introspective reports expanded dramatically in psychophysics with the experimental introduction of the magnitude-estimation methods for psychophysical scaling (45). Here justification based on an argument of "simplicity of judgment" was no longer applicable. Indeed experimental observers occasionally required a fair amount of instruction and training before they could adequately perform the tasks required by the experimental design. Yet the overwhelming concern was how to interpret the numerical judgment. Was it really an estimator of some quantitative feature of the observer's experience? This interrogatory objection was presented most diligently by Graham and Ratoosh (23) and Torgerson (50), but these criticisms did not impede the massive application of magnitude-estimation techniques to a variety of scaling problems.

The fact is that a useful method for systematically accumulating information will always overpower theoretical arguments that prove the method illegitimate. It was true for Fechner, and it remained true for Stevens. For, as the philosopher Nelson Goodman (21) has remarked, "The case against the measurability of almost any property is overwhelming—until the property is measured. Consistency and objectivity are the products of measurement, not prerequisites for it."

The primary justification for using these techniques of phenomenal report is that the data are systematic, reproducible, and can be plausibly interpreted. Thus a determination of the absolute threshold of visual sensitivity based on judgments of the presence or absence of an increment of light against a background (27) continues to be the accepted and routine technique for studying the psychophysics of vision. Qualms about judgmental bias, even when the experimenter serves as the observer, hardly exist. The data from experiments of this kind confirm too many well-founded beliefs to be rejected because of methodological objections to the natural interpretation of the observer's report.

Yet doubt prevailed among the experimentalists. The early experiments of Irwin and Preston (28), and later the research of Verplanck et al. (51), showed response-dependent effects in psychophysical judgments. The results were interpreted in a variety of ways, but the primary notion was that subjective judgment is only loosely coupled to the stimulus objective of the judgment. The judgment is constrained to a greater or less extent by variables that influence the response structure in some unknown way. These variables as a class have all been designated "response-bias" variables. They constitute the substance of a variety of psychological disciplines that fall under rubrics such as personality, motivation, and attitudes. Sometimes these response-bias variables are construed as having a feedback effect on the perceptual nature of the stimulus itself (12); that is, they are thought to modify the receptor system so that the perceptual qualities are changed. Nevertheless this view, once called the "new look" in perception, has not developed into a viable substantive area of research.

To cope with this intrusive issue that relates so forcefully to topics in psychology far beyond the psychophysical laboratory, theoreticians, beginning with Smith and Wilson (42) and unfolding fully through the exceptional efforts of Tanner and Swets (47), implemented a modus vivendi between scientists interested in the performance of sensory systems and researchers concerned with the methodological issues. We call the general structure of these abstractions *two-parameter decision theories*. This name emphasizes that the observer's responses are to be construed as volitional decisions about the stimulus events arranged by the experimenter. Furthermore these decisions are not only based on the experimenter-controlled events, but also on events (independent?) interpretable as motivational, attitudinal, or instructional. These theories therefore separate the observed response measures into a part attributable to the stimulus variables and an independent part that represents other psychological factors.

SIGNAL-DETECTION THEORY: AN EXAMPLE
OF TWO-PARAMETER DECISION PROBLEMS

We introduce the theory of signal detectability by first considering a paradigmatic experiment. As we examine the experiment we will introduce richness into the description. This leads naturally to a characterization of models of the experiment that culminates in a two-parameter decision theory.

An experimental observer is placed in an isolated environment where he has two keys available, one labeled yes, the other labeled no. He is instructed that on a sequence of successive trials, defined by some arbitrary stimulus display (perhaps a clock face with a moving hand), he is to decide whether a particular signal, say a weak sound, is present or absent. If he decides that it is present, he is to press the button marked yes, whereas if he thinks it is absent, he is to press no. If the signal is presented on every trial, as it might be in an audiometric examination, then the percentage of times the observer reports hearing the signal can be determined. If that proportion is less than one, the signal is appropriately weak and may be called near-threshold.

Note that if the observer knows the signal will be presented continuously, he may say yes on every trial whether he hears the signal or not. We may interpret this tendency to reply yes as a fact of the observer's personality, independent of his ability to detect the signal. We presume that among the yes responses to actual auditory experience there may be possible yes reports independent of the auditory experience and dependent only on response bias. The observer's report may not faithfully report his state of mind. Consequently our paradigmatic experiment fails to distinguish between actual sensory performance of the observer and his response bias. It is impossible in this experiment to estimate independently the sensory components and the bias components of the observer's judgments and decisions.

This experimental problem is resolved by only presenting the signal on some fixed proportion of trials in some irregular order. Therefore if maybe 50% of the trials do not contain a signal, then the experimenter is able to calculate two independent measures of yes responses. One represents the proportion of times the observer reported the signal present when in fact it was present; the other is the proportion of times the observer reported the signal present when it was not present. We call the first of these proportions a hit, and the second a false alarm. The hit proportion tells us something about how the sensory system is operating, and the false alarms inform us of the observer's response bias, that is, his tendency to say yes regardless of the presence of the signal.

If in the preceding experiment the false alarm proportion was greater than zero, then the experimenter could assume that the observer did not hear the signal during some of the trials on which the signal actually was presented and the observer reported yes. This implies that the experimenter was not aware of the values, motives, or attitudes that the observer exhibited when using the yes button. Although it may seem plausible to assume that he has no greater reason for pressing the button saying yes than he does for pressing the button saying no, such an assumption leaves uncontrolled the actual performance variables.

One way to gain control over these variables is to use methods that have been developed to train animals; that is, appropriate rewards and costs are given to the observer that are contingent upon the joint occurrences of signal presentation and response (cf. the chapter by Stebbins in this *Handbook*). When the observer becomes aware (or is made aware) of the contingencies between his performance and objects of his desire or aversion, then we may expand the experiment to determine something about the response structure itself.

An arrangement of benefits and costs contingent upon the experimenter's presentation and the observer's response is called a payoff function (15). It often takes the form of a matrix that shows the value to be received and costs to be leveled contingent upon responses relative to the signal presentation. The entries in the payoff matrix are often shown in monetary terms, although occasionally the entries represent other objects with positive or negative incremental utility to the observer. Table 1 shows an example of a monetary payoff matrix. The matrix is fully symmetric; that is, a hit receives a reward equal and opposite to a false alarm. Notice that two other stimulus-response contingencies are contained in this simple payoff matrix: a response of no when a stimulus is present (called a miss), and no when the stimulus is absent (called a correct rejection). The full symmetry of the matrix is represented by equal and opposite values in these cells also. The symmetry referred to here is only an objective description of the matrix. The effects of the payoffs may or may not be psychologically symmetric.

Although the payoff function in Table 1 may represent what is intuitively the appropriate payoff for the experiment, it is not unreasonable to believe that an observer could discriminate just as well if the payoff function were modified into the matrix shown in Table 2.

In this matrix the observer is heavily rewarded for hits and only very lightly fined for false alarms. In this case we would expect the proportion of yes responses to increase dramatically, which would of course increase both the hit and false alarm rates. If the same observer under the same conditions were faced with each of these matrices separately, one would presume that any difference in response proportions would reflect not a difference in sensory capabilities but rather a change in response bias. Thus any theory that

TABLE 1. *Fully Symmetric Payoff Matrix*

Response	Signal	No Signal
Yes	$1	−$1
No	−$1	$1

TABLE 2. *Asymmetric Payoff Matrix: High Probability of Yes Response*

Response	Signal	No Signal
Yes	$1	−1¢
No	−1¢	10¢

purports to represent performance in these experiments would have to distinguish between consistent sensory behavior between the experiments and variations in response bias that the payoff functions would induce. Furthermore we would expect the theory to deal with these two questions independently. That is, variations in response bias should not influence the perceptual processes and, likewise, changes in the perceptual parameters—for example, alterations of auditory threshold—should not modulate response bias.

If we keep the auditory threshold fixed and vary the response bias with different payoff matrices, we observe data relating hits and false alarms as shown in Figure 1. These data points show how changes in the hits and false alarms may proceed as the observer increases his yes responses. The data (16) represent values of different payoff functions. The payoff function that generated the low probability of saying yes is like the matrix in Table 3. The data showing a high probability of yes are the consequences of a payoff matrix like the one shown in Table 2.

All of the data points shown in Figure 1 represent shifts in response proportions induced by the same signal, but with different payoff matrices, and therefore are presumed to represent equal subjective sensitivity. Consequently such data graphs are often called isosensitivity functions. They represent the equivalent of the operating characteristic (OC) curve of the statistician, and the receiver operating characteristic (ROC) curve of the electrical engineer. Com-

TABLE 3. *Asymmetric Payoff Matrix: Low Probability of Yes Response*

Response	Signal	No Signal
Yes	10¢	−$1
No	−1¢	10¢

monly the acronym ROC is used to describe the functions fitted to such data, in which case psychologists interpret it as response operating characteristics.

It is known that changes in response bias can be induced by a variety of methods (16), and consequently it can be assumed that the various experimental factors that induce bias all affect a single parameter. This is not necessarily true in all contexts, but in this experiment there is no room for more than a sensitivity parameter and a parameter to represent bias variables. This implies that although response bias effects may vary in their deep structure as a result of the experimental factors that influence this bias, more complex experiments are needed to detect such changes. Having issued this warning, we now assume that all experimental treatments that induce response bias changes are represented by the same process. For many experiments, including the numerous complex ones we cite, this assumption is reasonable.

THEORY OF SIGNAL DETECTABILITY

In the experiment described above our observer was listening to a weak acoustic signal. With equivalent justification, however, we can construe the observer as making decisions among various kinds of abstract events that could be represented in a variety of different ways. We adopt this interpretation as the most useful for developing a theory and interpret the events presented to the experimental observer as numerical quantities induced by the experimental stimuli. The simplest assumption is that the quantity associated with no signal is represented by the value "0" and the quantity represented by the presence of a signal is given an arbitrary numerical assignment, say, "2."

The important thing to recognize about the nature of empirical events in general and the mental processing of environmental stimuli in particular is that although essentially identical physical events are repeatedly presented, their effects on the organism are presumed to vary from occasion to occasion. The most common and plausible assumption about the nature of this variation is that the environmental quantity is distributed normally. In the context of signal-detection theory, we assume this about all effects induced by stimulus events. For this example the nonstimulus 0 and the stimulus 2 represent the means of two normally distributed variables. The second parameter of the normal distribution is the standard deviation. To again simplify the initial assumptions of the theory, we presume that the standard deviation (SD) of both

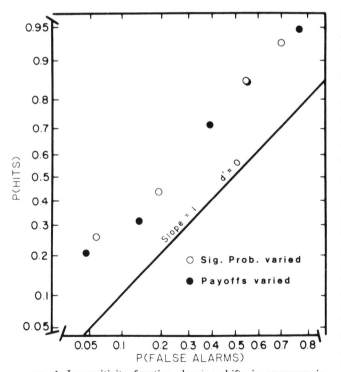

FIG. 1. Isosensitivity function showing shifts in responses induced by changes in payoffs when same signal is presented. Coordinate system adjusts proportions to match normal probability distribution.

the 0 and 2 distributions are equal to each other and that both are equal to unity. If we then portray these two distributions as in Figure 2, they overlap as shown.

The abscissa in Figure 2 is the magnitude of the psychic effect of the occurrence of one of the events. The presence of the overlap of the two distributions is the fundamental theoretical process that causes the difficulty inherent in the decision. In other words, if both distributions did not overlap in a significant way, then an event drawn from the distribution with 0 mean would be (almost) absolutely and consistently distinguishable from an event drawn from the distribution with mean = 2. The significant overlap indicates that an event drawn from one distribution could have been drawn from the other with only moderately different probability. Therefore it is incumbent on the observer to estimate not only how likely an event is to arise from one distribution, but also how likely one distribution is to be sampled. What are the a priori probabilities that events will be drawn from each distribution? These presentation probabilities are often selected to be equal, as in our example above, but whether they are or not, they must be factored into the decision process. Observers may discover these probabilities themselves. This is commonly attributed to learning processes that occur during the course of an experiment. Alternatively information about the a priori probabilities of the stimuli can be included in the overt instructions to the observer.

In any case we may begin with the symmetric assumption (i.e., events are drawn from the 0 and 2 distributions with equal likelihood). To represent numerical values along the abscissa, we may select units of the standard deviation as a natural metric. These correspond to the widely tabled values of the function z—values of the unit normal distribution with zero mean (38). In Figure 2 these units have been marked on the abscissa.

This representation shows that if an observer is asked to decide whether a particular event has been drawn from the 0 or 2 distribution, then a reasonable procedure is to construct a decision point on the abscissa, say at the point marked C in Figure 2, and call all observations greater than C, 2, and all observations less than C, 0. The location of the criterion point obviously depends on features of the experimental conditions that the observer understands or that he is exposed to during the course of the experiment, such as the payoff matrices, the signal presentation probabilities, his attitude about the use of the words *zero* and *two*, and his willingness to take risks.

Assuming that the value of C is fixed by the observer after some preliminary groping for an appropriate criterion point, then we note that the conditional response probabilities P (two$|$2) and P(two$|$0) or P(zero$|$0) and P(zero$|$2) can be represented by the integrals or areas of these distributions from the cut point to the right (or left). The relative sizes of these areas depend on how far apart the means of the two distributions are located. In this example this distance d is 2. If the signal were represented by a distribution with mean = 4 and SD = 1, the two distributions would overlap less, and the hits would be greater relative to the false alarms for any cut point. This mean difference d, when normalized by the value of SD, is represented by the symbol d'. Since SD = 1, in this instance, then $d = d'$.

The portion in Figure 2 under the 2 distribution at the right of C shows the probability of correctly reporting that an event came from the 2 distribution and represents a hit = P (two$|$2). Notice also that the shaded portion of the zero distribution to the right of

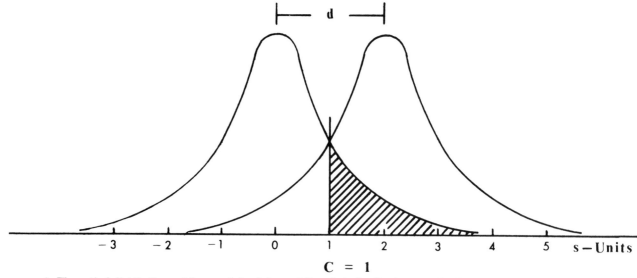

FIG. 2. Theoretical distributions of theory of signal detectability. *Left distribution*, nonstimulus effects; *right distribution*, stimulus effects. *Shaded portion* to *right* of C, criterion, represents proportion of false alarms.

C will also be reported as coming from the two distribution, and this probability—P (two|0)—represents a false alarm. The areas to the left of the cut point C under each of the distributions represent the complementary probabilities of a miss and a correct rejection. Observe that the parameters, d' and C, completely capture the nature of the underlying process.

The following expressions summarize the geometric concepts that we have been using. Equation 1 shows that d' is the difference between the means normalized by the standard deviation

$$d' = (\mu_s - \mu_n)/\text{SD} \tag{1}$$

where μ_s is the mean of the 2 distribution (signal) and μ_n is the mean of the 0 distribution (no signal). For our numerical example the value of d' is $(2 - 0)/1 = 2$. The parameter C is represented by the z score of the cut point referenced to the 0 distribution. Because it is just halfway between the two means, its value is 1.

In this example we have talked about theoretical values of a theoretical structure. There is no empirical content in the material discussed so far except for the integrals of the distributions of Figure 2 that represent the response probabilities generated by the observer. Consequently, although in the example here we talk as though we know the nature and location of the distributions, the problem is quite the reverse in any actual application of the theory. In reality we must use our knowledge of the observer's empirical response probabilities and work backward to construct the underlying structure from which those response probabilities might arise.

Insofar as the signals and nonsignals in any given experiment are unmarked with arithmetical values, the notion that the abscissa of the underlying perceptual structure is a numerical representation must depend on the response probabilities themselves. One way to do this is to assume that the observer calculates a likelihood ratio $l(x)$ by taking the ratio of the value of the ordinate $f_s(z)$ of the signal distribution at the observing point z and the value of the no-signal ordinate $f_n(z)$ at the same point as shown in Equation 2

$$l(x) = f_s(z)/f_n(z) \tag{2}$$

If we then redefine the cut point C as a ratio of such ordinates at $C = z$, then we can define a new response bias measure β, as shown in Equation 3

$$\beta = f_s(C)/f_n(C) \tag{3}$$

Since the value of C in our example above (Fig. 2) is just at the point that the distributions cross, the heights of the ordinates of the distributions are equal, and $\beta = 1$. The observer's decision rule is then reduced to the principle: if $l(x) > \beta$, say 2, if $l(x) < \beta$, say 0.

Such a simple and transparent theory hardly seems likely to serve as a candidate for a revolutionary way of thinking about psychological problems concerning human judgment, yet this is exactly the result of the theory of signal detectability. It has spawned new appreciation of the possibilities of representing human nature as a function of behavioral variables, the interactions and invariances of which are constrained by a more or less well-formed mathematical structure. Obviously many questions arise. They are dealt with in various ways later, but three that come to mind most immediately are mentioned here.

First, what happens if the standard deviations of the signal and no-signal distributions are not equal? In principle nothing serious occurs except that an additional parameter must be estimated from the data. The symmetry of the isosensitivity function around the minor axis is distorted or, if the data are plotted in normal probability coordinates rather than linear probability coordinates, the best-fitting line to the data points tilts away from a 45° line. The interpretation of such differences in variability between the no-signal and signal distributions is open to any ripe imagination; the central experimental problem is to design techniques for administering events about which decisions are to be made that give rise to distributions with equal variability. Such experimental methods are becoming better understood. They rest primarily upon requiring observers to make judgments about differences of ratios of pairs of events rather than absolute judgments about the events themselves. Thus instead of asking an observer to judge the presence or absence of some weak signal, we ask the observer to judge whether the second of two signals presented on each occasion is greater or less than the first.

A second question independent of the first concerns methods for assessing the reliability of the estimated parameters. This statistical issue has been examined from time to time and there are both parametric (22) and nonparametric (40) methods for comparing data obtained within these experimental contexts.

Once the theory of signal detectability is proposed as a basis for understanding decisions, a common question arises. Can some procedure be prescribed based on the payoff matrices and the sensitivity of the observer that will permit the observer to maximize or optimize the payoffs in a given situation? That is, is there some criterion point that is "best" for the particular payoff matrix and the observer's sensitivity? This is not only an intriguing theoretical issue for scientists ranging from economists to psychotherapists; it is of great practical importance because decisions for action often depend on poorly discriminable events and payoff matrices having utilities that may not be entirely obvious. Thus it would be helpful to know, for example, where to set the cut point for the selection of personnel for programs that require expensive and extensive training when selection is based on tests or other measures that yield signals that are difficult to distinguish. Solutions to this problem clearly depend on the kinds of decision rules that are used. An early discussion of some of these decision rules can be found in reference 39 and in the extensive analysis of optimum decision procedures contained in the important dissertation by Marill (34).

Stated as a rule of thumb, data obtained to determine whether people optimize in the sense of maximizing expected value or percent correct show that individual performance departs systematically from optimum behavior. Examples from Green (24) are buttressed by additional references cited here. In general terms the responses of people tend to be more conservative than theories of optimization predict. In dealing with this issue, some elaboration to enhance the stark simplicity of the original theory of signal detectability is needed. In particular questions about how response bias is modulated constitute, at the practical level, a most important class of problems. Signal processing by the sensory systems has been almost entirely preempted by the study of the physiological transduction systems. This work is reinforced by psychophysical studies and the methodologies based on developments of signal detectability theory, but it seems clear that the primary contributions of this theory will come from a deeper understanding of how the response structure itself is organized by the cognitive and affective aspects of a person's nature.

CRITICISMS OF THEORY OF SIGNAL DETECTABILITY AND DEVELOPMENT OF ALTERNATIVE THEORIES

A change in experimental method such as that produced by the theory of signal detectability offers a new way to view experiments and data in an old area. As such, it leads to conflicts, objections, reactions, and new alternatives. This investiture of a new theory declares it open for opposition and makes it important for scientific progress. Theories die more often from not being attacked than from being the objects of extensive criticism.

Generally the objections to the theory of signal detectability take two major forms. First, the theoretical structure is often construed as too weak. That is, the distributions that underlie the response structure are arbitrary, underivable from more fundamental principles, unconnected with known facts about the physiological structure of the organism, and unrejectable by data collected in ways that the theory requires. This class of objections is a natural reaction to statistical models in general, especially if the distribution functions are not derivable from simple mechanisms intrinsic to the substantive area. Consequently experimentalists and theoreticians have searched for ways to generate signal-detection–like distributions from known physiological mechanisms or from other structures that spread across more than sensory mechanisms.

Examples of such countertheories are the choice theory of Luce (30), the neural counting models of McGill (35), and the enlargement by Durlach and Braida (6) of the theory of signal detectability. All these theories more or less willingly accept the central tenet of the theory of signal detectability, namely that a two-parameter decision theory is essential. The issues that are raised by these theoreticians concern the origin of the underlying decision distribution, the nature of the mechanisms by which these distributions are modulated, and the plausibility of the neurological source of information internal to the person making the decisions.

A second source of objection to the theory of signal detectability is that it does not fit the data. This is quite the reverse of the first objection, where the theory is construed as too weak to be successful because it fits all data without illuminating any. The second objection is based on experiments for which the theory is silent but which yield data one would not expect if a literal interpretation of the theory were forced on the experiment. A classic example of objections of this kind are displayed in the experiments reported by Parducci and Sandusky (37). Let us turn to a brief overview of such work referred to above to help deflect overreaction to our critical remarks.

In his seminal book, *Individual Choice Behavior*, Luce (30) proposed one of the first alternatives to the theory of signal detectability. The theory postulates that the conditional probabilities of response in the presence or absence of a signal depend on the values of two hypothetical ratio scales, one called α and the other called v. The α scale is construed as a measure of the similarity between the event presented to the person and some standard event (e.g., the mean of an underlying noise distribution) for which a response of a particular kind is appropriate. The v scale is simply a numerical value of the bias parameter and is estimated from the data based on the formulas of Equations 4 and 5

$$P \text{ (hit)} = \alpha/(\alpha + v) \tag{4}$$

$$P \text{ (false alarm)} = 1/(1 + v) \tag{5}$$

where hit and false alarm probabilities (P) are the same as defined in SIGNAL-DETECTION THEORY: AN EXAMPLE ..., p. 105.

In plotting the isosensitivity functions derivable from both the signal-detectability and the choice-theoretic model, Luce (ref. 30, p. 61–62) makes the important point that "although the ROC curves from the two models are practically indistinguishable, there is a significant difference of interpretation. In the model of signal detectability the subject selects a cutoff point along a decision axis, whereas in the axiom 1 model, he selects a response bias. The latter model and its interpretation seem to be more readily generalized to more complex experiments." Unfortunately the applicability of choice theory to more complex experiments has not materialized significantly. The author has abandoned this theory for a model based on hypotheses of a nonpsychological nature. Such hypotheses, which are often represented as physiological, have been used to motivate alternative mathematical structures for signal detection. Specifically this second class of alternative models arises from the belief that known neurophysiological facts should temper the nature of psychological theory. Although there can be no question that in principle such an assertion is true, it is not at all clear that through the use of verbal report, contact will be made with such underlying physiological mechanisms. The likelihood that the neurophysiology generating verbal responses has even highly indirect access to uncoded information about activities in the sensory pathways seems extremely small. On the other hand, if it is argued that the information in the sensory pathways limits what can be reported by the observer, then there may indeed be constraints on the observer's responses that are attributable to the physiological structure of the sensory system.

A first example of such a theory is McGill's neural counting model for energy detection as a basis for auditory amplitude discrimination (35). McGill proposes a counting mechanism for sensory amplitude detection. The general idea is that the flow of information arising in a receptor is monitored somewhere in the central nervous system in terms of a count of the number of arriving impulses. These undifferentiated impulses may arise in a variety of channels, but when they come together at the counter, they simply add additional counts. The pulses transmitted through each channel must follow certain rules—for example, that the rate of impulse transmission is proportional to the energy in the signal for that channel. Notice that the incoming signal is activating a series of parallel channels, each of which may be pulsing at its own rate. As the counter collects these impulses over a short but well-defined period it exhibits different counts even though the signal energy remains constant at the receptor. Thus the variability of stimulus effects on the active biological system is explained.

The statistics of such a counting mechanism are well understood. The counts generate a Poisson distribution. This distribution has the special property that a single statistic (λ) estimates both the mean, which is the representation of central tendency, and the variance, or spread, of the distribution.

McGill demonstrates that if energy change is selected as the appropriate metric of the physical amplitude variable, much of the classic psychophysical data can be generated by this simple counter. There is no need to introduce what the author considers the unnecessary complications of cognitive likelihood ratio analysis. McGill does not closely examine the topic of response criteria, preferring to return to an earlier mode when experimenters fixed criteria by using well-practiced observers who exactly understood the task. Consequently he is prepared to perform analyses of experimental variations of stimulus displays in which the false alarm rate is held constant by some experimental technique. Once that assumption is granted, he is able to describe the outcomes of experiments in which variations in signal energy, signal-to-noise ratio, the presence of pure tones in noise, and the constant proportionality of Weber's law are all derivable.

The central thrust of his criticism of the theory of signal detectability is that it does not physically analyze the stimulus. This reduces its potential for predicting the nature of the response structure independently of the data generated in an experiment. It is of unquestionable value to be able to predict in advance the consequences of a particular stimulus, given that we have exercised control over the cognitive components of the judgmental process. The advantages of such an approach in any engineering context are obvious.

A possible notion motivating such theories is that because the nervous system emits easily recognizable pulses and because the mean pulse rate is roughly proportional to the intensity of the applied irritation to the neural tissue, the mean pulse rate is the object of the primary decision. Note that McGill's attempt to reduce the role of decision processes does not extend to Luce and Green's (31) adaptation and modification of this model from one that counts to one that times. Rather Luce and Green explain the nature of the control over the sensitivity parameter exercised by the stimulus but recognize the existence of bias as more than an experimental problem.

The strong physiological substrate of the counting model of McGill and other similar models is not found in the approach to the problem of intensity discrimination proposed by Durlach and Braida (6). They imply that the theory of signal detectability is incomplete. It does not cope with the interrelations between intensity resolution, intensity magnitude, categorical judgment, and other features of discrimination and scaling that all seem closely related. Their basic model for sensitivity and bias is equivalent to the theory of signal detectability. They assume, however, that the incoming sensory information, in addition to generating a decision variable, is influenced by other factors, construed as noise, that contribute to the random nature of the decision. This noise is thought to arise from two aspects that they call sensation noise and memory noise. The sensation noise is analogous to the noise characteristics of the stimulus set and consequently is completely determined by the stimulus. On the other hand, because certain variations in response structure appear to be associated with the way in which the experiment is conducted, they construe that another form of noise is introduced by the effects of memory. Memory itself is thought to be divided into two operating modes: a sensory mode in which an icon or representation of the actual stimulus is preserved by some rehearsal mechanism, and a context-coding mode (a labeling process) in which the observer attempts to assign a name to the signal contingent on the set of possible signals (the context) in which the specific stimulus is embedded. Notice that the strategy of this approach consists of adopting the basic signal-detectability model and then adding to it additional representations that permit the estimation of additional parameters. These parameters improve precision and permit the model to represent a variety of experimental paradigms. The implicit criticism behind the theory is that although two-parameter decision theory does represent a formidable set of data, there are other interconnected experimental paradigms that are not accommodated by the theory. This point is made more explicit by some of the recent work of Parducci and Sandusky (37). In their experiments they alter the context in which the signal presentations are given, showing that biasing effects of probability of signal presentation, for example, are the reverse of those predicted by the theory of signal detectability when response optimization is assumed. In general their data demonstrate that various cognitive attitudes can be introduced into an experiment to alter the response structure in ways that the bias parameter does not accommodate.

DECISION THEORY AND THE THRESHOLD

I have not yet remarked on the relation between the development of the theory of signal detectability and the classic concept of the psychophysical threshold. The threshold notion itself dates at least from the late sixteenth century, when philosophers puzzled over the question of the identity of indiscernibles. The formalization of the notion of the threshold may have begun with the research of Weber (53) and his demonstration of the empirical law bearing his name. Details of the theory of the threshold were developed in 1860 by Fechner in *Elemente der Psychophysik* (7), along with a set of methods to determine the values of absolute and differential thresholds. These classic methods of threshold determination and the concepts and statistics of the psychometric function are a representation of theory similar to that of Blackwell (1), which deals with questions of false alarms and other so-called invalid modes of response. For a general overview see Galanter (14).

The central idea of modern interpretations of threshold theories is to adjust the proportion of hits generated by response bias according to the proportion of false alarms. We assume that the observer occasionally guesses correctly when he or she is unable actually to detect the presence of a signal. When this correction-for-guessing theory is coupled with the classic threshold model, one accounts for the presence of false alarms by estimating a second parameter that represents the degree of guessing. Whereas the classic theory presumes that there is a physiological limit below which signals will not produce any effect and above which signals will always produce a mental effect, this revision decouples the threshold-divided conscious-

ness from the verbal behavior of the observer. The theory becomes a two-parameter decision theory.

To account for response variability, the threshold may drift around its mean value as time passes according to (perhaps) a normal distribution. Consequently signals weaker than the mean threshold will occasionally be detected, whereas signals that are above the mean will be reported much more frequently. Within the framework of such a theory, response biases increase the chance that the experimental observer will report as a signal an event that in fact is not a signal. Consequently his bias will increase all of his hit percentages by some proportionate amount. This linear increase in hits and false alarms as his propensity to say yes increases is represented by a correction-for-guessing formula in which

$$P \text{ (true detections)} = \frac{P \text{ (hits)} - P \text{ (false alarms)}}{100 - P \text{ (false alarms)}} \quad (6)$$

A prediction of this theory is that hits and false alarms will trace an isosensitivity function that extends from the upper right-hand corner of Figure 3 to some arbitrary intercept on the ordinate. This intercept is the true probability of detecting a signal and represents the unbiased hit probability for a signal of given strength.

The fact that the data in Figure 3 curve down as they approach the ordinate enables us to reject such a theory out of hand. This does not imply, however, that a threshold theory is in principle incapable of characterizing the isosensitivity data. One can develop a more sophisticated threshold theory by assuming that in addition to guessing that signals are present when in fact they are not, the observer may also report that signals are absent when in fact they are present. Thus, like the observer's mind, the observer's response structure may be in one of two states. He or she may either be in a detection-reporting state, in which case he will report the signal as present when it is absent, or he may be in a non–detection-reporting state, in which case he will report the signal as not present when it is. The observer presumably reports the state that he is in, which may be induced by the presence or absence of the signal or by other response-bias factors. Thus he may falsify a proportion of his responses about each of his perceptual states.

This modification of the classic threshold theory produces a two-limbed isosensitivity function that is shown in Figure 3. Notice that it would be extremely difficult to select either decision theory on the basis of observed isosensitivity data. By adding a variety of additional states to the observer's mental equipment, it is possible to approximate, to any degree of precision, data from a variety of experiments. This has been shown in detail by Norman (36), who presents various multistate threshold models.

Although it is not necessary to reject the concept of

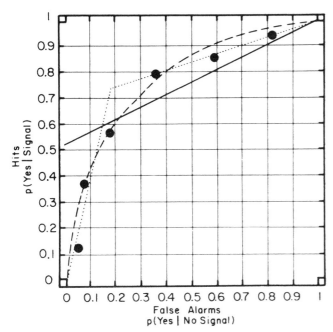

FIG. 3. Isosensitivity graph; coordinates are linear proportions. The 3 functions represent 3 different theories. *Solid line,* threshold theory; *dashed line,* theory of signal detectability; *dotted line,* two-limbed threshold theory. [From Galanter (11). In: *Yearbook of Science and Technology,* edited by D. I. Eggenberger. Copyright © 1966 by McGraw-Hill Book Company. Used with permission of McGraw-Hill Book Company.]

the threshold to retain the advantages of a two-parameter decision theory, the wide acceptance of the theory of signal detectability has resulted in questions concerning the true existence of the threshold. The theory of signal detectability makes the notion of a threshold meaningless insofar as the events to be classed as one kind either do or do not differ in the statistical sense from the events to be classed as another kind. If the two distributions of the events differ, and if he is given a sufficiently large sample, then regardless of the minuteness of the difference, the observer will be able to make the discrimination. A threshold in such a process does not exist, except insofar as the observer's sample sizes are not sufficient to permit reliable discrimination. In principle, of course, discrimination between distributions with even the most minute differences is always possible.

We move now from considerations of methodological niceties, and why the theory of signal detectability is attractive, to whether the theory itself has made any significant contributions to the study of topics having their own intrinsic substantive interest. I begin this examination by turning first to the area of vigilance and reviewing here some research on this topic that has resulted from considerations of the theory of signal detectability.

VIGILANCE AND WATCH KEEPING

Vigilance and watch keeping are concerned with

detection and identification under conditions of high uncertainty—temporal or spatial. In the usual vigilance experiment, the experimental observer has minimal information about the time or visual location of the stimulus for a particular presentation. The consistent experimental finding is that detection and identification performance deteriorates from the beginning to the end of the watch. The rate of deterioration depends on a number of variables, primarily on the initial detection probability (48). Other factors such as target stability also influence the watch keeping, but a common question is whether the deterioration may represent some slow decay of the sensory system in terms of a loss of sensitivity or whether the phenomenon is attributable to biasing factors such as fatigue or boredom. A two-parameter decision theory with experiments designed to distinguish among these alternatives should shed some light on these problems.

Early in the development of the theory of signal detectability, Broadbent (4) and Mackworth (32, 33) examined the application of the theory on the watch-keeping task. I now review some of their work and collateral reports that show how these topics have influenced experiments on the vigilance process. It should be noted that some of the later two-parameter decision models, such as the counting model of McGill, may provide deeper explanations for the vigilance phenomenon than do simple detection theories. Swets (46), in his excellent review of recent vigilance experiments, points out the need to distinguish between the theory of signal detectability as an explanatory model of the watch-keeping task and as a useful analytic procedure for data reduction. Generally, however, the tenor of research using the theory of signal detectability is to try to test the model. This line appears consistently in the research, and, like Swets, we consider this effort a rather empty exercise.

Although time uncertainty has been a central parameter studied by psychophysicists, vigilance experiments, because of the protracted times needed, have minimally exploited these models. The difficulty of coupling decision theory involving discrete responses with a presumably continuous process is the nub of the issue. For example, a currently intractable problem is the study of skilled motor performance. The experiments in this field are aimed at the measurement of work-load decrements in the performance of skilled operators. The problem exhibits itself because of the high quality of motor performance in general. Crashes, although catastrophic, are extremely rare events and are not heralded by proportionately large departures from routine error rates. Although the performance may continue with great precision until a catastrophic event occurs, however, there is a strong and probably correct intuition that the catastrophe is preceded by changes in effort—both cognitive and perceptual—required to maintain the requisite precision. Techniques for the study of such work-load decrement problems, including secondary-task deterioration, may force the expansion of decision-theory ideas back to the examination of the continuous case. At this time I simply note the lack of such a rapprochement and suggest the importance of its study.

Finally, I remark on the connection between practical and theoretical issues that are nicely intertwined in the vigilance situation. Although not as dramatic as some of the possible applications of the theory of signal detectability to the medical and pharmacological areas, watch keeping and the performance that depends on it are among the most consequential jobs in a high-technology environment. The air-traffic control specialist is a prime example of the demands on vigilance made by complex man-machine systems.

Two fairly recent books, one by Broadbent (4) and the other by Mackworth (33), represent contemporary thinking about the problem of vigilance as interpreted by models of decision theory. Broadbent reports eight different experiments conducted throughout the 1960s that demonstrate unequivocally that d', the sensitivity parameter of the signal-detection model, is the same at the end of a vigilance-requiring work day as at the beginning. This represents a substantiation within vigilance theory that the observed decrease in detection during a watch-keeping task is due to an upward shift in the criterion. An extremely important result of Broadbent's continuing work, however, concerns experiments in which the rate of occurrence of events reported is high. Under such conditions there tend to be decrements in d' that result in fewer detection responses unless there are compensating criterion shifts. This suggests that to optimize vigilance performance, payoff functions must be introduced that are time dependent and that increase the value of reporting signals as the watch time increases.

Paralleling and supporting the work of Broadbent are the extensive experiments of Mackworth (33). In his book *Vigilance and Attention*, he summarizes the findings of a variety of experiments. Like Broadbent's results, those of Mackworth all point to an interpretation based on an upward shift of criterion. This yields a decrease in the hit rate during monotonous decision-making tasks. Mackworth interprets this as evidence for a habituation of neural responses to noise events. This habituation effect is quite general and also includes neural responses to the "wanted" stimuli. Consequently observers exhibit a reduction in vigilance performance.

Whereas it may seem that the most telling use of two-parameter decision theory is to discount the role of sensory change as a modulator of behavior, some work has shown that indeed where either volitional or sensory effects could occur, some changes are attributable to sensory effects. Cahoon (5) required observers to detect 30 bright flashes in a series of dimmer flashes over a period of 2 h under four different levels of oxygen deprivation. The oxygen deprivation ranged from sea-level environments to levels corresponding to 5,100-m altitude. The experimenter demonstrated

that d', the sensitivity parameter, decreased with increasing oxygen deprivation, whereas β, the response bias parameter, showed little variation across levels of oxygen concentration. Other performance tests administered by the experimenter also showed positive correlations with values of d'. This suggests that in situations where known effects on sensory systems occur, alterations in the detection parameter also occur. Similar results are reported by Loeb et al. (29), in which vigilance performance was compared among experimental subjects that had been administered d-amphetamine, chlorpromazine, benactyzine, and a placebo. The results demonstrate unequivocally that the placebo yields performance changes that are represented by shifts in the criterion toward greater conservatism. Under the influence of the placebo, there was no change in d'. The tranquilizers, however, both decreased d' and shifted the criterion measure. The stimulant, on the other hand, resulted in essentially constant d' and β for the duration of the vigil. One may conclude that the stimulant improved performance insofar as the commonly observed vigilance decrement did not occur. Mackworth (32) has also reported data that show the stabilizing effects of amphetamine in the vigilance situation. These results and others reviewed by Swets (46) demonstrate the power of the signal-detection model to characterize those features of a person that are differentially affected by environmental change.

In the vigilance task the general amplitude level of the environment and the changes to be detected are extremely low: the task is inducive to quiescent states. The payoffs, however, are designed toward high attensity. The results show that for small-amplitude modulations, one sets a higher and higher criterion level on what will be accepted as a signal. This passage of the sensory systems into quiescence is an analogue of the act of falling asleep. Whether sleep is itself a reduction in sensitivity of the receptor systems or an increase in the criterion for the representation of an external environmental change is a question that is not fully understood. There is no doubt that detection levels during sleep are enormously reduced, and it is probable that both processes work together to accentuate this phenomenon; but if vigilance is the complement of sleep, then its study may yield insights into this most common, yet poorly understood, modulation of sensory functioning.

PERCEPTION AND PSYCHOPHYSICS

Topics in perception were always thought to be illuminated, if not explained, by psychophysical data. In addition psychophysical experiments have often asked the basic perceptual questions about the limits and constraints on the sensory side of the perception process. Thus the growth of decision theory in the study of psychophysical functions constitutes a natural development, while its applications in more perceptual areas depend on the philosophical stance of the investigator. Topics in perception have consistently divided theorists into two major opposing camps: the nativists, Gestalt psychologists, holists, or organization theorists versus the empiricists, learning theorists, choice theorists, and associationists. The central issue dividing the two groups is whether perceptual events as a basis for cognition are intrinsic to the structural constraints of the organism and the physical constraints of the world—the Gestalt position—or are the result of accidental contingencies and highly probable consequences that arise in a relatively universal way among all members of a given population in their commerce with the physical world based on the associative structures of their neural tissue—the associationist position. The argument consequently is genetic. How do the observable perceptual organizations develop?

The advent of two-parameter decision theory in no way resolves the primary nativist-empiricist controversy. Indeed it does not address the question, although it has been suggested elsewhere that the associationists' doctrine may in fact be representable as a pure decision-theory problem. This view, which has never been considered seriously, is enunciated in the following quotation (10):

> But in [association] theory, stimuli are simply discriminable events. Any organization that the stimuli possess must be based upon connections of discrimination, or orderings over manipulable variables of the stimuli. The kind of rebuttal that [association] theory gives to these ideas is the proposal that, for the human adult, the organizations may exist, but such organizations are simply an elaborate construction out of basic stimulus elements (i.e., discriminative responses) that results from having learned certain things. We now merely project this acquired knowledge upon the environment. Thus, the [association] theorist believes that the perceptual world, the world that we see, is composed of two parts. First the discriminative [response] elements that we have called stimuli, and second a mental operation imposed on stimuli as a result of prior knowledge. The prior knowledge that the [association] theorist uses to get some organization onto the stimuli was called (by Wundt, 1894), the *apperceptive mass*. Although it was thought of by the classical psychologist as an image of one kind or another, many modern [associationists] presume that the apperceptive mass is some form of bias on previously learned responses. These responses and their biases, when made in the presence of certain stimuli, are the only evidence of an organization of the stimuli. In essence, the [associationist] argues that the visual world is constructed from discriminative components [or responses] held together or organized, as a result of our having learned certain [other] responses. These [other] responses, when they were made in the past, yielded outcomes of value which led to biases that now suggest an organization of the physical stimuli. But these stimuli are as disconnected as ever. It is only what is said or done about them that leads us to assume they are organized.

Such a strung-out view of perceptual processes as merely response bias is hard to swallow. On the other hand, it is not inconceivable that many of the perceptual puzzles—the illusions, for example—may represent the effects of biasing variables in the perceptual system. Such biases may function to provide compensation for the flexible and deformable energy ensembles at our receptors. Thus the perceptual world can be formed into coherent and continuous stretches and expanses as the disjunct glimpses, and overheard phrases become assembled into the nicely filled up and infinitely extendable world of sight and sound.

Recall, however, our earlier comments about the role of amplitude discrimination on perception, and note that if such a distinction is valid, then the associationistic analysis may apply only to the affective side of perception. This position is by no means as patently rejectable as is the view that the cognitive features of the world are merely learned associations. Emotional responses to the elemental components of discrimination could well serve as the building blocks of human affective nature. The Pavlovian conditioning of the autonomic nervous system and its role in the generation of feelings are well documented. To attribute to the psychophysically isolated features of the perceptual world, the role of merely conditioned stimuli in no way devalues their relevance to understanding human nature.

FECHNER'S PROBLEM

The research reported in *Elemente der Psychophysik* by Fechner in 1860 (7) established the empirical procedures for conducting psychophysical experiments to determine critical benchmarks of sensory functioning: the absolute threshold, the differential threshold, and the identifiability of stimuli. These various matching techniques and constant stimulus methods compose the central arsenal of psychophysical experimentation. Fechner's goal was more extensive than the mere development of experimental technologies, however. Indeed his intention was to resolve the mind-body problem in scientific terms. This problem, the connection between consciousness and the material environment, has been a crucial question in western philosophic thought for thousands of years. Modern science resolves it either by rejecting the concept of consciousness and replacing it with the parametric values of behavioral laws or by regarding conscious activity as the subtle physicochemical rumbling of the central nervous system; but the phenomenon itself does not melt away under these explanatory rubrics. Rather we either turn our backs on it or reduce it to nonequivalent material activities that are putatively scientific.

Fechner, on the other hand, was not so cavalier. His concern for the problem of consciousness and its relation through the sensory systems to the physical world was to be solved by the development of a mathematical model that would represent the dynamics of conscious function in terms of an equation that related numerical representations of consciousness to numerical representations of the energy values of the physical environment. Furthermore he demanded that the basis on which the numerical representation of conscious events was generated had to be intrinsically nonintrospective and thus based only on judgments of the sort discussed in earlier paragraphs. That is, only judgments of matching or equivalence on the one hand, or asymmetric judgments of greater or less on the other were sufficiently primitive to preclude bias of the conscious experience by verbal or cultural phenomena. The introspective examination of consciousness was eschewed by Fechner as being no more legitimate than the prior attempts by epistomologists to establish the nature of consciousness through personal introspection and armchair research.

This work resulted in the well-known Massformel, Fechner's law. This states that the experiential consequences of environmental energies can be numerically represented by the logarithm of an appropriate metric of the energy continuum. The promulgation of Fechner's law set the stage for a variety of experimental activities aimed at characterizing the nature of physical and conscious phenomena by explicating the transduction processes of the sensory systems (26). Such activity continues to the present day, because the examination of these neurological mechanisms bypasses Fechner's central question, which concerns the nature of conscious experience. This hardly fetches a smile among the legions of sensory psychophysicists, whereas it represented the heart of the theoretic enterprise to Fechner. The development of sensory scaling, as Fechnerian methods came to be called, and their extensions by Thurstone (49) to nonmetric external events had two consequences. First, as previously described, Fechner's experimental methods were extended and improved, in particular through the theory of signal detectability. The applications of Fechnerian scaling, on the other hand, turned toward the scaling of nonphysical events such as attitudes, mental abilities, and esthetics, areas in which Fechner himself pioneered (8).

This interest generated by Fechner in the measurement of consciousness fell to a group of experimentalists far removed from the classical psychophysical mold. Their concern was not with receptor functioning, a topic they considered irrelevant to the assessment of the mental events they were trying to measure. Rather, the intrinsic structure of Fechner's law became the object of their concern.

MAGNITUDE ESTIMATION—SCALING BY INTROSPECTIVE REPORT

The importance of psychophysical scaling depends on turning a technique to assess responses to environ-

mental events into a measure of their conscious effects on people. For instance, the acoustic engineers wanted to measure sound levels to reflect aspects of human response to the sound. In particular, questions arose regarding for example, whether the sounds were too loud, or interfered with other activities. Fechner's law seemed to help. The decibel, that is, a logarithmic transformation of acoustic energy, certainly represented how people experienced sounds better than the actual energy levels. Still the adequacy of this decibel representation left something to be desired. Engineers and psychophysicists needed to develop new psychophysical functions that approximated more closely the experiences subjects reported about the environments where they worked or lived.

During the middle 1950s, S.S. Stevens, at the psychoacoustic laboratory at Harvard University, continued to explore other methods for obtaining numerical representations of sensory experience. Generally his methods involve assigning numerical representations to stimulus presentations by direct introspection. The observer is then asked to report on the introspectively assessed experience. The data from a dozen of these experiments were compiled in a report by Stevens and Galanter (45) that showed an intrinsic nonlinearity between people's introspective judgments of the experiential effects of various stimulus domains and what turned out to be Fechnerian scales (18). These data demonstrated unequivocally that subjects could report numerically about some feature of their experience and that these reports generated smooth functions. Furthermore these functions exhibited a common structure: namely, a power function, which is of the form

$$\Psi = \alpha\Phi^\beta \tag{7}$$

where Ψ is the numerical report of the experience produced by physical stimulus Φ. When data conform to this function and are plotted in double logarithmic coordinates, the resulting straight line is represented by the slope parameter β. The intercept, α, may or may not be determined by the experimenter.

The usual procedure for collecting data in the magnitude-estimation experiment involves presenting to the observer a stimulus S^s, the standard, which is assigned a specific numerical value R^s, the modulus. In the case of sounds, the data shown in Figure 4 represent a series of judgments made about seven different stimuli when the stimulus value at 85 dB was assigned the modulus 100. As plotted in the double logarithmic coordinates of this figure, the slope, estimated by a least-squares solution for the best-fitting line, is about 0.60.

In general the slope parameter of magnitude-estimation functions varies from one sense department to another, but within a particular modality it is relatively insensitive to large variations in experimental procedure. This observation led Stevens and his colleagues to argue that magnitude-estimation tech-

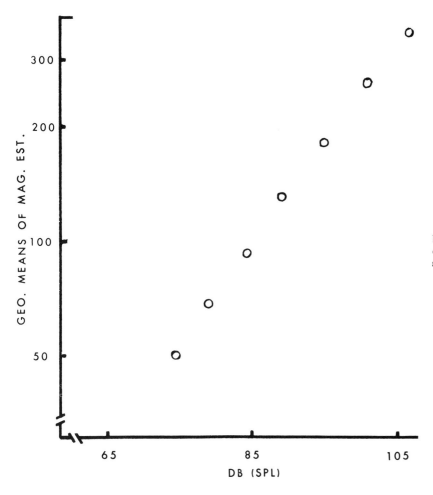

FIG. 4. A magnitude-estimation function based on geometric means of judgments of 10 observers. Standard stimulus of 85 dB was assigned the modulus 100.

niques yield a psychophysical law that is superior to Fechner's law because it is less subject to biasing effects from experimental context or manipulation than those generated by scaling methods based on Fechner's law.

The main consequence that followed the development of the magnitude-estimation techniques was the wholesale application of these methods to a variety of problems for which sensory scales of environmental events could serve some practical purpose. These procedures have given rise to the establishment of engineering standards for the calculation of such subjective experiences as loudness (44) and annoyance of aircraft overflight sounds (9); there are other scales such as the utility scale of money (12) that are not yet standard but are widely applicable.

One of the early criticisms directed at methods of magnitude estimation concerned the fact that most of the experimental data were based on averages, calculated across subject populations. That is, the construction of a scale of loudness depended on judgments made by a sample of subjects who judged the loudness of a set of sounds. Stevens (43) said that he preferred to interpret magnitude-estimation judgments as a public opinion poll. The problem is that data from experiments consisting of repeated trials on individuals often yielded functions less smooth than group

data. Individual data functions often displayed cusps and breaks that most probably revealed the existence of biases of one type or another. These data showed departures from the smooth power function commonly observed in group data. This might be because the individual observer, on recognizing a signal as one he has heard before, may recall his numerical assignment to the recognized signal and repeat it. Insofar as his original judgment was not in error, this tendency can only improve the quality of the data by reducing the variability of judgment. If the original judgment was off target, however, the repetition merely increases the reliability of the deviant judgment and exacerbates the departures from linearity. The consequence may be a function with well-defined breaks, cusps, or flyers.

Evidence that observers do use the same judgments for repeated presentations of the same stimuli has been reported by Galanter et al. (17). When individuals were presented with a second pass through nine different stimuli, about 20% of their second judgments were identical to their first responses. To minimize this effect we have adopted a procedure in which successive passes through the stimulus set are made only after a shift in S^s and R^s. This technique generates individual-observer data that are fit by a power function about as well as group data. With this method the magnitude-estimation technique becomes a viable method for assessing the perceptual judgments of individuals. By constantly shifting the standard and the modulus, the observer is forced to use different numerical values even though he may believe that the stimulus is the same as one he has heard before. The results of the application of this technique to a single observer are shown in Figure 5. Data from a similar experiment using a constant standard and modulus are also plotted here. We see that the variable standard and modulus function is as regular and linear as similar functions obtained from groups.

To accept magnitude-estimation judgments as data is to accept introspective report. Insofar as such judgments represent subjective magnitudes, we may question the nature of the events about which magnitudes are reported. Clearly the magnitudes are not those of the experience of the stimulus. Observers consistently deny examining an image of the stimulus in making their judgment. It is the stimulus effect that is reported, an effect we think represents the feelings or emotions generated or modulated by the stimulus. The easiest kind of magnitude judgments to obtain from subjects are those that represent some affective aspect of the stimulus, such as annoyances, or worth or value. The ability of people to represent numerically how they feel has been exploited in our research to

measure such personally and socially important attitudes as the seriousness of criminal acts (41), the value of money (19), annoyance of aircraft overflights (20), and the desirability of various events (13). Note should also be taken of a different interpretation: observers may simply be making the "stimulus error." That is, they are merely reporting an interpretation of the stimulating conditions based on their experience with the sources of the stimulus dynamics. This position has been developed most effectively by Warren and Warren (52).

The development of magnitude-estimation scaling and its implications for practical and theoretical issues (e.g., see ref. 25) bring the wheel of psychophysical studies full circle. The earliest work in psychophysics was designed to catch consciousness in the scientific net. This effort was abandoned with the development of the biological and neurophysiological disciplines and their application to sensation and perception. At first, though, the limitations of instrumentation and technique forced these studies to depend on behavioral data. Within this context the data from the psychophysical observer was accepted only if it was generated in a most reduced form. The data had to be emitted as though from a decerebrate preparation. Interpretation and introspective exploration were precluded as appropriate response modes. Judgments of equivalence or difference construed as minimal representations of sensory functioning were the only tolerable experimental devices.

The reach of these data limited the interpretation placed on the theories for which the data were collected. Clearly if the data represent at most relative frequencies of binary judgments, the quintessential feature of sensory experience is carefully concealed from the experimenter. The development of this minimal psychophysics was not only a necessary beginning but was important for the development of many behavioral theories and models that gave us new insight into the nature of the response structure of the human observer. The details of these insights, however, were still shrouded by the limitations in the response mechanisms that were accepted as generating the data base.

The need for this behavioral radicalism was attributable primarily to the intrinsically unwieldy and unreliable results from the introspective methods used by Wundt at Leipzig and by Titchener at Cornell. Although the psychophysicists deplored the descriptive ramifications of the introspective report, they were hard pressed to deny the importance of the structural properties of the experience that the introspection provided. The Gestalt movement in Germany attempted to retain the relevant introspections while discarding the introspective method. This led to ingenious demonstrations that relied for their validity on the punch they gave to consciousness. The psychophysical methods themselves were used when they applied to the resolution of dichotomous questions. The nature of extended experience, however, appeared

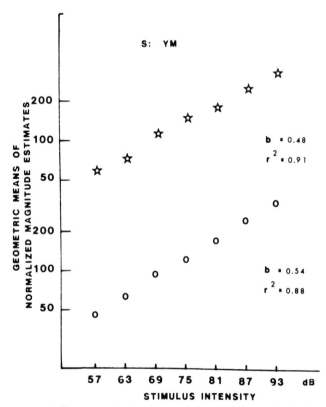

FIG. 5. Two magnitude-estimation functions for a single observer. *Circles*, judgments made with constantly shifting standard and modulus; *stars*, judgments made with standard stimulus equal to 69 dB assigned the modulus 100. Functions are displaced on ordinate to separate data.

not to yield to the abstract constructions based on these binary judgments.

We have seen in this final section how psychophysics has returned to a weak form of introspection. The scaling methods that rely on an exploration of consciousness provide some hope that we may enrich our understanding of human perceptual functioning by relaxing our demands on the observer. We must try to release the ambient mind from the mold constructed by the radical behaviorists. This enrichment of our data base will expand our comprehension of the subtle and complex issues that are involved in the day-to-day commerce between the human being and his environment.

The preparation of this chapter was supported in part by a grant from the U.S. National Aeronautics and Space Administration. Part of the research reported here was supported by the U.S. Office of Naval Research.

GENERAL REFERENCES*

ANNETT, J., AND L. PATERSON. Training for auditory detection. *Acta Psychol.* 27: 420–426, 1967.

BAEKELAND, F., AND P. HOY. Vigilance before and after sleep. *Percept. Mot. Skills* 31: 583–586, 1970.

BANKS, W. P. Criterion change and response competition in unlearning. *J. Exp. Psychol.* 82: 216–223, 1969.

BERNBACH, H. A., AND G. H. BOWER. Confidence ratings in continuous paired-associate learning. *Psychon. Sci.* 21: 252–253, 1970.

BERNSTEIN, I. H., M. H. CLARK, AND R. R. BLAKE. Sensitivity and decisional factors in the psychological refractory period. *Percept. Psychophys.* 7: 33–37, 1970.

BOTHE, G. B., AND L. E. MARKS. Absolute sensitivity to white noise under auxiliary visual stimulation. *Percept. Psychophys.* 8: 176–178, 1970.

BROWN, A. E., AND H. K. HOPKINS. Interaction of the auditory and visual sensory modalities. *J. Acoust. Soc. Am.* 41: 1–6, 1967.

BROWN, J., AND D. A. ROUTH. Recognition assessed by d' and by a nonparametric alternative (the A-index) as a function of the number of choices. *Q. J. Exp. Psychol.* 22: 707–719, 1970.

CARTERETTE, E. C., AND M. COLE. Comparison of the receiver operating characteristics for messages received by ear and by eye. *J. Acoust. Soc. Am.* 34: 172–178, 1962.

CARTERETTE, E. C., M. P. FRIEDMAN, AND M. J. WYMAN. Feedback and psychophysical variable in signal detection. *J. Acoust. Soc. Am.* 39: 1051–1055, 1966.

CLEMENT, D. E., AND K. E. HOSKING. Scanning strategies and differential sensitivity in a visual signal detection task: intrasubject reliability. *Psychon. Sci.* 22: 323–324, 1971.

COLQUHOUN, W. P., AND A. D. BADDELEY. Role of pretest expectancy in vigilance decrement. *J. Exp. Psychol.* 68: 156–160, 1964.

CREELMAN, C. D. Human discrimination of auditory duration. *J. Acoust. Soc. Am.* 34: 582–593, 1962.

DAVENPORT, W. G. Vibrotactile vigilance: the effects of cost and values on signal detection. *Percept. Psychophys.* 5: 25–28, 1969.

DOROSH, M. E., J. E. TONG, AND D. R. BOISSONEAULT. White noise, instructions, and two-flash fusion with two signal detection procedures. *Psychon. Sci.* 20: 98–99, 1970.

EARLE, D. C., AND G. LOWE. Channel, temporal and composite uncertainty in the detection and recognition of auditory and visual signals. *Percept. Psychophys.* 9: 177–181, 1971.

EIJKMAN, E., AND J. H. VENDRIK. Can a sensory system be specified by its internal noise? *J. Acoust. Soc. Am.* 37: 1102–1109, 1965.

ELFNER, L. F., AND W. R. DELAUNE. Detection of shift in binaural images: a rating method approach. *Percept. Psychophys.* 8: 158–160, 1970.

EMERICH, D. S. ROCs obtained with two signal intensities presented in random order, and a comparison between yes/no and rating ROCs. *Percept. Psychophys.* 3: 35–40, 1968.

FRIEDMAN, M. P., E. C. CARTERETTE, L. NAKATANI, AND A. AHUMADA. Comparisons of some learning models for response bias in signal detection. *Percept. Psychophys.* 3: 5–11, 1968.

GALANTER, E. Contemporary psychophysics. In: *New Directions in Psychology*, edited by T. Newcomb. New York: Holt, 1962, p. 89–156.

GESCHEIDER, G. A., W. G BARTON, M. R. BRUCE, J. H. GOLDBERG, AND M. J. GREENSPAN. Effects of simultaneous auditory stimulation on the detection of tactile stimuli. *J. Exp. Psychol.* 81: 120–125, 1969.

GESCHEIDER, G. A., J. H. WRIGHT, AND M. B. EVANS. Reaction time in the detection of vibrotactile signals. *J. Exp. Psychol.* 77: 501–504, 1968.

GROSS, H. A., BOYER, W. N., AND GUYOT, G. W. Determination of a DL using two point tactual stimuli: a signal detection approach. *Psychon. Sci.* 21: 198–199, 1970.

GURALNICK, M. J., AND K. G. HARVEY. Response requirements and performance in a visual vigilance task. *Psychon. Sci.* 20: 215–217, 1970.

HARDY, G. R., AND D. LEGGE. Cross modal induction of changes in sensory thresholds. *Q. J. Exp. Psychol.* 20: 20–29, 1968.

HATFIELD, J. L., AND D. R. SODERQUIST. Practice effects and signal detection indices in an auditory vigilance task. *J. Acoust. Soc. Am.* 46: 1458–1463, 1969.

HATFIELD, J. L., AND D. R. SODERQUIST. Coupling effects and performance in vigilance tasks. *Hum. Factors* 12: 351–359, 1970.

HELMHOLTZ, H. VON. *Treatise on Physiological Optics* [Leipzig: Voss, 1909–1911]. New York: Dover Reprint, 1962.

HERSHMAN, R. L., AND D. SMALL. Tables for d' for detection and localization. Perception and localization. *Percept. Psychophys.* 3: 321–323, 1968.

HUMA, A. L. Auditory detection and optimal response biases. *Percept. Psychophys.* 15: 425–433, 1974.

JACOBS, D. C., AND E. GALANTER. Estimates of utility function parameters from signal detection experiments. New York: Columbia Univ., Psychophys. Lab. Rep., 1974, vol. 32, p. 1–46.

JERISON, H. J., AND R. M. PICKETT. Vigilance: the importance of the elicited observing rate. *Science* 143: 970–971, 1964.

JOHANSON, A. M. The influence of incentive and punishment upon reaction-time. *Arch. Psychol.* 54: 2–8, 1922.

KINCHLA, R. A., AND L. G. ALLAN. Visual movement perception: a comparison of sensitivity to vertical and horizontal movement. *Percept. Psychophys.* 8: 399–405, 1970.

KINTSCH, W. An experimental analysis of single stimulus tests and multiple-choice tests of recognition memory. *J. Exp. Psychol.* 76: 1–6, 1968.

KOPP, I., AND I. LIVERMORE. Differential discriminability or response bias: a signal detection analysis of categorical perception. *J. Exp. Psychol.* 101: 179–182, 1973.

LINKER, E., M. E. MOORE, AND E. GALANTER. Taste thresholds, detection models and disparate results. *J. Exp. Psychol.* 67: 59–66, 1964.

LOEB, M., AND J. R. BINFORD. Examination of some factors influencing performance on an auditory monitoring task with one signal per aversion. *J. Exp. Psychol.* 83: 40–44, 1970.

LUCAS, P. A. Human performance in low-signal probability tasks. *J. Acoust. Soc. Am.* 42: 153–178, 1967.

MARTIN, E., AND A. W. MELTON. Meaningfulness and trigram recognition. *J. Verb. Learn. Verb. Behav.* 9: 126–135, 1970.

MILOSEVIC, S. Effect of time and space uncertainty on a vigilance task. *Percept. Psychophys.* 15: 331–334, 1974.

---

* These general references provide an excellent overview of the material presented in this chapter; specific references cited in the text follow.

MUNSINGER, H., AND K. GUMMERMAN. Simultaneous visual detection and recognition. *Percept. Psychophys.* 3: 383–386, 1968.

MURDOCK, B. B., JR. Signal detection and short-term memory. *J. Exp. Psychol.* 70: 443–447, 1965.

MURPHY, E. H., AND P. H. VENABLES. Ear asymmetry in the threshold of fusion of two clicks: a signal detection analysis. *Q. J. Exp. Psychol.* 22: 288–300, 1970.

PASTORE, R. E., AND C. J. SCHEIRER. Signal detection theory: consideration for general application. *Psychol. Bull.* 81: 945–958, 1974.

RYDER, P., R. PIKE, AND L. DALGHISH. What is the signal in signal detection? *Percept. Psychophys.* 15: 479–482, 1974.

SHIPLEY, E. F. A signal detection theory analysis of a category judgment experiment. *Percept. Psychophys.* 7: 38–42, 1970.

STURMER, G. VON. Time perception, vigilance and decision theory. *Percept. Psychophys.* 3: 197–200, 1968.

SWETS, J. A., AND T. G. BIRDSALL. Deferred decision in human signal detection: a preliminary experiment. *Percept. Psychophys.* 2: 15–28, 1967.

SWETS, J. A., J. MARKOWITZ, AND O. FRANZEN. Vibrotactile signal detection. *Percept. Psychophys.* 6: 83–88, 1969.

SWETS, J. A., AND S. T. SEWALL. Invariance of signal detectability over stages of practice and levels of motivation. *J. Exp. Psychol.* 66: 120–126, 1963.

TANNER, T. A., J. A. RANK, AND R. C. ATKINSON. Signal recognition as influenced by information feedback. *J. Math. Psychol.* 7: 259–274, 1970.

TORGERSON, W. S. *Theory and Methods of Scaling.* New York: Wiley, 1958.

VIEHMEISTER, N. F. Intensity discrimination: performance in three paradigms. *Percept. Psychophys.* 8: 417–419, 1970.

WESTERNDORF, D. H., AND R. FOX. Binocular detection of positive and negative flashes. *Percept. Psychophys.* 15: 61–65, 1974.

REFERENCES

1. BLACKWELL, H. R. Psychophysical thresholds, experimental studies of methods of measurement. Ann Arbor: Univ. of Michigan Eng. Res. Bull. No. 36, 1953.

2. BOYNTON, R. M., AND J. W. ONLEY. A critique of the special status assigned by Brindley to "psychophysical linking hypotheses" of "class A." *Vision Res.*, 2: 383–390, 1962.

3. BRINDLEY, G. S. *Physiology of the Retina and the Visual Pathway.* Baltimore, MD: William & Wilkins, 1960.

4. BROADBENT, D. E. *Decision and Stress.* New York: Academic, 1971.

5. CAHOON, R. L. Vigilance performance under hypoxia. *J. Appl. Psychol.* 54: 479–483, 1970.

6. DURLACH, N. I., AND L. D. BRAIDA. Intensity perception. I. Preliminary theory of intensity resolution. *J. Acoust. Soc. Am.* 46: 372–383, 1969.

7. FECHNER, G. T. *Elemente der Psychophysik.* Leipzig: Breitkopf & Hartel, 1860.

8. FECHNER, G. T. *Zur Experimentalen Aesthetik.* Leipzig: Hirzel, 1871.

9. FEDERAL AVIATION ADMINISTRATION. *Certification Procedure Federal Aviation Regulations,* Part 36, 1971, Washington, D.C.: Federal Aviation Administration, 1971.

10. GALANTER, E. *Textbook of Elementary Psychology.* San Francisco: Holden-Day, 1966.

11. GALANTER, E. Signal detection. In: *Yearbook of Science & Technology,* edited by D. I. Eggenberger. New York: McGraw-Hill, 1966, p. 387–389.

12. GALANTER, E. Psychological decision mechanisms and perception. In: *Handbook of Perception,* edited by E. Carterette and M. Friedman. New York: Academic, 1974, vol. 2, chapt. 4, p. 85–125.

13. GALANTER, E. *Utility Scales of Monetary and Non-Monetary Events.* New York: Columbia Univ. Press, 1975. (Psychophys. Lab. Tech. Rep. PLR-36.)

14. GALANTER, E. Psychophysics: an overview. In: *International Encyclopedia of Psychiatry, Psychology, Psychoanalysis, and Neurology,* edited by B. Wolman. New York: Aesculapius, 1977, p. 283–288.

15. GALANTER, E., AND M. GERSTENHABER. On thought: the extrinsic theory. *Psychol. Rev.* 63: 218–227, 1956.

16. GALANTER, E., AND G. L. HOLMAN. Some invariances of the isosensitivity function and their implications for the utility function of money. *J. Exp. Psychol.* 73: 333–339, 1967.

17. GALANTER, E., G. M. KARSTEN, AND N. L. HABER. Magnitude estimation functions for individuals. *Meeting Psychonomic Soc., November 1978, San Antonio, TX.*

18. GALANTER, E., AND S. MESSICK. The relations between category and magnitude scales of loudness. *Psychol. Rev.* 68: 363–372, 1961.

19. GALANTER, E., AND P. PLINER. Cross-modality matching of money against other continua. In: *Sensation and Measurement: Papers in Honor of S. S. Stevens,* edited by H. R. Moskowitz and B. Scharf. Dordrecht: Reidel, 1974, p. 65–76.

20. GALANTER, E., R. D. POPPER, AND T. B. PERERA. Annoyance scales for simulated VTOL and CTOL overflights. *J. Acoust. Soc. Am.* 62(S1), Dec., 1977, p. S8(A).

21. GOODMAN, N. Science and simplicity. In: *Philosophy of Science Today,* edited by S. Morgenbesser. New York: Basic Books, 1967, vol. 7, p. 68–78.

22. GOUREVITCH, V., AND E. GALANTER. A significance test for one parameter isosensitivity functions. *Psychometrike* 32: 25–33, 1967.

23. GRAHAM, C., AND P. RATOOSH. Notes on some inter-relations of sensory psychology, perception, and behavior. In: *Psychology: A Study of a Science,* edited by S. Koch. New York: McGraw-Hill, 1962, vol. 4, p. 483–514.

24. GREEN, D. M. Psychoacoustics and detection theory. *J. Acoust. Soc. Am.* 32: 1189–1203, 1960.

25. GREEN, D. M., AND R. D. LUCE. Variability of magnitude estimates: a timing theory analysis. *Percept. Psychophys.* 15: 291–300, 1974.

26. HELMHOLTZ, H. VON. *Handbuch der physiologischen Optik* (3rd ed.). Leipzig: Voss, 1909–1911.

27. HOOD, D. C. Visual sensitivity. In: *International Encyclopedia of Psychiatry, Psychology, Psychoanalysis, and Neurology,* edited by B. Wolman. New York: Aesculapius, 1977.

28. IRWIN, F. W., AND M. G. PRESTON. Avoidance of repetition of judgments across sense modalities. *J. Exp. Psychol.* 21: 511–520, 1937.

29. LOEB, M., G. R. HAWKES, AND E. A. ALLUISI. The influence of *d*-amphetamine, benactyzine, and chlorpromazine on performance in an auditory vigilance task. *Psychon. Sci.* 3: 29–30, 1965.

30. LUCE, R. D. *Individual Choice Behavior.* New York: Wiley, 1959.

31. LUCE, R. D., AND D. M. GREEN. A neural timing theory for response times and the psychophysics of intensity. *Psychol. Rev.* 79: 14–57, 1972.

32. MACKWORTH, J. F. The effect of amphetamine on detectability of signals in a vigilance task. *Can. J. Psychol.* 19: 104–110, 1965.

33. MACKWORTH, J. F. *Vigilance and Attention: A Signal Detection Approach.* Baltimore, MD: Penguin, 1970.

34. MARILL, T. *Detection Theory and Psychophysics.* Cambridge: MIT Press, 1956.

35. MCGILL, W. Neural counting mechanisms and energy detection in audition. *J. Math. Psychol.* 4: 351–376, 1967.

36. NORMAN, D. A. Sensory thresholds response bases and the neural quantum theory. *J. Math. Psychol.* 1: 88–120, 1964.

37. PARDUCCI, A., AND A. J. SANDUSKY. Limits on the applicability of signal detection theories. *Percept. Psychophys.* 7: 63–64, 1970.

38. PEARSON, E. S., AND H. O. HARTLEY. *Biometrica Tables for Statisticians.* New York: Cambridge, 1958, vol. 1.

39. PETERSON, W. W., T. G. BIRDSALL, AND W. C. FOX. The theory of signal detectability. *IRE Trans. Prof. Group Inform. Theory* 4: 171–212, 1954.

40. POLLACK, I., D. A. NORMAN, AND E. GALANTER. An efficient non-parametric analysis of recognition memory. *Psychon. Sci.* 1: 327–328, 1964.

41. SELLIN, T., AND M. E. WOLFGANG. *The Measurement of Delinquency.* New York: Wiley, 1964.

42. SMITH, M., AND E. H. WILSON. A model of the auditory threshold and its application to the problem of the multiple observer. *Psychol. Monogr.* 67: 67(9), 1953.

43. STEVENS, S. S. *Measurement: Definitions and Theories*, edited by C. W. Churchman and P. Ratoosh. New York: Wiley, 1959.

44. STEVENS, S. S. Perceived level of noise by Mark VII and decibels (E). *J. Acoust. Soc. Am.* 51: 575–593, 1972.

45. STEVENS, S. S., AND E. GALANTER. Ratio scales and category scales on a dozen perceptual continua. *J. Exp. Psychol.* 54: 377–412, 1957.

46. SWETS, J. A. Signal detection theory applied to vigilance. In: *Vigilance: Theory, Operational Performance, and Physiological Correlates*, edited by R. R. Mackie. London: Plenum, 1977.

47. TANNER, W. P., JR., AND J. A. SWETS. A decision making theory of visual detection. *Psychol. Rev.* 61: 401–409, 1954.

48. TEICHNER, W. H. The detection of a simple visual signal as a function of time of watch. *Hum. Factors* 16: 339–353, 1974.

49. THURSTONE, L. L. A law of comparative judgment. *Psychol. Rev.* 34: 273–286, 1927.

50. TORGERSON, W. S. Distances and ratios in psychophysical scaling. *Acta Psychol.* 19: 201–205, 1961.

51. VERPLANCK, W. S., J. W. COTTON, AND G. H. COLLIER. Previous training as a determinant of response dependency at the threshold. *J. Exp. Psychol.* 45: 10–14, 1953.

52. WARREN, R. M., AND R. P. WARREN. A critique of S. S. Stevens' "New Psychophysics." *Percept. Mot. Skills* 16: 797–810, 1963.

53. WEBER, E. H. *De pulsu, resorptione, auditu et tactu: annotationes anatomicae et physiological.* Leipzig: 1834.

54. WUNDT, W. *Lectures on Human and Animal Psychology.* New York: McMillan, 1894.

CHAPTER 4

Sensory function in animals

W. C. STEBBINS

C. H. BROWN

M. R. PETERSEN

Primate Laboratory, Kresge Hearing Research Institute, University of Michigan, Ann Arbor, Michigan

CHAPTER CONTENTS

IN THE ANALYSIS of sensations—the various ways in which organisms receive, process, and react to information about the events in their environment—two approaches have prevailed. Physiologists have monitored the electrical activity of receptors and of more central structures in response to sensory stimulation in a variety of creatures other than humans; psychologists, using the introspective methods of psychophysics, have relied on human language to discover how human beings respond to or judge the sensory stimuli that impinge upon them. As a consequence there are now two largely unrelated bodies of data, each with its accompanying theoretical framework. On the one hand, our understanding of the function of the nervous system in lower animals—of the transduction and subsequent treatment of a variety of forms of energy from the environment—has come to us largely from the laboratory of electrophysiology. Our conceptions of stimulus transduction and central processing are essentially based on findings from nonhumans. On the other hand, human psychophysics has provided us with an elaborate conceptual schema and considerable knowledge of human sensory acuity and perceptual judgments based on behavior in response to verbal instructions.

Until recently, and for reasons that are not entirely clear, many physiologists have avoided dealing with behavior. The anesthetized acute animal preparation has proven its worth many times over and has certainly provided much of the basis for modern sensory neurophysiology. Although not the most natural or biological preparation, it continues to enjoy considerable popularity and to produce theoretical and systematic conceptions about nervous function. In the long run, however, the findings from such acute experiments must account for the behavior of the awake intact animal in continual interaction with its environment. Sooner or later the awake animal must be directly questioned about the stimuli that control its behavior.

The resistance of some physiologists to deal with behavior lies, perhaps, in their apprehension that the results will somehow be less objective and more difficult to quantify than those they obtain from the quieter and less "willful" physiological preparations to which they are accustomed (1). Behavior is considered more whimsical, more variable, and subject to a host of unknown (perhaps unknowable) influences than are events that take place at a cellular level. Darwin and continuity of species notwithstanding, is it possible that the sensations of lower animals are not amenable to direct scientific inquiry? This was the view clearly expressed by Claude Bernard a century ago in his treatise on experimental medicine (2). Many physiologists are now engaged in behavioral experiments on sensory processing. It is but one purpose of this chapter to lay these old canards to rest once and for all.

In his exclusive treatment of human sensory capacities the psychophysicist has elaborated on a century-old tradition of verbal question and introspective report and has created a virtual science of human sensation. An approach so dependent on human language precludes comparative analysis of sensory phenomena. Interestingly enough, at issue are philosophical problems similar in nature to those just discussed with regard to the physiologist's reluctance to engage in behavioral experimentation. The origins of psychophysics are found in the mid-nineteenth century in the old mind-body dualism that set human beings apart from other animals on the grounds that the mind was peculiarly human and its functions could be precisely measured by meticulously constructed introspective procedures (see ref. 15). The suggestion that sensation was of the mind and could be explored only in humans was, of course, antithetical to the Darwinian model of continuity of species.

As we show in this chapter, it is indeed possible in many instances to circumvent language in the process of questioning animals about their sensory experiences. In examining some of the more complex perceptual phenomena, however, the language barrier appears insurmountable. The problem is exacerbated because the definition of these phenomena is inextricably tied to language—often in terms of the instructions given the subject before the experiment. It is therefore impossible to devise animal experiments that are directly analogous to those that have been carried out on human subjects. Are we then to regard these examples as phenomena unique to humans? Even complex perceptual experiences have some biological generality, and their existence and measurement in other animals without benefit of language may shed some light on the evolution of sensory systems and the selective pressures that have played a part in it. To extend the analysis of perceptual phenomena to lower animals, however, the language barrier must be overcome.

It is reasonable to expect that any complete account of sensory function must deal, at some level, with both physiological processing in humans and sensory acuity in other animals as measured by their behavior. Recent improvements in electrical recording techniques have made it possible to measure, with considerable precision and with noninvasive techniques, electrical activity evoked by sensory stimulation in humans (16, 41). In this chapter we describe some of the procedures that have permitted us to probe animals other than humans for quantitative information about their sensory resolving power and for the ways in which they discriminate or perceive sensory events. The subject, awake and intact, is first behaviorally trained by operant conditioning procedures and then tested with some of the more common methods of human psychophysics (see ref. 54).

Conditioning procedures permit a form of nonverbal communication with nonhuman subjects. They serve as a substitute for the instructions generally given to human subjects, and they also allow a response that is directly analogous to the yes-no or brighter-dimmer of human psychophysics. By the use of these procedures the naïve (in some cases wild) animal is brought under control and becomes, in time, a reliable and trusted observer in the sensory laboratory, rivaling his human counterpart. When behavioral training is completed, the limits of sensory resolution (threshold), discrimination, and perception are examined by psychophysical methods.

This chapter is divided into three sections. The first discusses the principles of operant conditioning relevant to animal psychophysics. We emphasize those procedures used in initial training, in establishing stimulus control of the animal's behavior, and in obtaining stable behavioral base lines prior to measuring sensory acuity or perceptual judgment. In the second section selected examples of sensory experiments designed to answer a variety of questions are presented to illustrate the wide range of problems that these kinds of behavioral procedures address. Finally, in the third section the more complex aspects of sensory perception are treated. Included are descriptions of those few experiments that have attempted to go beyond problems of sensory acuity or resolution and that have used the techniques of animal psychophysics to deal with the issues of behavioral judgments of stimulus continua (e.g., intensity, frequency) or sensory scaling, matching, and illusions.

Throughout the chapter we stress what we consider to be the relevant issues and the available laboratory methods for preparing and behaviorally testing an animal to determine how it senses or perceives exteroceptive stimulation. The experimental examples that have been selected illustrate the reliability and precision one can expect with animals, given the appropriate procedures.

BEHAVIORAL PRINCIPLES

Procedures that permit the analysis of sensory processes in nonhuman animals awaited the development of an objective, rigorous science of behavior. The insistence of earlier investigators such as Bernard (2) that the characteristics of the nonhuman's sensory and perceptual systems would forever remain unknown merely reflected the inability of science at that time to provide a satisfactory account of behavior without invoking unobservable and hypothetical processes. To compound the problem, these covert processes of a conscious mind were considered uniquely human and, in fact, formed a part of the definition of what it meant to be human. Historically it is possible to cite several scientific movements that forced a major reevaluation of this view of the determinants of behavior. For example, Darwin's views of evolutionary continuity were applied to behavior and led to an anecdotal period in nineteenth century psychology in which mental faculties were attributed to animals. In reaction to this mentalism or ascription of conscious thought to animals, Morgan (32) suggested a more parsimonious account of animal behavior that emphasized the role of environmental factors in animal behavior without resorting to unobservables. Morgan's effort was prompted by Pavlov's discovery that the simple reflexes identified by nineteenth century physiologists were malleable and susceptible to a wide range of environmental influences; stimuli originally without effect could, through appropriate associative conditioning, evoke responses formerly elicited only by unconditioned stimuli. And, finally, Watson (60) integrated the principles of Morgan and others with Pavlov's (34) reflex conditioning and applied them to the control and analysis of both human and animal behavior. These developments in experimental psychology together with the Darwinian notion of species continuity led in time to the formulation of a set of general principles sufficient for a systematic description of the factors responsible for the origin and control of all behavior, animal and human alike. The empirical realization and subsequent refinement of Watson's ideas about the importance of environmental events in the establishment and maintenance of all behaviors was provided by Skinner in *The Behavior of Organisms* (49).

Operant and Respondent Conditioning

Within the context of this chapter, an important consequence of the development of an objective science of behavior was that the tools necessary for inquiry into sensory phenomena in animals became available. Hence, a major impediment to the study of animal sensory processes—the lack of a common communication channel—was overcome by the devising of interactive situations in which the animal, by its behavior in the presence of a particular stimulus, revealed its sensory capabilities; the experimenter, in turn, informed the animal of the propriety of its behavior by arranging specific consequences for specific types of responses to different stimuli.

For heuristic reasons we here consider behavior as being composed of several smaller units called responses. Similarly, the environment can be reduced to simpler units called stimuli. Over the past 40 years learning theorists have recognized two different classes of responses—operants and respondents. Operants are often referred to as instrumental or voluntary responses; respondents are thought of as reflexive or involuntary. More specifically, respondents are elicited and controlled exclusively by antecedent stimulus conditions, whereas operants are responses whose probability of occurrence depends on the nature of the past consequences of those responses. Questions have been raised about the other traditional criteria (24) used to distinguish the two response classes (19, 47), leading to suggestions that what defines a response as

operant or respondent is independent of any inherent characteristic of the response itself, but instead depends on the particular learning paradigm in which it occurs. Here we need only consider the methodologic distinctions between the conditioning procedures out of which the two response types emerge.

In respondent conditioning a novel stimulus or CS (the conditioned stimulus) is temporally associated with an eliciting or unconditioned stimulus (US), which evokes some unconditioned response. After repeated association of the CS and US, the CS acquires the ability to evoke a conditioned response related in some fashion to the unconditioned response. For example, after repeated pairings of a light with an electric foot shock, the light (CS) might elicit components of a complex motor response (e.g., leg flexion) originally evoked by the foot shock (US). In the prototypical operant conditioning experiment the emission of the operant response (R) in the presence of a discriminative stimulus (S^D) results in the presentation of a reinforcer (S^R, or consequence) that increases the future probability of the response. For instance, we might arrange for a rat to receive a food pellet if it presses a lever when a red lamp is lit. With continued training the rat will immediately press the lever when the red lamp is lit, pausing only long enough to consume the reinforcer.

Figure 1 contains a schematic summary of the two conditioning procedures in the form of state diagrams. This form of notation is a useful and unambiguous way of describing conditioning procedures (see ref. 51). The individual circles (states) indicate the status of the procedures at different times; the labeled arrows indicate transitions between the states and contain the temporal or response requirements necessary to effect the transitions. State diagrams describe the specific contingent relation among stimuli, responses, and reinforcers characteristic of the two conditioning procedures. In respondent conditioning the only contingency in effect is the one between the CS and the US. The two periods of time (T) shown in the respondent conditioning state diagram of Figure 1 refer to the

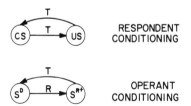

FIG. 1. State diagrams of respondent and operant conditioning procedures. Diagrams shown here and in Fig. 3 describe sequential response contingencies, stimulus presentations, and temporal events that occur under the conditions of the experiment. The respondent conditioning state diagram specifies that a conditioned stimulus (CS) of duration T is presented and its termination is followed immediately by an unconditioned stimulus (US) of duration T. The operant conditioning diagram indicates that the operant response (R) in the presence of the discriminative stimulus (S^D) produces a positive reinforcer (S^{R+}) of duration T.

durations of the CS and the US. Thus the diagram specifies that a CS of some arbitrary duration, T, is presented and, upon termination, is followed immediately by a US, also of some arbitrary duration, T. The CS, in a sense, predicts the US. Thus the former becomes a sufficient condition for an elicited response (42). Note that the response does not appear in the state diagram; it is in one sense an incidental feature of the conditioning procedure and bears no contingent relation to the stimuli.

The response plays a much more active role in determining the sequence of events in operant conditioning, which is basically a three-term contingency: the S^D sets the occasion for an R, which produces a positive reinforcer (S^{R+}) of duration T. Thus the reinforcer is presented if and only if the response is emitted in the presence of the discriminative stimulus. As a consequence, operant conditioning procedures generally afford more precise and direct control over the likelihood of a response during a stimulus than respondent conditioning procedures. The CS in respondent conditioning and the S^D in operant conditioning are the stimuli that the animal psychophysicist manipulates to determine an animal's sensitivity. Because the stimulus events of interest are often subtle and barely perceptible, the experimenter must be confident that any observed alterations in response probability are primarily a function of changes in the physical dimensions of the stimulus rather than a reflection of variation in the amount of control the stimulus conditions exert over the response.

In a conventional respondent conditioning experiment after several CS-US pairings, the CS is presented alone to estimate its degree of control over the conditioned response. After a few such presentations the CS loses its ability to elicit the response, necessitating occasional reconditioning trials in which the CS and US are again paired. The gradual loss of the CS's eliciting function after each reconditioning phase makes reliable sensitivity measures difficult. In contrast, in operant conditioning the S^D does not elicit the response but rather specifies the context in which it will produce a reinforcer. Thus the experimenter need not be concerned that the alterations in response probability that occur during different stimuli are a function of continuous changes in some nonsensory, associative property of the S^D related to the conditioning process; the contingent relations among stimulus, response, and reinforcer remain invariant.

Schedules of Stimulus Presentation and Reinforcement

In operant conditioning the experimenter follows a prescribed set of rules—a schedule—for determining when and for how long a stimulus should be presented, under what conditions a response (or responses) produces a reinforcer, and the consequences of a response

during stimulation. Although there are numerous ways of generating different sequential relations among stimuli, responses, and reinforcers, the design of most experiments in animal psychophysics requires only the more basic schedules. One can arrange for a discriminative stimulus or reinforcer to be presented after a particular number of responses, or after the passage of some minimum period of time ending with a response. In a fixed-ratio schedule an event is made contingent upon the execution of some constant number of responses; in a variable-ratio schedule the precise number of responses required changes from one stimulus presentation or reinforcer to the next, but varies around a mean value established by the experimenter. Similarly, in a fixed-interval schedule the first response after some constant period of time produces a scheduled consequence; under a variable-interval schedule the consequence follows the first response after a period of time that changes with each succeeding discriminative stimulus or reinforcer. Each of these schedules produces a predictable, stereotyped pattern of responding. Generally the variable schedules are more useful because they produce a nearly constant, steady-response base line against which very small changes in behavior following introduction of a stimulus can be reliably measured. Specific details on the use of these schedules appear, where relevant, in subsequent sections of this chapter.

Development of Stimulus Control

In discrimination training, responses are selectively reinforced in the presence of one stimulus and not in the presence of others, so that responding comes under the control of that stimulus relative to other stimuli. On the basis of its behavior the subject can be said to be discriminating one stimulus from all others, including irrelevant or extraneous cues in the test environment. For example, to train a pigeon to discriminate the presence of a light from its absence we might reinforce pecks at an illuminated response disk but withhold reinforcement for pecks at the same disk when it is darkened. Two criteria must be met to conclude that the animal's response is under stimulus control of the S^D (lighted key). First, the probability of a response must be much higher during the S^D than at any other time; second, changes in some property of the S^D must produce obvious yet orderly changes in response probability. The first criterion is generally satisfied in the training phase of psychophysical experiments by showing that the animal responds only during the S^D and not when it is absent. The second criterion is fulfilled in a testing phase in which a selected dimension (e.g., intensity, wavelength) of the stimulus is systematically varied through a wide range of values. Thus the intensity of light, for example, might be varied in a graded fashion to determine response probability as a function of stimulus intensity. If the subject is attending to the light, we expect an orderly decline in response probability as the animal's threshold for detecting the light is approached.

A refinement of the basic three-term stimulus-response-reinforcer relation that animal psychophysicists frequently use is the requirement of an explicit cue-producing or observing response. In this way, presentation of the discriminative stimulus is contingent upon the execution of a response distinct from the one that occurs in the presence of the S^D. Once the S^D has been presented, a different but usually compatible response (the stimulus-reporting response) is required to produce the primary reinforcer. As a result of its temporal contiguity with the primary reinforcer, the S^D acquires reinforcing properties in its own right; its presentation serves as an effective way of maintaining the observing response. The observing response ensures that the S^D is presented only when the animal is "attending" to the stimulus situation and not when it is engaged in some competing activity (e.g., grooming, sleeping).

In procedures that use positive reinforcement an additional deterrent to responses being emitted outside the proper stimulus context is a brief interruption of the experimental session whenever such responses occur. That is, reporting responses emitted in the absence of the S^D produce a time-out or temporary suspension of the experiment. Because experimental animals normally adopt strategies that maximize the rate of reinforcement, any behavior that results in a reduction of reinforcement density is avoided. Thus, in time, responses are for the most part emitted only under proper stimulus conditions.

Auditory Stimulus Control in Guinea Pig

An illustration of the application of the principles of operant conditioning to the acquisition and maintenance of stimulus control is provided by a training and testing procedure developed to behaviorally assess the guinea pig's auditory sensitivity (35, 39).

During testing the guinea pig is confined in a hardware cloth cage placed in a sound-attenuated booth (see Fig. 2). The well-trained subject nose-presses the left-hand illuminated disk (observing disk D_O) until it detects a tone presented from a transducer positioned directly above the disk. The subject then quickly moves to the right-hand disk (reporting disk, D_R), nose-presses it a single time, and collects a small, parsley-flavored food pellet from the tray mounted between the disks. Despite its apparent simplicity, this behavioral sequence is the product of an extensive training regimen in which the individual components of the final chain of responses have been progressively added in a systematic fashion.

The final procedure is schematized in Figure 3. This sequence begins with both disk lights illuminated (reporting disk light on, L_R; observing disk light on, L_O).

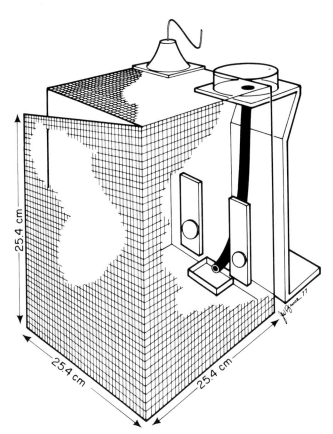

FIG. 2. Schematic view of testing chamber used in determining the guinea pig's audibility function. Response disks are 3.8 cm above the floor and 11.5 cm apart. Feeder tray located midway between response disks projects 3.3 cm into chamber. Speaker is positioned directly over left disk. [From Prosen, Petersen, Moody, and Stebbins (39).]

After a variable time interval (VT), ranging from 1 to 30 s (mean 10 s), a null state—one in which no new stimulus is introduced to the animal, but which is a required step in the programming sequence—is entered. If the animal emits an observing response (R_O) within 2 s of entry into this state, a tone is presented; if no R_O is emitted during this period, the system simply returns to the initial state and the sequence begins again. This 2-s null state, termed a limited hold, effectively limits the time during which a tone may be produced by an R_O and prevents subjects from waiting for a period of time equal to the longest interval programmed (30 s) and then responding on the observing disk (D_O) and on the reporting disk (D_R) in rapid succession. In the absence of a limited hold this strategy would effectively produce a reinforcer. Once a tone is presented the subject must complete a reporting response (R_R) within 3 s to receive a food pellet. After delivery of the food pellet the sequence is reinitiated. Failure to report the tone within the specified 3-s period has no consequence other than returning the subject to the start of the sequence. Any R_R made in the absence of the tone (i.e., during the first two states) initiates a time-out (TO) during which all lights are extinguished and the entire experiment is halted for 15 s.

The initial step in most positive reinforcement procedures is to increase the effectiveness of the primary reinforcer by depriving subjects of it for some period of time prior to testing. A common food-deprivation regimen used with adult animals is to deprive them to some fraction (e.g., 80%) of their free-feeding weight and maintain them at that level for the duration of the experiment. In long-term experiments with subadult animals, however, it is necessary to devise a deprivation schedule that permits growth and development. Laboratory guinea pigs continue to gain

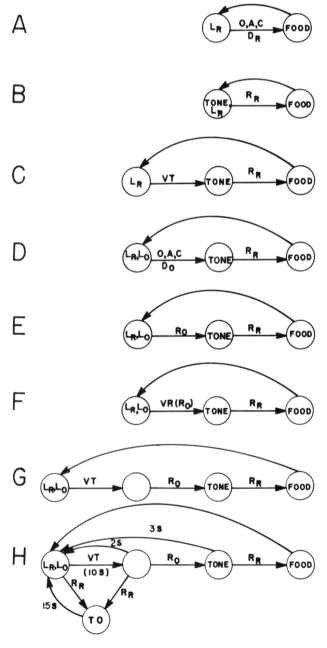

A

B

C

D

E

F

G

H

weight over the first 2–3 years of life. Thus to ensure healthy, viable experimental subjects, the diet provided for these animals must be designed to permit some weight gain. The feeding schedule used in this experiment allowed the guinea pigs a total of approximately 25 g per day of food pellets plus lab chow supplemented with fresh vegetables twice a week. The curves relating weight to the age of the animal in Figure 4 compare the growth of food-deprived animals and their free-feeding counterparts. Note that the feeding program merely slowed the growth of the experimental animals without halting it. Figure 4 also contains an average growth function for *Cavia aperea,* the closest wild relative of the domestic guinea pig, *Cavia porcellus.* Interestingly, the daily points for the experimental subjects closely follow the course of the *C. aperea* growth function. The deprivation schedule appears to maintain the experimental subjects (*C. porcellus*) at or near the weight at which *C. aperea* operates in the wild. The net result of the deprivation regimen was to produce healthy, well-motivated experimental animals that worked steadily through experimental sessions often lasting 2.5–3 h and during which 400–500 stimulus trials were presented.

Response Shaping

To train the guinea pig to press the illuminated disk with its nose it was necessary to initially reinforce the response units that approximate the act of nose-pressing and that occur naturally in the animal's response repertoire. Thus, during very early stages it was necessary to reinforce (in succession) approach, ori-

FIG. 3. State diagrams representing successive stages in a training regimen for guinea pigs for a two-response auditory testing procedure. Conditions for initial training are shown in *A*. Final testing procedure is shown in *H*. Intermediate stages *B–G* indicate addition of response contingencies until final conditions in *H* are in effect. *A*: first phase of training. Only the report disk light is on (L_R). Any orientation toward, approach, or contact (O, A, C) of report disk (D_R) produces a food pellet. The sequence begins anew after delivery of food pellet. *B*: second phase. There is a continuous tone; a nose-press of the reporting disk (R_R) turns the tone off for the duration of feeder operation and produces a food pellet. *C*: third phase. A tone is turned on aperiodically (VT); a reporting response (R_R) terminates the tone and produces food. *D*: phase four. Observing disk light (L_O) and reporting disk light (L_R) are both illuminated; any orientation toward, approach, or contact with the observing disk (D_O) initiates the tone and sets the occasion for an R_R. *E*: fifth stage. A nose-press of the observing disk (R_O) produces the tone. *F*: sixth phase. Variable ratio (VR) of R_O [VR (R_O)] must be completed to produce the tone. *G*: seventh phase. After passage of an aperiodic interval of time in the first state of this phase, a null state is entered. The null state simply designates a required programming state, which is associated with no change in stimulus conditions. Emission of an R_O while in the null state produces a tone. *H*: final procedure. An R_O must be emitted within 2 s of entry into the null state to produce a 3-s tone. Failure to complete an R_O during the 2-s null state or an R_R during the 3-s tone simply results in a return to the first state and the sequence starts anew. An R_R in the absence of a tone (i.e., during the first two states) results in a 15-s time-out (TO). An R_R during the tone produces a food pellet.

response to the stimulus; failure to cross results in delivery of an electric foot shock that can be terminated only by leaping the barrier. One disadvantage of the technique is that the animal is not required to perform any overt observing response prior to the S^D and thus might not be in an optimal position for receipt of the stimulus or in the same position on subsequent trials. As a result stimulus intensity varies with the animal's spatial relation to the source of the stimulus. Variability in the psychophysical data reflects this variability in stimulation.

It would be erroneous to conclude, however, that negative reinforcement procedures necessarily produce more variable data or require shorter training regimens than positive reinforcement procedures. Green (17) carefully compared the sensory data obtained using negative and positive reinforcement procedures for an experimental situation in which all variables other than the nature of the reinforcing stimulus were closely matched. He reported no difference between sensory measures obtained using appetitive versus aversive stimuli, and concluded that discrepancies reported by others probably reflected a failure to equate negative and positive reinforcement procedures in terms of behavioral contingencies and stability criteria.

The conditioned suppression procedure, a paradigm that has enjoyed some degree of popularity among animal psychophysicists, essentially represents a compromise between respondent, negative reinforcement, and positive reinforcement techniques (50). Originally conceived by Estes and Skinner (14) to provide an objective measure of anxiety, the technique takes advantage of the fact that animals react to a stimulus that predicts an impending, unavoidable shock by ceasing any ongoing activities. Animals are initially trained to respond on either a variable-interval or a variable-ratio schedule of food reinforcement. Once the subjects respond at a steady rate, a stimulus that terminates with a shock is presented. After several pairings of stimulus and shock the animals cease to respond in the presence of the shock-predicting stimulus. This technique shares the disadvantage of most other negative reinforcement procedures, namely, that few trials (20–30 at most) can be administered in a single session without disrupting performance of the base-line operant response. Another drawback of this method is that a warning stimulus must be presented for relatively long periods of time (10–30 s) if conditioned suppression is to be successful (3, 27). Hence, the effects of sensory adaptation may conceivably introduce some distortion into those sensory measures obtained by this technique.

SENSATION

Sensory experiments are conducted for the most part to determine minimum detectable energy levels or minimum discriminable differences along continua of wavelength, sound pressure, and so on. Human subjects are verbally instructed to attend to and report changes in stimulation on the appropriate stimulus dimension, but animals must be prepared for these experiments by the techniques described in the section BEHAVIORAL PRINCIPLES, p. 124. Their behavior is brought under stimulus control by the judicious use of operant conditioning procedures. The methods developed for human psychophysics are then applied to the animals to measure either their sensory acuity or the limits of their resolution of sensory events in their environment. The psychophysical methods prescribe rules for determining the functional relation between stimulus variation and behavior. Such rules permit the determination of threshold levels of stimulation in as unambiguous a manner as possible.

Threshold Procedures

When stimulus control has been achieved by the appropriate conditioning procedures so that experimental subjects are reliably discriminating between at least two values on the selected stimulus dimension, further values are presented in predetermined sequential formats and the subjects' responses noted. Threshold is usually defined as that value of the stimulus that is reported correctly 50% (in certain instances 75%) of the time. Due to small fluctuations in the stimulus and changes in the subject over time, threshold is necessarily a statistical concept and is the average of responses to repeated stimulus presentations. Stimuli may be ordered sequentially, i.e., according to their position on the continuum (low to high or high to low), randomly, or in a fixed relation to the subject's response to them. The selection of a particular psychophysical procedure is determined by the demands of the particular experiment. There is usually a trade-off between the ability to preserve stimulus control and the efficiency of the procedure with regard to the amount of data that can be obtained per unit time. Some of these procedures are described below.

In the method of limits, stimuli are usually presented in alternate ascending (low to high) and descending (high to low) sequences. In threshold experiments the ascending series starts well below threshold; the descending series begins with values that are clearly discriminable. Often it is difficult to maintain stimulus control with long ascending series, so in certain applications only descending series are used (see ref. 10). Threshold is defined as the average stimulus value of the response transitions in the various series (i.e., yes to no, and no to yes), and it may differ slightly between ascending and descending series. Starting points for the series are varied to prevent the subject from responding to the number in the sequence. The method of limits is relatively inefficient because only a small number of trials (those surrounding the response transition point) are used in the threshold calculation. This is a problem both in operant conditioning experiments where the number of positive reinforcements that can be given is limited and in experiments where a time-dependent process occurs rapidly (e.g., dark adaptation or recovery from a noise-induced threshold shift).

The method of constant stimuli dictates that a fixed set of stimulus values (usually 5 to 7), selected to bracket the subject's threshold, be presented in a random sequence. From the frequency of correct detections at each value a function is constructed and threshold is usually interpolated at the stimulus value corresponding to 50% correct (see Fig. 6). Stimulus control is ensured by presenting a slightly disproportionate number of stimuli above the threshold region. Reliable estimates of threshold are obtained by this method and, for that reason, it is often the method of choice in psychophysical experiments with animals. Unfortunately, like the method of limits, the method of constant stimuli is relatively inefficient because only a small portion of the data collected is used in the calculation of threshold.

The tracking or staircase method, which is a modification of the method of limits, represents a considerable improvement in efficiency over the other methods (see ref. 46). A stimulus changes in value as a consequence of the subject's response on the preceding trial. For example, on an intensive dimension the signal is attenuated for the trial after a correct detection, but after a trial in which the subject has failed to report its presence, the signal intensity is increased. As in the method of limits, threshold is determined from the region of response transition. Either the midpoint in stimulus intensity between correct detections and failure to report or simply the stimulus value for 50% correct detections may be used. This method permits rapid data collection and is extremely efficient, but because the stimuli are always close to threshold, breakdown in stimulus control is a potential hazard. In addition the method may not be suitable for some animals or for certain applications. It is possible, however, to bring the method into use gradually or even

to restore stimulus control by a variety of procedural changes (see ref. 31).

Sound Localization in Monkey

The method of constant stimuli is illustrated in a series of experiments in which monkeys were trained through operant conditioning procedures to report a change in the horizontal coordinate (azimuth) of a sound in space (7, 8). The animals were required to perform an observing response by making contact with a response disk, which resulted in the delivery of a series of tone pulses from a reference speaker located directly ahead. After a varying number of tone pulses from the reference speaker, a trial was presented in which the signal was delivered from a location to the right of the monkey. The signal was pulsed alternately from the two locations; if the monkey released the response disk during the trial it received a food reward. Release of the disk at any other time resulted in the occurrence of punishment in the form of a brief time-out (a temporary cessation of the experiment). The basic features of this procedure include the observing response (holding the response disk), the report response (releasing the response disk), and the presentation of catch trials. Catch trials, in which the stimulus or stimulus change to be detected is not presented, are an important feature of sensory experiments. These trials allow monitoring of the subject's rate of guessing and thus provide an indication of the degree of behavioral control exercised by the stimulus. In the present experiment, catch trials, in which the signal did not change location, were programmed to occur intermittently. Release of the response disk during these trials was followed by a brief time-out.

Figure 7 displays psychophysical functions for three monkeys obtained by the method of constant stimuli for the localization of an 8,000-Hz pure tone. The probability of detecting a change in signal location ascends monotonically with an increase in the magnitude of the change approaching 100% between 20° and 30°. This figure also shows that the individual perfor-

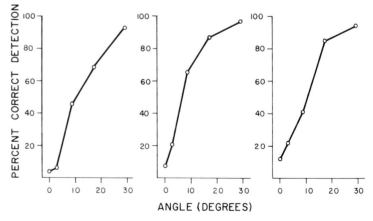

FIG. 7. Psychophysical functions for 3 monkeys. Percentage of correct detections of a change in location of an 8,000-Hz tone as a function of horizontal displacement of the tone in degrees of arc. Threshold or minimum audible angle is the angle in degrees of arc at which 50% correct detections occurred (i.e., about 11% for record at *left*). Percentage of catch trials (on which stimulus did not change location) to which the subject responded is displayed over the 0° azimuth point. [Adapted from Brown, Stebbins, et al. (8).]

mances of the three subjects were very similar. The dynamic range of each subject's performance varied from chance (near zero) to 100%. This indicated that the subject was under excellent stimulus control. The location of the signal was changed by presenting the tone through different speakers situated on an arc surrounding the subject. Thus a change in location was potentially confounded by a change in transducer. To demonstrate that the monkey's performance was dependent on the change in spatial location and independent of possible speaker differences, the speakers were exchanged between two locations, and the resulting psychophysical functions were found to be unchanged.

In sensory experiments there is always the possibility that other properties of the signal may vary with the independent variable. In auditory localization experiments, as the location of a constant intensity sound is changed, its apparent loudness may vary. Thus the subject's behavior may reflect the detection of a change in loudness rather than the detection of a change in location. In the localization study this problem was approached by randomly varying the sound pressure of each stimulus pulse. Irregularities in sensory data can often be a consequence of the failure to eliminate such confounding variables. Differences in performance among individuals may not always be an expression of sensory differences along the dimension selected, but they may occur because different components of multidimensional stimuli acquire control in different subjects (43).

Psychophysical experiments are directed at questions of minimum discriminable stimulus differences (e.g., difference thresholds), as in the example of stimulus location, or with regard to particular properties of the stimulus itself, such as wavelength or intensity. The absolute threshold is a special case, which most often deals with intensity and represents the minimum detectable energy level to which the animal responds. At issue is the absolute resolving power of the sensory system. In animal psychophysics a distinction between absolute and difference threshold experiments is related to the conditioning procedure, to the specification of the reinforcement contingency, and to the use of catch trials. In absolute threshold experiments the known condition is the absence of stimulation; in difference threshold experiments the known condition is stimulus equality. In the experiment on sound localization catch trials were based on acoustic stimuli coming from the same location; reinforcement was contingent upon a response to change in stimulus location. In the absolute threshold experiment catch trials are blank or stimulus-free intervals; reinforcement follows responses to stimulation.

Visual Acuity in Cat

To determine the absolute threshold of visual acuity in the cat, Bloom and Berkley (4) simultaneously presented test stimuli consisting of square-wave gratings varying in spatial frequency, and a standard stimulus, which was a uniform field adjusted to match the test or comparison gratings in overall luminance. Thus the standard was the absence of a grating, and the subject's visual acuity was determined by the finest grating that could be distinguished from the uniform field.

Each cat was trained to insert its head in a small Plexiglas chamber and to respond by pressing its nose against either the left or right of two response keys (thin, flat, Plexiglas disks). The keys were transparent to permit viewing of the visual stimuli. The stimulus associated with one key was the square-wave grating; the stimulus associated with the other key was the uniform field. The two stimulus displays were electronically generated on an oscilloscope screen. Each cat received liquid food reinforcement for pressing the response key associated with the test grating; responses to the key associated with the uniform field produced a time-out. The threshold for visual acuity (the highest spatial-frequency grating discriminable from the uniform field) was determined by the tracking method for targets at different distances from the subject. In Figure 8 threshold visual acuity as a function of viewing distance is presented for four cats. From these data Bloom and Berkley (4) have argued that the discontinuity in the curves serves as an index of the near point, or closest viewing distance, for optimum acuity in the cat.

Bloom and Berkley's experiment was readily modified from the measurement of the absolute threshold of visual acuity to the measurement of the differential threshold for visual resolution. The standard stimulus was a grating of fixed spatial frequency; test stimuli were comparison gratings of different spatial frequencies. The experiment measured the cat's ability to resolve differences in spatial frequency. Similarly, with grating contrast as the independent variable, the modulation transfer function for the cat was determined (M. A. Berkley, personal communication).

Relation of Psychophysics to Structure and Physiological Function

The methods of animal psychophysics are particularly useful in revealing structure-function relationships or relations between physiological processing and behavior when combined with anatomical or physiological procedures. The reliability and precision of these conditioning and psychophysical procedures are a match for the degree of resolution provided by the microscope or microelectrode. In the illustrations that follow we present examples of joint behavioral and anatomical or behavioral and physiological experiments. The advantages of such research strategies for investigating the nervous system are readily apparent.

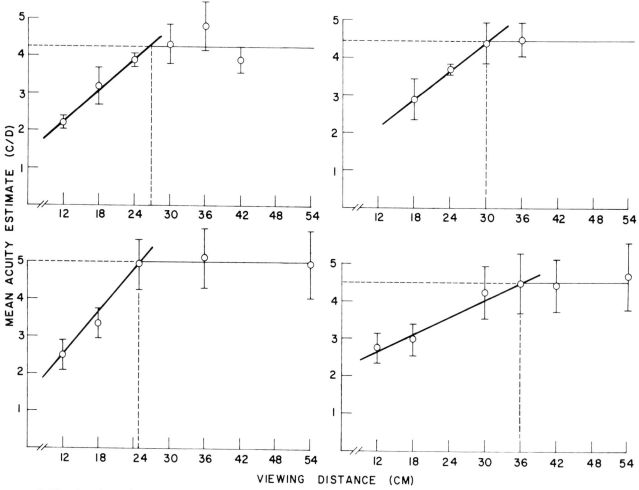

FIG. 8. Visual acuity and near point of accommodation in 4 cats. Mean visual acuity ± SD in cycles per degree (C/D) of visual angle is shown as a function of viewing distance. Intersection of the 2 line segments denotes the near point of accommodation. As viewing distance is increased visual acuity increases up to the near point but remains constant beyond it. [Adapted from Bloom and Berkley (4).]

Relation of Hearing Impairment and Inner Ear Damage in Guinea Pig

Microscopic observations of the mammalian inner ear have revealed the existence of two distinct populations of sensory receptors, the inner and the outer hair cells. It is conceivable that in certain properties inner and outer hair cells functionally parallel the cone and rod photoreceptors in the visual system. The outer hair cells, like the rods, may be the more sensitive of the two receptor cell types (11). Prosen, Petersen, Moody, and Stebbins (39) have sought to evaluate the hearing of the guinea pig with the outer hair cells missing. The training procedure has been described in *Auditory Stimulus Control in Guinea Pig*, p. 127. Briefly, operant conditioning techniques were used to train the animal to press a circular plastic disk with its nose. After training, the guinea pig pressed one disk as the observing response. The test tone was presented

after varying time intervals and if the tone was detected the subject pressed an adjacent disk and was reinforced with food. Thresholds were determined by the method of constant stimuli. After normal hearing thresholds had been determined, daily doses of kanamycin were administered by subcutaneous injection. The outer hair cells in the guinea pig are more susceptible than the inner hair cells to kanamycin poisoning, and at certain dose levels receptor damage is largely restricted to the outer hair cells located in the base of the cochlea that are associated with the detection of high-frequency acoustic stimuli (18). These effects may be observed in Figure 9, which illustrates the increase in threshold in a guinea pig after kanamycin treatment. This figure also depicts the pattern of relative destruction in the three rows of outer and the single row of inner hair cells, as observed post mortem in the organ of Corti. Although these results are consistent with the position that the outer hair cells are acoustically more sensitive than inner hair cells, Prosen, Petersen, Moody, and Stebbins (39) caution that such results by themselves do not favor this position over the alternative hypothesis that both inner and outer hair cells are equally sensitive and that the reduction in sensitivity after kanamycin poisoning results from the elimination of three-fourths of the total population of hair cells from a given segment of the cochlea. One may appreciate from experiments such as this that a variety and combination of experimental strategies are often required to adequately define the functional relationship between sensory structure and function.

Somatosensory Discrimination in Monkeys and Humans

A careful interlinkage of psychophysical experi-

ments on humans and monkeys (macaques), and physiological experiments on the monkey, has allowed Mountcastle and his colleagues (25, 33) to advance a physiological interpretation of human somatosensation. The psychophysical experiments illustrate that when humans and monkeys are tested under virtually identical circumstances their sensory performances on some somatosensory discriminations are essentially indistinguishable. In these experiments monkey and human subjects were trained to report the detection of mechanical oscillatory signals applied to the glabrous skin of the hand. The stimuli were sinusoidal vibrations of varying amplitude and frequency. The monkeys were trained to press a telegraph key after a step indentation (fixed displacement) of the skin by a stimulator. After a variable interval of time a sine-wave oscillation was superimposed on the step indentation. The detection of the oscillation was reported

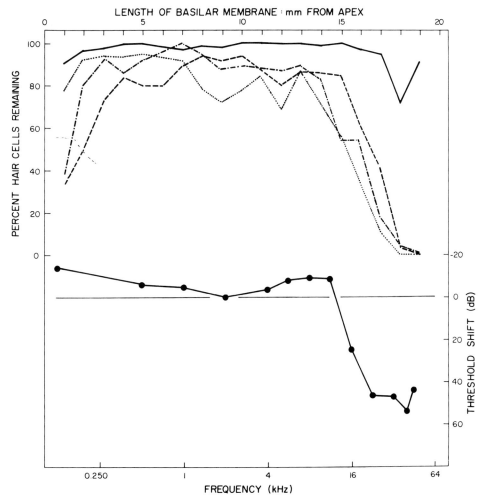

FIG. 9. Drug-induced hearing loss and cochlear lesions in guinea pig S5. *Top panel* represents a cytocochleogram, which indicates the number of receptor cells [one row of inner hair cells, IHC, and 3 rows of outer hair cells, OHC, remaining in each millimeter along basilar membrane of left cochlea after administration of ototoxic drug (200 mg/kg kanamycin sc for 15 days)]. ———, IHC; ······, OHC 1; –·–·–, OHC 2; – – – –, OHC 3. *Lower panel* represents the hearing loss associated with the cochlear damage. [From Prosen, Petersen, Moody, and Stebbins (39).]

by the release of the telegraph key. Correct responses were signaled by a light and reinforced; incorrect responses were followed by a brief time-out. Failure to report stimulation resulted in its termination without reinforcement, and such a failure or "miss" was followed by an intertrial interval. Thresholds for the detection of vibration were interpolated from psychophysical functions generated by the method of constant stimuli for different frequencies of vibration. The relation between threshold of detection and vibratory frequency is presented in Figure 10 for five human and six monkey subjects. These functions demonstrate that as signal frequency increases, the signal amplitude at threshold decreases for frequencies up to 200–300 Hz for both species. These functions also illustrate that the detection of vibration on the skin is essentially the same for macaques and humans.

To evaluate possible neural substrates for this behavioral function the average frequency-threshold function for the six monkeys was compared with the scatter plot of response threshold for fibers in the median nerve as shown in Figure 11. The perception of mechanical oscillation in humans is not uniform with respect to oscillation frequency. Low-frequency oscillations occasion a well-localized flutter; high frequencies cause a more diffusely localized hum. Thresholds for low-frequency flutter (2–30 Hz) in both humans and monkeys were markedly elevated by the

application of a local cutaneous anesthesia; the thresholds for high-frequency vibrations were unaffected (33, 58). On the basis of these results, Mountcastle et al. (33) have noted that the detection of low-frequency flutter is mediated by rapidly adapting fibers associated with Meissner's corpuscles located in the dermal ridges; the detection of high-frequency vibration is mediated by subdermal Pacinian corpuscles. The sensory dichotomy is corroborated by the thresholds for stimulation of median nerve fibers associated with the two receptor populations presented in Figure 11B and D.

Mountcastle et al. (33) observed that when the amplitude of stimulation was increased above threshold a level was eventually reached above which the fiber's response became phase locked and fired synchronously with the period of the signal. These levels are presented as the tuning points in Figure 11A and C. This phenomenon may be characterized as an atonal interval, a term that denotes the span between the just-detectable amplitude for a particular frequency and the amplitude at which the oscillation subjectively displays a definite pitch.

This issue was experimentally addressed by LaMotte and Mountcastle (25), who adapted their behavioral procedure to determine the frequency difference threshold in the monkey. In the behavioral experiment, contact with the response key resulted in

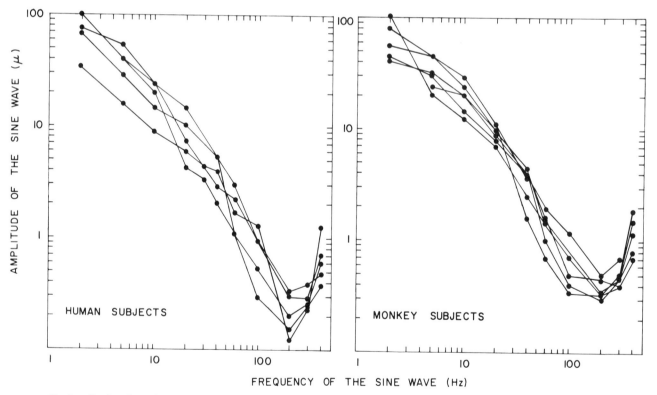

FIG. 10. Amplitude of mechanical vibration at threshold plotted as a function of oscillation frequency in individual humans ($n = 5$) and monkeys ($n = 6$). Vibration was a sinusoidal oscillation varying in amplitude and applied to the glabrous skin of the hand. [From Mountcastle et al. (33).]

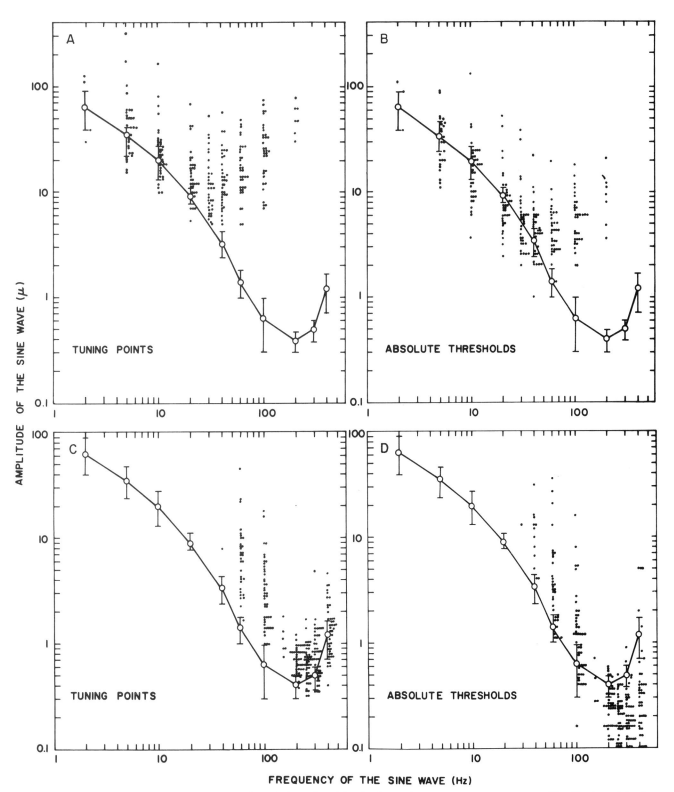

FIG. 11. Correlation of activity in first-order somatosensory neurons with vibratory detection thresholds. ○—○, Mean (± SE) frequency-threshold function for 6 monkeys; ●, thresholds for neural activity recorded from fibers in the monkeys' median nerves. *Panels A* and *B* show phase locking (or tuning) and absolute thresholds recorded from rapidly adapting myelinated fibers that are probably associated with Meissner corpuscles. *Panels C* and *D* show corresponding phase locking (tuning) and absolute thresholds recorded from Pacinian afferent fibers. [From Mountcastle et al. (33).]

the delivery of two successive signals differing in frequency of oscillation—a standard followed by a comparison. After onset of the comparison signal, the subject was required to release one response key and then report if the comparison signal was of higher or lower frequency than the standard by contacting a second response key (if higher) or withholding contact from it (if lower). The standard signal was 30 Hz and the test stimuli, which ranged from 24 to 36 Hz, were behaviorally adjusted to be equal in subjective intensity at several different amplitude levels above detection threshold. Average curves for the discrimination of oscillation frequency are shown in Figure 12 for five human and five monkey subjects. These data are scaled with regard to the detection threshold for flutter vibration. The results indicate that both human and monkey observers are unable to discriminate between the frequencies of two oscillatory signals until the amplitude of oscillation is elevated approximately 7 dB over the threshold for detection. The signal amplitude required for frequency discrimination is the same as the level at which fibers characteristically begin to phase lock (the entrainment or tuning threshold). This correspondence suggests that flutter frequency, or tonality, is temporally represented by the phase locking of neurons. The correspondence between monkey and human acuity, the high degree of similarity in receptor structure between the two species, and the agreement between physiological and psychophysical measures in the monkey support the contention that human somatosensation of flutter vibration is coded in the median nerve in a fashion similar to that of the monkey. As illustrated by the work of Mountcastle and his associates (25, 33, 58) the combination of physiological observations and psychophysical measurements across species holds promise as one of the more powerful approaches to understanding the basis of human sensation.

Criteria for Selection of Behavioral Procedures

The selection of the appropriate procedure in animal psychophysical experiments depends on a number of factors related to the purpose of the experiment. The most important are time and the level of precision required. Unfortunately, experiments that can be completed in a matter of days or a few weeks may yield only a tenuous yes-or-no answer with a moderate-to-high degree of variability. Statistically there is safety in numbers; many subjects may be used to counter

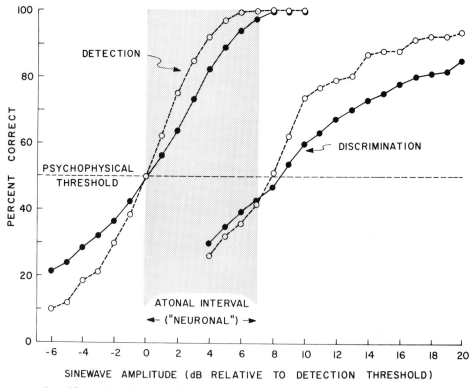

FIG. 12. Atonal interval and somatosensation of flutter. Psychophysical functions on *left* represent detection of a 30-Hz mechanical oscillation in both human (○—○) and monkey (●—●) as a function of oscillation amplitude. *Curves* on *right* indicate ability of human and monkey observers to discriminate a 30-Hz flutter from oscillations of different frequency (24 Hz or 36 Hz) as a function of oscillation amplitude. *Shaded zone* denotes atonal interval, and it brackets the range in amplitude corresponding to absolute threshold and the tuning threshold for β-sized afferents, believed to be the Meissner afferents. Abscissa is scaled relative to the amplitude associated with the detection threshold (4.8 μm). [From LaMotte and Mountcastle (25).]

individual variability. The positive reinforcement operant conditioning procedures that have been advocated are not time saving (perhaps some day they will be), but we believe that they provide for both greater validity and reliability in the data, particularly for individual subjects (29, 55). As will become further evident in the section PERCEPTION, this page, these procedures also enable us to ask considerably more complicated and sophisticated questions regarding the behavioral aspects of sensory processing.

Selection of an appropriate and discrete observing response in animal psychophysical experiments has several advantages. We have already mentioned the value of controlling the animal's attention prior to introduction of the stimulus. Equally important, requiring an observing response can help to guarantee a replicable position of the sensory end organ relative to the stimulus transducer. The observing response of holding or contacting a response disk renders the subject silent and motionless—a condition conducive to, for example, stable audiometric testing (7, 35, 39, 56). The optimal observing response may be specific for each animal and sensory modality under investigation. In Blough's visual tracking procedure (5) pigeons were required to insert their heads in a positioning hole. Henton et al. (20) in an olfactory discrimination study taught pigeons to insert their heads in an aperture in the stimulus chamber. Loop and Berkley (26) in a visual discrimination study trained cats to press the display screen with their noses for the observing response. In these examples the response topography was selected to standardize and optimize the subject's position for the controlled presentation of the stimulus.

In animal psychophysical studies stimulus artifacts may appear in one of two forms: extraneous stimuli can substitute for the experimental stimulus and acquire control over the subject, or properties of the experimental stimulus can modify and confound the assessment of the subject's sensitivity. With respect to the former, Blough (5) has reported that in an early version of his visual tracking study with pigeons, reinforcement delivery became a discriminative stimulus for responses on only one of the two response keys. As a consequence, the subject's performance was controlled by the delivery of reinforcement and not by the value of the visual stimulus. A test for this artifact is provided by turning off the signal-generating apparatus and observing whether the subject continued to respond and receive reinforcement. The second class of stimulus artifact results in threshold estimates that do not reflect the organism's actual sensitivity. In an early determination of pure-tone threshold in the guinea pig, Prosen, Petersen, Moody, and Stebbins (39) noted that the subject's threshold of hearing was unexpectedly elevated at 16,000 and 32,000 Hz. In subsequent measurements of the sound field it was observed that the closed-circuit video camera used to monitor the subject's performance emitted a narrow-

band signal centered at 15,700 and 31,400 Hz. This high-frequency signal produced by the video camera masked the detection of the test signal. When the camera was turned off, thresholds at the previously masked points fell to expected values. Another concern is that threshold may, for some reason, be dependent on the psychophysical method used. This possibility has been explored by the determination of the absolute threshold of hearing in the monkey by three different methods (55). Monkeys were trained by operant conditioning to release contact with a response disk during, and only during, tone presentation to receive food reinforcement. Tones were presented according to one of three psychophysical procedures: the method of constant stimuli, the method of limits, and the method of tracking. Audiograms were constructed from the data showing the relationship between absolute threshold of audibility and tonal frequency. The audiogram in Figure 13 indicates that the thresholds generated by all three psychophysical methods coincide and are, therefore, independent of the method.

PERCEPTION

Sensory scaling of physical continua, stimulus matching, and the sensory illusions are distinct from the threshold or acuity-directed measures described in the previous section. There is an extensive experimental literature based on findings from human subjects, but the generality of these phenomena to other animals has not been adequately demonstrated. Although we would not argue for a qualitative distinction between these so-called perceptual events and sensory ones, there are important differences that have a direct bearing on the design of experiments with nonhuman animals. For example, in threshold experiments, stim-

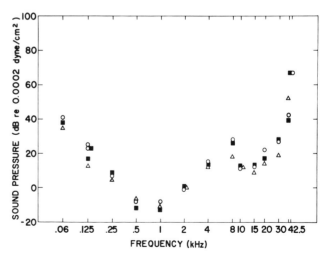

FIG. 13. Auditory threshold function for left ear of one monkey, M-17, determined by psychophysical methods of limits, constant stimuli, and tracking. ○, Method of limits; ■, method of constant stimuli; △, tracking. [From Stebbins (55).]

ulus off (in the determination of absolute thresholds) and physical equality of stimuli (for difference thresholds) are conditions that are specifiable in advance of the experiment. The experimental design—specifically the statement of the contingencies of reinforcement—is based on being able to specify those conditions. In the perceptual experiment such prior specification is not possible. In treating scaling, matching, and the illusions, the physical and subjective scales are different, at least in human subjects, and this fact precludes the use of selective reinforcement with animals. In other words, in the perceptual experiment we cannot state a relation between behavior and some stimulus value as reinforcible before the experiment. In fact, it is often that very relation that the experiment seeks to uncover.

In the measurement of loudness, for example, two pure tones of different frequency are required to be matched on the basis of loudness; the first tone is a standard or reference, and the subject is required to vary the second tone until it equals the standard on the dimension referred to in the verbal instructions as loudness. Because the pure-tone threshold function is a limiting case of the equal-loudness function, it is apparent that equal loudness is not equal sound pressure. Therefore, to reinforce an animal's behavior under the condition of stimulus equality, i.e., equal sound pressure, is to prejudge equal loudness and perhaps build into the animal a new scale that may be due to training and not to the characteristics of the animal's sensory system. Other alternatives equally without merit are 1) to assume that equal-loudness functions in an animal parallel the animal's threshold function (in humans at high sound pressures even this relation breaks down), or 2) in animals with pure-tone threshold functions, similar to those found in humans, to also assume similar loudness functions.

It is for this class of experiments, by our definition perceptual, that the language barrier between animal subject and human experimenter appears particularly impenetrable. Definitions of these perceptual events studied experimentally in human subjects are inseparable from human language—that is, from a set of instructions to the subject. Is it possible that both the logarithmic relation and the power function, so often found in experiments on humans, are somehow artifacts of language? Are loudness, brightness, and the products of sensory scaling applicable only to those animals that have language? Until many of these psychophysical concepts are separated from their complete dependence on language there will be no direct way, for example, of constructing equal-loudness contours for the monkey or a bril scale for the mole. An interest in looking beyond problems of stimulus resolution or sensory acuity stems from a belief that perceptual events are not limited to humans, that there is species continuity, that many of the phenomena are a product of basic sensory mechanisms (in some instances, nonstimulus variables may also play a role), and that we need to develop procedures that are completely independent of language. Extension to lower animals is a major goal, but procedures that do not rely on language may throw some light on the poorly understood effects of the instructional variable on psychophysical judgments in humans.

Loudness Judgment in Monkeys

Several years ago we developed a strategy for providing a nonlinguistic analogue to the study of loudness in animals (53) by taking advantage of the built-in relation between the intensity of stimulation and the latency of an animal's behavioral response to that stimulation. Selective reinforcement is not required. The basic latency-intensity relation is relatively common and has been reported wherever graded activity is seen, from the cellular level in acute experimental animals (59) to complex information-processing experiments with humans (38, 52). A typical function is shown in Figure 14. The stimulus is a pure tone and the function spans the greater part of the dynamic range of hearing of the primate—here an Old World monkey.

The animal is trained to depress a telegraph key in response to a visual signal and to release it very quickly (reinforcement depends on it) in response to a pure tone. After training, and when a stable base line has been obtained, the sound pressure level of the tone is varied over a wide range (29, 53). It was first determined that the placement of the latency-intensity function along the abscissa depended on the frequency of tonal stimulation. It seemed a reasonable assumption that equal latencies at different frequencies represented measures of equal sensory effect—that is, equal loudness. Contours based on equal latencies (reaction times) are shown for one monkey in Figure 15 [from data of Pfingst et al. (36)]. We reasoned further that if an equivalence could be demonstrated in human subjects between loudness functions based on language (verbal instructions) and those based on equal reaction times, our argument for the status of loudness perception in lower animals might be strengthened. In fact, as we later discovered, Chocholle (9) had done the appropriate experiment in 1940; we replicated his results (unpublished observations), as did Pfingst et al. [Fig. 16; (36)].

Moody (30) has taken the procedure one step further and proposed an animal model for the study of loudness recruitment. Recruitment in humans refers to an abnormally rapid increase in perceived loudness with an increase in sound pressure in certain cases of sensorineural hearing loss. Hypothetical latency-intensity functions for a normal and an impaired ear are shown in Figure 17. For the impaired ear, hearing loss is evident at low sound pressure levels (SPL) near threshold and as high as 45 dB. At 50 dB and above, both ears function alike. Some comparable data from a monkey exposed to potentially damaging sound are

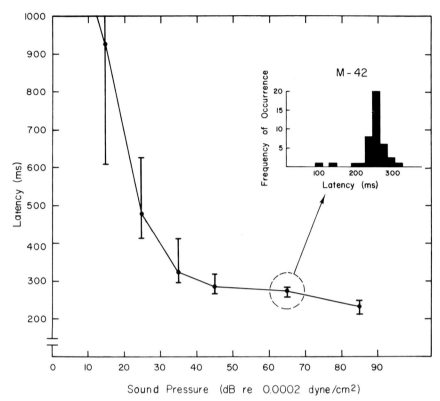

FIG. 14. Median reaction time as a function of stimulus intensity for one monkey, M-42. *Vertical lines*, semi-interquartile ranges. *Inset*: frequency distribution of reaction times at 65-dB sound pressure level from the function of reaction time and stimulus intensity.

shown in Figure 18. The animal's left ear was exposed; both ears were tested immediately and again 24 h after exposure. Temporary recruitment was demonstrated in the left ear. Recently, using this same reaction time method, we have been able to confirm recruitment in a human patient with hearing loss (W. C. Stebbins and D. B. Moody, unpublished observations). Clearly there are some disadvantages of the reaction time method. For example, increased variability in response latency close to absolute threshold somewhat diminishes the effective resolution of the method at lower sound pressure levels. The demonstrated comparability of a procedure for studying perception in human subjects that does not rely on language with one that does, however, provides justification for its use in the analysis of comparative perception.

In measuring loudness recruitment in monkeys, Pugh et al. (40) have shown close agreement between the reaction-time procedure and the input-output function for the N_1 component of the eighth nerve action potential. Under base-line conditions of normal hearing the reciprocal of the N_1 amplitude as a function of intensity was adjusted to fit the behavioral latency-intensity function. After noise exposure both functions shifted together, showed the recruitment effect just described, and were closely parallel during the course of recovery to normal hearing. To the extent, then, that reaction time is a measure of loud-

ness, the primary N_1 component of the eighth nerve action potential is related to loudness perception.

Brightness Scaling in Pigeon

The loudness experiment using reaction time (53) represented an attempt to determine a psychological or behavioral scale of a physical continuum in animals. One advantage of the method is that it generated a continuous or analogue scale for the latency variable. In human psychophysics such scales are often based on the subject assigning some number to a physical quantity or being instructed to fractionate (halve or double) a selected dimension of the stimulus. The result is a discrete or digital scale. Herrnstein and Van Sommers (21) attempted to obtain such a scale for brightness in the pigeon and, by so doing, to establish a scaling procedure for use with animals. As the authors point out, animals have not been used in scaling experiments because the way in which they are instructed—that is, differentially reinforced for responding to stimuli on a particular continuum—would build into the animal the very scale the experimenter is attempting to derive. On the other hand, the animal will not attend to the continuum unless it is in some way instructed to do so.

Pigeons were trained to peck at a transilluminated disk: they were reinforced with food for pecking at a

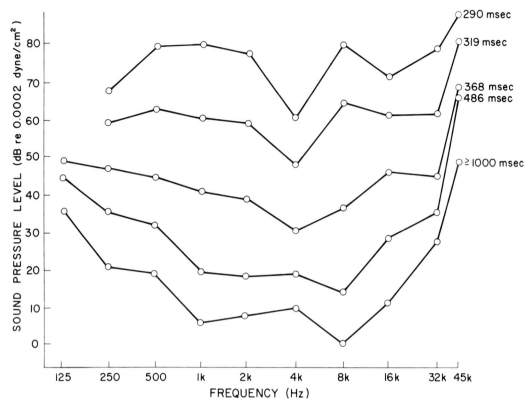

FIG. 15. Equal-latency contours for one monkey derived from latency-intensity functions for the same animal. [From Pfingst et al. (36).]

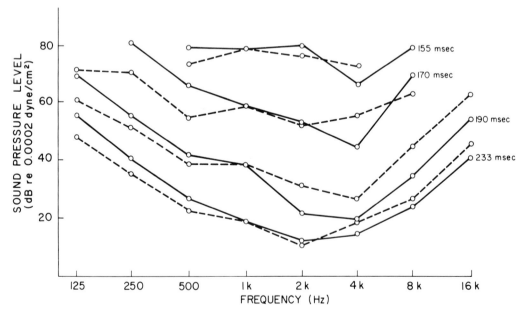

FIG. 16. Equal-latency contours (—) and equal-loudness contours (----) for one human subject. Loudness contours are based on verbal instructions to the subject. [From Pfingst et al. (36).]

rate determined by the intensity of the light behind the disk. During training five luminances spaced at 6-dB intervals were correlated with five response rates; the highest rate was required under the highest luminance. At each intensity the prescribed range of rates

was reinforced. Ranges at adjacent intensities were nonoverlapping. Figure 19 shows the training curves for each bird; the functions have slopes of about 1 except at the highest intensities.

After initial training four test stimuli were added.

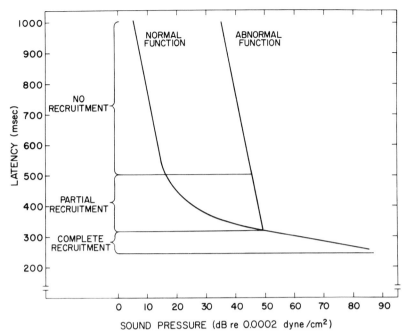

FIG. 17. Hypothetical latency-intensity functions obtained from a normal and abnormal ear. The abnormal function shows recruitment. [From Moody (30), with permission of S. Karger AG, Basel.]

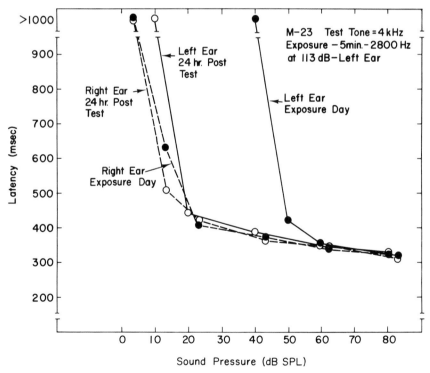

FIG. 18. Latency-intensity functions obtained from one monkey immediately and again 24 h after a monaural sound exposure (5-min exposure, 2,800 Hz at 113 dB, left ear; test tone 4 kHz). [From Moody (30), with permission of S. Karger AG, Basel.]

The intensities of these stimuli were fixed at the midpoints (geometric mean) between successive pairs of the five training stimuli so that the nine stimuli were arranged in a series at 3-dB intervals. The rein-forcement rules for the original five training stimuli remained unchanged. No reinforcement was given, however, for responding to the test stimuli. The order of stimulus presentation was random. Responding to

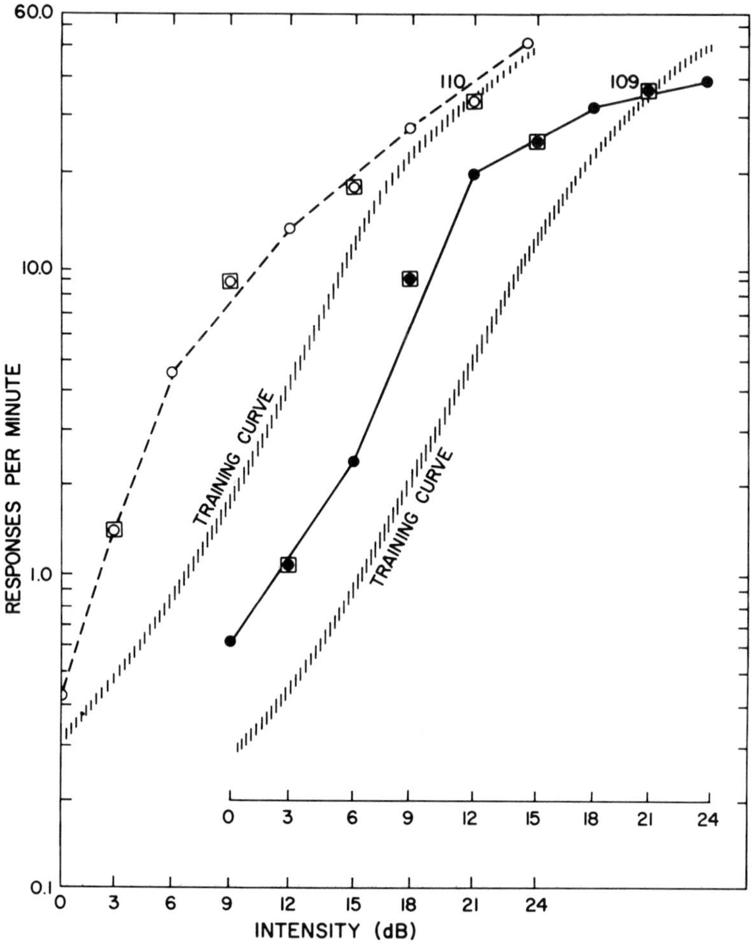

FIG. 19. Rate of pecking as a function of the luminance of the stimulus for two different pigeons (109 and 110). *Training curve* shows prescribed rate of responding at the training stimuli (0, 6, 12, 18, and 24 dB). *Points* enclosed in *squares* give rates obtained with test stimuli (3, 9, 15, and 21 dB) in whose presence responding was never reinforced. [From Herrnstein and Van Sommers (21). Copyright 1962 by the American Association for the Advancement of Science.]

these test stimuli was maintained in the absence of reinforcement, presumably because they were not readily discriminable from the adjacent training stimuli. The hope, then, was that the birds would scale the test luminances by their rates of response relative to the adjacent training stimuli.

Response rates for each subject, as a function of intensity for all nine luminances together, are shown in Figure 19. As the authors indicate, the birds are responding to the test stimuli at a rate close to the geometric mean of the rates at the adjacent training stimuli. Such a result indicates that the birds were scaling brightness as if it were a power function of luminance—a result consistent with what Stevens had found with human observers (57). Unfortunately, other interpretations based on the data are possible; further, intervals of only 3 dB do not provide sufficient resolution to reject other hypotheses. The experiment may be subject to the same criticism that Herrnstein and Van Sommers (21) had hoped to avoid—namely, that the animals have been trained to make a specific perceptual judgment. Clearly the selection of a logarithmic scale of training and test stimuli may have provided a bias toward scaling according to a power function. As the authors point out, alternative training

curves must be attempted in order to substantiate their conclusions. Nevertheless, this experiment was a tour de force and suggests the kind of effort and strategy that are necessary if we are to probe animals about the ways in which they perceive the world about them.

Visual Aftereffects in Monkey

The sensory illusions are probably the least understood of the perceptual phenomena. The most well known are undoubtedly the visual illusions—the reversible figures such as the Necker cube, illusions of extent such as the Müller-Lyer figure, and illusions of motion and of aftereffect such as those combined in the rotating (Archimedes) spiral. In an attempt to quantify the response to these illusions, human subjects have been verbally instructed to indicate extent or direction or to make a comparison between two figures with respect to size or length and so on. Certain parameters of stimulation have been shown to reliably change the subject's response—to enhance or even abolish the illusion. The physiological basis for the illusions, however, remains unknown. Although many of the illusions are contrived figures, they are often based on naturally occurring illusions—for example, the apparent motion of trees or other stationary objects after visual fixation of a swiftly flowing stream.

The study of illusions in animals is also hampered by the difficulty of setting the reinforcement contingency without also affecting the animal's behavior with respect to the illusions. The problem is demonstrated by an ingenious experiment by Scott and Milligan (48) to determine whether monkeys experience a visual motion aftereffect after viewing a rotating spiral. Humans typically report apparent shrinkage of a stationary object or pattern immediately after fixation of a spiral rotating in a clockwise direction, if the spiral is drawn counterclockwise outward, and apparent expansion after viewing the same spiral turning in a counterclockwise direction.

Scott and Milligan trained their monkeys initially to report the actual shrinkage or expansion of a circle presented on an oscilloscope screen. They were reinforced with food for responding on the right of two levers when an expanding circle appeared and for responding on the left lever when a contracting circle was presented. Incorrect responses were punished by shock. Responses on trials when the circle was not moving received neither food nor shock. The animals were also trained to fixate yet not respond to a spiral that was motionless and that was presented immediately prior to the expanding or contracting circle.

Training was considered complete after the animal had effectively learned to fixate the spiral when it was presented and immediately thereafter to respond correctly on the right lever for an expanding circle or on the left lever for a contracting one.

In order then to measure or test the extent of the illusion, the spiral was rotated in one direction or the other at different speeds of rotation on two-thirds of the trials. The subjects were trained to fixate the moving spiral in the same way they had fixated it when it was motionless. On the remaining trials the original training conditions were in effect—that is, the spiral was motionless before the circle contracted or expanded. On these trials reinforcement was given for correct responses and shock for incorrect responses. On the test trials, when the spiral was moving, subjects were neither shocked nor reinforced with food for responding to the two slower rates of circle movement (1.7 and 3.4 minarcs/s). However, they were reinforced for responding correctly and shocked for incorrect responses at the higher circle rates of expansion or contraction.

Scott and Milligan's hypothesis, already verified in human subjects, was that the postrotational illusion would either add to or subtract from the actual rate of change of circle size. That it did is evident from their results for one animal presented in Figure 20. Left-lever responses (for contracting circles) are shown for

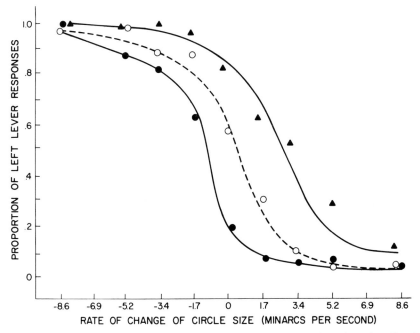

FIG. 20. Influence of visual motion aftereffect induced by viewing a rotating spiral, on ability of one monkey to report direction of change in size of an expanding or contracting circle. Proportion of left lever responses reflects animal's ability to correctly identify circle contraction. Circle was contracting (negative numbers) or expanding (positive numbers) at different rates noted on abcissa and was viewed immediately after fixation of a spiral, which was either stationary (○), rotating in a clockwise direction (▲), or in a counterclockwise direction (●). Extent of the illusion was measured by horizontal displacement of function obtained under clockwise condition or of function obtained under counterclockwise condition from function obtained under the stationary condition. [From Scott and Milligan (48).]

different rates of change of circle size. Lack of preferred lever position is indicated by the approximately equal number of responses on each lever to the non-moving circle after fixation of a stationary spiral. The extent of the illusion is illustrated by the displacement to the left of the function that followed fixation of the spiral rotating in the counterclockwise direction and in the displacement to the right of the function that represents viewing of the circle after fixation of the spiral rotating in the clockwise direction. The extent of the illusion for apparent contraction is -1.62 minarcs/s. The authors have indicated that these are well within the range of findings for humans.

The difficulties regarding reinforcement contingencies in perceptual experiments with animals can be seen in the instability or drift of the monkeys' perceptual behavior. The monkeys were reinforced for reporting the higher rates of circle expansion and contraction after spiral fixation; incorrect responses were punished. Neither shock nor food was given under the more difficult discrimination conditions—that is, after responses to the lower rates of circle expansion and contraction. It is entirely conceivable that animals, with lengthy training, discriminated the conditions under which reinforcement was given from those under which it was withheld; in fact, the authors suggested this possibility. With inadequate stimulus control one might expect behavioral instability and drift. Furthermore, reinforcement of responses to the change in size of the circle after spiral fixation is subject to the criticism that rather than questioning the animal about the way it perceives the illusion, the experimenters are training it to respond as man does under similar conditions. There is no obvious escape from this dilemma; at present it is not clear that any alternative strategies are available. Have we encountered, as these authors have suggested, a principle of "psychophysical indeterminacy"?

Use of Generalization Procedure

One training and testing method that is essentially bias free and has been used in the study of the Müller-Lyer (arrowhead) illusion (28) is the generalization procedure. It is based on the finding that an animal reinforced for responding to one stimulus value on a continuum will respond less frequently to other values that are presented without reinforcement. The attenuation in behavior as the distance along the stimulus continuum from the original training stimulus is increased is called the generalization gradient. The gradient, in a sense, provides a measure of perceived distance along the continuum from the original training stimulus and, as a result, a measure of perceived distance between any two nontraining stimuli. Because reinforcement is given for responses to only one stimulus, the perceptual judgment of distance along the continuum is not biased by the training procedure.

Unfortunately, there are at least two drawbacks to the generalization procedure. The gradient changes shape over time so that the data must often be gathered in a single session. Consequently subjects can only be tested once; replication is usually not feasible. More serious is the fact that the data are so variable that fine resolution of the subjective or perceptual scale along the continuum is not possible.

SUMMARY

In the last two decades substantial progress has been made in the analyses by behavioral procedures of sensory processes in awake animals. Operant conditioning has provided the basis for a viable methodology by permitting the translation from verbal instructions in man to an explicit set of reinforcement contingencies in animals. Although the procedures are often time consuming, they can be effective in training animals to observe sensory events as precisely and reliably as humans. On comparative perception the findings to date are more meager and have been provided by only a few suggestive experiments. A major goal of further research in this area must be the development of a greater variety of training and testing procedures that will not exert undue influence on the animal's perceptual response and yet will lead to precise and stable estimates of perceptual judgment.

The authors' research reported in the chapter was supported by research grants from NSF (BNS74-20050) and NINCDS (NS05077).

The authors wish to thank M. A. Berkley, G. Gourevitch, J. E. Hawkins, Jr., D. B. Moody, and J. A. Nowack for their helpful comments on the manuscript.

REFERENCES

1. BARBER, S. B. Sense organs. In: *Encyclopedia of Biological Sciences* (2nd ed.), edited by P. Gray. New York: Van Nostrand Reinhold, 1970, p. 843–845.
2. BERNARD, C. *An Introduction to the Study of Experimental Medicine*, transl. by H. C. Greene. New York: Henry Schuman, 1949.
3. BLACKMAN, D. E. Conditioned suppression and the effects of classical conditioning on operant behavior. In: *Handbook of Operant Behavior*, edited by W. K. Honig and J. E. R. Staddon. Englewood Cliffs, NJ: Prentice-Hall, 1977, p. 340–363. (Century Psychol. Ser.)
4. BLOOM, M., AND M. A. BERKLEY. Visual acuity and the near point of accommodation in cats. *Vision Res.* 17: 723–730, 1977.
5. BLOUGH, D. S. A method for obtaining psychophysical thresholds from the pigeon. *J. Exp. Anal. Behav.* 1: 31–43, 1958.
6. BRADY, J. V. Behavioral stress and physiological change: a comparative approach to the experimental analysis of some psychosomatic problems. *Trans. NY Acad. Sci.* 26: 483–496, 1964.
7. BROWN, C. H. Auditory Localization in Primates: The Role of Stimulus Bandwidth. Ann Arbor: Univ. of Michigan, 1976. Dissertation.

8. BROWN, C. H., M. D. BEECHER, D. B. MOODY, AND W. C. STEBBINS. Localization of pure tones by Old World monkeys. *J. Acoust. Soc. Am.* 63: 1484–1492, 1978.

9. CHOCHOLLE, R. Variation des temps de réaction auditif en fonction de l'intensité à diverse fréquences. *Année. Psychol.* 41: 65–124, 1940.

10. DALLAND, J. I. The measurement of ultrasonic hearing. In: *Animal Psychophysics: The Design and Conduct of Sensory Experiments*, edited by W. C. Stebbins. New York: Plenum, 1970, p. 21–40.

11. DALLOS, P., AND C.-Y. WANG. Bioelectric correlates of kanamycin intoxication. *Audiology* 13: 277–289, 1974.

12. DE VILLIERS, P. Choice in concurrent schedules and a quantitative formulation of the law of effect. In: *Handbook of Operant Behavior*, edited by W. K. Honig and J. E. R. Staddon. Englewood Cliffs, NJ: Prentice-Hall, 1977, p. 233–287. (Century Psychol. Ser.)

13. EDIGER, R. D. Care and management. In: *The Biology of the Guinea Pig*, edited by J. Wagner and P. Manning. New York: Academic, 1976, p. 5–12.

14. ESTES, W. K., AND B. F. SKINNER. Some quantitative properties of anxiety. *J. Exp. Psychol.* 29: 390–400, 1941.

15. FECHNER, G. T. *Elements of Psychophysics* (transl. by H. E. Adler and edited by E. G. Boring and D. H. Howes). New York: Holt, 1966.

16. GALAMBOS, R. Electrophysiological measurement of human auditory function. In: *The Nervous System. Human Communication and its Disorders*, edited by D. B. Tower and E. L. Eagles. New York: Raven, 1975, vol. 3, p. 181–190.

17. GREEN, S. Auditory sensitivity and equal loudness in the squirrel monkey (*Saimiri sciureus*). *J. Exp. Anal. Behav.* 23: 255–264, 1975.

18. HAWKINS, J. E. Drug ototoxicity. In: *Handbook of Sensory Physiology*, edited by W. D. Keidel and W. D. Neff. Berlin: Springer-Verlag, 1976, vol. 3, p. 707–748.

19. HEARST, E., AND H. M. JENKINS. *Sign Tracking: The Stimulus-Reinforcer Relation and Directed Action*. Austin, TX: Psychonomic Soc., 1974.

20. HENTON, W. W., J. C. SMITH, AND D. TUCKER. Odor discrimination in pigeons. *Science* 153: 1138–1139, 1966.

21. HERRNSTEIN, R. J., AND P. VAN SOMMERS. Method for sensory scaling with animals. *Science* 135: 40–41, 1962.

22. HINELINE, P. N. Negative reinforcement and avoidance. In: *Handbook of Operant Behavior*, edited by W. K. Honig and J. E. R. Staddon. Englewood Cliffs, NJ: Prentice-Hall, 1977, p. 364–414. (Century Psychol. Ser.)

23. HUTCHINSON, R. R. By-products of aversive control. In: *Handbook of Operant Behavior*, edited by W. K. Honig and J. E. R. Staddon. Englewood Cliffs, NJ: Prentice-Hall, 1977, p. 415–431. (Century Psychol. Ser.)

24. KIMBLE, G. A. *Hilgard and Marquis' Conditioning and Learning*. Englewood Cliffs, NJ: Prentice-Hall, 1961.

25. LAMOTTE, R. H., AND V. B. MOUNTCASTLE. Capacities of humans and monkeys to discriminate between vibratory stimuli of different frequency and amplitude: a correlation between neural events and psychophysical measurements. *J. Neurophysiol.* 38: 539–559, 1975.

26. LOOP, M. S., AND M. A. BERKLEY. Temporal modulation sensitivity of the cat. I. Behavioral measures. *Vision Res.* 15: 555–561, 1975.

27. LYON, D. O. Conditioned suppression: operant variables and aversive control. *Psychol. Rec.* 18: 317–338, 1968.

28. MALOTT, R. W., AND M. K. MALOTT. Perception and stimulus generalization. In: *Animal Psychophysics: The Design and Conduct of Sensory Experiments*, edited by W. C. Stebbins. New York: Plenum, 1970, p. 363–400.

29. MOODY, D. B. Reaction time as an index of sensory function. In: *Animal Psychophysics: The Design and Conduct of Sensory Experiments*, edited by W. C. Stebbins. New York: Plenum, 1970, p. 277–302.

30. MOODY, D. B. Behavioral studies of noise-induced hearing loss in primates: loudness recruitment. In: *Advances in Oto-Rhino-Laryngology: Otophysiology*, edited by M. Lawrence, J. E. Hawkins, Jr., and W. P. Work. Basel: Karger, 1973, vol. 20, p. 82–101.

31. MOODY, D. B., M. D. BEECHER, AND W. C. STEBBINS. Behavioral methods in auditory research. In: *Handbook of Auditory and Vestibular Research Methods*, edited by C. A. Smith and J. A. Vernon. Springfield, IL: Thomas, 1976, p. 439–495.

32. MORGAN, C. L. *An Introduction to Comparative Psychology*. London: Scott, 1894.

33. MOUNTCASTLE, V. B., R. H. LAMOTTE, AND C. GIANCARLO. Detection thresholds for stimuli in humans and monkeys: comparison with threshold events in mechanoreceptive afferent nerve fibers innervating the monkey hand. *J. Neurophysiol.* 35: 122–136, 1972.

34. PAVLOV, I. P. *Conditioned Reflexes: An Investigation of the Physiological Activity of the Cerebral Cortex*. London: Oxford Univ. Press, 1927.

35. PETERSEN, M. R., C. A. PROSEN, D. B. MOODY, AND W. C. STEBBINS. Operant conditioning in the guinea pig. *J. Exp. Anal. Behav.* 27: 529–532, 1977.

36. PFINGST, B. E., R. HIENZ, J. KIMM, AND J. M. MILLER. Reaction-time procedure for measurement of hearing. I. Suprathreshold functions. *J. Acoust. Soc. Am.* 57: 421–430, 1975.

37. POILEY, S. M. Growth tables for 66 strains and stocks of laboratory animals. *Lab. Anim. Sci.* 22: 759–779, 1972.

38. POLLACK, J. D. Reaction time to different wave-lengths at various luminances. *Percept. Psychophys.* 3: 17–24, 1968.

39. PROSEN, C. A., M. R. PETERSEN, D. B. MOODY, AND W. C. STEBBINS. Auditory thresholds and kanamycin-induced hearing loss in the guinea pig assessed by a positive reinforcement procedure. *J. Acoust. Soc. Am.* 63: 559–566, 1978.

40. PUGH, J. E., JR., D. B. MOODY, AND D. J. ANDERSON. Electrophysiological studies of loudness recruitment. In: *Electrocochleography*, edited by R. J. Ruben, C. Eberling, and G. Salomon. Baltimore: Univ. Park, 1976, p. 471–478.

41. REGAN, D. *Evoked Potentials in Psychology, Sensory Physiology, and Clinical Medicine*. London: Chapman & Hall, 1972.

42. RESCORLA, R. A. Conditioned inhibition of fear. In: *Fundamental Issues in Associative Learning*, edited by N. J. Mackintosh and W. K. Honig. Halifax: Dalhousie Univ. Press, 1969, p. 65–89.

43. REYNOLDS, G. S. Attention in the pigeon. *J. Exp. Anal. Behav.* 4: 203–208, 1961.

44. RILLING, M. Stimulus control and inhibitory processes. In: *Handbook of Operant Behavior*, edited by W. K. Honig and J. E. R. Staddon. Englewood Cliffs, NJ: Prentice-Hall, 1977, p. 432–480. (Century Psychol. Ser.)

45. ROOD, J. P. Ecological and behavioral comparisons of three genera of Argentine cavies. *Anim. Behav. Monogr.* 5: pt. 1, 1972.

46. ROSENBERGER, P. B. Response-adjusting stimulus intensity. In: *Animal Psychophysics: The Design and Conduct of Sensory Experiments*, edited by W. C. Stebbins. New York: Plenum, 1970, p. 161–184.

47. SCHWARTZ, B., AND E. GAMZU. Pavlovian control of operant behavior: an analysis of autoshaping and its implications for operant conditioning. In: *Handbook of Operant Behavior*, edited by W. K. Honig and J. E. R. Staddon. Englewood Cliffs, NJ: Prentice-Hall, 1977, p. 52–97. (Century Psychol. Ser.)

48. SCOTT, T. R., AND W. L. MILLIGAN. The psychophysical study of visual motion aftereffect rate in monkeys. In: *Animal Psychophysics: The Design and Conduct of Sensory Experiments*, edited by W. C. Stebbins. New York: Plenum, 1970, p. 341–361.

49. SKINNER, B. F. *The Behavior of Organisms*. New York: Appleton, 1938.

50. SMITH, J. Conditioned suppression as an animal psychophysical technique. In: *Animal Psychophysics: The Design and Conduct of Sensory Experiments*, edited by W. C. Stebbins. New York: Plenum, 1970, p. 125–159.

51. SNAPPER, A. G., J. Z. KNAPP, AND H. K. KUSHNER. Mathematical description of schedules of reinforcement. In: *Theory of Reinforcement Schedules*, edited by W. N. Schoenfeld. New York: Appleton, 1970, p. 247–275.

52. SNODGRASS, J. G., R. D. LUCE, AND E. GALANTER. Some experiments on simple and choice reaction time. *J. Exp. Psychol.* 74: 1–17, 1967.

53. STEBBINS, W. C. Auditory reaction time and the derivation of equal loudness contours for the monkey. *J. Exp. Anal. Behav.* 9: 135–142, 1966.

54. STEBBINS, W. C. (editor). *Animal Psychophysics: The Design and Conduct of Sensory Experiments.* New York: Plenum, 1970.

55. STEBBINS, W. C. Studies of hearing and hearing loss in the monkey. In: *Animal Psychophysics: The Design and Conduct of Sensory Experiments,* edited by W. C. Stebbins. New York: Plenum, 1970, p. 41–66.

56. STEBBINS, W. C. Hearing of the anthropoid primates: a behavioral analysis. In: *The Nervous System. Human Communication and its Disorders,* edited by D. B. Tower and E. L. Eagles. New York: Raven, 1975, vol. 3, p. 113–123.

57. STEVENS, S. S. On the psychophysical law. *Psychol. Rev.* 64: 153–181, 1957.

58. TALBOT, W. H., I. DARIAN-SMITH, H. H. KORNHUBER, AND V. B. MOUNTCASTLE. The sense of flutter-vibration: comparison of the human capacity with response patterns of mechanoreceptive afferents from the monkey hand. *J. Neurophysiol.* 31: 301–334, 1968.

59. TOWE, A. L., AND R. W. MORSE. Dependence of the response characteristics of somatosensory neurons on the form of their afferent input. *Exp. Neurol.* 6: 407–425, 1962.

60. WATSON, J. B. *Behaviorism.* New York: Norton, 1930.

CHAPTER 5

Organization of the thalamocortical complex and its relation to sensory processes

E. G. JONES | *James L. O'Leary Division of Experimental Neurology and Neurological Surgery and McDonnell Center for the Study of Higher Brain Function, Washington University School of Medicine, St. Louis, Missouri*

CHAPTER CONTENTS

AT THE PRESENT TIME it may seem arguable that a survey of such a heterogeneous region as the thalamus can have much value. The thalamus of even the most generalized mammal is a complex of many nuclei with different connectional relationships and, inevitably, different functions. Not surprisingly, therefore, anatomical and physiological work in the last 20 years has tended to emphasize aspects of individual nuclei, by contrast with the work of earlier generations of scientists whose approach was rather more regional. However, as work progresses on the functional role of individual thalamic nuclei, certain general principles of organization common to all or to large groups of nuclei are emerging. In what follows attention is drawn to some of these principles and, without presenting an excessive amount of detail, the stage is set for the in-depth discussions of the individual sensory systems that follow in succeeding chapters. Other reviews from slightly different viewpoints are in Jones (236, 237) and Berman and Jones (45).

HISTORICAL PERSPECTIVE

The earliest history of thalamic studies has been described by Walker (524), Clarke and O'Malley (94), and Meyer (340). The development of ideas regarding thalamic organization in the twentieth century has been reviewed by Berman and Jones (45) and is only alluded to briefly here.

Several early workers had recognized that the thalamus is divided into anterior, lateral, and medial groups of nuclei by the internal medullary lamina. The nomenclature that is in widest use today for describing the individual nuclei dates from the work in the 1920s and 1930s of the students of G.C. Huber in the United States [see especially Bodian (54), Gurdjian (195), and Rioch (423)] and of D'Hollander in Belgium [e.g., D'Hollander and Gerebtzoff (110, 111)]. In a series of comparative studies on the more common experimental animals these workers adopted some of the earlier terms of Nissl (369, 370) and extended and systematized them. In this style, a thalamic nucleus is named essentially on the basis of its belonging to a particular group of nuclei and according to its position within that group. Hence nucleus ventralis posterior lateralis (the ventroposterolateral nucleus) is the lateral division of the most posterior nucleus of the ventral nuclear group. This usage was adopted in two of the most authoritative works of the period (90, 524), and many other valuable early accounts of the thalamus in which different nomenclatures were used are now rarely quoted [e.g., Friedemann (154), Pines (397), Ramón y Cajal (413), M. Rose (444), and Vogt (523)]. Traces of Rose's nomenclature remain in such terms as *ventrobasal complex;* Vogt's nomenclature can be discerned in some of the terms applied to the higher primate thalamus. Rose's term *nuclear complex* retains some usefulness where it is desirable to refer collectively to an aggregation of nuclei, such as those of the medial geniculate body, that are related to one another on topographic, connectional, and functional grounds.

Most of the early experimental anatomical work on the thalamus was conducted with the cellular (retrograde) degeneration technique after ablation of the cerebral cortex. It commenced with the early studies of Nissl (370) and Monakow (344, 345), continued through the 1930s with the work of Walker (524), of LeGros Clark and his collaborators (e.g., refs. 91, 92), and of many others, and culminated with that of J.E. Rose and Woolsey (438–442) in the 1940s. This work has left us with several familiar definitions and concepts, some of which are particularly relevant to any consideration of the thalamus as a sensory relay center.

Studies conducted with the cellular degeneration technique provided a connectional basis for the subdivisions of the dorsal part of the diencephalon that had previously been made on ontogenetic and phylogenetic grounds (90, 127, 215, 432). Thus it is possible to distinguish between nuclear aggregations that stand in direct relation to the cerebral cortex and constitute the dorsal thalamus and those aggregations (the reticular nucleus, ventral lateral geniculate nucleus, and zona incerta) that have closer affinities with the subthalamic region and constitute the ventral thalamus. A further noncortically related region, the epithalamus, is composed of the paraventricular and habenular nuclei. From the embryonic anlage of the epithalamus, the pretectal nuclei develop (432).

Within the cortically related, dorsal thalamus two major types of nuclear aggregation have been distinguished, mainly on the basis of their differential responses to regional ablations of the cortex. These are the principal nuclei, all or most of which undergo severe retrograde atrophy after removal of appropriate areas of the cortex, and the nuclei of the internal medullary lamina. Though it has sometimes been contested [e.g., Murray (359)], these intralaminar nuclei are generally reported to show a mild to moderate degree of retrograde reaction after destruction of the cortex, but severe degeneration after destruction of the striatum, i.e., of the caudate nucleus and putamen (129, 401–403). The intralaminar nuclei include the centre médian and parafascicular nuclei (90) and certain nuclei sometimes termed the midline group. This latter term is rather confusing and is probably best avoided, since it includes not only representatives of the intralaminar group but also elements of the epithalamus and certain nuclei that should be more correctly classified as principal nuclei (441).

Each principal nucleus of the thalamus projects to one or more fields of the cerebral cortex. These fields can be defined in terms of cytoarchitectonics and often in terms of electrophysiological properties (439, 441, 442). In a sense, each principal thalamic nucleus is a dependency of its cortical target field, since it degenerates when the target is destroyed. In terms of sensory function, however, the cortical target is necessarily dependent on its input from the principal thalamic nucleus.

The old custom of dividing the principal nuclei into extrinsic (relay) nuclei and intrinsic (association) nuclei is being abandoned. Extrinsic nuclei were considered to be those (such as the ventral and anterior groups and the geniculate bodies) that receive afferents from extrathalamic sources and project to so-called primary areas of the cortex. Intrinsic nuclei were considered to be those (such as the medial, lateral, and posterior groups) that were thought to receive inputs only from other thalamic nuclei and to project to association cortex (433, 438). With the passage of time, however, and with the development of more refined anatomical techniques it has become clear that probably every thalamic nucleus receives afferent fibers from at least one extrathalamic source.

After cortical ablations some principal thalamic nuclei do not undergo the same severity of retrograde reaction as others. This has lead to another somewhat confusing concept of *essential* and *sustaining* thalamocortical projections. These are probably best explained by quoting the original words of J.E. Rose and Woolsey (443). According to these authors, a cortical area receives an essential projection from a given thalamic nucleus "if destruction of such an area alone causes marked degenerative changes in the nucleus." By contrast, "if two cortical areas are considered, and if destruction of neither of them leads to degenerative changes in a thalamic nucleus or to only slight alterations but if a simultaneous destruction of both causes a profound degeneration of the thalamic element, … both areas receive *sustaining projections* from this nucleus." Although certain alternative explanations are possible, the usual interpretation of a sustaining projection is that it is formed by collateral branches of thalamic axons passing to more than one cortical field. As we shall see, subsequent work with more sensitive techniques has sometimes borne out this viewpoint, but in certain situations the failure of a thalamic nucleus to degenerate after ablation of its target field may be due to causes other than the existence of sustaining collaterals terminating in another field.

BASIC SUBDIVISIONS OF THALAMUS
IN REPRESENTATIVE MAMMALS

Figure 1*A–I* shows a series of frontal sections through the thalamus of a cat to illustrate the general configuration of the dorsal thalamic nuclei in a representative mammal. At anterior levels (Fig. 1*A, B*) the three anterior nuclei are seen, together with the parataenial nucleus lying always deep to the stria medullaris and probably best considered a component of the medial group of nuclei. The medial group also includes the mediodorsal nucleus (seen more posteriorly in Fig. 1*C, D*) and the medioventral or reuniens nucleus (Fig. 1*A*).

The mediodorsal and medioventral nuclei are separated from one another by the central medial nucleus, which lies in the midline but expands laterally within the internal medullary lamina as the paracentral and central lateral nuclei (Fig. 1*B, C*). These, at slightly more posterior levels, separate the anterior group from the lateral mass of the dorsal thalamus, which consists of the dorsally placed lateral nuclei and the ventrally placed ventral nuclei. The most anterior of the lateral nuclei, the lateral dorsal nucleus, breaks through the internal medullary lamina to become closely associated with the anterior group (Fig. 1*B*). Immediately posterior to the lateral dorsal nucleus lie the lateral posterior nucleus and the pulvinar nucleus (Fig. 1*D–G*). The former of these consists of several nuclear aggregations (a nuclear complex; Fig. 1*F*), and some parts of it should be regarded as equivalent to certain of the nuclei of the primate pulvinar.

The ventral nuclei consist of anteriorly situated ventroanterior and ventrolateral nuclei that are not clearly distinguishable in nonprimates (Fig. 1*A–C*) and a ventroposterior nucleus or ventrobasal complex, divisible into a lateral (ventroposterolateral or external) subnucleus and a medial (ventroposteromedial or arcuate) subnucleus (Fig. 1*D*).

Medially, at levels posterior to the medioventral nuclei, the ventromedial complex is found consisting of a principal ventromedial nucleus, a submedial nucleus, and a basal ventromedial nucleus (Fig. 1*B–E*). Posteriorly the ventral nuclei give place to the medial geniculate complex of nuclei with an intervening, somewhat ill-defined region referred to as the posterior complex (Fig. 1*E–G*). The borders of this with the overlying lateral posterior complex are also difficult to define. The medial geniculate complex comprises a rather cell-sparse dorsal group of nuclei, a cell-dense ventral nucleus, and a medial magnocellular nucleus lying along the medial lemniscus (Fig. 1*E–H*).

The nuclei of the internal medullary lamina are particularly well defined at posterior levels and consist of the centre médian and parafascicular nuclei (Fig. 1*D, E*). These, together with several condensations of cells in the posterior complex, collectively termed the suprageniculate nucleus (Fig. 1*E, F*), form the poste-

rior surface of the dorsal thalamus and are separated from the pretectal nuclei by a thin medial medullary lamina.

The lateral geniculate complex (Fig. 1*D–I*) is an outgrowth of the lateral nuclear mass, only partially separated from it by a thin medullary lamina. It consists of laminar and medial interlaminar nuclei that are parts of the dorsal thalamus and are collectively termed the dorsal lateral geniculate complex. To these are added the ventral lateral geniculate nucleus lying within the optic tract (Fig. 1*E–H*) and, more or less continuous with its two fellow components of the ventral thalamus, the reticular nucleus and the zona incerta (Fig. 1*A–G*). All three are separated from the dorsal thalamus by the external medullary lamina.

Figures 2*A–D*, 3*A–C*, and 4, taken from macaque monkeys, supplement those of the cat thalamus and serve to demonstrate the expanded size and clear nuclear subdivisions of the primate pulvinar, as well as the additional subdivisions of the ventral nuclear complex that only become distinct in primates. Also shown are the relatively expanded centre médian nucleus and the more well defined suprageniculate nucleus with its extension along the medial medullary lamina, the limitans nucleus. The small pregeniculate nucleus (Fig. 2*A*) is the primate equivalent of the ventral lateral geniculate nucleus.

SENSORY RELAY NUCLEI

The so-called sensory relay nuclei of the dorsal thalamus include the following: the ventroposterior nucleus, which receives the terminations of the medial lemniscus and spinothalamic tract; the basal ventromedial or taste relay nucleus; the lateral and medial geniculate nuclei, forming the visual and auditory relay centers, respectively. To these should be added elements of the ventrolateral complex of nuclei that transmit afferent information to the motor and premotor cortex, and also elements of the lateral posterior-pulvinar complex, which form essential components of an extrageniculostriate visual pathway. In a number of the sensory systems the thalamic relay nuclei can be shown to be organized along similar lines. As more and more data become available it seems likely that certain principles of organization may prove to be common to all the relay nuclei. Therefore it is convenient to consider the several nuclei together. Any sensory system presenting unique problems or concepts is reviewed separately.

Topographic Organization

The ventroposterior and the medial and lateral geniculate nuclei each contain a detailed representation of the related receptor surface (5, 261, 326, 437, 449, 531). This organization is dependent in the first instance on the systematic ordering of incoming afferent fibers and is reflected in the nature of the projection upon the cerebral cortex.

In all three relay nuclei, afferent fibers enter in an orderly manner and terminate on similarly arrayed groupings of neurons. Perhaps the most striking example of this is in the ventral nucleus of the medial geniculate complex. In the cat [Fig. 5; (255, 351, 352)] and probably in other animals as well, bundles of afferent fibers ascending in the brachium of the inferior colliculus enter the ventral nucleus of the medial geniculate complex from its ventromedial aspect. From there the fibers run sequentially along the den-

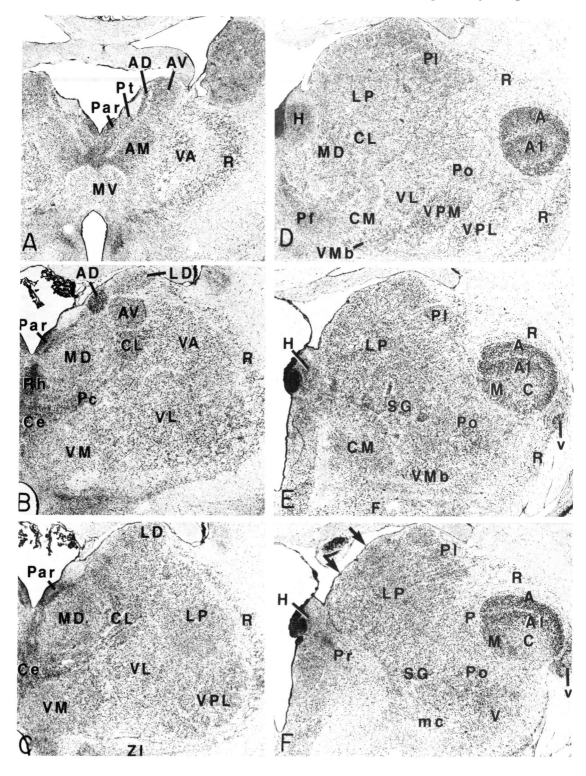

dritic fields of a series of thalamocortical relay neurons. The neurons, when stained in their entirety with the Golgi method and observed in a section cut in the

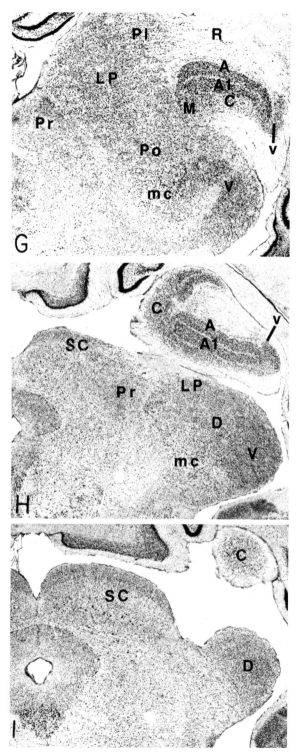

FIG. 1. *A–I*: frontal sections through thalamus of a cat showing in rostrocaudal sequence the nuclei mentioned in text.* Thionine stain; × 10. (Photographed from material kindly provided by Dr. A. L. Berman.)

frontal plane, form a series of parallel, more or less dorsoventrally oriented strips, each with an inward-curving ventral end that becomes partially coiled near the point of entry of the afferent fibers. Over the anteroposterior extent of the nucleus the strips of cells seen in a single section are aligned so as to form a number of more or less sagittally oriented sheets with coiled ventromedial ends. Along these sheets, and following their contours, run the incoming fibers, many of which are distributed to each sheet. Morest (351–353) has referred to the sheets of cells and fibers as laminae, through these, unlike the larger laminae of the lateral geniculate nucleus, are not visible in conventional Nissl-stained sections.

It is also clear that the dendritic fields of one lamina encroach to a considerable extent upon other adjacent laminae. And the branching pattern of the afferent fibers is such that each entering fiber forms several branches that run along more than one row of cells (Fig. 4). Therefore the laminae are not totally independent entities.

The systematic relationship between incoming fibers and chains of thalamocortical relay cells forms the basis of the tonotopic organization that exists in the medial geniculate nucleus. A recording microelectrode driven dorsal to ventral through the nucleus, thus paralleling the planes of the fiber and cell sheets, encounters mainly neurons activated by the same or

* Abbreviations for many of the figures in this chapter: AI, first auditory field; AII, second auditory field; AD, anterodorsal nucleus; AM, anteromedial nucleus; AV, anteroventral nucleus; BIC, brachium of inferior colliculus; CB, Clare-Bishop area; CL, central lateral nucleus; CM, centre médian nucleus; CN, caudate nucleus; Ep, posterior ectosylvian area; F, fields of Forel; G, gustatory cortex; GLd, dorsal lateral geniculate nucleus; H, habenular nuclei; Ia, agranular insular cortex; Id, dysgranular insular cortex; Ig, granular insular cortex; L,Lim, limitans nucleus; LD, lateral dorsal nucleus; LG, lateral geniculate complex; A,A1,C, laminar nucleus of dorsal nucleus; M, medial interlaminar nucleus of dorsal nucleus; v, ventral nucleus; LM, medial lemniscus; LS, lateral sulcus; MD, mediodorsal nucleus; MG, medial geniculate complex; MGd,D, dorsal nuclei; MGM, magnocellular nucleus; MGP,MGv,V, ventral nucleus; MT, middle temporal area; MV, medioventral (reuniens) nucleus; OT, optic tract; P, posterior nucleus of Rioch; Pa, postauditory area; Par, paraventricular nuclei; Pc, paracentral nucleus; Pes, posterior ectosylvian area; Pf, parafascicular nucleus; Pi, parainsular area; Pl, pulvinar nucleus (cat); Pla, anterior pulvinar nucleus; Pli, inferior pulvinar nucleus; Pll, lateral pulvinar nucleus; Plm, medial pulvinar nucleus; Po, posterior complex; Pr, pretectal nuclei; Pt, parataenial nucleus; R, reticular nucleus; Rh, rhomboid nucleus; Ri, retroinsular area; RL, rostrolateral auditory area; RN, red nucleus; SI, first somatic sensory area; SII, second somatic sensory area; SF, suprasylvian fringe area; SG, suprageniculate nucleus; Sm, submedial nucleus; STS, superior temporal sulcus; T,T1–3, temporal areas; V, vestibular area; VA, ventral anterior nucleus; VB(Vb), ventrobasal complex; VL, ventral lateral complex; VLc, caudal nucleus; VLo, oral nucleus; VM, principal ventromedial nucleus; VMb, basal ventromedial nucleus; VPI, ventroposteroinferior nucleus; VPL, ventroposterolateral nucleus; VPLc, caudal division; VPLo, oral division; VPM, ventroposteromedial nucleus; WM, white matter; ZI, zona incerta; 1–21, numbered areas of cerebral cortex; I–VI, layers of cerebral cortex.

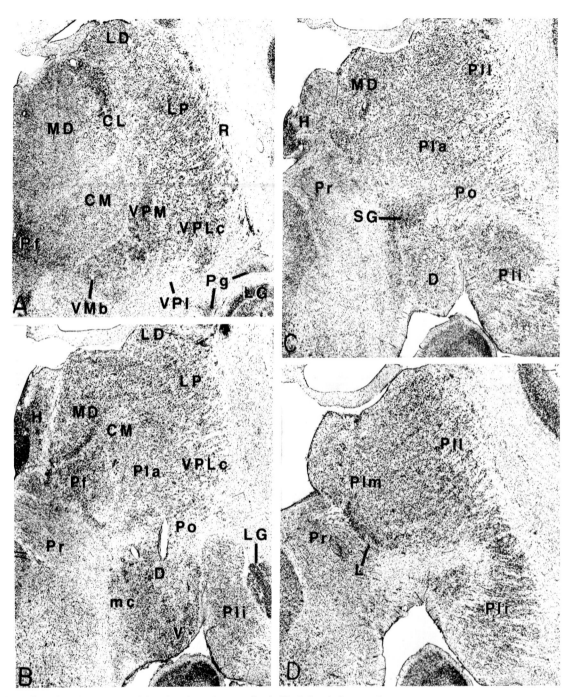

FIG. 2. *A–D*: frontal sections in rostrocaudal order through posterior half of the thalamus of a rhesus monkey showing subdivisions of pulvinar, ventral, and medial geniculate complexes and certain related nuclei. For abbreviations see footnote to Fig. 1 legend. Thionine stain; × 8.

closely similar tones. By contrast a microelectrode driven lateral to medial, and thus across the sheets (Fig. 6), encounters neurons that are activated by progressively higher pitches of sound (5). This systematic tonotopic shift becomes less obvious as the electrode enters the part of the nucleus in which the cell sheets become coiled. From these studies it is clear that a shift in the mediolateral dimension of the medial

geniculate nucleus represents a shift along the basilar membrane. The dorsoventral dimension seemingly represents a position along the length of the basilar membrane. Insufficient work has yet been done to show any shift in topographic properties with a move in the anteroposterior dimension, i.e., in the plane of the cell and fiber sheets. By analogy with the ventroposterior nucleus, discussed in the next paragraph one

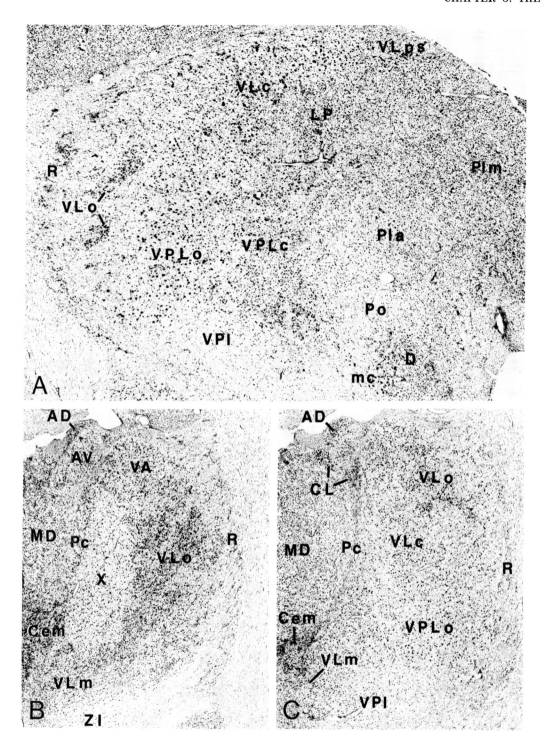

FIG. 3. Sagittal section, *A*, and frontal sections, *B*, *C*, rostral to Fig. 2*A* showing certain more anterior subdivisions of the ventral nuclear complex of monkey. For abbreviations see footnote to Fig. 1 legend. Thionine stain; *A*: × 15; *B*, *C*: × 12.

would anticipate that little change would occur. It is possible, however, that receptive-field properties other than that of location on the basilar membrane (i.e., frequency of sound) could change.

There is reason to believe that the topographic organization of the ventroposterior nucleus is based on principles similar to those observed in the medial geniculate nucleus. As determined by evoked-potential and single-unit studies (358, 399, 437), the body surface is represented as a series of concentric lamellae passing through the dorsoventral extent of the nucleus, each lamella more or less representing a body part, though

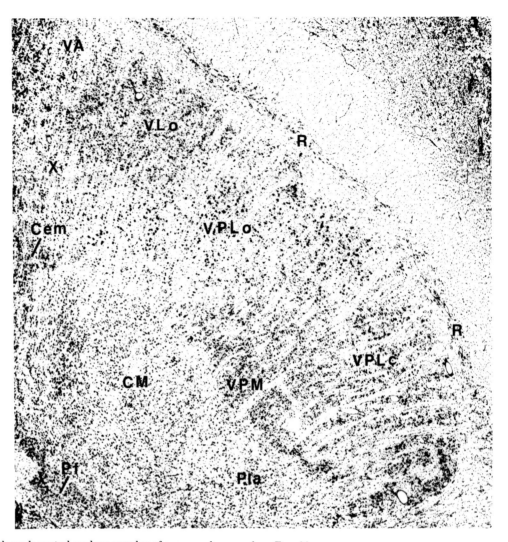

FIG. 4. Horizontal section through ventral nuclear complex of a cynomolgus monkey. For abbreviations see footnote to Fig. 1 legend. Thionine stain; × 18.

not, as commonly stated, a dermatome (314). The lamellae are curved slightly, the convexity being lateral (Figs. 7, 9). In most animals, the lamellae are aligned so that those representing the most caudal body parts lie anterolaterally, with progressively more rostral body parts and the trigeminal region represented in sequence more and more posteromedially (Figs. 7, 9). There are some distortions in relation to the enlarged representations of the hand, foot, and digits in many animals and of the trigeminal nerve in those animals in which the nose and perioral regions are the major sensory area of the body surface (437, 531). But in general the lamellae extend through the anteroposterior dimensions of the nucleus, thus resembling those of the medial geniculate nucleus. In the ventroposterior nucleus, unlike in the medial geniculate, there is evidence for a functional difference between dorsal and ventral parts of the lamellae. Deep receptors tend to be represented anterodorsally and superficial receptors more ventrally and posteriorly

(Fig. 9; see also Figs. 12, 27). There is even reason to believe that there may be separate body representations in each part (245).

The lamellae of electrophysiological studies on the ventroposterior nucleus, like those of the medial geniculate nucleus, are to some extent conceptual conveniences and are not clearly defined in Nissl-stained preparations. Fibers of the medial lemniscus enter the nucleus in serial order (413, 457), however, and each one seems to distribute spraylike clusters of terminal ramifications at intervals within one or more laminar groupings of cells (Figs. 8, 9). An individual terminal spray may merge with that generated by other fibers to make a cluster. The clusters are clearly demonstrated by anterograde labeling after small lesions or isotope injections in localized regions of the dorsal column nuclei [(43, 200); see also Fig. 9B], and they are usually elongated anteroposteriorly following the curves of the lamellae. Terminal clusters derived from axons leaving the deep part of the cuneate nucleus end dorsally in the ventroposterior nucleus and those derived from the superficial part of the cuneate nucleus end ventrally (200). Individual lemniscal axons do not terminate throughout the dorsoventral extent of the lamellae of the body representation but at selected levels within lamellae, although over a relatively long anteroposterior distance.

The terminal clusters serve to encompass narrow, elongated groupings of thalamocortical relay cells whose axons project as a group upon the cortex [Fig. 37; (246, 281)]. One of the most striking morphological demonstrations of this is visible in conventional Nissl-stained preparations of the ventroposteromedial nucleus in certain rodents and marsupials [Fig. 10; (509)]. Here, individual cell groups receive groups of axons carrying sensory input from a single mystacial vibrissa and each projects to a segregated grouping of cells in the somatic sensory cortex. Each of the cortical cell groups, clearly separated from one another, is related to a single vibrissa. A demonstration of the elongated nature of the clusters in monkeys is obtained from single-unit recordings. If a microelectrode is driven into the ventroposterior nucleus horizontally from behind (245, 246), the receptive-field and modality properties of the successively encountered units do not change over quite long distances (Fig. 11). By contrast, dorsal-to-ventral or lateral-to-medial penetrations encounter sudden changes in receptive fields over quite short distances (Fig. 12).

The lamellar type of organization appears to be basic, but within this there is clearly another, smaller unit of organization formed by small, usually elongated groups of cells receiving afferent input of the same type, or from the same part of the peripheral receptive surface, and projecting as a group upon the sensory cortex. It is possible that not all types of afferent input to a sensory nucleus necessarily conform to this pattern. The distribution of individual spinothalamic fibers to the ventral nuclei, for example, has been described as far more diffuse than that of the lemniscal fibers (457).

The dorsal nucleus of the lateral geniculate complex (referred to hereafter simply as the lateral geniculate nucleus) also shows a well-defined topological pattern. In many mammalian species, and probably in the majority, the retinotopic representation is repeated several times in a series of cellular laminae. In carnivores, many primates, and certain other highly visual forms, many or all of these laminae are clearly separated from one another by interlaminar plexuses of fibers. The cellular laminae are not to be regarded in the same light as the lamellae of cells described in the medial geniculate and ventroposterior nuclei, for each lamina in the lateral geniculate nucleus contains a total representation of the appropriate visual half-field.

The elongated clusters of cells and associated afferent fibers within the topological lamellae of the ventroposterior nucleus have as their counterparts in the lateral geniculate nucleus the so-called projection column [Fig. 13; (449)]. A projection column is a line of cells that is oriented at right angles to all of the sheetlike laminae of the lateral geniculate nucleus; it receives afferent input from ganglion cell axons representing a single point in the visual field and projects to a localized patch of visual cortex. The representation of a single retinal point in one lamina is aligned with other representations of that point in other laminae and, where appropriate, with those of the homonymous point (in the contralateral retina) in intervening laminae. Therefore a projection column representing a point in the binocular visual field extends as a line

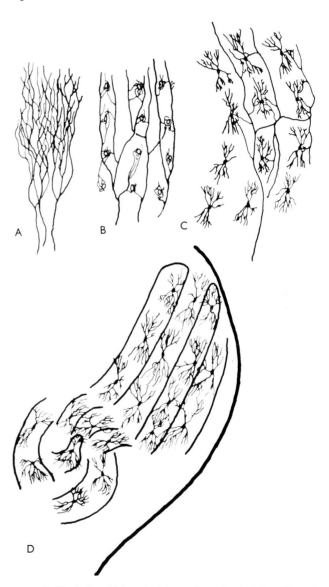

FIG. 5. Ventral medial geniculate nucleus of cat. *A*: bundling of afferent fibers. *B*: overlap of terminal clusters of individual fibers. *C*: distribution of a single fiber to more than one lamellar arrangement of thalamocortical relay cells. *D*: parallel, lamellar configuration of dendritic fields of thalamocortical relay cells, with ventromedial ends of lamellae coiled. [From Morest (352), by permission of Cambridge University Press.]

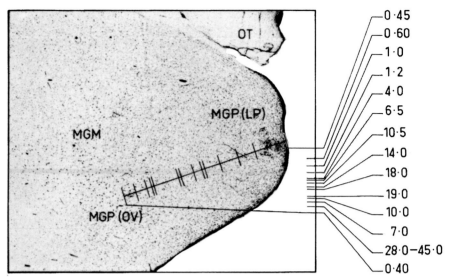

FIG. 6. Systemic, low to high progression of best frequencies recorded from single units in ventral medial geniculate nucleus of a cat, in electrode penetration oriented across rows of cells and fibers illustrated in Fig. 5. For abbreviations see footnote to Fig. 1 legend. [From Aitkin and Webster (5).]

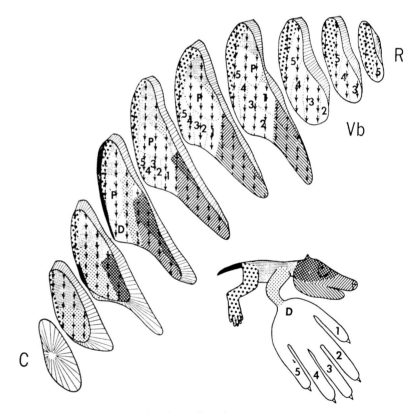

FIG. 7. Rostral (R) to caudal (C) series of schematic sections through ventrobasal complex of a raccoon showing typical mammalian plan of representation of body parts as defined in a systematic microelectrode mapping study. [From Welker (531).]

across all laminae and projects as a kind of unit to the visual cortex (Fig. 13). Perhaps the most dramatic way of demonstrating this anatomically is to make a small lesion in a part of the visual-field representation in the striate (visual) cortex. Because the representation in the cortex is determined by the representation in the lateral geniculate nucleus, this leads after an appropriate survival time to retrograde degeneration in a column extending at right angles across all cellular laminae (Fig. 14). Because a projection column is

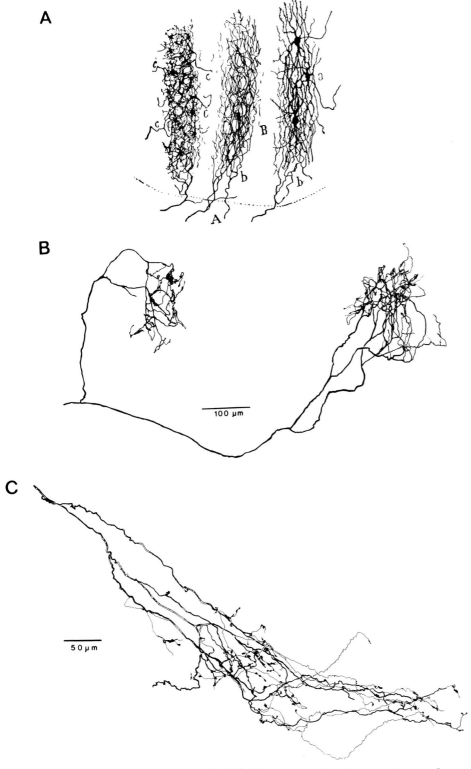

FIG. 8. *A*: Golgi preparation from a horizontal section through mouse ventrobasal complex, showing lamellar distribution of aggregations of lemniscal fibers (*left*), of corticothalamic fibers (*middle*), and of thalamocortical relay cells (*right*) upon which the fibers terminate. *B, C*: single medial lemniscal fibers anterogradely labeled by injection of horseradish peroxidase in medial lemniscus of cats. Sagittal sections. [*A*: from Cajal (413) by permission of Instituto Cajal, Madrid; *B, C*: from unpublished material of W. T. Rainey and E. G. Jones.]

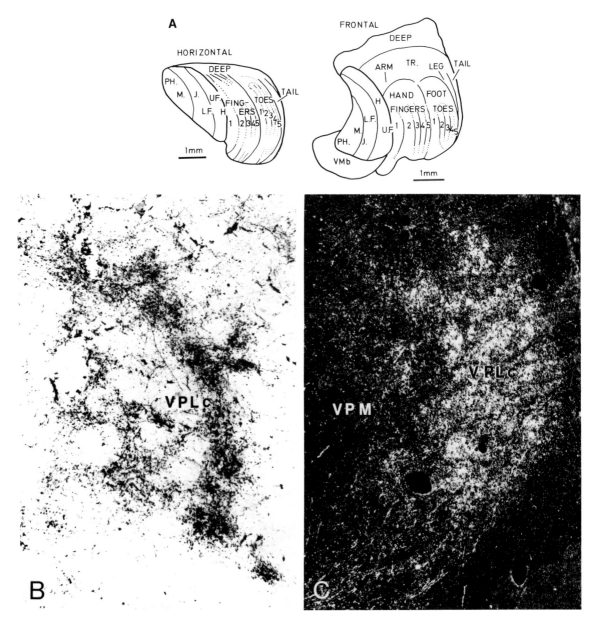

FIG. 9. *A*: schematic drawings on horizontal (*left*) and frontal (*right*) sections of monkey ventrobasal complex, showing division of complex into a large cutaneous and a smaller deep component. In cutaneous portion, body parts are represented as a series of lamellae, as determined from microelectrode recordings. *B*: horizontal section showing labeling of terminal ramifications of lemniscal fibers arising from small group of cells in dorsal column nuclei, and extending as a rod that follows contours of a lamella. Horseradish peroxidase, no counterstain; × 300. *C*: dark-field photomicrograph from a frontal section showing anterograde labeling of terminal aggregations of lemniscal fibers; each cluster represents a rod, like that in *B*, cut in cross section. For abbreviations see footnote to Fig. 1 legend. Autoradiograph × 200. [*A*: from Jones and Friedman (245); *B*: from Jones et al. (246); *C*: from Tracey, Jones, et al. (513).]

probably comparable to the elongated cell clusters described for the ventroposterior nucleus, sequences of projection columns related to a particular degree of retinal eccentricity (from the fovea) and aligned anteroposteriorly presumably correspond to the lamellae described in the other two nuclei (Fig. 13, *lower*). In this way the orderly mapping of the visual half-field is laid down in the individual laminae of the lateral geniculate complex.

The part of a projection column found in an individual lamina is laid down by the mode of distribution of retinal fibers entering that lamina. These are fibers of variable size (187) that give rise to cypress-tree-like arborizations enveloping the dendrites of the lateral geniculate cells. The arborizations have their long axes aligned perpendicular to the plane of the lamina (187, 379, 413, 498, 505). Generally the arborization is confined to a single lamina, but within a lamina, as in the other two relay nuclei, adjacent arborizations overlap to a considerable extent.

Topographic ordering of the inputs to other principal thalamic nuclei has also been demonstrated. There is good evidence in the ventrolateral complex for a lamellar organization with subsidiary elongated focal clusters comparable to that in the ventroposterior nucleus but based on cerebellar inputs (19, 20, 361, 506). Similarly, in the lateral posterior nucleus of the cat, afferent fibers from the superior colliculus are distributed in a series of parallel, slablike formations (176) that show increased density of acetylcholinesterase activity (184).

Cell Types

The cell types of all the principal thalamic nuclei show many similarities. As before, however, we confine our description to the three sensory relay nuclei. Again, most of our knowledge is derived from studies on nonprimates, particularly the cat, and more detail is available for the lateral geniculate nucleus than for the other two nuclei (145, 186, 187, 197, 354, 410). Two major cell types have been identified in Golgi preparations. Certain other forms have also been described, but in all except the lateral geniculate nucleus (see below, this subsection) it is uncertain to what extent these represent variants of the two major types.

The thalamic relay cell or principal cell is large, its soma usually measuring from 20 to 50 μm in diameter. In Golgi preparations it is distinguished (Fig. 15) by a large number of long, stout dendrites that tend to radiate out rather symmetrically in all directions,

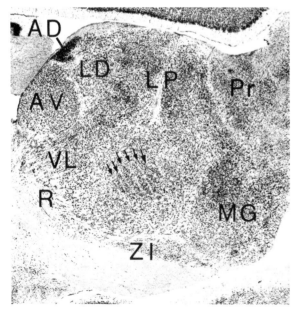

FIG. 10. Oblique parasagittal section showing (*arrows*) six rows of cells in VPM nucleus of a marsupial phalanger, each providing input to similar clumps of cortical cells that represent the mystacial vibrissae. For abbreviations see footnote to Fig. 1 legend. Thionine stain, × 12.

branching several times as they do so. The dendritic field of such a cell is, thus, often in the shape of a ball, though it may undergo some variation at nuclear and interlaminar boundaries. The dendrites give off numerous protrusions from their surfaces. The protrusions are larger, thicker, and fewer in number than the dendritic spines of a typical spiny cell in other parts of the brain, and they seem to form the major synaptic sites for afferent axon terminals (see Fig. 24). The axons of the relay cells are thick; they are often said to pass to the cerebral cortex giving off few or no collaterals within the nucleus of origin, but intracellular injection studies are beginning to demonstrate such collaterals [see Fig. 23; (2, 155)]. In the lateral geniculate nucleus of the cat, LeVay and Ferster (305) brought forth ultrastructural and other evidence indicating that two somewhat dissimilar types of principal cell originally identified in Golgi preparations by Guillery [Fig. 15; (187)] are probably the cells that selectively receive inputs from different categories (X and Y) of retinal ganglion cell. This classification is tending to be borne out by intracellular injection studies (155). A similar morphological distinction has been made between principal cells in the ventroposterior nucleus (391), and in that nucleus large and small cells have been found to project to layers IV and I, respectively, of the cerebral cortex (393a). But the differences have not been subjected to physiological verification.

The second major category of thalamic cell has been described as common by some authors but rare by others. It is small (10–20 μm) and usually has no more than three or four relatively short dendrites. The dendrites leave the perikaryon at variable angles so that the cell may appear triangular, fusiform, or ovoid (Fig. 16). The major distinguishing feature of these dendrites is their possession of numerous long, thin, often highly branched protrusions that give rise to large, bulbous dilatations at irregular intervals. These dilatations form the light microscopic correlate of an unusual class of presynaptic dendrite when viewed ultrastructurally (see Figs. 21–24). This smaller cell type also seems to have an extensive, locally ramifying axon.

The usual interpretation of this second small cell class has been that it is a Golgi type II cell or interneuron with its axon confined entirely to the nucleus in which it lies. Studies involving labeling of thalamic cells by retrograde transport of tracer injected into the cerebral cortex, for a time, cast some doubt on this interpretation. The early studies conducted with this technique suggested that virtually every neuron in the labeled part of the appropriate thalamic nucleus contained the marker (248, 293, 311, 371, 550). This seemed to imply either that the smaller cells have collateral axon branches to the cortex or that they are not uniformly distributed throughout the nucleus. This discrepancy has still not been completely resolved. Winfield et al. (544) and LeVay and Ferster (305) have pointed out that in light microscopy the unlabeled interneurons may be too small to be distin-

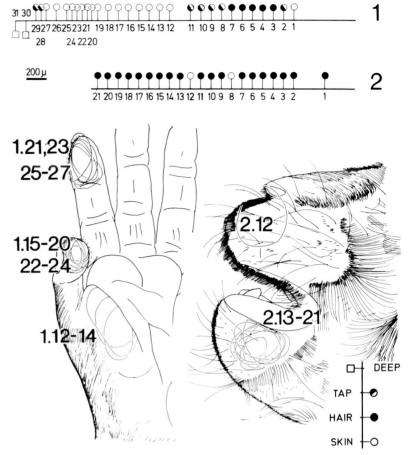

FIG. 11. Receptive fields of selected sequences of units recorded from two electrode penetrations made horizontally from behind through the VPLc (*1*) and VPM (*2*) nuclei of a monkey. In sequences illustrated, units had very similarly situated peripheral receptive fields and responded to same type of stimulus (see key figure). Units for which no receptive fields are illustrated were related to other body parts. For abbreviations see footnote to Fig. 1 legend. [From Jones et al. (246).]

guished from neuroglial cells. LeVay and Ferster (305) consider that interneurons may account for as many as 25% of the neurons in the lateral geniculate nucleus of the cat. On the other hand, the morphology of some cells projecting to the visual cortex from the lateral geniculate nucleus strongly resembles that of Golgi-impregnated interneurons (155, 341).

This brief description has mentioned only two principal classes of cell. Types that seem to be transitional between the principal cell and the interneuron and long- and short-axoned interneurons have also been described (376, 510, 519). It is by no means ruled out that some of the cells described as interneurons may, indeed, have a collateral to the cortex (519).

Afferent Axons

Two major axon types are observed entering each principal thalamic nucleus (187, 197, 255, 328, 354, 360, 501, 510). These form the ascending pathway to the nucleus and the descending pathway to it from its related area of the cerebral cortex. The ascending

fibers have been described earlier in general terms. The ascending fibers have a relatively constant structure. Each terminal branch breaks up into a relatively compact grapelike configuration some 150–250 μm in extent (Figs. 17, 18). The terminals within this mass are large, bulbous, and recognizable at the light microscopic level. In experiments in which the afferent fibers are labeled by degeneration or by transport of radioactive or other markers, each arborization appears as a relatively narrow, condensed mass (Fig. 18). However, a single fiber can often give rise to more than one arborization (Fig. 8) ending at different levels in one of the representational lamellae of a nucleus such as the ventroposterior.

The terminal arborizations do not, as was once believed, embrace the cell somata of thalamic neurons, but form synaptic contacts on the dendrites. Tömböl (510) has used their size and the size of the dendritic trees of the relay neurons in the ventroposterior nucleus of the cat to calculate that a single neuron should receive a minimum of 10 of these afferent fibers. Because in all the principal nuclei there is a consider-

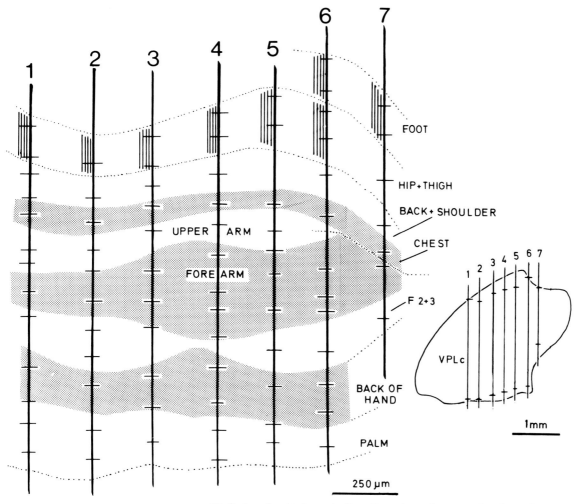

FIG. 12. Series of vertical penetrations through monkey ventrobasal complex records single units (*bars*) and multiunit activity (*stipple* or *lines*) related to same body part at a constant depth implying rodlike representation of smaller body parts within broader lamellar pattern. *Stipple* indicates cutaneous, *lines* deep receptive fields. [From Jones and Friedman (245).]

able overlap of terminal arborizations derived from different fibers, the number, and therefore the degree of convergence, is probably substantially greater. The topographic ordering to be found in the sensory relay nuclei is determined by bundles of afferent fibers with substantial overlap rather than by single, spatially segregated fibers. Nevertheless, bundles of fibers derived from different sources may show some spatial segregation. In the ventrolateral complex, for example, bundles of fibers derived from the interposed nucleus of the cerebellum do not overlap those derived from the dentate nucleus (19, 20).

The second type of afferent fiber that has been consistently recognized arises in the cerebral cortex (Fig. 17). Generally these fibers are much thinner than the ascending afferents and in all nuclei run long, relatively straight courses with few major branches. Along their length these thin fibers give off short side branches ending in one or two small terminal swellings.

Other such swellings may be seen on the parent fiber itself.

The corticothalamic fibers respect the topographic organization of the relay nucleus, for fibers arising in one part of the cortical representation project back only to the appropriate part of the relay nucleus [(112, 188, 249, 257, 336, 517; for other references, see citations for *Axon Bundling*, p. 184]. Injection of tracer at one point in a cortical area, thus, leads to labeling of terminal ramifications in only one part of the relay nucleus (Fig. 19B; see also Fig. 32). If the injection is relatively large it may label a zone that is comparable to one of the afferent lamellae already discussed and that extends in a narrow zone through the full antero-posterior and dorsoventral extent of the nucleus (Fig. 19B); if small it labels a narrower zone related only to the grouping of cells projecting to the point injected in the cortex (see Fig. 32). In the lateral geniculate nucleus this would be a projection column, in the

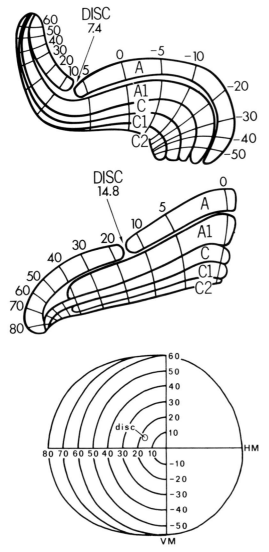

FIG. 13. *Upper and middle*: schematic sagittal (*upper*) and frontal (*middle*) sections of laminar dorsal lateral geniculate nucleus of a cat. *Upper*: projection columns representing degrees of visual-field eccentricity above and below horizontal meridian (0). *Middle*: projection columns representing points of increasing eccentricity from vertical meridian (0). *Disc*, zone of absent cells representing relative position of the optic disk. *Lower*: mode of projection of visual half-field onto individual laminae. Each projection column seems to form a part of a lamellar distribution of afferent fibers and the cells upon which they terminate, which in turn, represent an arclike portion of visual field. Note larger representation of parts of field closest to fixation point. Laminae A_1 and C_1, in receiving fibers only from ipsilateral eye, represent a smaller part of hemifield and are thus shorter than laminae A, C, and C_2, which receive fibers from the contralateral eye. *HM*: horizontal meridian; *VM*: vertical meridian. [*Upper* and *middle figures*: from Kaas et al. (260, 261).]

ventroposterior nucleus an anteroposterior rod (Fig. 20).

At the moment it is uncertain whether the large and the small types of afferent axon described here always arise in lower centers and in the cerebral cortex, respectively. In the lateral nuclear complex of the cat

(309) and in the inferior pulvinar nucleus of the squirrel monkey, although most large fibers with grapelike terminal arborizations arise in the superior colliculus (387), a small proportion may also arise in the cerebral cortex (331). In the ventral lateral and centre médian nuclei the smaller type of fiber, in addition to arising in the cerebral cortex, appears to originate from the globus pallidus (201).

A third major input to each thalamic nucleus, to be described later, emanates from the reticular nucleus (see VENTRAL THALAMUS, p. 196). These axons have not yet been separately identified, but their endings are known from electron microscopy.

Synaptic Organization

Numerous electron microscopic studies have been made of the synaptic organization of the thalamic relay nuclei. The following account, though very generalized, seems to be broadly applicable to all nuclei and to rodents, cats, and primates; it is derived from the work of many authors (97, 145, 189, 192, 197, 201, 250, 251, 255, 308, 325, 359, 394, 409, 498, 501, 543, 550).

A feature that has attracted the attention of all workers is the presence of large aggregations of dendrites and axon terminals often more or less completely encapsulated by a wrapping of thin astrocytic processes (Figs. 21, 22; see also Fig. 24). These complexes have often been referred to as glomeruli or synaptic islands, but neither term is completely appro-

FIG. 14. Columnlike zone of retrograde degeneration extending across all laminae of lateral geniculate nucleus of a monkey following a small lesion in one part of visual-field representation in striate cortex. *Arrow* indicates an unrelated region of additional degeneration. [From Kaas et al. (261).]

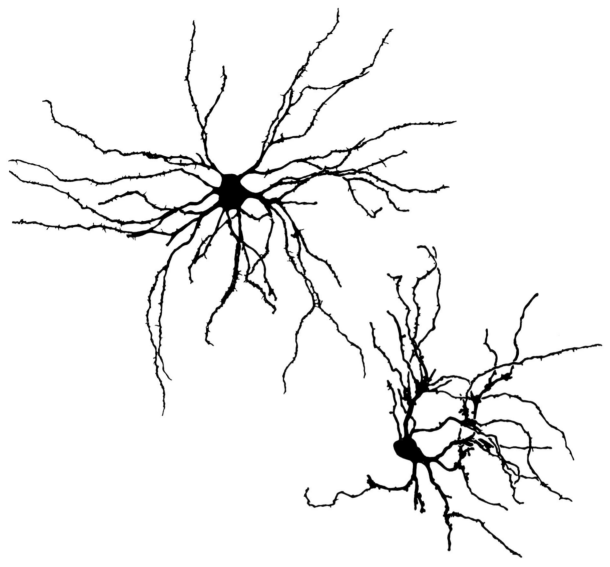

FIG. 15. Drawings of Golgi preparations from lateral geniculate nucleus of a cat showing two types of thalamocortical relay neurons. Larger type is typical of such neurons in most principal thalamic nuclei. Dendritic protrusions and appendages are major sites of synaptic contact with ascending afferent fibers. × ~300. [From Guillery (187).]

priate, since the formations are probably not isolated units but parts of larger complexes spreading over a wider area. Three elements form the major constituents of each synaptic aggregation. There are slight differences in the numbers and in the relative disposition of each element from nucleus to nucleus and from species to species, but the fundamental organization is the same. The terminal arborization of an ascending afferent may contribute terminal bulbs to many synaptic complexes. The large terminal bulbs contain spherical synaptic vesicles and make asymmetrical synaptic contacts with one or more dendritic protrusions or dendrites that are probably derived from both thalamocortical relay cells and from interneurons. Similar synaptic contacts are also made with a somewhat larger number of other processes that also

contain synaptic vesicles (Figs. 21, 22; see also Fig. 24). These latter processes, besides receiving synaptic contacts from the ascending afferents, make multiple synaptic contacts with the associated dendrites. The contacts have symmetrical membrane complexes, and the associated vesicles are flattened or pleomorphic in aldehyde-fixed material, suggesting an inhibitory function. The parent processes are unlike axons, since they contain ribosomes and rough endoplasmic reticulum (Figs. 21, 22); they appear to be the locally ramifying, highly branched dendritic processes of the small interneuron described above [Fig. 16; (145)]. This cell may also give rise to somatodendritic synapses. The axon of the interneuron gives rise to true axon terminals containing flattened vesicles as well; such terminals are occasionally seen ending on both conventional and

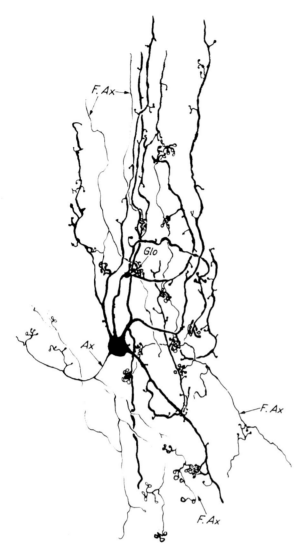

FIG. 16. Golgi preparation of a typical thalamic interneuron showing interrelationship of grapelike dendritic appendages and axonal branches (*F.Ax*) with one another in formation of synaptic islands or glomeruli (*Glo*). × ~300. [From Szentágothai (500).]

presynaptic dendrites toward the periphery of a synaptic complex (Figs. 21, 22, 24). A final feature of the synaptic complex is the presence of numerous adhesive-type contacts, linking together axon terminals, dendrites, and cell somata within and around the complex.

The transmitter agent at the ascending afferent synapse is unknown, though several have been investigated (237). That at the dendrodendritic and axodendritic synapses made by the interneurons is also unknown, though some small neurons in the lateral geniculate nucleus are thought to be GABAergic (483), a term derived from γ-aminobutyric acid (GABA).

The complex synaptic aggregations to which the ascending afferent fibers and the curious presynaptic dendrites contribute are formed on the dendrites of the thalamocortical relay cells and of the interneurons

quite close to the cell somata. Corticothalamic fibers, by contrast, terminate in large numbers on the more peripheral parts of the dendrites and on the parts of the presynaptic dendrites outside the synaptic complexes [Figs. 22, 24; (251, 375)]. The corticothalamic terminals are recognizable by their small size and rather dense cytoplasmic matrix; they contain spherical synaptic vesicles and end with asymmetrical membrane thickenings. There is some reason to believe that these terminals may release glutamate or aspartate as their transmitter agents (24a, 152, 321, 485). In the lateral geniculate nucleus some but not all may be associated with bands of cholinesterase staining (150).

Terminals of axons emanating from the reticular nucleus (Fig. 24) have flattened synaptic vesicles and end in symmetric membrane complexes on dendrites or somata of relay neurons (348, 378) also outside the glomeruli. These terminals appear to be GABAergic (224).

The complex synaptic circuitry outlined here has not yet been correlated with the synaptic events occuring in the thalamus during passage of sensory impulses. An afferent volley invariably leads to the production of excitatory postsynaptic potentials (EPSPs) in the thalamocortical relay cells (4, 12, 68). But the action made by the synapses of the ascending afferents upon the presynaptic dendrites of the interneurons is uncertain. If it is in the nature of the usually understood form of presynaptic inhibition (135, 138), the effect would be to reduce the amount of their transmitter released, possibly by depolarization, as in the spinal cord (138). Then the ascending afferent, besides activating the relay cell, might have the effect of nearly simultaneously releasing it from a tonic inhibition provided by the presynaptic dendrites. On the other hand, if the effect of the ascending afferent is to cause the presynaptic dendrites to release their transmitter, either locally or synchronously after discharge of the interneuron, their effect on the relay cell would presumably occur only after a significant delay and therefore could lead to a postexcitatory inhibition of the relay cell. In either case, the circuitry could account for the often prolonged and profound inhibition that tends to follow activation of relay cells in thalamic nuclei by afferent impulses (4, 12, 68, 227, 365). The subsequent attenuation of this inhibitory aftereffect might result from self-inhibition of the inhibitory interneurons via the serial and reciprocal synapses that their presynaptic dendrites make with one another. It could also be mediated by their axons that also end upon the presynaptic dendrites in inhibitory type synapses.

Postexcitatory inhibition of thalamocortical relay cells has sometimes been attributed to effects mediated by recurrent collaterals of thalamocortical axons ending on inhibitory interneurons (12). Collaterals of this type do not seem to be particularly common in morphological studies, and some workers have denied

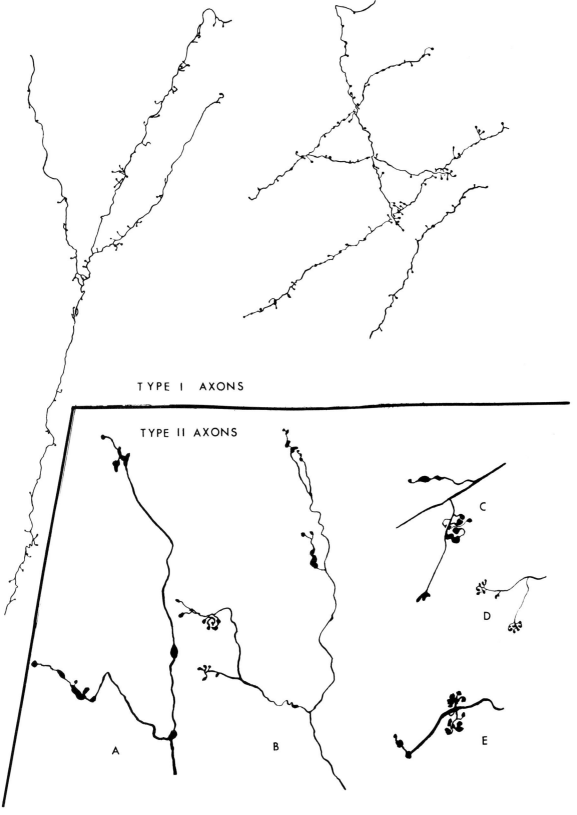

TYPE I AXONS

TYPE II AXONS

FIG. 17. Drawings of Golgi preparations showing terminal portions of type I, or corticothalamic, and of type II, or retinal afferent fibers, from lateral geniculate nucleus of the cat. These are typical of comparable fibers in other principal thalamic nuclei. [From Guillery (187).]

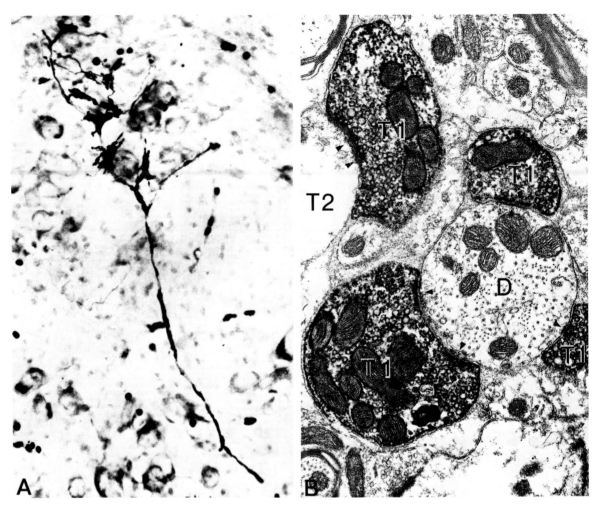

FIG. 18. *A*: photomicrograph of one of the terminal branches of a medial lemniscal axon filled with horseradish peroxidase in cat ventrobasal complex. × 400. *B*: electron micrograph of labeled terminals (*T1*) from a similar axon. *Arrowheads*, points of synaptic contact on a dendrite (*D*) and on a dendritic terminal (*T2*). × 50,000. [From unpublished material of W. T. Rainey and E. G. Jones.]

their existence but they are now being recognized again in intracellular injection studies [Fig. 23; (155)]. Nevertheless, most recent studies of synaptic mechanisms emphasize direct afferent inputs to inhibitory interneurons as well as to relay cells (67, 130, 349, 472).

The role of the corticothalamic fibers is also far from clear. The terminals of these fibers are situated peripheral to the main afferent fiber synapse and their effect on both the relay cells and the interneurons may be expected to be modulatory. Cortical stimulation prior to the passage of an afferent volley may either facilitate or inhibit transmission of that volley through the appropriate relay nucleus (e.g., 47, 266, 526). However, the relevant synaptic circuitry for these effects has not been fully established. Burchfiel and Duffy (66) have concluded that the somatic sensory cortex may normally exert a tonic inhibitory effect over its thalamic relay nucleus. In the lateral geniculate nucleus, Pettigrew (395) first suggested and Schmielau and Singer (462, 472) later elaborated a view that

corticothalamic fibers and their interactions with geniculate interneurons could subserve certain mechanisms of stereoscopic vision.

The role of the presumably GABAergic and inhibitory input from the reticular nucleus in synaptic transmission through the thalamus is considered in the section on the reticular nucleus and other parts of the ventral thalamus (see VENTRAL THALAMUS, p. 196).

SUBDIVISIONS IN RELATION TO AFFERENT PATHWAYS AND CORTICAL PROJECTIONS

Certain thalamic nuclear complexes such as the medial geniculate body, though often regarded as a functional unit, consist of a number of subsidiary nuclei. The significance of these nuclei often lies in their receiving different components of the relevant ascending sensory pathways and in their projecting to independent areas of the cerebral cortex. Even within

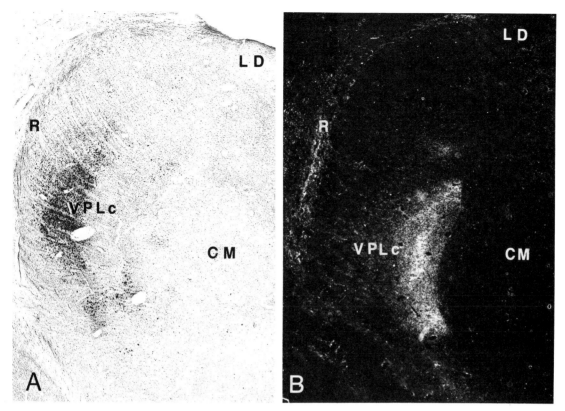

FIG. 19. Ventrobasal complexes of monkeys after large injections of tracer in hand representations of somatic sensory cortex. *A*: lamellar configurations of thalamocortical relay cells retrogradely labeled with horseradish peroxidase. *B*: lamellar configurations of corticothalamic fiber terminations anterogradely labeled with tritiated amino acids. For abbreviations see footnote to Fig. 1 legend. *A*: × 12; *B*: × 17.

a relatively homogeneous nucleus, such as the lateral geniculate, particular cell groups may receive different inputs and project to separate cortical areas. At the other end of the scale two obviously distinct nuclei, such as the lateral geniculate and parts of the pulvinar, may receive independent components of a particular sensory system but project to the same areas of the cortex.

Medial Geniculate Complex

The medial geniculate body of all mammals consists of three major nuclei, and further subdivisions can be recognized within one of these [Figs. 1, 2; (72, 258, 352, 380, 413)]. Each of the major nuclei receives a different component of the ascending auditory pathways and in general projects to an independent cortical area. The ventral nucleus of the medial geniculate complex is the recipient of fibers from the central nucleus of the inferior colliculus (15, 85, 255, 353) and is reciprocally connected with the first auditory field, or AI (14, 85, 112, 285, 542). In the ventral nucleus, cells show the complex laminar organization and fine tonotopic organization that is also present in AI (see the chapter by Aitkin, Irvine, and Webster in this volume of the *Handbook*). The dorsal nucleus of the medial genicu-

late complex is composed of three or more subsidiary nuclei that have been given various names, depending on the investigator and the species examined. Most of the relevant data come from the cat (112, 352) and monkey (72, 258). These nuclei receive auditory fibers from the brain stem that seem to travel deep in the midbrain tegmentum rather than in the lateral lemniscus (85), though some may come from the external or pericentral nuclei of the inferior colliculus (15, 285). Within the dorsal nucleus individual cells seem to have much broader turning curves than in the ventral nucleus (5). Each subdivision of the dorsal nucleus appears to be related to one of the several fields of the auditory cortex outside AI [Fig. 25; (72, 85, 112, 542)], but there may be some overlap, at least in the cat (14, 542). Since each of the fields outside AI also contains a separate representation of the auditory frequency range (338, 553), each field may be concerned with different aspects of auditory sensation, although too little work has been done on the individual fields for any relevant data to have emerged. The differential subcortical and cortical relationships of the various nuclear groups of the dorsal nucleus of the medial geniculate complex could provide a fertile field for future study.

The third major nucleus of the medial geniculate

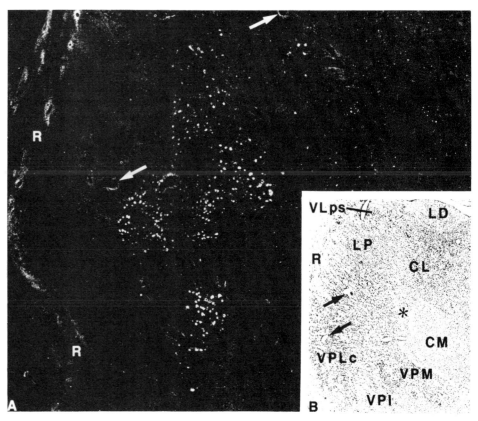

FIG. 20. *A*: dark-field photomicrograph showing thalamocortical relay cells, retrogradely labeled with horseradish peroxidase after a single relatively small injection in the hand area of SI. Though falling within a lamella in an appropriate part of body representation in ventrobasal complex (*B*), the cells form subsidiary clusters. These may correspond to groups of cells receiving input from individual bundles of afferent types. For abbreviations see footnote to Fig. 1 legend. *A*: × 20; *B*: × 5. [From Jones et al. (257).]

complex, the magnocellular nucleus, receives inputs from a number of sources including the ascending auditory pathways (350, 353) and the superior colliculus (176). It is usually also regarded as receiving spinothalamic fibers (56, 273), but it seems questionable that these fibers do indeed terminate around the large cells that characterize the nucleus (20, 238). Units in the magnocellular nucleus respond to polymodal stimuli, including auditory stimuli (3, 398). This nucleus appears to belong to a class of nuclei different from the others of the medial geniculate complex; these project to single cortical fields and their axons terminate in layers III and IV, but the magnocellular nucleus appears to project widely over most fields of the auditory and adjacent regions, and its axons terminate primarily in layer I (239, 443, 447). The possible significance of this pattern of organization is considered in the section OTHER DIFFUSE THALAMOCORTICAL SYSTEMS, p. 194.

Somatic Sensory Relay Nuclei

The major thalamic relay center in the somatic sensory system is the ventroposterior nucleus (Figs. 1–

4), which receives the fibers of the medial lemniscus. The use of the term *ventroposterior nucleus* is subject to a great deal of confusion; in the traditional accounts of many species it includes regions that are clearly not somatic sensory in the usual sense. In nearly all species it often has been taken to include a medial parvocellular component, the basal ventromedial nucleus (Figs. 1, 3) that forms the thalamic relay for gustatory impulses (69); in higher primates it also includes an anterior division, the pars oralis of the ventroposterolateral nucleus (Figs. 2–4), which does not receive lemniscal fibers and is part of the thalamic relay primarily for cerebellar inputs to the motor cortex (19–21, 156, 488). To avoid this confusion, J. E. Rose and Mountcastle (437) reintroduced M. Rose's (444) older term *ventrobasal complex* to include only those parts of the ventral nuclear mass activated by somesthetic stimuli, which in their study were light touch, pressure, and movement of joints. In most nonprimates the ventrobasal complex is coextensive with the ventroposterolateral nucleus in which fibers from the dorsal column nuclei terminate, together with the ventroposteromedial nucleus in which fibers from the trigeminal complex terminate (40, 57, 185, 200, 238, 319, 320, 473,

474). It excludes, however, the taste relay nucleus and, it excludes the so-called pars oralis of the ventroposterolateral nucleus of primates.

The cortical relationships of the ventrobasal complex have become more fully understood in recent years. In earlier studies cells of the ventrobasal complex were thought to project only to the first somatic sensory area, or SI (398, 443). It is now clear that its efferent axons reach both SI and the second somatic sensory area (SII) in all mammals [Fig. 26; (72, 191, 199, 247, 250, 253, 451, 452, 547)]. Experiments using the method of antidromic activation of thalamic cells by cortical stimulation indicate that though many cells of the ventrobasal complex in the cat project only to SI, a moderate proportion project by axon collaterals to both SI and SII (17, 327). This has been confirmed by anatomical experiments involving double-labeling techniques [Fig. 23; (233, 480)]. A few cells of the ventrobasal complex project only to SII (330, 480). There is reason to believe that identical anatomical arrangements exist in the monkey (E. G. Jones, unpublished observations).

The ventrobasal complex provides an example not

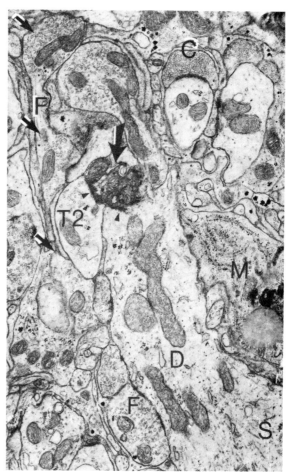

FIG. 22. Electron micrograph from ventrobasal complex of cat showing a medial lemniscal terminal (*large arrow*) degenerating 4 days after destruction of contralateral dorsal column nuclei. This terminal is making synaptic contact (*arrowheads*) with a presynaptic dendrite containing ribosomes (*T2*) and with a proximal dendrite (*D*) close to its point of origin from its parent cell soma (*S*). Presumed axon terminals (*F*) of interneurons arise as dilatations (*smaller arrows*) of a single axon. Small terminal (*C*) is a presumed corticothalamic fiber terminal; *M* indicates a microglial cell. × 10,000.

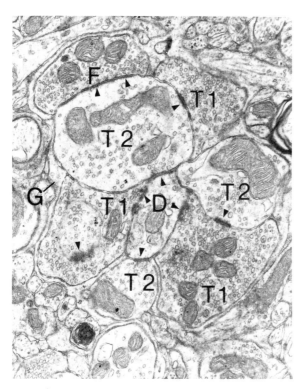

FIG. 21. Electron micrograph from the ventrobasal complex of a cat showing some of characteristic features of synaptic aggregations found in most thalamic nuclei. Dendritic protrusion (*D*) is postsynaptic (*arrowheads*) to terminals (*T1*) of ascending afferent fibers and to presumed presynaptic dendrites (*T2*). Presynaptic dendrites are themselves postsynaptic to ascending afferent terminals and to flattened vesicle-containing terminals (*F*). Both presynaptic dendrites and *F*-type terminals appear to be derived from interneurons of type illustrated in Fig. 14. *G* indicates ensheathing astroglial processes. × 20,000.

only of a thalamic nucleus providing the major input to two cortical areas but also of a true collateral thalamocortical projection. The fact that the branches distribute to homologous parts of the body representation in both SI and SII (250) is another example of the remarkable degree of connectional specificity demonstrated by the nervous system during the course of its development.

Two other aspects of the thalamic relationships of SI and SII require attention:

1. The first somatic sensory area in many species, especially carnivores and primates, is divided into three cytoarchitectonic fields (areas 3, 1, and 2) that lie within the total body representation as demonstrated by the recording of surface-evoked potentials and illustrated in the now popular so-called homun-

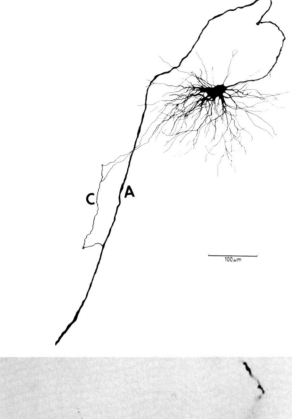

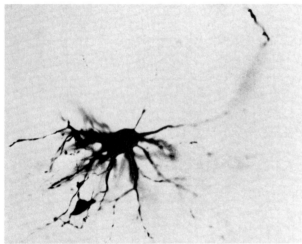

FIG. 23. Drawing (*above*) and photomicrograph (*below*) showing a thalamocortical relay cell injected with horseradish peroxidase in cat ventrobasal complex. Axon (*A*) gives off a collateral (*C*) within nucleus. (By courtesy of Dr. B. Walmsley.)

cular form. Area 3 is further divided into an area (3b) of highly granular cortex, and an area (3a) of attentuated granulation intervening between area 3b and the motor cortex. In the primate each field of SI tends to be specifically activated by different categories of peripheral stimulus. Area 3a responds to stimulation of group I muscle afferents, area 3b mainly but not exclusively to stimulation of slowly adapting mechanoreceptors in skin, area 1 mainly but not exclusively to stimulation of rapidly adapting mechanoreceptors in skin and subcutaneous tissues, and area 2 to movement of joints (99, 162, 208, 317, 389, 396, 403, 532).

This implies that each field receives input from separate populations of thalamic neurons, each specifically activated by only one category of somesthetic stimulus. Area 3a may be somewhat different, since, unlike the other fields, some of its neurons are said to receive convergent input from both muscle and cutaneous nerves (208). Inputs to areas 1 and 2 are thought to be relayed by the contralateral dorsolateral funiculus of the spinal cord, whereas inputs to areas 3a and 3b are thought to be mediated by the contralateral dorsal columns (126). Both tracts distribute to the ventrobasal complex via the medial lemniscus and, as might be expected from the distribution of units with different response properties, the fibers carrying impulses from the dorsolateral funiculus are distributed dorsal to those carrying impulses from the dorsal columns (314).

2. The anatomy of the ventrobasal projection to SI has been the source of some confusion. Early studies with the retrograde degeneration technique (93, 424) seemed to imply that fibers passing to areas 1 and 2 were collateral branches of those passing to area 3. This depended on the observation that destruction of areas 1 and 2 led to relatively little retrograde change in the ventrobasal complex, whereas destruction of these in conjunction with area 3 led to substantially greater retrograde degeneration than after removal of area 3 alone. Though this seemed to provide evidence of a sustaining projection, as outlined in the historical introduction, it could not be easily reconciled with the physiological evidence of modality-specific thalamocortical projections from separate cells to the three fields. Now it has been shown that after destruction of area 3b and injection of horseradish peroxidase in areas 1 and 2, the retrogradely transported label accumulates in intact rather than in shrunken cells (257). Therefore it seems unlikely that collateral projections to areas 3, 1, and 2 exist. The differential cellular changes seen in the ventrobasal complex after ablation of each of the fields may stem from the fact that area 3 receives an extremely dense projection made up of very thick fibers from many cells in the ventrobasal complex, whereas areas 1 and 2 receive a much sparser projection made up of very fine fibers from many fewer cells (239, 253).

In the monkey, the thalamic cells projecting to the different fields are situated in different parts of the ventrobasal complex (Fig. 27). Poggio and Mountcastle (399) originally showed that neurons responsive to cutaneous stimulation are situated in a central core of the ventrobasal complex, while those responsive to stimulation of deep tissues are situated anterodorsally. Loe et al. (314) then showed that the central cutaneous core receives its input via the medial lemniscus and that the anterodorsal deep shell received its inputs via the dorsolateral funiculus of the spinal cord. The deep shell also receives inputs from the external cuneate nucleus (61). Friedman and Jones (156) next showed that the central cutaneous core projects to areas 3b and 1, while the anterodorsal deep shell projects to areas 3a and 2. It now seems apparent that within the central cutaneous core there may be separate populations of neurons projecting to areas 3b and 1 (245, 366). There is reason to believe that separate representatives of the body surface may exist in the central cutaneous core and in the deep shell (245). Independ-

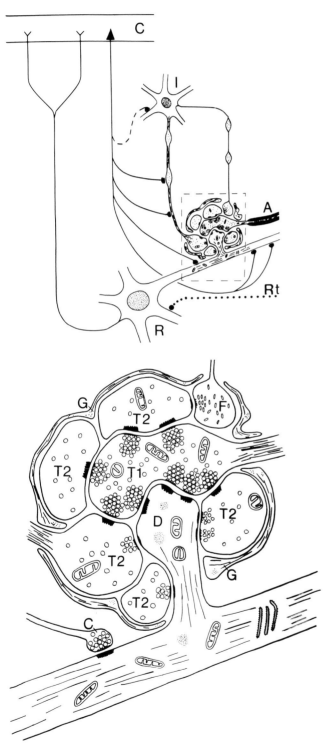

ent cells within each of these may, therefore, project to the separate representations described (263) in the four architectonic fields of SI of monkeys.

Areas 3a, 3b, 1, and 2 are present in the cat and certain other species. Area 3a, is also known to be a specific receiving zone for group I muscle afferents in the cat (296, 383, 385). There is recent evidence for independent representations of separate submodality properties in other parts of the cat SI (136a). In the cat, the thalamic input is uniformly dense over areas 3a, 3b, 1, and 2 (282). In some species such as the rat the fields may not be readily distinguishable in the same sense as in monkeys and cats, and the SI representation seems to be coextensive with an area of highly granular cortex apparently analogous to area 3b (530) and receiving inputs from the ventrobasal complex (451, 549). There is some evidence, however, that parts of the thalamus, either in or adjacent to the ventrobasal complex, and confusingly called "SII of the thalamus" by Emmers (143), project to the relatively less granular cortex around the granular area that forms the heart of the SI representation (118). This part of the thalamus receives the central projections of fibers traveling in the contralateral dorsolateral funiculus of the spinal cord, and it appears to contain a full representation of the contralateral half of the body surface (143, 509). There is an obvious parallel between this organization and that described in the monkey, but it is still difficult to say that the functional organization in the two species is necessarily identical.

The dorsal column, the dorsolateral funicular, and the central trigeminal projections to the ventrobasal complex have been well established. Somewhat less work has been devoted to the spinocervicothalamic system that, together with these others, constitutes the medial lemniscus. In cats and rats (55, 319, 320) its fibers seem to terminate mainly in anterior parts of the contralateral ventrobasal complex, and in this region electrophysiological studies (295) indicate interactions between spinocervicolemniscal inputs and dorsal column lemniscal inputs on thalamocortical relay cells projecting to SI. In monkeys (60) a sparse projection occupies medial parts of the VPLc nucleus. Some lateral cervical nucleus cells projecting to the thalamus have collaterals to the pretectum (42).

FIG. 24. Schematic drawing indicating synaptic relationships typical of majority of thalamic nuclei. Dendritic protrusions (D) of thalamocortical relay cells (R) receive terminals (T1) of ascending afferent fibers (A) and presynaptic dendrites (T2) of interneurons (I). Presynaptic dendrites and probably conventional dendrites of interneurons are also postsynaptic to afferent fiber terminal and sometimes to one another (not shown). Axons of interneurons also terminate (F) mainly on presynaptic dendrites. The complex synaptic aggregation tends to be ensheathed in astrocytic processes (G). Outside this, corticothalamic terminals (C) end on relay cell dendrites and on presynaptic dendrites of interneurons. On the relay cell, most cortical terminals are distally situated. Terminals of reticular nucleus axons (Rt) also terminate on or close to somata of relay neurons.

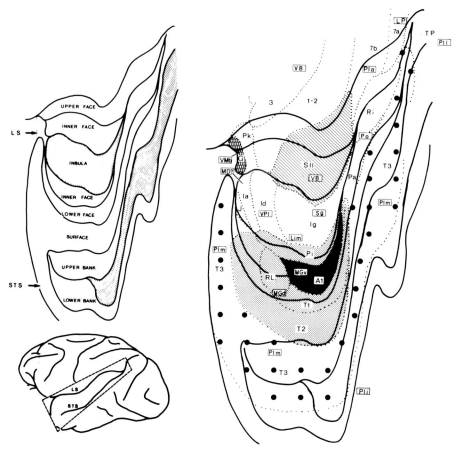

FIG. 25. Orthographic reconstruction of cytoarchitectonic fields in vicinity of lateral and superior temporal sulci of rhesus monkey. Method of making the reconstruction is as illustrated at *left*. Thalamic nuclei projecting to individual fields are indicated by letters in small boxes. For abbreviations see footnote to Fig. 1 legend. [From Jones and Burton (239).]

The ventrobasal projection to SII is a matter of some confusion, primarily because of the failure of many workers to recognize that SII as originally defined by surface-recorded evoked potentials (552) consists of more than one entity. Haight (196) has shown that in the cat a more dorsal and anterior part contains a full-body representation and shows unitary responses identical to those in SI and in the ventrobasal complex. This part of the conventionally drawn SII is the only part to receive thalamic fibers from the ventrobasal complex (210), and it would be desirable to reserve the term SII for this part (Figs. 25, 28).

The remainder of SII as originally defined lies dorsal and posterior to the part receiving from the ventrobasal complex; it contains neurons with large peripheral receptive fields that respond to multimodal and often nociceptive stimuli (196). This part receives input from the posterior complex of the thalamus (210, 355, 480). Though originally described by Carreras and Andersson (81), the neuronal responses typical of this zone had been related to SII as a whole. It is clear that similar divisions with differential thalamic connections

and differential response properties are also present in what was originally called SII in monkeys [Fig. 25; (72, 534)].

Fibers arising in many laminae of the spinal cord and trigeminal nucleus caudalis, including the marginal zone and substantia gelatinosa (18, 82, 160, 161, 286, 403a, 514, 536), terminate within the ventrobasal complex along with those of the medial lemniscus. For a time, work in the cat and rat suggested that all spinothalamic fibers terminated only in the posterior group and in a rather ill defined region along the anterior and dorsal surface of the ventrobasal complex and separate from the region of termination of lemniscal afferents [Fig. 29; (56, 238)]. Recent work on the cat indicates that some spinothalamic fibers do indeed terminate among the lemniscal fibers in the ventrobasal complex (101a). In monkeys the principal regions of termination of spinothalamic fibers are in the ventrobasal complex and in the ventral part of the relay to motor cortex (VPLo), thus forming a potential route for the relay of short-latency somatic sensory information to the motor cortex (18, 20, 513). Spinotha-

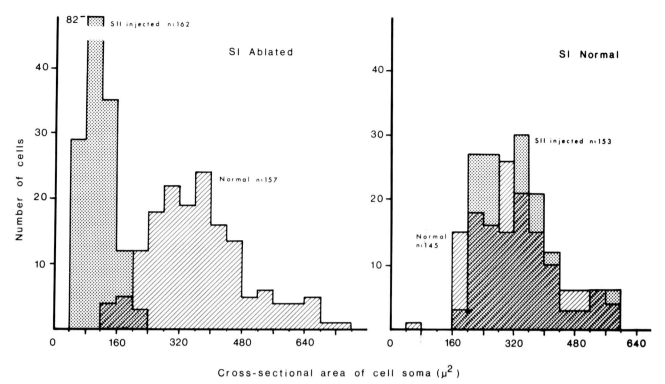

FIG. 26. Data from experiments in cats in which cells of ventrobasal complex projecting to SII were retrogradely labeled with horseradish peroxidase (*right*) in a normal animal and (*left*) in an animal in which SI had been removed 6 months previously. Retrogradely labeled cells (*stipple*), in comparison with unlabeled cells in ventrobasal complex of contralateral side (*hatching*), are markedly shrunken on side on which SI was ablated, indicating that normally these cells have collateral axon branches to both areas. For abbreviations see footnote to Fig. 1 legend. [From Jones (233).]

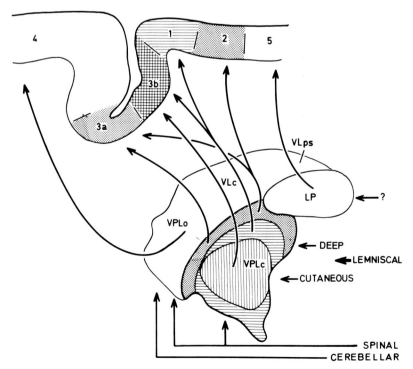

FIG. 27. Schematic figure showing on sagittal sections the pattern of input-output connections of ventrobasal complex and certain adjacent thalamic nuclei in monkey. For abbreviations see footnote to Fig. 1 legend. [From Jones and Friedman (245).]

lamic recipient cells in the ventrobasal complex responsive to thermal stimuli have now been shown to project to SI (272a).

The status of the zone of spinal fiber terminations peripheral to the ventrobasal complex is still a matter of some uncertainty. Evidence in the cat suggests that the fibers terminating in it arise to a large extent in the marginal layer of the contralateral dorsal horn (82, 514), perhaps implying a role for this part of the thalamus in nociception. The region has not been explored electrophysiologically, but it is known in the cat to project to areas of the cortex that have not usually been considered to be involved in thermo- or nociception. These include the third somatic sensory area (SIII), which lies posterior to SI (502). This area is activated at short latency by peripheral stimulation, contains a full representation of the body surface (103), and projects to the spinal cord (100). It appears likely that a similar region, perhaps coextensive with the supplementary sensory area (52, 383) and lying in the superior parietal lobule, is also present in primates (254). There is no evidence at all, however, to implicate this in thermo- or nociception.

Two other regions of the dorsal thalamus in which spinothalamic fibers terminate in all species are the intralaminar system of nuclei and a further, rather ill defined, and frequently misunderstood region termed the *posterior complex* of nuclei (Figs. 1, 3, 29). In the cat some spinothalamic fibers that arise from cells in the marginal layer and laminae VII and VIII of the spinal cord (82) terminate around a group of large, densely staining cells in the caudal part of the central lateral nucleus [Fig. 29; (238, 334)]. Earlier reports of spinal terminations in the centre médian and parafas-

cicular nuclei of the cat were clearly based on a failure to demonstrate adequately the cytoarchitecture in this region. The same situation is found in monkeys (273), though here the caudal, large cells of the central lateral nucleus are often included in the densocellular (paralamellar) component of the mediodorsal nucleus. In rats and many other smaller mammals with less well defined intralaminar nuclei the zone of intralaminar terminations appears to be incorporated in the parafascicular nucleus (319, 336, 430). Spinothalamic fibers ending here in rats have been reported to arise only in the deeper laminae of the spinal cord (168).

The posterior complex is a composite of several nuclei. Of these, the suprageniculate-limitans, magnocellular medial geniculate, and lateral and intermediate divisions have little to do with the somatic sensory system. The medial division of the posterior complex, extending forward from just beneath the magnocellular nucleus of the medial geniculate complex in the cat, embraces the caudal pole of the ventrobasal complex and overlaps it dorsally so as to become more or less continuous with the region of spinal terminations lying dorsal and rostral to the ventrobasal complex (Fig. 1). The greater part of this region, which also receives spinal and trigeminal fibers (56, 57), has sometimes been referred to as the intermediate or inferior nucleus of the lateral nuclear complex or even as a part of the lateral posterior nucleus (319, 423). The region can be identified in rats (248) and monkeys, though its relationships to the surrounding nuclei are somewhat altered [Figs. 2, 43; (72, 144)].

Although there have been reports that spinal fibers terminate in the magnocellular nucleus of the medial

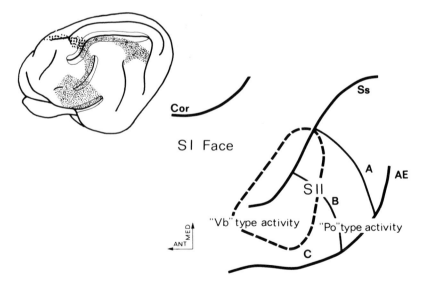

FIG. 28. *Left*: distribution (*stipple*) of cortical projections of posterior complex of thalamic nuclei in cats. *Right*: distribution of neurons with lemniscal (VB-type) and nonlemniscal (Po-type) response properties in anterior ectosylvian gyrus of cat. These occupy different parts of area previously designated SII on basis of surface-evoked potentials and correspond to regions receiving from ventrobasal and posterior complexes of thalamus. A, B, C are previously identified zones of Carreras and Andersson (81). For abbreviations see footnote to Fig. 1 legend. [From Haight (196).]

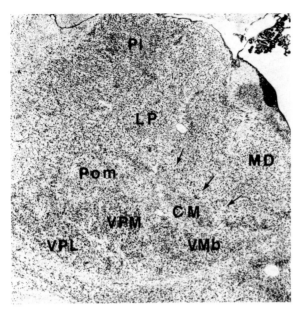

FIG. 29. Cytoarchitecture of two regions receiving spinothalamic terminals in the cat. These include medial division of posterior complex (*Pom*) and a group of large cells of central lateral nucleus (*arrows*) that are often mistakenly regarded as belonging to the centre médian nucleus (*CM*). Thionine stain; × 10. For other abbreviations see footnote to Fig. 1 legend. [From Jones and Burton (238).]

geniculate complex (56, 273, 319), a more conservative interpretation (238, 361) would be that these end around smaller cells that are actually caudal extensions of the medial division. Similarly, although dorsal column lemniscal or spinocervicolemniscal fibers have sometimes been reported to terminate in the medial division of the posterior complex, the number of fibers appear to be minimal in comparison with those from the spinal cord.

The response properties of neurons in the spinal part of the posterior group are such that they have been implicated by some investigators in pain mechanisms (84, 398, 533). There is also evidence, however, that many neurons may be specifically activated by innocuous stimuli (102, 446). Both of these types of response are perhaps explicable, since the medial division seems to receive its spinal input from laminae IV to VI of the contralateral spinal cord (82), in which spinothalamic tract cells with both types of property are found (537). The cortical target of this spinothalamic part of the posterior group forms a region lying above and behind the part of SII receiving fibers from the ventrobasal complex (210, 355) and referred to in the monkey as the retroinsular area (Figs. 25, 28, 29). There is some extremely circumstantial evidence to implicate this area in pain perception (72).

Gustatory Nucleus

The thalamic relay for gustatory impulses forms a compact, easily recognizable mass of small cells at the posteromedial border of the ventroposteromedial nucleus. Traditionally it has been referred to as the pars parvocellularis of the ventroposteromedial nucleus (Figs. 1, 2), but it was included in the ventromedial complex by J. E. Rose and Mountcastle (436) on the grounds that, unlike the rest of the ventroposterior nucleus (ventrobasal complex), it was not activated by somatic sensory stimuli. This has, unfortunately, led to a certain amount of confusion, for the term *ventromedial complex* has now tended to become synonymous with the term *taste nucleus*. The ventromedial complex, however, also includes principal, interventral, and submedial nuclei; therefore, to avoid further confusion Berman and Jones (45) in 1973 coined the term *basal ventromedial nucleus* for the taste relay. It has been recognized in virtually all mammals and reaches an unusually large size in ungulates (433). There is some reason to believe that the histologically identifable part of the nucleus may consist of two parts, the taste relay and a second part projecting to nongustatory parts of the cortex (283). The nongustatory part may be the thalamic terminus for second-order vagal afferents (107). A vagal relay medial to the taste relay region completes a systematic topographic sequence in which, on passing medially from the ventroposterolateral nucleus, the representation of cervical spinal nerves gives way in sequence to the contralateral trigeminal nerve, then to parts of both trigeminal nerves in the ventroposteromedial nucleus, and thereafter to the ipsilateral facial, glossopharyngeal, and vagus nerves in the basal ventromedial nucleus (28, 51, 142, 294, 373, 436, 437).

The basal ventromedial nucleus seems to receive the majority of its gustatory afferents, not directly from the nucleus solitarius of the medulla oblongata, but from a secondary relay center in the dorsal part of the pons (372, 373). It is not completely clear whether this is identical to the parabrachial nucleus, which also furnishes an input to the basal ventromedial nucleus (450). In other respects its anatomical organization, so far as it is known, resembles that of the ventrobasal complex. Perhaps the most striking similarity is the nature of its cortical projection. The basal ventromedial nucleus projects to a gustatory focus within the representation of the tongue in SI (Fig. 25) and to a second more ventrally placed area lying close to SII and the insular cortex [Fig. 25; (35, 36, 70, 72)]. It is highly likely, although not proved, that this is a true, collateral type of thalamocortical projection, for the basal ventromedial nucleus undergoes more severe retrograde degeneration after destruction of both areas than after destruction of the SI projection area alone (36).

Vestibular Relay

Though responses to vestibular nerve stimulation could clearly be elicited in certain parts of the thalamus (74, 343, 398), the general consensus had been that no fibers emanating from the vestibular nuclei reached the thalamus directly, i.e., without an intervening relay (503). However, there is now good evidence for a modest vestibulothalamic projection arising from the part of the vestibular nuclear complex in which spinal afferents terminate (300, 446, 513).

Early work on the thalamic and cortical representation of the vestibular nerve in the cat tended to focus attention on the vicinity of the magnocellular medial geniculate nucleus (343, 398) and on a cortical projection zone buried in the banks of the anterior suprasylvian sulcus (16, 298, 342, 525). A comparable vestibular projection area appears to be present in area 2 of the monkey SI cortex in which it overlaps part of the representation of the head (335). In the monkey, however, the parts of the thalamus that have recently attracted most attention as the principal vestibular relay to the cortex are the ventral nuclei. The thalamic terminus of vestibular efferents has been shown in the monkey to be in the relay to motor cortex, VPLo (20, 300), although field potentials and single-unit activity elicited by vestibular stimulation can be demonstrated over the ventroposteroinferior nucleus (74, 105) as well. The VPLo does not project to the area 2 vestibular focus, but there is suggestive evidence that VPI may project to it as well as to the dysgranular insular cortex [Fig. 25; (72)].

Visual Relay Nuclei

The thalamic connections of the visual system are somewhat bewildering in their complexity and in the degree to which the different components interrelate with one another. There are two major circuits: one, leading from the optic tract through the lateral geniculate nucleus to the primary visual cortex (and in some animals to other areas as well), may be termed the geniculostriate system; the other, leading from the optic tract to the pretectum and superior colliculus and thence via the lateral nuclear complex of the thalamus to areas outside the primary visual cortex, may be termed the extrageniculostriate system [Figs. 30, 31; (231, 463)]. Although there is evidence that at least in some species the geniculostriate system is involved in visual discrimination and the extrageniculostriate system in orientation toward visual stimuli (44, 83, 463), separation of the two is to a large extent merely a descriptive convenience, because they interconnect at many levels.

Geniculostriate System

In outlining the patterns of connectivity in the geniculostriate system it is desirable to present data from the carnivore and primate separately, for the greatly different configurations of the lateral geniculate complexes in the two orders make a single unifying account difficult. Other species have been studied less intensively, but from published accounts it may be

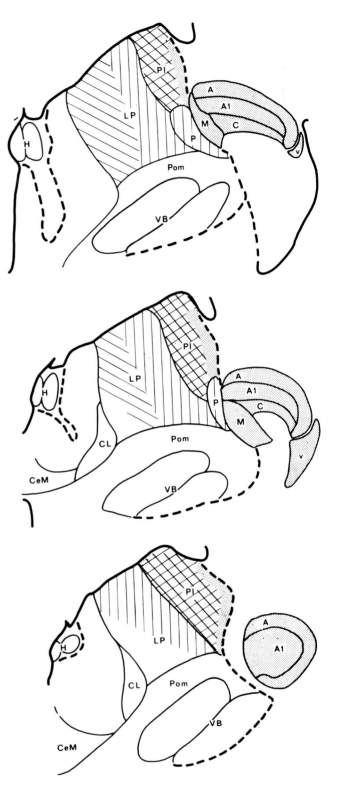

FIG. 30. Frontal sections through thalamus of cat showing schematically the differential distribution of fibers from retina (*stipple*), from certain pretectal nuclei (*cross hatching*), from visual areas of cortex (*vertical hatching*), and from superficial layers of superior colliculus (*oblique hatching*). Compare Fig. 1F. For abbreviations see footnote to Fig. 1 legend.

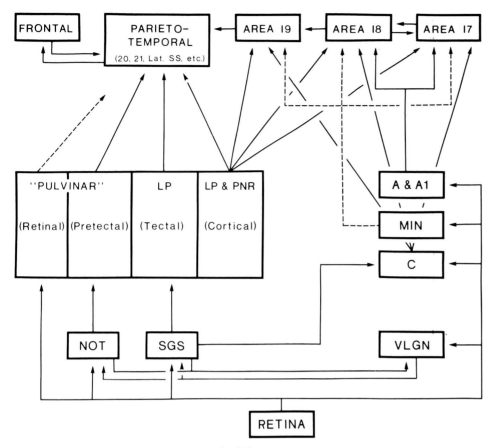

FIG. 31. Schematic diagram illustrating patterns of afferent and thalamocortical connectivity in geniculocortical and extrageniculocortical parts of visual system as currently understood in cat. A, A_1, C: layers of dorsal lateral geniculate nucleus; Lat. SS: lateral suprasylvian area; LP & PNR: lateral posterior nucleus and posterior nucleus of Rioch; MIN: medial interlaminar nucleus of dorsal lateral geniculate; NOT: nucleus of optic tract; SGS: stratum griseum superficiale of superior colliculus; VLGN: ventral lateral geniculate nucleus.

assumed that the overall connectional patterns are similar.

In the cat, optic tract fibers emanating from the contralateral eye terminate in lamina A and in at least two subsidiary laminae (C and C_2) of the collective C-laminae (Figs. 1, 30). Fibers from the ipsilateral eye terminate in the A_1-lamina, as well as in the C_1-lamina that intervenes between the C- and C_2-laminae (190, 216). There is relatively little overlap of ipsi- and contralaterally arising fibers in the interlaminar zones (190).

Axons terminating in the A- and A_1-laminae generally arise from retinal ganglion cells with both brisk-sustained and brisk-transient discharge properties (95, 124, 125, 159, 217, 540, 541). These are thought to be equivalent to the X- and Y-cells defined by their different capacities for spatial summation (144a). It seems clear that X- and Y-fibers terminate upon separate populations of cells in the A- and A_1-laminae. In the cat these two laminae project to both areas 17 and 18, (i.e., visual areas I and II), but area 17 receives both X- and Y-cell inputs, whereas area 18 receives

only Y-cell inputs (484). This would imply that lateral geniculate cells receiving Y-type fibers send collateral axon branches to both area 17 and area 18. It was originally suggested on morphological grounds (164) that the axons of the larger cells of the A- and A_1-laminae branched in this fashion; this was apparently confirmed by Stone and Dreher (484), using antidromic techniques, and though support was not forthcoming in the subsequent study of LeVay and Ferster (305), Giesert (167) has now indicated that approximately 10% of the cells in the A- and A_1-laminae may project to both areas.

The C-laminae of the feline lateral geniculate nucleus, as well as receiving X- and Y-cell inputs, also receive the axons of a third category of retinal ganglion cells with sluggish discharge patterns, or W-cells (159, 540, 541). The cortical relationships of the C-laminae are quite different from those of the A- and A_1-laminae. Whereas the fibers emanating from the A- and A_1-laminae terminate in layers IV and VI of areas 17 and 18, those from the C-laminae terminate in layer I and in layer IV in zones lying superficial and deep to the A-laminae terminations (Fig. 41). In addition their terminations spread rather diffusely from areas 17 and 18 into adjacent cortical areas that do not receive fibers from the A- and A_1-laminae (306, 408). The functional significance of this is uncertain, but it clearly forms a different kind of thalamocortical relationship of the lateral geniculate complex.

A further nucleus of the cat lateral geniculate complex (exclusive of the ventral lateral geniculate nucleus) also receives fibers from both retinae and seems to contain a complete representation of the appropriate visual half-field. This is the medial interlaminar nucleus [Figs. 1, 30, 31; (165, 205, 280, 301, 449)]. Its cortical projection is at least to areas 18 and 19 and possibly to other areas as well (167, 323). A small lateralmost portion of the pulvinar nucleus also receives a direct retinal input [Fig. 30, 31; (47, 193)]. The cortical relationships of this area are not completely clear, but on topological grounds (209) it may be expected to project to areas of cortex which, though probably visual in function (386), are even further removed from the primary visual cortex.

Extrageniculostriate System

Entering the thalamus from the pretectum and superior colliculus, the extrageniculostriate system gains access to the cortex, often to the same areas of cortex as those mentioned above, by way of the lateral nuclear complex (46, 47, 167, 176, 180–184, 209, 269, 408 497, 518, 520).

In general terms, the lateral nuclear complex of the cat consists of four, more or less parallel, roughly anteroposteriorly disposed bands (Figs. 1F, 30, 31). 1) A medial, large-celled component receives fibers from the superficial, visually activated layers of the superior colliculus (176). 2) A second component lying lateral to this receives fibers from several areas of the visual cortex; this component (518) includes the so-called posterior nucleus of Rioch (423), which is found only in carnivores (Fig. 1E). 3) The third component forms most of the pulvinar nucleus of the cat and receives fibers from the nucleus of the optic tract (including the olivary nucleus), the only nucleus of the pretectum to receive direct retinal projections (46). 4) The fourth and most lateral component at the extreme lateral margin of the pulvinar nucleus is the retinal recipient zone described above (46).

The cortical projections of these four components of the lateral nuclear complex include a number of cortical areas usually termed extrastriate that lie in the middle and posterior suprasylvian gyri of the cat (Fig. 31). Most of these contain representations of the visual field (329, 386), and the fiber systems terminating in the various components of the lateral nuclear complex are distributed in a topographically organized manner compatible with this. The areas are necessary for various forms of visual discriminations in the cat (479) and are clearly comparable to the peristriate and

inferotemporal regions of primates (231, 529). The evidence to date is that thalamocortical fibers leaving most of the thalamic components of the extrageniculostriate system terminate in circumscribed architectonic fields with their endings in layers III and IV of the cortex. Most of the components of the lateral nuclear complex could, therefore, be considered typical thalamic relay nuclei. There is reason to believe, however, that the part of the complex receiving fibers from areas 17, 18, and 19 of the visual cortex may project in a more diffuse manner to areas 17, 18, and 19 and to several other areas that have specific inputs from other thalamic nuclei (170).

The emphasis in the account just given has been on separating out, for the sake of clarity, the several components of the thalamic visual system of the cat. It would be wrong, however, to create the impression that these are entirely separate pathways, for they come together in several places. When the following points are considered, not only does any separation appear rather artificial, but also the task of trying to make some functional sense of the individual components becomes rather formidable. 1) The nucleus of the optic tract and the superficial layers of the superior colliculus are reciprocally connected with one another and with the ventral lateral geniculate nucleus, which is another retinal recipient region (46, 176). 2) The superficial layers of the superior colliculus project to the deeper C-laminae of the lateral geniculate nucleus (176, 512). 3) Parts of some thalamic nuclei project rather diffusely over several cortical areas. 4) Most of the cortical areas receiving inputs from the various components of the visual thalamus are interconnected by corticocortical fibers (170, 209). 5) Most of these areas project back to the superficial (visual) layers of the superior colliculus and to a lesser extent to the nucleus of the optic tract (163, 267).

For the sake of further simplicity this account has focused on the cat, for which most anatomical detail is known. Nevertheless, the broader outlines of the circuitry described seem to be applicable to monkeys. In monkeys the lateral geniculate nucleus projects only to area 17, but there are differential laminar terminations of the parvo- and magnocellular laminae (226, 318) and of cells in subsidiary and interlaminar zones (78). There is a segregation of X- and Y-type inputs to the parvo- and magnocellular layers (458, 469). Moreover, tectal, pretectal, and retinal inputs to extrageniculate parts of the thalamus seem to dominate different parts of the inferior pulvinar nucleus (30–34, 166, 174, 202, 203, 211, 330, 387, 417). These project to several parts of the peristriate and inferotemporal cortex (33, 72, 516), and one at least seems to provide a diffuse input terminating in layer I of several cortical areas, including area 17 (33, 374).

From work on insectivores and nonsimian primates by Diamond and his colleagues it is clear that, in these species also, the thalamic visual system must be considered in terms of a retinogeniculostriate system and of a system arising in the pretectum and tectum that gains access to extrastriate cortex via one or more components of the lateral nuclear complex and pulvinar (174, 202, 203, 309, 310, 406, 429). A similar duality undoubtedly exists in all mammals. All of these studies clearly show that the lateral nuclear mass can no longer be dismissed as a vague associational nucleus, for it forms one of the major relay centers of the thalamus.

CORTICOTHALAMIC RECIPROCITY

Very little is know about the function of corticothalamic fibers, but the principle of reciprocal connections between a thalamic relay nucleus and its cortical target area is now so well established that it is strange to recall that the very existence of these fibers was once hotly debated (see Berman and Jones (45) for references). It can probably be stated categorically that if a cortical area projects to any nucleus of the dorsal thalamus it is indicative that the nucleus will also send fibers to that cortical area. This statement applies equally to the principal and to the intralaminar nuclei. It excludes nuclei of the ventral thalamus such as the ventral lateral geniculate and reticular, which though receiving corticofugal fibers do not project to the cortex (141, 234, 477).

The principle of thalamocortical and corticothalamic reciprocity was in the minds of workers some years ago in regard to the major relay nuclei (112), and all recent work tends to confirm it (23, 39, 163, 173, 188, 219, 220, 249, 290, 308–310, 314). The degree of interlocking of topography in the thalamocortical and corticothalamic systems of the principal relay nuclei is remarkable. The terminations of corticothalamic fibers emanating, for example, from a part of the body representation in SI form a lamella exactly comparable to that formed by medial lemniscal fibers and thalamocortical relay cells (Fig. 19). A small focal injection of axoplasmically transported tracer in the visual cortex labels terminal ramifications only around the group of cells forming the projection column in the lateral geniculate nucleus that projects to that focus in the visual cortex (517). A similar focal injection of the somatic sensory cortex (257) gives a narrow rodlike zone of labeling that extends anteroposteriorly through the ventrobasal complex and around cells projecting to the zone injected. This reciprocal relationship can be shown dramatically in experiments in which thalamocortical relay cells are retrogradely labeled and the corticothalamic terminals around them are anterogradely labeled in the same experiment by injection of a retrograde and an anterograde tracer at the same point in the cortex (Fig. 32).

In many of the earlier studies on corticothalamic connections it was noted that corticothalamic fibers passed back, not simply to the principal relay nucleus, but to an additional nucleus that was not thought to

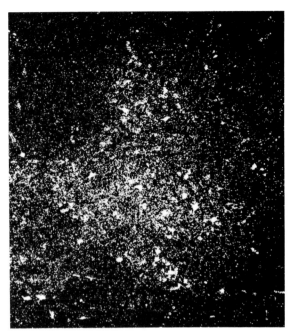

FIG. 32. Dark-field photomicrograph from ventrobasal complex of a rat in which tritiated amino acids and horseradish peroxidase were injected at same site in SI cortex. Grains representing anterograde labeling of terminal ramifications of corticothalamic fibers have same distribution as retrogradely labeled thalamocortical relay cells projecting to same cortical site. × 50.

project to the particular cortical area being studied. In many cases the additional nuclear group receiving such fibers proved to be part of the intralaminar system, but the visual areas had additional projections to parts of the lateral nuclei as well as to the lateral geniculate nucleus, and the auditory areas had projections to nuclei other than the medial geniculate. With the development of more sensitive techniques for tracing fiber pathways in the central nervous system, many of these apparent discrepancies have been resolved. In some cases the demonstration of an apparently nonreciprocal corticothalamic projection, such as that once described from SI and SII to parts of the posterior complex (249, 253, 420), was probably due to involvement of an adjacent area (area 5 or the insular cortex) by the lesions used to promote degeneration of corticothalamic fibers (502). In the case of the intralaminar system of nuclei it is now clear that these nuclei have substantial cortical projections (248, 487). Their cortical projection patterns seem to be less tightly organized than those of the main nuclei in the sense that a given intralaminar nucleus tends to project to a region of cortex rather than to a specific field or fields. Nevertheless, it is clear that the cortical target of any intralaminar nucleus will include those cortical fields that send corticothalamic fibers to it (see Fig. 34).

In the case of the auditory cortex each of the various fields projects to its principal relay nucleus within the medial geniculate complex as well as to the magnocellular nucleus of the complex (112). The magnocellular nucleus projects widely over all the auditory and certain adjacent fields, a pattern of organization orginally postulated by J. E. Rose and Woolsey (443) and later confirmed (239, 447). In the visual system, part of the lateral nuclear complex receiving corticothalamic fibers from the primary areas is separate from the parts projecting to other cortical fields. Like the intralaminar and the magnocellular medial geniculate nuclei, this cortically dominated part of the lateral complex projects to widespread areas of the cortex, including the areas from which it receives fibers (170, 518). In common with the intralaminar nuclei, the thalamocortical fibers emanating from this part of the lateral complex and from the magnocellular medial geniculate nucleus end primarily in layer I of the cortex and not in the middle layers. The rule, thus, seems to be that each cortical area receives thalamic input from a principal nucleus and from a second, relatively less specific nucleus, and that the cortical area projects back to both.

Just as the two or more thalamic nuclei receiving corticothalamic fibers from a particular cortical area seem to send their thalamocortical fibers to terminate in different layers of that area, so the cells giving rise

to the two or more sets of corticothalamic projections also seem to be situated in different layers. Where corticothalamic cells have been identified by retrograde labeling from injections of tracer into a principal relay nucleus, they have proved to be, without exception, the modified pyramidal cell of layer VI of the cortex [Fig. 33; (170, 232, 256, 271, 318, 428, 431, 545, 547)]. In the striate cortex of the monkey there is evidence that cells projecting to the magnocellular and parvocellular layers of the lateral geniculate nucleus have somata in different sublayers of layer VI (318). By contrast with the corticogeniculate projection cells, those providing the additional corticothalamic projection to the inferior pulvinar nucleus are relatively large, true pyramidal cells and are found in smaller numbers in layer V of the striate cortex (318). This makes it unlikely that the axons projecting to the inferior pulvinar are collaterals of those projecting to the lateral geniculate nucleus or vice versa. In the cat and rabbit Guillery (188) and Giolli and Pope (173) had intimated from study of the pattern of axonal degeneration ensuing from visual cortical lesions that corticogeniculate axons could be fine collaterals of those passing to the lateral posterior nucleus. There is still the possibility, however, that those passing to the

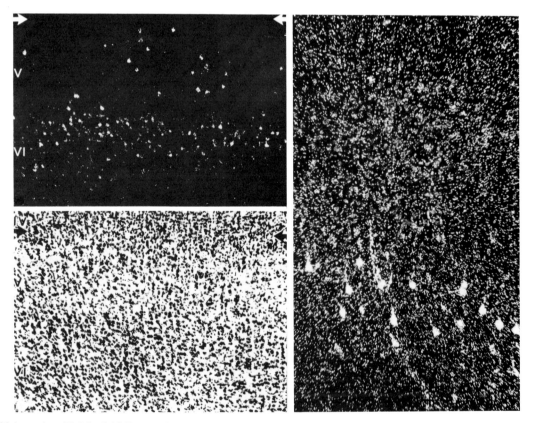

FIG. 33. *Left*: dark-field (*upper*) and bright-field (*lower*) photomicrographs at same magnification and from same field showing retrograde labeling of many corticothalamic cells in layer VI with a smaller number in layer V. SI cortex of a squirrel monkey. Thionine counterstain, × 50. *Right*: retrograde labeling of corticothalamic neurons in layer VI of monkey SI cortex following injection of [³H]D-aspartate in the ventrobasal complex. × 200. [*Left*: from Jones and Wise (256); *right*: from Jones (237).]

lateral posterior nucleus are collaterals of corticotectal axons as originally suggested by Ramón y Cajal (413), for the cell somata of origin of corticotectal cells also reside in layer V (218, 318, 548).

It is thought that many corticotecal neurons in the cat visual cortex are activated monosynaptically as part of the first cortical response to an afferent input (385). This seems to depend on the presence at the junction of layers V and VI (see Fig. 40) of a band of thalamic axon terminals deriving from the lateral geniculate nucleus but separate from the more prominent band in layers III and IV (123, 225, 306, 445). The possibility exists, also, that many corticothalamic cells are activated as part of the early cortical response to a peripheral stimulus and thus exert their effect quickly and directly upon the thalamic cells from which they are receiving input (204). This view is not, however, shared by all workers, since some corticothalamic cells are activated at rather long latencies and can have receptive fields of a type that implies input from other cortical neurons (65a, 169a). There is some evidence that corticothalamic neurons projecting to the lateral geniculate nucleus may use glutamate or aspartate as their transmitter agent (24a, 104, 152, 485). Layer VI cells in many cortical areas can be selectively labeled by [^{3}H]D-aspartate injected into the cortex or by retrograde transport of the material when injected into the thalamus (Fig. 33).

A second, smaller population of corticothalamic cells has now been found in layer V of most other cortical areas that have been studied (Fig. 33). And it seems likely that they project to the intralaminar or other thalamic nucleus that provides the nonprimary thalamic input to the relevant area (86). In all cortical areas, the primary thalamic input has a band of terminals at the junction of layers V and VI [see Fig. 40; (239, 428, 545, 546, 549)]; hence corticothalamic cells in both layers V and VI of all areas may be activated directly by thalamocortical impulses. In addition to having a small population of corticothalamic cells, layer V of most other cortical areas contains the somata of some corticotectal neurons as well as the somata of corticostriatal and pyramidal tract neurons. Cajal (413) originally suggested that some corticothalamic fibers passing to the ventral nuclear complex could be the collaterals of pyramidal tract axons. This seems to be ruled out, however, by the fact that corticothalamic cells of layer V generally have much smaller somata and lie deeper in layer V than those giving rise to the other subcortical projections (256, 547), and by the double-labeling study of Catsman-Berrevoets and Kuypers (87).

FINER ORGANIZATION OF THALAMOCORTICAL PROJECTION

The topographic representation pattern in the principal relay nuclei is faithfully transmitted by thalamocortical fibers to the appropriate sensory area or

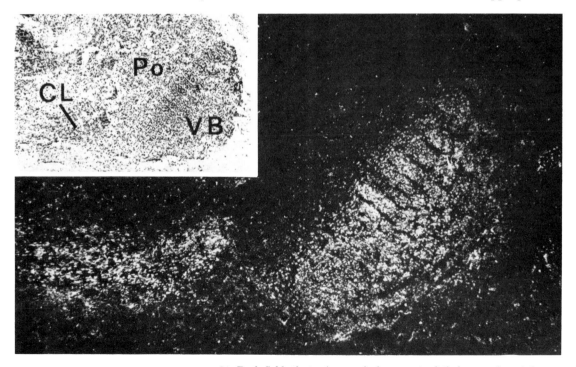

FIG. 34. Dark-field photomicrograph from part of thalamus of an infant rat shown in *inset*. Thalamocortical relay cells are retrogradely labeled both in ventrobasal complex and in central lateral nucleus following injection of horseradish peroxidase in maturing SI cortex. Note clustering of cells in *VB*, which is thought to be basis of axonal bundling in the cortex. Thionine counterstain; × 75; *inset* × 30. For abbreviations see footnote to Fig. 1 legend. [From Wise and Jones (549).]

areas of the cerebral cortex. In this way is built up the topographic map that can be delineated in evoked potential and single-unit studies. Presumably, representation patterns in cortical areas outside the primary sensory areas are also determined by the thalamic inputs, but ordered corticocortical projections from the primary areas themselves may also play a role.

Axon Bundling

Thalamocortical fibers from the relay nuclei enter the cortex in bundles that seem to emanate from small groups of thalamic relay cells activated from closely similar peripheral receptive fields and often by the same types of receptor. The best illustrations of this bundling occur in the projections to the aggregations of granule cells or "barrels," each of which represents a mystacial or other vibrissa in the SI cortex of rodents and certain other forms (276, 549). In the visual cortex, bundles of fibers from different lateral geniculate laminae form the basis of the ocular dominance columns (307, 468). Possibly the best example of the grouping of thalamic cells that seems to underlie this bundling of thalamocortical fibers is in the ventroposteromedial nucleus of the thalamus in those species with cortical barrels, as already pointed out (Figs. 10, 34, 35), for

here the collections of cells receiving individual vibrissal inputs and projecting to a barrel form recognizable aggregates separate from their neighbors. The rodlike configurations of thalamocortical relay cells in the ventrobasal complex (Figs. 20, 34, 36, 37), and the cells along a projection column in the lateral geniculate nucleus, are probably comparable to the cell aggregates projecting to a cortical barrel, and similar aggregates are found in the thalamic relay to motor cortex (see Fig. 43). It is probable that bundling of thalamocortical fibers is a feature of the thalamic input from all sensory relay nuclei to their appropriate areas of the cortex and that this bundling forms the basis of many of the columnar characteristics of intracortical organization (see the chapter by Scheibel in this volume of the *Handbook*). In many areas of the cortex the bundles and their terminal ramifications often lie side by side and cannot always be demonstrated in isolation (233). Nevertheless, small lesions or injections of tracer in a thalamic nucleus usually reveal focal patches of degeneration or label in the cortex. These patches are commonly of a diameter approximately corresponding to that of a physiologically defined column (0.5–1.0 mm). Within the bundle of axons terminating in such a patch, there is the possibility that single axons may terminate preferentially in dif-

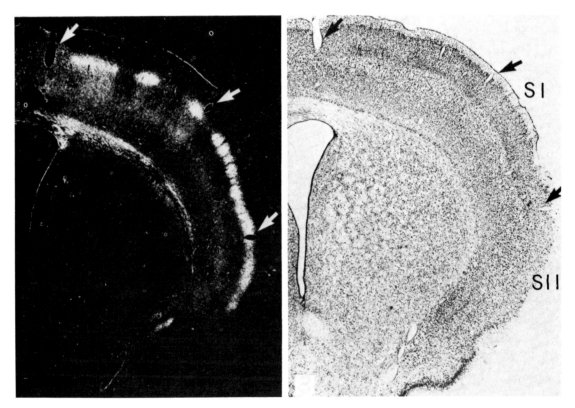

FIG. 35. Dark-field and bright-field photomicrographs from immediately adjacent sections through first and second somatic sensory areas (*SI* and *SII*) of cortex of a rat, stained for degenerating axons (*left*) and with thionine (*right*) 4 days after destruction of thalamic ventrobasal complex. *Arrows* indicate same blood vessels. Note clustered nature of terminal ramifications of thalamocortical fibers and in *SI* their restriction to zones of aggregated granule cells. × 150. [From Wise and Jones (549).]

ferent layers or on different cells, though this has only been demonstrated in the visual cortex to date [see Fig. 41; (171, 226)].

Since the columnlike organization of cells in the sensory cortex is maintained irrespective of whether bundles of thalamocortical fibers can be demonstrated in isolation or not, it may be assumed that even in areas where these lie side by side there is no greater overlap in the terminal ramifications of individual bundles than of afferent fibers in the thalamus (Fig. 35). Thus the topographic projection of the sensory surface is maintained. In the motor cortex the restricted nature of the thalamocortical axon distribution probably ensures the close coupling between columns of output cells related to motoneurons involved in movements of a small part of the body and the

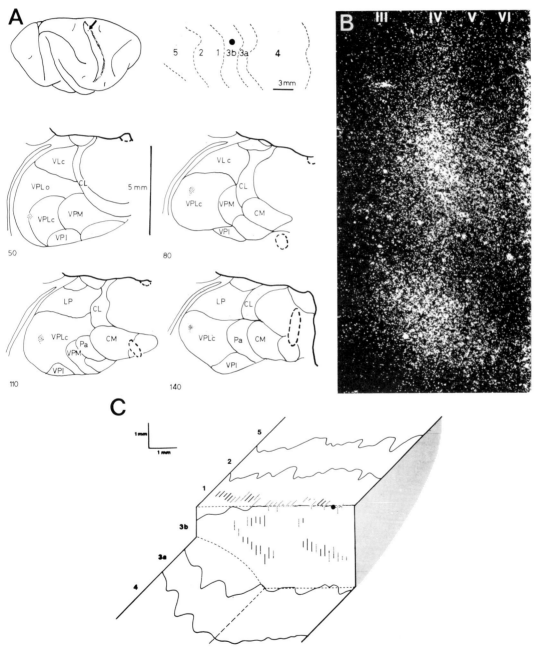

FIG. 36. *A*: punctate injection of retrograde tracer in one field (area 3b) of monkey SI cortex leads to retrograde labeling of rod of cells in ventrobasal complex of the thalamus. *B*: focal injections of tritiated amino acids in the ventrobasal complex leads to anterograde labeling of focal zones of termination in the SI cortex. *C*: when reconstructed on an unfolded surface map, foci are seen to form parts of short strips. For abbreviations see footnote to Fig. 1 legend. [*A*: from Jones (236a); *B*: from Friedman and Jones (155a); *C*: from Jones et al. (246).]

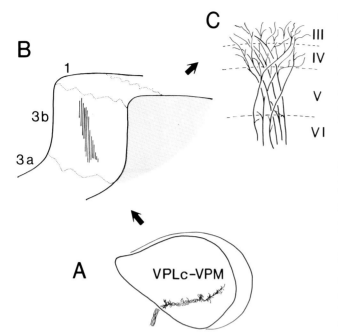

FIG. 37. Schematic figures indicating basis for thalamic projection to columns in somatic sensory cortex. A bundle of lemniscal axons, of like place and modality properties, terminates along length of a rod of thalamocortical relay cells (*A*) whose bundled axons (*B*, *C*) project to a common focus in a field of the postcentral gyrus. For abbreviations see footnote to Fig. 1 legend. [From Jones et al. (246).]

input to them from afferents arising in tissues stimulated during these movements (22, 22a).

Laminar Terminations

Thalamocortical fibers terminating in the main sensory areas of the neocortex have a pattern of laminar distribution somewhat different from those terminating in surrounding areas and in the frontal, parietal, and temporal association cortex (239). Only in the highly granular areas (3b, 17, and the first auditory area) do thalamic fibers arising in the principal thalamic nucleus terminate in layer IV, though this is the layer that is conventionally described as the thalamic recipient layer in all areas except the agranular motor and premotor cortex. Even in the highly granular (koniocortical) areas, thalamic afferent terminals extend into the deeper half of the overlying layer III. In all nonkoniocortical areas, thalamic afferents from the principal nuclei avoid layer IV, partially or even entirely, and terminate among the large pyramidal cells in the deeper half of layer III [Figs. 38, 39; (239)].

A feature shared by all those areas in which thalamic terminals are found only in layer III is that the thalamocortical fibers ending in these areas are remarkably fine and few in number and apparently give rise to relatively few terminals. This again contrasts with the thick, numerous, and densely terminating fibers in the koniocortical areas (232, 239, 253). Thus, there appears to be some truth in the old maxim that

the degree of granularity of an area reflects the number and density of thalamic afferents terminating in it, though it is difficult to ascertain the grounds upon which this belief arose. It seems likely that the relative paucity of thalamocortical fibers and their small size are in some way linked to the lack of a dramatic retrograde cellular response in the thalamus after removal of, for example, parts of the temporal cortex (524) or areas 1 and 2 (93, 424).

The existence of thalamic fiber terminations in the sensory cortex in layers other than layers III and IV, has recently been recognized. Those terminating at the junction of layers V and VI and apparently present in all areas (Fig. 40) have already been discussed in connection with the corticothalamic system of fibers. Where the overlying of layer III and IV terminations are broken up into recognizable patches, such as the barrels of the somatic cortex and the ocular dominance columns of the visual cortex, the terminals in the deeper layers form similar patches that are in register with those in the overlying layers (535, 549), and the deeper terminals often arise from collaterals of fibers destined to terminate in the overlying layers [Fig. 42; (148, 299)].

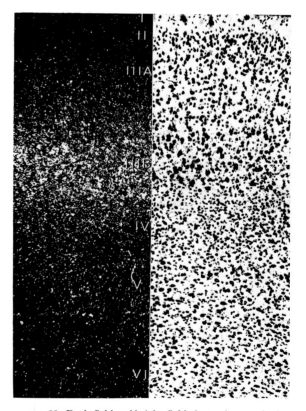

FIG. 38. Dark-field and bright-field photomicrographs from same part of area 5 of a monkey in which tritiated amino acids were injected in lateral posterior nucleus. Autoradiographically labeled terminal ramifications of thalamocortical fibers are predominately distributed to large-celled part of layer III (layer IIIB) instead of to layer IV. Thionine counterstain. × 70. [From Jones and Burton (239).]

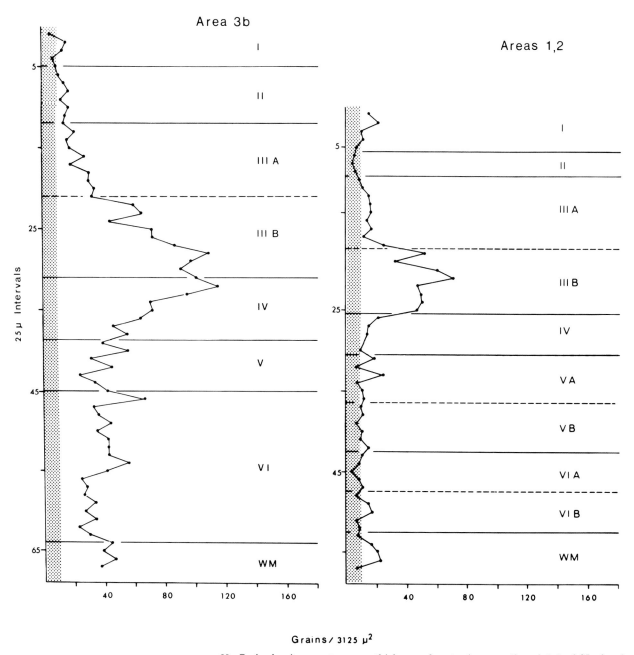

FIG. 39. Grain density counts across thickness of cortex in areas 3b and 1–2 of SI of a rhesus monkey following injection of tritiated amino acids in the thalamic ventrobasal complex. Peaks of grain density are either in layer IIIB alone or at border of layers IIIB and IV. Additional small peaks are seen in layer V or VI. Background indicated by *stipple*. For abbreviations see footnote to Fig. 1 legend. [From Jones and Burton (239).]

Additional thalamic fiber terminations have at times been described in the superficial part of layer I of many cortical areas [Fig. 39; (250, 538)]. Recent studies have not always demonstrated layer I projections when an injection of tracer is confined to the principal relay nucleus (233, 549). But fibers of several other thalamic nuclei do reach layer I. These other nuclei include the magnocellular medial geniculate nucleus and parts of the ventral, lateral, medial, anterior, and pulvinar complexes (27, 78, 117, 212, 214, 239, 283, 303, 393a, 447). Whether the intralaminar nuclei send fibers to layers I and VI or only to layer VI (Fig. 40) is still debated (214a, 233). The visual cortex is a rather special case (Fig. 41): the A- and A₁-laminae in the cat and the parvocellular laminae in the monkey project only to layers IV and VI, whereas the C-laminae of the cat lateral geniculate and the magnocellular laminae and certain subsidiary cell groups of the mon-

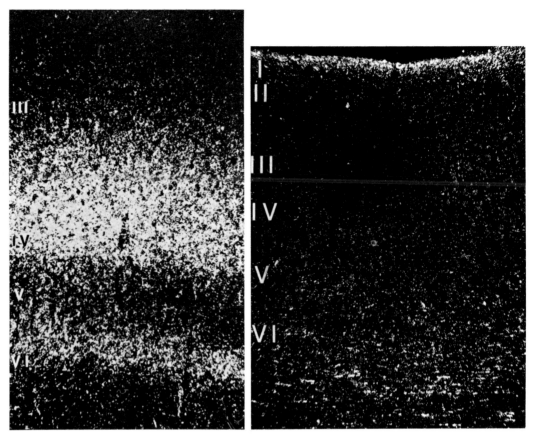

FIG. 40. *A*: dark-field photomicrograph from area 3b of squirrel monkey showing labeling of terminal ramifications in layer VI as well as in layers III–IV following injection of tritiated amino acids in ventrobasal complex. × 70. *B*: dark-field photomicrograph from cingulate cortex of cat following injection of tritiated amino acids in thalamic intralaminar nuclei. Unlike that in *A*, major cortical projection demonstrated is to outer part of layer I. There is labeling of fibers in layer VI and in underlying white matter. × 50. [*A*: from Jones and Burton (239)].

key or prosimian lateral geniculate project to layer I as well, or to layer I alone (78, 150a, 226, 306).

Any differential effects of the layer I and the deeper thalamocortical terminations have not yet been discovered. One possibility is that, as already discussed, the terminations at the junction of layers V and VI provide direct, rapid, monosynaptic input to efferent cells, some of which may then serve to modulate further sensory impulse traffic en route to that cortical area. The layer III and IV terminations seem to arrive at the layer from which further intracortical processing commences. Cells in these layers mainly project to or within the supragranular layers from which ipsilateral corticocortical and commissural projections arise (235, 241, 256). The layer I terminations, arising as they do from somewhat diffusely projecting nuclei, and terminating seemingly on the peripheralmost parts of the dendrites of cells in all layers, may in some way affect levels of cortical excitability rather than being directly concerned in the elaboration of sensory information. This hypothesis, however, is largely conjectural, and much further work is required to determine whether it is valid.

The excitatory transmitter agent used at any of the thalamocortical synapses has not been established (237).

OTHER RELAY NUCLEI

Though the emphasis throughout the present account has been on those thalamic nuclei that form more or less direct relays to the sensory areas of the cortex, every principal nucleus is, in a sense, a relay nucleus. With certain exceptions the organization of the majority follows the same general principles as already outlined, and in many cases the relevant nuclei are indirectly concerned with sensory mechanisms. What follows is a brief review of the connectional relationships of some nuclei about which we have convincing data.

Mediodorsal Nucleus

Certain parts of the mediodorsal nucleus that usually can be distinguished cytoarchitectonically receive fibers from the olfactory cortex and, as a consequence,

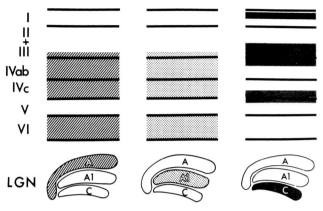

FIG. 41. Differential laminar distributions of thalamocortical fibers arising from A- and C-laminae of cat lateral geniculate nucleus. For abbreviations see footnote to Fig. 1 legend. [From LeVay and Gilbert (306).]

units in the mediodorsal nucleus can be activated by stimulation of the lateral olfactory tract (228). Other parts of the mediodorsal nucleus project to medially and laterally situated areas of the frontal cortex (26, 116, 117, 283). The lateralmost projection field seems to include the agranular insular cortex as well. It is interesting that the same areas of frontal cortex to which the mediodorsal nucleus projects also receive subcortical inputs from certain nuclei of the amygdala. The amygdaloid nuclei involved also project to the mediodorsal nucleus itself (284). The amygdaloid projections to frontal cortex form but one of several recently recognized direct subcortical inputs to the neocortex that bypass the thalamus. Others include the ascending noradrenergic (496), serotoninergic (98, 198), and dopaminergic (230) pathways from the brain stem, as well as that from the substantia innominata (114, 242, 275), which is probably cholinergic (339).

Ventral Lateral Complex

The ventral lateral nuclear complex includes several nuclei that are particularly distinct in higher primates. They form the thalamic relays to the motor and premotor areas of the cortex. At the moment there is a great deal of confusion, partly because of a genuine lack of data, and partly because in some studies on thalamocortical connections of the ventral lateral complex the various nuclear divisions have not been adequately delineated in the experimental material. Furthermore, some nuclei that have previously been described as separate seem to form parts of a common nucleus. One of the clearest ways of delineating the nuclei of the primate ventrolateral complex is on the basis of their afferent connections [(Fig. 43; (19–21, 257–265, 481, 486, 513)]. Though not afflicted by the same welter of names, the ventrolateral complex of other species is probably organized along similar lines.

In the monkey the projection of the internal segment of the globus pallidus to the pars oralis of the ventral lateral nucleus (VLo) seems clear (289, 363,

513), and it is probable (Fig. 44) that this does not overlap the projection of the deep cerebellar nuclei or of the substantia nigra to the thalamus. The VLo relays to area 6 (513) but whether it has differential connections with the supplementary motor area and with other more lateral parts of area 6 is not yet known.

Cerebellar fibers distribute throughout a common nucleus (Fig. 43) that includes regions previously identified as the pars caudalis of the ventrolateral nucleus (VLc), the pars oralis of the ventroposterolateral nucleus (VPLo), the pars postrema of the ventrolateral nucleus (VLps), and nucleus X (19–21). The cerebellar terminations do not overlap the terminal territory of medial lemniscal fibers or that of pallidal or substantia nigral fibers; but some spinothalamic and vestibular axons terminate in parts of the same regions. The terminal territory of the spinothalamic fibers extends forward from the lemniscal terminal nucleus, the pars caudalis of the ventroposterolateral nucleus (VPLc) [Fig 44; (20, 41, 58, 59, 245)]. The cortical target of the cerebellar relay nucleus is area 4 only (19–21).

The pars reticulata of the substantia nigra projects to a medial part of the ventrolateral complex (VLm) that is perhaps more correctly labeled part of the ventromedial complex (VM), since this is the termination of nigral fibers in other species [Figs. 1–4; (25, 27, 96, 146, 146a, 212)]. Some of the nigral cells projecting to the thalamus have axon branches to the superior colliculus (38) and may be GABAergic (113, 277, 327). The cortical target of VLm is uncertain in primates but probably includes medial and anterior areas of cortex (214). In rats, the VM nucleus projects to layer I over virtually the whole cortex. Somewhat suprisingly, recent studies have rather convincingly disproved the long-established teaching that the red nucleus provides an input to the ventral lateral complex (139, 223).

Pulvinar

What little is known of the pulvinar and lateral nuclear complex in general has been reviewed during the consideration of the visual system. With the exception of the lateral dorsal nucleus, the subdivisions mentioned here account for the greater part of the lateral complex in nonprimates. In primates the anterior (oral), medial, and lateral nuclei of the pulvinar (Fig. 2) have not been the subjects of detailed study. None of these appear to be primarily visual in their relationships. The anterior nucleus seems to project to a subdivision of area 5 in the parietal lobe (72, 244, 257) and the medial nucleus mainly to the cortex in the depths of the superior temporal sulcus and at the tip of the temporal lobe (72, 516). The medial nucleus has projections to the amygdala (73) and is also said to project to the frontal eye fields (62, 515, 516).

The lateral nucleus of the pulvinar seems to project to cortex lying at the junction of the parietal, temporal, and occipital lobes, including large parts of what was called area 19 by Brodmann (64). None of the areas to which it projects, however, appear to be closely related to the visual system. Visual areas outside the striate cortex appear to be the targets mainly of the inferior nucleus of the pulvinar.

The only known subcortical inputs to the pulvinar are those that reach its inferior nucleus from subcortical visual centers (see *Extrageniculostriate System*, p. 180). Apart from the cerebral cortex (384) no extrathalamic source has yet been convincingly shown to project to the other pulvinar nuclei.

Suprageniculate-Limitans Nucleus

Closely associated with the pulvinar is the combined suprageniculate-limitans nucleus, best seen in primates (Fig. 2) and usually considered a part of the

FIG. 42. Laminar distribution in visual cortex of single thalamocortical fibers thought to arise from Y-type (*this page*) and X-type (*facing page*) relay neurons in A-laminae of cat lateral geniculate nucleus. [From Ferster and LeVay (148).]

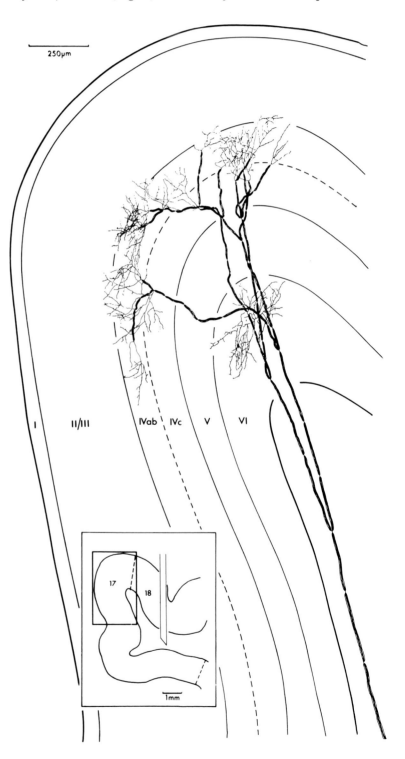

posterior complex. This forms the major thalamic relay for the ascending outflow of the deep layers of the superior colliculus (31, 176). In view of the known functions of the deep collicular layers (see chapter by Schiller in this volume of the *Handbook*) one would expect the suprageniculate-limitans nucleus to be in some way concerned with visuomotor interactions. It is, therefore, somewhat surprising that the suprageniculate-limitans nucleus projects not to visual, parietal, or frontal cortex but to the granular field of the insular cortex [Fig. 25; (72, 209)].

Anterior Group and Lateral Dorsal Nucleus

The anterior nuclei (Figs. 1*A*, *B*) form the thalamic relays to certain cortical areas on the medial surface of the frontal lobe, to the cingulate and retrosplenial cortex, and to cortical areas bounding the hippocampal

formation (70, 248, 283, 303, 368, 425, 471, 554). One of the nuclei, the anterodorsal, even projects to a part of the hippocampal formation itself, the subiculum (470, 554). It would appear that the closely associated medioventral (reuniens) nucleus also projects to the hippocampus (213). Although it had been known for some time that the hippocampal formation projects to certain of the anterior nuclei and possibly to the medioventral nucleus (493), these are the first indications that the hippocampal formation receives fibers from the dorsal thalamus. These observations, together with those on the mediodorsal nucleus, show that the dorsal thalamus is related to archicortex and paleocortex and not simply to neocortex as had been long supposed. The fornical fibers terminating in the anterior nuclei, can, therefore, be considered as corticothalamic fibers, and it is interesting that ultrastructurally their probable terminals have the distribution and

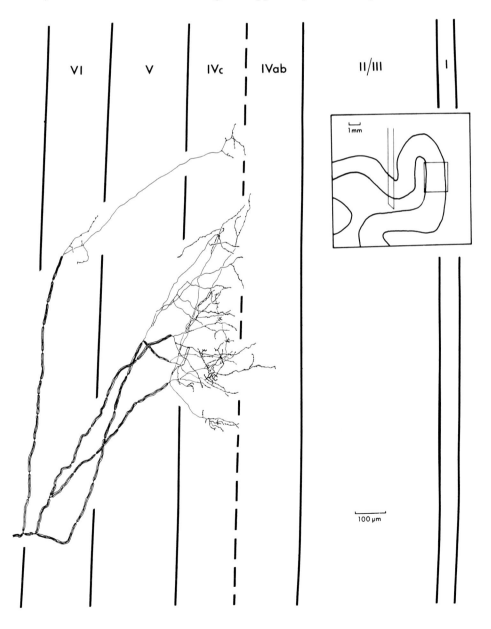

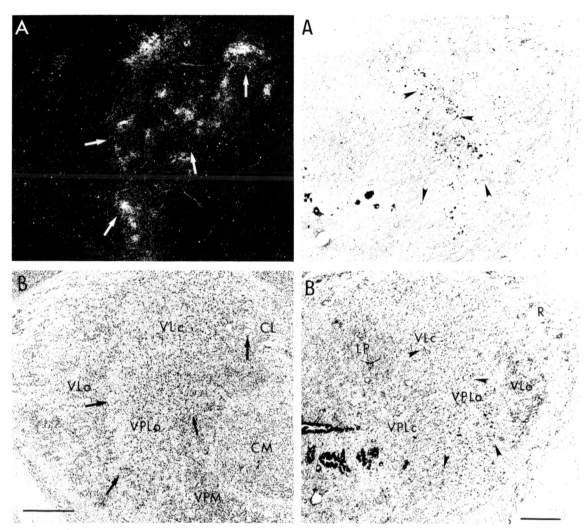

FIG. 43. *Left*: dark-field, *A*, and bright-field, *B*, photomicrographs showing anterograde labeling of dentatothalamic axons in patches confined to common VPLo-VLc nucleus of monkey. Sagittal section, anterior to left. *Arrows*, same blood vessels. *Right*: adjacent uncounterstained, *A*, and counterstained, *B*, sagittal sections showing retrograde labeling of thalamic cells restricted to common VPLo-VLc nucleus following an injection of tracer in cortical area 4. *Arrows*, same blood vessels. Blood to left is in electrode tracks; anterior is to right. For abbreviations see footnote to Fig. 1 legend. [From Asanuma, Thach, and Jones (20).]

appearances of corticothalamic terminals in other nuclei (106). As in other thalamic nuclei, large, glomerular-related terminals in the anterior nuclei are derived from the major subcortical input to the nuclei, in this case the mamillothalamic tract (106). Whether this tract distributes fibers to the medioventral nucleus is unknown.

The anterior nuclei contain the highest concentrations of muscarinic cholinergic receptors in the thalamus (445a).

The lateral dorsal nucleus, despite its name, is perhaps more appropriately included with the anterior nuclei because of its position internal to the part of the internal medullary lamina that encloses the anterior group. Its cortical projection has been variously described as being the cingulate gyrus (116, 117, 248, 426) and area 7 of the parietal cortex (209, 425, 427), and it may have a substantial layer I projection (426). The fornix is a major source of afferent connections to the lateral dorsal nucleus (521); these fibers probably arise in cortical areas adjacent to the subiculum hippocampi (493) and even in the hippocampus itself. Other inputs appear to come from as yet ill-defined areas of the medullary reticular formation (315).

Other Principal Nuclei

The status of two other thalamic nuclei, the submedial nucleus and the paratenial nucleus, is uncertain. Each seems to project, respectively, to inferior

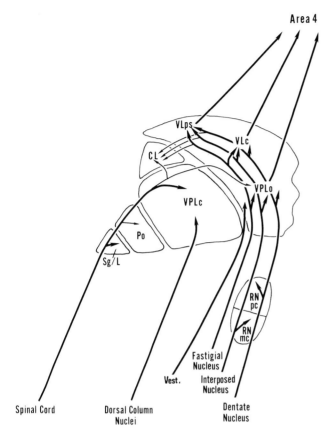

FIG. 44. Schematic outline of input-output connections of thalamic relay to area 4 of motor cortex in monkeys. Also illustrated are differential distributions of dorsal column-lemniscal and spinothalamic terminations in thalamus. *Vest*, vestibular input. For other abbreviations see footnote to Fig. 1 legend. [Adapted from Asanuma, Thach, and Jones (20).]

and to medial frontal cortex (248), but the areas have not been clearly identified. Since the paratenial nucleus has also been said to project to a part of the striatum, the nucleus accumbens (492), it may be more properly regarded as an intralaminar nucleus.

INTRALAMINAR NUCLEI

The nuclei within the internal medullary lamina have for a long time been regarded as quite different from the principal nuclei. The nuclei (Figs. 1–4) are made up of a rostral or central commissural (433) group (central lateral, paracentral, and central medial), and a more caudal pair, the parafascicular and centre médian, that are said to have grown out of the rostral group in the course of evolution (90). The centre médian is present in many but not all species. It is absent, for example, in rodents and marsupials; it reaches its largest size in the primates.

Unlike the cells of the principal nuclei that have symmetrical or bitufted dendritic fields, the predominant cells of all the intralaminar nuclei exhibit what

has been called an isodendritic appearance (414, 415). The shape of the dendritic field is much more elongated, and it is thought by Ramón-Moliner and Nauta (415) to resemble that of cells in the brain stem reticular formation. The dendrites, however, do have protrusions resembling those of relay cells in the principal nuclei. Moreover, despite reports to the contrary, a population of typical thalamic interneurons is present (206), and the synaptic organization is said to be the same as that in the principal nuclei (201).

In Nissl-stained sections the cells of the rostral group show variations in size and staining density that in some cases correlate with differences in afferent input. From the available data, at least, it seems clear that the intralaminar nuclei cannot be regarded as a diffusely organized system in which many afferent systems terminate indiscriminately.

The most clear-cut segregation of an afferent system within the intralaminar nuclei occurs in the large, caudalmost cells of the central lateral nucleus that receive fibers from the contralateral side of the spinal cord [Fig. 29; (238, 334, 335)]. These cells have sometimes been erroneously included in the centre médian, parafascicular, or mediodorsal nuclei. Apart from the spinothalamic tract, no other sensory pathways send fibers directly to the intralaminar nuclei.

Anterior to the caudally placed large cells, the central lateral nucleus consists of smaller cells, and separate groups appear to receive fibers from the pretectum (46) and the deep layers of the superior colliculus (116). Their terminations are overlapped to some extent by fibers emanating from the deep cerebellar nuclei (212), but those from the cerebellar nuclei extend in a more rostral direction and invade the paracentral and central medial nuclei. The most rostral, dorsal, and medial projections within the intralaminar system, incorporating parts of the central lateral, paracentral, and central medial nuclei lying in relation to the anterior thalamic nuclei, come from both rostral and caudal parts of the brain stem reticular formation (140, 362) and certain other brain stem regions (282, 315). It is uncertain whether any of these various afferents to the intralaminar nuclei are collaterals of those directed to principal nuclei.

The centre médian nucleus receives afferent fibers mainly from the internal segment of the globus pallidus, rather than from the cerebellum as commonly supposed (212, 289, 333). Because the centre médian nucleus has little connectional relationship with any sensory pathway, it is difficult to provide a morphological basis for the reports of neurons within it that are activated by polymodal and nociceptive peripheral stimuli (8).

The afferent connections of the parafascicular nucleus are somewhat confusing. In cats and primates it clearly does not receive fibers from the spinal cord, yet in rodents and marsupials it does (335, 336, 430). It is tempting to regard the part that receives spinal fibers in these lower forms as being simply comparable to the caudal large-celled part of the central lateral nucleus in other species. However, a part of the central lateral nucleus also receives spinal fibers in the lower forms, so the discrepancy cannot be resolved.

The various nuclei and subnuclei of the intralaminar system appear to be heavily interconnected so that when labeled by autoradiography or by degeneration, the fibers arising in one part appear to spread throughout most other parts of the complex. Contrary to once-popular supposition, they do not seem to project to any other dorsal thalamic nuclei, though large numbers of fibers emanating from them traverse the ventral anterior nucleus.

The factor common to all the intralaminar nuclei is their heavy projection to the striatum—the caudate nucleus, and putamen (101, 248, 292, 360, 400–402). Generally speaking, this appears to be organized such that those parts of the intralaminar complex receiving fibers from (and projecting to) a particular cortical region send fibers to terminate in the part of the striatum that receives corticostriatal fibers (272, 291) from that part of the cortex.

For some years it was believed by many that the sole target of the intralaminar nuclei was the striatum and that the cellular reaction seen in the intralaminar nuclei after lesions of the cortex was a transneuronal degenerative effect occasioned by removal of a source of afferents to the nuclei (128, 402). This was contested by other workers (359) who regarded the cellular changes in the intralaminar nuclei as being true retrograde degeneration. More recent work carried out with axoplasmic transport methods has indicated that both striatal and cortical projections emanate from all components of the intralaminar complex (248, 291, 360, 487). The striatal projection, however, is undoubtedly heavier than that to the cortex (234).

The projection of the intralaminar nuclei to the cortex appears to be unlike that of the principal nuclei. Not only do the fibers of an individual nucleus appear to be distributed regionally instead of according to architectonic fields, but the fibers end rather diffusely either in layers I and VI (119–121, 233, 316) or in layer VI alone [Fig. 40B; (214a)]. As yet, there is no information whether these fibers are collaterals of the thalamostriatal fibers. The topography of the system is still incompletely worked out, but the more anterior and medial nuclei (central medial and paracentral) appear to project to medial and rostral parts of the cortex, the parafascicular nucleus to rostral and lateral parts of the frontal lobe, the centre médian nucleus to the motor areas, and the central lateral nucleus to the somatic sensory and parietal cortex (37, 248, 283, 322, 487). Axons of some cells in the central lateral or paracentral nuclei may even reach the visual cortex (37, 78). This topography is very similar to that originally established by identification of the regions of cortex in which long-latency recruiting responses commenced after electrical stimulation of the individual intralaminar nuclei (230).

The cerebral cortex also projects upon the intralaminar nuclei, as might be supposed, in an appropriately organized manner. The first somatic sensory area, for example, projects back to the relevant part of the central lateral nucleus (Fig. 17) and the motor cortex to the centre médian nucleus in monkeys (257, 402, 487), though not in the cat, where it projects to the central lateral nucleus (212).

The functional significance of the intralaminar projection upon the cortex is still a matter of conjecture. It clearly cannot be regarded simply as another sensory pathway, for apart from the reticular formation the only major sensory pathway ending in it is the spinothalamic. All of the other inputs are in some way related to the motor system, including those parts of the pretectum, superior colliculus, and brain stem reticular formation that are involved in visuomotor coordination. In this case it may be significant that cells in the caudal part of the central lateral nucleus discharge in relation to eye movements (459) and that stimulation in the region can produce eye movements (460). This part of the central lateral nucleus is connected with the frontal eye fields in monkeys (7, 24).

For the moment, the best interpretation of the role of the cortical projection from the intralaminar complex is probably the old one that these fibers in some way control levels of cortical excitability. Thus they have been implicated in mediating recruiting responses, barbiturate spindling, and the effects of reticular formation stimulation on cortical arousal (507). There seems to be little evidence, however, that the output of the intralaminar nuclei relays first in the ventral anterior nucleus of the thalamus, as often supposed. Effects comparable to those elicited by stimulation of the intralaminar nuclei (230, 356), when obtained by stimulation of the ventral anterior nucleus, probably result from stimulation of the efferent fibers of the intralaminar nuclei.

This is little information available about the transmitter characteristics of intralaminar cells, through glutamate or aspartate have been suggested (485). All parts of the nuclear complex contain rather high concentrations of opiate receptors and enkephalin-containing fibers and show a relatively high density of acetylcholinesterase staining (237).

OTHER DIFFUSE THALAMOCORTICAL SYSTEMS

Certain other thalamocortical projections that do not seem to be constrained by architectonic boundaries in the cortex have already been alluded to, and it remains for them to be summarized. Certain of the nuclei giving rise to these diffuse projections may provide an input to the auditory, visual, and adjacent areas that is comparable to that furnished by the intralaminar nuclei to other areas.

One of the most obvious of these nuclei is the magnocellular medial geniculate nucleus. The afferent inputs to this nucleus have rarely been well described, because the nucleus has usually been taken to form part of a large and somewhat arbitrarily defined posterior group of nuclei. Hence it is often difficult to be certain from the literature that recordings have actually been made from its characteristic large cells, or that anatomically labeled pathways actually ended in relation to these cells. It is clear that though the cells are predominately auditory in their properties, their tuning curves are far broader than those of the other nuclei of the medial geniculate complex (3), a condition that implies a rather nonspecific organization. The cells in the general vicinity of the magnocellular nucleus, as well as responding to auditory stimuli, also respond to vestibular and to certain forms of somatic sensory stimuli. The stimuli to which the cells respond have been variously described as either noxious (84, 398) or innocuous (102) in character. The effects have been thought to be mediated by spinothalamic fibers that are said to terminate in the magnocellular nucleus (56, 273). However, there is some reason to believe that the magnocellular cells themselves are not directly contacted by spinal fibers (238). The only surely known sources of afferent fibers to the magnocellular nucleus are the inferior colliculus (85, 350, 353, 504) and the deepest layer of the superior colliculus (176). All of the fields of the auditory cortex also project to it (112). Its afferent connectivity, therefore, also fits the idea of the nucleus being nonspecifically, or at least somewhat diffusely, organized but having a preponderance of auditory connections. In addition to having a rather diffusely organized cortical projection (443), which seems to terminate in layer I of all the auditory fields (239, 447), the magnocellular nucleus is thought to project also to the striatum (207, 447).

In the lateral geniculate nucleus the C-laminae of the cat or the magnocellular laminae and interlaminar cells of primates project diffusely to layer I of the cortex (78, 226, 306, 408). In the lateral nuclear complex a part of the lateral posterior nucleus or pulvinar that receives fibers from several visually related areas of the cortex projects to layer I of all them, including the striate cortex (170, 323, 374). The response properties of neurons in the relevant part of the lateral posterior nucleus or pulvinar have not been fully documented, although many cells are clearly visual in their responses (175), and stimulation in the lateral nuclear complex can apparently affect excitability levels in the striate cortex (64). Certain of the C-laminae also receive afferents from the superficial layers of the superior colliculus (176). So far as they have been studied, the magnocellular laminae and interlaminar zones in the primate show similar inputs and similar connectional patterns. Though it has been argued that the A- and A1-laminae of the cat may also receive afferents other than those emanating from the retina (270), these suggestions have not been subjected to rigorous proof. At the moment, therefore, there seems every reason to believe that the A- and A1-laminae of the cat and the parvocellular laminae of the monkey form a more specific thalamocortical system than that passing through the C- or the magnocellular laminae.

The possibility of other diffusely organized thalamocortical systems has recently come into prominence again with the observations of Herkenham (213) and of Krettek and Price (283) that the ventromedial nucleus of the rat may project diffusely to layer I over wide areas of the cortex. There is good evidence in many species that the ventromedial nucleus or its equivalent in primates (the medial nucleus of the ventrolateral complex) is the principal thalamic relay for ascending fibers from the pars reticulata of the substantia nigra (80, 96, 146, 422). Interestingly, the cortical projection of the ventromedial nucleus does not include the traditional motor areas of the cortex, but it does seem to include areas to which direct, dopaminergic fibers of the substantia nigra and ventral tegmental area project (25).

Among other thalamic nuclei that may also give rise to diffuse layer I cortical projections are the anteromedial nucleus (303, 383), lateral dorsal nucleus (426), and parts of the ventroanterior and ventrolateral nuclei (88, 158). In the case of the latter nuclei, which have been traditionally related to the frontal lobe (524), there are several reports of projections to the parietal lobe as well (115, 268, 425). In the cat the cells projecting to the parietal cortex lie close to those projecting to the motor cortex and within the region of termination of efferent fibers of the deep cerebellar nuclei (212). The part of the suprasylvian gyrus to which these cells project includes at least one of several so-called polysensory regions of the cortex in which occur maximal barbiturate spindling, recruiting responses, and responses to stimulation of the brain stem reticular formation (507), and in which cells show convergence of visual, auditory, and somatic sensory input (48, 73, 131–134). Another such region lies within areas 4 and 6 of the frontal lobe, also within the projection zone of cells receiving cerebellar afferents in the ventral nuclear complex.

The polysensory areas have never been satisfactorily explained in anatomical terms, for they appear to overlie parts of several cytoarchitectonic areas that each receive afferent projections from different principal thalamic nuclei. They appear, however, to lie at focal sites of intralaminar nuclear projections. The implication therefore, is that a further thalamocortical system, perhaps derived from the intralaminar nuclei, may overlie the more specific projections to these areas and may be responsible under appropriate conditions for recruiting, spindling, reticular activation, and polysensory responses.

It has not been determined to what extent nuclei other than the intralaminar, but having diffuse projections, may be involved in mediating long-latency, recruiting, or other types of nonspecific response. Jasper (230), however, pointed out that though recruiting-type responses may be observed in areas such as the auditory and visual, these cannot be obtained by stimulation of the intralaminar nuclei. Possibly the responses in these areas are mediated by diffusely projecting nuclei such as the magnocellular medial geniculate nucleus, lateral posterior nucleus, or C-laminae of the lateral geniculate nucleus.

Stimulation of the lateral nuclear complex has been found to affect the excitability of neurons in the visual cortex (64), and stimulation of the ventromedial nucleus has long been known to lead to recruiting-type responses in the cingulate regions (230). In the case of the apparently diffuse projections from the ventrolateral nuclear complex, Sasaki and his co-workers (453–455) have described a cerebellothalamocortical pathway relaying in the ventral lateral complex and seemingly also involved in recruiting and spindling responses of the parietal cortex.

After a period of time in which work on diffuse thalamocortical systems lost most of its former popularity, a new interest now seems to be stirring. At the present time this primarily rests on observations made with anatomical techniques that clearly show that the idea of a one-to-one connection between a thalamic nucleus and a cortical field, an idea that has dominated our thinking for nearly three decades, need not be necessarily exclusive. With the further documentation of diffuse thalamocortical relays, it is likely that these will regain some of their former popularity.

VENTRAL THALAMUS

By convention (91, 127, 432) the ventral thalamus is taken to include the ventral lateral geniculate nucleus and the reticular nucleus, together with the zona incerta and the closely related fields of Forel (Figs. 1–3). Originally their separation from the dorsal thalamus was based on phylogenetic and ontogenetic grounds, but subsequent work on their connectional relationships has tended to support this, for none of them seem to project to the cerebral cortex or striatum.

Ventral Lateral Geniculate Nucleus

As pointed out in an earlier section, the ventral lateral geniculate nucleus is reciprocally connected with the superficial, visual layers of the superior colliculus (141, 176, 182, 202, 203, 495) and the visual nuclei of the pretectum (46). In highly visual species the size of the ventral lateral geniculate nucleus and the complexity of cellular lamination in it increase in proportion to the large size of the midbrain visual centers (1, 91, 367). Other inputs include the optic tract and certain areas of the visual cortex (221, 301, 518). Other efferent projections of the ventral nucleus include those to the zona incerta, to the nuclei of the assessory optic system, and to the ventral lateral geniculate nucleus of the opposite side. It is the only known thalamic nucleus to have a commissural projection. The ventral lateral geniculate nucleus is a major site of termination of catecholamine and sero-

tonin containing fibers arising in the locus coeruleus and dorsal nucleus of the midbrain raphe (53, 98, 170, 302, 332, 496), though these regions project to other thalamic nuclei as well (450, 513).

Zona Incerta and Fields of Forel

The zona incerta and fields of Forel show a pattern of connectivity similar to that of the ventral lateral geniculate nucleus, but more in relation to the sensorimotor system. The zona incerta in particular receives afferent fibers from the sensorimotor cortex, from the cerebellum, and from the spinal cord (56, 57, 249, 334), and neurons in it may be activated at short latency by somesthetic stimuli (108). Both the zona incerta and fields of Forel also receive fibers from the deepest layer of the superior colliculus (176), from certain of the deep nuclei of the pretectum (46, 180), and from the mesencephalic reticular formation (140), none of which are visual in their connectional relationships. At least one of these, the anterior pretectal nucleus, however, receives medial lemniscal fibers (42, 320) and efferents from the somatic sensory cortex (249). Unlike the ventral lateral geniculate nucleus, the efferent connections of the zona incerta and fields of Forel are not well known and their roles in sensorimotor activities, if any, are unknown. Some cells in them appear to project to the spinal cord (292a).

Reticular Nucleus

Neither the ventral lateral geniculate nucleus, nor the zona incerta, nor the fields of Forel are connected with the dorsal thalamus. The reticular nucleus, however, is intimately related to the dorsal thalamus; apart from the apparent interconnections among the nuclei of the internal medullary lamina, it is the only thalamic nucleus to effect intrathalamic connections. Their synaptic terminations have already been discussed. The reticular nucleus forms a thin sheet, two or three cells thick, covering the anterior, lateral, and ventral surfaces of the dorsal thalamus (Figs. 1–4). It probably incorporates in the cat a small region known as the perigeniculate nucleus. All thalamocortical and corticothalamic fibers, and probably all thalamostriate and pallidothalamic fibers therefore pass through the reticular nucleus; it is clearly in a position to monitor all activity entering and leaving the dorsal thalamus and passing to and from these sources. That it does so is indicated by the anatomical observations that at least the first three groups of fibers mentioned distribute terminals to the nucleus as they traverse if [Figs. 45, 46; (2, 148, 234, 347, 377, 413, 456). There is some evidence that these fibers may be derived from collateral branches of the traversing fibers. Physiological studies also show that stimulation of medial parts of the thalamus or the subcortical white matter lead to high-frequency burst discharges in the reticular nucleus (157, 461).

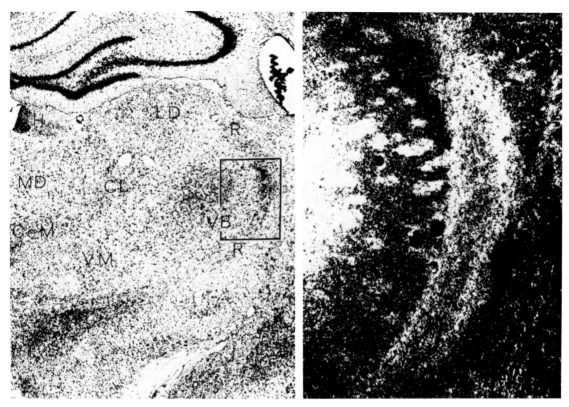

FIG. 45. Dark-field photomicrograph (*right*) from region indicated by box in bright-field photomicrograph of a thionine-counterstained autoradiograph (*left*), showing labeling of terminal ramifications of corticothalamic fibers in thalamic reticular nucleus (*R*) of rat following injection of tritiated amino acids in the SI cortex. For other abbreviations see footnote to Fig. 1 legend. *Left*, × 90. [From Jones (234).]

Though it was once believed that the reticular nucleus projected widely and diffusely upon the cerebral cortex (89, 434), this idea has tended to be discounted by recent work with anterograde and retrograde tracers (234, 248). Instead, the only output of the nucleus appears to be into the dorsal thalamus. Efferent connections with the striatum and midbrain have also been postulated (270, 413, 456), but none of them have been confirmed (234). Every nucleus of the dorsal thalamus receives fibers from the reticular nucleus, and it has been noted, at least in the ventrolateral complex, that the temporal characteristics of the inhibitory postsynaptic potentials generated in the ventrolateral complex by stimulation of more medial parts of the thalamus are very similar to those of the bursting discharges simultaneously being produced in the reticular nucleus (157, 404, 461). The reticular nucleus may therefore provide an inhibitory effect on dorsal thalamic neurons, tending to reduce their levels of excitability immediately after the firing of a thalamocortical volley and immediately after their activation by corticothalamic fibers. This inhibitory effect is probably mediated by γ-aminobutyric acid (GABA), the transmitter agent thought to be produced by reticular nucleus neurons: both these neurons and their

probable terminals in the dorsal thalamus can be stained immunocytochemically with antiserum to the GABA-synthetic enzyme, glutamic acid decarboxylase [Fig. 47; (224)]. Furthermore, the dorsal thalamic nuclei contain very high concentrations of high-affinity GABA receptors (384).

The degree of specificity in the system is difficult to assess. Each dorsal thalamic nucleus, as its efferent fibers traverse the reticular nucleus, distributes terminals to a fairly constant part of it [Fig. 41; (234, 235)]. All areas of the neocortex also project to it (79, 234, 347, 421), and the topography in this system is such that corticothalamic fibers destined to terminate in a particular dorsal thalamic nucleus distribute fibers to the same part of the reticular nucleus that receives afferents from that dorsal thalamic nucleus. Furthermore, a dorsal thalamic nucleus receives fibers from the same part of the reticular nucleus that its afferents and efferents traverse (234). Certain parts of the reticular nucleus are, therefore, dominated by a particular sensory system and the neurons can have appropriate peripheral receptive fields (347, 489, 490). Despite this apparent specificity there is a great deal of overlap in the terminations of the various dorsal thalamic nuclei; moreover, the cells of the reticular nucleus have ex-

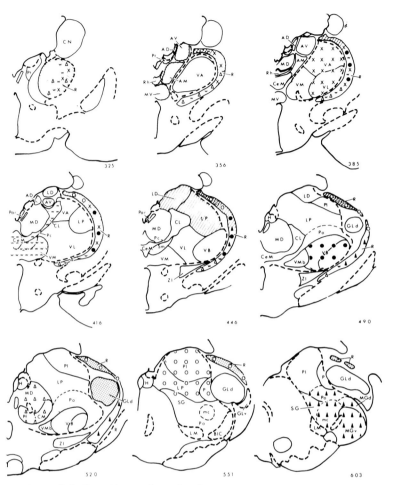

FIG. 46. Projection drawings of series of frontal sections at intervals indicated by numbers, showing overlapping sectors of cat reticular nucleus related to different groups of dorsal thalamic nuclei. For clarity, symbol related to one particular group of dorsal thalamic nuclei appears on one section only. For abbreviations see footnote to Fig. 1 legend. [From Jones (234).]

tremely long dendrites that spread widely over the surface of the dorsal thalamus (413, 456). It is highly likely, therefore, that a single cell receives inputs from many dorsal thalamic nuclei and many cortical areas. The apparently inhibitory effect of the reticular nucleus on the dorsal thalamus may therefore be a generally diffuse one, perhaps controlling a general level of thalamic arousal rather than being specifically related to sensory processing.

Though once thought to be a final relay in the reticular activating pathway from the brain stem to the cortex (230), the lack of a cortical projection and the failure to identify any major brain stem pathways terminating in it tend to preclude the reticular nucleus from this role. To date the only brain stem afferents that have been convincingly identified as passing to the reticular nucleus arise, like those to the other components of the ventral thalamus, from certain of the deeper nuclei of the pretectum (46) and possibly from the underlying mesencephalic reticular formation (140). The reticular nucleus contains high concentrations of nicotinic cholinergic receptors (237), and its neurons respond to iontophoretically applied acetyl choline (29).

THALAMIC INPUTS FROM BRAIN STEM RETICULAR FORMATION

Electrical stimulation in the vicinity of the midbrain reticular formation can facilitate the transmission of an afferent volley through a thalamic relay nucleus such as the lateral geniculate (122, 153, 405, 482, 539). The effect is a long-latency one and may be brought about by disinhibition in the relay nucleus (67, 472). Field potentials recorded in the lateral geniculate nucleus during reticular stimulation resemble the pontogeniculooccipital (PGO) waves recorded from the pons, lateral geniculate nucleus, and occipital cortex during paradoxical sleep (67, 472). The reticular input to the thalamus may, therefore, serve to control levels of thalamic activity during sleep and arousal.

Direct reticular formation inputs to the principal

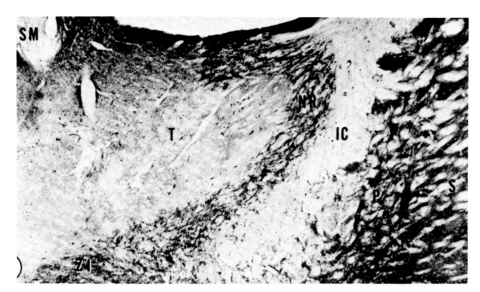

FIG. 47. Heavy immunocytochemical staining of GABAergic neurons in reticular nucleus (Rt) of rat thalamus. Antiserum to glutamic acid decarboxylase. For abbreviations see footnote to Fig. 1 legend. [From Houser et al. (224).]

relay nuclei of the thalamus are not particularly obvious. As mentioned in an earlier section, the reports of a few cells retrogradely labeled in the locus ceruleus, parabrachial nucleus, dorsal raphe nucleus and various other parts of the reticular formation following injection of tracer in the principal nuclei could have been due to involvement of fibers of passage projecting to other sites. Of the sensory relay nuclei, only the gustatory nucleus appears to receive a significant input from the parabrachial nuclei (372, 373, 450) and caudal medulla (315), and the ventral lateral geniculate nucleus receives a significantly heavier catecholamine and serotonin input than the dorsal (98, 496).

Brain stem reticular projections can be demonstrated to the intralaminar nuclei (140, 315, 362). But because these do not project to the relay nuclei, it is difficult to see how they could directly mediate the reticular effect on thalamic transmission. It is possible that they could mediate an effect indirectly through their projections to cerebral cortex, reticular nucleus, or striatum, and this could conceivably account for the long latency of the effect of reticular stimulation (see reviews in refs. 67 and 472). A relay through the reticular nucleus is the more appealing because of its presumed inhibitory effect on the thalamus and because it is itself inhibited by stimulation of the reticular formation (555). Whether the reticular nucleus is recruited by direct projections from the midbrain or indirectly via other thalamic structures remains an open question.

REFERENCES

1. ABLANALP, P. Some subcortical connections of the visual system in tree shrews and squirrels. *Brain. Behav. Evol.* 3: 155–168, 1970.
2. AHLSEN, G., S. LINDSTROM, AND E. SYBIRSKA. Subcortical axon collaterals of principal cells in the lateral geniculate body of the cat. *Brain Res.* 156: 106–109, 1978.
3. AITKIN, L. M. Medial geniculate body of the cat: responses to tonal stimuli of neurons in medial division. *J. Neurophysiol.* 36: 275–283, 1973.
4. AITKIN, L. M., AND C. W. DUNLOP. Inhibition in the medial geniculate body of the cat. *Exp. Brain Res.* 7: 68–83, 1969.
5. AITKIN, L. M., AND W. R. WEBSTER. Medial geniculate body of the cat: organization and responses to tonal stimuli of neurons in ventral division. *J. Neurophysiol.* 35: 365–380, 1972.
6. AKERT, K. Comparative anatomy of frontal cortex and thalamofrontal connections. In: *The Frontal Cortex and Behavior*, edited by J. M. Warren and K. Akert. New York: McGraw-Hill, 1964, p. 372–396.
7. AKERT, K., AND K. HARTMAN-VON MONAKOW. Relationships of precentral, premotor and prefrontal cortex to the mediodorsal and intralaminar nuclei of the monkey thalamus. *Acta. Neurobiol. Exp.* 40: 7–25, 1980.
8. ALBE-FESSARD, D., AND L. KRUGER. Duality of unit discharges from cat centrum medianum in response to natural and electrical stimulation. *J. Neurophysiol.* 25: 3–20, 1962.
9. ALLMAN, J. M., J. H. KAAS, R. M. LANE, AND F. M. MIEZIN. A representation of the visual field in the inferior nucleus of the pulvinar in the owl monkey (*Aotus trivirgatus*). *Brain Res.* 40: 291–302, 1972.
10. AMARAL, D. G., AND W. M. COWAN. Subcortical afferents to the hippocampal formation in the monkey. *J. Comp. Neurol.* 189: 573–592, 1980.
11. ANDERSEN, P., S. A. ANDERSSON, AND S. LANDGREN. Some properties of the thalamic relay cells in the spino-cervico-lemniscal path. *Acta. Physiol. Scand.* 68: 72–83, 1966.
12. Andersen, P., J. C. Eccles, and T. A. Sears. The ventro-basal nucleus of the thalamus: types of cells, their responses and their functional organization. *J. Physiol. London* 174: 370–399, 1964.
13. ANDERSEN, P., K. JUNGE, AND O. SVEEN. Cortico-thalamic

facilitation of somatosensory impulses. *Nature London* 214: 1011–1012, 1967.

14. ANDERSEN, R. A., P. L. KNIGHT, AND M. M. MERZENICH. The thalamocortical and corticothalamic connections of AI, AII, and the anterior auditory field (AAF) in the cat: evidence for two largely segregated systems of connections. *J. Comp. Neurol.* 194: 663–701, 1980.

15. ANDERSEN, R. A., G. L. ROTH, L. M. AITKIN, AND M. M. MERZENICH. The efferent projections of the central nucleus and the pericentral nucleus of the inferior colliculus in the cat. *J. Comp. Neurol.* 194: 649–662, 1980.

16. ANDERSSON, S., AND B. E. GERNANDT. Cortical projection of vestibular nerve in cat. *Acta Otolaryngol.* 116: 10–18, 1954.

17. ANDERSSON, S. A., S. LANDGREN, AND D. WOLSK. The thalamic relay and cortical projection of group I muscle afferents from the forelimb of the cat. *J. Physiol. London* 183: 576–591, 1976.

18. APPLEBAUM, A. E., R. B. LEONARD, D. R. KENSHALO, JR., R. F. MARTIN, AND W. D. WILLIS. Nuclei in which functionally identified spinothalamic tract neurons terminate. *J. Comp. Neurol.* 188: 575–586, 1979.

19. ASANUMA, C., W. T. THACH, AND E. G. JONES. Anatomical evidence for segregated focal groupings of efferent cells and their terminal ramifications in the cerebellothalamic pathway. *Brain Res. Rev.* 5: 267–297, 1983.

20. ASANUMA, C., W. T. THACH, AND E. G. JONES. Distribution of cerebellar terminations and their relation to other afferent terminations in the thalamic ventral lateral region of the monkey. *Brain Res. Rev.* 5: 237–265, 1983.

21. ASANUMA, C., W. T. THACH, AND E. G. JONES. Cytoarchitectonic delineation of the ventral lateral thalamic region in monkeys. *Brain Res. Rev.* 5: 219–235, 1983.

22. ASANUMA, H., J. FERNANDEZ, M. E. SCHEIBEL, AND A. B. SCHEIBEL. Characteristics of projections from the nucleus ventralis lateralis to the motor cortex in the cat: an anatomical and physiological study. *Exp. Brain Res.* 20: 315–330, 1974.

22a. ASANUMA, H., AND I. ROSÉN. Topographical organization of cortical efferent zones projecting to distal forelimb muscles in the monkey. *Exp. Brain Res.* 14: 243–256, 1972.

23. AUER, J. Terminal degeneration in the diencephalon after ablation of frontal cortex in the cat. *J. Anat.* 90: 30–41, 1956.

24. BARBAS, H., AND M.-M. MESULAM. Organization of afferent input to subdivisions of area 8 in the rhesus monkey. *J. Comp. Neurol.* 200: 407–433, 1981.

24a. BAUGHMAN, R. W., AND C. D. GILBERT. Aspartate and glutamate as possible neurotransmitters in the visual cortex. *J. Neurosci.* 4: 427–439, 1981.

25. BECKSTEAD, R. M. Convergent thalamic mesencephalic projections to the anterior medial cortex in the rat. *J. Comp. Neurol.* 166: 403–416, 1976.

26. BECKSTEAD, R. M. An autoradiographic examination of corticocortical and subcortical projections of the medio-dorsal projection (prefrontal) cortex in rat. *J. Comp. Neurol.* 184: 43–62, 1979.

27. BECKSTEAD, R. M., V. B. DOMESICK, AND W. J. H. NAUTA. Efferent connections of the substantia nigra and ventral tegmental area in the rat. *Brain Res.* 175: 191–218, 1979.

28. BECKSTEAD, R. M., J. R. MORSE, AND R. NORGREN. The nucleus of the solitary tract in the monkey: projections to the thalamus and brain stem nuclei. *J. Comp. Neurol.* 190: 259–282, 1980.

29. BEN-ARI, Y., R. DINGLEDINE, I. KANAZAWA, AND J. S. KELLY. Inhibitory effects of acetylcholine on neurones in the feline nucleus reticularis thalami. *J. Physiol. London* 261: 647–671, 1976.

30. BENDER, D. B. Retinotopic organization of macaque pulvinar. *J. Neurophysiol.* 46: 672–693, 1981.

31. BENEVENTO, L. A., AND J. H. FALLON. The ascending projections of the superior colliculus in the rhesus monkey (*Macaca mulatta*). *J. Comp. Neurol.* 160: 339–361, 1975.

32. BENEVENTO, L. A., AND M. REZAK. Extrageniculate projec-

tions to layers VI and I of striate cortex (area 17) in the rhesus monkey (*Macaca mulatta*). *Brain Res.* 96: 51–55, 1975.

33. BENEVENTO, L. A., AND M. REZAK. The cortical projections of the inferior pulvinar and adjacent lateral pulvinar in the rhesus monkey (*Macaca mulatta*): an autoradiographic study. *Brain Res.* 108: 1–24, 1976.

34. BENEVENTO, L. A., M. REZAK, AND R. SANTOS-ANDERSON. An autoradiographic study of the projections of the pretectum in the rhesus monkey (*Macaca mulatta*): evidence for sensorimotor links to the thalamus and oculomotor nuclei. *Brain Res.* 127: 197–218, 1977.

35. BENJAMIN, R. M., AND K. AKERT. Cortical and thalamic areas involved in taste discrimination in the albino rat. *J. Comp. Neurol.* 111: 231–260, 1959.

36. BENJAMIN, R. M., AND H. BURTON. Projection of taste nerve afferents to anterior opercular-insular cortex in squirrel monkey (*Saimiri sciureus*). *Brain Res.* 7: 221–231, 1968.

37. BENTIVOGLIO, M., G. MACCHI, AND A. ALBANESE. The cortical projections of the thalamic intralaminar nuclei, as studied in cat and rat with the multiple fluorescent retrograde tracing technique. *Neurosci. Lett.* 26: 5–10, 1981.

38. BENTIVOGLIO, M., D. VAN DER KOOY, AND H. G. J. M. KUYPERS. The organization of the efferent projections of the substantia nigra in the rat. A retrograde fluorescent double labeling study. *Brain Res.* 174: 1–17, 1979.

39. BERESFORD, W. A. Fiber degeneration following lesions of the visual cortex of the cat. In: *Neurophysiologie und Psychophysik des visuallen Systems*, edited by R. Jung and H. Kornhuber. Berlin: Springer-Verlag, 1961, pp. 247–255.

40. BERKLEY, K. J. Different targets of different neurons in nucleus gracilis of the cat. *J. Comp. Neurol.* 163: 285–303, 1975.

41. BERKLEY, K. J. Spatial relationships between the terminations of somatic sensory and motor pathways in the rostral brainstem of cats and monkeys. I. Ascending somatic sensory inputs to lateral diencephalon. *J. Comp. Neurol.* 193: 283–317, 1980.

42. BERKLEY, K. J., A. BLOMQVIST, A. PELT, AND R. FLINK. Differences in the collateralization of neuronal projections from the dorsal column nuclei and lateral cervical nucleus to the thalamus and tectum in the cat: an anatomical study using two different double-labeling techniques. *Brain Res.* 202: 273–290, 1980.

43. BERKLEY, K. J., J. GRAHAM, AND E. G. JONES. Differential incorporation of tritiated proline and leucine by neurons of the dorsal column nuclei in the cat. *Brain Res.* 132: 485–505, 1977.

44. BERLUCCHI, G., J. M. SPRAGUE, J. LEVY, AND A. C. DIBERARDINO. Pretectum and superior colliculus in visually guided behavior and in flux and form discrimination in the cat. *J. Comp. Physiol. Psychol.* 78: 123–172, 1972.

45. BERMAN, A. L., AND E. G. JONES. *The Thalamus and Basal Telencephalon of the Cat. A Cytoarchitectonic Atlas With Sterotaxic Coordinates.* Madison: Univ. of Wisconsin Press, 1982.

46. BERMAN, N. Connections of the pretectum in the cat. *J. Comp. Neurol.* 174: 227–254, 1977.

47. BERMAN, N., AND E. G. JONES. A retino-pulvinar projection in the cat. *Brain Res.* 134: 237–248, 1977.

48. BIGNALL, K. E. Comparison of optic efferents to primary visual and polysensory areas of cat neocortex. *Exp. Neurol.* 17: 327–343, 1967.

49. BILLINGS-GAGLIARDI, S., V. CHAN-PALAY, AND S. L. PALAY. A review of lamination in area 17 of the visual cortex of *Macaca mulatta.* *J. Neurocytol.* 3: 619–629, 1974.

50. BISHOP, P. O., W. KOZAK, W. R. LEVICK, AND G. J. VAKKUR. The determination of the projection of the visual field onto the lateral geniculate nucleus in the cat. *J. Physiol. London* 163: 503–539, 1962.

51. BLOMQUIST, A. J., R. M. BENJAMIN, AND R. EMMERS. Thalamic localization of afferents from the tongue in squirrel monkey (*Saimiri sciureus*) *J. Comp. Neurol.* 118: 77–87, 1962.

52. BLOMQUIST, A. J., AND C. A. LORENZINI. Projection of dorsal roots and sensory nerves to cortical sensory motor regions of

squirrel monkey. *J. Neurophysiol.* 28: 1195–1205, 1965.

53. BOBILLIER, P., S. SEGUIN, F. PETITJEAN, D. SALVERT, M. TOURET, AND M. JOUVET. The raphe nuclei of the cat brain stem: a topographical atlas of their efferent projections as revealed by autoradiography. *Brain Res.* 113: 449–486, 1976.

54. BODIAN, D. Studies on the diencephalon of the Virginia opossum. Part I. The nuclear pattern in the adult. *J. Comp. Neurol.* 71: 259–324, 1939.

55. BOIVIE, J. The termination of the cervicothalamic tract in the cat. An experimental study with silver impregnation methods. *Brain Res.* 19: 333–360, 1970.

56. BOIVIE, J. The termination in the thalamus and zona incerta of fibres from the dorsal column nuclei (DCN) in the cat. An experimental study with silver impregnation methods. *Brain Res.* 28: 459–490, 1971.

57. BOIVIE, J. The termination of the spinothalamic tract in the cat. An experimental study with silver impregnation methods. *Exp. Brain Res.* 112: 331–353, 1971.

58. BOIVIE, J. Anatomical observations on the dorsal column nuclei, their thalamic projection and the cytoarchitecture of some somatosensory thalamic nuclei in the monkey. *J. Comp. Neurol.* 178: 17–48, 1978.

59. BOIVIE, J. An anatomical reinvestigation of the termination of the spinothalamic tract in the monkey. *J. Comp. Neurol.* 186: 343–370, 1979.

60. BOIVIE, J. Thalamic projections from lateral cervical nucleus in monkey. A degeneration study. *Brain Res.* 198: 13–26, 1980.

61. BOIVIE, J., AND K. BOMAN. Termination of a separate (proprioceptive?) cuneothalamic tract from external cuneate nucleus in monkey. *Brain Res.* 224: 235–246, 1981.

62. BOS, J., AND L. A. BENEVENTO. Projections of the medial pulvinar to orbital cortex and frontal eye fields in the rhesus monkey (*Macaca mulatta*). *Exp. Neurol.* 49: 487–496, 1975.

64. BRODMANN, K. *Vergleichende Lokalisationslehre der Grosshirnrinde in ihren Prinzipien dargestellt auf Grund des Zellenbaues.* Leipzig: J. A. Barth, 1909, p. 324.

65. BROWN, T. S., AND L. A. MARCO. Effects of stimulation of the superior colliculus and lateral thalamus on visual evoked potentials. *Electroencephalogr. Clin. Neurophysiol.* 22: 150–158, 1967.

65a. BULLIER, J., AND G. H. HENRY. Ordinal position and afferent input of neurons in monkey striate cortex. *J. Comp. Neurol.* 193: 913–936, 1980.

66. BURCHFIEL, J. E., AND F. H. DUFFY. Corticofugal influence upon cat thalamic ventrobasal complex. *Brain Res.* 70: 395–411, 1974.

67. BURKE, W., AND A. M. COLE. Extraretinal influences on the lateral geniculate nucleus. *Rev. Physiol. Biochem. Pharmacol.* 70: 395–411, 1974.

68. BURKE, W., AND A. J. SEFTON. Discharge patterns of principal cells and interneurones in lateral geniculate nucleus of rat. *J. Physiol. London* 187: 201–212, 1966.

69. Burton, H., and R. M. Benjamin. Central projections of the gustatory system. In: *Handbook of Sensory Physiology. Chemical Senses. Taste*, edited by L. M. Beidler. New York: Springer-Verlag, vol. 4, pt. 2, p. 148–164.

70. BURTON, H., AND F. EARLS. Cortical representation of the ipsilateral chorda tympani nerve in the cat. *Brain Res.* 16: 520–523, 1969.

71. BURTON, H., D. J. FORBES, AND R. M. BENJAMIN. Thalamic neurons responsive to temperature changes of glabrous hand and foot skin in squirrel monkey. *Brain Res.* 24: 179–180, 1970.

72. BURTON, H., AND E. G. JONES. The posterior thalamic region and its cortical projection in New World and Old World monkeys. *J. Comp. Neurol.* 168: 249–301, 1976.

73. BUSER, P., AND K. E. BIGNALL. Nonprimary sensory projections on the cat neocortex. *Int. Rev. Neurobiol.* 10: 111–165, 1965.

74. BÜTTNER, U., AND V. HENN. Thalamic unit activity in the alert monkey during natural vestibular stimulation. *Brain Res.* 103: 127–132, 1976.

75. CALDWELL, R. B., AND R. R. MIZE. Superior colliculus neurons which project to the cat lateral posterior nucleus have varying morphologies. *J. Comp. Neurol.* 203: 53–66, 1981.

76. CAMPBELL, C. B. G. The visual system of insectivores and primates. *Ann. NY Acad. Sci.* 167: 388–403, 1969.

77. CAMPOS-ORTEGA, J. A., AND W. R. HAYHOW. On the organization of the visual cortical projection to the pulvinar in *Macaca mulatta. Brain Behav. Evol.* 6: 394–423, 1973.

78. CAREY, R. G., D. FITZPATRICK, AND I. T. DIAMOND. Layer I of striate cortex of *Tupaia glis* and *Galago senegalensis*: projections from thalamus and claustrum revealed by retrograde transport of horseradish peroxidase. *J. Comp. Neurol.* 186: 393–438, 1979.

79. CARMAN, J. B., W. M. COWAN, AND T. P. S. POWELL. Cortical connexions of the thalamic reticular nucleus. *J. Anat.* 98: 587–598, 1964.

80. CARPENTER, M. B., K. NAKANO, AND R. KIM. Nigrothalamic projections in the monkey demonstrated by autoradiographic techniques. *J. Comp. Neurol.* 165: 401–415, 1976.

81. CARRERAS, M., AND S. A. ANDERSSON. Functional properties of neurons of the anterior ectosylvian gyrus of the cat. *J. Neurophysiol.* 26: 100–126, 1963.

82. CARSTENS, E., AND D. TREVINO. Laminar origins of spinothalamic projections in the cat as determined by the retrograde transport of horseradish peroxidase. *J. Comp. Neurol.* 182: 151–165, 1978.

83. CASAGRANDE, V. A., AND I. T. DIAMOND. Ablation study of the superior colliculus in the tree shrew (*Tupaia glis*). *J. Comp. Neurol.* 156: 207–237, 1974.

84. CASEY, K. L. Unit analysis of nociceptive mechanisms in the thalamus of the awake squirrel monkey. *J. Neurophysiol.* 29: 727–750, 1966.

85. CASSEDAY, J. H., I. T. DIAMOND, AND J. K. HARTING. Auditory pathways to the cortex in *Tupaia glis. J. Comp. Neurol.* 166: 303–340, 1976.

86. CATSMAN-BERREVOETS, C. E., AND H. G. J. M. KUYPERS. Differential laminar distribution of corticothalamic neurons projecting to the VL and the center median. An HRP study in the cynomolgus monkey. *Brain Res.* 154: 359–365, 1978.

87. CATSMAN-BERREVOETS, C. E., AND H. G. J. M. KUYPERS. A search for cortico-spinal collaterals to thalamus and mesencephalon by means of multiple retrograde fluorescent tracers in cat and rat. *Brain Res.* 218: 15–34, 1981.

88. CAVINESS, V. S., JR., AND D. O. FROST. Tangential organization of thalamic projections to the neocortex in the mouse. *J. Comp. Neurol.* 194: 335–369, 1980.

89. CHOW, K. L. Regional degeneration of the thalamic reticular nucleus following cortical ablations in monkeys. *J. Comp. Neurol.* 92: 227–240, 1952.

90. CLARK, W. E. LEGROS. The structure and connections of the thalamus. *Brain* 55: 406–470, 1932.

91. CLARK, W. E. LEGROS, AND R. H. BOGGON. The thalamic connections of the parietal and frontal lobes of the brain in the monkey. *Philos. Trans. R. Soc. London Ser. B* 224: 313–359, 1935.

92. CLARK, W. E. LEGROS, AND D. W. C. NORTHFIELD. The cortical projection of the pulvinar in the macaque monkey. *Brain* 60: 126–142, 1937.

93. CLARK, W. E. LEGROS, AND T. P. S. POWELL. On the thalamocortical connexions of the general sensory cortex of *Macaca. Proc. R. Soc. London Ser. B* 141: 467–487, 1953.

94. CLARKE, E. C., AND C. D. O'MALLEY. *The Human Brain and Spinal Cord.* Berkeley: Univ. of California Press, 1968.

95. CLELAND, B. G., R. MORSTYN, H. C. WAGNER, AND W. R. LEVICK. Long-latency retinal input to lateral geniculate neurones of the cat. *Brain Res.* 91: 306–310, 1975.

96. COLE, M., W. J. H. NAUTA, AND W. R. MEHLER. The ascending efferent projections of the substantia nigra. *Trans. Am. Neurol. Assoc.* 89: 74–78, 1964.

97. COLONNIER, M., AND R. W. GUILLERY. Synaptic organization in the lateral geniculate nucleus of the monkey. *Z. Zellforsch.*

Mikrosk. Anat. 62: 333–355, 1964.

98. CONRAD, L. C., C. M. LEONARD, AND D. W. PFAFF. Connections of the median and dorsal raphe nuclei in the rat: an autoradiographic and degeneration study. *J. Comp. Neurol.* 156: 179–205, 1974.

99. COSTANZO, R. M., AND E. P. GARDNER. Multiple-joint neurons in somatosensory cortex of awake monkeys. *Brain Res.* 214: 321–333, 1981.

100. COULTER, J. D., L. EWING, AND C. CARTER. Origin of primary sensorimotor cortical projections to lumbar spinal cord of cat and monkey. *Brain Res.* 103: 366–372, 1976.

101. COWAN, W. M., AND T. P. S. POWELL. The projection of the midline and intralaminar nuclei of the thalamus of the rabbit. *J. Neurol. Neurosurg. Psychiatry* 18: 266–279, 1955.

101a. CRAIG, A. D., AND H. BURTON. Spinothalamic terminations in the ventroposterolateral nucleus of the cat. *Soc. Neurosci. Abstr.* 5: 705, 1979.

102. CURRY, M. J. The exteroceptive properties of neurones in the somatic part of the posterior group (PO). *Brain Res.* 44: 439–462, 1972.

103. DARIAN-SMITH, I., J. ISBISTER, H. MOK, AND T. YOKOTA. Somatic sensory cortical projection areas excited by tactile stimulation of the cat: a triple representation. *J. Physiol. London* 182: 671–689, 1966.

104. DAVIES, L. P., AND G. A. R. JOHNSTON. Uptake and release of D- and L-aspartate by rat brain. *J. Neurochem.* 26: 1007–1014, 1976.

105. DEECKE, L., D. W. F. SCHWARZ, AND J. M. FREDRICKSON. Nucleus ventroposterior inferior (VPI) as the vestibular thalamic relay in the rhesus monkey. I. Field potential investigation. *Exp. Brain Res.* 20: 83–100, 1975.

106. DEKKER, J. J., AND H. G. J. M. KUYPERS. Quantitative EM study of projection terminals in the rat's AV thalamic nucleus. Autoradiographic and degeneration techniques compared. *Brain Res.* 117: 399–422, 1976.

107. DELL, P. Corrélations entre le système végétif et le système de la vie de relation. Mésencéphale, diencéphale et cortex cérébral. *J. Physiol. Paris* 44: 471–557, 1952.

108. DENAVIT, M., AND E. KOSINSKI. Somatic afferents to the cat subthalamus. *Arch. Ital. Biol.* 106: 391–411, 1968.

109. DEVITO, J. L. Projections from the cerebral cortex to intralaminar nuclei in monkey. *J. Comp. Neurol.* 136: 193–201, 1969.

110. D'HOLLANDER, F. Recherches anatomiques sur les couches optiques. La Topographie des noyaux thalamiques. *Névraxe* 14, 15: 469–519, 1913.

111. D'HOLLANDER, F., AND A. GEREBTZOFF. Les couches optiques et leurs connexions. Synthèse de nos recherches anatomie-expérimentales. *Bull. Acad. R. Med. Belg.* 4: 305–314, 1939.

112. DIAMOND, I. T., E. G. JONES, AND T. P. S. POWELL. The projection of the auditory cortex upon the diencephalon and brain stem in the cat. *Brain Res.* 15: 205–340, 1969.

113. DICHIARA, G., M. L. PORCEDDU, M. MORELLI, M. L. MULAS, AND G. L. GESSA. Evidence for a GABAergic projection from the substantia nigra to the ventromedial thalamus and to the superior colliculus of the rat. *Brain. Res.* 176: 273–284, 1979.

114. DIVAC, I. Magnocellular nuclei of the basal forebrain project to neocortex, brain stem and olfactory bulb. Review of some functional correlates. *Brain Res.* 93: 385–398, 1975.

115. DIVAC, I., J. H. LAVAIL, P. RAKIC, AND K. R. WINSTON. Heterogeneous afferents to the inferior parietal lobule of the rhesus monkey revealed by the retrograde transport method. *Brain Res.* 123: 197–207, 1977.

116. DOMESICK, V. B. Projections from the cingulate cortex in the rat. *Brain Res.* 12: 296–320, 1969.

117. DOMESICK, V. B. Thalamic relationships of the medial cortex in the rat. *Brain Behav. Evol.* 6: 457–483, 1972.

118. DONALDSON, L., P. J. HAND, AND A. R. MORRISON. Cortical-thalamic relationships in the rat. *Exp. Neurol.* 47: 448–458, 1975.

119. DONOGHUE, J. P., AND F. F. EBNER. The laminar distribution and ultrastructure of fibers projecting from three thalamic

120. DONOGHUE, J. P., AND F. F. EBNER. The organization of thalamic projections to the parietal cortex of the Virginia opossum. *J. Comp. Neurol.* 198: 365–388, 1981.

121. DONOGHUE, J. P., K. L. KERMAN, AND F. F. EBNER. Evidence for two organizational plans within the somatic sensory-motor cortex of the rat. *J. Comp. Neurol.* 183: 647–664, 1979.

122. DOTY, R. W., P. D. WILSON, J. R. BARTLET, AND J. PECCI-SAAVEDRA. Mesencephalic control of lateral geniculate nucleus in primates. I. Electrophysiology. *Exp. Brain Res.* 18: 189–203, 1973.

123. DRÄGER, U. C. Autoradiography of tritiated proline and fucose transported transneuronally from the eye to the visual cortex in pigmented and albino mice. *Brain Res.* 82: 284–292, 1974.

124. DREHER, B., Y. FUKADA, AND R. W. RODIECK. Identification, classification, and anatomical segregation of cells with X-like and Y-like properties in the lateral geniculate nucleus of Old World primates. *J. Physiol. London* 258: 433–452, 1976.

125. DREHER, B., AND A. J. SEFTON. Properties of neurons in cat's dorsal lateral geniculate nucleus: a comparison between medial interlaminar and laminated parts of the nucleus. *J. Comp. Neurol.* 183: 47–64, 1979.

126. DREYER, D. A., R. J. SCHNEIDER, C. B. METZ, AND B. L. WHITSEL. Differential contribution of spinal pathways to body representation in postcentral gyrus of *Macaca mulatta*. *J. Neurophysiol.* 37: 119–145, 1974.

127. DROOGLEEVER-FORTUYN, A. E. Die Ontogenie der Kerne des Zwischenhirns beim Kaninchen. *Arch. Anat. Physiol. Anat. Abt.* 303–352, 1912.

128. DROOGLEEVER-FORTUYN, J. Anatomical basis of cortico-subcortical relationships. *Electroencephalogr. Clin. Neurophysiol.* 4: 149–162, 1953.

129. DROOGLEEVER-FORTUYN, J., AND R. STEFENS. On the anatomical relations of the intralaminar and midline cells of the thalamus. *Electroencephalogr. Clin. Neurophysiol.* 3: 393–400, 1951.

130. DUBIN, M. W., AND B. G. CLELAND. The organization of visual inputs to interneurons of the lateral geniculate nucleus of the cat. *J. Neurophysiol.* 40: 410–427, 1977.

131. DUBNER, R. Single cell analysis of sensory interaction in anterior lateral and suprasylvian gyri of the cat cerebral cortex. *Exp. Neurol.* 15: 255–273, 1966.

132. DUBNER, R., AND F. J. BROWN. Response of cells to restricted visual stimuli in an association area of cat cerebral cortex. *Exp. Neurol.* 20: 70–86, 1968.

133. DUBNER, R., AND L. T. RUTLEDGE. Recording and analysis of converging input upon neurons in cat association cortex. *J. Neurophysiol.* 27: 620–634, 1964.

134. DUBNER, R., AND L. T. RUTLEDGE. Intracellular recording of the convergence of input upon neurons in cat association cortex. *Exp. Neurol.* 12: 349–369, 1965.

135. DUDEL, J., AND S. W. KUFFLER. Presynaptic inhibition at the crayfish neuromuscular junction. *J. Physiol. London* 155: 543–562, 1961.

136. DYKES, R. W., J. D. DUDAR, D. G. TANJI, AND N. G. PUBLICOVER. Somatotopic projections of mystacial vibrissae on cerebral cortex of cats. *J. Neurophysiol.* 40: 997–1014, 1977.

136a. DYKES, R. W., D. D. RASMUSSON, AND P. B. HOELTZELL. Organization of primary somatosensory cortex in the cat. *J. Neurophysiol.* 43: 1527–1546, 1980.

137. DYKES, R. W., M. SUR, M. M. MERZENICH, J. H. KAAS, AND R. J. NELSON. Regional segregation of neurons responding to quickly adapting, slowly adapting, deep and Pacinian receptors within thalamic ventroposterior lateral and ventroposterior inferior nuclei in the squirrel monkey (*Samiri sciureus*). *Neuroscience* 6: 1687–1692, 1981.

138. ECCLES, J. C., R. M. ECCLES, AND F. MAGNI. Central inhibitory action attributable to presynaptic depolarization produced by muscle afferent volleys. *J. Physiol. London* 159: 147–166, 1961.

139. EDWARDS, S. B. The ascending and descending projections of

nuclei to the somatic sensory-motor cortex of the opossum. *J. Comp. Neurol.* 198: 389–420, 1981.

the red nucleus in the cat: an experimental study using an autoradiographic tracing method. *Brain Res.* 48: 45–63, 1972.

140. EDWARDS, S. B., AND J. S. DE OLMOS. Autoradiographic studies of the projections of the midbrain reticular formation: ascending projections of nucleus cuneiformis. *J. Comp. Neurol.* 165: 417–431, 1976.

141. EDWARDS, S. B., A. C. ROSENQUIST, AND L. A. PALMER. An autoradiographic study of the ventral lateral geniculate projections in the cat. *Brain Res.* 72: 282–287, 1974.

142. EMMERS, R. Localization of thalamic projections of afferents from the tongue in the cat. *Anat. Rec.* 148: 67–74, 1964.

143. EMMERS, R. Organization of the first and second somesthetic regions (SI and SII) in the rat thalamus. *J. Comp. Neurol.* 124: 215–227, 1965.

144. EMMERS, R., AND K. AKERT. *A Stereotaxic Atlas of the Brain of the Squirrel Monkey (Saimiri sciureus).* Madison: Univ. of Wisconsin Press, 1963, p. 102.

144a. ENROTH-CUGELL, C. C., AND J. G. ROBSON. The contrast sensitivity of retinal ganglion cells of the cat. *J. Physiol. London* 187: 517–534, 1966.

145. FAMIGLIETTI, E. V., JR., AND A. PETERS. The synaptic glomerulus and the intrinsic neuron in the dorsal lateral geniculate nucleus of the cat. *J. Comp. Neurol.* 144: 285–334, 1972.

146. FAULL, R. L. M., AND J. B. CARMAN. Ascending projections of the substantia nigra in the rat. *J. Comp. Neurol.* 132: 73–92, 1968.

146a. FAULL, R. L. M., AND W. R. MEHLER. The cells of origin of nigrotectal, nigrothalamic and nigrostriatal projections in the rat. *Neuroscience* 3: 989–1002, 1978.

147. FELDMAN, S. G., AND L. KRUGER. An axonal transport study of the ascending projection of medial lemniscal neurons in the rat. *J. Comp. Neurol.* 192: 427–454, 1980.

148. FERSTER, D., AND S. LEVAY. The axonal arborizations of lateral geniculate neurons in the striate cortex of the cat. *J. Comp. Neurol.* 182: 923–944, 1978.

149. FINLEY, J. C. W., J. L. MADERDRUT, AND P. PETRUSZ. The immunocytochemical localization of enkephalin in the central nervous system of the rat. *J. Comp. Neurol.* 198: 541–565, 1981.

150. FITZPATRICK, D., AND I. T. DIAMOND. Distribution of acetylcholinesterase in the geniculostriate system of *Galago senegalensis* and *Aotus trivirgatus:* evidence for the origin of the reaction product in the lateral geniculate body. *J. Comp. Neurol.* 194: 703–719, 1980.

150a. FITZPATRICK, D., K. ITOH, M. CONLEY, AND I. T. DIAMOND. The projection of the lateral geniculate body to extrastriate cortex in the owl monkey and squirrel monkey. *Soc. Neurosci. Abstr.* 7: 830, 1981.

151. FITZPATRICK, K., AND T. J. IMIG. Projections of auditory cortex upon the thalamus and midbrain in the owl monkey. *J. Comp. Neurol.* 177: 437–556, 1978.

152. FONNUM, F., J. STORM-MATHISEN, AND I. DIVAC. Biochemical evidence for glutamate as neurotransmitter in corticostriatal and corticothalamic fibres in rat brain. *Neuroscience* 6: 863–873, 1981.

153. FOOTE, W. E., R. J. MACIEWICZ, AND J. P. MORDES. Effect of midbrain raphe and lateral mesencephalic stimulation on spontaneous and evoked activity in the lateral geniculate of the cat. *Exp. Brain Res.* 19: 124–130, 1974.

154. FRIEDEMANN, M. Die Cytoarchitektonik des Zwischenhirns der Cercopitheken mit besonderer Berücksichtigung des Thalamus opticus. *J. Psychol. Neurol. Leipzig* 18: 309–378, 1911.

155. FRIEDLANDER, M. J., C.-S. LIN, L. R. STANFORD, AND S. M. SHERMAN. Morphology of functionally identified neurons in lateral geniculate nucleus of the cat. *J. Neurophysiol.* 46: 80–129, 1981.

155a. FRIEDMAN, D. P., AND E. G. JONES. Focal projection of electrophysiologically defined groupings of thalamic cells on the monkey somatic sensory cortex. *Brain Res.* 191: 249–252, 1980.

156. FRIEDMAN, D. P., AND E. G. JONES. Thalamic input to areas 3a and 2 in monkeys. *J. Neurophysiol.* 45: 59–85, 1981.

157. FRIGYESI, T. L., AND R. SCHWARTZ. Cortical control of thalamic sensorimotor relay activities in the cat and the squirrel monkey. In: *Corticothalamic Projections and Sensorimotor Activities,* edited by T. L. Frigyesi, E. Rinvik, and M. D. Yahr. New York: Raven, 1972, p. 161–195.

158. FROST, D. O., AND V. S. CAVINESS, JR. Radial organization of thalamic projections to the neocortex in the mouse. *J. Comp. Neurol.* 194: 369–394, 1980.

159. FUKUDA, Y., AND J. STONE. Retinal distribution and central projections of Y-, X-, and W-cells of the cat's retina. *J. Neurophysiol.* 37: 749–772, 1974.

160. FUKUSHIMA, T., AND F. W. L. KERR. Organization of trigeminothalamic tracts and other thalamic afferent systems of the brainstem in the rat: presence of gelatinosa neurons with thalamic connections. *J. Comp. Neurol.* 183: 169–184, 1979.

161. GANCHROW, D. Intratrigeminal and thalamic projections of nucleus caudalis in the squirrel monkey (*Saimiri sciureus*): a degeneration and autoradiographic study. *J. Comp. Neurol.* 178: 281–312, 1978.

162. GARDNER, E. P., AND R. M. COSTANZO. Properties of kinesthetic neurons in somatosensory cortex of awake monkeys. *Brain Res.* 214: 301–320, 1981.

163. GAREY, L. J., E. G. JONES, AND T. P. S. POWELL. Interrelationships of striate and extrastriate cortex with the primary relay sites of the visual pathway. *J. Neurol. Neurosurg. Psychiatry* 31: 135–157, 1968.

164. GAREY, L. J., AND T. P. S. POWELL. The projection of the lateral geniculate nucleus upon the cortex in the cat. *Proc. R. Soc. London Ser. B* 169: 107–126, 1967.

165. GAREY, L. J., AND T. P. S. POWELL. The projection of the retina in the cat. *J. Anat.* 102: 189–222, 1968.

166. GATASS, R., E. OSWALDO-CRUZ, AND A. P. B. SOUSA. Visuotopic organization of the cebus pulvinar: a double representation of the contralateral hemifield. *Brain Res.* 152: 1–16, 1978.

167. GEISERT, E. E., JR. Cortical projections of the lateral geniculate nucleus in the cat. *J. Comp. Neurol.* 190: 793–812, 1980.

168. GEISLER, G. J., JR., D. MENETREY, AND A. I. BASBAUM. Differential origins of spinothalamic tract projections to medial and lateral thalamus in the rat. *J. Comp. Neurol.* 184: 107–126, 1979.

169. GEREBTZOFF, M. A. Systèmatisation des connections thalamo-corticales. *Cellule* 46: 5–54, 1937.

169a. GILBERT, C. D. Laminar differences in receptive field properties of cells in the cat primary visual cortex. *J. Physiol. London* 268: 391–421, 1977.

170. GILBERT, C. D., AND J. P. KELLY. The projections of cells in different layers of the cat's visual cortex. *J. Comp. Neurol.* 163: 81–105, 1975.

171. GILBERT, C. D., AND T. N. WIESEL. Morphology and intracortical projections of functionally characterized neurones in the cat visual cortex. *Nature* 280: 120–125, 1979.

172. GIOLLI, R. A., AND M. D. GUTHRIE. The primary optic projections in the rabbit. An experimental degeneration study. *J. Comp. Neurol.* 136: 99–126, 1969.

173. GIOLLI, R. A., AND J. E. POPE. The mode of innervation of the dorsal lateral geniculate nucleus and the pulvinar of the rabbit by axons arising from the visual cortex. *J. Comp. Neurol.* 147: 129–143, 1973.

174. GLENDENNING, K. K., J. A. HALL, I. T. DIAMOND, AND W. C. HALL. The pulvinar nucleus of *Galago senegalensis. J. Comp. Neurol.* 161: 419–457, 1975.

175. GODFRAIND, J. M., M. MEULDERS, AND C. VERAART. Visual properties of neurons in pulvinar, nucleus lateralis posterior and nucleus suprageniculatus thalami in the cat. I. Qualitative investigation. *Brain Res.* 44: 503–526, 1972.

176. GRAHAM, J. An autoradiographic study of the efferent connections of the superior colliculus in the cat. *J. Comp. Neurol.* 173: 629–654, 1977.

177. GRAHAM, J., AND V. A. CASAGRANDE. A light microscopic and electron microscopic study of the superficial layers of the superior colliculus of the tree shrew (*Tupaia glis*). *J. Comp. Neurol.* 191: 133–151, 1980.

178. GRAHAM, J., C.-S. LIN, AND J. H. KAAS. Subcortical projections of six visual cortical areas in the owl monkey, *Aotus trivirgatus*. *J. Comp. Neurol.* 187: 557–580, 1979.

179. GRANT, G., J. BOIVIE, AND H. SILFVENIUS. Course and termination of fibres from the nucleus Z of the medulla oblongata. An experimental light microscopical study in the cat. *Brain Res.* 55: 55–70, 1973.

180. GRAYBIEL, A. M. Some extrageniculate visual pathways in the cat. *Invest. Opthalmol.* 11: 322–332, 1972.

181. GRAYBIEL, A. M. Some thalamocortical projections of the pulvinar-posterior system of the thalamus in the cat. *Brain Res.* 22: 131–136, 1970.

182. GRAYBIEL, A. M. Studies on the anatomical organization of posterior association cortex. In: *The Neurosciences: Third Study Program*, edited by F. O. Schmitt and F. G. Worden. Cambridge, MA: MIT Press, 1974, p. 205–214.

183. GRAYBIEL, A. M., AND D. M. BERSON. Autoradiographic evidence for a projection from the pretectal nucleus of the optic tract to the dorsal lateral geniculate complex in the cat. *Brain Res.* 195: 1–12, 1980.

184. GRAYBIEL, A. M., AND D. M. BERSON. Histochemical identification and afferent connections of subdivisions in the lateralis posterior-pulvinar complex and related thalamic nuclei in the cat. *Neuroscience* 5: 1175–1238, 1980.

185. GROENEWEGEN, H. J., A. J. P. BOESTEN, AND J. VOOGD. The dorsal column nuclear projections to the nucleus ventralis posterior lateralis thalami and the inferior olive in the cat: an autoradiographic study. *J. Comp. Neurol.* 162: 505–517, 1975.

186. GROFOVÁ, I., AND E. RINVIK. An experimental electron microscopic study on the striatonigral projection in the cat. *Exp. Brain. Res.* 11: 249–262, 1970.

187. GUILLERY, R. W. A study of Golgi preparations from the dorsal lateral geniculate nucleus of the adult cat. *J. Comp. Neurol.* 128: 21–50, 1966.

188. GUILLERY, R. W. Patterns of fiber degeneration in the dorsal lateral geniculate nucleus of the cat following lesions in the visual cortex. *J. Comp. Neurol.* 130: 197–222, 1967.

189. GUILLERY, R. W. The organization of synaptic interconnections in the laminae of the dorsal lateral geniculate nucleus of the cat. *Z. Zellforsch. Mikrosk. Anat.* 96: 1–38, 1969.

190. GUILLERY, R. W. The laminar distribution of retinal fibers in the dorsal lateral geniculate nucleus of the cat: a new interpretation. *J. Comp. Neurol.* 138: 339–367, 1970.

191. GUILLERY, R. W., H. O. ADRIAN, C. N. WOOLSEY, AND J. E. ROSE. Activation of somatosensory areas I and II of cat's cerebral cortex by focal stimulation of the ventrobasal complex. In: *The Thalamus*, edited by D. P. Purpura and M. D. Yahr. New York: Columbia Univ. Press, 1966, p. 197–206.

192. GUILLERY, R. W., AND M. COLONNIER. Synaptic patterns in the dorsal lateral geniculate nucleus of the monkey. *Z. Zellforsch. Mikrosk. Anat.* 103: 90–108, 1970.

193. GUILLERY, R. W., E. E. GEISERT, JR., E. H. POLLEY, AND C. A. MASON. An analysis of the retinal afferents to the cat's medial interlaminar nucleus and its rostral thalamic extension, the "geniculate wing". *J. Comp. Neurol.* 194: 117–142, 1980.

194. GUILLERY, R. W., AND J. H. KAAS. A study of normal and congenitally abnormal retinogeniculate projections in cats. *J. Comp. Neurol.* 143: 73–100, 1971.

195. GURDJIAN, E. S. The diencephalon of the albino rat. Studies on the brain of the rat No. 2. *J. Comp. Neurol.* 43: 1–114, 1927.

196. HAIGHT, J. R. The general organization of somatotopic projections to SII cerebral neocortex in the cat. *Brain Res.* 44: 483–502, 1972.

197. HAJDU, F., G. SOMOGYI, AND T. TÖMBÖL. Neuronal and synaptic arrangements in the lateralis posterior-pulvinar complex of the thalamus in the cat. *Brain Res.* 73: 89–104, 1974.

198. HALARIS, A. E., B. E. JONES, AND R. Y. MOORE. Axonal transport in serotonin neurons of the midbrain raphe. *Brain Res.* 107: 555–574, 1976.

199. HAND, P. J., AND A. R. MORRISON. Thalamocortical projections from the ventrobasal complex to somatic sensory areas I and II. *Exp. Neurol.* 26: 291–308, 1970.

200. HAND, P. J., AND T. VAN WINKLE. The efferent connections of the feline nucleus cuneatus. *J. Comp. Neurol.* 171: 83–109, 1977.

201. HARDING, B. N., AND T. P. S. POWELL. An electron microscopic study of the centre-median and ventrolateral nuclei of the thalamus in the monkey. *Philos. Trans. R. Soc. London Ser. B* 279: 357–412, 1977.

202. HARTING, J. K., W. C. HALL, AND I. T. DIAMOND. Evolution of the pulvinar. *Brain Behav. Evol.* 6: 424–452, 1973.

203. HARTING, J. K., W. C. HALL, I. T. DIAMOND, AND G. F. MARTIN. Anterograde degeneration study of the superior colliculus in *Tupaia glis*: evidence for a subdivision between superficial and deep layers. *J. Comp. Neurol.* 148: 361–386, 1973.

204. HARVEY, A. R. A physiological analysis of subcortical and commissural projections of areas 17 and 18 of the cat. *J. Physiol. London* 302: 507–534, 1980.

205. HAYHOW, W. R. The cytoarchitecture of the lateral geniculate body in the cat in relation to the distribution of crossed and uncrossed optic fibers. *J. Comp. Neurol.* 110: 1–64, 1958.

206. HAZLETT, J. C., C. R. DUTTA, AND C. A. FOX. The neurons in the centromedian-parafascicular complex of the monkey (*Macaca mulatta*): a Golgi study. *J. Comp. Neurol.* 168: 41–73, 1976.

207. HEATH, C. J. Distribution of axonal degeneration following lesions of the posterior group of thalamic nuclei in the cat. *Brain Res.* 21: 435–438, 1970.

208. HEATH, C. J., J. HORE, AND C. G. PHILLIPS. Inputs from low threshold muscle and cutaneous afferents of hand and forearm to areas 3a and 3b of baboon's cerebral cortex. *J. Physiol. London* 257: 199–227, 1976.

209. HEATH, C. J., AND E. G. JONES. Anatomical organization of the suprasylvian gyrus of the cat. *Ergeb. Anat. Entwicklungsgesch.* 45: 3–64, 1971.

210. HEATH, C. J., AND E. G. JONES. An experimental study of ascending connections from the posterior group of thalamic nuclei in the cat. *J. Comp. Neurol.* 141: 397–426, 1971.

211. HENDRICKSON, A., M. E. WILSON, AND M. J. TOYNE. The distribution of optic nerve fibers in *Macaca mulatta*. *Brain Res.* 23: 425–427, 1970.

212. HENDRY, S. H. C., E. G. JONES, AND J. GRAHAM. Thalamic relay nuclei for cerebellar and certain related fiber systems in the cat. *J. Comp. Neurol.* 185: 679–714, 1979.

213. HERKENHAM, M. The connections of the nucleus reuniens thalami: evidence for a direct thalamo-hippocampal pathway in the rat. *J. Comp. Neurol.* 177: 589–610, 1978.

214. HERKENHAM, M. The afferent and efferent connections of the ventromedial thalamic nucleus in the rat. *J. Comp. Neurol.* 183: 487–517, 1979.

214a. HERKENHAM, M. Laminar organization of thalamic projections to the rat neocortex. *Science* 207: 532–534, 1980.

215. HERRICK, C. J. *An Introduction to Neurology* (2nd ed.). Philadelphia, PA: Saunders, 1918, p. 394.

216. HICKEY, T. L., AND R. W. GUILLERY. An autoradiographic study of retinogeniculate pathways in the cat and the fox. *J. Comp. Neurol.* 156: 239–253, 1974.

217. HOFFMAN, K. P., J. STONE, AND S. M. SHERMAN. Relay of receptive-field properties in dorsal lateral geniculate nucleus of the cat. *J. Neurophysiol.* 35: 518–531, 1972.

218. HOLLÄNDER, H. On the origin of the corticotectal projections in the cat. *Exp. Brain Res.* 21: 433–439, 1974.

219. HOLLÄNDER, H. Projections from the striate cortex to the diencephalon in the squirrel monkey (*Saimiri sciureus*). A light microscopic radioautographic study following intracortical injections of ³H leucine. *J. Comp. Neurol.* 155: 425–440, 1974.

220. HOLLÄNDER, H., AND L. MARTINEZ-MILLAN. Autoradiographic evidence for a topographically organized projection from the striate cortex to the lateral geniculate nucleus in the rhesus monkey. (*Macaca mulatta*). *Brain Res.* 100: 407–411, 1975.

221. HOLLÄNDER, H., AND D. SANIDES. The retinal projection to

the ventral part of the lateral geniculate nucleus. An experimental study with silver-impregnation methods and axoplasmic protein tracing. *Exp. Brain Res.* 26: 329–342, 1976.

222. HOLLÄNDER, H., J. TIETZE, AND H. DISTEL. An autoradiographic study of the subcortical projections of the rabbit striate cortex in the adult and during postnatal development. *J. Comp. Neurol.* 184: 783–794, 1979.

223. HOPKINS, D. A., AND D. G. LAWRENCE. On the absence of a rubrothalamic projection in the monkey with observations on some ascending mesencephalic projections. *J. Comp. Neurol.* 161: 269–293, 1975.

224. HOUSER, C. R., J. E. VAUGHN, R. P. BARBER, AND E. ROBERTS. GABA neurons are the major cell type of the nucleus reticularis thalami. *Brain Res.* 200: 341–354, 1980.

225. HUBEL, D. H. An autoradiographic study of the retino-cortical projections in the tree shrew (*Tupaia glis*) *Brain Res.* 96: 41–50, 1975.

226. HUBEL, D. H., AND T. N. WIESEL. Laminar and columnar distribution of geniculo-cortical fibers in the macaque monkey. *J. Comp. Neurol.* 146: 421–450, 1972.

227. IWAMURA, Y., AND S. INUBUSHI. Regional diversity in excitatory and inhibitory receptive-field organization of cat thalamic ventrobasal neurons. *J. Neurophysiol.* 37: 910–919, 1974.

228. JACOBSON, S., AND J. Q. TROJANOWSKI. Corticothalamic neurons and thalamocortical terminal fields: an investigation in rat using horseradish peroxidase and autoradiography. *Brain Res.* 85: 385–401, 1975.

229. JACKSON, J. C., AND R. M. BENJAMIN. Unit discharges in the mediodorsal nucleus of the rabbit evoked by electrical stimulation of the olfactory bulb. *Brain Res.* 75: 193–201, 1974.

230. JASPER, H. H. Unspecific thalamocortical relations. In: *Handbook of Physiology. Neurophysiology*, edited by J. Field, H. W. Magoun, and V. E. Hall. Washington, DC: Am. Physiol. Soc., 1960, sect. 1, vol. II, chapt. 53, p. 1307–1321.

231. JONES, E. G. The anatomy of extrageniculostriate visual mechanisms. In: *The Neurosciences: Third Study Program*, edited by F. O. Schmitt and F. G. Worden. Cambridge, MA: MIT Press, 1974, p. 215–227.

232. JONES, E. G. Lamination and differential distribution of thalamic afferents within the sensory-motor cortex of the squirrel monkey. *J. Comp. Neurol.* 160: 167–203, 1975.

233. JONES, E. G. Possible determinants of the degree of retrograde neuronal labeling with horseradish peroxidase. *Brain Res.* 85: 249–253, 1975.

234. JONES, E. G. Some aspects of the organization of the thalamic reticular complex. *J. Comp. Neurol.* 162: 285–308, 1975.

235. JONES, E. G. Varieties and distribution of non-pyramidal cells in the somatic sensory cortex of the squirrel monkey. *J. Comp. Neurol.* 160: 205–267, 1975.

236. JONES, E. G. Functional subdivision and synaptic organization of the mammalian thalamus. In: *International Review of Physiology. Neurophysiology IV*, edited by R. Porter. Baltimore, MD: University Park, 1980, p. 173–245.

236a.JONES, E. G. Anatomy of cerebral cortex: columnar input-output organization. In: *Organization of the Cerebral Cortex*, edited by F. O. Schmitt, F. G. Worden, G. Adelman, and S. G. Dennis. Cambridge, MA: MIT Press, 1981, p. 199–235.

237. JONES, E. G. The thalamus. In: *Biochemical Neuroanatomy*, edited by P. Emson. New York: Raven, 1982.

238. JONES, E. G., AND H. BURTON. Cytoarchitecture and somatic sensory connectivity of thalamic nuclei other than the ventrobasal complex in the cat. *J. Comp. Neurol.* 154: 395–432, 1974.

239. JONES, E. G., AND H. BURTON. Areal differences in the laminar distribution of thalamic afferents in cortical fields of the insular, parietal and temporal regions of primates. *J. Comp. Neurol.* 168: 197–247, 1976.

240. JONES, E. G., AND H. BURTON. A projection from the medial pulvinar to the amygdala in primates. *Brain Res.* 104: 142–147, 1976.

241. JONES, E. G., H. BURTON, AND R. PORTER. Commissural and cortico-cortical "columns" in the somatic sensory cortex of primates. *Science* 190: 572–574, 1975.

242. JONES, E. G., H. BURTON, C. B. SAPER, AND L. SWANSON. Midbrain, diencephalic and cortical relationships of the basal nucleus of Meynert and related structures in primates. *J. Comp. Neurol.* 167: 385–419, 1976.

243. JONES, E. G., J. D. COULTER, H. BURTON, AND R. PORTER. Cells of origin and terminal distribution of corticostriatal fibers arising in the sensory-motor cortex of monkeys. *J. Comp. Neurol.* 173: 53–80, 1977.

244. JONES, E. G., J. D. COULTER, AND S. H. C. HENDRY. Intracortical connectivity of architectonic fields in the somatic sensory, motor and parietal cortex of monkeys. *J. Comp. Neurol.* 181: 291–347, 1978.

245. JONES, E. G., AND D. P. FRIEDMAN. Projection pattern of functional components of thalamic ventrobasal complex on monkey somatosensory cortex. *J. Neurophysiol.* 48: 521–544, 1982.

246. JONES, E. G., D. P. FRIEDMAN, AND S. H. C. HENDRY. Thalamic basis of place- and modality-specific columns in monkey somatosensory cortex: a correlative anatomical and physiological study. *J. Neurophysiol.* 48: 545–568, 1982.

247. JONES, E. G., AND R. Y. LEAVITT. Demonstration of thalamo-cortical connectivity in the cat somato-sensory system by retrograde axonal transport of horseradish peroxidase. *Brain Res.* 63: 414–418, 1973.

248. JONES, E. G., AND R. Y. LEAVITT. Retrograde axonal transport and the demonstration of non-specific projections to the cerebral cortex and striatum from thalamic intralaminar nuclei in the rat, cat and monkey. *J. Comp. Neurol.* 154: 349–377, 1974.

249. JONES, E. G., AND T. P. S. POWELL. The projections of the somatic sensory cortex upon the thalamus in the cat. *Brain Res.* 10: 369–391, 1968.

250. JONES, E. G., AND T. P. S. POWELL. The cortical projection of the ventroposterior nucleus of the thalamus in the cat. *Brain Res.* 12: 127–151, 1969.

251. JONES, E. G., AND T. P. S. POWELL. An electron microscopic study of the mode of termination of cortico-thalamic fibres in the thalamic relay nuclei of the cat. *Proc. R. Soc. London Ser. B* 172: 173–185, 1969.

252. JONES, E. G., AND T. P. S. POWELL. Electron microscopy of synaptic glomeruli in the thalamic relay nuclei of the cat. *Proc. R. Soc. London Ser. B* 172: 153–171, 1969.

253. JONES, E. G., AND T. P. S. POWELL. Connexions of the somatic sensory cortex of the rhesus monkey. III. Thalamic connexions. *Brain* 93: 37–56, 1970.

254. JONES, E. G., AND T. P. S. POWELL. Anatomical organization of the somatosensory cortex. In: *Handbook of Sensory Physiology. Somatosensory System*, edited by A. Iggo. New York: Springer-Verlag, 1973, vol. 2, p. 579–620.

255. JONES, E. G., AND A. J. ROCKEL. The synaptic organization in the medial geniculate body of afferent fibres ascending from the inferior colliculus. *Z. Zellforsch. Mikrosk. Anat.* 113: 44–66, 1971.

256. JONES, E. G., AND S. P. WISE. Size, laminar and columnar distribution of efferent cells in the sensory-motor cortex of primates. *J. Comp. Neurol.* 175: 391–438, 1977.

257. JONES, E. G., S. P. WISE, AND J. D. COULTER. Differential thalamic relationships of sensory-motor and parietal cortical fields in monkeys. *J. Comp. Neurol.* 183: 833–882, 1979.

258. JORDAN, H. The structure of the medial geniculate nucleus (MGN): a cyto and myeloarchitectonic study in the squirrel monkey. *J. Comp. Neurol.* 148: 469–479, 1973.

259. JORDAN, H., AND H. HOLLÄNDER. The structure of the ventral part of the lateral geniculate nucleus. A cyto- and myeloarchitectonic study in the cat. *J. Comp. Neurol.* 145: 259–271, 1972.

260. KAAS, J. H., R. W. GUILLERY, AND J. M. ALLMAN. Discontinuities in the dorsal lateral geniculate nucleus corresponding to the optic disc: a comparative study. *J. Comp. Neurol.* 147: 163–179, 1973.

261. KAAS, J. H., R. W. GUILLERY, AND J. M. ALLMAN. Some principles of organization in the dorsal lateral geniculate nucleus. *Brain Behav. Evol.* 6: 253–299, 1973.

262. KAAS, J. H., C.-S. LIN, AND V. A. CASAGRANDE. The relay of

ipsilateral and contralateral retinal input from the lateral geniculate nucleus to striate cortex in the owl monkey: a transneuronal transport study. *Brain Res.* 106: 371–378, 1976.

263. KAAS, J. H., R. J. NELSON, M. SUR, C. H. LIN, AND M. M. MERZENICH. Multiple representations of the body within the primary somatosensory cortex of primates. *Science* 204: 521–523, 1979.

264. KAITZ, S. S., AND R. T. ROBERTSON. Thalamic connections with limbic cortex. II. Corticothalamic projections. *J. Comp. Neurol.* 195: 527–545, 1981.

265. KALIL, K. Projections of the cerebellar and dorsal column nuclei upon the thalamus of the rhesus monkey. *J. Comp. Neurol.* 195: 25–50, 1981.

266. KALIL, R. E., AND R. CHASE. Corticofugal influence on activity of lateral geniculate neurons in the cat. *J. Neurophysiol.* 33: 459–474, 1970.

267. KANASEKI, T., AND J. M. SPRAGUE. Anatomical organization of pretectal nuclei and tectal laminae in the cat. *J. Comp. Neurol.* 158: 319–337, 1974.

268. KASDON, D. L., AND S. JACOBSON. The thalamic afferents to the inferior parietal lobule of the rhesus monkey. *J. Comp. Neurol.* 177: 685–706, 1978.

269. KAWAMURA, S., J. M. SPRAGUE, AND K. NIIMI. Corticofugal projections from the visual cortices to the thalamus, pretectum and superior colliculus in the cat. *J. Comp. Neurol.* 158: 339–362, 1974.

270. KELLY, J. P., AND C. D. GILBERT. The projections of different morphological types of ganglion cells in the cat retina. *J. Comp. Neurol.* 163: 65–80, 1975.

271. KELLY, J. P., AND D. WONG. Laminar connections of the cat's auditory cortex. *Brain Res.* 212: 1–16, 1981.

272. KEMP, J. M., AND T. P. S. POWELL. The cortico-striate projection in the monkey. *Brain* 93: 525–546, 1970.

272a. KENSHALO, D. R., JR., G. J. GIESLER, R. B. LEONARD, AND W. D. WILLIS. Responses of VPLc neurons in the primate thalamus to noxious thermal stimuli. *Soc. Neurosci. Abstr.* 5: 612, 1979.

273. KERR, F. W. L. The ventral spinothalamic tract and other ascending systems of the ventral funiculus of the spinal cord. *J. Comp. Neurol.* 159: 335–356, 1975.

274. KERR, F. W. L., AND H. H. LIPPMAN. The primate spinothalamic tract as demonstrated by anterolateral cordotomy and commissural myelotomy. *Adv. Neurol.* 4: 147–156, 1974.

275. KIEVIT, J., AND H. G. J. M. KUYPERS. Basal forebrain and hypothalamic connections to frontal and parietal cortex in the rhesus monkey. *Science* 187: 660–662, 1975.

276. KILLACKEY, H. P., AND S. LESHIN. The organization of specific thalamocortical projections to the posteromedial barrel subfield of the rat somatic sensory cortex. *Brain Res.* 86: 469–472, 1975.

277. KILPATRICK, I. C., M. S. STARR, A. FLETCHER, T. A. JAMES, AND N. K. MACLEOD. Evidence for a GABAergic nigrothalamic pathway in the rat. I. Behavioral and biochemical studies. *Exp. Brain Res.* 40: 45–54, 1980.

278. KIM, R., K. NAKANO, A. JAYARAMAN, AND M. B. CARPENTER. Projections of the globus pallidus and adjacent structures: an autoradiographic study in the monkey. *J. Comp. Neurol.* 169: 263–290, 1976.

279. KING, G. W. Topology of ascending brainstem projections to nucleus parabrachialis in the cat. *J. Comp. Neurol.* 615–638, 1980.

280. KINSTON, W. J., M. A. VADAS, AND P. O. BISHOP. Multiple projection of the visual field to the medial portion of the dorsal lateral geniculate nucleus and the adjacent nuclei of the thalamus of the cat. *J. Comp. Neurol.* 136: 295–315, 1969.

281. KOSAR, E., AND P. J. HAND. First somatosensory cortical columns and associated neuronal clusters of nucleus ventralis posterolateralis of the cat: an anatomical demonstration. *J. Comp. Neurol.*, 198: 515–539, 1981.

282. KOTCHABHAKDI, N., E. RINVIK, K. YINGCHAREON, AND F. WALBERG. Afferent projections to the thalamus from the perihypoglossal nuclei. *Brain Res.* 187: 457–462, 1980.

283. KRETTEK, J. E., AND J. L. PRICE. The cortical projections of the mediodorsal nucleus and adjacent thalamic nuclei in the rat. *J. Comp. Neurol.* 171: 157–191, 1977.

284. KRETTEK, J. E., AND J. L. PRICE. Projections from the amygdaloid complex to the cerebral cortex and thalamus in the rat and cat. *J. Comp. Neurol.* 172: 687–722, 1977.

285. KUDO, M., AND K. NIIMI. Ascending projections of the inferior colliculus in the cat: an autoradiographic study. *J. Comp. Neurol.* 191: 545–556, 1980.

286. KUMAZAWA, T., E. R. PERL, P. R. BURGESS, AND D. WHITEHORN. Ascending projections from marginal zone (Lamina I) neurons of the spinal dorsal horn. *J. Comp. Neurol.* 162: 1–12, 1975.

287. KÜNZLE, H. Thalamic projections from the precentral motor cortex in *Macaca fascicularis. Brain Res.* 105: 253–267, 1976.

288. KÜNZLE, H. An autoradiographic analysis of the efferent connections from premotor and adjacent prefrontal regions (areas 6 and 9) in *Macaca fascicularis. Brain Behav. Evol.* 15: 185–234, 1978.

289. KUO, J. S., AND M. B. CARPENTER. Organization of pallidothalamic projections in the rhesus monkey. *J. Comp. Neurol.* 151: 201–236, 1973.

290. KUSAMA, T., K. OTANI, AND E. KAWANA. Projections of the motor, somatic sensory, auditory and visual cortices in cats. In: *Progress in Brain Research. Correlative Neurosciences. Fundamental Mechanisms*, edited by T. Tokizane and J. P. Schadé. Amsterdam: Elsevier, 1966, vol. 21A, pt. A, p. 292–322.

291. KUYPERS, H. G. J. M. Discussion. In: *The Thalamus*, edited by D. P. Purpura and M. D. Yahr. New York: Columbia Univ. Press, 1966, p. 122–127.

292. KUYPERS, H. G. J. M., J. KIEVET, AND A. C. GROEN-KLEVANT. Retrograde axonal transport of horseradish peroxidase in the rat's forebrain. *Brain Res.* 67: 211–218, 1974.

292a. KUYPERS, H. G. J. M., AND V. A. MAISKY. Retrograde axonal transport of horesradish peroxidase from spinal cord to brain stem cell groups in the cat. *Neurosci. Lett.* 1: 9–14, 1975.

293. LAEMLE, L. K. Cell populations of the lateral geniculate nucleus of the cat as determined with horesradish peroxidase. *Brain Res.* 100: 650–656, 1975.

294. LANDGREN, S. Thalamic neurons responding to cooling of the cat's tongue. *Acta. Physiol. Scand.* 48: 255–267, 1960.

295. LANDGREN, S., A. NORDWALL, AND C. WENGSTRÖM. The location of the thalamic relay in the spino-cervico-lemniscal path. *Acta. Physiol. Scand.* 65: 165–175, 1965.

296. LANDGREN, S., AND H. SILFVENIUS. Projection to cerebral cortex of group I muscle afferents from the cat's hind limb. *J. Physiol. London* 200: 353–372, 1969.

297. LANDGREN, S., AND H. SILFVENIUS. Nucleus Z, the medullary relay in the projection path to the cerebral cortex of group I muscle afferents from the cat's hindlimb. *J. Physiol. London* 218: 551–571, 1971.

298. LANDGREN, S., H. SILFVENIUS, AND D. WOLSK. Vestibular, cochlear and trigeminal projections to the cortex in the anterior suprasylvian sulcus of the cat. *J. Physiol. London* 191: 561–573, 1967.

299. LANDRY, P., AND M. DESCHÊNES. Intracortical arborizations and receptive fields of identified ventrobasal thalamocortical afferents to the primary somatic sensory cortex in the cat. *J. Comp. Neurol.* 199: 345–372, 1981.

300. LANGE, W., J. A. BÜTTNER-ENNEVER, AND U. BÜTTNER. Vestibular projections to the monkey thalamus: an autoradiographic study. *Brain Res.* 177: 3–18, 1979.

301. LATIES, A. M., AND J. M. SPRAGUE. The projection of optic fibers to the visual centers in the cat. *J. Comp. Neurol.* 127: 35–70, 1966.

302. LEGER, L., K. SAKAI, D. SALVERT, M. TOURET, AND M. JOUVET. Delineation of dorsal lateral geniculate afferents from the cat brain stem as visualized by the horseradish peroxidase technique. *Brain Res.* 93: 490–496, 1975.

303. LEONARD, C. M. The prefrontal cortex in the rat. I. Cortical projection of the mediodorsal nucleus. II. Efferent connections. *Brain Res.* 12: 321–343, 1969.

304. LEONTOVICH, T. A., AND G. P. ZHUKOVA. The specificity of neuronal structure and topography of the reticular formation in the brain and spinal cord of carnivora. *J. Comp. Neurol.* 121: 347–380, 1963.

305. LEVAY, S., AND D. FERSTER. Relay cell classes in the lateral geniculate nucleus of the cat and the effects of visual deprivation. *J. Comp. Neurol.* 172: 563–584, 1977.

306. LEVAY, S., AND C. D. GILBERT. Laminar patterns of geniculocortical projection in the cat. *Brain Res.* 113: 1–19, 1976.

307. LEVAY, S., D. H. HUBEL, AND T. N. WIESEL. The pattern of ocular dominance columns in macaque visual cortex revealed by a reduced silver stain. *J. Comp. Neurol.* 159: 559–576, 1975.

308. LIEBERMAN, A. R., AND K. E. WEBSTER. Presynaptic dendrites and a distinctive class of synaptic vesicle in the rat dorsal lateral geniculate nucleus. *Brain Res.* 42: 196–200, 1972.

309. LIN, C. S., AND J. H. KAAS. Projections from cortical visual areas 17, 18, and MT onto the dorsal lateral geniculate nucleus in owl monkeys. *J. Comp. Neurol.* 173: 457–474, 1977.

310. LIN, C. S., AND J. H. KAAS. The inferior pulvinar complex in owl monkeys: architectonic subdivisions and patterns of input from the superior colliculus and subdivisions of visual cortex. *J. Comp. Neurol.* 187: 655–678, 1979.

311. LIN, C. S., K. E. KRATZ, AND S. M. SHERMAN. Percentage of relay cells in the cat's lateral geniculate nucleus. *Brain Res.* 131: 167–173, 1978.

312. LINDVALL, O., AND A. BJÖRKLUND. The organization of the ascending catecholamine neuron systems in the rat brain as revealed by the glyoxylic acid fluorescence method. *Acta. Physiol. Scand. Suppl.* 412: 1–48, 1974.

313. LINDVALL, O., A. BJÖRKLUND, R. Y. MOORE, AND U. STENEVI. Mesencephalic dopamine neurons projecting to neocortex. *Brain Res.* 81: 325–331, 1974.

314. LOE, P. R., B. L. WHITSEL, D. A. DREYER, AND C. B. METZ. Body representation in ventrobasal thalamus of macaque: a single-unit analysis. *J. Neurophysiol.* 40: 1339–1355, 1977.

315. LOEWY, A. D., J. H. WALLACH, AND S. MCKELLAR. Efferent connections of the ventral medulla oblongata in the rat. *Brain Res. Rev.* 3: 63–80, 1981.

316. LORENTE DE NÓ, R. Cerebral cortex: architectonics, intracortical connections. In: *Physiology of the Nervous System*, edited by J. F. Fulton. London: Oxford, 1949, p. 274–301.

317. LUCIER, G. E., D. C. RÜEGG, AND M. WEISENDANGER. Responses of neurones in motor cortex and in area 3A to controlled stretches of forelimb muscles in cebus monkeys. *J. Physiol. London* 251: 833–853, 1975.

318. LUND, J. S., R. D. LUND, A. E. HENDRICKSON, A. H. BUNT, AND A. F. FUCHS. The origin of efferent pathways from the primary visual cortex, area 17, of the macaque monkey as shown by retrograde transport of horseradish peroxidase. *J. Comp. Neurol.* 164: 287–303, 1975.

319. LUND, R. D., AND K. E. WEBSTER. Thalamic afferents from the dorsal column nuclei. An experimental anatomical study in the rat. *J. Comp. Neurol.* 130: 301–312, 1967.

320. LUND, R. D., AND K. E. WEBSTER. Thalamic afferents from the spinal cord and trigeminal nuclei. An experimental anatomical study in the rat. *J. Comp. Neurol.* 130: 313–328, 1967.

321. LUND-KARLSEN, R., AND F. FONNUM. Evidence for glutamate as a neurotransmitter in the corticofugal fibres to the dorsal lateral geniculate body and the superior colliculus in rats. *Brain Res.* 151: 457–468, 1978.

322. MACCHI, G., A. QUATTRINI, P. CHINZARI, G. MACHESI, AND G. CAPOCCHI. Quantitative data on cell loss and cellular atrophy of intralaminar nuclei following cortical and subcortical lesions. *Brain Res.* 89: 43–59, 1975.

323. MACIEWICZ, R. J. Thalamic afferents to areas 17, 18, and 19 of cat cortex traced with horseradish peroxidase. *Brain Res.* 84: 308–312, 1975.

324. MACLEOD, N. K., T. A. JAMES, I. C. KILPATRICK, AND M. S. STARR. Evidence for a GABAergic nigrothalamic pathway in the rat. II. Electrophysiological studies. *Exp. Brain Res.* 40: 55–61, 1980.

325. MAJOROSSY, K., AND M. RÉTHÉLYI. Synaptic architecture in the medial geniculate body (ventral division). *Exp. Brain Res.* 6: 306–323, 1968.

326. MALPELI, J. G., AND F. H. BAKER. The representation of the visual field in the lateral geniculate nucleus of *Macaca mulatta. J. Comp. Neurol.* 161: 569–594, 1975.

327. MANSON, J. The somatosensory cortical projections of single nerve cells in the thalamus of the cat. *Brain Res.* 12: 489–492, 1969.

328. MASON, C. A., AND J. A. ROBSON. Morphology of retinogeniculate axons in the cat. *Neuroscience* 4: 79–97, 1979.

329. MASON, R. Functional organization in the cat's pulvinar complex. *Exp. Brain Res.* 31: 51–66, 1978.

330. MATHERS, L. H. The synaptic organization of the cortical projection to the pulvinar of the squirrel monkey. *J. Comp. Neurol.* 146: 43–60, 1972.

331. MATHERS, L. H. Ultrastructure of the pulvinar of the squirrel monkey. *J. Comp. Neurol.* 146: 15–42, 1972.

332. MCBRIDE, R. L., AND J. SUTIN. Projections of the locus coeruleus and adjacent pontine tegmentum in the cat. *J. Comp. Neurol.* 165: 265–284, 1975.

333. MCGUINESS, C. M., AND G. M. KRAUTHAMER. The afferent projections to the centrum medianium of the cat as demonstrated by retrograde transport of horseradish peroxidase. *Brain Res.* 184: 255–270, 1980.

333a. MCLEOD, J. G. The representation of the splanchnic afferent pathways in the thalamus of the cat. *J. Physiol. London* 140: 462–478, 1958.

334. MEHLER, W. R. Further notes on the center median nucleus of Luys. In: *The Thalamus*, edited by D. P. Purpura, and M.D. Yahr. New York: Columbia Univ. Press, 1966, p. 109–122.

335. MEHLER, W. R. Some observations on secondary ascending afferent systems in the central nervous system. In: *Pain*, edited by R. S. Knighton and P. R. Dumke. Boston: Little, Brown, 1966, p. 11–32.

336. MEHLER, W. R. Some neurological species differences—a posteriori. *Ann. NY Acad. Sci.* 167: 424–468, 1969.

337. MEHLER, W. R., M. E. FEFERMAN, AND W. J. H. NAUTA. Ascending axon degeneration following anterolateral chordotomy. An experimental study in the monkey. *Brain* 83: 718–750, 1960.

338. MERZENICH, M. M., AND J. F. BRUGGE. Representation of the cochlear partition on the superior temporal plane of the macaque monkey. *Brain Res.* 50: 275–296, 1973.

339. MESULAM, M. M., AND G. W. VAN HOESEN. Acetylcholinesterase-rich projections from the basal forebrain of the rhesus monkey to neocortex. *Brain Res.* 109: 152–157, 1976.

340. MEYER, A. *Historical Aspects of Cerebral Anatomy*. London: Oxford, 1971, p. 230.

341. MEYER, G., AND K. ALBUS. Topography and cortical projections of morphologically identified neurons in the visual thalamus of the cat. *J. Comp. Neurol.* 201: 353–374, 1981.

342. MICKLE, W. A., AND H. W. ADES. A composite sensory projection area in the cerebral cortex of the cat. *Am. J. Physiol.* 170: 682–689, 1952.

343. MICKLE, W. A., AND H. W. ADES. Rostral projection pathway of the vestibular system. *Am. J. Physiol.* 176: 243–246, 1954.

344. MONAKOW, C. VON. Weitere Mittheilungen über durch Exstirpation circumscripter Hirnrindenregionen bedingte Entwicklungshemmungen des Kaninchengehirns. *Arch. Psychiatr. Nervenkr.* 12: 141–156, 535–549, 1882.

345. MONAKOW, C. VON. Experimentelle und pathologisch-anatomische Untersuchungen über die Haubenregion, den Sehügel und Beiträgen zur Kenntniss früh erworbener Gross- und Kleinhirndefecte. *Arch. Psychiatr. Nervenkr.* 27: 1–128, 386–478, 1895.

346. MONTERO, V. M., AND R. W. GUILLERY. Degeneration in the dorsal lateral geniculate nucleus of the rat following interruption of the retinal or cortical connections. *J. Comp. Neurol.* 134: 211–242, 1968.

347. MONTERO, V. M., R. W. GUILLERY, AND C. N. WOOLSEY. Retinotopic organization within the thalamic reticular nucleus demonstrated by a double label autoradiographic technique.

Brain Res. 138: 407–422, 1977.

348. MONTERO, V. M., AND G. L. SCOTT. Synaptic terminals in dorsal lateral geniculate nucleus from neurons of the thalamic reticular nucleus: an electron microscope autoradiographic study. *Soc. Neurosci. Abstr.* 6: 838, 1980.

349. MOONEY, R. D., M. W. DUBIN, AND A. C. RUSOFF. Interneuron circuits in the lateral geniculate nucleus of monocularly deprived cats. *J. Comp. Neurol.* 187: 533–544, 1979.

350. MOORE, R. Y., AND J. M. GOLDBERG. Ascending projections of the inferior colliculus in the cat. *J. Comp. Neurol.* 121: 109–135, 1963.

351. MOREST, D. K. The neuronal architecture of the medial geniculate body of the cat. *J. Anat.* 98: 611–630, 1964.

352. MOREST, D. K. The laminar structure of the medial geniculate body of the cat. *J. Anat.* 99: 143–160, 1965.

353. MOREST, D. K. The lateral tegmental system of the midbrain and the medial geniculate body: study with Golgi and Nauta methods in cat. *J. Anat.* 99: 611–634, 1965.

354. MOREST, D. K. Synaptic relationships of Golgi type II cells in the medial geniculate body of the cat. *J. Comp. Neurol.* 162: 157–193, 1975.

355. MORRISON, A. R., P. J. HAND, AND J. O'DONOGHUE. Contrasting projections from the posterior and ventrobasal thalamic nuclear complexes to the anterior ectosylvian gyrus of the cat. *Brain Res.* 21: 115–121, 1970.

356. MORUZZI, G., AND H. W. MAGOUN. Brain stem reticular formation and activation of the EEG. *Electroencephalogr. Clin. Neurophysiol.* 1: 455–473, 1949.

357. MOUNTCASTLE, V. B. Modality and topographic properties of single neurons of cat's somatic sensory cortex. *J. Neurophysiol.* 20: 408–434, 1957.

358. MOUNTCASTLE, V. B., AND E. HENNEMAN. Pattern of tactile representation in thalamus of cat. *J. Neurophysiol.* 12: 85–100, 1949.

359. MURRAY, M. Degeneration of some intralaminar thalamic nuclei after cortical removals in the cat. *J. Comp. Neurol.* 127: 341–368, 1966.

360. NAUTA, H. J. W., M. B. PRITZ, AND R. J. LASEK. Afferents to the rat caudatoputamen studied with horseradish peroxidase. An evaluation of a retrograde neuronanatomical method. *Brain Res.* 67: 219–238, 1974.

361. NAUTA, W. J. H. An experimental study of the fornix system in the rat. *J. Comp. Neurol.* 104: 247–272, 1976.

362. NAUTA, W. J. H., AND H. G. J. M. KUYPERS. Some ascending pathways in the brain stem reticular formation. In: *Reticular Formation of the Brain*, edited by H. H. Jasper, L. D. Proctor, R. S. Knighton, W. C. Noshay, and R. T. Costello. Boston, MA: Little, Brown, 1958, p. 3–20.

363. NAUTA, W. J. H., AND W. R. MEHLER. Projections of the lentiform nucleus in the monkey. *Brain Res.* 1: 3–42, 1966.

364. NAUTA, W. J. H., AND D. G. WHITLOCK. An anatomical analysis of the nonspecific thalamic projection system. In: *Brain Mechanisms and Consciousness*, edited by J. F. Delafresnaye. Springfield, IL: Thomas, 1954, p. 81–116.

365. NELSON, P. G., AND S. D. ERULKAR. Synaptic mechanisms of excitation and inhibition in the central auditory pathway. *J. Neurophysiol.* 26: 908–923, 1963.

366. NELSON, R. J., AND J. H. KAAS. Connections of the ventroposterior nucleus of the thalamus with the body surface representations in cortical areas 3b and 1 of the cynomologus macque (*Macaca fascicularis*). *J. Comp. Neurol.* 199: 29–64, 1981.

367. NIIMI, K., T. KANASEKI, AND T. TAKIMOTO. The comparative anatomy of the ventral nucleus of the lateral geniculate body in mammals. *J. Comp. Neurol.* 121: 313–323, 1963.

368. NIIMI, K., M. NIIMI, AND Y. OKADA. Thalamic afferents to the limbic cortex in the cat studied with the method of retrograde axonal transport of horesradish peroxidase. *Brain Res.* 145: 225–238, 1978.

369. NISSL, F. Die Kerne des Thalamus beim Kaninchen. *Neurol. Zentralbl.* 8: 549–550, 1889.

370. NISSL, F. Die Grosshirnanteile des Kaninchens. *Arch. Psychiatr. Nervenkr.* 52: 867–953, 1913.

371. NORDEN, J. J., AND J. H. KAAS. The identification of relay neurons in the dorsal lateral geniculate nucleus of monkeys using horseradish peroxidase. *J. Comp. Neurol.* 182: 707–726, 1978.

372. NORGREN, R. Taste pathways to hypothalamus and amygdala. *J. Comp. Neurol.* 166: 17–30, 1976.

373. NORGREN, R., AND C. M. LEONARD. Ascending central gustatory pathways. *J. Comp. Neurol.* 150: 217–237, 1973.

374. OGREN, M. P., AND A. E. HENDRICKSON. The distribution of pulvinar terminals in visual areas 17 and 18 of the monkey. *Brain Res.* 137: 343–350, 1977.

375. OGREN, M. P., AND A. E. HENDRICKSON. The morphology and distribution of striate cortex terminals in the inferior and lateral subdivisions of the *Macaca* monkey pulvinar. *J. Comp. Neurol.* 188: 179–199, 1979.

376. OGREN, M. P., AND A. E. HENDRICKSON. The structural organization of the inferior and lateral subdivisions of the *Macaca* monkey pulvinar. *J. Comp. Neurol.* 188: 147–178, 1979.

377. O'HARA, P. T., AND A. R. LIEBERMAN. Thalamic reticular nucleus: anatomical evidence that cortico-reticular axons establish monosynaptic contact with reticulo-geniculate projection cells. *Brain Res.* 207: 153–156, 1981.

378. O'HARA, P. T., A. J. SEFTON, AND A. R. LIEBERMAN. Mode of termination of afferents from the thalamic reticular nucleus in the dorsal lateral geniculate nucleus of the rat. *Brain Res.* 197: 503–506, 1980.

379. O'LEARY, J. L. A structural analysis of the lateral geniculate nucleus of the cat. *J. Comp. Neurol.* 73: 405–430, 1940.

380. OLIVER, D. L., AND W. C. HALL. Subdivisions of the medial geniculate body in the tree shrew (*Tupaia glis*). *Brain Res.* 86: 217–227, 1975.

381. OLIVER, D. L., AND W. C. HALL. The medial geniculate body of the tree shrew, *Tupaia glis*. I. Cytoarchiture and midbrain connections. *J. Comp. Neurol.* 182: 423–458, 1978.

382. OLIVER, D. L., AND W. C. HALL. The medial geniculate body of the tree shrew, *Tupaia glis*. II. Connections with the neocortex. *J. Comp. Neurol.* 182: 459–494, 1978.

383. OSCARSSON, O., AND I. ROSÉN. Short-latency projections in the cat's cerebral cortex from skin and muscle afferents in the contralateral forelimb. *J. Physiol. London* 182: 164–184, 1966.

384. PALACIOS, J. M., J. K. WAMSLEY, AND M. J. KUHAR. High affinity GABA receptors—autoradiographic localization. *Brain Res.* 222: 285–307, 1981.

385. PALMER, L. A., AND A. C. ROSENQUIST. Visual receptive fields of single striate cortical units projecting to the superior colliculus in the rat. *Brain Res.* 67: 27–42, 1974.

386. PALMER, L. A., A. C. ROSENQUIST, AND R. J. TUSA. The retinotopic organization of lateral suprasylvian visual areas in the cat. *J. Comp. Neurol.* 177: 237–256, 1978.

387. PARTLOW, G. D., M. COLONNIER, AND J. SZABO. Thalamic projections of the superior colliculus in the rhesus monkey, *Macaca mulatta*. A light and electron microscopic study. *J. Comp. Neurol.* 72: 285–318, 1977.

388. PASIK, P., T. PASIK, J. HÁMORI, AND J. SZENTÁGOTHAI. Golgi type II interneurons in the neuronal circuit of the monkey lateral geniculate nucleus. *Exp. Brain Res.* 17: 18–34, 1973.

389. PAUL, R. L., M. MERZENICH, AND H. GOODMAN. Representation of slowly and rapidly adapting cutaneous mechanoreceptors of the hand in Brodmann's areas 3 and 1 of *Macaca mulatta*. *Brain Res.* 36: 229–249, 1972.

391. PEARSON, J. C., AND D. E. HAINES. Somatosensory thalamus of a prosimian primate (*Galago senegalensis*). II. An HRP and Golgi study of the ventral postero-lateral nucleus (VPL). *J. Comp. Neurol.* 190: 559–580, 1980.

392. PECCI SAAVEDRA, J., O. L. VACCAREZZA, AND T. A. READER. Ultrastructure of cells and synapses in the parvocellular portion of the cebus monkey lateral geniculate nucleus. *Z. Zellforsch. Mikrosk. Anat.* 89: 462–477, 1968.

393. PENFIELD, W., AND H. JASPER. *Epilepsy and the Functional Anatomy of the Human Brain.* Boston, MA: Little, Brown, 1954.

393a. PENNY, G. R., K. ITOH, AND I. T. DIAMOND. Thalamic cells of different sizes project to different layers of the somatic cortex. *Soc. Neurosci. Abstr.* 7: 834, 1981.

394. PETERS, A., AND S. L. PALAY. The morphology of laminae A and A1 of the dorsal nucleus of the lateral geniculate body of the cat. *J. Anat.* 100: 451–486, 1966.

395. PETTIGREW, J. D. The importance of early visual experience for neurons of the developing geniculo-striate system. *Invest. Ophthalmol.* 11: 386–393, 1972.

396. PHILLIPS, C. G., T. P. S. POWELL, AND M. WIESENDANGER. Projection from low-threshold muscle afferents of hand and forearm to area 3a of baboon's cortex. *J. Physiol. London* 217: 419–446, 1971.

397. PINES, J. L. Zur Architectonik des Thalamus opticus beim Halbaffen (*Lemur catta*). *J. Psychol. Neurol. Leipzig* 33: 31–72, 1927.

398. POGGIO, G. F., AND V.B. MOUNTCASTLE. A study of the functional contributions of the lemniscal and spinothalamic systems to somatic sensibility. Central nervous mechanisms in pain. *Bull. Johns Hopkins Hosp.* 106: 266–316, 1960.

399. POGGIO, G. F., AND V. B. MOUNTCASTLE. The functional properties of ventrobasal thalamic neurons studied in unanesthetized monkeys. *J. Neurophysiol.* 26: 775–806, 1963.

400. POWELL, T. P. S., AND W. M. COWAN. The connexions of the midline and intralaminar nuclei of the thalamus of the rat. *J. Anat.* 88: 307–319, 1954.

401. POWELL, T. P. S., AND W. M. COWAN. A study of thalamo-striate relations in the monkey. *Brain* 79: 364–390, 1956.

402. POWELL, T. P. S., AND W. M. COWAN. The interpretation of the degenerative changes in the intralaminar nuclei of the thalamus. *J. Neurol. Neurosurg. Psychiatry* 30: 140–153, 1967.

403. POWELL, T. P. S., AND V. B. MOUNTCASTLE. Some aspects of the functional organization of the cortex of the postcentral gyrus of the monkey: a correlation of findings obtained in a single unit analysis with cytoarchitecture. *Bull. Johns Hopkins Hosp.* 105: 133–162, 1959.

403a.PRICE, D. D., R. DUBNER, AND J. W. HU. Trigeminothalamic neurons in nucleus caudalis responsive to tactile, thermal, and nociceptive stimulation of monkey's face. *J. Neurophysiol.* 39: 936–953, 1976.

404. PURPURA, D. P. Intracellular studies of synaptic organization in the mammalian brain. In: *Structure and Function of Synapses*, edited by G. D. Pappas and D. P. Purpura. New York: Raven, 1972, p. 257–302.

405. PURPURA, D. P., J. G. MCMURTRY, AND K. MAEKAWA. Synaptic events in ventrolateral thalamic neurons during suppression of recruiting responses by brain stem reticular stimulation. *Brain Res.* 1: 63–76, 1966.

406. RACZKOWSKI, D., AND I. T. DIAMOND. Projections from the superior colliculus and the neocortex to the pulvinar nucleus in *Galago*. *J. Comp. Neurol.* 200: 231–254, 1981.

407. RACZKOWSKI, D., AND A. C. ROSENQUIST. Connections of the parvocellular C laminae of the dorsal lateral geniculate nucleus with the visual cortex in the cat. *Brain Res.* 199: 447–451, 1980.

408. RACZKOWSKI, D., AND A. C. ROSENQUIST. Retinotopic organization in the cat lateral posterior-pulvinar complex. *Brain Res.* 221: 185–191, 1981.

409. RALSTON, H. J., III. The synaptic organization of lemniscal projections to the ventrobasal thalamus of the cat. *Brain Res.* 14: 99–115, 1969.

410. RALSTON, H. J., III. Evidence for presynaptic dendrites and a proposal for their mechanism of action. *Nature London* 230: 585–587, 1971.

411. RALSTON, H. J., III, AND K. L. CHOW. Synaptic reorganization in the degenerating lateral geniculate nucleus of the rabbit. *J. Comp. Neurol.* 147: 321–350, 1973.

412. RALSTON, H. J., III, AND M. M. HERMAN. The fine structure of neurons and synapses in the ventrobasal thalamus of the cat. *Brain Res.* 14: 77–97, 1969.

413. RAMÓN Y CAJAL, S. *Histologie du Système Nerveux de l'Homme et des Vertébrés* (transl. by S. Azoulay). Paris: Maloine, 1909–1911.

414. RAMÓN-MOLINER, E. Specialized and generalized dendritic

patterns. In: *Golgi Centennial Symposium: Perspectives in Neurobiology*, edited by M. Santini. New York: Raven, 1975, p. 87–100.

415. RAMÓN-MOLINER, E., AND W. J. H. NAUTA. The isodendritic core of the brain stem. *J. Comp. Neurol.* 126: 311–335, 1966.

416. RAYMOND, J., D. DEMÊMES, AND R. MARTY. Voies et projections vestibulaires ascendantes émanant des noyaux primaires: étude radioautographique. *Brain Res.* 111: 1–12, 1976.

417. REZAK, M., AND L. A. BENEVENTO. A comparison of the organization of the projections of the dorsal lateral geniculate nucleus, the inferior pulvinar and adjacent lateral pulvinar to primary visual cortex (area 17) in the macaque monkey. *Brain Res.* 167: 19–40, 1979.

418. RICHARDO, J. A. Efferent connections of the subthalamic region in the rat. I. The subthalamic nucleus of Luys. *Brain Res.* 202: 257–272, 1980.

419. RINVIK, E. The corticothalamic projection from the pericruciate and coronal gyri in the cat. An experimental study with silver-impregnation methods. *Brain Res.* 10: 79–119, 1968.

420. RINVIK, E. The corticothalamic projection from the second somatosensory cortical area in the cat. An experimental study with silver impregnation methods. *Exp. Brain Res.* 5: 153–172, 1968.

421. RINVIK, E. Organization of thalamic connections from motor and somatosensory cortical areas in the cat. In: *Corticothalamic Projections and Sensorimotor Activities*, edited by T. Frigyesi, E. Rinvik, and M. D. Yahr. New York: Raven, 1972, p. 57–90.

422. RINVIK, E. Demonstration of nigrothalamic connections in the cat by retrograde axonal transport of horseradish peroxidase. *Brain Res.* 90: 313–318, 1975.

423. RIOCH, D. McK. Studies on the diencephalon of carnivora. I. Nuclear configurations of the thalamus, epithalamus and hypothalamus of dog and cat. *J. Comp. Neurol.* 49: 1–120, 1979.

424. ROBERTS, T. S., AND K. AKERT. Insular and opercular cortex and its thalamic projection in *Macaca mulatta*. *Schweiz. Arch. Neurol. Neurochir. Psychiatr.* 92: 1–43, 1963.

425. ROBERTSON, R. T., AND T. J. CUNNINGHAM. Organization of corticothalamic projections from parietal cortex in cat. *J. Comp. Neurol.* 199: 569–586, 1981.

426. ROBERTSON, R. T., AND S. S. KAITZ. Thalamic connections with limbic cortex. I. Thalamocortical projections. *J. Comp. Neurol.* 195: 501–527, 1981.

427. ROBERTSON, R. T., AND E. RINVIK. The corticothalamic projections from parietal regions of the cerebral cortex. Experimental degeneration studies in the cat. *Brain Res.* 51: 61–79, 1973.

428. ROBSON, J. A., AND W. C. HALL. Connections of layer VI in striate cortex of the grey squirrel (*Sciurus carolinensis*). *Brain Res.* 93: 133–139, 1975.

429. ROBSON, J. A., AND W. C. HALL. The organization of the pulvinar in the grey squirrel (*Sciurus carolinensis*). I. Cytoarchitecture and connections. *J. Comp. Neurol.* 173: 355–388, 1977.

430. ROCKEL, A. J., C. J. HEATH, AND E. G. JONES. Afferent connections to the diencephalon in the marsupial phalanger and the question of sensory convergence in the "posterior group" of the thalamus. *J. Comp. Neurol.* 145: 105–129, 1972.

431. ROMAGNANO, M. A., AND R. J. MACIEWICZ. Peroxidase labeling of motor cortex neurons projecting to ventrolateral nucleus in the cat. *Brain Res.* 83: 469–473, 1975.

432. ROSE, J. E. The ontogenetic development of the rabbit's diencephalon. *J. Comp. Neurol.* 77: 61–129, 1942.

433. ROSE, J. E. The thalamus of the sheep: cellular and fibrous structure and comparison with pig, rabbit and cat. *J. Comp. Neurol.* 77: 469–523, 1942.

434. ROSE, J. E. The cortical connections of the reticular complex of the thalamus. *Res. Publ. Assoc. Res. Nerv. Ment. Dis.* 30: 452–479, 1952.

435. ROSE, J. E., AND V. B. MOUNTCASTLE. The thalamic tactile region in rabbit and cat. *J. Comp. Neurol.* 97: 441–489, 1952.

436. ROSE, J. E., AND V. B. MOUNTCASTLE. Activity of single

neurons in the tactile thalamic region of the cat in response to a transient peripheral stimulus. *Bull. Johns Hopkins Hosp.* 94: 238–282, 1954.

437. ROSE, J. E., AND V. B. MOUNTCASTLE. Touch and kinesthesis. In: *Handbook of Physiology. Neurophysiology*, edited by J. Field, H. W. Magoun, and V. E. Hall. Washington DC: Am. Physiol. Soc., 1959, sect. 1, vol. I, chapt. 17, p. 387–429.

438. ROSE, J. E., AND C. N. WOOLSEY. A study of thalamocortical relations in the rabbit. *Bull. Johns Hopkins Hosp.* 73: 65–128, 1943.

439. ROSE, J. E., AND C. N.WOOLSEY. The orbitofrontal cortex and its connections with the mediodorsal nucleus in rabbit, sheep and cat. *Res. Publ. Assoc. Res. Nerv. Ment. Dis.* 27: 210–232, 1948.

440. ROSE, J. E., AND C. N. WOOLSEY. Structure and relations of limbic cortex and anterior thalamic nuclei in rabbit and cat. *J. Comp. Neurol.* 89: 279–347, 1948.

441. ROSE, J. E., AND C. N. WOOLSEY. Organization of the mammalian thalamus and its relationships to the cerebral cortex. *Electroencephalogr. Clin. Neurophysiol.* 1: 391–403, 1949.

442. ROSE, J. E., AND C. N. WOOLSEY. The relations of thalamic connections, cellular structure and evocable electrical activity in the auditory region of the cat. *J. Comp. Neurol.* 91: 441–466, 1949.

443. ROSE, J. E., AND C. N. WOOLSEY. Cortical connections and functional organization of the thalamic auditory system of the cat. In: *Biological and Biochemical Bases of Behavior*, edited by H. F. Harlow and C. N. Woolsey. Madison: Univ. of Wisconsin Press, 1958, p. 127–150.

444. ROSE, M. Das Zwischenhirn des Kaninchens. *Mem. Acad. Pol. Sci. Lett. Ser. B* 8: 1–108, 1935.

445. ROSENQUIST, A. C., S. B. EDWARDS, AND L. A. PALMER. An autoradiographic study of the projections of the dorsal lateral geniculate nucleus and the posterior nucleus in the cat. *Brain Res.* 80: 71–93, 1974.

445a.ROTTER, A., N. J. M. BIRDSALL, A. S. V. BURGEN, P. M. FIELD, E. C. HULME, AND G. RAISMAN. Muscarinic receptors in the central nervous system of the rat. I. Technique for autoradiographic localization of the binding of [³H]propylbenzilylcholine mustard and its distribution in the forebrain. *Brain Res. Rev.* 1: 141–165, 1979.

446. ROWE, M. J., AND B. J. SESSLE. Somatic afferent input to posterior thalamic neurones and their axon projection to the cerebral cortex in the cat. *J. Physiol. London* 196: 19–35, 1968.

447. RYUGO, D. K., AND H. P. KILLACKEY. Differential telencephalic projections of the medial and ventral divisions of the medial geniculate body of the rat. *Brain Res.* 82: 173–177, 1974.

448. SAKATA, H., T. ISHIJIMA, AND Y. TOYODA. Single unit studies on ventrolateral nucleus of the thalamus in the cat: its relation to the cerebellum, motor cortex and basal ganglia. *Jpn. J. Physiol.* 16: 42–60, 1966.

449. SANDERSON, K. J. The projection of the visual field to the lateral geniculate and medial interlaminar nuclei in the cat. *J. Comp. Neurol.* 143: 101–108, 1971.

450. SAPER, C. B., AND A. F. LOEWY. Efferent connections of the parabrachial nucleus in the rat. *Brain Res.* 197: 291–318, 1980.

451. SAPORTA, S., AND L. KRUGER. The organization of thalamocortical relay neurons in the rat ventrobasal complex studied by the retrograde transport of horseradish peroxidase. *J. Comp. Neurol.* 174: 187–208, 1977.

452. SAPORTA, S., AND L. KRUGER. The organization of projections to selected points of somatosensory cortex from the cat ventrobasal complex. *Brain Res.* 178: 275–298, 1979.

453. SASAKI, K., Y. MATSUDA, S. KAWAGUCHI, AND N. MIZUNO. On the cerebellothalamo-cerebral pathway for the parietal cortex. *Exp. Brain Res.* 16: 89–103, 1972.

454. SASAKI, K., Y. MATSUDA, H. OKA, AND N. MIZUNO. Thalamocortical projections for recruiting responses and spindling-like responses in the parietal cortex. *Exp. Brain Res.* 22: 87–96, 1975.

455. SASAKI, K., T. SHIMONO, H. OKA, T. YAMAMOTO, AND Y. MATSUDA. Effects of stimulation of the midbrain reticular formation upon thalamocortical neurones responsible for cortical recruiting responses. *Exp. Brain Res.* 26: 261–273, 1976.

456. SCHEIBEL, M. E., AND A. B. SCHEIBEL. The organization of the nucleus reticularis thalami: a Golgi study. *Brain Res.* 1: 43–62, 1966.

457. SCHEIBEL, M. E., AND A. B. SCHEIBEL. Patterns of organization in specific and nonspecific thalamic fields. In: *The Thalamus*, edited by D. P. Purpura, and M. D. Yahr. New York: Columbia Univ. Press, 1966, p. 13–46.

458. SCHILLER, P. H., AND J. G. MALPELI. Functional specificity of lateral geniculate nucleus laminae of the rhesus monkey. *J. Neurophysiol.* 41: 788–797, 1978.

459. SCHLAG, J., I. LETHINEN, AND M. SCHLAG-REY. Neuronal activity before and during eye movements in thalamic internal medullary lamina of the cat. *J. Neurophysiol.* 37: 982–995, 1974.

460. SCHLAG, J., AND M. SCHLAG-REY. Induction of oculomotor responses from thalamic internal medullary lamina in the cat. *Exp. Neurol.* 33: 498–508, 1971.

461. SCHLAG, J., AND M. WASZAK. Characteristics of unit responses in nucleus reticularis thalami. *Brain Res.* 21: 286–288, 1970.

462. SCHMIELAU, F., AND W. SINGER. The role of visual cortex for binocular interactions in the cat lateral geniculate nucleus. *Brain Res.* 120: 359–361, 1977.

463. SCHNEIDER, G. E. Two visual systems. *Science* 163: 895–902, 1969.

464. SCHWARZ, D. W. F., AND J. M. FREDRICKSON. Rhesus monkey vestibular cortex: a bimodal primary projection field. *Science* 172: 280–281, 1971.

465. SCOLLO-LAVIZZARI, G. S., AND K. AKERT. Cortical area 8 and its thalamic projection in *Macaca mulatta. J. Comp. Neurol.* 121: 259–269, 1963.

466. SEFTON, A. J., AND W. BURKE. Reverberatory inhibitory circuits in the lateral geniculate nucleus of the rat. *Nature London* 205: 1325–1326, 1965.

467. SHANKS, M. F., AND T. P. S. POWELL. An electron microscopic study of the termination of thalamocortical fibres in areas 3b, 1 and 2 of the somatic sensory cortex in the monkey. *Brain Res.* 218: 35–48, 1981.

468. SHATZ, C. J., S. LINDSTRÖM, AND T. N. WIESEL. The distribution of afferents representing the right and left eyes in the cat's visual cortex. *Brain Res.* 131: 103–116, 1972.

469. SHERMAN, S. M., J. R. WILSON, J. H. KAAS, AND S. V. WEBB. X- and Y-cells in the dorsal lateral geniculate nucleus of the owl monkey (*Aotus trivirgatus*). *Science* 192: 475–477, 1976.

470. SHIMAZU, H., N. YANAGISAWA, AND B. GAROUTTE. Corticopyramidal influences on thalamic somatosensory transmission in the cat. *Jpn. J. Physiol.* 15: 101–124, 1965.

471. SHIPLEY, M. T., AND K. E. SØRENSON. On the laminar organization of the anterior thalamus projections to the presubiculum in the guinea pig. *Brain Res.* 86: 473–477, 1975.

472. SINGER, W. Control of thalamic transmission by corticofugal and ascending reticular pathways in the visual system. *Physiol. Rev.* 57: 386–420, 1977.

473. SMITH, R. L. The ascending fiber projections from the principal sensory trigeminal nucleus in the rat. *J. Comp. Neurol.* 148: 423–445, 1973.

474. SMITH, R. L. Axonal projections and connections of the principal sensory trigeminal nucleus in the monkey. *J. Comp. Neurol.* 163: 347–375, 1975.

475. SOUSA-PINTO, A. Cortical projections of the medial geniculate body in the cat. *Ergeb. Anat. Entwicklungsgesch.* 48: 1–40, 1973.

476. SPATZ, W. B. Thalamic and other subcortical projections to area MT (visual area of superior temporal sulcus) in the marmoset *Callithrix jacchus. Brain Res.* 99: 129–134, 1975.

477. SPATZ, W. B., AND G. ERDMANN. Striate cortex projections to the lateral geniculate and other thalamic nuclei: a study using degeneration and autoradiographic tracing methods in the marmoset (*Callithrix jacchus*). *Brain Res.* 82: 91–108, 1974.

478. SPATZ, W. B., J. TIGGES, AND M. TIGGES. Subcortical projections, cortical associations, and some intrinsic interlaminar

connections of the striate cortex in the squirrel monkey (*Saimiri*). *J. Comp. Neurol.* 140: 155–174, 1970.

479. SPRAGUE, J. M., J. LEVY, A. DIBERARDINO, AND G. BERLUCCHI. Visual cortical areas mediating form discrimination in the cat. *J. Comp. Neurol.* 172: 441–488, 1977.

480. SPREAFICO, R., N. L. HAYES, AND A. RUSTIONI. Thalamic projections to the primary and secondary somato-sensory cortices in cat: single and double retrograde tracer studies. *J. Comp. Neurol.* 203: 67–90, 1981.

481. STANTON, G. B. Topographical organization of ascending cerebellar projections from the dentate and interposed nuclei in *Macaca mulatta*. An anterograde degeneration study. *J. Comp. Neurol.* 190: 699–733, 1980.

482. STERIADE, M., G. OAKSON, AND A. DIALLO. Reticular influences on lateralis posterior thalamic neurons. *Brain Res.* 131: 55–71, 1977.

483. STERLING, P., AND T. L. DAVIS. Neurons in cat lateral geniculate nucleus that concentrate [³H]-gamma-aminobutyric acid (GABA). *J. Comp. Neurol.* 192: 737–749, 1980.

484. STONE, J., AND B. DREHER. Projection of X- and Y-cells of the cat's lateral geniculate nucleus to areas 17 and 18 of visual cortex. *J. Neurophysiol.* 36: 551–567, 1973.

485. STREIT, P. Selective retrograde labeling indicating the trasmitter of neuronal pathways. *J. Comp. Neurol.* 191: 429–464, 1980.

486. STRICK, P. L. Light microscopic analysis of the cortical projection of the thalamic ventrolateral nucleus in the cat. *Brain Res.* 55: 1–24, 1975.

487. STRICK, P. L. Multiple sources of thalamic input to the primate motor cortex. *Brain Res.* 88: 372–377, 1975.

488. STRICK, P. L. Anatomical analysis of ventrolateral thalamic input to primate motor cortex. *J. Neurophysiol.* 39: 1020–1031, 1976.

489. SUGITANI, M. Electrophysiological and sensory properties of the thalamic reticular neurons related to somatic sensation in rats. *J. Physiol. London* 290: 79–95, 1979.

490. SUMITOMO, I., M. NAKAMURA, AND K. IWANA. Location and function of the so-called interneurons of rat lateral geniculate body. *Exp. Neurol.* 51: 110–173, 1976.

491. SWANSON, L. W. An autoradiographic study of the efferent connections of the preoptic region in the rat. *J. Comp. Neurol.* 167: 227–256, 1976.

492. SWANSON, L. W., AND W. M. COWAN. A note on the connections and development of the nucleus accumbens. *Brain Res.* 92: 324–330, 1975.

493. SWANSON, L. W., AND W. M. COWAN. An autoradiographic study of the organization of the efferent connections of the hippocampal formation in the rat. *J. Comp. Neurol.* 172: 49–84, 1977.

494. SWANSON, L. W., AND W. M. COWAN. The connections of the septal region in the rat. *J. Comp. Neurol.* 186: 621–656, 1979.

495. SWANSON, L. W., W. M. COWAN, AND E. G. JONES. An autoradiographic study of the efferent connections of the ventral lateral geniculate nucleus in the albino rat and the cat. *J. Comp. Neurol.* 156: 143–163, 1974.

496. SWANSON, L. W., AND B. K. HARTMAN. The central adrenergic system. An immunofluorescence study of the location of cell bodies and their efferent connections in the rat utilizing dopamine-beta-hydroxylase as a marker. *J. Comp. Neurol.* 163: 467–505, 1975.

497. SYMONDS, L. L., A. C. ROSENQUIST, S. B. EDWARDS, AND L. A. PALMER. Projections of the pulvinar–lateral posterior complex to visual cortical areas in the cat. *Neuroscience* 6: 1995–2020, 1981.

498. SZENTÁGOTHAI, J. The structure of the synapse in the lateral geniculate body. *Acta Anat.* 55: 166–185, 1963.

499. SZENTÁGOTHAI, J. Models of specific neuron arrays in thalamic relay nuclei. *Acta Morphol. Acad. Sci. Hung.* 15: 113–124, 1967.

500. SZENTÁGOTHAI, J. Neuronal and synaptic architecture of the lateral geniculate body. In: *Handbook of Sensory Physiology. Visual Centers of the Brain*, edited by R. Jung. New York: Springer-Verlag, 1973, vol. 7, pt. 3B, p. 141–176.

501. SZENTÁGOTHAI, J., J. HÁMORI, AND T. TÖMBÖL. Degeneration and electron microscope analysis of the synaptic glomeruli in the lateral geniculate body. *Exp. Brain Res.* 2: 283–301, 1966.

502. TANJI, D. G., S. P. WISE, R. W. DYKES, AND E. G. JONES. Cytoarchitecture and thalamic connectivity of third somatosensory area of cat cerebral cortex. *J. Neurophysiol.* 41: 268–284, 1978.

503. TARLOV, E. The rostral projections of the primate vestibular nuclei: an experimental study in macaque, baboon and chimpanzee. *J. Comp. Neurol.* 135: 27–56, 1969.

504. TARLOV, E. C., AND R. Y. MOORE. The tecto-thalamic connections in the brain of the rabbit. *J. Comp. Neurol.* 126: 403–435, 1966.

505. TELLO, F. Disposición microscopica y estructura del cuerpo geniculado externo. *Trab. Lab. Invest. Biol. Univ. Madrid* 3: 39–62, 1904.

506. THACH, W. T., AND E. G. JONES. The cerebellar dentatothalamic connection: terminal field, lamellae, rods and somatotopy. *Brain Res.* 169: 168–172, 1979.

507. THOMPSON, R. F. *Foundations of Physiological Psychology.* New York: Harper & Row, 1967, p. 474–528.

508. THOMPSON, R. F., R. M. JOHNSON, AND J. J. HOOPES. Organization of auditory, somatic sensory, and visual projections to association fields of cerebral cortex in the cat. *J. Neurophysiol.* 26: 343–364, 1963.

509. TOMASULO, K. C., AND R. EMMERS. Spinal afferents to SI and SII of the rat thalamus. *Exp. Neurol.* 26: 482–497, 1970.

510. TÖMBÖL, T. Short neurons and their synaptic relations in the specific thalamic nuclei. *Brain Res.* 3: 307–326, 1967.

511. TÖMBÖL, T., F. HAJDU, AND G. SOMOGYI. Identification of the Golgi picture of the layer VI cortico-geniculate projection neurons. *Exp. Brain Res.* 24: 107–110, 1975.

512. TORREALBA, F., G. D. PARTLOW, AND R. W. GUILLERY. Organization of the projection from the superior colliculus to the dorsal lateral geniculate nucleus of the cat. *Neuroscience* 6: 1341–1360, 1981.

513. TRACEY, D. J., C. ASANUMA, E. G. JONES, AND R. PORTER. Thalamic relay to motor cortex: afferent pathways from brain stem, cerebellum, and spinal cord in monkeys. *J. Neurophysiol.* 44: 532–554, 1980.

514. TREVINO, D. L., AND E. CARSTENS. Confirmation of the location of spinothalamic neurons in cat and monkey by the retrograde transport of horseradish peroxidase. *Brain Res.* 98: 177–182, 1975.

515. TROJANOWSKI, J. Q., AND S. JACOBSON. Medial pulvinar afferents to frontal eye fields in rhesus monkey demonstrated by horseradish peroxidase. *Brain Res.* 80: 395–411, 1974.

516. TROJANOWSKI, J. Q., AND S. JACOBSON. A combined horseradish peroxidase–autoradiographic investigation of reciprocal connections between superior temporal gyrus and pulvinar in squirrel monkey. *Brain Res.* 85: 347–353, 1975.

517. UPDYKE, B. V. The patterns of projection of cortical areas 17, 18 and 19 onto the laminae of the dorsal lateral geniculate nucleus in the cat. *J. Comp. Neurol.* 163: 377–395, 1975.

518. UPDYKE, B. V. Topographic organization of the projections from cortical areas 17, 18 and 19 onto the thalamus, pretectum and superior colliculus in the cat. *J. Comp. Neurol.* 173: 81–122, 1977.

519. UPDYKE, B. V. A Golgi study of the class V cell in the visual thalamus of the cat. *J. Comp. Neurol.* 186: 603–620, 1979.

520. UPDYKE, B. V. Projections from visual areas of the middle suprasylvian sulcus onto the lateral posterior complex and adjacent thalamic nuclei in cat. *J. Comp. Neurol.* 201: 477–506, 1981.

521. VALENSTEIN, E. S., AND W. J. H. NAUTA. A comparison of the distribution of the fornix system in the rat, guinea pig, cat and monkey. *J. Comp. Neurol.* 113: 337–364, 1959.

522. VAN DER LOOS, H. Barreloids in mouse somatosensory thalamus. *Neurosci. Lett.* 2: 1–6, 1976.

523. VOGT, C. La myéloarchitecture du thalamus du cercopithéque. *J. Psychol. Neurol. Leipzig* 12: 285–324, 1909.

524. WALKER, A. E. *The Primate Thalamus.* Chicago: Univ. of

Chicago Press, 1938, p. 321.

525. WALZL, E. M., AND V. B. MOUNTCASTLE. Projection of vestibular nerve to cerebral cortex of cat (Abstract). *Am. J. Physiol.* 159: 595, 1949.

526. WATANABE, T., K. YANAGISAWA, J. KANZAKI, AND Y. KATSUKI. Cortical efferent flow influencing unit responses of medial geniculate body to sound stimulation. *Exp. Brain Res.* 2: 302–317, 1966.

527. WEBER, J. T., AND J. K. HARTING. The efferent projections of the pretectal complex: an autoradiographic and horseradish peroxidase analysis. *Brain Res.* 194: 1–28, 1980.

528. WEBSTER, K. E. The cortico-striatal projection in the cat. *J. Anat.* 99: 329–337, 1965.

529. WEISKRANTZ, L. The interaction between occipital and temporal cortex in vision: an overview. In: *The Neurosciences: Third Study Program,* edited by F. O. Schmitt, and F. G. Worden. Cambridge, MA: MIT Press, 1974, p. 189–204.

530. WELKER, C. Receptive fields of barrels in the somatosensory neocortex of the rat. *J. Comp. Neurol.* 166: 173–189, 1976.

531. WELKER, W. I. Principles of organization of the ventrobasal complex in mammals. *Brain Behav. Evol.* 7: 253–336, 1974.

532. WERNER, G., AND B. L. WHITSEL. Topology of the body representation in somatosensory area I of primates. *J. Neurophysiol.* 31: 856–869, 1968.

533. WHITLOCK, D. G., AND E. R. PERL. Afferent projections through ventrolateral funiculi to thalamus of cat. *J. Neurophysiol.* 22: 133–148, 1959.

534. WHITSEL, B. L., L. M. PETRUCELLI, AND G. WERNER. Symmetry and connectivity in the map of the body surface in somatosensory area II of primates. *J. Neurophysiol.* 32: 170–183, 1969.

535. WIESEL, T. N., D. H. HUBEL, AND D. LAM. Autoradiographic demonstration of ocular-dominance columns in the monkey striate cortex by means of transneuronal transport. *Brain Res.* 79: 273–279, 1974.

536. WILLIS, W. D., R. B. LEONARD, AND D. R. KENSHALO, JR. Spinothalamic tract neurons in the substantia gelatinosa. *Science* 202: 986–988, 1978.

537. WILLIS, W. D., D. L. TREVINO, J. D. COULTER, AND R. A. MAUNZ. Responses of primate spinothalamic tract neurons to natural stimulation of the hindlimb. *J. Neurophysiol.* 37: 358–372, 1974.

538. WILSON, M. E., AND B. G. CRAGG. Projections from the medial geniculate body to the cerebral cortex in the cat. *Brain Res.* 13: 462–475, 1969.

539. WILSON, P. D., J. PECCI-SAAVEDRA, AND R. W. DOTY. Mesencephalic control of lateral geniculate nucleus in primates. II. Effective loci. *Exp. Brain Res.* 18: 204–213, 1973.

540. WILSON, P. D., M. H. ROWE, AND J. STONE. Properties of relay cells in cat's lateral geniculate nucleus: a comparison of W-cells with X- and Y-cells. *J. Neurophysiol.* 39: 1193–1209, 1976.

541. WILSON, P. D., AND J. STONE. Evidence of W-cell input to the cat's visual cortex via the C laminae of the lateral geniculate nucleus. *Brain Res.* 92: 472–478, 1975.

542. WINER, J. A., I. T. DIAMOND, AND D. RACZKOWSKI. Subdivisions of the auditory cortex of the cat: the retrograde transport of horseradish peroxidase to the medial geniculate body and posterior thalamic nuclei. *J. Comp. Neurol.* 176: 387–418, 1977.

543. WINFIELD, D. A. The synaptic organization of glomeruli in the magnocellular and parvocellular laminae of the lateral geniculate nucleus in the monkey. *Brain Res.* 198: 55–62, 1980.

544. WINFIELD, D. A., K. C. GATTER, AND T. P. S. POWELL. An electron microscopic study of retrograde and orthograde transport of horseradish peroxidase to the lateral geniculate nucleus of the monkey. *Brain Res.* 92: 462–467, 1975.

545. WISE, S. P. The laminar organization of certain afferent and efferent fiber systems in the rat somatosensory cortex. *Brain Res.* 90: 139–142, 1975.

546. WISE, S. P., S. H. C. HENDRY, AND E. G. JONES. Prenatal development of sensorimotor cortical projections in cats. *Brain Res.* 138: 538–544, 1977.

547. WISE, S. P., AND E. G. JONES. Cells of origin and terminal distribution of descending projections of the rat somatic sensory cortex. *J. Comp. Neurol.* 175: 129–157, 1977.

548. WISE, S. P., AND E. G. JONES. Topographic and columnar distribution of the corticotectal projection from the rat somatic sensory cortex. *Brain Res.* 133: 223–235, 1977.

549. WISE, S. P., AND E. G. JONES. Developmental studies of thalamocortical and commissural connections of the rat somatic sensory cortex. *J. Comp. Neurol.* 178: 187–208, 1978.

550. WONG-RILEY, M. T. T. Neuronal and synaptic organization of the normal dorsal lateral geniculate nucleus of the squirrel monkey, *Saimiri sciureus. J. Comp. Neurol.* 144: 25–59, 1972.

551. WONG-RILEY, M. T. T. Demonstration of geniculocortical and callosal projection neurons in the squirrel monkey by means of retrograde axonal transport of horseradish peroxidase. *Brain Res.* 79: 267–272, 1974.

552. WOOLSEY, C. N. Organization of somatic sensory and motor areas of the cerebral cortex. In: *Biological and Biochemical Bases of Behavior,* edited by H. F. Harlow, and C. N. Woolsey. Madison: Univ. of Wisconsin Press, 1958, p. 63–81.

553. WOOLSEY, C. N. Electrophysiological studies on thalamocortical relations in the auditory system. In: *Unfinished Tasks in the Behavioral Sciences,* edited by A. Abrams, H. H. Garner, and J. E. Toman. Baltimore: Williams & Wilkins, 1964, p. 45–57.

554. WYSS, J. M., L. W. SWANSON, AND W. M. COWAN. A study of subcortical afferents to the hippocampal formation in the rat. *Neuroscience* 4: 463–476, 1979.

555. YINGLING, C. D., AND J. E. SKINNER. Selective regulation of thalamic sensory relay nuclei by nucleus reticularis thalami. *Electroencephalogr. Clin. Neurophysiol.* 41: 476–482, 1976.

CHAPTER 6

The brain stem reticular core and sensory function

ARNOLD B. SCHEIBEL | *Departments of Anatomy and Psychiatry and*
Brain Research Institute, University of
California, Los Angeles, California

OUR CONCEPTIONS OF THE NATURE and role of the brain stem reticular core have undergone considerable changes in the 20-year period that separates the writing of this chapter from its predecessor in the first edition of this *Handbook* on the nervous system. The change is fundamental, both qualitatively and quantitatively, and reflects not only the application of new techniques to problems of reticular form and function but also the fruits of mature reflection on a body of data already rich and varied by 1957. In essence, the monolithic interneuronal pool of the early 1950s has become a structural and biochemical mosaic of suborgans—interactive, yet individuated. The functional expressions of the core reflect this heterogeneity of substrate at every level of the central nervous system. Rostral influences of the core have proved to be particularly fruitful fields for investigation, and here the entire subject area of sleep and wakefulness and the various states of perceptive awareness have become

vastly enriched over the rudimentary notions of the early 1950s. The story of descending reticulospinal systems has also gained, not only in richness of detail but also in the addition of an entirely new concept, i.e., reticular mediation and suppression of nociceptive sensation.

To provide a state-of-the-art review, emphasis in this chapter is placed on the development of concepts, both structural and functional, rather than on an exhaustive review of the literature. From the enormous range of data relevant to reticulospinal systems I focus on those relating to the reception and modulation of sensory inputs.

TERMINOLOGY

In almost a century of work no fully satisfactory term has been developed for designating the complex of neuronal cell pools and associated fibers that make up the core of the brain stem. The most common designation, the reticular formation, is of course an entirely descriptive name of uncertain parentage. It was undoubtedly used by the early brain stem morphologists to describe the reticulated, pepper-and-salt appearance resulting from a seemingly unpatterned admixture of neurons and myelinated fibers. A more recent and equally unsatisfactory name, the nonspecific system, is defensible only on the basis of its more functional derivation, that is, the totality of those neuronal elements that are not part of the specific (earlier recognized, sensory-related) ascending relays such as the dorsal column–medial lemniscus and anterolateral (spinothalamic) complexes. This nomenclature serves to memorialize a classic discovery: the presence of multiple systems ascending in parallel and exerting qualitatively different effects on thalamus and cortex. But the connotations of nonspecificity are unfortunate. Earlier conceptions of a heterogeneous grab bag of interneurons interspersed without much pattern among the more ordered files of ascending and descending tracts have been shown to be incorrect. We are only now becoming aware of the complex and elegant interdigitation of multiple, individually signatured cell systems, characterized by idiosyncratic morphology, synaptic chemistry, input-output streams, and functional roles. In fact, the nonspecific systems are at least as highly ordered, and often a good deal more complex, than the specific systems. Another term enjoying popularity in the 1950s and 1960s, the ascending reticular activating system (ARAS) (174), has limited relevance today because the roster of known ascending functions transcends cortical activation.

As a function of these terminological difficulties, a tendency has developed to exclude certain nuclei from the domain of the reticular core as their projections, or their biochemistry, become better known. Thus Brodal (32a) has proposed separation of the lateral reticular nucleus (nucleus of the anterolateral system), the nucleus reticularis tegmenti pontis of Bechterew, and the paramedian reticular cell group on the basis of their significant cerebellar projections, because this trajectory has been considered, until recently, exotic for reticular neurons. In the same way, the locus coeruleus and the nuclei of the raphe seem to be developing autonomous status as their individual biochemical characteristics become familiar (47, 72, 73). Should the trend continue, the consequence, while not a neurobiological disaster, probably would necessitate some new generic referent such as "nuclei of the brain stem core," or perhaps an item-by-item muster. For some years it has been our preference to refer to all the intrinsic nuclei of the brain stem, exclusive of cranial nerve nuclei with their related structures and large relay centers such as the olives, red nucleus, and substantia nigra, as the brain stem reticular core (224, 229). This convention is followed here, no matter what the current state of knowledge about individual input-output systems or chemistry may be. In this way, we maintain a nominally classic position without in any way prejudicing the present and future role of any item in the subset.

In attempting to develop a unifying concept, consider that all reticular neurons are interneurons. Their neurites (axons and dendrites) reach neither the receptive periphery of the organism, with one possible exception (see ref. 84), nor the organs of motor performance, such as muscles and glands. Ignoring the interneuron systems of the spinal cord (which are remarkably similar in many ways), we consider the reticular core of the medulla, pons, and mesencephalon. The presumably analogous elements of the diencephalon are squeezed into rather thin, medially lying plates bearing an enlarged nuclear grouping caudally (the centre médian–parafascicular complex) and two lateral, upward-curving winglike extensions (the intralaminar system) that anatomically separate the dorsomedial from the ventrolateral thalamus. These thalamic components are also considered because of

their functional interdependence with the brain stem core. A brief section on the nucleus reticularis thalami, the thin, platelike extension of subthalamus that now appears to mediate essentially all thalamocortical interactions, completes the roster.

HISTORICAL DEVELOPMENT OF CONCEPTS

Our current notions of the structural organization and functional role of the reticular core are based on a series of seminal reports scattered through the literature of the first half of the twentieth century. Each of these reports, viewed in retrospect, contained data or ideas prescient of findings made a decade or more later, and each fell on remarkably stony soil. In fact, it was not until the late 1940s that reticular formation research became fashionable, and in one form or another it has remained so, due largely to the great interest in its most notable neural products—sleeping and dreaming.

In the first decade of the twentieth century Ramón y Cajal (203a) called attention to the interneuron-like organization of the core, likening the constituent cells to higher order (third, fourth, and fifth) relay neurons for both sensory and motor systems. He called attention to the bifurcation and multiple-branching patterns of some of their axons and projections, both rostral and caudal. The sensory and motor collaterals feeding the core, identified by Cajal in his Golgi sections, also were seen by Kohnstamm and Quensel (133) with more conventional techniques. Their suggestion that a common pooling or sampling of afferent inputs might form a "centrum receptorium" or "sensoring commune" within the reticular formation was clearly an idea ahead of its time.

The caudally directed axons described by Cajal were identified as projecting upon spinal cord by means of the retrograde studies of Kohnstamm (132) and van Gehuchten (75) and the anterograde (Marchi) material of Lewandowsky (145). The definitive Marchi description of reticulospinal axons, however, was that of Papez (190), who described three major descending bundles. This work was later confirmed and extended by a number of studies, including those by Niemer and Magoun (180), Torvik and Brodal (264), and Nyberg-Hansen (182), and are now in the process of redefinition through the use of radioactively tagged amino acids, horseradish peroxidase, and more selective stimulation methods (194, 195, 284, 285).

The possible functional role of these descending paths in modulating spinal output was considered by Allen (6), but these ideas were not to come to fruition until more than a decade later, in the studies by Magoun and Rhines (160, 205) on brain stem reticular override (inhibition and facilitation) of ongoing spinal motor activity. The classic studies of the latter investigators, which strongly implied non-Sherringtonian (i.e., nonreciprocal) processes, were modified in the investigations of Sprague and Chambers (255) using the nonanesthetized preparation. A more detailed understanding of the mechanisms involved in reticular control of spinal outflow has developed with the demonstrations of inhibitory postsynaptic potentials (IPSP) in α-motoneurons following stimulation of medial medullary reticular zones (87, 108, 151), and of a combination of spindle activation and excitatory postsynaptic potentials (EPSP) in γ-motoneurons after stimulation of appropriate facilitatory areas of the brain stem (54, 85).

Of more relevance to our own concern with the impact of the reticular core on sensory mechanisms is the long series of observations by Hess and colleagues (98–100) and Bremer (30, 31), starting in the 1930s, concerning the possible role of brain stem systems in sleep and wakefulness. In some of the earliest experiments performed on chronically implanted nonanesthetized animals, Hess showed that slow repetitive stimulation of a number of sites inside (and outside) the brain stem could produce behavioral states indistinguishable from spontaneous sleep. Such results seemed irrational to the scientific community at the time because they implied that sleep was an active process. The studies of Bremer (30, 31), on the other hand, were more consonant with ideas of the time. He showed that following complete decerebration, the resulting cerveau isolé preparation generated a sleeping electrocorticographic pattern that continued without interruption until the animal's death. It should be pointed out here that Loomis et al. (153) and Gibbs et al. (77) had demonstrated in the preceding year that the electroencephalographic pattern characteristic of sleep was the high-voltage slow-wave sequence or θ-rhythm. Bremer interpreted his findings to mean that a tonic ascending flow of corticipetal impulses was necessary to maintain the wakeful state. The only ascending systems known at the time were the dorsal column–medial lemniscus and spinothalamic tracts (anterolateral lemniscus). He concluded that these were the necessary agents and that a constant influx of sensory information produced wakefulness. These data satisfied intuitive notions of the nature of sleep and, with necessary amendations of the activating agency involved (as discussed later in this section), provided the dominant substrate of thinking on this subject for the next 20 years.

In a significant series of papers that appeared between 1936 and 1943, Dempsey and Morison and other associates of Alexander Forbes (51–53, 172, 173) defined some of the functional characteristics of the rostral portion of an extralemniscal path reaching cerebral cortex. Its medial location, widespread projection on cortex, sensitivity to anesthesia or hypnotics, and the characteristic pattern of stimulus-locked recruitment potentials that followed its stimulation at slow frequencies were of considerable, if not immediately recognized, importance. Further studies by Hanberry and Jasper and associates (91, 92, 110, 111) and

by Penfield (193) emphasized the apparent pacemaking role of this thalamic nonspecific system and culminated in the concept of the centrencephalon. For the first time since Hughlings Jackson (107) the geographical hierachy of brain levels was brought under question. The cortex was, in fact, made penultimate to the upper end of the brain stem and the principle of thalamocortical circulation proposed earlier by Ramón y Cajal (203a), Campion (38), and Dusser de Barenne and McCulloch (57) gained support and some degree of experimental verification.

The studies of Bremer and of the Forbes group reached maturity in the report by Moruzzi and Magoun (174) describing reticular control over cortical activity and its relation to the spectrum of conscious states from vigilance to deep sleep. More importantly, Lindsley and Magoun and various collaborators (148–150) were able to identify the ascending activating system by selective lesions of lemniscal and extralemniscal (reticular core) systems. The original interpretation of Bremer (30, 31) was now modified as it became clear that "tonus cerebrale" was maintained by ascending projections from the reticular core rather than by the sensory lemnisci themselves. The final thalamocortical link was assumed to involve the thalamic nonlemniscal system of Forbes' group, although Moruzzi and Magoun were careful to point out that they were not yet able to specify details of the structural substrate for the ARAS. It was assumed, however, that the core of the brain stem exerted its effects on the cortex over a series of polysynaptic channels forged by chains of short-axoned cells. Golgi studies demonstrated that these paths actually depended on oligosynaptic and, in some cases, on monosynaptic channels to the cortex (222, 224, 230, 271, 272); these data have since been confirmed by intracellular analyses (159).

In the early 1950s, the entire concept of the sleeping state still included two basic assumptions that were soon to be proved fallacious. The first, as we have seen, was the idea of sleep as a passive state, and the second was that of sleep as an essentially unimodal phenomenon marked only by quantitative gradations from superficial to deep. Yet, published data already existed to the contrary: Hess and associates (98–100) had demonstrated that slow repetitive stimulation was capable of producing apparently natural sleep in implanted, unrestrained cats, and a number of workers had already published records correlating low-voltage fast-wave rhythms with a curious type of sleep marked by movements of parts of the body (53, 98, 128, 204, 206). Nevertheless it was the studies by Dement and Kleitman (50, 130) that finally identified this as a qualitatively different type of sleeping behavior (REM, rhombencephalic, paradoxical sleep). The reports of Rossi and associates (216–218) and of M. Jouvet and D. Jouvet and Michel (115–118) provided an anatomicophysiological basis for this complex of sleep states, relating them to specific areas of the lower

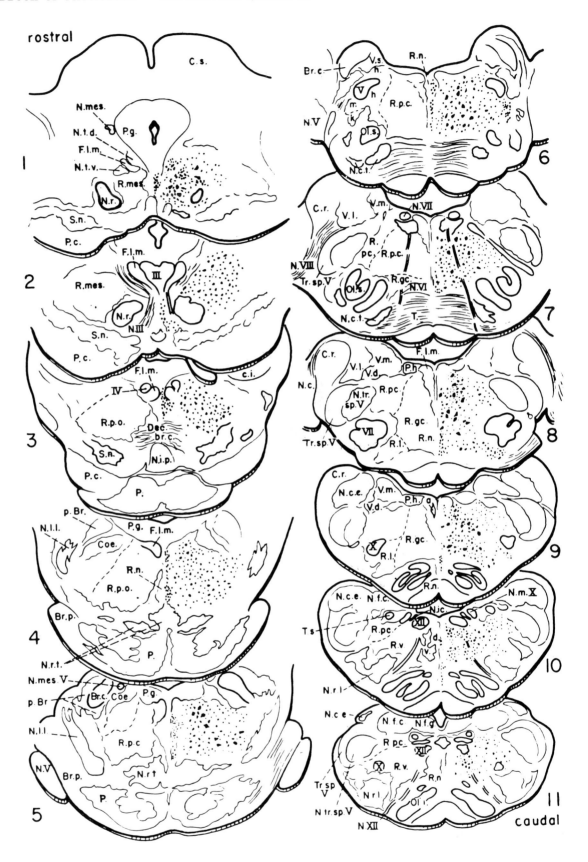

brain stem. Thus within a few years it had become clear that the reticular core was just as certainly a mosaic of functionally distinct zones as was the cerebral neocortex.

Another significant aspect of reticular core activities was revealed by Galambos (74) and Hernandez-Peon (97). They were able to relate the size of sensory-evoked potentials to the focus of active interest momentarily expressed by implanted, freely mobile animals. Golgi studies (224, 229, 271) document the penetration of appropriate sensory processing nuclei and cortical stations by reticular collaterals. Today it seems likely that the process of delimitation of the focus of consciousness with concordant suppression of those sensory inputs temporarily relegated to a secondary role may well be a function of the reticular core in cooperation with the thalamic nonspecific system. A more recently discovered component of this phenomenon is the selective gating effect exerted by the mesencephalic tegmentum jointly with frontal granular cortex over the nucleus reticularis thalami (250, 291). The possible role of these conjoint functions of the brain stem and diencephalic reticular formation in the moment-to-moment interplay of levels of perceptive awareness, the "searchlight of consciousness" (49), is discussed in *Nucleus Reticularis Thalami*, p. 245.

ORGANIZATION OF RETICULAR CORE

Cell Groups

Cytoarchitectonic study of the grouping of cell bodies throughout the brain stem core reveals a number of nuclei varying somewhat in size, shape, and position, depending on the species examined and the particular prejudices of the examiner. The most detailed investigation, that by Olszewski and Baxter (187, 188) in human beings, shares the same criticism as others of this type. Nuclear divisions must often be determined arbitrarily, and cell body morphology, which serves as primary criterion for this type of study, frequently has little functional relevance (see discussion that accompanies ref. 187; see also ref. 66). Nonetheless most investigators, using a group of structural techniques, would undoubtedly agree on the following fairly conservative roster of reticular core nuclei (Fig. 1). Added support has come from the use of histochemical and histofluorescent techniques, although results reported from the use of the latter are not entirely congruent with earlier descriptions.

Most posterior in the brain stem and just rostral to the decussation of the pyramids are the small-celled systems of the nucleus reticularis ventralis and the more dorsolateral nucleus reticularis parvocellularis. Somewhat more rostral in the medulla the large-celled groupings of nucleus reticularis gigantocellularis become visible, and these elements, with an admixture of smaller cells, extend at least one-third of the distance into the pontile tegmentum, where they become known as nucleus reticularis pontis caudalis. The very large neuronal elements disappear in the upper half of the pons, where this cell column is confluent with the nucleus reticularis pontis oralis. Much of the reticular formation of the mesencephalon is included in the somewhat diffusely bordered nucleus cuneiformis (see Fig. 2), generally considered to be the most rostral part of the brain stem reticular nuclei, although extensions of the system continue as dorsal and ventral leaves through thalamus and subthalamus, respectively.

The region of the midline is occupied by a somewhat discontinuous group of subnuclei known collectively as the nuclei of the raphe (Fig. 2). These have been subdivided according to cytoarchitectonic criteria into six groups by Taber and associates (262, 263) and into nine subnuclei by Dahlstrom and Fuxe and associates (47, 72, 73), using histofluorescence methods. The paramedian nuclear complex (see Fig. 1) lies between the raphe elements and the axons of the hypoglossal nucleus in caudal medulla and, like the nucleus reticularis tegmenti pontis and the lateral reticular nucleus, projects largely to the cerebellum. Because of the latter's close associations with the anterolateral fascic-

---

FIG. 1. Equally spaced transverse Nissl-stained sections through brain stem of cat show grouping of cells in reticular core. *Dots* on *right* indicate specific cell bodies, while *dashed lines* on *left* indicate approximate boundaries of major reticular nuclei. Terminology and nuclear areas are based on studies by Olszewski of the rabbit, with minor modifications. The following list of abbreviations refers only to structures making up reticular core. *a*, Accessory group of paramedian reticular nucleus; *d*, dorsal group of paramedian reticular nucleus; *h*, region poor in cells of Meesen and Olszewski surrounding motor trigeminal nucleus; *k*, cell group k of Meesen and Olszewski; *m*, cell group m of Meesen and Olszewki; *N. ic.*, nucleus intercalatus; *N.r.l.*, lateral reticular nucleus; *N.r.t.*, nucleus reticularis tegmenti pontis; *N.t.d.*, dorsal tegmental nucleus; *N.t.v.*, ventral tegmental nucleus; *P.g.*, periaqueductal gray; *P.h.*, nucleus prepositus hypoglossi; *R. gc.*, nucleus reticularis gigantocellularis; *R.l.*, nucleus reticularis lateralis (of Meesen and Olszewski); *R. mes.*, reticular formation of mesencephalon; *R.n.*, nucleus of the raphe; *R.pc.*, nucleus reticularis parvocellularis; *R.p.o.*, nucleus reticularis pontis oralis; *R.p.c.*, nucleus reticularis pontis caudalis; *R.v.*, nucleus reticularis ventralis; *v*, ventral group of paramedian reticular nucleus. [From Brodal (32).]

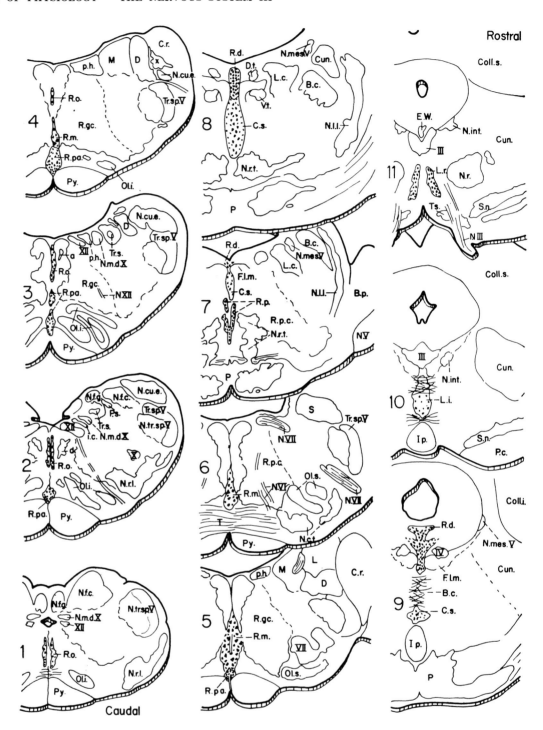

ulus and its rather different dendritic morphology (see *Dendritic Patterns*, this page), question has been raised about the validity of its inclusion under the umbrella of reticular nuclei. Similar questions have been raised about the norepinephrine-rich cells of the locus coeruleus (see Fig. 1) in the dorsolateral pons. In each case judgments will differ, but I feel that despite the varied trajectories and diverse chemical signatures of these nuclear groups, nothing is to be lost by such generalizations.

In the final analysis there are sufficient similarities across all of these apparently diverse groups (i.e., their brain stem locations, their interneuronal nature, the diversity of their inputs, and the multiplicity of their output channels) to warrant such common grouping.

Dendritic Patterns

The relatively segregated nature of the cytoarchitectonic maps drawn or photographed from the usual cell body stains becomes less convincing when compared with material prepared by techniques (Golgi, methylene blue) that show the entire dendritic array (Fig. 3). The dendrite systems of the reticular core, with a few exceptions, are characterized by long, relatively unramified shafts that, at least in brain stem cross sections, diverge radially from the cell body.

Dendrites of the lateral reticular nuclei and the more dorsal elements of the paramedian group depart from this schema in favor of a shorter, more ramified pattern. On the whole, the typical reticular cell presents the appearance of the classic interneuron or motorneuron with a radially dispersed dendritic array that has been called isodendritic by Ramón-Moliner and Nauta (203). The shafts are long, and in small rodents they may extend over one-third of the brain stem cross section being examined (224). As a result dendrites from cells in one neuronal field may penetrate deeply into another field or nucleus, effectively blurring the cytoarchitectonic territories established on the basis of cell body location alone.

Despite the extensive circumferential patterns described by these domains, idiosyncratic modifications appear when the stem is viewed in planes of section other than the usual transverse or coronal plane. Sagittal sections reveal that the majority of medium-sized and large neurons of the medial half of the brain stem, particularly in upper medulla and pons, possess dendritic envelopes flattened in the rostrocaudal dimension (29, 224, 271). The resulting compression along the long axis of the brain stem results in series of flattened dendritic domains, recalling a stack of poker chips (Fig. 4). Although this analogy clearly has its limitations, it nevertheless calls attention to the pos-

---

FIG. 2. Equally spaced transverse thionine-stained sections through brain stem of adult cat. Outlines, made by means of a projection apparatus, were checked under microscope and details entered. Nuclei of the raphe are indicated by *dots*; density and sizes of *dots* serve to give an approximate impression of architecture of various nuclei. *a*, Accessory group of paramedian reticular nucleus; *B.c.*, brachium conjunctivum cerebelli; *B.p.*, brachium pontis; *Coll.i.*, inferior colliculus; *Coll.s.*, superior colliculus; *C.r.*, restiform body; *C.s.*, nucleus centralis superior; *Cun.*, nucleus cuneiformis; *d*, dorsal group of paramedian reticular nucleus; *d*, descending (spinal) vestibular nucleus; *D.t.*, dorsal tegmental nucleus (Gudden); *E.W.*, Edinger-Westphal nucleus; *F.l.m.*, medial longitudinal fasciculus; *i.c.*, nucleus intercalatus; *Ip.*, interpeduncular nucleus; *L.*, lateral vestibular nucleus (Deiters'); *L.c.*, locus coeruleus; *L.i.*, nucleus linearis intermedius; *L.r.*, nucleus linearis rostralis; *M*, medial vestibular nucleus; *N.c.t.*, nuclei of trapezoid body; *N.cu.e.*, external cuneate nucleus; *N.f.c.*, cuneate nucleus; *N.f.g.*, gracile nucleus; *N.int.*, nucleus interstitialis (Cajal); *N.l.l.*, nuclei of lateral lemniscus; *N.m.d.X*, dorsal motor vagus nucleus; *N.mes.V*, mesencephalic trigeminal nucleus; *N.r.*, red nucleus (n. ruber); *N.r.l.*, nucleus reticularis lateralis (nucleus funiculi lateralis); *N.r.t.*, nucleus reticularis tegmenti pontis (Bechterew); *N.tr.sp.V*, nucleus of spinal trigeminal tract; *N.III, V, VI, VII, XII*, cranial nerves; *Ol.i.*, inferior olive; *Ol.s.*, superior olive; *P*, griseum pontis; *P.c.*, cerebral peduncle; *p.h.*, nucleus prepositus hypoglossi; *P.s.*, nucleus parasolitarius; *Py.*, pyramid; *R.d.*, nucleus raphe dorsalis; *R.gc.*, nucleus reticularis gigantocellularis medullae oblongatae; *R.m.*, nucleus raphe magnus; *R.o.*, nucleus raphe obscurus; *R.p.*, nucleus raphe pontis; *R.pa.*, nucleus raphe pallidus; *R.p.c.*, nucleus reticularis pontis caudalis; *S*, superior vestibular nucleus; *S.n.*, substantia nigra; *T*, trapezoid body; *Tr.s.*, solitary tract; *Tr.sp.V*, spinal trigeminal tract; *Ts.*, ventral tegmental nucleus of Tsai; *V.t.*, ventral tegmental nucleus (Gudden); *x*, group x of Brodal and Pompeiano; *III, IV, VII, X, XII*, cranial motor nerve nuclei. [From Taber (262).]

sibility of considerable degrees of modular organization in a neuropil originally thought to be without demonstrable structure. The domains described here, with their minimal extension along the rostrocaudal

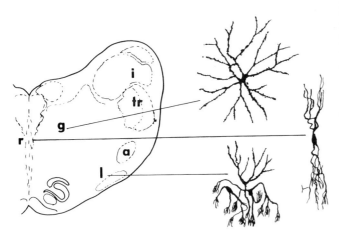

FIG. 3. Dendritic patterns in brain stem reticular core (based on Golgi-stained sections): *g*, nucleus gigantocellularis; *r*, nucleus of the raphe; *l*, lateral reticular nucleus, which has many of the features of sensory relay nuclear cells and probably serves, in part, that function for the adjacent spinothalamic tract; *i*, inferior cerebellar penduncle; *tr*, descending root and nucleus of the trigeminal nerve; *a*, nucleus ambiguus.

axis, mimic the localized terminal configuration of afferents entering the substance of the core at these levels from both ascending and descending tracts (Fig. 4). Matching of the postsynaptic receptive neuropil to patterns generated by the presynaptic influx are common in the nervous system. In this case one apparent result would be to limit the "receptive field" (not used in the usual peripheral sense) of the recipient neuron to a population of presynaptic terminals entering at that level only. The output of each such cell would accordingly represent a sample of synaptic transactions occurring at a specific cross-sectional level of the stem. The general concept of large numbers of chips or modules, aside from having familiar overtones in today's world of computer technology, adds a dimension of manageability to the description of neuropil and has been found to be applicable at other levels of the central nervous system (261).

We still know remarkably little about the intimate structure and function of dendrites. After Gerlach's (76) use of carmine stains led to the initial discovery of dendrites, and after a brilliant period of description by Golgi (80), Cajal (203a), and the great first generation of "silver anatomists," they were virtually forgotten for almost 40 years. The canonical neuron became a sphere, and it was thought that synaptic activity developing more than 200 μm from the cell

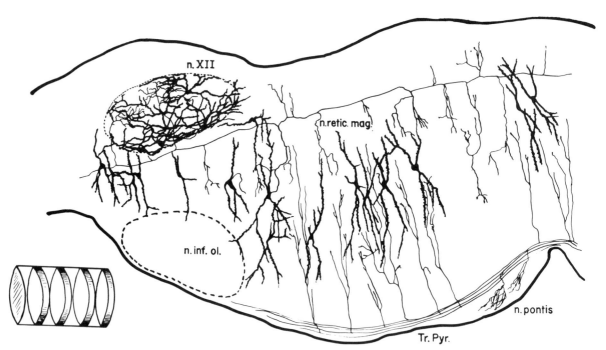

FIG. 4. Sagittal section through lower half of brain stem of 10-day-old rat. Most of dendrite mass of reticular-core cells is organized along dorsoventral axis as seen in this type of section, with marked compression along rostrocaudal axis. This orientation places dendrites parallel to terminal presynaptic components, which in this case arise from pyramidal tract (*Tr. Pyr.*) and from a single axon of a magnocellular reticular neuron (*n. retic. mag*). This type of dendrite organization, which is especially characteristic of reticular cells of medial two-thirds of core, produces sets of 2-dimensional modular neuropil fields leading to stack-of-chips analogy (see *inset, lower left*). This is contrasted with dendritic patterns in adjacent hypoglossal nucleus (*n. XII*); *n. inf. ol.*, inferior olive; *n. pontis*, the pons. [From Scheibel and Scheibel (224).]

body could safely be ignored. The reemergence in the 1950s of the dendrite as an anatomically and physiologically interesting entity, first as a decremental conductor and then, under a group of specified conditions, as a structure capable of generation and propagation of spikes (59, 200, 254), has measurably enriched concepts of neuropil function.

The classification of dendrites in the reticular core is that produced by Ramón y Cajal. The long, straight, somewhat spine-covered protoplasmic processes that he drew as a result of observations in perinatal animals, however, do not represent the most generalized case. Evidence now indicates that with increasing maturity most of the dendrite spines are lost, leaving scattered excrescences whose functions remain enigmatic (223). Furthermore the long, straight profiles are resculpted into more tortuous patterns, bending around the increasing bulk of maturing "through fibers" (Fig. 5). Perhaps as a partial function of this change, groups of dendrites are now reorganized into tightly packed complexes or bundles (223), each of which may include from 3 to 10 or more dendritic elements. Within these fascicles, as elsewhere in the

maturing nervous system (221), pairs and trios of dendrite shafts may run closely adjacent to each other for hundreds of micrometers, facing membranes lying within 100 Å or less of each other, frequently without recognizable intervening structures. In the majority of cases studied with electron microscopy no membrane specializations (such as membrane thickening, increased electron density, and synaptic vesicles) have been described along these interfaces (162, 236). The functional significance of such relationships is still unknown. It has been suggested, however, that these bundles may function as storage sites for central programs (235) or else may provide a setting for interactive local processes, electrochemical in nature, among the closely adjacent elements (67, 244). In the latter case the configuration of molecules rich in glycoprotein and sialic acid making up the extended membrane would conceivably be modulated and coupled by rapidly mobile divalent cations (especially Ca^{2+} and Mg^{2+}) operating in the hyaluronate-rich extraneuronal compartment intervening between facing membrane pairs. The postulated longitudinal sequences of macromolecular complexes have been suggested as carriers of

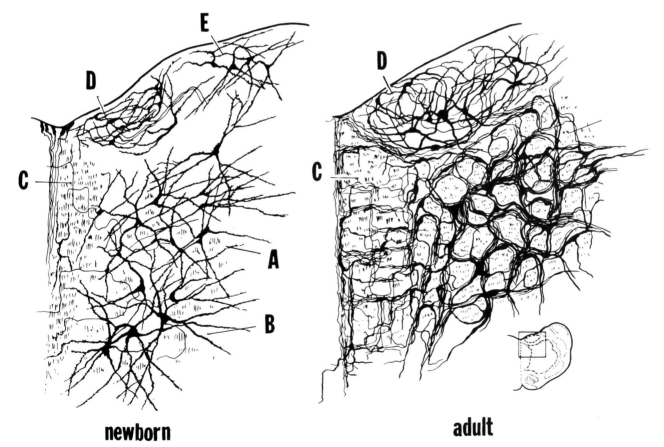

newborn   **adult**

FIG. 5. Cross sections through same level of medulla of newborn and adult cats showing apparent loss of dendritic spines and apparent regrouping of reticular cell dendrites into bundles. Neurons include those of most rostral part of n. reticularis parvocellularis (*A*) and of n. reticularis gigantocellularis (*B*). *C*, medial longitudinal fasciculus; *D*, n. prepositus hypoglossi; *E*, medial vestibular nucleus. Rapid Golgi variant. Original magnification × 160. [From Scheibel, Davies, and Scheibel (223).]

coded information relevant to the output performance characteristic of the neuron groups involved (235, 236).

Whatever the ultimate role of dendrite bundles may be, the dendrite shafts themselves are richly invested over most of their nonapposed surfaces with presynaptic terminals. These represent the influx not only of collateral and terminal fibers of the long ascending (spinothalamic, spinoreticular) and descending (pyramidal, extrapyramidal) tracts but also of the complex intrareticular and conduction systems generated by reticular elements at all levels of the neuraxis.

The segregation of afferents on selected portions of the individual dendrite shafts that has proved to be so characteristic of axodendritic organization in hippocampus (155) and cerebral neocortex (79) appears less evident in the core. On the other hand, individual dendrite branches appear, through their position, to be closely and selectively related to one or more input systems. I have previously suggested the analogy of reticular cell dendrites reaching toward their sources of innervation. This selective loading of individual shafts by synaptic terminals from the fiber systems toward which the dendrite shaft points is illustrated in Figure 6.

Ultrastructural studies of synaptic morphology in the core have been limited. Those that have been reported indicate no particular surprises (29). Synaptic glomeruli of the type reported in sensory relay nuclei such as the lateral geniculate (260) have apparently not been seen.

Quantitative light-microscopic studies by Kositzyn (134) indicate an average synaptic density of 20 dendrites per 100 μm^2 in the gigantocellular region, a figure slightly lower than that suggested by the electron-microscopic evaluation of Bowsher and Westman (29). In addition to the usual type of individual or cluster synaptic terminal patterns, many creeping synapses (i.e., reiterative contacts from a single fiber) have been noted (Fig. 7). A very rough tentative figure of 7,560 synapses per "average polydendritic neuron" has been suggested by Bowsher and Westman (29). Their degeneration studies suggest that only one in 1,000 of these may be of direct spinal origin. There are no data at present to document quantitatively the source of the remainder of the presynaptic terminal arrays. Golgi data (A. B. Scheibel, unpublished data) indicate, however, that the vast majority of these have intrareticular origins.

Afferent Systems

As already indicated in the section HISTORICAL DEVELOPMENT OF CONCEPTS, p. 214, the reticular core receives a remarkably heterogeneous input made up of both collaterals and terminals from ascending and descending tracts. Notable among these are the anterolateral systems (spinothalamic tracts), elements of the solitary complex (n. solitarius), descending trigeminal and vestibular nuclei, and the pyramidal and

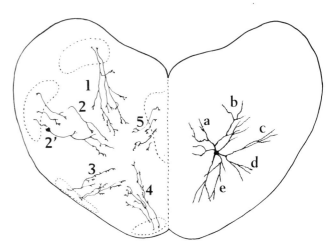

FIG. 6. Dendrite system a is oriented toward axons from medial longitudinal fasciculus (5); dendrite system b is oriented toward axons from vestibular nuclear complex (1); c corresponds to descending trigeminal system (2); d corresponds to spinothalamics (3); e is oriented toward axons from corticospinal fibers (4).

extrapyramidal systems (32a, 33, 203a, 220, 224, 271, 272). Note that the medial lemniscus appears specifically excluded from contributions to the system (163, 224, 272). In addition to this rich influx from fiber systems passing through the brain stem, the reticular core appears to be supplied quite specifically by an ascending spinoreticular bundle (216) and by descending axons from the cerebellum (278), thalamic nonspecific nuclei (239), and the nucleus reticularis thalami (227, 230). It would appear to be organized, quite literally, to monitor activity in almost every portion of the neuraxis and in virtually every passing fiber system.

A considerable body of physiological data supports the anatomical findings that indicate a convergence of fibers, collateral or terminal, on the brain stem reticular core. Although evoked potential studies (256) suggest reticular response to many input channels, it is the single-unit study above all others that has proved instructive in this matter. Both extracellular (8, 19, 27, 28, 223a) and intracellular (105, 159) techniques have emphasized polysensory convergence on individual elements of the core. Patterns of convergence have proved wide but not unlimited, each reticular cell tending to have its own unique mix of input terminals (Fig. 8).

Early qualitative studies emphasized the convergence of inputs from several parts of the body and from multiple neural systems on individual reticular units (8, 223a). Thus a single reticular element of the midbulb or upper bulb could readily be shown to be driven by shocks to the sciatic or saphenous nerve, ipsilaterally or contralaterally, to surface polarization of the anterior lobe of the cerebellum, to nose pressure or whisker pulls, to auditory (and occasionally visual) stimuli, and to cortical stimulation. Some corticoreticular pathways were shown by Magni and Willis (159)

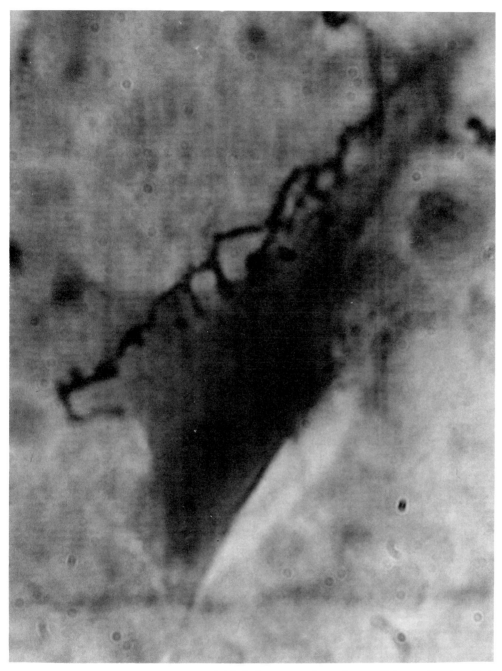

FIG. 7. Reticular neuron from gigantocellular nucleus in a 10-day-old cat. A single terminating afferent establishes a series of terminal boutons along proximal portion of dendrite and cell body. Golgi modification × 440.

to be of short latency and probably monosynaptic nature, which undoubtedly indicated reticular activation by collaterals or terminals of pyramidal fibers. Later studies by Peterson et al. (195) suggested that excitation originating in pericruciate regions is distributed bilaterally in the nucleus gigantocellularis and nucleus pontis caudalis but ipsilaterally in the nucleus pontis oralis. These authors also concluded on the basis of the wide dispersion of excitatory postsynaptic

potential (EPSP) latencies, that a large part of the effects of cortical excitation on reticular elements was mediated by multisynaptic loops. Such driving effects were very frequently followed by prolonged periods of depression. The early component of this phase was believed to be due to inhibitory postsynaptic potentials (IPSPs) and afterhyperpolarization evoked by the cortical stimulus. The later components, lasting 300 ms or longer, were attributed to temporary cessa-

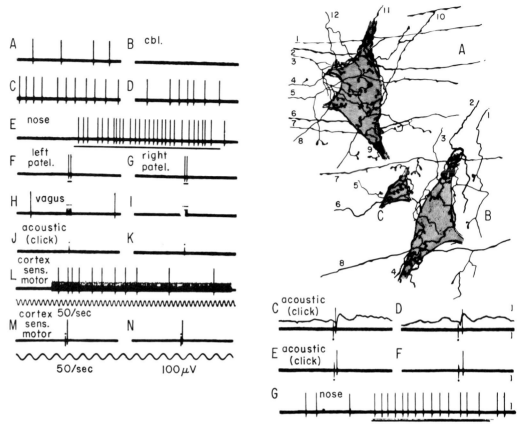

FIG. 8. Convergence of heterogeneous afferents on single elements of brain stem reticular core, demonstrated physiologically and histologically. Strips A–N (*left*) and C–G (*bottom right*) illustrate patterns of spike discharge of 2 elements of bulboreticular formation. At *left*, A is firing spontaneously; B is inhibited by cerebellar polarization; C rebounds following cessation of polarization; D returns to more normal discharge pattern; E is stimulated by nose pressure; F and G are stimulated by patellar tendon taps administered bilaterally; H and I are unaffected by short trains of vagal stimulation; J and K are unaffected by auditory clicks; L is driven by repetitive cortical stimulation; M and N show, with aid of expanded time base, that latency of the corticifugal discharge to the bulboreticular unit is very short. Strips C–F (*bottom right*) show that another bulboreticular unit that is sensitive to pressure to nose (G) can also be driven by auditory clicks (C and D). This rather minimal effect is unmasked (E and F) when spontaneous activity of unit is inhibited by cerebellar polarization. A–C *top right*, bulboreticular cells, lying within several hundred μm of each other, in a 10-day-old kitten. Axons from a number of fiber systems were traced to these cells, although only terminal portions are shown. Horizontally running fibers such as A1–A7 and B7–B8 appear to belong to spinoreticular and long reticuloreticular components, while B1–B4, approached from dorsal and lateral aspects of bulb, represent sensory collaterals and cerebelloreticular collaterals. All records from locally anesthetized, paralyzed (Flaxedil) cat. [From Scheibel and Scheibel (224).]

tion of activity in recurrent neuronal loops within the reticular core itself.

Golgi studies (A. B. Scheibel, unpublished data) and experimental anatomic investigations (7, 122) indicate the presence of significant tectoreticular projections. Fibers originating in dorsal tectum, primarily in the deeper portions of the superior colliculus, follow both crossed and uncrossed pathways caudally, reaching the pontomedullary core, where they terminate with varying density patterns within n. pontis oralis, n. pontis caudalis, and n. gigantocellularis. That a substantial portion of this pathway is monosynaptic is evidenced by the short-latency reticular EPSPs following its activation, as demonstrated by Udo and Mano (268) and Peterson et al. (195).

The organization of afferent systems discharging via collaterals or terminals into the reticular core has proved to be both a fascinating and frustrating area for investigation. Initial microelectrode studies (8, 223a) revealed only general patterns of polysensory convergence. A more exacting analysis of input organization into medulla, pons, and mesencephalic tegmentum by Bell et al. (19) has, however, produced useful data. Bell and colleagues have concluded that in the lower two-thirds of the brain stem, the face is the body component most commonly represented in the synaptic ensemble of reticular neurons; such terminals project unilaterally (primarily ipsilaterally) and are concentrated in highly restricted fields. The forelimb is another commonly represented element of the body. Corresponding fibers that show no obvious side preference are concentrated in restricted fields when they are ipsilaterally represented. The hindlimb, trunk, and tail constitute the least frequently represented zones and involve bilateral projections characterized by wide receptive fields. Idiosyncratic differences have also been noted between the pontomedullary and mesencephalic tegmental areas for face and anterior and posterior body representations, respectively. This indicates a rather high degree of somatic afferent terminal organization within the core.

Somewhat different findings were reported by Bowsher et al. (28), who found that all units encountered in the gigantocellular region of the rostral bulb could be driven by somatic stimulation and that 65% of these showed heterosensory convergence (with sound or light, or both). This figure closely coincides with the proportion of large, bouton-covered polydendritic neurons (66%) that Bowsher and his co-workers have described in this region, in contradistinction to a smaller oligodendritic neuron with a small, round cell body, one or two spine-free dendrites, and a very low loading (5–6 boutons/100 μm^2) of synaptic spines.

Although these values probably represent our best estimates to date of patterns of sensory representation along the brain stem reticular core, several factors are undoubtedly operating to make this a dynamic rather than static configuration, with possibilities for widespread variation under certain conditions. For one thing, reticular neurons appear to undergo rapid and profound degrees of adaptation or habituation (19, 103, 149, 226), especially to peripheral stimuli. Regular repetition of a stimulus of constant characteristics produces progressively smaller response patterns (Fig. 9). The percentage of reticular cells showing response habituation vary from 60% to 90%, depending on the technique and animal species used. Almost as many cells show dynamic changes to stimulus pairing (34, 149). This contrasts sharply with cells of the visual cortex, for example, that show response habituation of 5%–15% (275), thereby emphasizing the plastic, reactive nature of core neurons and their afferent sensibility to the immediacy and relevance of a stimulus.

In addition a number of neurons (at least in the pontomedullary area) have been shown to follow sensitivity cycles of relatively fixed duration. During this time the modality of inputs to which they are sensitive shows rather dramatic changes (225). As an example, a reticular unit that is initially responsive to exteroceptive activities, such as contralateral stimulation of the sciatic nerve or ipsilateral superficial stimuli to face and snout, or both, may become entirely refractory to both of these while reflecting, alternatively, certain interoceptive phenomena, such as respiration or gastrointestinal activities. I have had the opportunity to record, without interruption, from a small number of such units for periods of up to 9 h (Fig. 10, ref. 225). Although the parameters of cycling tend to vary for each cell, the total length of each cycle ap-

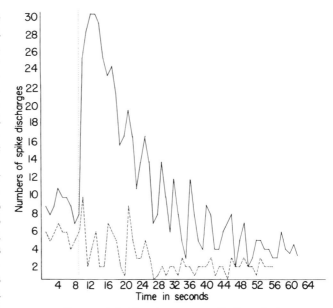

FIG. 9. Contrast in habituation patterns of bulboreticular neuron exposed to repetitive sciatic stimulation at 2 V, 1/s, 0.5-ms pulse width. *Solid line*, first series of stimuli; *dashed line*, second series of stimuli, delivered following a 3-min rest period after habituation had been achieved; *dotted vertical line*, time of onset of stimuli. Oscillatory variations in number of spike discharges per stimulus during period of habituation seem characteristic of this process. All records from locally anesthetized, paralyzed (Flaxedil) cat. [Adapted from Scheibel and Scheibel (226).]

proximates 90–100 min, with about twice as much time spent in the exteroceptive-responsive phase as in the interoceptive phase. At the time these results were reported they did not seem to be temporally related to variations in the coincidentally recorded electrocorticogram, particularly with regard to sleeping vs. waking records. In the interim, however, it has come to seem more probable that individual sequencing of reticular-unit activity may well be time locked to major swings of the rest-activity cycle (129, 130).

Axonal Outflow: General Picture

It is the length and distribution of their axonal systems that most clearly identify cells of the reticular core as being truly interneuronal in nature. A spectrum of pathway lengths and trajectories exists, and in larger mammals, primates, and human beings, it is conceivable that these may never be known in complete detail, since the branching patterns are so intensive and so closely intermingled, the axons so diverse in origin and distribution. As already noted, it seems unlikely that any reticular cell axon reaches elements of the receptor systems or effector apparatus, although an exception to the former may exist in reported tegmental outflow fibers to the retina (84). However, the potential range of axonal paths within the central nervous system is enormous. If generalizations are possible, it may perhaps be said that cells along the more ventral and lateral periphery of the core tend to

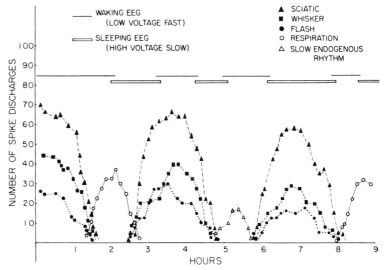

FIG. 10. Cyclic response of single medullary reticular neuron whose activity was continuously monitored for 9 h. Nearly 3 complete cycles of exogenously driven and endogenously driven activity are charted here. Periods of sensitivity to exogenous inputs are almost twice as long as those to slow endogenous rhythms. *Line-bar* notation above curves indicates no clear-cut relationship between these swings and states of consciousness of animal. Recent reevaluation of all of these data, however, throws this interpretation open to question. All records from locally anesthetized, paralyzed (Flaxedil) cats. [Adapted from Scheibel and Scheibel (225).]

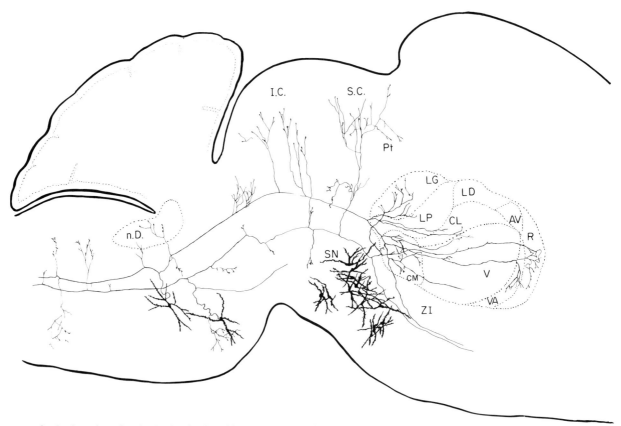

FIG. 11. Sagittal section of entire brain of 7-day-old mouse showing 2 reticular cells in gigantocellular nucleus of rostral medulla. Both cells emit axons that bifurcate and course rostrad and caudad. A number of collaterals are given off by each axon, some of which reach cranial nerve nuclei, such as Deiters' component of vestibular complex (*n.D.*); both inferior and superior colliculi (*I.C.* and *S.C.*); and pretectum (*Pt*). *CM*, centre médian; *LP*, lateral posterior; *LG*, lateral geniculate; *LD*, lateral dorsal; *CL*, central lateral; *AV*, anterior ventral; *V*, ventral complex; *VA*, ventral anterior; *R*, nucleus reticularis thalami; *ZI*, zona incerta; and *SN*, substantia nigra. [From Scheibel and Scheibel (224).]

have a more limited axonal distribution, whereas those in a more central location tend to project for longer distances. Classic among the latter are the larger neurons of the gigantocellularis, pontis caudalis, and pontis oralis nuclei, and perhaps n. cuneiformis, which are most likely to generate bifurcating axons running for long distances both rostrally and caudally. The branches of many of these, especially in upper pons and lower medulla, may extend without interruption both to spinal cord and to cerebral cortex (Fig. 11). These form the basis for short-latency ascending and descending core effects and undoubtedly represent only a fraction of the available complement of axons. Actually a spectrum of axonal lengths can be found to range from relatively limited trajectories (but not true short-axoned cells) to the great majority of intermediate-length elements. These elements connect various levels of the brain stem core and undoubtedly comprise the great majority of axons of the system. It is not yet known what proportion of these cells project, via large branches, to multiple major structures (i.e., spinal cord, cerebellum, basal ganglia, and cerebral hemispheres) instead of a single major trajectory or target. Furthermore the problem is not one that is easily addressed by any of the tracking methods available, including tagged amino acids and horseradish peroxidase. Limited numbers of trajectories can be worked out by means of methodical retrograde stimulation of intracellularly recorded neurons. Such a task is obviously laborious and requires a long-range commitment of time. Golgi analysis of serial thick sections through the brains of small laboratory animals, especially the young mouse and rat, offers an alternative that provides us with models of the various axonal trajectory complexes that may exist (Fig. 12).

Reticular cell axons are also remarkable for the richness of their smaller side branches or collaterals. The apparent frequency with which these emerge from the parent axon and the enormous range of target neuropil fields that they innervate (224) have been discussed. In fact there is probably no nuclear field or structural entity within the neuraxis that does not receive reticular axonal collaterals of varying sizes and lengths (including, of course, other portions of the core itself). On the basis of patterns studied in the young rodent, we have postulated (224) that if the average reticular collateral is 100 μm long and if one collateral emerges at some angle from the parent axon every 100 μm, then it can be conceived that a cylindrical volume, the area of potential interaction, surrounds each axon for virtually its entire course. Postsynaptic elements in this zone are particularly likely to receive synaptic contributions from this axon and may be considered to be, in a sense, under major synaptic control of this element, even though they are also receptive to many other inputs. The nature of intrareticular synaptic activities mediated by the local collateral systems is not entirely known. Studies by Ito et al. (105), however, indicate that "the pontomedullary reticular formation includes two groups of neurons, one of which inhibits, and the other excites, respectively, the reticular neurons themselves through abundant collaterals of their descending and ascending axons." (p. 225 in ref. 105).

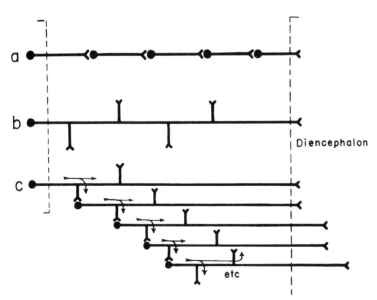

FIG. 12. Several possible conduction circuits through reticular core of the brain stem: *a*, type of chaining of short-axoned cells hypothesized by Moruzzi and Magoun (174) and by a number of other workers to explain conduction characteristics marked by slow transmission, long latency, and recruiting; *b*, single, long-axoned cell, reaching from bulb (*dashed line* at *left*) to diencephalon, illustrating type of conductor found in large numbers in reticular formation; *c*, the many collaterals of long conductors, as in *b*, may provide for more circuitous paths through reticular core, producing greater lateral dispersion and increasingly longer conduction times and longer latencies. [From Scheibel and Scheibel (224).]

An interesting functional question arises from the study of this system of multiple projections from single reticular neurons. Does activity generated by a reticular neuron propagate inexorably into every terminal, thereby exerting synaptic actions indiscriminately on all postsynaptic structures with which synaptic contacts are made? Effects as diffuse as this would seem to vary when compared with the focusing characteristics to which I have already alluded. Although specific gating mechanisms are still in question, evidence can be adduced that presynaptic inhibition, operating at the level of the individual target nucleus or field and probably mediated by indigenous local circuit neurons (Golgi type II), may be one of the mechanisms involved in adding selectivity to the multiplexed output of such reticular neurons (249).

Detailed descriptions of the termination of each axonal system are beyond the scope of this report. A few general comments can be made, however, regarding the major axonal outflow systems.

DESCENDING SYSTEMS. Descending systems appear to flow primarily from the medial two-thirds of the lower brain stem, particularly the medulla and pons (Fig. 13). The pontile projection appears largely ipsilateral; that from the medulla is both ipsilateral and contralateral. It was originally thought that most of these projection fibers came from large neurons in the n. reticularis gigantocellularis and the more rostral n.

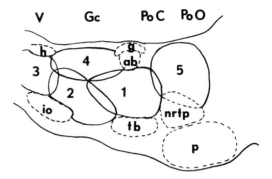

FIG. 14. Division of medial pontomedullary reticular cells into functional zones (*1–5*) on basis of somatomotor connections. *V*, n. ventralis; *Gc*, n. gigantocellularis; *PoC*, m. pontis caudalis; *PoO*, n. pontis oralis; *io*, inferior olive; *tb*, trapezoid body; *nrtp*, n. reticularis tegmenti pontis; *p*, pons; *h*, hypoglossal; *g*, genu; *ab*, abducens. [Adapted from Petersen (194).]

reticularis pontis caudalis and n. reticularis pontis oralis (264). [Subtle retrograde changes were more widespread, however, indicating a considerably wider derivation of these fibers, especially from smaller reticular neurons (A. Brodal, personal communication).] More recent fluorescence studies (47) indicate that a significant proportion of smaller cells, in a wider geographic distribution, may contribute to these projections, although the basic pattern appears essentially unchanged. Neurophysiological studies have begun to reveal spatial segregation of reticulospinal neurons on the basis of their spinal projection (see later in this section). Furthermore there is a considerable degree of shift from high to low conduction velocities between the pontine reticular formation and the caudal region of n. reticularis gigantocellularis.

Pontine reticular formation stimulation evokes monosynaptic EPSPs in spinal motoneurons transmitted over rapidly conducting reticulospinal fibers (87, 288), whereas stimuli originating caudal to the midpoint of n. reticularis gigantocellularis result in large, longer latency IPSPs in motoneurons (108). Despite the long-standing thesis that inhibitory phenomena depend on at least one intercalated sign-changing neuron (58), a notion that is now known to be overly limiting (104, 231), Ito (105) has recently shown that reticulospinal elements in the caudal region may be directly inhibitory. A considerable number of these caudally situated reticulospinal units appear to have slow conduction velocities, thereby explaining the longer latencies of reticular-evoked IPSPs in motoneurons supplying the hindlimbs.

At a more integrated level it is interesting to note that Grillner and Shik (88) have found that a 60-Hz stimulation of a region deep to inferior colliculus in tegmentum can produce locomotion on the treadmill in precollicular, postmammillary cats. Experimental studies indicate that the mechanism involves a descending slow-fiber system that activates spinal step-generating neurons (i.e., the spinal program for stepping). Such results might be explained if the noradre-

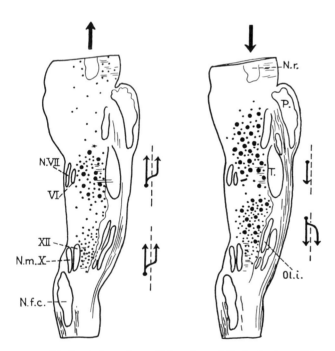

FIG. 13. Semischematic sagittal sections of the brain stem of the cat showing arrangement and distribution of reticular cells sending axons rostrally (*left*) and caudally (*right*). Despite considerable overlap caudally directed axons appear to arise somewhat more rostrad than do rostrally directed fibers. *Arrows* at *sides* of figures indicate that axon systems are both crossed and uncrossed except for fibers descending from the pons, which are uncrossed. [From Brodal (32).]

nergic reticulospinal system was activated from the mesencephalic locomotor region.

Recently reported studies by Willis et al. (285) have shed further light on descending reticular control over spinal sensory activity. Stimulus trains of 100 Hz or more at strengths as low as 25 μA applied to caudal raphe nuclei, especially the n. raphe magnus, are sufficient to greatly inhibit activity of spinothalamic tract cells and of dorsal horn interneurons. The effect appears to show considerable specificity because inhibition of the N_3 (third negative neural potential) component of the dorsally derived spinal cord negative potential (17) and of the late-burst discharges of spinothalamic tract neurons and interneurons is more profound than inhibition of the N_1 or N_2 (first and second negative neural potentials, respectively) waves and of the early-burst discharges. This element of reticulospinal control appears to be conducted over a pathway that is at least partially myelinated and that travels in the dorsolateral fasciculus. It is of particular interest that responses to both tactile and noxious stimuli are inhibited.

Recent studies by Peterson and his colleagues (194, 195) provide evidence that areas of selective projection originate within the medial pontomedullary reticular formation. As indicated in Figure 14, five zones have been identified. Zone 1 appears to exert an excitatory effect on motoneurons at all levels of the spinal cord, whereas zones 2 and 3 stimulate motoneurons supplying axial musculature of the neck and back. In addition zone 3 (the most caudal of the five zones) is a powerful inhibitor of cervical motoneurons. Zone 4 exerts its maximal effect on cervical motoneurons, providing both excitation and inhibition; zone 5, which primarily occupies the area anatomically identified as n. pontis oralis, appears to have no appreciable effect on spinal motor outflow.

Further information regarding the projection paths of axons originating in the paramedian pontine reticular formation has been supplied by means of the radioautographic studies by Graybiel (86). Neurons in the central pons appear to send an axonal projection of considerable size to the abducens nucleus and n. prepositus hypoglossi. More rostral pontine sites project primarily to nearby tegmentum and the central gray substance. More caudal areas (including the upper pole of the magnocellular complex and the n. pontis caudalis) generate a decussating system of axons reaching the contralateral abducens nucleus, n. prepositus hypoglossi, and parts of the vestibular complex (Fig. 15). These studies support earlier Golgi investigations in underlining numerous reticuloreticular paths of varying lengths and a strong contingent of collateral or terminal elements in the pretectum. In addition rostral areas of the pontile core (n. pontis oralis near its juncture with midbrain tegmentum) send rather heavy projections to the pars compacta of the substantia nigra and the subthalamic nucleus of Luys. These anatomical findings support the earlier

physiological studies by Bender and Shanzer (20, 21), which called attention to the upper pontine tegmentum as a center for several types of oculomotor control. In company with Peterson and associates (194, 195), Bender and Shanzer also emphasized the degree of specification that local pontile reticular zones achieve in their innervation of various structures associated with visual tracking.

Regarding sites of termination, reticulospinal fibers of pontine origin seem to terminate bilaterally in lamina VIII and adjacent parts of lamina VII. Contralateral terminations are primarily established by means of fibers crossing in the anterior commissure. Axons of medullary origin terminate primarily in lamina VII, although a small number seem to reach lamina IX, where they may end directly on both α- and γ-motoneurons (182).

SYSTEMS INVOLVED IN SUPPRESSION OF PAIN. Recent evidence indicates that the reticular core, under control of enkephalin-binding neurons of the periaqueductal gray matter, can modulate and suppress nociceptor systems at the spinal level. Although the full state of core involvement is not yet known, it seems clear that both the dorsal raphe nucleus (184) and the n. centralis inferior of the raphe complex (185) exert potent effects in suppression of pain in rats and cats. The system appears to be serotonergic in nature (though other chemically signatured systems may also be involved) and the descending fiber systems appear to be of both small and medium caliber. Repetitive stimulation in these sites appears to suppress behavioral reactions elicited by strong pinches to the tail or to the four limbs and modifies the threshold of the jaw-opening reflex obtained by tooth pulp stimulation. All of these inhibitory reactions are depressed by the opiate antagonist naloxone (184). At the spinal level, activity in neurons of laminae I and V appears to be selectively inhibited by raphe stimulation, the mechanism appearing to be postsynaptic in nature (23, 146). Lamina I cells are selectively activated by slowly conducting myelinated fibers (A-δ-) or unmyelinated C-fibers, or both (42, 265, 266), in both cat and monkey and appear to be primarily responsive to intense mechanical, thermal, or noxious stimulation (199, 286). Neurons of lamina V are also driven by noxious stimulation but are also responsive to wide-field convergent cutaneous stimuli (198, 286). Both of these cell systems appear to contribute to the formation of the spinothalamic tract (265, 266, 286) in conjunction with less well-defined elements in laminae VII–VIII (144). Willis (284) has identified the raphe magnus as another source of inhibitory control over spinothalamic tract cells (via the dorsolateral fasciculi). The n. reticularis gigantocellularis seems capable of producing both inhibitory and facilitatory effects on these target cells, so the mechanisms involved may be somewhat more complex. Because inhibitory effects still occur following lesions of the dorsolateral fasciculi (site of

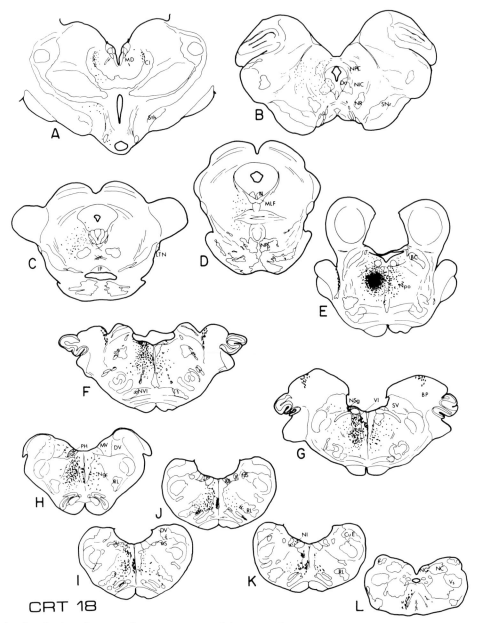

CRT 18

FIG. 15. Radioautographic analysis of projections from pontile tegmentum to abducens nucleus and nucleus prepositus hypoglossi in cat. Injection site is shown in heavy black in section *E*. Distribution of silver grain overlying efferent pathways traced from deposit is shown by *dots*. Of special interest is labeling in the ipsilateral abducens nucleus (*VI*) in section *G* and the nucleus prepositus hypoglossi (*PH*) in sections *H* and *J*. Considerable labeling also occurs throughout medial magnocellular portion of tegmentum, both at level of injection site and more caudally. Most intensive labeling appears in rostral part of nucleus gigantocellularis, (*Ngc*). Rostral projections are more sparse and are found mainly in mesencephalic tegmentum, ventral half of pretectal region, and in accessory oculomotor nuclei including interstitial nucleus of Cajal (*NIC*), and nucleus of posterior commissure (*NPC*). In thalamus, discrete accumulations appear at juncture of central lateral (*Cl*) and medial dorsal (*MD*) nuclei. *NR*, nucleus ruber; *SN*, substantia nigra; *IP*, interpeduncular nucleus; *LTN*, lateral terminal nucleus; *MLF*, medial longitudinal fasciculus; *NPp*, nucleus papilliformis; *BC*, brachium conjunctivum; *Npo*, nucleus pontis oralis; *NSG*, nucleus supragenualis; *SV*, superior vestibular nucleus; *BP*, brachium pontis; PH, nucleus prepositus hypogloss; *MV*, medial vestibular nucleus; *Dr*, descending vestibular nucleus; *NI*, nucleus intercalatus; *cuE*, external cuneate nucleus; *NG*, nucleus gracilis; *NC*, nucleus cuneatus; *f*, cell groups f of Brodal. [Adapted from Graybiel (86).]

the descending serotonergic system), Willis believes that the pathway involved may be one of the classic reticulospinal tracts.

The pathways linking periaqueductal gray matter with the raphe systems are not well worked out. Autoradiographic studies by Ruda (219), however, suggest that neurons in the ventral periaqueductal region project ventrally and caudally on elements of the raphe nuclear complex, and Golgi studies clearly show such axons collateralizing within the substance of the raphe system (A. B. Scheibel, unpublished data).

A recent report on the discovery of a nonpeptide morphinelike compound in the cell bodies of the raphe magnus (78) may be of interest in this regard. Significant concentrations of the substance have also been found in adjacent nuclear fields of the medial vestibular nuclei, n. prepositus hypoglossi, n. gigantocellularis, and in the fastigial nucleus of the cerebellum. These five zones are known to be interconnected by recurrent loops of varying lengths. Their conjoint, caudally directed output via axons of the n. raphe magnus and n. gigantocellularis may provide an important aspect of suprasegmental override acting on spinal sensory systems—in this case the system concerned with the reception and initial elaborations of nociceptive stimuli.

ASCENDING SYSTEMS. The ascending systems have been at least partially identified by a combination of electrophysiological, neurohistological (i.e., Golgi and various tracking methods), histochemical, and fluorescent techniques. Reticular axons appear to ascend through upper medulla, pons, and mesencephalon in several loose bundles on each side of the midline. Small numbers of fascicles run through more lateral areas of the core in the general region of the central tegmental tract. The major pathway bifurcates at the mesodiencephalic interface (33, 177, 212, 224, 229), sending a dorsal leaf into the medial one-third of the thalamus and a ventral leaf through the zona incerta and subthalamus. The dorsal leaf terminates primarily ipsilaterally among nuclear elements of the medial (nonspecific) thalamus, although in rodents a substantial collateral fraction crosses the midline to end contralaterally. Despite statements to the contrary (165), some collaterals and terminals definitely synapse in the centre médian–parafascicular complex, whereas the majority project somewhat more rostrally into the centralis medialis, reuniens, and rhomboidalis nuclei and into the more lateral intralaminar extensions (n. centralis lateralis and n. paracentralis). Fibers of the

ventral leaf appear to collateralize or terminate, or both, in the substance of the hypothalamus and the septal-basal forebrain region. The latter serves as a powerful intergrating and dispersal area en route to hippocampus and neocortex. Both anatomical and electrophysiological evidence suggest that approximately 10% of ventral leaf fibers project without synaptic interruption onto the cerebral neocortex, most probably to the anterior one-third of the hemisphere (159, 224, 229).

The major portion of this ascending relay system and its secondary projections to limbic cortex and cerebral neocortex appear to be cholinergic in nature (247, 248). Over the past 10 years histofluorescent techniques, developed by Falck and Hillarp and colleagues (63, 64) and applied specifically to the reticular core by Dahlstrom and Fuxe and their co-workers (47, 72, 73), have revealed a series of ascending aminergic pathways, both serotonergic and adrenergic, as well as powerful dopaminergic systems related more specifically to substantia nigra and perinigral outflow. Figures 16 and 17 summarize the approximate position and extent of these systems. They are also dealt with in relation to their specific nuclei in CHOLINERGIC NEURONS, p. 232 and in CATECHOLAMINERGIC NEURONS, p. 233.

Analysis of the ascending systems by means of Golgi impregnations has stressed the polyvalent nature of reticular connections and their participation in many noncore systems. Both terminals and collaterals have been traced to the mesencephalic tectum and into both medial and lateral geniculate nuclei (224, 229, 271, 272). Physiological correlates for these projections have been provided in a series of papers by Doty and his colleagues (16), who obtained varying degrees of facilitation or inhibition, or both, from multiple core sites in mesencephalic and pontine tegmentum. Parallel studies by Singer (249) suggest that facilitation of transmission through the lateral geniculate nucleus may depend largely on disinhibition and only minimally on postsynaptic excitation. Because systemic applications of atropine and scopolamine abolish these effects of reticular stimulation (W. Singer, unpublished observation), it may be inferred that cholinergic core systems are involved.

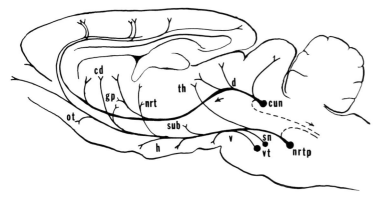

FIG. 16. Drawing of generalized small mammalian brain, showing some elements of ascending cholinergic reticular system of pons and mesencephalon and their projections throughout the neuraxis. *Dashed lines* represent probable but not fully established pathways. *cd*, Caudate nucleus; *cun*, n. cuneiformis; *d*, dorsal leaf of ascending reticular projection; *gp*, globus pallidus; *h*, hypothalamus; *nrt*, n. reticular thalami; *nrtp*, n. reticularis tegmenti pontis; *ot*, optic tract; *sn*, substantia nigra; *sub*, subthalamus; *th*, thalamus; *v*, ventral leaf of ascending reticular formation; *vt*, ventral tegmental nucleus. [Adapted from Shute and Lewis (248).]

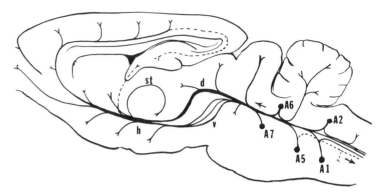

FIG. 17. Some major projections of noradrenergic systems of reticular core and their apparent terminal areas. Major pathways are ascending ones, using both dorsal leaf (*d*) and ventral leaf (*v*) of familiar reticular core pathways. Cell group *A6* (locus coeruleus) undoubtedly projects to cerebellum, tectum, lower brain stem, and spinal cord; medullary cell groups *A1* and *A5* may do so. *h*, Hypothalamus; *st*, stria terminalis. Most data from rat brain. [Adapted from Ungerstedt (269a).]

Evoked-potential studies of Lindsley (147) have shown how conditioning stimulation of the mesencephalic tegmentum facilitates the resolution of evoked visual-cortical responses to paired light flashes. At a behavioral level, Fuster and Uyeda (70) demonstrated that reticular stimulation in chronically implanted monkeys resulted in reduced reaction time and fewer perceptual errors in a tachistoscopic discrimination task. Although these effects might depend on reticularly induced changes in geniculate excitability alone, there is also evidence from changes in slow-wave patterns and from single-unit activity to support direct participation of the reticular elements in synaptic activity of the visual cortex (16, 121, 249). Analysis of the structure of the visual cortex in rodents and kittens, by use of Golgi methods, reveals the presence of the typical vertical fibers ascending from white matter to cortical surface, parallel to and often in repetitive synaptic contact with the apical shafts of pyramids that Lorenté de Nó (156) called "pluriareal" afferents. We have studied these elements in very small mice where they could be traced for long distances in a single section, and it seems highly probable that they are indeed terminals of corticipetal projections from the brain stem core or thalamic nonspecific nuclei, or both (230). If so this would supply the structural substrate for the physiological effects just noted.

Golgi studies have also revealed the presence of collaterals and terminals from ascending core fibers; they enter the ventrobasal nucleus of the thalamus and cross the more regular ensembles of synaptic fields generated by the terminating medial lemniscus. These fibers have been assumed to play a gain-setting role in somatosensory thalamic activities. Studies such as those by Yamamoto (290) and Melzack et al. (167) tend to support this notion. Yamamoto showed that trains of pulses to the reticular formation resulted in a 50% increase in response of many ventrobasal cells (fully half responded to reticular core stimulation), this response lasting for as long as 30 s. Further functional evidence of participation of the core in ventrobasal activity has been provided by McGowan-Sass and Eidelberg (164) and Lelord and Maho (142), who demonstrated that ventrobasal responses exhibit changes during habituation or conditioning. Thus a combination of structural and functional evidence documents participation of axon collaterals or terminals of reticular core origin in a number of thalamic sensory nuclei and in related cortical zones. Similar data can be adduced for the presence of reticular fibers in sensory processing nuclei at more caudal levels (i.e., the nuclei gracilis and cuneatus, and the descending trigeminal nucleus).

Systems With Specific Chemical Signature

CHOLINERGIC NEURONS. A considerable amount of information is available on the nature of specific chemical substances that characterize several axonal projection systems of the reticular core. Histochemical studies by Shute and Lewis (247, 248) have revealed two presumably cholinergic ascending systems (see Fig. 16).

The first of these, the dorsal tegmental pathway, arises largely from the cells in the nucleus cuneiformis of the mesencephalic tegmentum. The axon system runs rostrally and somewhat dorsally, supplying tectum, pretectal area, geniculate bodies, thalamus, and possibly portions of the globus pallidus. The thalamopetal projection includes a limited number of terminals to the centre médian–parafascicular complex; denser projections to the intralaminar nuclei (particularly n. centralis lateralis); and a low-to-medium-density projection to the anterior thalamic nuclear complex, the medial portion of the posteroventral nucleus (ventrobasal complex), and the ventrolateral nucleus. Some fibers are reported to traverse the nucleus reticularis thalami. This system has been shown to contain both acetylcholinesterase (AChe) and pseudocholinesterase (Che).

The second of these cholinergic ascending systems, the ventral tegmental pathway, contains AChe but is devoid of Che; it arises from the pars compacta of the substantia nigra and from cells of the ventral tegmental area of the anterior mesencephalon. Because many of the latter group are usually included within the province of the reticular core, they are relevant to this description. The bundle is joined by ascending fibers from the nucleus tegmenti pontis, which sends some of its fibers to the cerebellum. The combined ventral tegmental ensemble of fibers traverses the zona incerta, the supramammillary region, and the lateral hypothalamic area, and it continues rostrally at least as far as the basal forebrain, where it is believed to interact with AChe-containing cells of globus pallidus, the entopeduncular nucleus, and the lateral preoptic area (see Fig. 16). Smaller components, either collaterals or terminals, appear to join the mammillothalamic bundle and terminate in the area of the anterior thalamic complex.

The pattern and distribution of the dorsal and ventral tegmental bundles are approximately congruent with the thalamic portions of the ascending reticular activating system as delimited in the cat by Starzl et al. (256). In addition, studies by Kanai and Szerb (120), among others, indicate that high-frequency stimulation of the mesencephalic tegmentum, which characteristically desynchronizes the electroencephalogram (174), causes a five- to sixfold increase in output of ACh from the cortex. Administration of atropine blocks electrocortical arousal without interfering with the enhanced ACh output, thereby strongly suggesting that the source of the ACh is the ascending presynaptic system itself, rather than elements of cortical derivation.

On the other hand, it seems unlikely that these cholinergic systems represent the sole substrate for cortical activation. Intracarotid injection of barbiturate does not necessarily disturb consciousness (277). Furthermore the thalamic nonspecific system that has been considered by some to be concerned with phasic aspects of the conscious state (110, 111) apparently is not cholinergically mediated, since recruitment phenomena (51) are not disturbed by systemic administration of atropine (152). Note also that recruitment waves are selectively depressed by mephenesin, which has no effect on arousal (126). It is unlikely, however, that the thalamic nonspecific system represents an activating agent distinct from the cholinergic systems discussed in this section, especially in light of the data of Schlag and Chaillet (239). These workers found that a lesion just caudal to the thalamus impairs its capacity to produce low-voltage fast-wave patterns characteristic of cortical activation but does not interfere with thalamic ability to drive cortical recruitment potentials. Thus the inference may be drawn that desynchronization of cortical rhythms consequent to high-frequency stimulation of the thalamic nonspecific system is most likely due to a caudal projection playing upon the major ascending activating system of the core. Such a system is demonstrated anatomically in *Afferent Systems*, p. 222, and *Nucleus Reticularis Thalami*, p. 245.

CATECHOLAMINERGIC NEURONS. Monoamine-containing neurons are now known to be widely distributed throughout the medulla, pons, and mesencephalon (9, 47, 72, 73). Increasingly sensitive fluorescence and histochemical methods pioneered by Falck and his co-workers (63, 64) have revealed throughout the reticular core a complex substructure of neurons containing significant quantities of dopamine, norepinephrine, or serotonin (5-HT). A rough correlation has been established between cell systems as demarcated by histofluorescence and those groupings already established by classic cytoarchitectonic methodology. In addition a significant number of projections from these cell systems have been detailed through use of a combination of methods uniquely suited to this new field of "chemoanatomy." For instance, catecholamine-containing axons have been found to fluoresce with particular intensity during the very early postnatal period, thereby providing opportunities for their direct tracking at this point in the life cycle without surgical or pharmacological intervention (158). Artificial accumulation of monoamine granules can be facilitated in the proximal portion of a cut axon because of rapid cellulifugal transport of the material up to the lesion point (47). Alternatively, accumulations can be stimulated by injections of colchicine along target pathways (46). Selective unilateral electrical stimulation of a monoamine pathway can deplete terminal amine and granule distribution after inhibition of amine synthesis (H. Arbuthnot, unpublished data). Finally, central noradrenergic neurons may be pharmacologically destroyed with a high degree of selectivity by 6-hydroxydopamine (269). These techniques used individually and in combination have allowed the reconstruction of a contrapuntal arrangement of neurons identified in rostrocaudal sequence as A_1 through A_{12} (catecholamine-rich) and B_1 through B_9 (serotonin-rich). Both groups are described in some detail by Dahlstrom and Fuxe (47); only a few salient features are mentioned here (see Fig. 17).

Cell groups A_1 through A_4 appear to vary in degree of fluorescence and extend rostrally in discontinuous array from the level of the pyramidal decussation to the nucleus of the facial nerve. The most caudal of these nuclei, A_1, sends descending fibers, bearing fine norepinephrine-rich terminals, into the spinal gray matter. Group A_5 is found in and around the fibers of the rubrospinal tract at the approximate level of the superior olive and sends its axons ventrolaterally, running parallel to motor roots of cranial nerves V and VII for short distances before turning rostrally or caudally, or both. Group A_6 is a highly localized and intensely fluorescing cluster that seems to be identical with the locus coeruleus (Fig. 18). Axon systems from this group have been traced down into the spinal cord, throughout the brain stem, up into the cerebral cortex, where dissemination of the fiber branches seems to be exceptionally wide [(112); Fig. 19], and into the cerebellar cortex; intriguing questions have been raised about the functional role of this third cerebellar afferent system. Fortunate Golgi studies also emphasize the extraordinarily wide dispersion of the axonal branches from single coerulean cells (Fig. 19). Cell groups A_7 and A_8 extend in discontinuous patches from the upper pontile into the lower mesencephalic

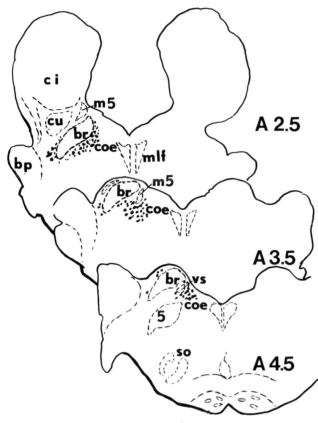

FIG. 18. Distribution of cell bodies containing catecholamine (norepinephrine) in dorsolateral tegmentum of pons of cat. Rostrally the cells appear grouped about brachium conjunctivum cerebelli (*br*) and extend somewhat beyond confines of locus coeruleus (*coe*). Further caudad some cells are located near ventricular surface. *bp*, Brachium pontis; *ci*, inferior colliculus; *cu*, nucleus cuneiformis; *mlf*, medial longitudinal fasciculus; *so*, superior olive; *m5*, main sensory nucleus of trigeminal nerve; *vs*, superior vestibular nucleus. *A 2.5, A 3.5*, and *A 4.5* indicate stereotaxic transverse plane of section. [Based on data of Chu and Bloom (42a).]

tegmentum and may represent many of the reticular neurons with long ascending axons. Cell groups A_9 and A_{10} seem to form an almost continuous crescent on each side of the midline, dorsal to the cerebral peduncle, and include initially all of the substantia nigra and parts of adjacent nonnigral tegmentum. Most but not all of these nuclei are source neurons for the dopamine-rich nigrostriatal pathways that have come to figure so prominently in our understanding of the pathogenesis of extrapyramidal disease (14, 24). There is some evidence of differentiation between medial and lateral nigroneostriatal dopaminergic pathways. Most intriguing is the evidence of Butcher et al. (35) that dopamine cell bodies in the medial part of the zona compacta and the presumably related terminals in the medial portion of the neostriatum show a less marked increase in fluorescence intensity after dopa loading than do the dopamine-containing cell bodies and terminals of the lateral portions of zona compacta and neostriatum, respectively.

One possible behavioral correlate of this chemoanatomical difference may be found in the recent studies of LeMoal et al. (143). These workers report that radio-frequency ablation of the ventral mesencephalic tegmentum in the rat provokes a specific behavioral syndrome appearing 8 days after lesioning and persisting for at least 210 days thereafter. The syndrome is characterized by hyperactivity and hyperreactivity during wakefulness, with only minor changes in sleep patterning and no statistically significant differences in the percentage of wakefulness and slow-wave sleep when compared with control animals. The percentage of desynchronized sleep is somewhat reduced but this is not in itself considered to be responsible for the hyperactive and hyperreactive state shown by the animals. The relatively long latency period (8 days) preceding appearance of the syndrome is considered by these authors to be due to a supersensitization process secondary to destruction of the A_{10} group of mesolimbic dopaminergic neurons. Furthermore it has been shown by Stinus et al. (259) that small doses of apomorphine or chronic administration of *d*-amphetamine (both dopaminomimetic drugs), or both, tend to reverse the locomotor hyperactivity characteristic of the ventral mesencephalic tegmental (VMT) syndrome. These workers suggest that the VMT A_{10} syndrome might provide a useful animal model for pathophysiological studies.

Rough quantitative figures available for group A_9 suggest the enormous extent and divergence of each element. Andén et al. (10) have estimated the number of dopamine-containing neurons on each side of the

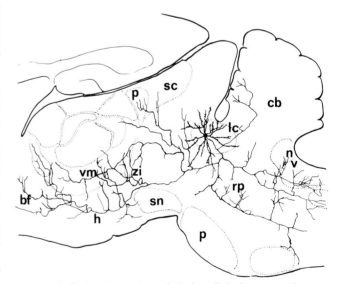

FIG. 19. Projection system of single cell in locus coeruleus as reconstructed from 2 adjacent Golgi-stained sections of 14-day-old mouse. *bf*, Basal forebrain; *cb*, cerebellum; *h*, hypothalamus; *lc*, locus coeruleus; *nv*, vestibular nuclear complex; *p*, pons; *rp*, nucleus raphe pontis; *sc*, superior colliculus; *sn*, substantia nigra; *vm*, ventromedial thalamus; *zi*, zona incerta. [Adapted from Scheibel and Scheibel (236a); used with permission of the New York Academy of Sciences.]

brain stem to be about 3,500 and the amount of dopamine in each terminal varicosity to be about 2.5 $\times 10^{-4}$ pg, with a concentration of 8,000 μg/g wet wt. They further suggest that the total terminal length of each axon is about 65 cm and each axon contains approximately 500,000 varicosities. It is therefore apparent that a relatively small cell ensemble can exert powerful and widespread effects on target organs.

It might be noted in passing that marked interspecies differences in the distribution of catecholamine varicosities in the brain stem reticular formation of the rat and the cat have been reported. As an example, Sladek (253) has contrasted the strongly fluorescing granule systems of the cat with matched areas in the reticular formation of the rat that appear virtually fluorescence free.

A majority of the A_{10} contingent of dopaminergic neurons terminate in the olfactory tubercle, the n. accumbens septi, the dorsolateral portion of the interstitial nucleus of the stria terminalis, and the central portion of the amygdaloid nucleus (9). This mesolimbic projection runs, in a sense, parallel to the lateral-lying nigrostriatal system (A_9), projects to a group of ventral- and rostral-lying stations, and is appreciably less rich in dopamine. Evidence of direct dopaminergic projections on the cerebral cortex has been supplied, however, by Fuxe et al. (71), who have traced pathways from cell bodies in the midbrain, probably from lateral A_{10} and medial A_9 (area ventralis tegmenti) to limbic and neocortical areas. The axons are thought to travel in the medial forebrain bundle and innervate all cortical zones to which the medial forebrain bundle is known to project.

SEROTONERGIC NEURONS. An equally complex, if more geographically limited, ensemble of nuclei makes up the serotonin-rich elements of the core. These are concentrated in discontinuous groups from the lower medulla through the mesencephalon, in and about the midline or raphe (see also Fig. 2). They generate a weak-to-moderate yellow fluorescence and are therefore usually accentuated by pretreatment of the animal with monoamine oxidase inhibitors. Group B_1 corresponds roughly with the nucleus raphe pallidus, although it probably includes at least several discrete cell groups. These are located in the caudal and ventral medulla from the level of the pyramidal decussation to the inferior olive. Group B_2 is made of small-to-medium-sized cells within the general area of the n. raphe obscurus. The cell bodies appear elongated and dorsoventrally oriented in the raphe. The nodulated axons of B_2 run caudally into spinal cord close to the midline and to axons descending from B_1. Group B_3 is a larger and more multivalent grouping that seems to extend at least from the middle one-third of the medulla into lower pons and includes elements of the slightly more lateral-lying n. paragigantocellularis (262) and the n. raphe magnus. A large number of axons appear to project caudally into the spinal cord.

Group B_4 appears to include a very limited aggregate of cell bodies just under the fourth ventricle, dorsal to the vestibular complex and VIth nerve nucleus. Group B_6 appears to be its rostral continuation into the pons, while B_5 cells are approximately congruent with the n. raphe pontis.

Nuclei B_7, B_8, and B_9 are all limited to the caudal portion of the mesencephalon and tend to transcend an exclusively raphe location, both dorsally and ventrally. Group B_7 represents a large population of closely packed cells centered in the n. dorsalis raphe but spilling over laterally into the third and fourth cranial nerves, the medial longitudinal fasciculus, and the periaqueductal gray matter. The cell bodies of group B_8 are located more ventrally along the midline and appear to include most or all of n. medianus raphe and n. linearis, whereas group B_9 is situated ventrolaterally, centered on the medial lemniscus and the immediately overlying reticular tegmentum.

The projections of the rostral group have been somewhat difficult to work out, but a remarkably broad pattern has begun to emerge, engaging significant amounts of diencephalon and telencephalon. Axons first run ventrally and then turn rostrally just above the n. interpeduncularis to form a bundle lying medial to the fasciculus retroflexus of Meynert and close to the lateral border of each fornix. These fibers are joined by fibers that are more laterally originating and similarly rich in serotonin, and they run within (or close to) the medial forebrain bundle. Some axons terminate in the mammillary body, while others are disseminated widely throughout limbic forebrain structures, the hypothalamus, and the n. suprachiasmaticus (3, 9, 10, 196).

Joint Golgi–electron-microscopic studies indicate that cell-dendrite systems of several of the raphe systems, particularly n. raphe pontis and n. linearis rostralis, are physically very close to blood vessels [(238); Fig. 20]. The dendrites of these two cell groups, in particular, are closely applied to the blood vessel walls and are frequently segregated from the vascular compartment only by a thin endothelial cell and intimal barrier. This raises questions about the possibility of special neurovascular relations. The raphe cells could be envisaged either as neurosecretory systems releasing substances into the circulation or else as receptors sensitive to certain circulating messenger substances. In view of their apparently obligatory role in the onset of sleep (115, 116), they might detect bloodborne substances such as cortisol and ACTH (169, 282), whose concentrations are time locked to circadian rhythms and possibly to the shorter rest-activity cycle of Kleitman (129, 130).

It is still too early to understand the significance of these individually signatured reticular-core projection systems and their complex pathways along the brain stem into the spinal cord, cerebellum, and diencephalic-telencephalic complex. Fuxe and his co-workers (73) suggest that the ascending norepinephrine sys-

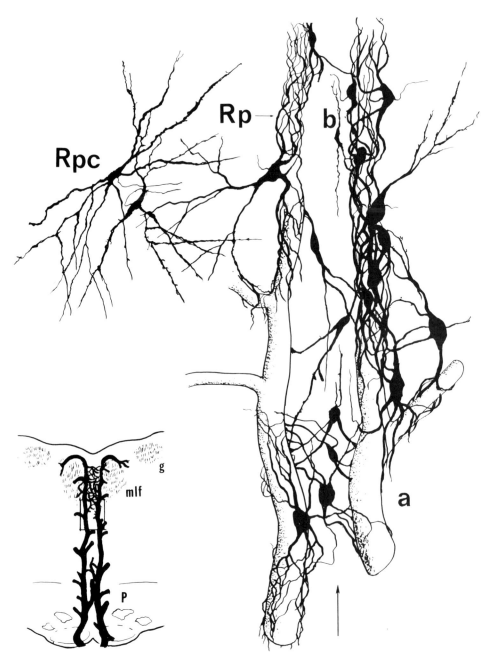

FIG. 20. Drawing of Golgi-stained cross section of 10-day-old kitten through pontile tegmentum showing how neurons of nucleus raphe pontis (*Rp*) climb along raphe blood vessels that are lightly impregnated (*a*) and unimpregnated (*b*). *Vertical arrow* indicates midline. Dendrites of some neurons bridge across midline and make contact with raphe vessels on both sides. *Inset,* part of the raphe vascular system at this level; *square,* area depicted in drawing. *Rpc*, nucleus reticularis pontis caudalis; *p*, pons; *mlf*, medial longitudinal fasciculus; *g*, genu of nerve VII. × 186. [From Scheibel, Tomiyasu, and Scheibel (238).]

tems are involved in the development of defense and attack behavior necessary to the organism's survival. Dopaminergic systems could supply the substrate of movement that might then be molded by the norepinephrinergic systems with their enormous arrays of collaterals penetrating into almost every portion of the nervous system. The dorsal ascending pathway, with its richer connections to thalamus and cerebral cortex, is conceived as being primarily concerned with varying levels of alertness, undoubtedly working in concert with the ascending cholinergic systems already described. The ventral pathway, with its preponderance of connections to hypothalamus and limbic system, might then be more closely related to autonomic activities (such as fear and rage) and the stigmata of threat-aggression (and possibly submission). Pathways descending from the more caudal norepineph-rine-containing nuclei might also be involved in such global reactions on the basis of their regulation of spinal reflex activity (decreasing transmission in short-latency pathways from flexor reflex afferents) and preganglionic systems of the sympathetic chain. Need-less to say, some of these norepinephrinergic neurons may generate the classic bifurcating axons now so familiar from Golgi impregnations, thereby further disseminating the effect.

An interesting footnote to these notions is supplied by the studies by Anlezark et al. (13), who showed that bilateral lesions of locus coeruleus in rats resulted in depletion of norepinephrine levels in cerebral cortex and diminished the rate of increase in running for food reward in a maze. Learning appeared to be absent in those rats with the most complete coerulean lesions. These authors contrasted these results with those of Lashley (140), who found that massive cerebral corti-cal lesions had little effect on the learning of simple tasks. They concluded that their data underline the significance of noradrenergic terminals in the cortex in the mediation of synaptic changes involved in learning.

The ascending components of the serotonin-rich raphe systems may be considered, in a very approxi-mate sense, to exert effects antagonistic to those of the norepinephrinergic system. In addition to the more obvious suppression of synchronized sleep by exten-sive raphe lesions or after *p*-chlorophenylalanine blockade by tryptophan hydroxylase (131), electrical stimualtion of raphe nuclei in the mesencephalon pro-duces behavioral signs of calmness and a sleeplike slow-wave pattern in the EEG (135). Furthermore, habituation to external stimuli, a physiological pattern characteristic of the reticular core (19, 103, 226), is reduced after such stimulation. In addition, behavioral effects of enhanced central norepinephrinergic trans-mission obtained by potentiation with drugs such as Catapresan are potentiated by tryptophan hydrox-ylase inhibition and inhibited by serotonin receptor stimulation caused by lysergic acid diethylamide (K. Fuxe, unpublished data).

Descending serotonergic activity is particularly ef-fective in the lumbosacral cord (70a), operating in both autonomic (8b) and somatic (73) systems. In rats with transected spinal cords the extensor hindlimb reflex is markedly increased by an increase in sero-tonin receptor activity (8a).

Ontogenetic studies by Olson and Seiger (186) indi-cate that all monoamine neuron systems in rat brain stem develop their chemical specifications within the period between the 12th day and the 15th day of gestation. This precocious appearance of mechanisms for synthesis and storage of amines antedates the development of terminal neuropil and establishment of normal synaptic functions. Olson and Seiger have speculated on a possible role (other than that of neural transmission) during ontogeny. Such a notion receives putative support from Pannese et al. (189) and Buz-nikov and co-workers (36), who have demonstrated, respectively, the early appearance of acetylcholines-terase in spinal autonomic ganglion neuroblasts prior to the onset of synaptic function and the apparently significant effect of transmitter substances in early embryogenesis of the sea urchin. Aghajanian and Bloom (2) have suggested that chemosensitivity an-tedates synaptogenesis, a conceptually attractive, if as yet unproved, concept. It is worth noting, however, that in my own experience to date, unusually intimate relationships have been found between the vascular compartment and two of the three major monoamin-ergic cell systems [(238); A. B. Scheibel, unpublished data]. It can be argued that this also suggests a neu-rohormonal role for aminergic systems in addition to their putative synaptic functions.

THALAMIC NONSPECIFIC SYSTEM

Since the time of Ramón y Cajal (203a) the central core of thalamic tissue surrounding the third ventricle has been recognized as structurally distinct from the massive surrounding bulk of thalamic nuclear fields. It has been only since 1939, however, when the studies by Forbes and Morison (68) were initially published, that the unique significance of this small complex of nuclei has begun to be appreciated. Ordinarily this core is not included in the overall category of brain stem reticular formation, although it probably derives from the archetypal brain stem interneuron just as do the neurons of the reticular core. Its dendrite systems appear to combine features of both isodendritic (gen-eralized) and allodendritic (specialized) patterning, and its outflow is frequently characterized by bifur-cating axons that run both rostrally and caudally. The neurons themselves present a broader range of pat-terns, both in size and in dendritic domain, than has been realized. The neuropil is particularly complex: it consists primarily of unmyelinated axonal components and, in the more posterior portion, is rich in synaptic glomeruli (283), a feature totally absent in the brain stem core. The reader may wish to consult the chapter by Jones in this *Handbook*.

The general scope of the system varies according to the investigator; terminology for this area, as else-where for the brain stem and the thalamus, is far from satisfactory. Cytoarchitectonic descriptions of the component nuclei have been attempted in whole or in part by Grünthal (89), Rioch (208, 209), Gurdjian (90), Krieg (137), Sheps (245), the Vogts (276), Hassler (94), Van Buren and Borke (273), and others; the classic descriptions of connections for the system are un-doubtedly those of Le Gros Clark and Boggon (43) and Walker (279).

Difficulties inherent in analysis of this portion of the thalamus cannot be overemphasized. Concepts of basic structural floor plans for the various subnuclei are still primitive, if they exist at all. Reliable information on input and output connections has just recently become available. Nonetheless these medial thalamic nuclei, together with the thalamus-enfolding lamina constituting the nucleus reticularis thalami, appear to play a vital role in modulation of all sensorimotor functions in the fine tuning of all state-dependent cortical activities and probably in the focusing of conscious processes. For this reason some consideration of the organization and function of the system seems indicated, no matter how abbreviated the attempt.

Cell Groups

The main nuclear masses constituting the thalamic nonspecific system as seen in cat coronal sections are shown in schematized form in Figure 21. These masses consist of paired nuclear fields organized in a rostrocaudal sequence flanking the third ventricle, and a group of smaller, unpaired, midline-bridging elements. The most caudal and prominent of the paired nuclei is the centre médian–parafascicular (CM-Pf) complex situated immediately anterior to the mesodiencephalic interface, the point where the major ascending projections from the reticular core separate into dorsal and ventral leaves. Progressing more anteriorly are the paracentral (Pc), central lateral (CL), anteromedial (AM), ventral medial (VM), and the parataenial nuclei (Pt). The unpaired groups include the periventricular complex (PVA and PVH), reuniens (RE), rhomboidal (Rh, not pictured), submedian (Sm), central medial (CM), and the more anterior complex of interanteromedial (IAM), anterior dorsal (AD), and anteroventral (AV) nuclei. Winglike extensions (the internal medullary laminae) from the paired nuclear masses, composed largely of the paracentral and central lateral nuclei, extend dorsolaterally to enfold the medial dorsal (MD) nucleus, which is not included in the roster of thalamic nonspecific nuclei. Surrounding the entire thalamus and separating it from the internal capsule is the nucleus reticularis thalami (R), which constitutes the external medullary lamina. The apparently unique role played by this thin platelike field is discussed in *Nucleus Reticularis Thalami*, p. 245.

It should be noted that marked interspecies variation exists in the structure of the thalamic nonspecific system, perhaps reflecting the rapidly changing form and function of the overlying cerebral cortices. In rodents, for instance, the parafascicular nucleus is the dominant component in the CM-Pf complex. Some investigators insist that no centre médian exists in the rat (165), and the numerous rat brain atlases available reflect this uncertainty. In carnivores such as the cat, centre médian approximates the parafascicular field in size, whereas in primates and human beings the parafascicular nucleus is appreciably smaller than the centre médian field, which now forms one of the most obvious landmarks of the posterior one-third of the diencephalon. The entire thalamic nonspecific system,

in relation to the total mass of the thalamus, becomes relatively (although not absolutely) smaller in primates and human beings. This appears to result from the tremendous increase in size of the relay nuclei and, in particular, of the dorsomedial and dorsolateral components that project to the enormously expanded association areas of cortex. The third ventricle is much more prominent in primates than in rodents or carnivores and makes much greater incursions on the domain of the unpaired central masses. In the human brain this central group is limited to an isolated anterior band of thalamic tissue bridging the ventricle, and even this is not present in approximately 30% of human subjects. The significance of this trend toward increased isolation of the two halves of the thalamus is unknown. We have speculated that it might reflect the progressive development of lateralization of function in the hemispheres (228–230).

Dendritic Patterns

Organization of the dendritic components of the thalamic nonspecific system is complex. Golgi studies in rodents (203a, 230, 233) tend to emphasize the impact of size and shape of the individual nuclear field on the form of dendritic domain. This seems especially true in the periventricular zone, in the immediately perifascicular portions of the parafascicular nucleus, and in the intralaminar zone and nucleus reticularis thalami. In addition, dendritic pattern reflects the orientation of axonal inputs. For instance, neurons of the reuniens, rhomboidal, and central medial nuclei, subject as they are to heterogeneous influx from a number of directions and from both halves of the thalamus, are characterized by dendritic systems radiating in all directions.

On the other hand a characteristically transverse orientation marks the dendritic domains of most parafascicular neurons. In the young rat the lateral dendritic mass extends several hundred micrometers outside the fasciculus retroflexus, running in parallel with at least two classes of axonal terminals (Fig. 22), which establish repetitive "climbing" contacts along these lateral parafascicular dendrites. The shorter medial dendrites seem to establish a very different type of crossover contact with periventricular axons running in a rostrocaudal direction.

A third pattern is shown by the immediately perifascicular dendrite segments, which are closely applied to the convexity of the fasciculus retroflexus from which a number of short terminal collaterals emerge. Neurons making up the field of the anterior medial nucleus show a predominantly transversely arranged dendrite pattern (Fig. 23). Here the relevant presynaptic components appear to consist of collaterals and terminals from contralateral cells crossing in the commissural system with a probable admixture of ipsilaterally and contralaterally derived corticothalamic axons descending via the inferior thalamic peduncle.

Comparable Golgi studies of the CM-Pf complex in

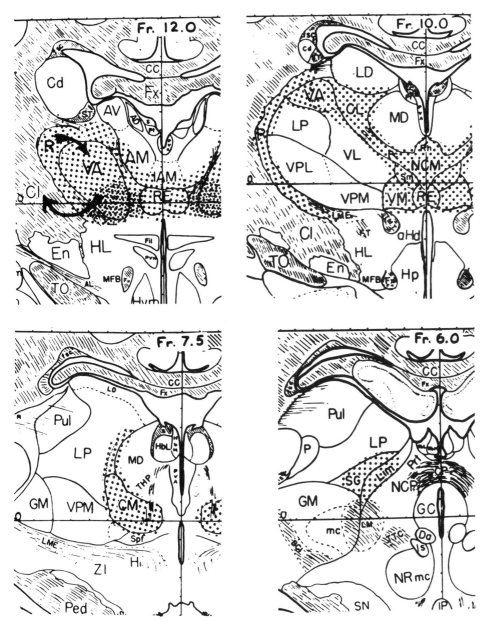

FIG. 21. Diagrammatic map of feline thalamic nonspecific system at four levels along the rostro-caudal axis, as determined by areas giving rise to recruiting responses. *AD*, anterodorsal nucleus; *aHd*, dorsal hypothalamic area; *AL*, ansa lenticularis; *AM*, anteromedial nucleus; *AV*, anteroventral nucleus; *BCI*, brachium of inferior colliculus; *CC*, corpus callosum; *Cd*, caudate nucleus; *Cl*, claustrum; *CL*, central lateral nucleus; *CM*, central medial nucleus; *CP*, posterior commissure; *Da*, nucleus of Darkschewitch; *En*, entopeduncular nucleus; *Fil*, filiform nucleus, *fsc*, subcallosal fasciculus; *FT*, thalamic fasciculus; *Fx*, fornix; *GC*, central gray matter; *GM*, medial geniculate body; *HbL*, lateral habenular nucleus; *HbM*, medial habenular nucleus; H_1, field of Forel; *HL*, lateral hypothalamus; *Hp*, posterior hypothalamus; *IAM*, interanteromedial nucleus; *IP*, interpeduncular nucleus; *Is*, interstitial nucleus; *LD*, lateral dorsal nucleus; *Lim*, nucleus limitans; *LM*, medial lemniscus; *LME*, external medullary lamina; *LP*, lateral posterior nucleus; *mc*, pars magnocellularis; *MD*, medial dorsal nucleus; *MFB*, medial forebrain bundle; *NCM*, central medial nucleus; *NCP*, posterior commissural nucleus; *NR*, red nucleus; *P*, posterior nucleus; *Pc*, paracentral nucleus; *Ped*, cerebral peduncle; *Prt*, pretectum; *Pt*, parataenial nucleus; *Pul*, pulvinar; *PVA*, anterior periventricular nucleus; *PVH*, periventricular hypothalamic nucleus; *R*, reticular nucleus; *RE*, nucleus reuniens; *S*, medullary stria; *SG*, suprageniculate nucleus; *Sm*, submedian nucleus; *SN*, substantia nigra; *Spf*, subparafascicular nucleus; *ST*, terminal stria; *THP*, habenulopeduncular tract; *TMT*, mammillothalamic tract; *TO*, optic tract; *TTC*, central tegmental tract; *VA*, ventral anterior nucleus, *VL*, ventral lateral nucleus; *VM*, ventral medial nucleus; *VPL*, ventral posterolateral nucleus; *VPM*, ventral posteromedial nucleus; *ZI*, zona incerta. *Arrows* in *upper left* diagram indicate 2 major directions of information flow at rostral pole of thalamus. *Dotted areas* represent zones from which recruitment responses were obtained. [Adapted from Jasper (110a).]

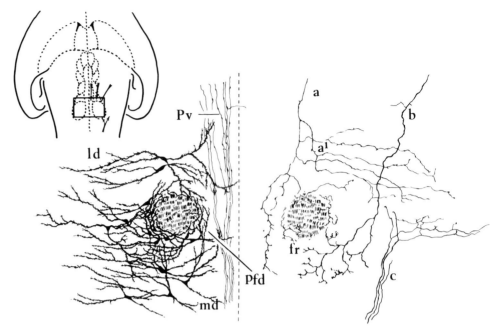

FIG. 22. Dendritic and axonal organization in posterior portion of medial thalamus in area of parafascicular nucleus of 12-day-old rat. Dendrites arranged primarily in mediolateral orientation. They are crossed by rostrocaudally oriented periventricular fiber bundles (*Pv*) and accompanied by collaterals from descending intralaminar fibers (*a*, *a*^{1}) and ascending reticular fibers (*c*). Axon (*b*), which may have come from nucleus reticularis thalami, bears a number of small terminal synaptic structures resembling axosomatic boutons. Modified rapid Golgi-impregnated section cut in horizontal plane. *Inset*: slightly schematized drawing of horizontal section through diencephalon and forebrain of young rat, showing location (*rectangle*) of area involved on each side of midline (*vertical dashed line*). *Arrows*, paths of converging afferents from more rostral areas. Other abbreviations: *ld*, lateral dendrite mass; *md*, medial dendrite mass; *pfd*, perifascicular dendrites; *fr*, fasciculus retroflexus (of Meynert). × 143. [From Scheibel and Scheibel (230).]

the monkey (95) reveal richer detail and a broader range of cell types. Two basic types of long-axoned (Golgi type I) neurons are found: one has essentially spine-free dendrites, whereas the other has densely spined dendritic systems. The latter type bears along its dendritic and somatic surfaces wisplike appendages, shorter than dendrites and longer than classic spines, each bearing its own spiny complement. The authors have named these microdendrites and apparently consider them to be another type of specialized postsynaptic structure. Short-axoned (Golgi type II) cells are present, though fewer in number. Many of their dendritic shafts are beaded and terminate in bulbous enlargements that appear to contribute to complex synaptic arrangements or tangles.

Electron-microscopic studies of the CM-Pf complex by Westman and Bowsher (283), by Harding and Powell (93), and by the Hazletts (96) have shed further light on the organization of the neuropil in the posterior one-third of the thalamic nonspecific system. Marked differences have been shown between this area and the brain stem reticular core. Westman and Bowsher (283) comment particularly on the absence of bouton-covered polydendritic neurons in the thalamic field and the predominance of a more simply domained nerve cell species characterized as oligodendritic. These cells are further characterized by the presence of electron-dense, mitochondria-containing, blunt-tipped protrusions on both dendritic and somal surfaces. The area is unusually rich in small unmyelinated axons and in axoaxonal synapses [a fact also noted by Pappas et al. (191)]. Of particular note is the presence of synaptic glomeruli (Fig. 24), structures now known to be common in nuclei of sensory processing systems (191, 202, 261) but not present in the reticular core of the brain stem (29). It seems likely that the synaptic tangles described by Hazlett et al. (95) at the light-microscope level are related to the synaptic glomeruli noted by Westman and Bowsher (283) with the electron microscope.

An analysis of CM-Pf organization in the cat, based on electrophysiological methods by Bénita and Condé (22), has provided useful insights into topographical limits and cell function. Neurons at the mesodiencephalic junction were divided into three major classes based on their modes of response to stimulus combinations from the reticular core, superior colliculus, and cerebellar dentate nucleus. From the topographical point of view, no significant difference was noted between centre médian and parafascicular fields. The major efferent cell of the nuclear complex was believed to be under the direct facilitatory control of the more caudal reticular core. The other cell types received varying mixtures of afferent terminals from the collic-

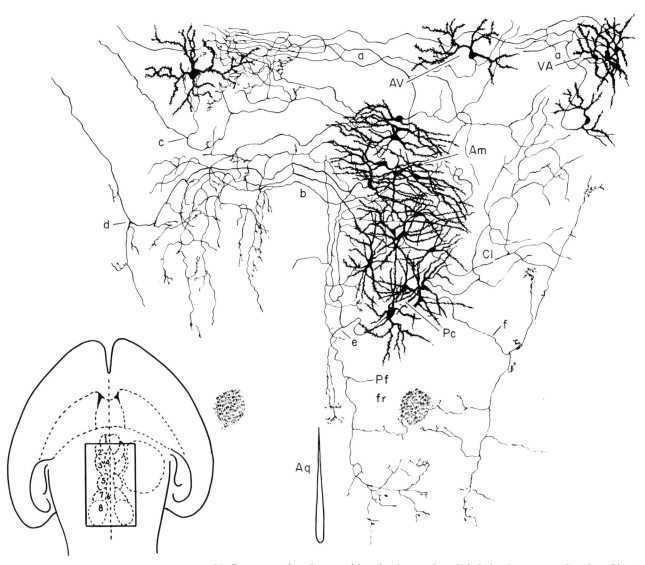

FIG. 23. Some axonal pathways of intralaminar and medial thalamic neurons of 14-day-old rat. Axon *a* from an anteromedial nuclear cell (*Am*) projects rostrally, both ipsilaterally and contralaterally. Axon *b* is the contralateral projection of an anteromedial neuron with both local and distant connections, while axons *c* and *d*, of similar derivation, project both rostrally and caudally on contralateral side. Axons *e* and *f* are from paracentral neurons (*Pc*), and both project rostrally and caudally. *Aq*, aqueduct of Sylvius; *AV*, anterior ventral nucleus; *Cl*, central lateral nucleus; *Pf*, parafascicular nucleus; *VA*, ventral anterior nucleus; and *fr*, fasciculus retroflexus. *Inset*: slightly schematized drawing of horizontal section through diencephalon and forebrain of young rat. *Rectangle*: area involved in figure. Modified rapid Golgi-stained section cut in horizontal plane. × 120. [From Scheibel and Scheibel (230).]

uli, the cerebellar dentate nucleus, and the recurrent loops generated by the CM-Pf output to putamen. These facilitatory inputs in turn drove neurons exerting inhibitory control over the output elements already mentioned. Such an organizational scheme is probably oversimplified; it has the further disadvantage of having been worked out in the chloralosane preparation with its well-known neuropharmacological idiosyncracies. It may nonetheless be useful in suggesting modes for further analysis of this complex region.

Very little information is yet available on the spe-

cific biochemical signatures of these thalamic nonspecific cell systems. However, Parent and Butcher (192) have provided introductory data on acetylcholinesterase (AChe) concentrations for a number of thalamic and hypothalamic nuclei. Among the nonspecific group they report very high levels of AChe in the anterior dorsal nuclei; moderate to strong AChe activity in the rhomboidal nucleus, most intralaminar nuclei, and the nucleus reticularis thalami; and very low activity in anterior ventral and parataenial nuclei. The functional significance of these differences is not yet apparent.

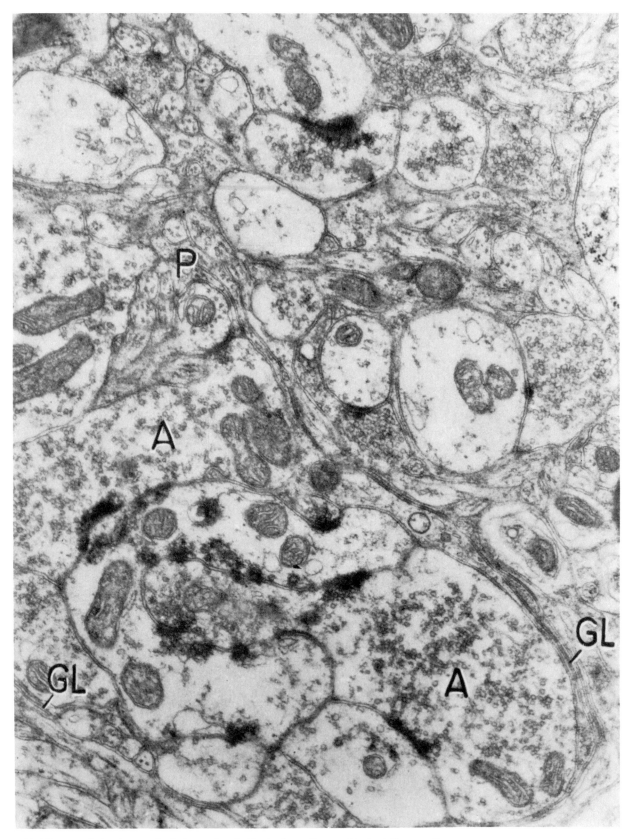

FIG. 24. Electron photomicrograph of glomerulus similar to those discussed in text. Surrounding glial sheaths (*GL*) encapsulate several presynaptic axonal processes (*A*) and a preterminal process (*P*) entering the complex. Midline thalamus, adult cat. × 16,000. [From Pappas et al. (191).]

Afferent Systems

The thalamic nonspecific system is virtually enfolded by the dorsal and ventral leaves (constituting the ascending projections) of the brain stem reticular core in the vertical plane, and by the fiber masses of the surrounding spinothalamic system in the horizontal plane. Shorter relays from tectal and tegmental stations penetrate the system's posterior face, whereas its anterior-inferior and lateral surfaces receive a broad spectrum of descending fibers from cortical and subcortical levels. In addition a complex (and as yet incompletely worked out) system of intrathalamic relays serves to interconnect the various neuropil fields of the medial and midline systems and generates powerful reciprocal connections with adjacent specific and association nuclei. The nonspecific fields thereby sit at a confluence of systems of caudal, rostral, and local derivation; this may be unique in the brain stem.

A combination of anatomical and physiological techniques have revealed many details about input arrangements. Spinal afferents from the anterolateral column reach the parafascicular and central lateral nuclei in the cat (11) and monkey (25, 166). The major spinal input to the centre médian, however, appears to project via the gigantocellular nucleus of the medullary reticular core (5, 27, 177), and this spinoreticulo–centre médian path is now believed to be the most important single somesthetic pathway to the caudal portion of the thalamic nonspecific system (26, 28). It should be added, however, that Mehler (165) believes the centre médian receives no afferents from spinal or brain stem sites and is the exclusive recipient of descending fibers from forebrain structures, especially globus pallidus and motor cortex.

The CM-Pf complex demonstrates both heterosensory and heterotopic convergence, although the lateral wing of the centre médian appears to "prefer" certain parts of the body (25). This may reflect specificities already established at the level of the reticular magnocellular nucleus (A. Mallart, D. Bowsher, and D. Albe-Fessard, unpublished observations, quoted in ref. 25). On the other hand, Kuypers (139) reports that in the chimpanzee there is differential distribution of the projections from various portions of the cortical motor strip area onto the CM field. Such data make it seem less likely that the centre médian represents an undifferentiated, isotropic field. Cortical sensory projections to CM appear to arise exclusively in somatosensory area II (4, 41) and are probably inhibitory in function, although it is not clear whether this effect is direct or relayed through the striatum and globus pallidus.

Afferents to CM from the limbic system via the fornix have been detailed by Valenstein and Nauta (270), whereas those from globus pallidus have been described by Nauta and Mehler (178); a cerebellar fastigial projection has been studied by Carpenter's group (40). Thus convergence on the posterior one-

third of the thalamic nonspecific system is of considerable scope even if the more caudal brain stem is not represented as Mehler maintains (165). Our own Golgi material strongly suggests that collaterals and fine terminals from a number of ascending systems do indeed terminate in the CM-Pf field—an observation that gains support from studies by Shute and Lewis (247) of the ascending cholinergic system.

Local connections with cells of the adjacent pretectum and with the more rostral nuclear fields of the nonspecific system are probably best seen in sensitive Golgi impregnations. In highly simplified form, the wealth of connections generated by bifurcating axons projecting from progressively rostrad nonspecific nuclei and the almost unlimited potential for internuclear communication that must exist in larger forms where the number of nerve cells increases sharply are illustrated in Figure 23. Notice, even in this illustration, that where not more than 2%–3% of elements are stained, how frequently collateral branches leave the larger axonal stems and penetrate adjacent nuclear zones both medial and lateral to the parent axon, in addition to projecting much longer distances in the rostrocaudal plane. This probably represents the basic scheme of internuclear organization and is similar in overall design to the intercommunicative connections seen throughout the brain stem reticular core.

The terminal structure of descending afferent connections from cortical and subcortical stations is still incompletely understood. Golgi studies suggest that descending thalamopetal systems to the ventrolateral pool of specific "relay" nuclei are of two predominant types (Fig. 25). One fiber species appears to terminate in a series of disklike neuropil fields, flattened in the anteroposterior dimension and stacked along that axis. A second fiber type generates series of cone-shaped plexuses, each of which branches more widely than preceding plexuses, though more sparsely, over the receptive field. I have discussed the possibility that these two terminal systems operate conjointly to form a neuropil matrix, resembling a three-dimensional set of Cartesian coordinates that may provide part of an address and retrieval system in specific thalamic fields (228, 232). Fiber systems with this degree of terminal organization have not been found in the nonspecific systems. Horizontal Golgi-stained sections (see Fig. 25) reveal a range of fibers generating multiply branched, variegated patterns found in areas both ipsilateral and contralateral to the site of origin. Some axon stems appear to supply one nucleus or one nuclear group. Others course through the entire rostrocaudal length of the thalamus, sending collaterals or terminals, or both, into most or all of the nonspecific nuclei and, in some cases, continuing into the mesencephalon.

The site of origin of these fiber types has not been determined, but a combination of axon degeneration methods, electrophysiological tracking techniques, and the more recent anterograde and retrograde meth-

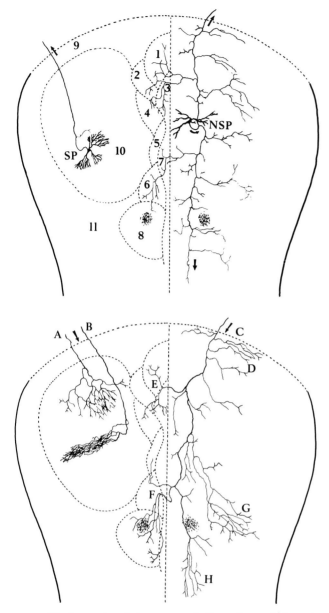

FIG. 25. Comparison between organizations of axonal elements of thalamic specific and nonspecific systems. Drawing based on a number of Golgi-stained sections of rat and mouse. *Top*: thalamofugal elements. A neuron of the ventrobasal complex (*10*) projects a virtually uncollateralized axon (*SP*) toward cortex. A neuron of the nonspecific system (*NSP*) generates an axon that bifurcates into rostral and caudal running branches, both of which are richly collateralized, ipsilaterally and contralaterally. *1*, Parataenial nucleus; *2*, anterior ventral nucleus; *3*, interanteromedial nucleus; *4*, anterior medial nucleus; *5*, paracentral nucleus; *6*, central lateral nucelus; *7*, central medial nucleus; *8*, centre médian–parafascicular complex; *9*, n. reticularis thalami; *10*, ventrobasal complex; and *11*, posterior thalamic complex. *Bottom*: descending thalamopetal elements (*A* and *B*) are axons running from cortex to parts of specific ventral nuclear complex. *A* is a characteristic 3-dimensional terminal while *B* is a 2-dimensional discoid arbor. *C* is an axon descending from cortex to nonspecific fields. Diffuse collateral system includes branches to area of nucleus reticularis (*D*) and area of ventral anterior nucleus (*D*) to contralateral nonspecific fields (*E* and *F*), to the posterior nuclear complex (*G*) and to the mesodiencephalic junction (*H*). [From Scheibel and Scheibel (230).]

odologies that use tagged amino acids and horseradish peroxidase, respectively, are beginning to provide some answers. A number of axonal contingents are known to originate throughout the orbitofrontal cortex, olfactory bulb and tract, amygdala, and septum and project through the hypothalamus, at least as far as the mesencephalic tegmentum (168, 176, 267). En route through the hypothalamus numerous fine collaterals are given off dorsally, reaching the most medial of the nonspecific group. These fibers undoubtedly represent part of the return limb of a thalamocorticothalamic arc established by the nonspecific thalamic system. More details of the relay from prefrontal cortex to the midline thalamic fields may be found in newer studies by Leichnetz and Astruc (141), whereas information on two-way relationships between nonspecific thalamus and prefrontal cortex is contained in the studies by Skinner and Lindsley and Yingling (250, 251).

The generally accepted pacemaking function of thalamic nuclei in the control of cerebral-cortical generators relies in part on these projections. Lindsley's group, in particular, has suggested that classic thalamic nonspecific effects on cortical activity such as recruitment are mediated entirely via thalamic prefrontal connections and rely on secondary corticocortical projections to spread the effect to central and caudal cortical stations, although as is noted later, there is now convincing evidence for direct fine-caliber thalamic nonspecific projections to many cortical areas. Relatively potent descending connections from the frontal eye fields (cortical area 8) on the anterior ventral, central lateral, and parafascicular nuclei (138) are of interest in view of the Schlags' studies of control of extraocular muscles by intralaminar nuclei (240, 243).

Axonal Outflow

Axonal projections from the thalamic nonspecific system include a wide variety of systems of varying lengths. As already indicated, axons leave most of the constituent fields, breaking up into a number of branch systems directed rostrally and caudally, as well as transversely (see Fig. 25). The former constitute both short and long relays functionally interconnecting the nonspecific nuclei, extending to and beyond the limiting nucleus reticularis thalami rostrolaterally and the mesencephalic tectum and tegmentum caudally. Physiological correlates of these sequences of rostrocaudal connections can be found in the studies by Starzl and Whitlock, who showed that following stimulation of the anterior end of the intralaminar system, "a wave was propagated to the posterior diffuse nuclei" (257). Evoked potentials, spindle bursts, and changes in single-unit activity that can be followed along the length of the intralaminar system following caudate stimulation (65, 136, 246) may all be due to these longitudinally directed intrathalamic fiber systems. Functional evidence for the laterally directed collateral branches extending into adjacent specific nuclei can be found in the studies by Purpura and his co-workers (201), who demonstrated the presence of frequency-specific control by intralaminar fields gating the input-output relations of cells in the nucleus ventrolateralis. This group of data may be taken as a paradigm rather than the limit of such relay-modulating activity.

The most abundantly documented extrathalamic projections are those that run rostrally and laterally into the putamen and, in somewhat smaller concentrations, into globus pallidus, caudate nucleus, and claustrum (45, 81, 119, 127, 179, 197). The projection to putamen from the CM-Pf complex appears topically organized, whereas projections from the intralaminar nuclei to the head of the caudate nucleus may not be.

The projection of nonspecific nuclei directly upon the cerebral cortex posed more serious problems for more than a decade. Physiological evidence clearly related these systems to cerebral cortex via the recruiting and augmenting potentials first described by the Forbes group (51, 52, 173). The classic hodological studies (43, 179, 279) did not demonstrate appropriate thalamocortical links, however, although Nauta and Whitlock (179) and Powell and Cowan (197) found projections to phylogenetically older portions of the cortex, especially prepyriform and entorhinal areas. Critical to the solution of this problem was the concept of "essential" and "sustaining" projections proposed by Rose and Woolsey (215). They suggested that in the case of a neuron whose major projective system collateralized widely en route to its destination, destruction of one group of terminal fibers need not result in retrograde changes in the cell bodies of origin. The uninjured sustaining collateral projections might well prove adequate in maintaining neuronal integrity.

More recent studies using tracking techniques of enhanced sensitivity have demonstrated fine thalamocortical projections such as those of the paracentral nucleus onto the cortex of cingulate gyrus and the orbitofrontal cortex, and those of the central lateral field onto the parietal-occipital area (175). Golgi studies in fortunate preparations have clearly demonstrated a powerful projection from the anterior one-third of the intralaminar system through the medial portion of the ventral anterior nucleus and n. reticularis thalami to orbitofrontal cortex [(230); Fig. 26]. In this case the axons generated by nuclear fields in the anterior midline thalamus may well be the significant or essential projection. Their functional characteristics as a relatively massive entity projecting from the anterior pole of thalamus have been explored by Skinner and Lindsley and Yingling (250–252) in a series of communications involving a reversible blockade of the inferior thalamic peduncle through the use of cryoprobes.

The enhanced sensitivity of modern tracking techniques, especially autoradiography, horseradish per-

oxidase, and kainic acid methods, is rapidly increasing the range of cortical areas now believed to be directly connected to the thalamic nonspecific system. These areas include virtually the entire range of sensorimotor strip areas in rat (289), cat (106), and monkey (48, 157); the visual cortex in the hedgehog (83); the extrastriate visual cortex in the cat (123); and broader areas of visually responsive parietal cortex (210, 211), the frontal lobe (125), and portions of anterior medial (retrospinal) cortex (18) in rat and cat, to name only a few. We must assume that the widely branching axon systems of thalamic nonspecific cells penetrate into substantial portions of the cortex, gating and modulating ongoing activity. The nature of these interactions is also under evaluation in physiological studies by Endo et al. (62), who have reported on the characteristics of postsynaptic potentials in pyramidal tract cells evoked by stimulation in the central lateral nucleus of the intralaminar zone.

Nucleus Reticularis Thalami

The nucleus reticularis thalami is of considerable interest to anyone concerned with thalamocortical interaction (Fig. 27). Anatomically this thin, curved, platelike nucleus is interposed between thalamus and cerebral cortex, and virtually all thalamically derived corticipetal fibers must traverse this field (203a, 227, 230). After early descriptions by Nissl (181) and Ramón y Cajal (203a), the structure evoked little interest until Morison and Dempsey (172, 173) called attention to the possible role of the nonspecific thalamic nuclei as part of a second corticipetal projection system parallel with classic sensory channels. Jasper (110) grouped the reticular nucleus with the midline and interlaminar nuclei and termed the complex the thalamic reticular system, thereby emphasizing the apparent functional unity of these components. Physiological studies by Hanberry and Jasper (92) identified the n. reticularis as the final common path for thalamic nonspecific systems projecting on the cortex. Retrograde degeneration studies by Rose and Woolsey (214) seemed to provide the anatomical substrate for such relations. Rose also cautioned, however, that changes noted in reticularis cells might be transneuronal in nature rather than retrograde (213). This view gained support from Carman et al. (39), who described a topically arranged corticifugal projection on the n. reticularis thalami. Golgi studies (227, 230) were then used to establish the caudally projecting path of reticularis axons (see Fig. 27), and these results were subsequently confirmed by degeneration studies (170). Evaluation of the Golgi material led to the conclusion that the probable role of this system was to modulate, via tonic or phasic inhibition, those thalamic cell groups whose axons penetrated the n. reticularis thalami (227, 230). Electrophysiological studies by Massion (161), Schlag and Waszak (241, 242, 280), and Yingling and Skinner (291), among others, have made

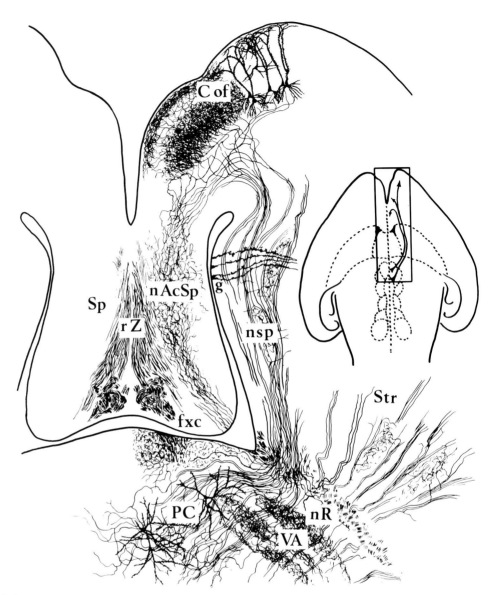

FIG. 26. Rostral projection of thalamic nonspecific system through inferior thalamic peduncle on orbitofrontal cortex (*C of*) of 50-day-old, partially demyelinated mouse. Axons from anterior thalamic nuclei, including paracentral (*PC*) and medial portion of ventral anterior (*VA*), project rostrally via inferior thalamic peduncle as nonspecific projection (*nsp*) past striatum (*str*) and branch widely in subgriseal white matter. Here some branches reach the nucleus accumbens septi (*nAcSp*). *nR*, nucleus reticularis thalami; *fxc*, columns of fornix; *sp*, septum; and *rZ*, radiation of Zuckerkandl. Ependymal neuroglial cells (*g*) line lateral ventricles. *Inset*: slightly schematized drawing of horizontal section through diencephalon and forebrain of young rat. *Rectangle*: area involved in figure. *Arrows*: position and course of thalamocortical nonspecific projection. Modified rapid Golgi-impregnated section cut in horizontal-oblique plane. × 113. [From Scheibel and Scheibel (230).]

this hypothesis increasingly tenable and have given substance to a previously suggested analogy likening the n. reticularis thalami to the screen grid in a triode or pentode vacuum tube (224). It now seems likely that the rhythmic thalamic oscillations constituting the "Adrian effect" (1) and the alternating sequences of EPSPs and IPSPs (excitatory and inhibitory postsynaptic potentials) characterizing unit activity in the somatosensory thalamus (12) are causally related to the phasic inhibition imposed by bursts of n. reticularis

neuronal activity. These phased bursts may also serve as the inhibitory source regulating recruiting responses and related synchronous electrocortical potentials. Thus the recurrent loop playing back on the thalamus by way of the n. reticularis thalami may provide a substrate that is crucial for thalamic and cortical synchronous activity.

Figure 28 shows, in schematic form, the two major routes for rostrally projecting impulses from the brain stem reticular core. The dorsal pathway relays in the

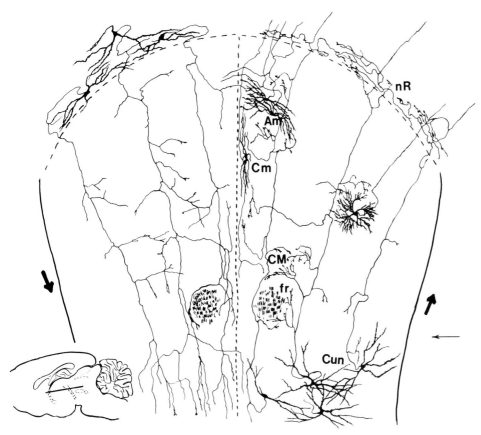

FIG. 27. Reciprocal connections between mesencephalic tegmental cells of the nucleus cuneiformis (*Cun*) and the nucleus reticularis thalami (*nR*), which may constitute part of thalamic gating system mentioned in text. *CM*, centre médian; *Cm*, central medial; *Am*, anterior medial nuclei; and *fr*, fasciculus retroflexus. Elements selected from several sections of 10-to-14-day-old rat. *Fine arrow*, mesodiencephalic interface. × 101.

thalamic nonspecific nuclei then proceeds rostrally toward cerebral cortex via the n. reticularis thalami. The ventral pathway traverses zona incerta and hypothalamus, thereby avoiding the n. reticularis entirely. The classic studies by Moruzzi and Magoun (174) emphasized the role of high-frequency stimulation of the brain stem core in desynchronizing the cortical EEG. Although similar stimuli, when applied to the thalamic intralaminar fields, produce equivalent effects, the studies of Schlag and Chaillet (239) and Weinberger and co-workers (281) have shown that the pathway responsible for the thalamically induced effect runs caudally through the mesencephalon. Tegmental lesions behind the point of stimulation abolish the cortical response but have no effect on the typical incrementing surface negative cortical waves induced by slow (6–12/s) thalamic intralaminar stimulation (51, 52). On the other hand, lesions involving the medial portion of ventral anterior nucleus, n. reticularis thalami (61, 124, 257, 274), or the inferior thalamic peduncle immediately anterior and ventral to these areas (250, 281) block development of cortical recruitment phenomena without affecting cortical desynchronization. Separate pathways would accordingly

appear to be involved in production of cortical synchronization and desynchronization. Consonant with these data is the finding by Jouvet and Jouvet (117) that ventrally placed lesions throughout septum, hypothalamus, subthalamus, and the interpeduncular region suppress desynchronized electrocortical patterns associated with rhombencephalic sleep, while dorsal lesions involving the posterior thalamus or the tegmentothalamic junction, or both, do not eliminate high-frequency cortical activity.

All of these data suggest that the ventral route alone may be effective as the pathway mediating cortical desynchronization, whereas the dorsal thalamic path, relaying in the nonspecific nuclear complex and projecting rostrally via the n. reticularis thalami, is responsible for high-voltage, slow-wave phenomena such as cortical spindling, recruitment waves, and synchronized sleep. The ventral leaf of the rostral projection of the reticular core thus appears to be the most likely afferent path mediating low-voltage, high-frequency cortical rhythms. It may be activated from thalamic levels either via antidromic stimulation of dorsal leaf fibers conducting caudally to the point of bifurcation with the ventral leaf, and then forward, or by ortho-

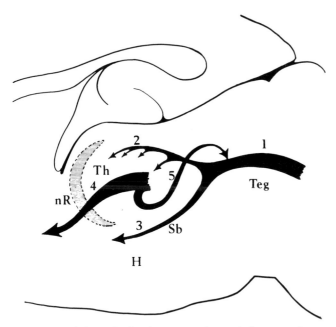

FIG. 28. Schematic drawing contrasting rostral course of axon systems from brain stem reticular core and nonspecific thalamic systems. Brain stem reticular axons (*1*) ascending through tegmentum (*Teg*); bifurcation occurs just caudal to thalamus, forming both the dorsal leaf (*2*), which terminates in thalamic intralaminar (*Th*) and dorsomedial fields, and the ventral leaf (*3*), which runs ventrolaterally through subthalamus (*Sb*) and hypothalamus (*H*) thereby swinging ventrally to nucleus reticularis thalami (*nR*). Axons of thalamic nonspecific system send caudally directed projection (*5*) back to tegmental level, while rostral component (*4*) perforates nucleus reticularis thalami and continues rostrally via inferior thalamic peduncle. [From Scheibel and Scheibel (230).]

dromic stimulation of caudally coursing axons of thalamic nonspecific cells projecting back on tegmental reticular neurons (see Fig. 25). As noted previously this ventral route includes many rostrally coursing projections originating in aminergic systems of the brain stem reticular core projecting toward subcortical and cortical target zones.

Another aspect of the relationship between n. reticularis and rostral and caudal centers is worth noting in view of the light it appears to shed on the entire issue of selective focusing of attention. The mesencephalic reticular formation and frontal granular (prefrontal) cortex exert complementary control over both unit activity and slow potential shifts in the n. reticularis thalami (251, 291). A significant proportion of tegmental cells (n. cuneiformis) and cells of the immediately overlying layers of deep tectum are multimodal (19). They respond to combinations of visual, somatic, and auditory stimuli with combinations of the last two modalities being the most numerous. The receptive fields of such multimodal cells show a considerable degree of congruence. For instance, a unit responding to hindlimb stimulation may have its auditory receptive field well to the rear, extending only as far anterior as the abdomen or trunk. These paired auditory and somatic maps maintain approximate reg-

ister and overlap the visuotopic map laid down in the more peripheral layers of superior colliculus (56, 82, 258). These data may indicate that each tectotegmental locus codes for a point in the three-dimensional space envelope around the organism. Data also exist that suggest the presence of a tectotegmental motor map closely matching the sensory map. Hess has used the term "visual grasp reflex" (100) to indicate the highly place-specified signature of motor stimuli in this area. Each stimulus produces a saccade that centers the fovea on the spatial point that is multimodally represented at the stimulation site. The utility of this type of sensorimotor organization in the conjoint control of head and eye movements is apparent, but there may well be further consequences.

Recent data (251, 291) indicate that tegmental stimulation produces positive-going, slow waves and temporary cessation of spike activity in the nucleus reticularis thalami, probably via a cholinergic mechanism (55). An external stimulus with alerting value produces the same effect, whereas unit-driving behavior results from medial thalamic stimulation in the presence of intact connections between thalamus and prefrontal cortex. Because reticularis bursts are associated with inhibition of neurons in specific thalamic nuclei (161, 241, 242), it can be assumed that inhibition of reticularis elements opens the gate for thalamocortical interaction. An increasing weight of evidence attests to the organizational specificity of the n. reticularis with regard to afferents originating in subjacent thalamus (170) as well as in overlying cortex (207), somatotopically and visuotopically (171). The tegmental projection onto this ensemble of n. reticularis sectors (see Fig. 27) also appears to be organized in congruent fashion (60). The resultant pattern resembles the leaves of a fan, spreading out toward cortex from the upper brain stem. Each leaf represents a specific peripheral sector and the sectors are multiply represented for mode as well as place specificity. Thus the reticularis gate exhibits a high degree of functional and spatial selectivity. Depending on the nature of the alerting stimulus (or site of central excitation), only that portion of n. reticularis will open (i.e., reticularis firing inhibited) which controls the appropriate subjacent thalamic sensory field. Information being processed and transmitted from this thalamic field alone may then gain access to cortex for further processing. It is tempting to speculate that in substrates such as this may reside the capacity for focusing attention, that "searchlight of consciousness" to which several authors (49) called attention in the Laurentian symposium on the brain stem reticular core.

OVERVIEW

Twelve years ago, in an attempt to summarize the probable range of activities characterizing the brain stem reticular core, the following roles were suggested: "determiner of operational modes, gating mechanism for all sensory influx, modulator and monitor of cortical function, readout mechanisms for the cortical differentiative and comparative processes, and gain manipulator for motor output." (p. 577 in ref. 229). That entity, whose behavior was painted in such broad strokes, was in turn described as "a mosaic of subcenters placed athwart all input and output systems of the neuraxis, receiving a constant sampling of information from activity ongoing in these systems. This mass of heterogeneous convergent data is integrated along the postsynaptic membrane of individual reticular neurons whose output represents an algebraic summation of these inputs. The output of these reticular-core elements, representing intensity rather than mode, is then projected rostrally and caudally to modulate the degree of synaptic drive on neurons spread widely throughout the cortex, brain stem, spinal cord, and, in some cases, as far peripherally as the first-order sensory cell." (p. 602 in ref. 229).

From a contemporary vantage point such descriptions seem almost too facile, invoking as they do an enormous range of neural mechanisms and processing capability. It is not so much that any of these operational roles have been proved fallacious, but rather that the anatomical and functional complexities that undoubtedly provide them with a substrate are becoming better appreciated. It is perhaps the difference between first viewing a countryside from great altitude and then from the top of a knoll. Impressions of general topography give way to analysis of detailed structural and functional ensembles. Formerly pertinent questions begin to fade—partially answered and partially replaced by others arising from the welter of new information made available by a closer vantage point.

Developments over the past decade and a half have brought the nonspecific systems of brain stem and thalamus into increasingly sharper focus. Of particular note is the high degree of order and specificity that the system complex shows. The general concept of reticular core as a pool of interneurons with a pluripotentium of functions undoubtedly remains intact. Yet the polysensory characteristics of reticular afferent patterns and the diversity of axonal trajectories seem increasingly compatible with a degree of functional specificity and target orientation that would have seemed unlikely only a few years ago.

Important insights into the chemical architecture of the reticular core have provided clues to the reticular control exerted over almost all other neural systems. The remarkably widespread axon systems, in particular those of the locus coeruleus, seem increasingly to mark this nucleus as "the reticular formation's reticular formation." The anatomical projections and functional interaction of the various aminergic systems may provide better understanding, not only of the subtleties of state-control-modulation of sensorimotor mechanisms but also of the basis for motivation and affect. Increasingly fine-grained data are becoming available on the interconnections of reticular core elements with brain stem nuclei, especially those nuclei mediating vestibulocochlear functions and eye movements. Such information may help clarify the mechanisms by which several types of meaningful contact between organism and environment are established and maintained. Even the substrate mechanisms responsible for selecting information from the streams of input that compete for thalamocortical processing and evaluation now appear isolable in the complementary interplay of tegmentum and medial thalamoprefrontal cortex acting on the ensembles of neurons that make up the nucleus reticularis thalami.

The introduction of a new generation of tracking techniques seems likely to continue to add detail and vigor to the picture. But in parallel with this new hodology there may also occur growth of new organizational concepts, some bearing little apparent relationship to axonal projections. More direct communications between reticular core neurons and the vascular system, and perhaps the ventricular fluid, may provide alternative routes for transfer of information that are only dimly seen at present. Local interactive processes between dendrites, based on nonpropagative ionic movements and the rapid reorganization of membrane-bound macromolecular systems, may also provide processing and storage capabilities of considerable importance. Who can deny that exploration of the reticular core has again entered on exciting times?

REFERENCES

1. ADRIAN, E. D. Rhythmic discharges from the thalamus. *J. Physiol. London* 113: 9P–10P, 1951.
2. AGHAJANIAN, G. K., AND F. E. BLOOM. The formation of synaptic junctions in developing rat brains: a quantitative electron microscopic study. *Brain Res.* 6: 716–727, 1967.
3. AGHAJANIAN, G. K., F. E. BLOOM, AND M. H. SHEARD. Electron microscopy of degeneration within the serotonin pathway of rat brain. *Brain Res.* 13: 266–273, 1969.
4. ALBE-FESSARD, D., AND E. GILLETT. Convergences d'afférences d'origines corticales et périphériques vers le centre médian du chat anesthésie ou éveillé. *Electroencephalogr. Clin. Neurophysiol.* 13: 257–269, 1961.
5. ALBE-FESSARD, D., AND A. MALLART. Réponses évoquées dans la formation réticulée bulbaire au niveau de noyau giganto cellularis d'Olzewski. Rôle de ces noyau dans la transmission

vers le centre médian du thalamus des afférences somatiques. *J. Physiol. Paris* 54: 271, 1962.
6. ALLEN, W. F. Formatio reticularis and reticulo-spinal tracts, their visceral functions and possible relationships to tonicity and clonic contractions. *J. Wash. Acad. Sci.* 22: 490–495, 1932.
7. ALTMAN, J., AND M. B. CARPENTER. Fiber projections of the superior colliculus in the cat. *J. Comp. Neurol.* 116: 157–178, 1961.
8. AMASSIAN, V. E., AND R. V. DEVITO. Unit activity in reticular formation and nearby structures. *J. Neurophysiol.* 17: 575–603, 1954.
8a. ANDÉN, N. E. Discussion of serotonin and dopamine in the extrapyramidal system. *Adv. Pharmacol.* 6: 347–349, 1968.
8b. ANDÉN, N. E., A. CARLSSON, AND N. A. HILLARP. Inhibition by 5-hydroxytryptophan of insulin-induced adrenalin deple-

tion. *Acta Pharmacol. Toxicol.* 21: 183–186, 1964.

9. ANDÉN, N. E., A. DAHLSTROM, K. FUXE, K. LARSSON, L. OLSON, AND U. UNGERSTEDT. Ascending monoamine neurons to the telencephalon and diencephalon. *Acta Physiol. Scand.* 67: 313–326, 1966.

10. ANDÉN, N. E., K. FUXE, B. HAMBERGER, AND T. HÖKFELT. A quantitative study on the nigro-neostriatal dopamine neuron system in the rat. *Acta Physiol. Scand.* 67: 306–312, 1966.

11. ANDERSON, F. D., AND C. M. BERRY. Degeneration studies of long ascending fiber systems in the cat brain stem. *J. Comp. Neurol.* 111: 195–229, 1959.

12. ANDERSON, P., AND T. A. SEARS. The role of inhibition in the phasing of spontaneous thalamocortical discharge. *J. Physiol. London* 173: 459–480, 1964.

13. ANLEZARK, G. M., T. J. CROW, AND A. P. GREENWAY. Impaired learning and decreased cortical norepinephrine after bilateral horns coeruleus lesions. *Science* 181: 682–684, 1973.

14. BARBEAU, A., T. L. SOURKES, AND G. F. MURPHY. Les catécholamines dans la maladie de Parkinson. In: *Monoamines et systéme nerveux centrale*, edited by J. de Ajuriaguerra. Paris: Masson et Cie, 1962.

15. BARTLETT, J. R., AND R. W. DOTY, SR. Influence of Mesencephalic stimulation on unit activity in striate cortex of squirrel monkeys. *J. Neurophysiol.* 37: 642–652, 1974.

16. BARTLETT, J. R., R. W. DOTY, J. PECCI-SAAVEDRA, AND P. J. WATSON. Mesencephalic control of lateral geniculate nucleus in primates. III. Modifications with state of alertness. *Exp. Brain Res.* 18: 214–224, 1973.

17. BEALL, J. E., A. E. APPLEBAUM, R. D. FOREMAN, AND W. D. WILLIS. Spinal cord potentials evoked by cutaneous afferents in the monkey. *J. Neurophysiol.* 40: 199–211, 1977.

18. BECKSTEAD, R. M. Convergent thalamic and mesencephalic projections to the anterior medial cortex in the rat. *J. Comp. Neurol.* 166: 403–416, 1976.

19. BELL, C., G. SIERRA, N. BUENDIA, AND J. P. SEGUNDO. Sensory properties of neurons in the mesencephalic reticular formation. *J. Neurophysiol.* 27: 961–987, 1964.

20. BENDER, M. B. The eye-centering system. A theoretical consideration. *Arch. Neurol. Psychiatry* 73: 685–699, 1955.

21. BENDER, M. B., AND S. SHANZER. Oculomotor pathways defined by electrical stimulation and lesions in the brain stem of the monkey. In: *The Oculomotor System*, edited by M. B. Bender. New York: Harper & Row, 1964, p. 81–140.

22. BÉNITA, M., AND H. CONDÉ. Intranuclear organization of the centre médian nucleus of thalamus. *J. Physiol. Paris* 64: 561–582, 1972.

23. BESSON, J. M., R. H. F. CATCHLOVE, P. FELTZ, AND D. LE BARS. Further evidence for postsynaptic inhibition on lamina V dorsal interneurons. *Brain Res.* 66: 531–536, 1974.

24. BIRKMAYER, W., AND O. HORNYKIEWICZ. Der L-Dioxyphenylalanin (=DOPA) Effekt bei der Parkinsons-Akinese. *Wien. Klin. Wochenschr.* 73: 787–788, 1961.

25. BOWSHER, D. The termination of secondary somatosensory neurons within the thalamus of *Macaca mulatta*: an experimental degeneration study. *J. Comp. Neurol.* 117: 213, 1961.

26. BOWSHER, D. Some afferent and efferent connections of the parafascicular-center median complex. In: *The Thalamus*, edited by D. P. Purpura and M. D. Yahr. New York: Columbia Univ. Press, 1966, p. 99–108.

27. BOWSHER, D., D. ALBE-FESSARD, AND A. MALLANT. Central extralemniscal afferents. *J. Anat.* 97: 151–152, 1963.

28. BOWSHER, D., A. MALLART, D. PETIT, AND D. ALBE-FESSARD. A bulbar relay to the centre median. *J. Neurophysiol.* 31: 288–300, 1968.

29. BOWSHER, D., AND J. WESTMAN. The gigantocellular reticular region and its spinal afferents: a light and electron microscope study in the cat. *J. Anat.* 106: 23–36, 1970.

30. BREMER, F. Cerveau "isolé" et physiologie du sommeil. *C. R. Soc. Biol.* 118: 1235–1241, 1935.

31. BREMER, F. Nouvelles recherches sur le mécanisme du sommeil. *C. R. Soc. Biol.* 122: 460–464, 1936.

32. BRODAL, A. *The Reticular Formation of the Brain Stem; Anatomical Aspects and Functional Correlations.* London: Oliver & Boyd, 1957.

32a. BRODAL, A. *Neurological Anatomy in Relation to Clinical Medicine* (2nd ed.). New York: Oxford Univ. Press, 1969.

33. BRODAL, A., AND G. ROSSI. Ascending fibers in brain stem reticular formation of cat. *Arch. Neurol. Psychiatry* 74: 68–87, 1955.

34. BURES, J., AND O. BURESOVA. Plasticity in single neurons and neural populations. In: *Short Term Changes in Neural Activity and Behavior*, edited by G. Horn and R. A. Hinde. Cambridge, England: Cambridge Univ. Press, 1970, p. 363–403.

35. BUTCHER, L., J. ENGEL, AND K. FUXE. L-DOPA induced changes in central monoamine neurons after peripheral decarboxylase inhibition. *J. Pharm. Pharmacol.* 22: 313–316, 1970.

36. BUZNIKOV, G. A., A. N. KOST, N. F. KUCHEROVA, A. L. MNDZHOYAN, N. N. SUVOROV, AND L. A. BERDYSHEVA. The role of neurohumours in early embryogenesis. III. Pharmacological analysis of the role of neurohumours in cleavage divisions. *J. Embryol. Exp. Morphol.* 23: 549–569, 1970.

38. CAMPION, G. C. Thalamo-cortical circulation of neural impulse; new integration of thalamo-cortical functioning. *Br. J. Med. Psychol.* 9: 203–217, 1929.

39. CARMAN, J. B., W. M. COWAN, AND T. P. S. POWELL. Cortical connections of the thalamic reticular nucleus. *J. Anat.* 98: 587–598, 1964.

40. CARPENTER, M. P., G. M. BRITTIN, AND J. PINES. Isolated lesions of the fastigial nuclei in the cat. *J. Comp. Neurol.* 109: 65–89, 1958.

41. CHANDLER, C. R. Thalamic Termination of Corticofugal Fibers from Somatic Sensory Areas I and II in the Cat. An Experimental Degeneration Study. Liverpool, England: Univ. of Liverpool, 1964. Ph.D. thesis.

42. CHRISTENSEN, B. N., AND E. R. PERL. Spinal neurons specifically excited by noxious or thermal stimuli: marginal zone of the dorsal horn. *J. Neurophysiol.* 33: 293–307, 1970.

42a. CHU, N. S. AND F. E. BLOOM. The catecholamine-containing neurons in the cat dorsolateral pontine tegmentum: distribution of the cell bodies and some axonal projections. *Brain Res.* 66: 1–21, 1974.

43. CLARK, W. E. LEGROS, AND R. H. BOGGON. On the connections of the medial cell groups of the thalamus. *Brain* 56: 83–98, 1933.

44. COHEN, B., AND M. FELDMAN. Relationship of electrical activity in pontine reticular formation and lateral geniculate body to rapid eye movement. *J. Neurophysiol.* 31: 806–817, 1968.

45. COWAN, W. M., AND T. P. S. POWELL. The projection of the midline and intralaminar nuclei of the thalamus of the rabbit. *J. Neurol. Neurosurg. Psychiatry* 18: 266–279, 1955.

46. DAHLSTROM, A. Effect of colchicine on transport of amine storage granules in sympathetic nerves of rat. *Eur. J. Pharmacol.* 5: 111–113, 1968.

47. DAHLSTROM, A., AND K. FUXE. Evidence for the existence of monoamine-containing neurons in the central nervous system. I. Demonstration of monoamines in the cell bodies of brain stem neurons. *Acta Physiol. Scand. Suppl.* 62: 1–55, 1964.

48. DEKKER, J. J., J. KIEVIT, S. JACOBSON, AND H. G. J. M. KUYPERS. Retrograde axonal transport of horseradish peroxidase in the forebrain of the rat, cat and rhesus monkey. In: *Golgi Centennial Symposium: Perspectives in Neurobiology*, edited by M. Santini. New York: Raven 1975, p. 201–208. (Golgi Centennial Symp., 1973.)

49. DELAFRESNAYE, J. F. (editor). *Brain Mechanisms and Consciousness.* Springfield IL: Thomas, 1954.

50. DEMENT, W., AND N. KLEITMAN. The relation of eye movements during sleep to dream activity: an objective method for the study of dreaming. *J. Exp. Psychol.* 53: 339–346, 1957.

51. DEMPSEY, E. W., AND R. S. MORISON. The production of rhythmically recurrent cortical potentials after localized thalamic stimulation. *Am. J. Physiol.* 135: 293–300, 1942.

52. DEMPSEY, E. W., R. S. MORISON, AND B. R. MORISON. Some afferent diencephalic pathways related to cortical potentials in the cat. *Am. J. Physiol.* 131: 718–731, 1941.

53. DERBYSHIRE, A. J., B. REMPEL, A. FORBES, AND E. F. LAMBERT. The effects of anesthetics on action potentials in the cerebral cortex of the cat. *Am. J. Physiol.* 116: 577–596, 1936.

54. DIETE-SPIFF, K., G. CARLI, AND G. POMPEIANO. Comparison of the effects of stimulation of the VIIIth cranial nerve, the vestibular nuclei or the reticular formation on the gastrocnemius muscle and its spindles. *Arch. Ital. Biol.* 105: 243–272, 1967.

55. DINGLEDINE, R., AND J. S. KELLY. Brain stem stimulation and the acetylcholine-evoked inhibition of neurones in the feline nucleus reticularis thalami. *J. Physiol. London* 271: 135–154, 1977.

56. DRÄGER, U. C., AND D. H. HUBER. Responses to visual stimulation and relationship between visual, auditory, and somatosensory inputs in mouse superior colliculus. *J. Neurophysiol.* 38: 690–713, 1975.

57. DUSSER DE BARENNE, J. G., AND W. S. McCULLOCH. Functional interdependence of sensory cortex and thalamus. *J. Neurophysiol.* 4: 304–310, 1941.

58. ECCLES, J. C. Postsynaptic inhibition in the central nervous system. In: *Neurosciences: A Study Program*, edited by G. C. Quarton, T. Melnechuk, and F. O. Schmitt. New York: Rockefeller Univ. Press, 1967, p. 408–426.

59. ECCLES, J. C., B. LIBET, AND R. R. YOUNG. The behavior of chromatolized motoneurons studied by intracellular recording. *J. Physiol London* 143: 11–40, 1958.

60. EDWARDS, S. B., AND J. S. DE OLMOS. Autoradiographic studies of the projections of the midbrain reticular formation ascending projections of nucleus cuneiformis. *J. Comp. Neurol.* 165: 417–431, 1976.

61. EIDELBERG, E., W. HYMAN, AND M. D. FRENCH. Pathways for recruiting responses in rabbits. *Acta Neurol. Latinoam.* 4: 279–287, 1962.

62. ENDO, K., T. ARAKI, AND K. ITO. Short latency EPSPs and incrementing PSPs of pyramidal tract cells evoked by stimulation of the nucleus centralis lateralis of the thalamus. *Brain Res.* 132: 541–546, 1977.

63. FALCK, B., AND N.-Å. HILLARP. On the cellular localization of catecholamines in the brain. *Acta Anat.* 38: 277–279, 1959.

64. FALCK, B., N.-Å. HILLARP, G. THIANE, AND A. TORP. Fluorescence of catecholamines and related compounds condensed with formaldehyde. *J. Histochem. Cytochem.* 10: 348–354, 1962.

65. FELTZ, P., G. KRAUTHAMER, AND D. ALBE-FESSARD. Neurons of the medial diencephalon. I. Somatosensory responses and caudate inhibition. *J. Neurophysiol.* 30: 55–80, 1967.

66. FEREMUTSCH, K., AND K. SIMMA. Beitrag zur Kenntnis der "Formatio reticularis medullae oblongatae et pontis" des Menschen. *Z. Anat. Entwicklungsgesch.* 121: 271–291, 1959.

67. FLEISCHHAUER, K., H. PETSCHE, AND W. WITTKOWSKI. Vertical bundles of dendrites in the neocortex. *Z. Anat. Entwicklungsgesch.* 136: 213–223, 1972.

68. FORBES, A., AND B. MORISON. Cortical response to sensory stimulation under deep barbiturate narcosis. *J. Neurophysiol.* 2: 112–128, 1939.

69. FRENCH, J. D., AND H. W. MAGOUN. Effects of chronic lesions in central cephalic brain stem of monkeys. *AMA Arch. Neurol. Psychiatry* 68: 591–604, 1952.

70. FUSTER, J. M., AND A. UYEDA. Facilitation of tachitoscopic performance by stimulation at midbrain tegmental points in the monkey. *Exp. Neurol.* 6: 384–406. 1962.

70a. FUXE, K. The distribution of monoamine nerve terminals in the central nervous system. *Acta Physiol. Scand. Suppl.* 248: 39–85, 1965.

71. FUXE, K., T. HÖKFELT, O. JOHANSSEN, G. JONSSON, P. LIDBRINK, AND A. LJUNGDAHL. The origin of the dopamine nerve terminals in limbic and frontal cortex. Evidence for mesocortical dopamine neurons. *Brain Res.* 82: 349–355, 1974.

72. FUXE, K., T. HÖKFELT, AND U. UNGERSTEDT. Central monoaminergic tracts. *Prin. Psychopharmacol.* 6: 87–96, 1970.

73. FUXE, K., T. HÖKFELT, AND U. UNGERSTEDT. Morphological and functional aspects of central monoamine neurons. In: *International Review of Neurobiology*, edited by C. C. Pfeiffer

and J. R. Smythies. New York: Academic, 1970, vol. 13, p. 93–126.

74. GALAMBOS, R. Suppression of auditory nerve activity by stimulation of efferent fibers to cochlea. *J. Neurophysiol.* 19: 424–437, 1956.

75. GEHUCHTEN, A. VAN. La degénérescence dite rétrograde. IV. Vibres réticulo-spinales ventrales. *Névraxe* 5: 88–107, 1903.

76. GERLACH, O. Von dem Rückenmark. In: *Strickers Handbuch*, 1871. [Cited by S. Ramon y Cajal in *Histologie du système nerveux de l'homme et des vertébrés* (transl. from Spanish by L. Azoulay). Paris: Maloine, 1909, vol. 1.]

77. GIBBS, F. A., H. DAVIS, AND W. G. LENNOX. The electroencephalogram in epilepsy and in conditions of impaired consciousness. *Arch. Neurol. Psychiatry* 34: 1133–1148, 1935.

78. GINTZLER, A. R., M. D. GERSHON, AND S. SPECTOR. A nonpeptide morphine-like compound: immunocytochemical localization in the mouse brain. *Science* 199: 447–448, 1978.

79. GLOBUS, A., AND A. B. SCHEIBEL. Synaptic loci on visual cortical neurons of the rabbit: the specific afferent radiation. *Exp. Neurol.* 18: 116–131, 1967.

80. GOLGI, C. *Opera Omnia*. Milan: Ulrico Hoepli, 1903, vols. 1 and 2.

81. GORBACHEVSKAIA, A. I. Proektsii nekotorykh intralaminarnykh iader talamus a na khtostatoe iadro in Roshek [English summary]. *Arkh. Anat. Gistol. Embriol.* 70: 58–63, 1976.

82. GORDON, B. Receptive fields in deep layers of cat superior colliculus. *J. Neurophysiol.* 36: 157–178, 1973.

83. GOULD, H. J., III, W. C. HALL, AND F. F. EBNER. Connections of the visual cortex in the hedgehog (*Parechinus hypomelas*). I. Thalamocortical projections. *J. Comp. Neurol.* 177: 445–472, 1978.

84. GRANIT, R. Centrifugal and antidromic effects on ganglion cells of retina. *J. Neurophysiol.* 18: 388–411, 1955.

85. GRANIT, R., AND B. HOLMGREN. Two pathways from brain stem to gamma ventral horn cells. *Acta Physiol. Scand.* 35: 93–108, 1955.

86. GRAYBIEL, A. M. Direct and indirect preoculomotor pathways of the brain stem: an autoradiographic study of the pontine reticular formation in the cat. *J. Comp. Neurol.* 175: 37–78, 1977.

87. GRILLNER, S., AND S. LUND. The origin of a descending pathway with monosynaptic action on flexor motoneurons. *Acta Physiol. Scand.* 74: 274–284, 1968.

88. GRILLNER, S., AND M. L. SHIK. On the descending control of the lumbosacral spinal cord from the "mesencephalic locomotor region." *Acta Physiol. Scand.* 87: 320–333, 1973.

89. GRÜNTHAL, E. Der Zellbau in Thalamus der Saüger und des Menschen. *J. Psychol. Neurol. Leipzig* 46: 41–112, 1934.

90. GURDJIAN, E. G. The diencephalon of the albino rat. Studies on the brain of the rat. No. 2. *J. Comp. Neurol.* 43: 1–114, 1927.

91. HANBERRY, J., C. AJMONE-MARSAN, AND M. DILWORTH. Pathways of non-specific thalamo-cortical projection system. *Electroencephalogr. Clin. Neurophysiol.* 6: 103–118, 1954.

92. HANBERY, J., AND H. JASPER. Independence of diffuse thalamo-cortical projection system shown by specific nuclear destructions. *J. Neurophysiol.* 16: 252–271, 1953.

93. HARDING, B. N., AND T. P. POWELL. An electron microscopic study of the centre-median and ventrolateral nuclei of the thalamus in the monkey. *Philos. Trans. R. Soc. London Ser. B* 279: 357–412, 1977.

94. HASSLER, R. Anatomy of the thalamus. In: *Introduction to Stereotaxis with an Atlas of the Human Brain*, edited by G. Schaltenbrand and P. Bailey. Stuttgart: Thieme, 1959, vol. 1, p. 230–290.

95. HAZLETT, J. C., C. R. DUTTA, AND C. A. FOX. The neurons in the centromedian—parafascicular complex of the monkey (*Macaca mulatta*): a Golgi study. *J. Comp. Neurol.* 168: 41–73, 1976.

96. HAZLETT, J. C., AND L. D. HAZLETT. Long axon neurons in the parafascicular and parafascicular posterolateral nuclei of the opossum: a Golgi study. *Brain Res.* 136: 543–546, 1977.

97. HERNANDEZ-PEON, R. Central mechanisms controlling con-

duction along central sensory pathways. *Acta Neurol. Latinoam.* 1: 256–264, 1955.

98. HESS, R., JR., W. P. KOELLA, AND K. AKART. Cortical and subcortical recordings in natural and artificially induced sleep in cats. *Electroencephalogr. Clin. Neurophysiol.* 5: 75–90, 1953.

99. HESS, W. R. Le sommeil. *C. R. Soc. Biol.* 107: 1333–1364, 1931.

100. HESS, W. R., S. BURGI, AND V. BUCHER. Motorische Funktion des Tektalund Tegmentalgebietes. *Monatsschr. Psyciatr. Neurol.* 112: 1–52, 1946.

101. HORNYKIEWICZ, O. How does L-DOPA work in Parkinsonism? In: *L-DOPA and Parkinsonism*, edited by A. Barbeau and F. H. McDowell. Philadelphia, PA: Davis, 1970.

102. HUNSPERGER, R. W., AND D. ROMAN. The integrative role of the intralaminar system of the thalamus in visual orientation and perception in the cat. *Exp. Brain Res.* 25: 231–246, 1976.

103. HUTTENLOCHER, P. R. Evoked and spontaneous activity in single units of medial brain stem during natural sleep and waking. *J. Neurophysiol.* 24: 451–468, 1961.

104. ITO, M., AND M. UDO. The origin of cerebellar-induced inhibition and facilitation in the neurons of Deiters and intracerebellar nuclei (Abstract). *Proc. Int. Congr. Physiol. Sci., 23rd, Tokyo, 1965*, p. 997.

105. ITO, M., M. UDO, AND N. MANO. Long inhibitory and excitatory pathways converging onto cat reticular and Deiters' neurons and their relevance to reticulofugal axons. *J. Neurophysiol.* 33: 210–226, 1970.

106. ITOH, K., AND N. MIZUNO. Direct projections from the mesodiencephalic midline areas to the pericruciate cortex in the cat. An experimental study with the horseradish peroxidase method. *Brain Res.* 116: 492–497, 1976.

107. JACKSON, J. H. *Selected Writings of John Hughlings Jackson*, edited by J. Taylor. London: Hodder and Stoughton, 1931, vols. 1 and 2.

108. JANKOWSKA, E., S. LUND, A. LUNDBERG, AND O. POMPEIANO. Inhibitory effects evoked through ventral reticulospinal pathways. *Arch. Ital. Biol.* 106: 124–140, 1968.

109. JANSEN, J., AND A. BRODAL. Experimental studies on the intrinsic fibers of the cerebellum. II. The cortico-nuclear projection. *J. Comp. Neurol* 73: 267–321, 1940.

110. JASPER, H. Diffuse projection systems: the integrative action of the thalamic reticular system. *Electroencephalogr. Clin. Neurophysiol.* 1: 405–420, 1949.

110a.JASPER, H. H. Thalamic reticular system. In: *Electrical Stimulation of the Brain*, edited by D. E. Sheer. Austin: Univ. of Texas Press, 1961, p. 277–287.

111. JASPER, H. H., R. NAQUET, AND E. E. KING. Thalamocortical recruiting responses in sensory receiving areas in the cat. *Electroencephalogr. Clin. Neurophysiol.* 7: 99–114, 1955.

112. JONES, B. E., A. E. HALARIS, M. MCILHANEY, AND R. Y. MOORE. Ascending projections of the locus coeruleus in the rat. I. Axonal transport in central noradrenaline neurons. *Brain Res.* 127: 1–21, 1977.

113. JONES, E. G., AND E. BURTON. Cytoarchitecture and somatic sensory connectivity of thalamic nuclei other than the ventrobasal complex in the cat. *J. Comp. Neurol.* 154: 395–432, 1974.

114. JONES, E. G., AND R. Y. LEAVITT. Retrograde axonal transport and the demonstration of non-specific projections to the cerebral cortex and striatum from thalamic intralaminar nuclei in the rat, cat, and monkey. *J. Comp. Neurol.* 154: 349–377, 1974.

115. JOUVET, M. Recherches sur les structures nerveuses et les mécanismes responsables des differentes phases du sommeil physiologique. *Arch. Ital. Biol.* 100: 125–260, 1962.

116. JOUVET, M. Neurophysiology of the states of sleep. *Physiol. Rev.* 47: 117–177, 1967.

117. JOUVET, M., AND D. JOUVET. A study of the neurophysiological mechanisms of dreaming. *Electroencephalogr. Clin. Neurophysiol. Suppl.* 24: 133–157, 1963.

118. JOUVET, M., AND F. MICHEL. Corrélations électromyographiques du sommeil chez le chat décortique at mesencéphalique chronique. *C. R. Soc. Biol.* 153: 422–425, 1959.

119. KAELBER, W. W., AND C. L. MITCHELL. The centrum medianum–central tegmental fasciculus complex. A stimulation,

120. KANAI, T., AND J. C. SZERB. Mesencephalic reticular activating system and cortical acetylcholine output. *Nature London* 205: 80–82, 1965.

121. KASAMATSU, T. Visual cortical neurons influenced by the oculomotor input: characterization of their receptive field properties. *Brain Res.* 113: 271–292, 1976.

122. KAWAMURA, K., A. BRODAL, AND G. HODDEVIK. The projection of the superior colliculus onto the reticular formation of the brain stem. An experimental anatomical study in the cat. *Exp. Brain Res.* 19: 1–19, 1974.

123. KENNEDY, H., AND C. BALEYDIER. Direct projections from thalamic intralaminar nuclei to extra-striate visual cortex in the cat traced with horseradish peroxidase. *Exp. Brain Res.* 28: 133–139, 1977.

124. KERR, F. W. L., AND J. L. O'LEARY. The thalamic source of cortical recruiting in the rodent. *Electroencephalogr. Clin. Neurophysiol.* 9: 461–476, 1957.

125. KIEVIT, J., AND H. G. J. M. KUYPERS. Organization of the thalamo-cortical connections to the frontal lobe in the rhesus monkey. *Exp. Brain Res.* 29: 299–322, 1977.

126. KING, E. E., AND K. UNNA. The action of mephenesin and other interneuron depressants on the brain stem. *J. Pharmacol. Exp. Ther.* 111: 293–301, 1954.

127. KITAI, S. T., J. D. KOCSIS, R. J. PRESTON, AND M. SUGIMORI. Monosynaptic inputs to caudate neurons identified by intracellular injection of horseradish peroxidase. *Brain Res.* 109: 601–606, 1976.

128. KLAUE, R. Die bioelekrische Tatigkeit der Grosshirnride im normalen Schlaf und in der Narkose durch Schlafmittel. *J. Psychol. Neurol. Leipzig* 47: 510–531, 1937.

129. KLEITMAN, N. The evolutionary theory of sleep and wakefulness. *Perspect. Biol. Med.* 7: 169–178, 1963.

130. KLEITMAN, N. *Sleep and Wakefulness*. Chicago: Univ. of Chicago Press, 1963.

131. KOE, B. K., AND A. WEISMAN. *p*-Chlorophenylalanine: a specific depletor of brain serotonin. *J. Pharmacol. Exp. Ther.* 154: 499–516, 1966.

132. KOHNSTAMM, O. Uber Urspramgskerne spinale Bahnen im Hirnstamm speciell über das Atomcentrum. *Arch. Psychiat. Nervenkrankh.* 32: 681–684, 1899.

133. KOHNSTAMM, O., AND F. QUENSEL. Das Centrum Receptorium (Sensorium) der Formatio Reticularis (Abstract). *Neurol. Zentralbl.* 27: 1046–1047, 1908.

134. KOSITZYN, N. S. Axo-dendritic relations in the brain stem reticular formation. *J. Comp. Neurol.* 122: 9–17, 1964.

135. KOSTOWSKI, W., AND E. GIACALONE. Stimulation of various forebrain structures and brain 5HT, 5HIAA and behaviour in rats. *Eur. J. Pharmacol.* 7: 176–179, 1969.

136. KRAUTHAMER, G., P. FELTZ, AND D. ALBE-FESSARD. Neurons of the medial diencephalon. II. Excitation of central origin. *J. Neurophysiol.* 30: 81–97, 1967.

137. KRIEG, W. J. S. The medial region of the thalamus of the albino rat. *J. Comp. Neurol.* 80: 381–413, 1944.

138. KUNZLE, H., AND K. AKERT. Efferent connections of cortical area 8 (frontal eye field) in *Macaca fascicularis*. A reinvestigation using the autoradiographic technique. *J. Comp. Neurol.* 173: 147–164, 1977.

139. KUYPERS, H. G. J. M. Discussion on centre median nucleus of Luys. In: *The Thalamus*, edited by D. P. Purpura and M. D. Yahr. New York: Columbia Univ. Press, 1966, p. 122–126.

140. LASHLEY, K. S. *Brain Mechanisms and Intelligence*. Chicago: Univ. of Chicago Press, 1929.

141. LEICHNETZ, G. R., AND J. ASTRUC. The efferent projections of the medial prefrontal cortex in the squirrel monkey (*Saimiri sciurens*). *Brain Res.* 109: 455–472, 1976.

142. LELORD, G., AND C. MAHO. Modifications des activités évoquées corticales et thalamique au cours d'un conditionnement sensoriel. I. Localisation des responses et variations avec la vigilance. *Electroencephalogr. Clin. Neurophysiol.* 27: 258–269, 1969.

143. LeMOAL, M., L. STINUS, AND D. GALEY. Radiofrequency lesion of the ventral mesencephalic tegmentum: neurological and behavioral considerations. *Exp. Neurol.* 50: 521–535, 1976.

144. LEVANTE, A., AND D. ALBE-FESSARD. Localisation dans les couches VII et VIII de Rexed des cellules d'origine d'un faisceau spin-réticulaire croise. *C. R. Acad. Sci. Ser. D* 274: 3007–3010, 1972.

145. LEWANDOWSKY, M. Untersuchungen über die Leitungs-bahnen des Truncus cerebri und ihren Zusammenhang mit denen der Medulla Spinalis und des Cortex cerebri. In: *Neurologische Arbeiten. Zweite Serie: weitere Beitäge zur Hirnanatomie*, Jena: G. Fischer, 1904, vol. 1, p. 63–150.

146. LIEBESKIND, J. C., G. GUILBAND, J. M. BESSON, AND J. L. OLIVERAS. Analgesia from electrical stimulation of the periaqueductal gray matter in the cat: behavioral observations and inhibitory effects on spinal cord interneurons. *Brain Res.* 50: 441–446, 1973.

147. LINDSLEY, D. B. The reticular system and perceptual discrimination. In: *Reticular Formation of the Brain*, edited by H. H. Jasper, L. D. Proctor, R. S. Kinghton, W. C. Noshay, and R. T. Costello. Boston, MA: Little, Brown, 1958, p. 513–534.

148. LINDSLEY, D. B., J. W. BOWDEN, AND H. W. MAGOUN. Effects upon the EEG of acute injury to the brain stem activating system. *Electroencephalogr. Clin. Neurophysiol.* 1: 475–486, 1949.

149. LINDSLEY, D. B., L. H. SCHREINER, W. B. KNOWLES, AND H. W. MAGOUN. Behavioral and EEG changes following chronic brain stem lesions in the cat. *Electroencephalogr. Clin. Neurophysiol.* 2: 483–498, 1950.

150. LINDSLEY, D. F., S. K. RANF, M. J. SHERWOOD, AND W. G. PRESTON. Habituation and modification of reticular formation neuron responses to peripheral stimulation in cats. *Exp. Neurol.* 41: 174–189, 1973.

151. LLINAS, R., AND C. A. TERZUOLO. Mechanisms of supraspinal actions upon spinal cord activities. Reticular inhibitory mechanisms on alpha-extensor motoneurons. *J. Neurophysiol.* 27: 579–591, 1964.

152. LOEB, C., F. MAGNI, AND G. F. ROSSI. Electrophysiological analysis of the action of atropine on the central nervous system. *Arch. Ital. Biol.* 98: 293–307, 1960.

153. LOOMIS, A. L., E. N. HARVEY, AND G. HOBART. Potential rhythms of the cerebral cortex during sleep. *Science* 81: 597–598, 1935.

154. LORENTE DE NÓ, R. Vestibulo-ocular reflex arc. *Arch. Neurol. Psychiatry* 30: 245–291, 1933.

155. LORENTE DE NÓ, R. Studies on the structure of the cerebral cortex. II. Continuation of the study of the ammonic system. *J. Psychol. Neurol.* 46: 117–177, 1934.

156. LORENTE DE NÓ, R. Cerebral cortex: architecture, intracortical connections, and motor projections. In: *Physiology of the Nervous System* (3rd ed.), edited by J. F. Fulton. New York: Oxford Univ. Press, 1949, p. 288–312.

157. MACCHI, G., M. BENTIVOGLIO, C. D'ATENA, P. ROSSINI, AND E. TEMPESTA. The cortical projections of the thalamic intralaminar nuclei restudied by means of the HRP retrograde axonal transport. *Neurosci. Letters* 4: 121–126, 1977.

158. MAEDE, T., AND A. DRESSE. Possibilités d'étude du trajet des fibres cérébrales monoaminergiques chez le rat nouveau-né. *C.R. Soc. Biol.* 162: 1626–1631, 1968.

159. MAGNI, F., AND W. D. WILLIS. Identification of reticular formation neurons by intracellular recording. *Arch. Ital. Biol.* 101: 681–702, 1963.

160. MAGOUN, H. W., AND R. RHINES. An inhibitory mechanism in the bulbar reticular formation. *J. Neurophysiol.* 9: 165–171, 1946.

161. MASSION, J. Intervention des voies cerebéllo-corticales et cortico-cérebelleuses dans l'organisation et la régulation du mouvement. *J. Physiol. Paris Suppl.* 67: 117A–170A, 1973.

162. MATTHEWS, M. A., W. D. WILLIS, AND V. WILLIAMS. Dendritic bundles in lamina IX of cat spinal cord. A possible source for electrical interaction between motoneurons? *Anat. Rec.* 171: 313–328, 1971.

163. MATZKE, H. A. The course of the fibers arising from the nucleus gracilis and cuneatus of the cat. *J. Comp. Neurol.* 94: 437–452, 1951.

164. McGOWAN-SASS, B. K., AND E. EIDELBERG. Habituation of somatosensory evoked potentials in the lemniscal system of the cat. *Electroencephalogr. Clin. Neurophysiol.* 32: 373–381, 1972.

165. MEHLER, W. R. Further notes on the center median nucleus of Luys. In: *The Thalamus*, edited by D. P. Purpura and M. D. Yahr. New York: Columbia Univ. Press, 1966, p. 109–122.

166. MEHLER, W. R., M. E. FEFERMAN, AND W. J. H. NAUTA. Ascending axon degeneration following anterolateral chordotomy. An experimental study in the monkey. *Brain* 83: 718–750, 1960.

167. MELZACK, R., K. W. KONRAD, AND B. DUBROWSKY. Prolonged changes in central nervous system activity produced by somatic and reticular stimulation. *Exp. Neurol.* 25: 416–428, 1969.

168. MILLHOUSE, O. E. A Golgi study of the descending medial forebrain bundle. *Brain Res.* 15: 341–363, 1969.

169. MILLS, J. N. Human circadian rhythms. *Physiol. Rev.* 46: 128–171, 1966.

170. MINDERHOUD, J. M. An anatomical study of the efferent connections of the thalamic reticular nucleus. *Exp. Brain Res.* 12: 435–446, 1971.

171. MONTERO, V. M., R. W. GUILLERY, AND C. N. WOOLSEY. Retinotopic organization within the thalamic reticular nucleus demonstrated by a double label autoradiographic technique. *Brain Res.* 138: 407–421, 1977.

172. MORISON, R. S., AND E. W. DEMPSEY. A study of thalamocortical relations. *Am. J. Physiol.* 135: 281–292, 1942.

173. MORISON, R. S., AND E. W. DEMPSEY. Mechanisms of thalamocortical augmentation and repetition. *Am. J. Physiol.* 138: 297–308, 1942.

174. MORUZZI, G., AND H. W. MAGOUN. Brain stem reticular formation and activation of the EEG. *Electroencephalogr. Clin. Neurophysiol.* 1: 455–473, 1949.

175. MURRAY, M. Degeneration of some intralaminar thalamic nuclei after cortical removals in the cat. *J. Comp. Neurol.* 127: 341–368, 1966.

176. NAUTA, W. J. H. Hippocampal projections and related neural pathways to the midbrain in the cat. *Brain* 81: 319–340, 1958.

177. NAUTA, W. J. H., AND H. G. KUYPERS. Some ascending pathways in the brain stem reticular formation. In: *Reticular Formation of the Brain*, edited by H. H. Jasper, L. D. Proctor, R. S. Knighton, W. C. Noshay, and R. T. Costello. Boston, MA: Little, Brown, 1958, p. 3–30.

178. NAUTA, W. J. H., AND W. R. MEHLER. Some efferent connections of the lentiform nucleus in monkey and cat. *Anat. Rec.* 139: 260, 1961.

179. NAUTA, W. J. H., AND D. G. WHITLOCK. An anatomical analysis of the nonspecific thalamic projection system. In: *Brain Mechanisms and Consciousness*, edited by J. F. Delafresnaye. Springfield, IL: Thomas, 1954, p. 81–104.

180. NIEMER, W. T., AND H. W. MAGOUN. Reticulo-spinal tracts influencing motor activity. *J. Comp. Neurol.* 87: 367–369, 1947.

181. NISSL, F. Die Kerne des Thalamus beim Kaninchen. *Tageblatt der 62 versamml, deutsch. Nat. Aerzte in Heidelberg, 1889.*

182. NYBERG—HANSEN, R. Sites and mode of termination of reticulo-spinal fibers in the cat. An experimental study with silver impregnation methods. *J. Comp. Neurol.* 124: 71–99, 1965.

183. OLIVERAS, J. L., J. M. BESSON, G. GUILBAND, AND J. C. LIEBESKIND. Behavioral and electrophysiological evidence of pain inhibition from midbrain stimulation in the cat. *Exp. Brain Res.* 20: 32–44, 1974.

184. OLIVERAS, J. L., Y. HOSOBUCHI, F. REDJEMI, G. GUILBAND, AND J. M. BESSON. Opiate antagonist, naloxone, strongly reduces analgesia induced by stimulation of a raphe nucleus (centralis inferior). *Brain Res.* 120: 221–229, 1977.

185. OLIVERAS, J. L., F. REDJEMI, G. GUILBAND, AND J. M. BESSON. Analgesia induced by electrical stimulation of the inferior centralis nucleus of the raphe in the cat. *Pain* 1: 139-145, 1975.

186. OLSON, L., AND A. SEIGER. Early prenatal ontogeny of central

monoamine neurons in the rat: fluorescence histochemical observations. *Z. Anat. Entwicklungsgesch.* 137: 301-316, 1972.

187. OLSZEWSKI, J. The cytoarchitecture of the human reticular formation. In: *Brain Mechanisms and Consciousness*, edited by J. F. Delafresnaye. Springfield, IL: Thomas, 1954, p. 54-76.

188. OLSZEWSKI, J., AND D. BAXTER. *Cytoarchitecture of the Human Brain Stem*. Philadelphia, PA: Lippincott, 1954.

189. PANNESE, E., L. LUCIANO, S. IURATO, AND E. REALE. Cholinesterase activity in spinal ganglia neuroblasts: a histochemical study at the electron microscope. *J. Ultrastruct. Res.* 36: 46-67, 1971.

190. PAPEZ, J. W. Reticulo-spinal tracts in the cat. Marchi method. *J. Comp. Neurol.* 41: 365-399, 1926.

191. PAPPAS, G. D., E. B. COHEN, AND D. P. PURPURA. Fine structure of synaptic and monosynaptic neuronal relations in the thalamus of the cat. In: *The Thalamus*, edited by D. P. Purpura and M. D. Yahr. New York: Columbia Univ. Press, 1966, p. 47-71.

192. PARENT, A., AND L. L. BUTCHER. Organization and morphologies of acetylcholinesterase-containing neurons in the thalamus and hypothalamus of the rat. *J. Comp. Neurol.* 170: 205-226, 1976.

193. PENFIELD, W. Epileptic automatisms and the centrencephalic integrating system. *Res. Publ. Assoc. Res. Nerv. Ment. Dis.* 30: 513-528, 1952.

194. PETERSON, B. W. Identification of reticulospinal projections that may participate in gaze control. *Neurosci. Res. Program Bull.* 18: 48-55, 1980.

195. PETERSON, B. W., M. E. ANDERSON, AND M. FILION. Responses of ponto-medullary reticular neurons to cortical, tectal, and cutaneous stimuli. *Exp. Brain Res.* 21: 19-44, 194.

196. POIRIER, L. J., E. G. MCGEER, L. LARCHELLE, P. L. MCGEER, P. BEDARD, AND T. BOUCHER. The effect of brain stem lesions on tyrosine and tryptophan hydroxylases in various structures of the telencephalon of the cat. *Brain Res.* 14: 147-155 1969.

197. POWELL, T. P. S., AND W. M COWAN. A study of thalamostriate relations in the monkey. *Brain* 79: 364-390, 1956.

198. PRICE, D. D., AND A. C. BROWE. Responses of spinal cord neurons to graded noxious and non-noxious stimuli. *Brain Res.* 64: 425-429, 1973.

199. PRICE, D. D., AND D. J. MAYER. Physiological laminar organization of the dorsal horn of *Macaca mulatta. Brain Res.* 79: 321-325, 1974.

200. PURPURA, D. P. Activation of "secondary" impulse trigger sites in hippocampal neurons. *Nature London* 211: 1317-1318, 1966.

201. PURPURA, D. P., T. L. FRIGYESI, J. G. MCMURTY, AND T. SCARF. Synaptic mechanisms in thalamic regulations of cerebello-cortical projection activity. In: *The Thalamus*, edited by D. P. Purpura, and M. D. Yahr. New York: Columbia Univ. Press, 1966, p. 153-172.

202. RALSTON, H. J., AND M. M. HERMAN. The fine structure of neurons and synapses in the ventrobasal thalamus of the cat. *Brain Res.* 14: 77-97, 1969.

203. RAMÓN-MOLINER, E., AND W. J. NAUTA. The isodendritic core of the brain stem. *J. Comp. Neurol.* 126: 311-335, 1966.

203a. RAMÓN Y CAJAL, S. *Histologie du système nerveux de l'homme et des vertébrés* [transl. from Spanish by L. Azoulay]. Paris: Maloine, 1909-1911, vols. 1 and 2.

204. RHEINBERGER, M. B., AND H. H. JASPER. Electrical activity of the cerebral cortex in the unanesthetized cat. *Am. J. Physiol.* 119: 186-196, 1937.

205. RHINES, R., AND H. W. MAGOUN. Brain stem facilitation of cortical motor response. *J. Neurophysiol.* 9: 219-229, 1946.

206. RIMBAUD, L., P. PASSOUANT, AND J. CADILHAC. Participation de l'hippocampe à la régulation des états de veille et de sommeil. *Rev. Neurol.* 93: 303-308, 1955.

207. RINVIK, E. Organization of thalamic connections from motor and somatosensory cortical areas in the cat. In: *Corticothalamic Projections and Sensorimotor Activities*, edited by T. Frigyesi, E. Rinvik, and M. D. Yahr. New York: Raven, 1972, p. 57-88.

208. RIOCH, D. M. Studies on the diencephalon of carnivora. I. The

nuclear configuration of the thalamus, epithalamus and hypothalamus of the dog and cat. *J. Comp. Neurol.* 49: 1-119, 1929.

209. RIOCH, D. M. A note on the centre médian nucleus of Luys. *J. Anat.* 65: 324-327, 1931.

210. ROBERTSON, R. T. Thalamic projections to visually responsive regions of parietal cortex. *Brain Res. Bull.* 1: 459-469, 1976.

211. ROBERTSON, R. T. Thalamic projections to parietal cortex. *Brain Behav. Evol.* 14: 161-184, 1977.

212. ROBERTSON, R. T., G. S. LYNCH, AND R. F. THOMPSON. Diencephalic distributions of ascending reticular systems. *Brain Res.* 55: 309-322, 1973.

213. ROSE, J. E. The cortical connections of the reticular complex of the thalamus. *Res. Publ. Assoc. Res. Nerv. Ment. Dis.* 30: 454-479, 1952.

214. ROSE, J. E., AND C. N. WOOLSEY. Organization of the mammalian thalamus and its relationships to the cerebral cortex. *Electroencephalogr. Clin. Neurophysiol.* 1: 391-403, 1949.

215. ROSE, J. E., AND C. N. WOOLSEY. Cortical connections and functional organization of the thalamic auditory system of the cat. In: *Biological and Biochemical Bases of Behavior*, edited by H. F. Harlow and C. N. Woolsey. Madison: Univ. of Wisconsin Press, 1958, p. 127-150.

216. ROSSI, G. F., AND A. BRODAL. Terminal distribution of spinoreticular fibers in the cat. *AMA Arch. Neurol. Psychiatry* 78: 439-453, 1957.

217. ROSSI, G. F., F. FAVALE, T. HARA, A. GIUSSANI, AND G. SACCO. Researches on the nervous mechanisms underlying deep sleep in the cat. *Arch. Ital. Biol.* 99: 270-292, 1961.

218. ROSSI, G. F., K. MINOBE, AND O. CANDIA. An experimental study of the hypnogenic mechanisms of the brain stem. *Arch. Ital. Biol.* 101: 470-492, 1963.

219. RUDA, M. Autoradiographic Study of the Efferent Projection of the Midbrain Central Gray to the Raphe Nuclei. Philadelphia: Univ. of Pennsylvania, 1975. (Ph.D. thesis).

220. SCHEIBEL, A. B. Axonal afferent patterns in the bulbar reticular formation (Abstract). *Anat. Rec.* 121: 361-362, 1955.

221. SCHEIBEL, A. B. Development of axonal and dendritic neuropil as a function of evolving behavior. In: *The Neurosciences, Fourth Study Program*, edited by F. O. Schmitt and F. G. Worden. Cambridge, MA: MIT Press, 1978, 381-398.

222. SCHEIBEL, M. E. Axonal efferent patterns in the bulbar reticular formation (Abstract). *Anat. Rec.* 121: 362, 1955.

223. SCHEIBEL, M. E., T. L. DAVIES, AND A. B. SCHEIBEL. Maturation of reticular dendrites: loss of spines and development of bundles. *Exp. Neurol.* 38: 301-310, 1973.

224. SCHEIBEL, M. E., AND A. B. SCHEIBEL. Structural substrates for integrative patterns in the brain stem reticular core. In: *Reticular Formation of the Brain*, edited by H. H. Jasper, L. D. Proctor, R. S. Knighton, W. C. Noshay, and R. T. Costello. Boston, MA: Little, Brown, 1958, p. 31-55.

225. SCHEIBEL, M. E., AND A. B. SCHEIBEL. Periodic sensory nonresponsiveness in reticular neurons. *Arch. Ital. Biol.* 103: 300-316, 1965.

226. SCHEIBEL, M. E., AND A. B. SCHEIBEL. The response of reticular units to repetitive stimuli. *Arch. Ital. Biol.* 103: 279-299, 1965.

227. SCHEIBEL, M. E., AND A. B. SCHEIBEL. The organization of the nucleus reticularis thalami: a Golgi study. *Brain Res.* 1: 43-62, 1966.

228. SCHEIBEL, M. E., AND A. B. SCHEIBEL. Patterns of organization in specific and nonspecific thalamic fields. In: *The Thalamus*, edited by D. P. Purpura and M. D. Yahr. New York: Columbia Univ. Press, 1966, p. 13-46.

229. SCHEIBEL, M. E., AND A. B. SCHEIBEL. Anatomical basis of attention mechanisms in vertebrate brains. In: *Neurosciences: A Study Program*, edited by G. C. Quarton, T. Melnechuk, and F. O. Schmitt. New York: Rockefeller Univ. Press, 1967, p. 577-602.

230. SCHEIBEL, M. E., AND A. B. SCHEIBEL. Structural organization of nonspecific thalamic nuclei and their projection toward cortex. *Brain Res.* 6: 60-94, 1967.

231. SCHEIBEL, M. E., AND A. B. SCHEIBEL. Terminal patterns in

cat spinal cord. III. Primary afferent collaterals. *Brain Res.* 13: 417–443, 1969.

232. SCHEIBEL, M. E., AND A. B. SCHEIBEL. Thalamus and body image—a model. *Biol. Psychiatry* 3: 71–76, 1971.

233. SCHEIBEL, M. E., AND A. B. SCHEIBEL. Input-output relations of the thalamic nonspecific system. *Brain Behav. Evol.* 6: 332–358, 1972.

234. SCHEIBEL, M. E., AND A. B. SCHEIBEL. Specialized organizational patterns within the nucleus reticularis thalami of the cat. *Exp. Neurol.* 34: 316–322, 1972.

235. SCHEIBEL, M. E., AND A. B. SCHEIBEL. Dendrite bundles as sites for central programs: an hypothesis. *Int. J. Neurosci.* 6: 195–202, 1973.

236. SCHEIBEL, M. E., AND A. B. SCHEIBEL. Dendrite bundles, central programs and the olfactory bulb. *Brain Res.* 95: 407–421, 1975.

236a. SCHEIBEL, M. E. AND A. B. SCHEIBEL. The anatomy of constancy. *Ann. NY Acad. Sci.* 290: 421–435, 1977.

237. SCHEIBEL, M., A. SCHEIBEL, A. MOLLICA, AND G. MORUZZI. Convergence and interaction of afferent impulses on single units of reticular formation, *J. Neurophysiol.* 18: 309–331, 1955.

238. SCHEIBEL, M. E., U. TOMIYASU, AND A. B. SCHEIBEL. Do raphe nuclei of the reticular formation have a neurosecretory or vascular sensor function? *Exp. Neurol.* 47: 316–329, 1975.

239. SCHLAG, J. D., AND P. CHAILLET. Thalamic mechanisms involved in cortical desynchronization and recruiting responses. *Electroencephalogr. Clin. Neurophysiol.* 15: 39–62, 1963.

240. SCHLAG, J., I. LEHTINEN, AND M. SCHLAG-REY. Neuronal activity before and during eye movements in thalamic internal medullary lamina of the cat. *J. Neurophysiol.* 37: 982–995, 1974.

241. SCHLAG, J., AND M. WASZAK. Characteristics of unit responses in nucleus reticularis thalami. *Brain Res.* 21: 286–288, 1970.

242. SCHLAG, J., AND M. WASZAK. Electrophysiological properties of units of the thalamic reticular complex. *Exp. Neurol.* 32: 79–97, 1971.

243. SCHLAG-REY, M., AND J. SCHLAG. Visual and presaccadic neuronal activity in thalamic internal medullary lamina of cat: a study of targeting. *J. Neurophysiol.* 40: 156–173, 1977.

244. SCHMITT, R. O., P. DEV, AND B. H. SMITH. Electrotonic processing of information by brain cells. *Science* 193: 114–120, 1976.

245. SHEPS, J. G. The nuclear configuration and cortical connections of the human thalamus. *J. Comp. Neurol.* 83: 1–56, 1945.

246. SHIMAMOTO, T., AND M. VERZEANO. Relations between caudate and diffusely projecting thalamic nuclei. *J. Neurophysiol.* 17: 278–288, 1954.

247. SHUTE, C. C. D., AND P. R. LEWIS. Cholinergic and monoaminergic pathways in the hypothalamus. *Br. Med. Bull.* 22: 221–226, 1966.

248. SHUTE, C. C. D., AND P. R. LEWIS. The ascending cholinergic reticular system: neocortical, olfactory, and subcortical projections. *Brain* 90: 497–520, 1967.

249. SINGER, W. Central core control of visual cortex function. In: *The Neurosciences, Fourth Study Program*, edited by F. O. Schmitt and F. Worden. Cambridge, MA: MIT Press, 1978, p. 1093–1110.

250. SKINNER, J. E., AND D. B. LINDSLEY. Electrophysiological and behavioral effects of blockade of the nonspecific thalamo-cortical system. *Brain Res.* 6: 95–118, 1967.

251. SKINNER, J. E., AND C. D YINGLING. Regulation of slow potential shifts in nucleus reticularis thalami by the mesencephalic reticular formation and the frontal granular cortex. *Electroencephalogr. Clin. Neurophysiol.* 40: 288–296, 1976.

252. SKINNER, J. E., AND C. D. YINGLING. Central gating mechanisms that regulate event-related potentials and behavior. In: *Progress in Clinical Neurophysiology. Attention, Voluntary Contraction, and Event-Related Cerebral Potentials*, edited by J. F. Desmedt. Basel: Karger, 1977, vol. 1, p. 30–69.

253. SLADEK, J. R. JR. Differences in the distribution of catecholamine varicosities in cat and rat reticular formation. *Science* 174: 410–412, 1971.

254. SPENCER, W. A., AND E. R. KANDEL. Electrophysiology of hippocampal neurons. IV. Fast prepotentials. *J. Neurophysiol.* 24: 272–285, 1961.

255. SPRAGUE, J. M., AND W. W. CHAMBERS. Control of posture by reticular formation and cerebellum in the intact, anesthetized and unanesthetized and in the decerebrated cat. *Am. J. Physiol.* 176: 52–64, 1954.

256. STARZL, T. E., C. W. TAYLOR, AND H. W. MAGOUN. Collateral afferent excitation of reticular formation of brain stem. *J. Neurophysiol.* 14: 479–496, 1951.

257. STARZL, T. E., AND D. G. WHITLOCK. Diffuse thalamic projection system in monkey. *J. Neurophysiol.* 15: 449–468, 1952.

258. STEIN, B. E., B. MAGALHÃES-CASTRO, AND L. KRUGER. Relationship between visual and tactile representations in cat superior colliculus. *J. Neurophysiol.* 39: 401–419, 1976.

259. STINUS, L., O. GAFFORI, H. SIMON, AND M. LEMOAL. Small doses of apomorphine and chronic administration of amphetamine reduce locomotor hyperactivity produced by radio-frequency lesions of dopaminergic A10 neurons area. *Biol. Psychiatry* 12: 719–732, 1977.

260. SZENTÁGOTHAI, J. The structure of the synapse in the lateral geniculate body. *Acta Anat.* 55: 166–183, 1963.

261. SZENTÁGOTHAI, J., AND M. A. ARBIB. Conceptual models of neural organization. *Neurosci. Res. Program Bull.* 12: 307–510, 1974.

262. TABER, E. The cytoarchitecture of the brain stem of the cat. I. Brain stem nuclei of the cat. *J. Comp. Neurol.* 116: 27–70, 1961.

263. TABER, E., A. BRODAL, AND F. WALBERG. The raphe nuclei of the brain stem in the cat. I. Normal topography and cytoarchitecture and general discussion. *J. Comp. Neurol.* 114: 161–187, 1960.

264. TORVIK, A., AND A. BRODAL. The origin of reticulo-spinal fibers in the cat. An experimental study. *Anat. Rec.* 128: 113–135, 1957.

265. TREVINO, D. L., J. D. COULTER, AND W. D. WILLIS. Location of cells of origin of spinothalamic tract in lumbar enlargement of the monkey. *J. Neurophysiol.* 36: 750–761, 1973.

266. TREVINO, D. L., R. A. MAUNZ, R. N. BRYAN, AND W. D. WILLIS. Location of cells of origin of the spinothalamic tract in the lumbar enlargement of cat. *Exp. Neurol.* 34: 64–77, 1972.

267. TSAI, C. The descending tracts of the thalamus and midbrain of the opossum. *J. Comp. Neurol.* 39: 173–216, 1925.

268. UDO, M., AND N. MANO. Discrimination of different spinal monosynaptic pathways converging onto reticular neurons. *J. Neurophysiol.* 33: 227–238, 1970.

269. UNGERSTEDT, U. 6-Hydroxy-dopamine induced degeneration of central monoamine neurons. *Eur. J. Pharmacol.* 5: 107–110, 1968.

269a. UNGERSTEDT, U. Stereotaxic mapping of the monoamine pathways in the rat brain. *Acta Physiol. Scand. Suppl.* 367: 1–48, 1971.

270. VALENSTEIN, E. S., AND W. J. H. NAUTA. A comparison of the distribution of the formix system in the rat, guinea pig, cat and monkey. *J. Comp. Neurol.* 113: 337–363, 1959.

271. VALVERDE, F. Reticular formation of the pons and medulla oblongata. A Golgi study. *J. Comp. Neurol.* 116: 71–99, 1961.

272. VALVERDE, F. Reticular formation of the albino rat's brain stem. Cytoarchitecture and corticofugal connections. *J. Comp. Neurol.* 119: 25–53, 1962.

273. VAN BUREN, J. M., AND R. C. BORKE. *Variations and Connections of the Human Thalamus.* New York: Springer-Verlag, 1972, vols. I and II.

274. VERZEANO, M., D. B. LINDSLEY, AND H. W. MAGOUN. Nature of recruiting response. *J. Neurophysiol.* 16: 183–195, 1953.

275. VINOGRADOVA, O. S., AND D. F. LINDSLEY. Extinction of reactions to sensory stimuli in single neurons of visual cortex in unanesthetized rabbits. *Federation Proc.* (Transl. Suppl.) 23: T241–T246, 1964.

276. VOGT, C., AND O. VOGT. Thalamus studien I–III. *J. Psychol. Neurol. Leipzig* 50: 32–154, 1941.

277. WADA, J., AND T. R. RASMUSSEN. Intracarotid amytal for the

lateralization of cerebral speech dominance. *J. Neurosurg.* 17: 266–282, 1960.

278. WALBERG, F., O. POMPEIANO, L. E. WESTRUM, AND E. HAUG-LIE-HANSSEN. Fastigioreticular fibers in cat. An experimental study with silver methods. *J. Comp. Neurol.* 119: 187–199, 1962.

279. WALKER, A. E. *The Primate Thalamus.* Chicago: Univ. of Chicago Press, 1938.

280. WASZAK, M. Firing patterns of neurons in the rostral and ventral part of nucleus reticularis thalami during EEG spindles. *Exp. Neurol.* 43: 38–58, 1974.

281. WEINBERGER, N. M., M. VELASCO, AND D. B. LINDSLEY. Effects of lesions upon thalamically induced electrocortical desynchronization and recruiting. *Electroencephalogr. Clin. Neurophysiol.* 18: 369–377, 1965.

282. WEITZMAN, E. D., D. FUKUSHIMA, C. NOGEIRE, H. ROFFWARG, T. F. GALLAGHER, AND L. HELLMAN. Twenty-four hour pattern of the episodic secretion of cortisol in normal subjects. *J. Clin. Endocrinol. Metab.* 33: 14–22, 1971.

283. WESTMAN, J., AND D. BOWSHER. Fine structure of the centro-median—parafascicular complex in the cat. *Brain Res.* 30: 331–337, 1971.

284. WILLIS, W. D. Descending pathways affecting spinal sensory systems. *Neurosci. Res. Program Bull.* 18: 63–66, 1980.

285. WILLIS, W. D., L. H. HABER, AND R. F. MARTIN. Inhibition of spinothalamic tract cells and interneurons by brain stem stimulation in the monkey. *J. Neurophysiol.* 40: 968–981, 1977.

286. WILLIS, W. D., D. L. TREVINO, J. D. COULTER, AND R. A. MAUNZ. Responses of primate spinothalamic tract neurons to natural stimulation of hindlimb. *J. Neurophysiol.* 37: 358–372, 1974.

287. WILSON, P. D., J. PECCI-SAAVEDRA, AND R. W. DOTY. Mesencephalic control of lateral geniculate nucleus in primates. II. Effective loci. *Exp. Brain Res.* 18: 204–213, 1973.

288. WILSON, V. J., AND M. YOSHIDA. Comparison of effects of stimulation of Deiters' nucleus and medial longitudinal fasciculus on neck, forelimb, and hindlimb motoneurons. *J. Neurophysiol.* 32: 743–758, 1969.

289. WISE, S. P., E. G. JONES. Cells of origin and terminal distribution of descending projections of the rat somatic sensory cortex. *J. Comp. Neurol.* 175: 129–157, 1977.

290. YAMAMOTO, T. Effects upon thalamic somatosensory transmission of reticular formation stimulation. *Tohoku J. Exp. Med.* 79: 369–384, 1963.

291. YINGLING, C. D., AND J. E. SKINNER. Regulation of unit activity in nucleus reticularis thalami by the mesencephalic reticular formation and the frontal granular cortex. *Electroencephalogr. Clin. Neurophysiol.* 39: 635–642, 1975.

CHAPTER 7

The beginnings of visual perception: the retinal image and its initial encoding

Appendix: Fourier transforms and shift-invariant linear operators

JOHN I. YELLOTT, JR. | *University of California, Irvine, California*
BRIAN A. WANDELL | *Stanford University, Stanford, California*
TOM N. CORNSWEET | *University of California, Irvine, California*

CHAPTER CONTENTS

SCOPE AND ORGANIZATION

The organizing theme of this chapter is the general question: What aspects of human visual perception can be thoroughly explained in physiological terms at the present time? This introductory section surveys the overall status of physiological explanations of visual phenomena. At present, tight explanatory links between perception and physiology are still largely confined to the level of the optics of the retinal image and its initial neural registration by the photoreceptors. However, understanding of the neural events that immediately follow quantum absorption is growing very rapidly: A number of perceptual phenomena seem tantalizingly close to complete explanation. The subsequent sections provide fairly detailed discussions of three special topics: *1*) high spatial frequency sensitivity or visual acuity (p. 260), *2*) color vision (p. 280), and *3*) light and dark adaptation (p. 293). The first two topics furnish outstanding examples of important visual phenomena that now seem to be thoroughly explainable in physical terms. The third topic is an example of a perceptual phenomenon that seems within reach of current physiological techniques and explanatory principles, but still some distance from a thoroughly satisfactory physical explanation. Finally, a mathematical *Appendix*, p. 302, outlines the Fourier analytic ideas underlying much current work in vision, and in particular the discussion of retinal imagery and spatial contrast sensitivity in our section VISUAL ACUITY p. 260.

PHYSIOLOGICAL EXPLANATION IN VISUAL SCIENCE: THREE CLASSES OF PERCEPTUAL PHENOMENA

The phenomena of human visual perception can be usefully divided into three classes. The smallest and most exclusive class consists of phenomena whose properties can presently be explained in terms of accepted physical principles together with well-established anatomical and physiological properties of the visual apparatus. In this class one can place two of the major phenomena of color vision—trichromacy at high-illumination levels and monochromacy (total color blindness) at low levels; and also the main features of visual detection of fine spatial detail—technically, the high-frequency end of the spatial contrast sensitivity function (the spatial "modulation transfer function" of the visual system). In addition one could include here various pathological effects having to do with visual field losses produced by lesions in the lower visual pathways (where the anatomical wiring diagrams are uncontroversial) and a few perceptual curiosities such as the blind spot (the 6° gap in the visual field produced by the hole in the receptor mosaic through which ganglion cell axons leave the retina) that can be attributed to straightforward anatomical considerations. The reader may be able to think of a few other candidates, but at the moment we do not think there are very many.

All of these class 1 phenomena can be conceptualized as a loss of information potentially available in the visual stimulus. In the case of color vision the visual system loses wavelength information, so that spectrally different lights are perceptually indistinguishable; in spatial vision the system loses high-frequency modulation information, so that stimuli which differ only in their fine detail cannot be discriminated; and the other cases mentioned above can be characterized in a similar fashion. This preoccupation with information loss is not accidental: The only perceptual phenomena universally acknowledged as being susceptible to explanation in physical terms are those that can be described as sensory losses of information—or equivalently (since information is ultimately carried by differences) in terms of a perceptual inability to discriminate between physically different stimuli. Brindley's (29) statement of the epistomological issue here has been especially influential:

> The main function of science, in those of its branches that have advanced beyond the primitively exploratory stage, is the formulation and testing of hypotheses which have exact and potentially observable implications. The inescapable implications of any hypothesis can necessarily be expressed in terms which appear either in the statement of the hypothesis, or in the background of generally accepted theory assumed in conjunction with it. For physiology, the terms used in stating the theoretical background are physico-chemical and anatomical; so it would seem that no physiological hypothesis that is also stated in physical, chemical and anatomical terms can ever predict the result of a sensory experiment, in which a report of sensations is concerned. There is, however, one class of predictions that can be made if we add to our theoretical background a single hypothesis that is very difficult to doubt. The additional hypothesis required is that whenever two stimuli cause physically indistinguishable signals to be sent from the sense organs to the brain, the sensations produced by these stimuli, as reported by the subject in words, symbols or actions, must also be indistinguishable. (p. 132–133).

Brindley's (29) assessment of other potential explanatory principles is also worth quoting, because it represents the most conservative position, and probably reflects the views of the majority of sensory physiologists:

> If a physiological hypothesis, i.e. a hypothesis about function that is stated in physical, chemical and anatomical terms, is to imply a given result for a sensory experiment, the background of theory assumed in conjunction with it must be enlarged to include hypotheses containing psychological terms as well as physico-chemical and anatomical. These may be called *psycho-physical linking hypotheses*. The one that has already been stated above, namely that physically indistinguishable signals sent from sense organs to the brain cause indistinguishable sensations, is the most general, and at the same time the most difficult to doubt, that has yet been proposed. It seems to me that it is the only one that is at present sufficiently secure to deserve inclusion in the body of generally accepted theory. (p. 134).

This degree of skepticism as to the value of other linking hypotheses is not universally shared, but at present there is apparently no general acceptance of any explanatory principle except the one endorsed here by Brindley.

The distinguishing property of the perceptual phenomena in our first class is that they can not only be characterized in terms of a loss of information, but in addition—and most important—we can confidently pinpoint the anatomical and physiological factors responsible for the specific form of the loss. Thus in the case of color vision, wavelength information is lost at the point of light absorption in the photoreceptors because any given receptor only records the fact that a photon has been absorbed, and not the wavelength of that photon [Rushton (112) calls this the "univariance" principle]. Consequently wavelength discrimination is only possible by virtue of a comparison between the quantum catches of receptors that have different absorption spectra, and the specific quantitative form of the chromatic information loss in human vision can be explained as an inevitable consequence of the limited variety of absorption spectra represented in the human retina: Night vision is monochromatic because all rods share the absorption spectrum of rhodopsin and daylight vision is trichromatic because there are three different cone pigments. In the case of spatial contrast sensitivity, high-frequency spatial information is lost because of the optical limitations of the eye: We cannot see ultrafine spatial details because they are washed out in the physical process of image formation and consequently never appear in the retinal image (though as we shall see in VISUAL ACUITY, p. 260, however, this story is complicated by a subsequent neurally imposed frequency cutoff that nearly—and quite mysteriously—matches the limits imposed by the optics). The anatomical and physiological factors responsible for the losses characterizing our other class 1 phenomena have already been noted in connection with their original descriptions.

In a second class, one can place a large number of visual phenomena for which one can envision plausible physiological models, but for which the specific anatomical or physiological mechanisms remain uncertain. Most of these can be characterized as information losses and fall into the explanatory framework common to our class 1 phenomena. The outstanding examples of class 2 phenomena are light and dark adaptation, i.e., changes in visual sensitivity due to changes in the mean illumination level. These effects might in principle be entirely accounted for in terms of photoreceptor properties (that is, one could readily imagine a visual system constructed in that fashion), and both psychophysical evidence and single-unit recordings indicate that receptors play a very substantial role in light adaptation: Changes in their sensitivity certainly account for a significant share in the overall perceptual effect. In the particular case of the phenomenon of rod saturation (the inability of rod-mediated vision to detect contrast at high-illumination levels) it has been suggested that the perceptual effect may be entirely explained in terms of a limiting of the rod outer segment membrane potential due to the closure of all of its sodium-permeable channels (97). However, in general it is clear that more proximal cells adapt to the prevailing visual environment and require some time to readjust when that environment changes. (12, 46) At the present time not enough is known about the quantitative properties of retinal circuits to support any definitive allocation of responsibility for the overall adaptation effect; this is an important target of current investigation.

The same can be said of many temporal phenomena; notably the inability to detect very rapid temporal modulation (flicker fusion), which might in principle by entirely explained in terms of the temporal smoothing properties of receptors—again, in the sense that one could construct plausible models on this basis, and also in the sense that receptors are known to act like temporal filters (26) and certainly play an important role in damping out rapid flicker. However, there is substantial evidence that "photopic flicker sensitivity is normally controlled, not by cone cells, but by the interactive pathways of the retina" (77).

Many other loss-like phenomena could also be placed in this second class, e.g., the subjective disappearance of stabilized retinal images, the suppression of low-frequency spatial contrast (together with such associated phenomena as mach bands), visual masking effects (28), various pattern and motion aftereffects [e.g., grating adaptation effects of the sort reported by Blakemore and Campbell (21), and Purkinje's waterfall illusion], and some aspects of depth perception [those related to pathological deficits in binocular stereopsis caused by developmental abnormalities that eliminate the disparity sensitive cortical neurons described by Barlow et al. (11)]. In all of those cases the

major barrier to full understanding is not the inability to construct plausible physiological models that could in principle account for the phenomena, but rather the lack of a sufficiently rich physiological data base to force consensus on a single specific model. What is needed, of course, is a detailed quantitative understanding of neural circuits, and especially of neural signals as they are actually transmitted, i.e., by transmitter substance release or electrical coupling. Studies aimed at obtaining information of that sort have only recently become technically possible (see, for example, ref. 12), and in fact it has only lately been established that receptors reduced their rate of transmitter release in response to light (102). This central fact is perhaps not surprising, since the membrane response to light is hyperpolarization, but it does pose a new challenge for modelers and also presents the functionally curious spectacle of a receptor-signaling mechanism that works hardest in the dark, when it has nothing to report.

Finally in connection with class 2 it is necessary to say something about heterochromatic brightness, which is the classic example of a visual phenomenon that cannot readily be described in terms of information loss, but instead both requires and suggests a physiological explanation based on some other principle. Intuitively it seems clear that lights can be at least roughly ordered on a dimension of "brightness" even when their colors are different—for example, one has no difficulty in judging that the sun is brighter than the sky—and the precise quantitative relationship between the physical properties of lights and their psychological classification in terms of brightness has been a long-standing psychophysical problem (78). Early experimental work suggested that brightness exactly satisfied an additive relationship: If light A matches light B in brightness, and C matches D, then the combination A + C (i.e., the physical superimposition of lights A and C on the retina) must match B + D [Abney's law (1)]. This additivity hypothesis has important practical implications in photometry and is officially embodied in applications of the Commission Internationale de l'Éclairage (C.I.E.) photopic luminosity curve (the "photopic standard observer") which supplies the spectral weighting function for automatic photometers. The extent to which it actually holds appears to depend on the nature of the brightness judgment required of an observer. When the observer is simply asked to make a direct brightness comparison between isolated steady lights, Abney's law fails quite dramatically (60). When brightness is measured by minimizing apparent flicker against a standard, the deviations from additivity are significant, though apparently tolerable for industrial standards (71). When measured by the relatively new technique of minimizing apparent contrast at a border (25, 127), additivity appears to hold within measurement error (71).

Suppose Abney's law is valid for some psychophysical context: How could one account for it physiologically? Clearly this is not a straightforward case of sensory loss of information potentially available in a physical stimulus, since the observer is not incapable of discriminating between heterochromatic lights equated for brightness—on the contrary, his task is to overlook their color differences and base his judgment on some perceptual dimension on which they are the same. What is at issue then is not an inability to discriminate, but rather an ability to classify discriminable stimuli in a systematic way. How can such an ability be brought within the scope of physiological explanation?

A first step is to determine the neural coding demands implied by the ability to classify stimuli in this particular fashion—in other words, what kinds of numbers (i.e., neural signals) would a mechanism have to assign to stimuli in order to match the observed psychophysical classification? The precise form of the relational structure implied by Abney's law has been informally understood for some time, and recently has been spelled out rigorously in two papers by Krantz (79, 80) which apply modern ideas of fundamental measurement theory to the classic problems of color vision. From the standpoint of physiological modeling, the essential result is that any device which classifies lights according to Abney's law must base its decision on a linear combination of the trichromatic color-matching coordinates—a condition that would be satisfied most naturally in the retina by a mechanism that based its output on a weighted average of the quantum catch in all three cone systems.

A second step is to imagine a sensory "channel" that carries the signal computed by our hypothetical brightness mechanism: operationally such a channel is defined simply in terms of the assumption that its response to two lights is the same whenever they produce the same value on the brightness dimension—e.g., the same value of weighted average quantum catch. Therefore, the state of this channel can be completely specified by a single real number. Physiologically, such a channel might be identified with the nonopponent ganglion cells found in primate retinas (42). Of course this channel is assumed to exist in parallel with other channels carrying information about other properties of the stimulus (notably, opponent ganglion cells carrying chromatic information), and on those channels the responses to two stimuli of equal brightness will generally not be identical. However, one can suppose that when brightness judgments are called for, the observer can somehow base his decisions solely on the output of the brightness channel, ignoring information on the other channels.

Now if such channels really existed (and an enormous amount of current work on many problems assumes more or less explicitly that they do), we could think of brightness in terms of a sensory loss along one channel, and in this way the psychophysical linking hypothesis described by Brindley would still in a sense apply. However, it will not apply strictly unless one can somehow manage to silence all the other channels, so that the observer's discriminations have to be based on the brightness channel alone. Unless this can be arranged, there remains an uncomfortable nonphysical component in the theory, namely the fact that we cannot predict what an observer *must* do in a brightness judgment task because we do not know what factors determine his ability or willingness to base his judgments on the proper channel. This nonobligatory "psychological" aspect of such multichannel models is epistemologically disturbing. Nevertheless, modeling along such lines seems to present the only obvious line of progress, since not many visual phenomena can be clearly characterized in terms that strictly fit the linking hypothesis quoted earlier. What seems likely is that converging evidence will gradually increase the apparent tangibility of certain specific sensory channels, so that it will eventually come to seem natural to regard them as legitimate entities in a physical theory—notwithstanding the possible psychological foibles of a still physically elusive human "observer" who reads their output. This in fact is already happening in the case of the brightness channel: There is reason to believe that this channel can be isolated by means of rapid flicker, so that discrimination tasks can be arranged that are only possible on the basis of its output, the chromatic channels being irrelevant (77). Conversely, the brightness channel itself can be silenced by requiring a discrimination between stimuli equated for brightness, and this results in rather dramatic perceptual effects (e.g., ref. 58a), which strongly support the idea that some fundamental cleavage in the visual system is being revealed.

Finally, in a third class one can place all those visual phenomena for which we have no clear conception of even the outlines of a physiological explanation. Most prominent here are phenomena involving memory—pattern recognition abilities in particular, but also such purely subjective phenomena as visual imagery and visual experience in dreams and hallucinations. Most aspects of three-dimensional spatial perception (especially monocular depth perception) should also be included here, along with most aspects of motion perception. In all these cases the phenomena cannot be characterized in terms of information loss along well-established visual pathways, and we have no clear understanding of how they might be related to neural mechanisms. Consequently the shape of their ultimate physiological explanations cannot easily be foreseen at the present time.

The following handbooks, textbooks, and review articles may be useful in gaining an overview of the current state of visual science: references 12, 35, 40, 50, 62, 66, 68, 73, 81, 90, 99, 106, 144.

VISUAL ACUITY

Overview

One of the most obvious aspects of visual experience is our limited ability to resolve spatial detail: If a black-and-white grating is made fine enough, it cannot be distinguished from a uniformly gray field. (At 25-cm viewing distance one can just tell the difference when the width of each bar is 40 μm.) Early in the 17th century the Spanish physician Daza de Valdes (in ref. 84) measured the spatial resolution ability of his patients by having them count grains of mustard in a line; by the end of that century Phillipe de La Hire had "calculated that the limiting fineness of vision was 1/8000 inch on the retina" (which corresponds to a grating in which each stripe subtends 0.6 min of visual angle, i.e., 0.83 cycle/min), and attributed this limit to the structure of the retina: ". . . such is the smallness of the net of which it is made up" [(84), p. 107]. Modern research on visual acuity, influenced by ideas from information theory and Fourier optics, has concentrated on the ability to detect sinusoidal spatial modulation, and has attempted to determine the specific limitations imposed first by the optical apparatus of the eye, and subsequently by neural factors. Under normal viewing conditions it turns out that smearing of the retinal image due to optical factors can account for the observed upper limit of resolution capacity [which according to contemporary measurements is essentially the same as that reported by de La Hire (in ref. 84), i.e., roughly 1 cycle/min]: The optics of the eye simply cannot transmit spatial information at higher frequencies. Consequently one can say that the invisibility of spatial detail beyond this resolution limit is due to the optics of the eye: No matter how the retina and subsequent neural stages of the visual system are designed, they cannot extract spatial information from a visual stimulus unless it is available in the retinal image. In this sense, the upper limits of the spatial resolution capacity of the visual system under normal viewing conditions can be regarded as well understood.

However, this simple story is complicated by the fact that local acuity outside the center of the retina—and also at the center under special conditions that eliminate the normal optical blurring—cannot be accounted for in terms of optical factors, but instead requires a neural explanation. At present not enough is known about the details of neural interactions to allow one to construct definitive models of spatial information processing in the visual system: A great many important facts have been discovered by single-unit recording and other modern techniques, but one still cannot confidently assign any specific aspect of spatial contrast vision to a specific neural mechanism. In this sense, firm understanding has still not progressed beyond the level of the physical properties of the retinal image. In fact it does not appear that we fully understand the general principles underlying the neural processes that limit visual acuity: In *Neural Limits of Visual Acuity*, p. 275, we point out that current physiologically motivated models for spatial contrast detection do not explain how the visual system is able to suppress the counterfeit spatial frequencies that should be generated by its relatively coarse

sampling of the retinal image. In a sense, we still do not understand the role played by the smallness of the retinal net.

This section first reviews the optical properties of the eye, with particular emphasis on factors that degrade the quality of the retinal image. Then we discuss the psychophysics of human spatial contrast sensitivity and attempt to relate these results to the optics of the eye and the physical and neural properties of the retina. The discussion centers around concepts derived from information theory and Fourier optics (27, 51, 62, 96); the mathematical details here are summarized in the *Appendix* to this chapter, p. 302. Other recent review articles related to the topic of this section are those by Westheimer (140), Thomas (124), Ripps and Weale (103), and Kelly (74). Le Grand's (84) classic text provides an extensive and authoritative discussion of visual acuity, and a recent theoretical paper by Snyder et al. (118) describes an interesting calculation of the spatial information capacity of the retina that takes into account quantum noise effects as well as the optical and anatomical factors considered here. [We do not deal explicitly with quantum noise because we are concerned with the ability to see fine spatial detail under optimal conditions, which means at illumination levels high enough to guarantee very high quantum signal-to-noise ratios in the retinal image. For general discussions of quantum noise effects in vision, see Barlow (10a) and Rose (108.)]

The Retinal Image

Strictly speaking, the term "retinal image'" is ambiguous, because from an optical standpoint the thickness of the retina is quite appreciable—an image in focus on its vitreal surface can be as much as 2 diopters out of focus at the outer segments of the photoreceptors, where vision is actually initiated. Throughout this discussion we use "retina" to mean the outer segment layer and "retinal image" to mean the image formed at that level of the retina. To understand the limits of visual acuity the first problem is to determine how the physical parameters of this image are related to those of the external scenes that give rise to it. We will assume that these scenes produce incoherent light, since that is the normal situation in natural vision. However, coherent light enters the discussion when we consider experiments that use interference techniques to create very high frequency retinal images. (The *Appendix* to this chapter, p. 302, describes the difference between coherent and incoherent imagery.)

RETINAL IMAGE REPRESENTATIONS OF OBJECT PROPERTIES. *Shape and size.* The strongest refractive surface in the eye is the anterior surface of the cornea, this air-to-cornea interface accounting for about two-thirds of the overall refractive power of the eye. Essentially all of the remaining refraction occurs at the surfaces and within the internal stria of the crystalline lens. The interacting effects of these various refractive elements are complex, but for a normal eye and a distant object, a good first-order approximation to their optical behavior can be made by substituting for all those elements a single thin lens with a focal length of 17 mm, located 17 mm in front of the retina, or about 7.5 mm behind the anterior surface of the cornea (45, 84, 144). The center of this equivalent lens is called the nodal point of the simplified eye. To find the location in the retinal image of any given point in a scene, one draws a straight line from the point through the nodal point of the eye, and the intersection of that line with the retina is the location of the corresponding region in the retinal image. Because the distance from the nodal point of the eye to the retina is about 17 mm, the size of the image of any object in the plane perpendicular to the line of sight, or as projected onto that plane, is given by

$$\frac{S_i}{S_o} = \frac{17}{d_o}$$

where S_o is the size of the object, or its projection on the perpendicular plane, and d_o is the distance from the nodal point of the eye to the object, in mm.

Object and retinal image sizes are often expressed in units of visual angle, that is, the angle subtended by the object or its image at the nodal point of the eye. For example, an object 1 m long, in a plane perpendicular to the line joining one of its ends with the nodal point of the eye at a distance of 100 m, subtends a visual angle of

$$\tan^{-1}\frac{1}{100} = 0.57° = 34'$$

Intensity relations. When an object that is radiating light is viewed, the intensity at each point in its image, that is, the number of quanta per unit time per unit area incident on the retina in the region corresponding to the object, is directly proportional to *a*) the intensity of light radiated by the object in the direction of the eye, and *b*) the area of the pupil of the eye. As the light travels from the objects to the retina it passes through various media, e.g., air, corneal tissue, etc., that absorb, reflect, or scatter some proportion of it, reducing the intensity of the image. If pupil size and the fraction absorbed, scattered, and reflected are fixed, the intensity of the retinal image is linearly related to the intensity of the light radiating from the object. Thus the retinal image contains information about an important physical parameter of the object, namely how much light it radiates in the direction of the eye. However, the reliability of that information depends upon the extent to which the pupil has a constant area. Because the normal pupil ranges in diameter from about 8 mm to 2 mm, the intensity of the retinal image of a given luminous object can vary over a range of about 16:1. Consequently, unless a brain mechanism knows the size of the pupil (information not directly available to introspection, for example), it cannot know this parameter exactly, but

only within an interval of roughly one log unit. The information contained in the retinal image about the relationships among the intensities of two or more sources seen simultaneously is much better, because pupil size affects all their images by the same factor.

In the natural environment in which the eye evolved most objects do not actively generate light, but instead, reflect light generated elsewhere. The intensity of the retinal image of a reflective object depends jointly on a property of the object, reflectance, and the intensity of incident light. The retinal images of reflective objects thus do not contain information specifying their reflectance directly, but only the product of incident illumination and reflectance. Because the reflectances of ordinary objects vary from about 90% to about 10%, that is, over a range of only about 10:1, while the incident illumination varies by more than 10^6:1 in our normal environment, the intensity of the retinal image of an object does not uniquely tell us the reflectance of the object. However, the retinal image does contain accurate information about the relative reflectances of two or more objects if it is known that they are equally illuminated. Over a broad range of light intensities (luminance > 1 cd/m^2) the increment-threshold intensity is proportional to the background intensity (i.e., $\Delta I/I$ = constant—Weber's law.) Consequently over this range reflectance differences that are visible at any illumination level will be visible at all levels.

Optical effects that blur the retinal image. When the object viewed is a point source, that is, a source of light that subtends a negligibly small visual angle (a star, for example), several properties of the eye will cause light from the source to be spread over some finite area of the retina.

Focus errors. Figure 1 represents a simplified eye looking at a point source. Some of the rays from the source are refracted by the equivalent lens, pass through the pupil, and strike the retina.

The rays in this figure are shown crossing in front of the retina, representing a condition where the image of the point source falls in front of the retina as it would in an uncorrected myopic (nearsighted) eye. If the pupil of the eye is circular, then the retinal light distribution predicted by geometrical optics will be a uniform disk whose diameter increases linearly with the distance between the retina and the point where the rays cross (that is, the focus error), and also linearly with the diameter of the pupil. This disk is called a "blur circle." (The shape of the distribution

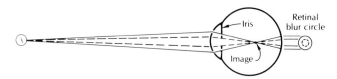

FIG. 1. Blur circles in a schematic misfocused eye for two different pupil sizes. [From Cornsweet (36).]

will be the same as the shape of the pupil. If the pupil were square, it would be a "blur square.") Blur circles for pupils of two different diameters are shown in Figure 1.

If two or more stars are imaged at the same time, each will form its own blur circle, and, because light intensities add linearly, the resulting retinal light distribution will simply be the sum of the individual blur circles. An extended source can be considered as an array of independent point sources, each of which forms its own blur circle. The resulting retinal light distribution is simply the sum of the distributions from each of these points. Since the blur circle for each point is identical, the defocused image of any object is simply the light distribution in the object convolved with the appropriate blur circle. [The operation of convolution is described mathematically in the *Appendix* to this chapter, *Shift-Invariant Linear Operators and Convolution*, p. 303 and TWO-DIMENSIONAL CASE, p. 304. Intuitively, this amounts to a smearing process in which each point in the object is imaged as a disk of light on the retina; the entire image of the subject is the sum of these (normally overlapping) disks.]

Aberrations. Even if a point source is focused as well as possible on the retina, the light from the source will still be distributed over a finite area as a result of imperfections or aberrations in the refractive system of the eye.

Spherical aberration (a consequence of differences in refractive power across the pupil as a function of distance from its center) varies strongly from one eye to another, within a given eye as a result of changes in accommodation, and from one meridian to another in the same eye.

Chromatic aberration results from differences in refractive power as a function of the wavelength of the incident light. When middle wavelength rays from a heterochromatic stimulus are in focus on the retina, rays from the blue end of the spectrum come to a focus in front of the retina and rays from the red end converge "behind" the retina. The magnitude of this aberration is relatively constant across individuals, and is quite substantial, as shown in Figure 2. Note that when the eye is accommodated for the red end of the spectrum, which seems to be the natural state of accommodation in viewing distant targets [(84), p. 45–46] deep blue light from the same target will be roughly 2 diopters out of focus.

Astigmatism (resulting from differences in refractive power as a function of meridional angle, i.e., for an eye with a horizontal line of sight, the power of the eye in a vertical plane might be different from its power in a horizontal plane) causes the retinal light distribution from each point in an object to be more or less elliptical in shape, the lengths of the major and minor axes of the ellipse depending upon the amount of astigmatism and the corresponding focus errors. Eyes differ greatly both in their amount of astigmatism and in its meridional orientation.

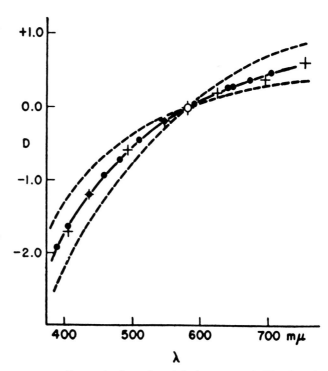

FIG. 2. Chromatic aberration of the human eye. λ, Wavelength; D, magnitude of chromatic aberration in diopters (assuming the eye is in perfect focus for 578 nm, D gives the power of the spectacle lens required to focus other wavelengths). *Solid line* and *solid dots*, average from 12 observers of Bedford and Wyszecki (19); *crosses*, average from 14 observers of Wald and Griffin (133); *dashed lines*, total range for all observations of Bedford and Wyszecki. [Adapted from Bedford and Wyszecki (19).]

Irregular refractive strengths over the surfaces of the eye, as in Figure 3, further degrade the image of each point in the object. The pattern of these irregularities varies considerably across observers and, for a given observer, across states of accommodation. Figure 3 shows a map of "isopower" lines across the pupil of one observer at zero accommodation; at higher levels of accommodation the map for this observer looks very different (125).

Coma refers to complex aberrations that arise as the angle between a collimated beam and the lens is varied. This effect has recently been shown to contribute importantly to the overall aberration of the eye, and to vary among different eyes (72).

Diffraction. Even if none of the aberrations just discussed were present in the eye, the light from a point source would spread over a finite region of the retina as a consequence of diffraction at the pupil. This can be thought of as an inevitable consequence of the fact that an optical instrument of limited size can only intercept a portion of the wave front arising from a source. The resulting distribution is approximately Gaussian, with a diameter that varies inversely with pupil diameter and directly with wavelength. (See Figs. 6 and 7.)

Scattering within the retina. As noted earlier the retina has an optically appreciable thickness: before

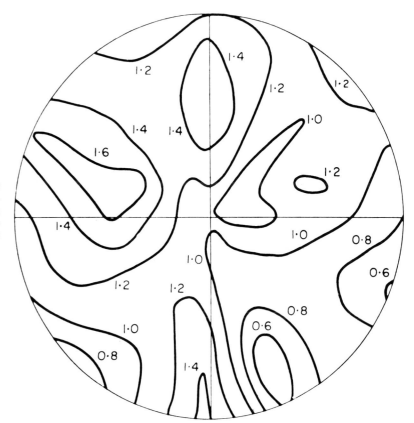

FIG. 3. Irregularities in refractive power across the pupil of a normal eye during relaxed accommodation (pupil diam, 7.2 mm). Contours join points of equal excess power (diopters). [From van den Brink (29a), with permission from Pergamon Press, Ltd.]

reaching the outer segments, light must pass through a layer of neural tissue that ranges from roughly 80 μm at the center of the fovea to nearly 400 μm at 5° eccentricity. This tissue and its vascular system must scatter some light, and that has generally been regarded as the functional explanation for its thinness in the region specialized for high acuity [but cf. Rodieck (106), p. 368]. Light that passes through the outer segment layer must also scatter upon reflection from the underlying tissues. Measurements of retinal scatter have recently been reported by Gorrand (52).

Pointspread and linespread functions. As a result of all of these factors, the light distribution in the focused retinal image of each point in an object is spread over a region of the retinal surface. The two-dimensional function that describes the image distribution for a single object point located at the origin is called the *pointspread function*: Figure 4 illustrates the concept for an idealized optical system consisting of a single lens. If the pointspread function is known for a given eye, the actual light distribution in the retinal image of any scene can be obtained by convolving the light distribution in the scene with the pointspread function. (In actuality the pointspread function varies with distance from the center of the fovea, and so in principle the entire set of pointspread functions must be known in order to derive the retinal image. However, because the high acuity phenomena that concern us here are mediated by the fovea, a single pointspread function is sufficient for present purposes.)

In practice, direct measurement of the pointspread function of the human eye is very difficult. (In fact, it has not yet been achieved.) But this function can be calculated from measurements of the *linespread function*, which are somewhat easier to obtain. The linespread function describes the cross section of the image of a thin (in principle, infinitely thin) line, as illustrated in Figure 5: If this function is known, and the optical system is circularly symmetrical (so that the linespread function does not depend on the orientation of the object line), the pointspread function can be derived from it by Fourier analytic methods, as outlined in the *Appendix* to this chapter, p. 302.

Figure 6 shows the foveal linespread function of the human eye for various pupil sizes [as measured by Campbell and Gubisch (33)], and Figure 7 shows the profiles of the corresponding pointspread functions as calculated by Gubisch (59). (In this instance it happens that the linespread and pointspread functions look roughly the same, but mathematically this need not always be the case.) These figures show two spread functions for each pupil size. The narrower function in each case is the theoretical spread that would result from diffraction at the pupil alone, while the wider function is the actual observed line or point spread. Notice that as pupil size increases the effect of diffraction at the pupil decreases but the actual spread

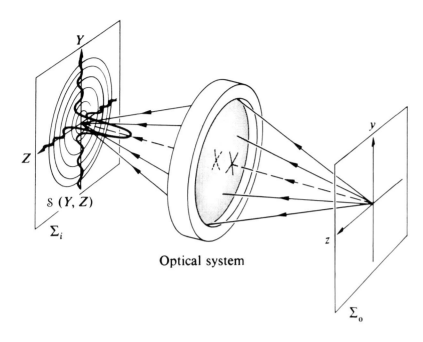

FIG. 4. Pointspread function of an optical system. Σ_o is the object plane, with coordinates y, z; Σ_i, is the image plane; $S(y,z)$, irradiance distribution produced in Σ_i by point source located at origin of Σ_o. Illustration is schematic. [From Hecht and Zajac (62).]

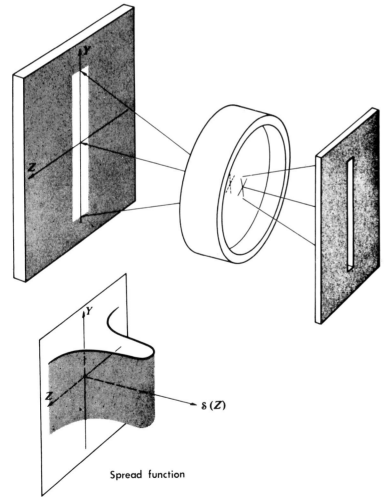

FIG. 5. Linespread function of an optical system. $S(Z)$ is the irradiance distribution in the image plane produced by an infinitely long thin line source in object plane. (The absence of secondary ripples here like those in Fig. 4 has no significance; both illustrations are schematic.) [From Hecht and Zajac (62).]

increases a bit due to the increased importance of other factors. For pupil diameters ≤2 mm (the lower limit in natural viewing) the observed spread functions are practically the same as those that would result from diffraction alone in an idealized optical system. (The light source here was a broad-band white light with a spectrum approximating the photopic luminosity function. Diffraction predictions were made by calculating monochromatic diffraction patterns for many different wavelengths and then weighting and averaging the resulting curves.)

The modulation transfer function. If the point-spread function of an optical system is known, the light distribution in the image of any object can be derived by convolving the light distribution in the object with the pointspread function. As mentioned above, the pointspread function can be derived from measures of the linespread function. An alternative procedure is to measure the *modulation transfer function* (MTF).

To measure the MTF one uses as an object a sinus-

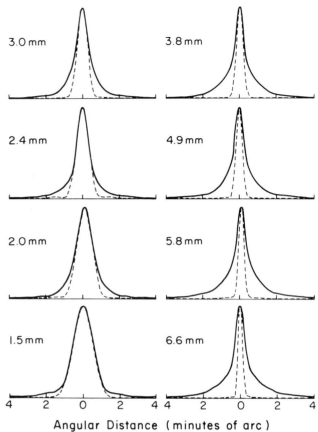

FIG. 7. Pointspread functions of the human eye for white light at various pupil diameters. *Solid curves,* radial profiles of theoretical pointspread functions calculated from linespread curves in Fig. 6. *Narrower dashed curves,* the point spread resulting from diffraction alone. [From Gubisch (59).]

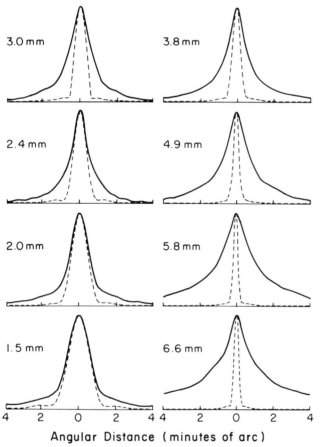

FIG. 6. Linespread functions of the human eye for white light at various pupil diameters. *Heavy dotted curves,* measured intensity (along horizontal axis) of retinal image of a line target as measured ophthalmoscopically. *Narrower dashed curves,* theoretical spread resulting from diffraction at the pupil alone. (All curves have been normalized to equal 1.0 at origin.) [From Campbell and Gubisch (33), with permission from Cambridge University Press.]

oidal grating, that is, a pattern for which intensity in one direction varies sinusoidally, while intensity is uniform in the orthogonal direction, as shown in Figure 8. The *contrast C* (or *modulation*) of such a grating is defined as

$$C = \frac{I_{max} - I_{min}}{I_{max} + I_{min}}$$

where I_{max} is the maximum intensity, I_{min} the minimum.

The image of such a grating will also have a sinusoidal intensity distribution, regardless of the nature of the pointspread function. (The convolution of a sine wave with any other function remains sinusoidal.) The ratio of image to object contrast is a measure of how well the optical system transfers the modulation of the object to the image plane. The fidelity of this transfer, that is, the value of this ratio, plotted as a function of the spatial frequency (i.e., cycles/deg) of the object grating, is the MTF of the optical system. (Figure 9 shows the MTF of a typical human eye for three different pupil sizes [as calculated by Gubisch (59) on the basis of the linespread data in Fig. 6]. For this optical system, and for all ordinary optical systems,

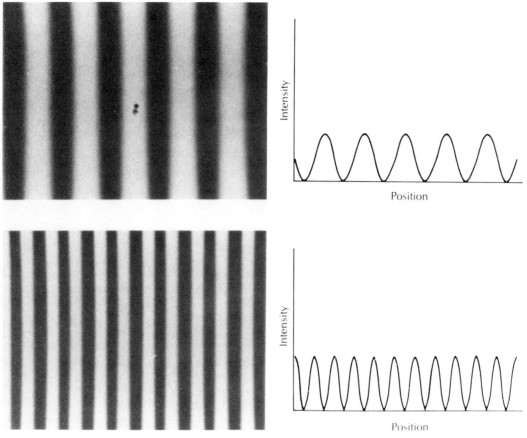

FIG. 8. Sinusoidal gratings. [From Cornsweet (36).]

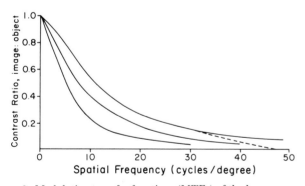

FIG. 9. Modulation transfer functions (MTFs) of the human eye for various pupil diameters. Each curve shows contrast reduction (i.e., retinal image contrast divided by the object contrast) imposed on sinusoidal targets as function of their spatial frequency. *Solid curves* (from *top* to *bottom*) correspond to pupil diameters of 2.4, 3.8, and 6.6 mm; *dashed curve* corresponds to 1.5 mm. MTFs calculated from linespread data of Fig. 6. [From Gubisch (59).]

the contrast ratio approaches one as the spatial frequency approaches zero. That is, for low spatial frequencies, the image contrast is as great as the object contrast, and as spatial frequency increases, the contrast in the image decreases relative to the object, until at very high frequencies (that is, for very closely spaced gratings) the image contrast is essentially zero regardless of the contrast of the object. Once the MTF

of an optical system is known its linespread and point-spread functions can be calculated by Fourier analytic methods. The mathematical details of this calculation are spelled out in the *Appendix* to this chapter, p. 302, but the essential fact is that the MTF is the absolute value (i.e., modulus) of the one-dimensional Fourier transform of the linespread function, or equivalently, the profile of the absolute value of the two-dimensional Fourier transform of the pointspread function. Before taking absolute values here, one has what is called the *optical transfer function* (OTF). When the OTF is entirely real and nonnegative—as will be the case when the optical system produces no phase shifts—the MTF and OTF are identical, and so the distinction need not be preserved. Both conditions are met by a well-focused eye, and in the vision literature one usually encounters only the MTF. However, it is important to keep in mind that the MTF by definition must be nonnegative and consequently does not reflect effects in which the OTF becomes negative for some spatial frequencies. Such effects can be produced by defocusing as discussed later in *Defocus and spurious resolution*, p. 268.

In general, then, if the MTF of a lens is known, the light distribution in the image of any object can be derived by *1*) analysis of the object into its Fourier spectrum, *2*) multiplication of the spectrum with the

MTF (or more precisely with the OTF, in cases where the MTF and OTF are not identical), and *3*) Fourier synthesis of the resulting product spectrum. Because of the directness of this operation the quality of an image-forming system is usually specified in terms of its MTF rather than its point- or linespread function.

Defocus and spurious resolution. As noted earlier, defocusing can be modeled by assuming that the image is convolved with a blur circle whose width is directly proportional to the distance between the retina and the actual location of the image plane. In the frequency domain this convolution corresponds to multiplication of the transfer function by the Fourier transform of a disk (Fig. A2 in the *Appendix* to this chapter, p. 302, illustrates this transform). Broadly speaking, the effect of the multiplication is to reduce contrast in the image, with greater reductions for higher frequencies. However, at a finer level of analysis (spelled out in the *Appendix* to this chapter, p. 302) it turns out that the actual effect will be to reduce contrast first to zero (i.e., as frequency increases); then to *reverse* the contrast of the image for higher frequencies—over this range absolute contrast first increases a bit, and then declines again to zero; next to re-reverse the contrast for the next range of frequencies, and so on. Thus a sinusoidal input with spatial frequency in one of the reversed contrast ranges will appear in the image 180 deg out of phase, i.e., with its peaks turned into valleys, and vice versa. In the optical literature, this phenomenon is known as "spurious resolution."

Figure 10 illustrates this process in terms of its effect on the MTF, and compares the theoretical optical results (dashed lines) with the actual effect of defocus on human contrast sensitivity as determined by Campbell and Green (32). (The dashed lines in the figure represent the MTF, which it will be recalled is the absolute value of the OTF, hence nonnegative. The contrast reversal regions correspond to intervals between the first and second zeros of the MTF, also between the third and fourth, etc. This illustrates the point that the MTF by itself is sometimes misleading, since it can only specify amplitude reductions, and not contrast reversals, which from a technical standpoint are phase-shift effects, the sinusoidal input being shifted by half a period in the output.)

The reader can observe these spurious resolution effects subjectively by carefully examining the upper spoke pattern in Figure 11 with one eye from a distance close enough that it is blurred on the retina. (The lower pattern is an out-of-focus photograph of the upper one, designed to illustrate how the latter will appear when viewed very close up.) The apparent contrast decreases toward the center of the figure, where spatial frequency is highest. Looking carefully, one can see a narrow ring or hourglass-like region where the contrast is zero. Inside that ring, the stripes are again visible, but with *reversed* contrast (a consequence of the convolution referred to above), then another ring and another contrast reversal, etc. If the observer has no astigmatism, the ring of zero contrast

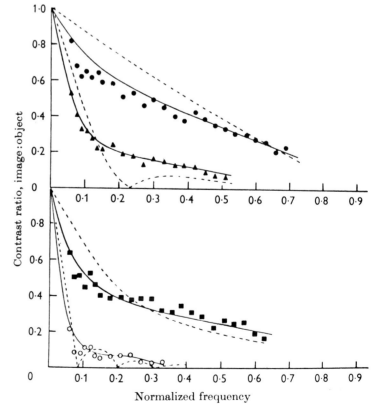

FIG. 10. Effects of defocus on human spatial contrast sensitivity (2-mm pupil). Data points show retinal image contrast reduction (inferred from threshold data of one observer) imposed on each spatial frequency as a function of defocus. *Upper panel*: ●, 1.5 diopters (myopic); ▲, 2.5 diopters. *Lower panel*: ■, 2.0 diopters, ○, 3.5 diopters. Spatial frequency expressed as fraction of highest frequency passed by the optics of the eye, i.e., 1.0 ≈ 60 cycles/deg. *Solid lines* drawn by hand through data points. *Dashed lines* show results predicted from diffraction alone. [From Campbell and Green (32), with permission from Cambridge University Press.]

will be round. If it is hourglass-shaped, the long axis of the hourglass is the meridian that yields the largest blur circle, and the orthogonal meridian will probably yield the smallest blur circle and thus the small axis of the hourglass. (The reader may also notice that when this spoke target is viewed from a distance at which it can be sharply resolved, the central region when fixated appears tinged with yellow. This is not due to macular screening pigment, because fixation on a blank portion of the page does not produce the same effect. We suspect this illusion may be related to the low density of blue cones in the central fovea, as discussed later in THE OPTICAL TRANSFER FUNCTION AND PHOTORECEPTOR SPACING, p. 270.)

Spatial Modulation Detection

HIGH-FREQUENCY RESOLUTION UNDER NORMAL VIEWING CONDITIONS. We have seen that for a number of physical reasons the retinal image is normally a degraded copy of the visual stimulus. The combined effect of all these degrading factors can be summarized

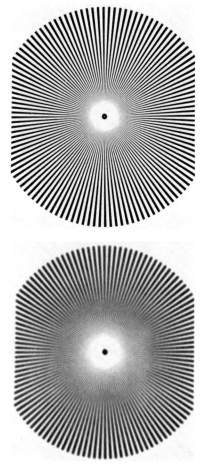

FIG. 11. *Top*: spoke target for demonstrating spurious resolution in human vision. See text for directions. *Bottom*: out-of-focus picture of spoke pattern illustrating spurious resolution in a photographic image.

by the MTF of the eye (or, more precisely, its OTF), which specifies the attenuation imposed on each spatial frequency in the stimulus and consequently allows us to determine how any stimulus will appear at the level of the retina. Clearly the visual system cannot detect stimulus information that is not physically present in the retinal image, and so the modulation transfer function sets an upper bound on the ability to resolve fine spatial detail under normal viewing conditions. ("Normal" here means incoherent illumination viewed with a natural pupil. Under special conditions, described below, it is possible to bypass the optics of the eye and form retinal images containing spatial frequencies higher than the normal cutoff.)

Suppose in particular that the stimulus is a vertical sinusoidal grating (as in Fig. 8) with intensity profile

$$B[1 + C \cos(2\pi\phi x)]$$

where x is measured in units of visual angle along the horizontal axis of the retina (i.e., degrees or minutes), ϕ is the spatial frequency (cycles/unit of visual angle), B is the mean intensity, and C is the contrast of the sinusoidal modulation. ($0 \leq C \leq 1$). At the level of the retina the image of this stimulus will take the form

$$aB[1 + t(\phi)C \cos(2\pi\phi x)]$$

where a is an attenuation factor representing light loss due to reflection and preretinal absorption in the ocular media, and $t(\phi)$ is the OTF of the eye evaluated at frequency ϕ. Consequently if we require an observer to discriminate between one stimulus in which $C = 0$ (i.e., a uniform field of intensity B) and another in which C is some nonzero value (in the extreme, $C = 1$) we are really asking him to discriminate between the retinal images aB and $aB[1 + t(\phi)C \cos(2\pi\phi x)]$. Obviously discrimination is impossible when $t(\phi) = 0$. The MTFs of Campbell and Gubisch [Fig. 9; (33)] show that for the human eye under optimal conditions, $t(\phi)$ vanishes around 50–60 cycles/deg. We can conclude from this that spatial contrast in the stimulus at frequencies higher than 1 cycle/min can never be detected because, in effect, it never reaches the retina: under normal viewing conditions this represents the physically imposed upper limit of visual acuity.

Of course it would be entirely possible for human contrast sensitivity to be substantially worse than the ideal limits imposed by optical considerations, and in fact this is the case under low light conditions and—at all intensity levels—for stimuli presented outside the fovea. However, under optimal conditions the performance of the visual system as a whole matches the upper limit imposed by the optics of the eye. Figure 12 shows psychophysical contrast thresholds for a variety of mean intensity levels as determined by van Ness and Bouman (126). These curves plot the smallest value of C at which an observer can discriminate $B[1 + C \cos(2\pi\phi x)]$ from a uniform field of intensity B. (Such plots are known as "spatial contrast sensitivity functions." Sometimes they are loosely referred to

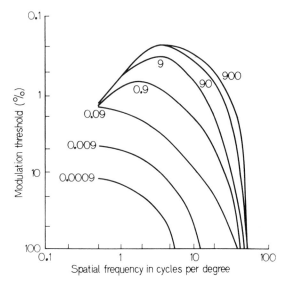

FIG. 12. Human spatial contrast thresholds for vertical sinusoidal gratings at various mean intensity levels (2-mm pupil, monochromatic light, wavelength 525 nm). *Each curve* plots threshold contrast as a function of spatial frequency for mean retinal illumination level (trolands) indicated by curve parameter (100% corresponds to contrast of 1.0). [Data from Van Ness and Bouman (126); figure from Westheimer (140).]

as "modulation transfer functions," by analogy to actual MTFs as determined for lenses and other imaging devices.) At the highest intensity levels ($B = 90$ and 900 trolands) contrast thresholds become independent of mean intensity (Weber's law), and discrimination becomes impossible when ϕ reaches approximately 55 cycles/deg (trolands = target luminance in candelas/m^2 × pupil area in mm^2). This is in good agreement with the upper limit of 50–60 cycles/deg predicted from the optical MTF. Many other psychophysical measurements have led to the same results (184). The data in Figure 12 were obtained with vertical gratings. Horizontal gratings give rise to similar values, but sensitivity to oblique gratings is somewhat worse. This difference disappears beyond a degree of retinal eccentricity ranging from 8° to 18° (20) and apparently is due to central effects, since it shows up in cortical evoked responses but not in the electroretinogram (91).

THE OPTICAL TRANSFER FUNCTION AND PHOTORECEPTOR SPACING. The fact that the normal retinal image never contains spatial frequencies higher than 1 cycle/min has implications for the optimal spacing of photoreceptors. Clearly, if the retina consisted simply of one giant receptor which integrated quantum catch over the entire retinal surface, the eye would be incapable of discriminating spatial modulation at all frequencies—i.e., it would be limited to registering only the overall mean intensity of the retinal image. On the other hand there would be no evident utility to packing in more individual receptors than is justified by the quality of optics of the eye. Fourier analytic considerations show that the optimal center-to-center spac-

ing between receptors should equal $(2\phi_c)^{-1}$, where ϕ_c is the highest spatial frequency that can be present in the retinal image. (This is the well-known "Sampling Theorem": its mathematical basis is spelled out in the *Appendix* to this chapter, p. 302). At this spacing the receptor mosaic is theoretically capable of providing an undistorted reproduction of any retinal image, i.e., no harmonic distortion will be introduced by the fact that the continuous optical image is sampled by an array of discrete receptors. Taking ϕ_c to be 1 cycle/min, this analysis implies an optimal center-to-center spacing of 0.5 minute. Osterberg's (95) cell counts of the human retina (Fig. 13) and the data of Polyak (98) indicate a peak cone density of roughly 150,000–200,000 cells/mm^2 at the center of the fovea; this corresponds to a spacing of 0.59–0.51 minute. Evidently in the central fovea there is a good match between the dimensions of the receptor mosaic and the optics of the eye: Any coarser sampling would lose (or distort) information potentially available in the retinal image, while any finer sampling would be superfluous, since it would never reveal any new information.

The idea that overall receptor density in the center of the retina has evolved to match the spatial frequency cutoff imposed by the optics of the eye raises the question of how this density should be parceled out among the three spectrally distinct classes of cones. At present there is no direct anatomical evidence as to the actual spacing of "red," "green," and "blue" cones in the human retina, because in primates there is no known way of identifying a cone's spectral class by its appearance alone. However, staining tech-

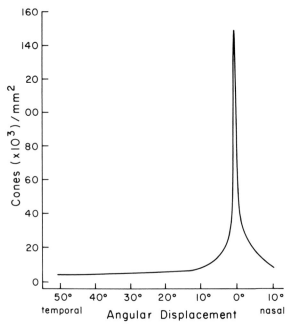

FIG. 13. Cone density as a function of distance from the center (0°) of the fovea. [Data from Osterberg (95); figure adapted from Ripps and Weale (103).]

niques that allow such an identification have recently been introduced and successfully applied to the baboon retina [see Marc and Sperling (94)]. Consequently it seems likely that definitive information on human cone spacing will be available before long, and so some speculation seems in order. Here we concentrate on the blue cones, whose spacing has long been a subject of controversy [(29), p. 240-244].

Clearly the key optical factor here is chromatic aberration, which as we have seen is quite substantial in the human eye (Fig. 2). Apparently when accommodation is entirely relaxed the eye is normally in focus for the red end of the spectrum [Ivanoff's data for 10 observers, cited in Le Grand (84), suggests a range from 625 nm to 725 nm]. Then with increasing accommodation the focal wavelength shifts downwards (sparing the eye some accommodative effort), reaching a lower limit around 500 nm for targets requiring 2.5 diopters of accommodation (40-cm viewing distance). Consequently retinal images in the range 400–500 nm are always out of focus by an amount ranging from 0 diopters to 2 diopters of myopia. This means that over the spectral range to which the blue cones are most sensitive the OTF of the eye goes to zero not at 60 cycles/deg but at some lower frequency, the exact value of which depends on pupil size and the assumed magnitude of "blue myopia." Sampling considerations in turn suggest that the density of blue cones ought to be lower than that of red and green cones.

To make an exact prediction of blue cone spacing based on the sampling theorem one needs to assume that the visual system is wired for some "typical" combination of pupil size and amount of blue myopia. Then one can calculate the spatial frequency cutoff of the corresponding optical transfer function—call this spatial frequency ϕ_b—and predict the blue cone spacing $s_b = (2\phi_b)^{-1}$. [Formulas for the OTF of a misfocused retinal image are given in the *Appendix*, Equations A17 and A18. As noted earlier in our discussion of spurious resolution (see *Defocus and spurious resolution*, p. 268) the OTF here goes monotonically to zero as frequency increases, and thereafter oscillates—within a monotonically shrinking envelope—between negative and positive values. For present purposes, it seems natural to identify the cutoff frequency ϕ_b with the first zero of the OTF.] The difficulty is that it is not obvious what pupil size and degree of blue myopia to assume. One plausible course is to assume the smallest normal pupil (2 mm diam) and 1–2 diopters of myopia—as though the retina were designed for distant viewing in bright light, with a focal wavelength of 675 nm [the average for Ivanoff's observers (in ref. 84)], and the blue cones spaced to sample an image in the range 400–500 nm. Then 1 diopter of blue myopia yields a cutoff frequency ϕ_b = 10.2 cycles/deg and a spacing s_b = 3′ visual angle, while 2 diopters yields ϕ_b = 4.8 cycles/deg, with s_b = 6.3′.

The later figure agrees closely with Marc and Sper-

ling's (94) measurement of blue cone spacing in the center (±0.5°) of the baboon fovea (mean = 6′), where overall cone density is roughly the same as in the human retina. However, in baboon, blue cone density is not maximal at the center of the fovea (as it is for both red and green cones) but instead at an eccentricity of 1°, where the spacing averages 3′—exactly the prediction for 1 diopter of blue myopia.

For the spacing of blue cones in the human retina we have only psychophysical evidence—based either on spatial mappings of detection thresholds for blue points superimposed on yellow backgrounds designed to silence the red and green cones (132, 141) or on visual acuity for targets visible only to blue cones (29, 41, 57). Both methods indicate that blue cone spacing in man has the same characteristics as in the baboon: The density is low in the very center of the fovea, with no evidence of any blue cones in a region subtending somewhere between 8′ (132) and 20′ (141). (Assuming a 6′-intercone distance we would expect only 2 blue cones in the first area and 11 in the second. Thus there is no serious discrepancy between these psychophysical observations of a "blue-blind" central zone and the notion that the spacing is actually constant at 6′ out to an eccentricity of ±0.5°). Outside this tiny central region the mapping technique (141) has produced an estimate of 10′ spacing out to 40′ from the center of the fovea, while acuity measurements with foveal targets yield spatial frequency cutoffs ranging from 9 ± 1 cycles/deg (41, 47) down to 4 cycles/deg (29). These cutoffs translate into blue cone spacings ranging from 3.33′ up to 7.5′—figures very close to the upper and lower spacings found in baboon fovea. [These estimates assume that the psychophysically determined spatial frequency cutoff is related to blue cone density by the sampling theorem. There is no necessary reason why this should be so, and it has been conjectured—e.g., by Brindley (29), that the poor acuity of the blue system is due to convergence of many blue cones onto the same second-order neuron rather than a sparsity of the cones themselves. However the weight of current evidence runs counter to that hypothesis.]

In summary then, what we know about blue cone spacing lends support to the idea that not only is overall foveal cone density matched to the overall spatial frequency cutoff of the retinal image, but in addition the same principle governs the individual densities of the various color systems. In a nutshell, blue cones are relatively sparse because from their spectral perspective the retinal image is always relatively coarse. This idea in turn raises intriguing questions as to how the visual system integrates spatial information arising from receptor systems that have different sampling capabilities. Speculation on this topic, however, would carry us too far afield.

BYPASSING THE OPTICS OF THE EYE. Using coherent light (e.g., from a laser source) it is possible to create interference patterns on the retina that contain spatial frequencies well beyond the normal 1-cycle/min cut-off. The technique, introduced in the 1930s by Le Grand (84), involves forming on the retina a diffraction pattern equivalent to the one produced by a pair of small apertures illuminated by the same coherent source. (In this case the eye acts like an optical computer of Fourier transforms as noted in the *Appendix* to this chapter, p. 302.) This procedure allows one to bypass the normal optical limitations of the eye (except for scattering within the retina itself), and determine whether the neural components of the visual system are capable of resolving spatial frequencies higher than those normally present in the retinal image. Figure 14 shows contrast thresholds as a function of spatial frequency measured under these conditions by Campbell and Green (32). The basic finding is that here, just as in normal viewing, resolution becomes impossible at spatial frequencies on the order of 1 cycle/min. (This was also found by Le Grand (84), Westheimer (138), and Green (58). The only exceptional results are those of Byram (31), who obtained limits on the order of 2.5 cycles/min. These results are discussed later in *Neural Limits of Visual Acuity*, p. 275.) Figure 15 shows a comparison between contrast thresholds obtained with interference patterns and normal targets at the same mean retinal illuminance: In both cases the high-frequency portions of the curves are fairly well fitted by straight lines (in this semilog plot) with the line for normal viewing having a somewhat steeper slope—necessarily, since in this case the

effective contrast at the retina is attenuated by the MTF of the optics of the eye, which does not affect the contrast of the interference targets.

Why should the postoptical components of the visual system be incapable of resolving spatial modulation beyond 1 cycle/min? Clearly from the standpoint of design efficiency such a limitation makes sense, since under normal viewing conditions no higher frequencies would ever be informative about the outside world—i.e., they could only arise as a result of optical phenomena within the eye itself. However, the question still arises as to the actual mechanisms responsible for the loss. Two kinds of factors need to be considered: first, purely physical limitations imposed by the size and spacing of the photoreceptors and by residual optical spreading that affects interference targets as well as normal ones; and second, physiological limitations due to neural mechanisms.

Physical factors affecting resolution of interference targets. Dimensions of receptor array. Anatomical evidence (95, 98, 104) indicates that in the central fovea [what Polyak (98) called the "foveola," a circular region 80′ across] the cone outer segments form a dense array of tightly packed cylinders, each having a cross section shaped somewhere between a circle and a hexagon—so that seen end-on "the entire formation here resembles an evenly distributed mosaic, like the cobblestones in an old fashioned pavement" [(98), p. 269; see Fig. 18 below). Receptor width in this region is approximately 0.25 min, the length of the outer

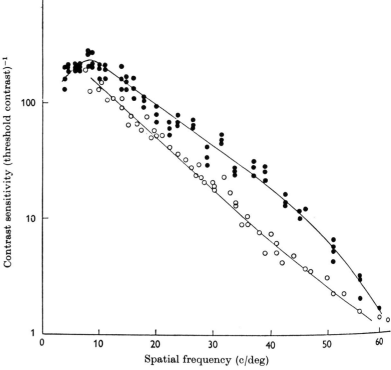

FIG. 14. Spatial contrast-sensitivity functions for sinusoidal interference targets formed with a coherent source; wavelength, 633 nm. Data for two observers; smooth curves drawn by hand through data points. Mean illumination level, 500 trolands. [From Campbell and Green (32), with permission from Cambridge University Press.]

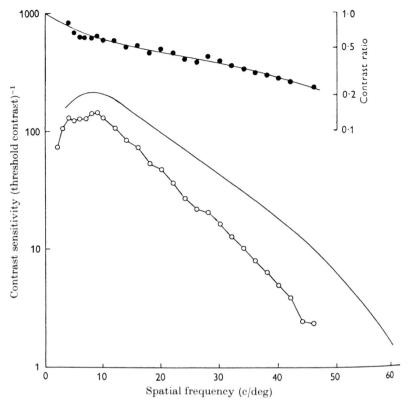

FIG. 15. Spatial contrast-sensitivity functions for interference fringes and normal targets at same mean retinal illuminance (500 trolands). Continuous smooth curve in *lower portion* of figure taken from data (*closed circles*) of Fig. 14 (i.e., these are interference target thresholds). *Open circles* show contrast thresholds for targets viewed normally, i.e., through the optics of the eye. *Closed circles* in the *top portion* show the ratio between the two curves below: this is an inferred measure of the modulation transfer function of the optics of this observer's eye. [From Campbell and Green (32), with permission from Cambridge University Press.]

segments is roughly 30 times their width, and the center-to-center distance between receptors is approximately 0.5 min. The foveola contains approximately 10^4 cones and no rods. As one moves out from the central fovea, cone density falls off approximately as the inverse distance from the center (as shown in Fig. 13), and the cones themselves become shorter and fatter. Conversely, rod density increases, reaching a peak approximately 20° from the center. (Rod dimensions are not of primary importance here because the upper limits of visual acuity are always obtained at mean illumination levels high enough to guarantee rod saturation.)

Residual optical factors. In terms of these dimensions it would not take a great deal of optical spreading within the retina to produce an effective spatial resolution cutoff of 1 cycle/min. As an example (motivated by the roughly linear falloff in semilog coordinates shown in Fig. 14) an optical spread corresponding to the MTF $e^{-\pi s}$ (where s denotes spatial frequency in cycles/min) would reduce contrast by 95% (i.e., from 1.0 to 0.05) at 1 cycle/min. The corresponding point-spread function in this case (which is given explicitly by Eq. A17 in the *Appendix*, p. 302) would be roughly Gaussian, with a height of 0.64 at the origin and 0.05 one min away. Thus light would be spread over a circular region having an effective radius of 3 receptors. In other words, the 1-cycle/min cutoff obtained with interference targets could be produced by a relatively small spread of light within the retina itself.

The actual behavior of light within the retina is far from fully understood. (Ref. 117 surveys the relatively new field of photoreceptor optics, which studies the waveguide properties of receptors.) However, Gorrand (52) has recently reported a few measurements of retinal scattering based on a new ophthalmoscopic technique that allows one to decompose the linespread function into two separate components corresponding to preretinal spread and scattering within the retina. (The technique used to produce the linespreads in Fig. 6 lumps both together.) Psychophysical methods can also be used to separate preretinal and intraretinal spread (32): The top portion of Figure 15 represents a psychophysical estimate of the preretinal MTF. Both physical and psychophysical methods yield about the same value for preretinal spread in the fovea (52), and agree in showing hardly any intraretinal spread in that region (where the retina is, of course, very thin). Consequently it seems fairly certain that optical spreading is not the major factor limiting foveal acuity for interference patterns—though in view of the relatively large effect to be expected from even a very small spread, and the fact that only a few physical measurements have so far been reported, it cannot be concluded that it plays no role at all.

Outside the fovea Gorrand's (52) measurements show that retinal scatter becomes more appreciable. For example at 6° eccentricity the contrast of a 7-cycle/deg interference grating is reduced by a factor around 0.7, and that of an 11-cycle/deg grating by 0.4.

However, here it is even more certain that retinal spreading is not the major factor limiting acuity, because at 6° the highest resolvable frequency for interference patterns is 6–8 cycles/deg (see ref. 58; Fig. 16). In other words a 7-cycle/deg grating that has an effective contrast at the outer segments of 0.7 is just at the threshold of visibility, whereas at the center of the retina the same frequency can be detected when its contrast is less than 0.005 (Fig. 12). Evidently postoptical differences between these two regions of the retina must be responsible for an effective contrast reduction of more than two log units.

Receptor sampling effects. The first postoptical factor that differentiates various regions of the retina, is of course, receptor density (Fig. 13). We have already noted that in the center of the fovea, receptor density matches the value prescribed by the sampling theorem for reconstructing inputs up to 60 cycles/deg, and this is also the psychophysical acuity limit for that region. If receptor density is the critical factor limiting visual acuity it is natural to expect that local acuity should be systemically related to local receptor density. Green (58) has measured local acuity for interference gratings in 30-min patches out to 8° eccentricity and compared the results to local receptor densities based on Osterberg's (95) cell counts. Figure 16 shows his results. It can be seen that out to 2° there is a striking agreement

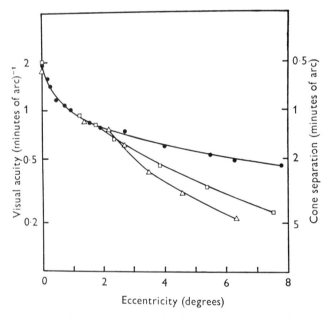

FIG. 16. Comparison between local spatial acuity for interference targets (633 nm) and intercone spacing at various distances from the center of the fovea (0° eccentricity). *Closed circles* show center-to-center intercone distances (1/distance in min). *Open points* show local spatial acuity for two observers. Visual acuity here is arbitrarily defined as twice the highest resolvable spatial frequency in cycles/min. This definition allows a direct comparison between local spatial acuity and local cone density: if acuity and cone density were matched according to the sampling theorem, both should fall on a common curve—as they do out to 2°. Targets subtended 32.4 min; mean intensity level was 1,200 trolands. [From Green (58), with permission from Cambridge University Press.]

between local spatial acuity (i.e., highest resolvable spatial frequency) and local interreceptor spacing: Letting s_d denote the highest resolvable frequency at distance d from the center of fovea, and w_d the center-to-center receptor spacing at distance d, Figure 16 shows that out to $d = 2°$

$$s_d = (2w_d)^{-1}$$

As Green pointed out, this relationship has a natural interpretation in terms of information theory. As we noted earlier, Fourier analytic considerations (the Whittaker-Shannon sampling theorem, described in the *Appendix*, p. 302) show that a two-dimensional array of sample points spaced w units apart (e.g., an array of photocells located at the nodes of a checkerboard with square size $w \times w$) permits perfect reconstruction of any image in which the highest spatial frequency does not exceed $(2w)^{-1}$. On this basis one can say that from 0° to 2° local spatial resolution capacity equals "the theoretical limits for a mosaic of receptors" [Green (58)].

However, this neat relationship should not be interpreted as an explanation of local spatial acuity, because the sampling theorem does not imply that spatial frequencies above $(2w)^{-1}$ simply vanish when sampled by an array with interreceptor distance w—in the sense that their sampled output will be indistinguishable from that produced by a uniform field. Rather, $(2w)^{-1}$ only represents the highest frequency that can be resolved without distortion: If a regular sampling array is confronted with frequencies above this limit it *can* transmit them, but their sampled output will be identical to that produced by lower frequencies. In communication theory this sort of distortion is known as "aliasing" (27, 96). [The mathematical details are explained in the *Appendix* to this chapter, p. 302, which also provides a figure illustrating the effect (Fig. A4).] To avoid aliasing in artificial image transmission systems one must prefilter the input to ensure that the sampling array never receives spatial frequencies higher than $(2w)^{-1}$: Mathematically this is accomplished by convolving the input with a pointspread function whose MTF vanishes at $(2w)^{-1}$. (Ideally this MTF should be 1.0 at all lower frequencies for optimum efficiency, but this usually cannot be achieved in practice because the corresponding point spread must contain negative regions.) In the human eye, of course, such prefiltering is normally performed by the optical transfer function, which vanishes at 1 cycle/min—the appropriate cutoff for receptor spacing in the central fovea. However, outside this region the optically imposed frequency cutoff will not be appropriate for the coarser sampling dimensions of the receptor mosaic (and of course with interference targets it does not operate at all, except for residual spreading within the retina itself). Consequently on sampling grounds alone there is no reason why spatial frequencies above $(2w)^{-1}$ should be entirely invisible in a retinal interference pattern—one might just as reasonably expect that substantially higher frequencies could be detected, though their appearance would be that of low-frequency counterparts produced by aliasing.

In summary then, residual optical spreading within the retina cannot account for the limits of visual acuity for interference targets: In the center of the fovea it is apparently physically negligible, and outside the center its effects, while physically appreciable, are nowhere near large enough to explain the dramatic decline in acuity. Out to 2° local resolution capacity matches the $(2w)^{-1}$ sampling theorem limit, but this relationship is itself more of a puzzle than an explanation of visual acuity, because sampling considerations alone do not imply that higher spatial frequencies should be invisible: The $(2w)^{-1}$ limit only specifies the range of frequencies that can be transmitted without distortion, and some additional mechanism is necessary to explain why higher frequencies are apparently undetectable. Beyond 2° spatial resolution capacity is substantially worse than the sampling theorem cutoff. Finally, it should be noted that local spatial acuity in scotopic (rod-mediated) vision is best around 4° from the center of the fovea, while rod density is greatest around 20° (124). Thus it appears that receptor geography alone cannot account for any spatial acuity limits. Consequently in order to explain the overall spatial resolution capacity of the visual system one has to turn to neural mechanisms.

Neural Limits of Visual Acuity

We have seen that everywhere on the retina the highest detectable spatial frequency either equals or falls below the aliasing cutoff implied by local receptor density. The problem now is to understand how these limits are produced by neural mechanisms. In the recent past, spatial contrast detection has been the subject of a great deal of theoretical work aimed at constructing physiologically realistic models that can account for psychophysical phenomena in terms of the receptive-field properties of cells in the visual pathway (53–55, 142). This kind of neural model building has reached quite a high level of sophistication, and one might imagine that even though many details remain to be worked out, at least the general neural principles underlying spatial contrast sensitivity are well understood—in the same way that we understand the principles underlying trichromacy.

However, if one begins to trace the flow of spatial contrast information up the visual pathway, beginning with the distribution of quantum catch in the receptor mosaic, one immediately encounters a theoretical road block that does not seem to be dealt with by any of the current models. This section focuses on this difficulty, which we shall call the "aliasing problem." The conclusion of our analysis is that because of this problem it is not at all clear that current theories of spatial contrast detection actually capture the fundamental principles underlying the neural mechanisms that limit visual acuity. To make this point we first give a brief overview of current theoretical ideas, and then explain why something more seems necessary to account for the limits of visual acuity.

PSYCHOPHYSICAL POINTSPREAD MODELS. In his review of theories of visual acuity, Le Grand [(84), p. 102] distinguished a class of "continuous theories" which "voluntarily neglect the discontinuous receptive structure of the retina." Current models for spatial contrast sensitivity (that is, models designed to account for the spatial contrast sensitivity function and similar data) are continuous theories, and we shall argue that as a consequence they cannot give a complete account of visual acuity. All of the models we have in mind are motivated primarily by the well-known antagonistic center-surround receptive-field organization first identified in retinal ganglion cells, and now known to characterize cells at every level of the visual pathway from receptors (16–18, 47) to level IV of the striate cortex (68). The discovery of this general organizational feature of the visual system corroborated Ernst Mach's (in ref. 101a) nineteenth century prediction—based entirely on perceptual analysis—that the light distribution in the retinal image must be spatially filtered by neural processes of lateral inhibition and excitation. To model this process it is natural to imagine that the neural components of the visual system operate on the retinal image in a fashion analogous to an optical pointspread function, but with the important difference that optical pointspread functions must be nonnegative, whereas a neural point spread can be both positive and negative. (This is critical, because a nonnegative point spread necessarily produces an MTF that is maximal at the origin and consequently could not explain the nonmonotonic shape of human spatial contrast sensitivity functions obtained at moderate-to-high mean luminance levels—e.g., the curves above 0.09 troland in Fig. 12.) If this neural filtering were linear its effect could be directly combined with the point spread produced by the optics of the eye to yield an overall pointspread function which, convolved with any stimulus, would yield its "neural image." The contrast in this neural image would then determine the limits of spatial contrast sensitivity: if the neural contrast for a given spatial frequency is zero when its physical contrast is 1.0, the frequency must be undetectable.

Figure 17A and B illustrate this kind of model in its basic form. Figure 17A shows spatial contrast sensitivity functions for several observers obtained in an experiment by Kelly and Savoie (76) that concentrated on the low-frequency end of the spatial spectrum. Also shown is a theoretical curve of the form $s^2 e^{-s}$ which provides a good fit for all observers. Suppose now that spatial contrast detection obeys the following model: the stimulus pattern S is first convolved with a pointspread function P (which combines both optical and neural spread) and the result $P*S$ is Fourier transformed to obtain its amplitude spectrum. If for any

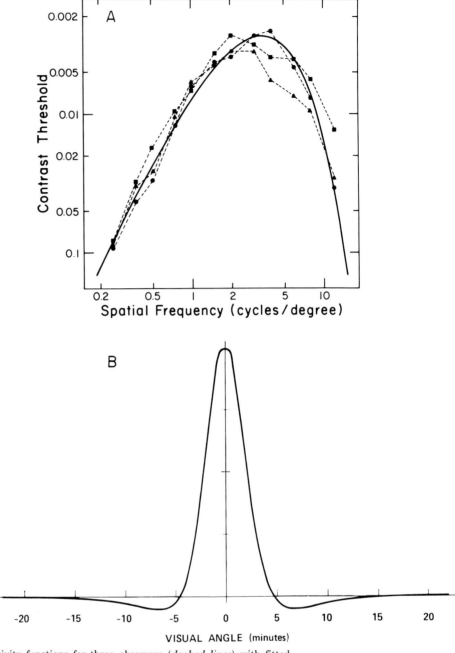

FIG. 17. *A*: spatial contrast-sensitivity functions for three observers (*dashed lines*) with fitted function $s^2 e^{-s}$ (*solid curve*), which can be regarded as the overall "modulation transfer function" of the human visual system. *B*: pointspread function obtained by Fourier inversion of the smooth curve in Figure 17*A*. [From Kelly (74).]

spatial frequency the amplitude spectrum exceeds a fixed threshold t, the observer detects contrast. When the stimulus is a sinusoidal grating of the form $1 + C \cos 2\pi s x$, where s is spatial frequency in cycles/unit of x (e.g., cycles/deg) and C is contrast, then detection will occur when $C|T_p(s)| = t$, where $|T_p(s)|$ is the absolute value of the Fourier transform of the point-spread function P. In other words, $|T_p(s)|$ is the modulation transfer function of this model visual system. Thus in this model the threshold contrast $C(s)$ for

detecting a sinusoid of frequency s is inversely proportional to $|T_p(s)|$, and so the spatial contrast sensitivity function $(C(s))^{-1}$ (e.g., as plotted in Fig. 17*A*) is directly proportional to the modulation transfer function of the visual system. Consequently to obtain the psychophysical pointspread function P (up to a constant factor reflecting the threshold t) one can simply calculate the inverse Fourier transform of the spatial contrast sensitivity function. Figure 17*B* (74) shows the outcome of applying this principle to the contrast sensitivity function (i.e., the fitted curve) in Figure 17A. The result, according to this model, should be the overall pointspread function of the visual system, incorporating both optical and neural effects. The function in Figure 17B is obviously reminiscent of the center-surround organization of the receptive fields of retinal ganglion cells, and so it is tempting to suppose that spatial contrast sensitivity can be explained physiologically by a combination of optical blurring and lateral neural mechanisms of a kind that are well established.

This kind of model was first employed in connection with sinusoidal contrast detection by Schade (115), who had in mind the practical task of incorporating human contrast sensitivity into the design of television systems. In effect, the human visual system could in this fashion be treated as the final stage in a series of linear filtering operations. Subsequent psychophysical work (see ref. 66, chapt. 1) coupled with results from neurophysiology (ref. 66, chapt. 2) has led to a considerable elaboration of the basic idea. Current models (36a, 53, 142) are designed to take account of the inhomogeneity of the visual field (by allowing the psychophysical pointspread function to change shape as a function of retinal position), and of the possibility that each point on the retina is served by several "mechanisms" or "channels," each having its own point spread (hence, its own spatial bandwidth) and its own sensitivity to the temporal parameters of the stimulus (i.e., some channels prefer flashes, others slow changes). For example, the recent model of Wilson and Bergen (142) assumes four channels at each point on the retina.

These psychophysical pointspread models account for the limits of local visual acuity in terms of the effective contrast transmitted by the most sensitive local channel, i.e., the channel which imposes the smallest contrast reduction on high spatial frequencies. If the output of this channel is below threshold for a grating of physical contrast 1.0, the limit of acuity has been reached. (Actually the detection process is currently assumed to involve "probability summation" between channels, so that the less-sensitive channels still contribute something to detection even when other, better tuned, channels are present. This makes a difference in estimating channel bandwidths, but is irrelevant to our main point here.)

Now there is no question that the most highly evolved of these psychophysical spread models can make good predictions of spatial contrast sensitivity functions, and of contrast thresholds for certain other stimuli besides sinusoidal gratings. Why then do we say that they are not obviously capable of accounting for the limit of visual acuity, which after all is only the high-frequency cutoff of the contrast sensitivity function? Put more broadly, could not lateral neural processes act in a manner analogous to optical point spread and thereby limit visual acuity by reducing the effective contrast of high-frequency retinal images?

The answer, in a nutshell, is that by neglecting the discontinuous receptive structure of the retina (i.e., the receptor sampling process) these models bypass the aliasing problem mentioned earlier, BYPASSING THE OPTICS OF THE EYE, Receptor sampling effects, p. 274. The key point is that spatial frequencies above the aliasing cutoff implied by local receptor density must be represented in the *input* to the neural part of the visual system as counterfeit low frequencies and therefore cannot be filtered out by the kind of static pointspread operations envisioned by current models. The next section explains this point in detail.

SPATIAL AMBIGUITY OF THE RECEPTOR IMAGE: THE ALIASING PROBLEM. Suppose that in a given patch of retina the receptors are laid out in a checkerboard array (i.e., each centered on an intersection), with center-to-center interreceptor distance w deg, and receptor width pw ($0 < p \leq 1$). Then suppose we image on this patch a vertical sinusoidal grating of frequency f cycles/deg and contrast C (i.e., a grating of the form $1 + C \cos 2\pi f x$). The aliasing cutoff in our patch is $(2w)^{-1}$: If f is always below this limit we know that in principle it can be reconstructed from its sampled image. However, if $f > (2w)^{-1}$ it can be shown that its sampled image will be identical to that produced by a lower frequency sinusoid of the form $1 + C \cos 2\pi(w^{-1} -f)x$, i.e., a sinusoid of frequency $w^{-1} -f$ and contrast C'. (This is worked out in the *Appendix* to this chapter, p. 302: see Eq. A23. The contrast reduction from C to C' is due entirely to integration over the surface area of the receptor). For example, if $w = 0.008°$ (0.5 min) and $pw = 0.004°$, as in the center of the fovea, the aliasing cutoff $(2w)^{-1}$ is 60 cycles/deg, and a 90-cycle/deg grating of contrast C will produce the same sampled image as a 30-cycle/deg grating of contrast $0.6C$. Similary, if $w = 0.033°$ (2 min) and $pw = 0.008°$ (to simulate the dimensions at 8° eccentricity) the aliasing cutoff is 15 cycles/deg and a 25-cycle/deg grating of contrast C produces the same sampled image as a 5-cycle grating of contrast $0.8C$.

Thus as a consequence of the aliasing possibilities inherent in receptor sampling there is an intrinsic spatial ambiguity in the input to the visual system: Any given distribution of quantum catch in the receptor mosaic—say a distribution consistent with spatial frequency f—could either have been produced by a real stimulus having frequency f, or by a higher frequency (here, $w^{-1} -f$) masquerading as f. However, the psychophysical literature tells us that frequencies greater than $(2w)^{-1}$ are seen as uniform fields, while lower frequencies are seen as spatially modulated. This means that the neural component of the visual system somehow manages to solve the aliasing problem without prefiltering the retinal image—a feat television engineers might well envy. How is it possible?

To forestall potential misunderstandings and objections, four points should be noted immediately. First, it should be clear that under the assumptions we began with (the realism of which we discuss in a moment) no neural mechanism of any kind can discriminate between the *stationary* retinal images of real spatial frequencies and their aliases (e.g., between 30 cycles/deg and 90 cycles/deg when $w = 0.5$ min) This is so because after sampling by the receptors these images present identical inputs to any subsequent neural process.

Second, it should not be thought that aliasing is only a real possibility with unnatural stimuli such as interference patterns. That is true in the center of the fovea, where the spatial limits of the eye match the aliasing cutoff of the receptors, but outside that small region the retina must be routinely exposed to spatial frequencies above its local aliasing cutoffs, because the optical quality of the retinal image remains roughly constant out to 30° (84) while receptor density decreases dramatically. (The example for 8° eccentricity given earlier illustrates this point.) Consequently the aliasing problem is one the visual system encounters in its normal operation, and presumably must be designed to solve.

Third, it is natural to wonder whether aliasing is only a mathematical possibility that depends critically on the unrealistic assumption of precisely regular receptor spacing. Certainly the real geometry of the receptor mosaic is not nearly as regular as that of our checkerboard model, and the exact consequences of irregular receptor spacing pose an open theoretical problem. However, one can get some immediate insight by constructing sampling arrays that simulate the actual distribution of receptors in real retinas. We have used Polyak's photographs of the human retina [(98), p. 268] to construct arrays of pinholes that simulate the sampling effects of the central fovea (by simply poking a pin through the apparent center of each receptor). When such an array is superimposed on gratings simulating frequencies beyond 60 cycles/deg (e.g., displayed on a television screen) one sees aliasing effects in the form of moire patterns that look like low-frequency "worms"—broad, elongated, irregular shapes that change as the grating moves (Fig. 18 illustrates the effect). This shows that the irregularities of actual receptor spacing do not automatically eliminate aliasing effects. Rather, it seems that they make these effects less exact: instead of a frequency beyond the $(2w)^{-1}$ cutoff aliasing back into a single lower frequency (e.g., 90 cycles/deg aliasing into 30 cycles/deg), it looks as though the effect of irregularity is to scatter a given high frequency into a range of lower frequencies, giving rise to patterns comparable to low-frequency spatial noise. However, there is no obvious reason why these low-frequency patterns should not be detected by the visual system and used to discriminate very high frequency gratings from uniform fields. In other words, the realities of receptor geography do not seem likely to provide a solution to the aliasing problem.

Finally, if aliasing is a real visual phenomenon (i.e.,

a real problem of the visual system, rather than simply a theoretical possibility), why has it not been revealed in previous experiments, i.e., in form of acuity values higher than the aliasing cutoff? (Of course, in a sense these would be artificial acuities mediated by a kind of false resolution, because the frequencies actually seen would not be physically present in the retinal image. However, that is not the issue.) Perhaps it has, because the acuity literature is too enormous for a thorough review, but the fact that one does not find results of this sort reported routinely could very well be due to three points of methodology. To demonstrate super acuity mediated by aliasing one must first ensure that frequencies higher than the local aliasing cutoff actually reach the retina. Consequently measurements in the fovea made with ordinary stimuli could never be expected to yield acuities higher than 60 cycles/deg. Second, it is essential to control image motion (i.e., by flashing the stimulus, or stabilizing its retinal image) because when motion is allowed the visual system has available information that in principle could allow it to discriminate between real spatial frequencies and counterfeits due to aliasing (e.g., if the eye moves at v deg/s a real 30-cycle/deg grating produces 30 v Hz flicker at each receptor, while a 90-cycles/deg grating masquerading as 30 cycles/deg will produce 90 v Hz flicker). As far as we know all of the experiments measuring acuity with interference targets have allowed sustained viewing with natural eye movements. Third, because detection of aliased frequencies would be a somewhat unnatural task, it seems essential to use an objective psychophysical method, e.g., forced choice discrimination between uniform and spatially modulated fields. This point is underscored by the exceptional results of Byram (31) mentioned earlier. He reported acuity limits as high as 150 cycles/deg, but stressed that the choice of an upper limit depended on what one was willing to accept as a legitimate experience of spatial contrast: At his highest values, regular square-wave gratings appeared as "wriggling curved line segments" [(31), p. 273]. Because Byram gave few details of his methods, and all other interference experiments have produced acuity values approximating 60 cycles/deg, his results may have been due to some artifact. However, it is also possible that he happened to achieve conditions facilitating actual detection of aliased frequencies.

Outside the fovea aliasing could be expected to show itself with ordinary stimuli, provided they were flashed or presented as stabilized images and objective psychophysical methods were used. We are not aware of any experiments satisfying both requirements. However, Le Grand (84) mentions the interesting point that in the periphery of the retina, unlike the fovea, acuity is significantly better for flashed targets than for steady ones. It seems conceivable that this is due to false resolution mediated by aliasing, though other explanations based on the greater prevalence of transient ganglion cells in the periphery are also plausible.

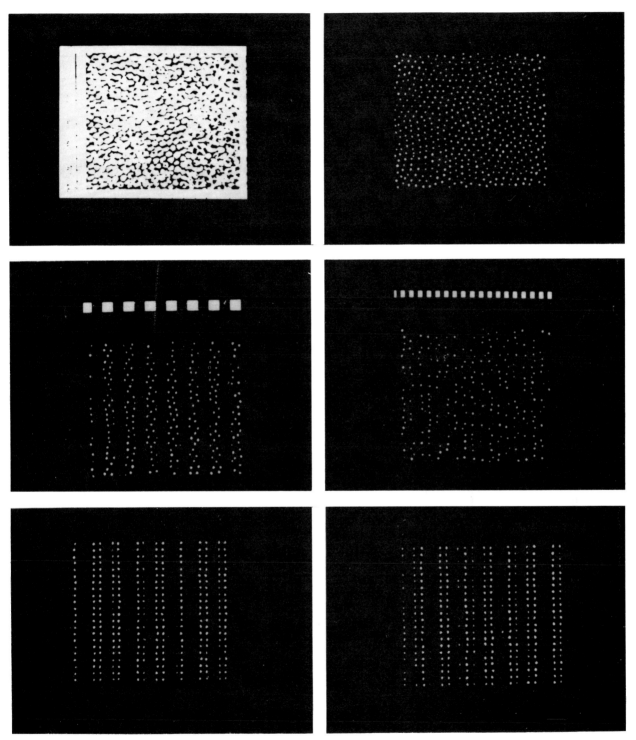

FIG. 18. The *top* and *middle rows* illustrate aliasing by an array of photoreceptors. *Top left*: photomicrograph of a 12′ × 13′ patch of human retina near the center of the fovea. The mean center-to-center distance between receptors is 0.53′, implying an aliasing cutoff of 57 cycles/deg. *Top right*: sampling grid made by punching a pinhole through the center of each receptor in the 12′ × 13′ patch. *Middle left*: 30-cycle/deg square wave grating seen through the pinhole grid. *Middle right*: 80-cycle/ deg square wave grating seen through the pinhole grid. Note the appearance of broad curved line segments due to aliasing. The *bottom row* illustrates the effect of a regularly spaced (checkerboard) array of sampling points having roughly the same sample-point distance as the average value for the retinal array. *Bottom left*: 30-cycle/deg square wave grating seen through the regular sampling grid. *Bottom right*: 80-cycle/deg square wave grating seen through the regular sampling grid. [*Top left* from Polyak (98), p. 268.]

CONCLUSIONS. The preceding line of analysis suggests two puzzles. First, because of sampling effects, visual acuity measured by the highest spatial frequency at which a sinusoidal interference pattern can be discriminated from a uniform field should be greater than the local sampling theorem limit everywhere on the retina. Second, spatial "noise" produced by aliased high frequencies should normally be present in the extrafoveal visual field. The fact that neither phenomenon ordinarily occurs perceptually seems to imply that the visual system has some active mechanism for suppressing counterfeit spatial frequencies, i.e., a mechanism that prevents false resolutions that would otherwise contaminate its spatial analysis of the retinal image. As far as we know, current neural models for spatial contrast detection do not explicitly provide such a mechanism, and consequently our ability to trace the flow of spatial information through the visual pathway has a missing link. We will not try to guess the nature of this link, except to make the obvious point that the most natural neural mechanism for suppressing aliased spatial frequencies would be one that relies on information supplied by retinal image motion. It is well known that during normal vision the retinal image is always in motion, and that when motion is artificially stopped vision fails almost immediately. This disappearance effect is usually attributed (in a functional sense) to a kind of neural boredom, but it also seems conceivable that the visual system is not so much concerned with suppressing unchanging spatial signals as with suppressing signals that are spatially ambiguous.

In any event it seems clear that the answer to these questions must come from studies that measure visual acuity under conditions that control retinal image motion. Kelly (75) has recently reported the first measurements of the spatial contrast sensitivity function for gratings that drift across the retina at a controlled velocity independent of the subject's eye movements. His measurements concentrate on lower frequencies and consequently are not directly related to our problem, but they do demonstrate clearly that spatial contrast sensitivity is sharply dependent on the rate of retinal image motion. Visual acuity must now be analyzed from this point of view.

COLOR VISION

Newton's prism experiments of 1666 showed that light comes in different degrees of refrangibility (today we would say different wavelengths or frequencies); that each wavelength in isolation produces its own unique color experience (i.e., the spectral colors); and that lights composed of wavelength mixtures generally produce color experiences indistinguishable from those produced by other mixtures that are physically entirely different (e.g., a red/green wavelength mixture is indistinguishable from a suitably adjusted yellow/blue mixture). For nearly 300 years this last fact was the outstanding problem of color vision. What causes the visual system to lose so much wavelength information? By the middle of the 19th century experiments by Maxwell had established the precise quantitative nature of this information loss, which at daylight levels of illumination takes the form of *trichromacy*: "Given any four lights, whether spectroscopically pure or not, it is always possible to place two of them in one half of a foveal photometric field and two in the other, or else three in one half and one in the other, and by adjusting the intensities of three of the four lights to make the two halves of the field indistinguishable to the eye." [(29), p. 199]. The psychophysical laws of color matching were formalized by the mathematician Grassman in 1853, and it became apparent that the set of color experiences could be modeled as a three-dimensional vector space, in which the three trichromatic "primaries" (that is, three lights of fixed wavelengths which can be weighted in intensity and mixed to match other lights of arbitrary composition) play the role of basis vectors: Just as any point in three-dimensional space can be produced by a linear combination of the vectors $(1, 0, 0)$, $(0, 1, 0)$, and $(0, 0, 1)$, so the color experience generated by any wavelength mixture L can be produced by a linear combination of primary lights A, B, C: Either $L = aA + bB + cC$ (where aA means a quanta/s at wavelength A, and + means the physical superposition of two lights—e.g., by overlapping the beams of two projectors) for some set of positive weights a, b, c, or one primary must be added to L to produce a match, in which case we interpret its weight as negative—so that, for example, $aA + L = bB + cC$. (For a thorough discussion of Grassman's laws and their measurement-theoretic implications, see Krantz, refs. 79, 80.)

Maxwell and Helmholtz (in 89a) independently recognized that trichromacy could be neatly explained by a physiological mechanism for light transduction suggested 50 years earlier by Thomas Young (in 89a). Impressed by the physical impossibility of equipping each retinal point with separate detectors for every wavelength, Young (in 89a) proposed that there might be only three broadband detectors, each corresponding to a "particle," analogous to a resonator, that responded best to some peak wavelength and more or less strongly to other wavelengths according to their distance from that peak. He supposed the peaks of the action spectra of his particles would correspond to the "three principle colors, red, yellow, and blue."

Modern work has exactly confirmed Young's proposal: "His particles are the π-electrons of the chromophores of the visual-pigment units of the cones." [See Rodieck (106), p. 714.] However, for a hundred years after its revival by Helmholtz and Maxwell (see ref. 89a), Young's model could not be physiologically confirmed, and in the absence of any clear understanding of the neural substrate of color vision, competing theories flourished. The most radical alternative (or so it seemed) was Hering's (66a) idea that photoreceptors might operate in an opponent-process fashion, with some substance being created by certain wavelengths and destroyed by others. Variations on Young's idea included the addition of more than three cone photopigments; the idea that each type of photopigment is (or is not) segregated into its own private set of receptors; the idea that the spectral sensitivities of the cones might be determined by optics rather than photochemistry, and the notion that the blue cones might be rods.

Many of these hypotheses could be decisively tested by psychophysical experiments (see chapt. 8 in ref. 29), and during the period 1850–1950 color science was largely dominated by psychophysics, which achieved some important successes. In the nineteenth century, perhaps the most notable example was König's demonstration (1894; see ref. 77a) that the action spectrum for detection in rod vision agrees with the absorption spectrum of the rod photopigment rhodopsin. That result (since confirmed by modern methods—see Fig. 21) showed that the spectral properties of rod vision at least could be explained by the absorption characteristics of a photopigment. In this century a comparable achievement is the long-term effort of W. S. Stiles to identify the spectral properties of the mechanisms underlying cone vision by the analysis of increment thresholds (120).

From the standpoint of industrial colorimetry, psychophysics alone was sufficient for the practical problem of specifying the color experiences produced by isolated lights of arbitrary spectral composition. [We say isolated because Grassman's laws do not predict the color experiences produced by juxtaposing two lights—e.g., the fact that white light turns pink when surrounded by a green field. These simultaneous contrast phenomena, which Land (82) has demonstrated so effectively, are still not fully understood.] However, psychophysical methods alone could not provide definitive answers to the fundamental questions: Are there really exactly three cone photopigments? If so what are their absorption spectra? Are the photopigment types segregated in different receptors? These questions persisted largely because the cone pigments of the human retina, unlike rhodopsin, could not be successfully isolated (and have not been to this day). The impasse was finally broken in the period 1950–1970 by two new techniques: retinal densitometry, which measures the absorption spectra of visual pigments in the living retina, and microspectrophotometry, which measures the absorption spectra of individual receptors. Both techniques have agreed in showing that besides rhodopsin, the human retina normally contains three cone pigments, which Rushton (112) has called erythrolabe (λ_{max} = 570), chlorolabe (λ_{max} = 540), and cyanolabe (λ_{max} = 440). Microspectrophotometry has shown in addition that these pigments are segregated in different receptors—the (so-called) "red," "green," and "blue" cones. [There are good grounds for objecting to these colorful labels—ex-

pressed, for example, by De Valois and De Valois (42) and in the chapter in this *Handbook* by De Valois and Jacobs. However, they are probably too convenient to be readily discarded.]

On the basis of these results—together with converging evidence from a hundred years of psychophysics and physiology—there is today general agreement that the normal human retina contains four photopigments (three cone pigments and rhodopsin), each housed in a separate class of receptors, and that this fact together with the inability of receptors to signal anything beyond their rate of quantum absorption (Rushton's univariance hypothesis) can account for the basic properties of color matching (e.g., see refs. 29, 106, 112, and chapts. 9–15 in ref. 40). The purpose of the present section is to show how the quantitative psychophysical facts of color matching arise from the underlying physiology of the retina. We first consider the special case of rod vision, which serves as an illustration of what can be expected in a monochromatic visual system—i.e., a system in which only one class of receptors is active, all of which share a common absorption spectrum. Then we extend the argument to cover dichromatic and trichromatic systems. We also briefly consider the major forms of color blindness, which can (probably) be explained in terms of losses or spectral distortions of one or more receptor systems. Our discussion does not extend beyond color phenomena that can be explained in terms of the absorption properties of receptors. Consequently we have nothing to say about such important perceptual phenomena as simultaneous color contrast, or about the neural mechanisms that process the color information supplied by the outer segments. On these topics the reader is referred to the chapter by De Valois and Jacobs in this *Handbook*.

Scotopic Spectral Sensitivity

Figure 19 is called the scotopic spectral sensitivity curve of the human eye. It represents psychophysical data, in that it was obtained by systematically varying physical parameters (intensity and wavelength) and measuring the corresponding perceptual effects. To obtain the curve in Figure 19, the subject was first fully dark adapted. Then flashes of light of a given wavelength and adjustable intensity were delivered to his peripheral retina, where rods are most densely packed, and, for each wavelength the intensity was found for which the flash was just on the threshold of visibility (i.e., the intensity for which it was reported to have been seen on 60% of the flashes). In other words, this is a plot of the effectiveness of light on the dark-adapted (scotopic) visual system as a function of wavelength—the scotopic visual action spectrum.

The ocular media absorb some quanta before they arrive at the retina, and the wavelength dependence of this absorption is plotted in Figure 20. When the spectrum in Figure 19 is corrected for the absorption shown in Figure 20, the result is as plotted with

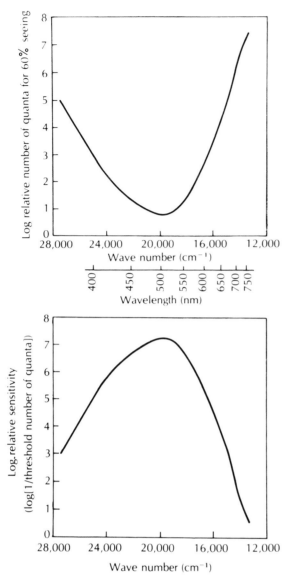

molecules within the rods. When a quantum passes through the space occupied by a rhodopsin molecule, it has some probability of being absorbed, and the absorption spectrum is really a plot of this probability as a function of wavelength. Now an extremely important question arises. When a quantum is absorbed by a rhodopsin molecule, does the resulting activity retain information about the wavelength of the absorbed quantum? All available evidence indicates the answer is no. Quanta of different wavelengths (and energies) may have different probabilities of being absorbed, but if a quantum is absorbed, the physiologically significant effect is apparently identical, regardless of the wavelength (or energy) of the quantum. Strong psychophysical evidence that the wavelength information is lost is that, if two patches of differing wavelengths are presented to a dark-adapted eye and their relative intensities are adjusted to compensate for the difference in scotopic sensitivity between the two wavelengths, the two patches will be completely indiscriminable, so long as the intensities of the patches are below the photopic threshold, so that only the scotopic system is operating. Any pair of lights that produce equal numbers of quantal absorptions are indistinguishable from each other. The information that the two patches are different in wavelength must therefore have been lost by the visual system, and that is true for all wavelengths. That information loss evidently occurs during the absorption of the quantum, all absorptions producing identical effects (the *cis-trans* isomerization of rhodopsin) regardless of the energy in the quanta. The differences in energy among absorbed quanta are evidently manifested in small temperature differences that are not signaled to the rest of the visual system.

The assumption that wavelength information is lost at the point of quantum absorption is generally referred to as the principle of "univariance," a term

FIG. 19. The scotopic visual action spectrum plotted two ways. Horizontal axis is linear with wave number (number of waves per cm). See text for explanation of data collection procedure. [From Cornsweet (36).]

symbols (×) in Figure 21. It is the action spectrum of that part of the scotopic visual system that is proximal to the ocular media. The dashed curve in Figure 21 is the absorption spectrum of rhodopsin. The coincidence of the dashed curve and the symbols in this figure, that is, the agreement between a psychophysically determined action spectrum and a physically measured absorption spectrum, is strong evidence for a physiological theory, namely, that the absorption of quanta by rods is the initial step in the crucial transduction of light into physiological signals, under scotopic conditions.

Monochromacy

The absorption spectrum of intact rods is primarily determined by the quantal absorption of the rhodopsin

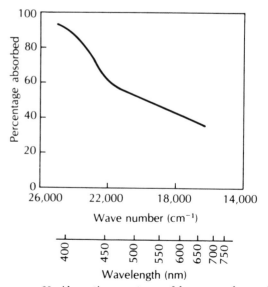

FIG. 20. Absorption spectrum of human ocular media. [From Ludvigh and McCarthy (89).]

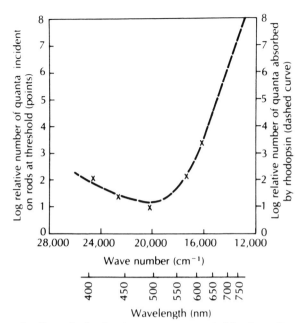

FIG. 21. Scotopic visual action spectrum corrected for absorption by ocular media (×) compared with absorption of rhodopsin (*dashed curve*). [From Cornsweet (36).]

introduced by Rushton (112). Because this hypothesis is central to understanding the relationship between the psychophysics and physiology of color vision, its meaning (and, of course, empirical validity) deserves close examination. Here we take univariance to mean that the effective input to the visual system is the quantum catch of the receptors, so that the response of any given receptor r_0 is some function $f_0(c_0, c_1, c_2, \ldots,\ )$ whose arguments are the quantum catches of r_0 itself, c_0, and the catches $c_1, c_2, \ldots$ of other receptors $r_1, r_2, \ldots$. Thus two stimuli that produce the same quantum catch in every receptor (i.e., the same values of $c_0, c_1, c_2, \ldots$) constitute identical inputs to the visual system and are necessarily indiscriminable. Note that this is not equivalent to assuming that the response of a receptor depends only on its own quantum catch—the special case in which f_0 depended on c_0 alone, and not on $c_1, c_2, \ldots$. This point is important because there have now been several demonstrations that receptor membrane potentials do depend on the quantum catch of more than one receptor (17, 18, 47) and one sometimes reads that such demonstrations disprove the univariance principle—which clearly they do not.

In fact there seems to be no evidence contradicting univariance. However, this does not mean the principle is undoubtable: Rodieck (106) points out that receptors could provide wavelength information by varying their output signal as a function of the position along the outer segment at which absorption occurs. (For example, quanta absorbed nearer the base might be more effective at modulating transmitter release.) Because the average position at which photons are absorbed depends on their wavelength (the mean distance traveled before absorption is inversely propor-

tional to the absorption probability) a device reading the output to a fixed number of absorptions could make a better-than-chance guess as to the wavelength of the stimulation if it knew where those absorptions had occurred. This would be a violation of univariance because the response of the visual system would depend on something more than quantum catch. However, it does not appear that the human visual system takes any significant advantage of this possibility. (We do not rule out the possibility that the mechanism suggested by Rodieck might produce failures of univariance in a psychophysical experiment designed specifically for the purpose, but we would expect any such failures to be very small.) At the moment then it seems safe to assume that univariance is strictly true and to develop a model of color vision based on that hypothesis. It is unlikely that future developments will force us to alter this assumption in any significant way.

Assuming univariance, lights that produce the same rate of quantum absorption in each receptor must be indistinguishable. To understand what this entails one needs a model of the light-absorption process. The standard first approximation is to assume that the light-catching parts of receptors (e.g., rod outer segments) can be treated simply as tubes filled with photopigment (e.g., rhodopsin) molecules; photopigment concentration is assumed to be uniform throughout the tube, and all quanta are assumed to enter the tube straight-on, and travel down its length until they are either absorbed or reach the end. In this case absorption can be modeled by a spatially homogeneous Poisson process in which the probability density for absorption of a quantum of wavelength λ_i at distance x along the outer segment is $a_i c\, e^{-a_i c x}$, where a_i is the chromophore absorptivity at λ_i (in other words, the intrinsic absorption spectrum of the photopigment), and c is the photopigment concentration. Then if the length of the outer segment is L, the probability, $P(i, c)$, that an incident quantum of wavelength λ_i will be absorbed during its journey down the receptor is

$$P(i, c) = 1 - e^{-a_i c L}$$

$P(i, c)$ is the absorption spectrum of the photoreceptor; it depends on both wavelength and concentration and is nonlinearly related to the intrinsic absorption spectrum of the photopigment.

If I_i quanta/s at wavelength λ_i are incident on the receptor, and the catch rate is small enough to leave the concentration c effectively unchanged, then the rate of absorption will be $P(i, c)I_i$ per second. Assuming that every receptor has the same absorption spectrum (e.g., only rods are active, and all have the same value of the product $a_i c L$), two uniform patches of light of wavelengths λ_1 and λ_2 are indistinguishable if their intensities, I_1, I_2, are adjusted so that

$$P(1, c)\, I_1 = P(2, c)\, I_2$$

Now it is obvious from this equation that at any fixed photopigment concentration level, any pair of monochromatic lights can be made indistinguishable by adjusting the intensity of one light. However, because the absorption spectrum $P(i, c)$ depends nonlinearly on c, it is also clear that in general, lights that produce equal absorptions at one concentration level will not necessarily do so at other levels. In other words, lights that are indistinguishable at one adaptation level need not match at all adaptation levels. This nonlinearity is formally awkward, and so it is natural to look for simplifying assumptions that can justify getting rid of it. If one requires a model that will guarantee the stability of color matches for all states of adaptation there are only two possibilities. One is that the product, $a_i cL$, is always small enough (≤ 0.2) to justify the approximation $1 - e^{-a_i cL} \approx a_i cL$. In this case two monochromatic lights match at any concentration if their intensity ratio I_1/I_2 equals the ratio a_2/a_1, and if this is true for any concentration it is true for all. Early estimates of the absorption probabilities of individual receptors suggested that $P(i, c)$ could be well approximated by $a_i cL$, but more recent measurements for both rods and cones yield values on the order of 0.5 or more [(106), p. 142–143], so this linear approximation assumption does not seem well founded.

The other alternative is to assume that photopigment concentration changes are negligible over the range of light intensities one is concerned with. In this case $P(i, c)$ can be regarded as a function of wavelength alone and written simply as P_i. Then the condition for indistinguishability of two monochromatic lights, L_1 and L_2, whose wavelengths are respectively λ_i and λ_2 is simply

$$P_1 I_1 = P_2 I_2$$

and for wavelength mixtures (say I_{ij} denotes the number of quanta/s at wavelength λ_j produced by L_i) the matching condition is

$$\sum_j P_j I_{1j} = \sum_j P_j I_{2j}$$

For the rod system this constant concentration assumption seems reasonable, because rods become visually ineffective (i.e., saturate) at intensity levels that bleach only a small fraction (ca. 10%) of the available rhodopsin (1a). For cones, on the other hand, visual matches can be disrupted by very intense adapting lights that bleach substantial fractions of photopigment (29), and so in this case a breakdown of the constant concentration assumption can have significant perceptual consequences. However, throughout most of the intensity range encountered in normal vision such breakdowns do not occur, and because the formal simplification permitted by that assumption is more important in cone vision (due to the additional complications introduced by the three-dimensionality of phototopic vision) it seems reasonable to adopt the hypothesis that for both cones and rods the photoreceptor absorption spectrum, $P(i, c)$, is independent of c, and for each receptor depends only on wavelength.

Thus we assume that all receptors of a given class can be characterized by a common absorption probability, P_i, that depends only on the wavelength, λ_i, via the intrinsic absorption spectrum, a_i of the photopigment common to that class. In that case, the requirement for indistinguishability of monochromatic lights by a given receptor system under all conditions is simply $P_1 I_1 = P_2 I_2$, and when several receptor systems are active—as we shall see in the following discussion—the requirement for indistinguishability is a straightforward multidimensional generalization of this equation.

As a consequence of the loss of wavelength information, the scotopic visual system is often said to be totally color-blind. That terminology can be misleading, however. A less ambiguous statement is that the scotopic system cannot discriminate among lights on the basis of their wavelength compositions. If two patches of differing wavelength composition are side by side, it is always possible to adjust the intensity of one until the two patches produce identical effects (numbers of absorptions and isomerizations) on the visual system, and thus to render them indistinguishable. Any visual system for which this is true is said to be monochromatic, or "totally color blind." Note that the term *monochromatic* does not in any sense refer to the perception of colors. If a totally color-blind person asserts that he sees a full spectrum of colors in the world, there is no class of evidence that can refute him. If he is truly monochromatic, what is missing is sensitivity to wavelength differences, and if he were to attribute color names to objects in the world, a manipulation of the intensity and wavelength of light reflected from objects would reveal that there was no *consistent relationship* between the wavelength composition of the reflected light and his color names.

Dichromacy

When the ambient light level is well above the cone threshold, the scotopic system evidently ceases to be functionally significant, and the cone, or photopic, system mediates normal human vision. Suppose that a person had both functional rods and cones, and all of his cones contained a pigment whose absorption spectrum was shifted with respect to rhodopsin, as in Figure 22. At low-light levels, only his rod system would operate and he would be a monochromat. At high levels, only his cone system would be functional, and he would still be a monochromat, since all of the arguments showing that the rod system is monochromatic would apply equally well. [Recent evidence indicates that the rod system can influence perception at relatively high light levels under certain conditions. See, for example, Stabell and Stabell (119). Those conditions are not relevant to the logic of this argument and will be neglected, here, to facilitate the discussion.]

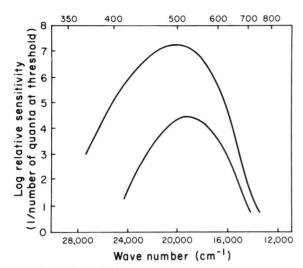

FIG. 22. Spectral sensitivity curve of rods (*upper curve*) compared with spectral sensitivity curve for a hypothetical set of cones (*lower curve*). Note that this lower curve does not represent any real set of cones and is strictly for explanatory purposes.

If a pair of patches of light of differing wavelengths are adjusted to be indiscriminable, that is, to produce equal numbers of absorptions, under scotopic conditions, and then the intensities of both patches are doubled but remain below the photopic threshold, the patches will still have equal effects on the visual system, and so will still be indiscriminable. If the intensities of both patches are now increased by a factor sufficient to raise them well above the cone threshold, the rods will cease contributing to vision and the visual action spectrum will shift to that of the cones. As a consequence, the probabilities of absorption of the various wavelength components will change and the patches will no longer match. However, it will now be possible to readjust the relative intensities of the two patches until they are again indiscriminable, and so the system is again monochromatic.

Now suppose that the intensities of the two patches were lowered until they were above the cone threshold but low enough that the rod system still functioned too. (This intensity range, between pure scotopic and pure photopic vision, is called mesopic vision.) If the intensities of the two patches were adjusted to produce equal absorption in the rods, they would have differing effects on the cones, and so the viewer could tell them apart. If the intensities were readjusted to produce a match for the cones, the rod signal would provide the information necessary to discriminate them. Therefore, a person with rods containing rhodopsin and cones containing a pigment with a different absorption spectrum would be a monochromat at high- or low-light levels, but would not be under mesopic conditions.

A fairly large class of humans (those afflicted with the form of color blindness known as *dichromacy*) have a normal rod system and a cone system that effectively consists of two kinds of receptors, differing in their absorption spectra (see curves for systems A and B in Figure 23A and B. When these people are presented with photopic stimuli, their visual systems contain two simultaneously operating cone subsystems, and their ability to discriminate wavelength mixtures has the same properties as the person described above under mesopic conditions.

If two patches of differing wavelength composition are adjusted in intensity to have identical effects on the A system, they will have differing effects on the B system, and vice versa. Thus, such a person is not a monochromat under photopic conditions. (He will be under scotopic conditions.) The point labeled 620 in Figure 23B is a representation of the effects on the A and B cone systems of a patch of light of wavelength 620 nm and an intensity of 1,000 $quanta \cdot s^{-1} \cdot mm^{-2}$. The location of that point in the two-dimensional space of Figure 23B is found simply by multiplying the intensity (1,000) by the proportion of quanta absorbed at 620 nm in each cone subsystem as plotted in Figure 23A.

The space in Figure 23B is linear. That is, if the intensity of the 620-nm stimulus were doubled, the number of quantal absorptions in each system would double, and a point representing this new stimulus would be twice as far from the origin. Thus, the dashed line in Figure 23B represents the effects of all intensities of 620-nm light. As noted above, this linearity only holds exactly as long as the intensity is not so great that a substantial fraction of either pigment is bleached. As a practical matter, this kind of linearity holds for almost all light levels experienced in the world. The space in Figure 23B represents the joint consequences of the action spectra of two visual subsystems, and we will call it the visual action space.

Suppose a second stimulus is now placed next to the first, at a wavelength of 560 nm and an intensity of 1,000 $quanta \cdot s^{-1} \cdot mm^{-2}$. Its effect on the A and B systems is represented by the dot labeled "560" in Figure 23B. The fact that this dot is not coincident with the point labeled "620" (i.e., that the effects of this stimulus are different from those of the first one) means that the two stimuli are discriminable (provided that the differences between their effects are not lost at any later stage in the system). Furthermore, changing the intensity of either patch would simply move its effect along the line connecting it with the origin, and thus there is no intensity adjustment that will render the two stimuli indiscriminable.

Now suppose that the patches are left the same, 1,000 $quanta \cdot s^{-1} \cdot mm^{-2}$ at 560 nm and 1,000 $quanta \cdot s^{-1} \cdot mm^{-2}$ at 620 nm, but a new component, 1,000 $quanta \cdot s^{-1} \cdot mm^{-2}$ at 500 nm, is added to the 620-nm patch. The effect on the visual system of this mixture (620 nm + 500 nm) of lights can be represented simply as the vector sum of the effects of each of its components, as in Figure 24, because the action space is

286

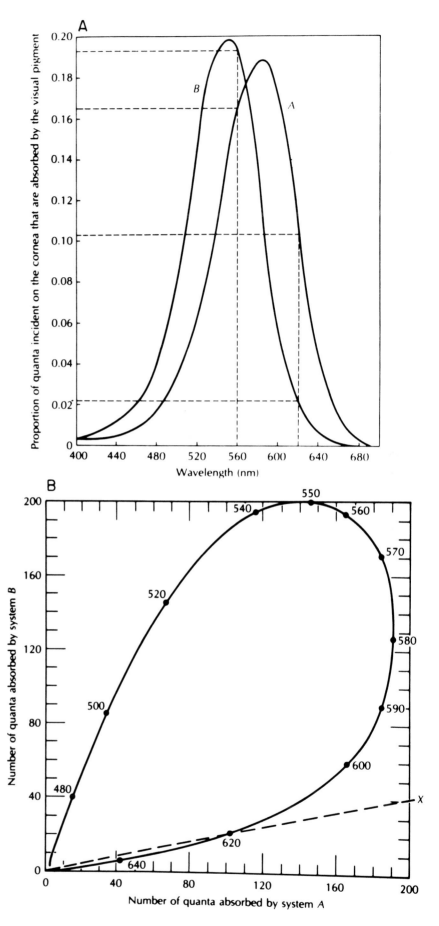

FIG. 23. *A*: absorption spectra for two classes of cones. (These are two of the three classes present in the normal human eye.) *B*: two-dimensional visual action space of a person whose eyes contain only the two kinds of cones plotted in *A*. See text for derivation of system B from A. [From Cornsweet (36).]

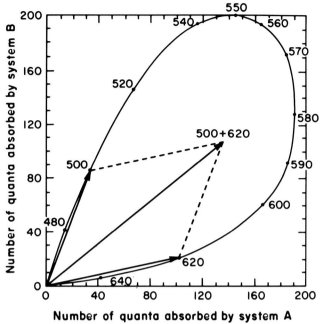

FIG. 24. A representation in two-dimensional action space of the effects of adding lights together. The result can be represented simply as the vector sum of the effects of the components.

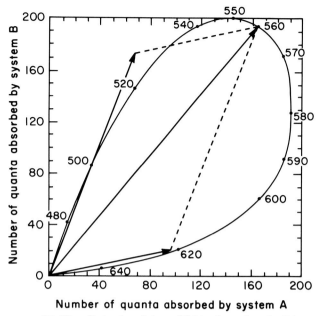

FIG. 25. The effects of a mixture of lights of wavelengths 500 nm and 620 nm and of appropriately chosen intensities (2,050 and 910 quanta·s^{-1}·mm^{-2}, respectively, in this example) will be identical to the effects of a light of 560 nm (at an intensity of 1,000 quanta·s^{-1}· mm^{-2}).

linear—that is, because each wavelength component produces a number of absorptions that is independent of the absorptions produced by the other component. The total number of absorptions in each pigment system is simply the sum of the absorptions that would have been produced by each wavelength component alone.

Now suppose that one patch delivers 1,000 quanta· s^{-1}·mm^{-2} at 560 nm and the other is a mixture of 2,050 quanta·s^{-1}·mm^{-2} at 500 nm and 910 quanta·s^{-1}· mm^{-2} at 620 nm. Figure 25 shows that the vector sum of the 500 and 620 nm mixture is represented by the same point in action space as is the patch of 560 nm at 1,000 quanta·s^{-1}·mm^{-2}. Because the effects of the mixture on both the A and B systems are identical with the effects of the 560-nm stimulus, the two patches must be indistinguishable. Furthermore, it is easy to see that, given a mixture of any two wavelengths, one shorter and one longer than 560 nm, intensities can be found for the two components of the mixture such that their vector sum equals the vector for the 560-nm patch. If it were possible to present stimuli of negative intensity (the physical representation of which will be discussed later), it should be clear that this property would not be restricted to a mixture of wavelengths one on each side of 560 nm, nor restricted to a mixture of just two wavelengths. In general, if negative intensities were possible and if a visual system contained just two classes of receptors whose action spectra were different, so that the effects of any mixture of wavelengths could be represented in a two-dimensional action space like that in Figure 23B, then the effects of any mixture of wavelengths could be

exactly matched by the effects of any other mixture of wavelengths if the intensities of two different wavelength components were properly adjusted. The effects of each mixture are found by vector addition of its components. The effects of the two mixtures are represented by two points in action space. By changing the intensity of any one wavelength component of a mixture, the effect of the mixture can be moved along a line parallel with the line through the origin representing the effects of that particular wavelength. If the intensity of a different wavelength is changed, the effects of the mixture move in a different direction. Therefore, by changing the intensities of any two wavelengths, the effects of a mixture can be placed anywhere in the two-dimensional action space; that is, any mixture can be made to match any other mixture by the adjustment of the intensities of any two components.

Consider the simple case illustrated in Figure 26, for which a match is to be made between a 620-nm patch and a mixture of 540 nm and 580 nm. If the match is to be made by adjusting the intensities of the 540-nm and 580-nm components, the 580-nm component must have an intensity of 790 quanta·s^{-1}·mm^{-2}, but the 540-nm component must have an intensity of −425 quanta·s^{-1}·mm^{-2}, which is not physically realizable. However, if the 540-nm component were moved from the patch containing the 580-nm component to the 620-nm patch and given an intensity of +425, the two patches would match. In general, if a match between two patches requires a negative intensity as represented in the action space, the match can be physically

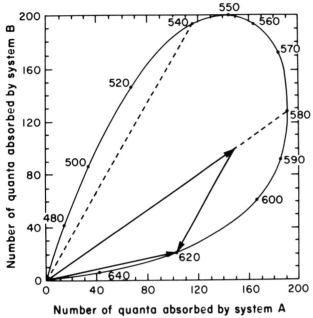

FIG. 26. If a mixture of two wavelengths is to match a third whose effects do not lie on a line between the two to be mixed, one of the two components of the mixture must have a negative intensity, as shown by the downward direction of the 500-nm vector. The physical realization of this negative vector requires the addition of 500 nm light of that magnitude to the 620-nm component.

of light, one containing any arbitrary mixture of wavelengths and the other any three wavelengths (except for a special case to be described below), and if the intensity of each of the three can be adjusted (including negative values, i.e., added as positive quantities to the other patch), it will always be possible to find a set of three intensities such that the two patches are indistinguishable. In three-dimensional action space, this is represented in the following way. The three actions of light (on the three color systems) of any single wavelength component are represented by a vector through the origin whose length is proportional to intensity and whose direction depends upon wavelength, and the actions of any mixture of wavelengths can be represented by the vector sum of its component vectors. Thus a patch containing an arbitrary mixture is represented by some vector or point in the action space. Given any set of three wavelengths in a second patch, the sum of their vectors can always be made to equal the vector representing the arbitrary mixture, if each intensity can be adjusted. However, this statement is only true so long as the vectors representing the three wavelengths do not all lie in the same plane. If they did, then a mixture of any two of them could be made indistinguishable from the third by the appropriate intensity adjustment. In other words, for

achieved by changing the sign of the intensity and adding it to the other patch instead.

The action space in Figure 23B is two dimensional because it represents the actions of lights on two systems, each of which is one dimensional (that is, the effect of light on each system depends only on the total number of quantal absorptions, not on their wavelengths). It follows that any visual system containing only two classes of receptors that differ in their absorption spectra must have the following property: any mixture of wavelengths can be exactly matched by any other mixture if the intensities of any two component wavelengths can be arbitrarily adjusted (including the realizable equivalent of negative intensities). A visual system with those properties is called dichromatic.

Trichromacy

Most humans cannot produce a match between two mixtures by adjusting the intensities of only two components. Three adjustments are required. That is, normal human vision is trichromatic and it must be represented by a three-dimensional action space. This is to be expected from the fact that the normal human visual system contains receptors with three different action spectra. One estimate of these spectra is shown in Figure 27, and Figure 28 is a representation of the corresponding three-dimensional action space.

If a normal human observer is shown two patches

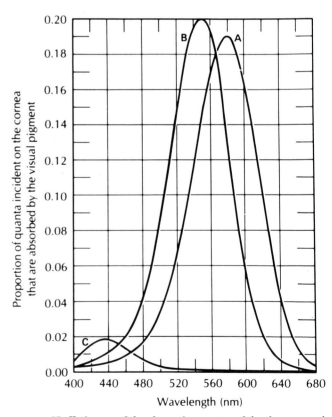

FIG. 27. Estimates of the absorption spectra of the three normal human cone pigments. [From Wald (131). Copyright 1964 by the American Association for the Advancement of Science.]

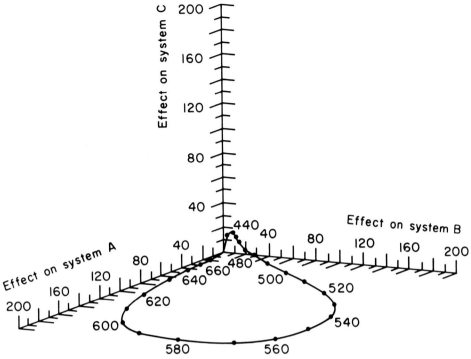

FIG. 28. Representation of the three-dimensional action space of the normal human visual system. The curved figure is the locus of the effect of the three systems of all wavelengths at a fixed intensity. [From Cornsweet (36).]

three wavelengths whose vectors all lie in the same plane, the three-dimensional visual system is, in effect, two dimensional. That condition can occur in normal human vision only in the long-wavelength region of the spectrum, where the blue-sensitive system provides a negligible contribution.

Color Blindness

The three-dimensional space in Figure 28 represents the actions of lights on the normal or trichromatic visual system. If the system were lacking any of the three normal color systems, its action space would collapse to a two-dimensional one, with axes corresponding to the two remaining color systems. This is precisely what seems to happen psychophysically in the type of "color blindness" known as dichromacy. By definition, a dichromat is a person who can match every light (i.e., any wavelength mixture) by adjusting the intensities of only two primaries, rather than the normal three. This color deficiency is further subdivided into three categories: protanopes (who need only a green and a blue primary), deuteranopes (who need only red and blue), and tritanopes (who need only red and green). Protanopia occurs in about 1% of males, deuteranopia also in about 1%, and tritanopia in 0.002%. (However, as noted earlier, everyone is apparently tritanopic in a tiny region at the center of the fovea.) For females (144) the corresponding frequencies are much lower for protanopia (0.02%) and deu-

teranopia (0.01%), but about the same for tritanopia (0.001%).

The simplest physiological explanation for this psychophysically defined color deficit is that one of the three cone types is missing: protanopes presumably lack the long-wavelength sensitive cones, deuteranopes the middle-wavelength sensitive cones, and tritanopes the short-wavelength sensitive cones. This idea is called the receptor-loss hypothesis and dates back to a suggestion in 1807 by Thomas Young (145). For many years its major competitor was the hypothesis that two of the normal cone systems might be neurally fused into one at a very early stage, thereby effectively creating a single system whose action spectrum would be a weighted average of its two components. Retinal densitometry seems to have disproved the latter hypothesis, since it shows that protanopes lack a long-wavelength photopigment, and deuteranopes lack a middle-wavelength pigment (112). Consequently, today the receptor-loss hypothesis is the generally accepted explanation of dichromacy.

However, recent work indicates that the classic version of that hypothesis needs to be amended somewhat. Suppose one assumes that not only do dichromats lack one of the three cone systems, but in addition their two remaining systems have the same action spectra as those of normal trichromatic observers—who in turn all share identical action spectra for all three of their cone systems. If we perform a confrontation experiment in which a trichromat adjusts the intensities of three primaries to produce a mixture M that matches any given light L, this expanded version of the receptor-loss hypothesis predicts that any dichromat must also perceive a match between M and L. This is so because the normal observer's match implies that M and L produce the same quantum catch in all three cone systems, and consequently they must also produce the same catch in whichever two of those systems are possessed by the dichromat.

By the same reasoning, the converse experiment should turn out differently: two patches that match to a dichromat will generally not match to a trichromat. Consider the set of mixtures represented by any line parallel to the axis representing system A in Figure 28. These mixtures have differing effects on a trichromatic visual system and can therefore be discriminated. However, because their effects lie along a line parallel to the axis representing the long-wavelength sensitive system (that is, they differ only in their effects on the long-wavelength sensitive system) a protanope would not be able to distinguish among them. (This line is called a *protanopic color-confusion line*.) Similarly, all mixtures whose effects would be plotted along any line parallel to the axis representing the middle-wavelength sensitive system would be indiscriminable to a deuteranope, etc. Thus dichromats cannot distinguish between the colors of certain objects that look different to most people, and so they are called *color-blind*.

Curiously, the idea that dichromats accept the same color matches as normal trichromats was for many years generally accepted, and widely cited as a proof of the receptor-loss hypothesis, even though there was really not much evidence to support it. Recently, Alpern and his collaborators (3–5) have made a systematic study of the question and have shown that in general, dichromats do not accept trichromats' matches, neither do they generally accept the matches of other dichromats. The differences between observers are fairly small, but well outside the bounds of measurement error.

To understand dichromacy in light of these results, one needs to consider the other major form of color blindness: the so-called trichromatic anomalous defects, which occur in about 5.5% of the male population and 0.4% of females (144). Anomalous trichromats are people who require three primaries to match every light (and consequently are trichromatic by definition), but whose intensity adjustments of those primaries are significantly different from those of "normal" trichromatic observers. Like the dichromats, anomalous trichromats are subdivided into three classes: protanomalous, deuteranomalous, and tritanomalous, according to the spectral range in which their differences from the norm are most apparent. If a patch of light containing an arbitrary wavelength mixture is to be matched by a mixture of short-, middle-, and long-wavelength primaries, a protanomalous observer requires a more intense long-wavelength primary than does a normal observer; a deuteranomalous

requires a more intense middle-wavelength primary, and so on. It is as if the protanomalous observer has a long-wavelength system whose action spectrum is shifted down toward lower wavelengths, so as to be relatively less sensitive to red light.

Now classically the anomalous trichromats were sharply distinguished from both dichromats and normal trichromats, as though they corresponded to three completely different underlying conditions: trichromats all had three "normal" cone systems; dichromats had only two of the three normal systems, and a third whose action spectrum was shifted away from the norm. The results of Alpern et al. (3–5) suggest a somewhat different story: Apparently there is random variation across the population in the exact location of the action spectra of each color system—as though every person constructed his own idiosyncratic visual system by sampling randomly from a collection of possible long-wavelength action spectra, and again from a collection of possible middle-wavelength spectra, and so on. In the continuum model, a dichromat is simply an unlucky person who happened to select, for example, a long-wavelength system that has effectively the same action spectrum as his middle-wavelength system, whereas an anomalous trichromat is not quite so unfortunate, having selected, for example, a long-wavelength action spectrum that is substantially shifted away from the model position but still does not entirely overlap the spectrum of his middle-wavelength system. "Normal trichromats" are those to whom chance has allocated three systems with action spectra that are all close to the modes of their respective populations. This model thus retains the essential feature of the receptor-loss theory of dichromacy—the idea that the dichromat has only two distinct cone action spectra instead of three—but blurs the old sharp distinctions between classes of normal and color-deficient observers, replacing them instead with purely statistical categories.

Dichromats are called *color-blind* not because they don't see colors, but because they confuse colors that appear clearly different to people with "normal" color vision. However, from an absolute standpoint, "normal" color vision is only a little less color blind than dichromacy. There is still an infinite set of mixtures of wavelengths that physically differ from each other and yet are indistinguishable to the trichromat. A monochromatic visual system loses all information about the wavelength composition of a stimulus, a dichromatic system loses a lot but not all such information, and the normal trichromatic system loses a little less than the dichromatic system.

The very large loss of wavelength information that occurs in trichromatic vision is exploited in many aspects of technology, especially in the printing, photographic, and television industries. That very long story is briefly mentioned here. If a television technician wants to show the audience a scene containing, say, a banana, and if the scene is to be viewed by an imaginary person whose visual system has lost no wavelength information (e.g., if his retina contains receptors with an infinite variety of action spectra and the rest of his nervous system retains information related to the differences among the outputs of these systems), the technician will have to deliver to the observer's eye a mixture of wavelengths that is identical to the mixture reflected by a banana, and that is, in fact, a very complex and continuous spectrum spanning the entire visible range of wavelengths. Thus his camera will have to be able to detect every wavelength independently, the screen of the receiver will have to contain an independently excitable phosphor that emits at each visible wavelength, and the electronics will have to permit the appropriate independent excitation of each of those phosphors. However, if the observer is as color-blind as a trichromat, the camera, receiver and electronics can be much simpler. Thus the typical studio color TV camera has three camera tubes within it, each viewing the same scene through a differently colored filter, so that there are three sensing systems whose action spectra are different. Similarly, the color receiver screen contains only three different phosphors each emitting light in a different region of the spectrum, and the electronics permit the relatively independent control of intensity of excitation of each.

Note that, because there is no operation in television reproduction that corresponds to the production of negative intensities, once any given set of phosphors has been chosen, there are some colors that cannot be reproduced. Referring to the action space in Figure 28, if the three phosphors each were to emit monochromatic light of a different wavelength, then the receiver can exactly reproduce any color whose action can be plotted as a point somewhere within the volume included in a triangular pyramid whose vertex is the origin and whose edges are the lines representing the effect of each of the three emitted wavelengths. However, the volume that includes all possible colors is roughly cone-shaped and convex everywhere except in the extremely long wavelength region of the spectrum; it includes and is larger than the pyramid-shaped volume that is enclosed by any finite set of wavelengths. In the television industry, phosphors are chosen to emit wavelengths whose vectors in action space include as much of the entire spectral volume as possible.

Seeing Colors

The reader will have noticed that in most of the preceding discussion we have refrained, sometimes with evident awkwardness, from mentioning any color names, like red, blue, and so on. In fact, none of the evidence or arguments presented so far has dealt with questions about the actual perception of colors. We have been concerned exclusively with discrimination or lack of it among patches of differing wavelength composition, and, paradoxically, the only definitions of the various forms of color blindness that are unambiguous are those that refer to discriminations, not to colors seen. However, once the preceding foundations have been established, many aspects of the perception of colors become easier to describe, systematize, and understand.

Each point in the trichromat's action space is a representation of the effects of some light, or mixture of lights, on his three color systems. Imagine the following simple procedure. We present various mixtures of wavelengths and intensities to a trichromat, mixtures represented by a broad sampling of points in the action space, and simply ask him to describe each mixture. (Each mixture is presented as a steadily illuminated patch on a dark background.) We can then map his descriptions onto the volume of action space and look for correspondences between his perceptions and the various combinations of actions on the three color systems. When this is done, the map displays certain regularities. The most obvious ones are: *1)* as the effects of a mixture move away from the origin, the stimulus is called "brighter," and *2)* all stimuli plotted along any straight line running through the origin are given the same hue name, e.g., orange, and stimuli not on the same line through the origin are given different names. Evidently, the hue name is somehow closely correlated with the *ratios* of excitations of the three systems and brightness is correlated with the strength of excitation. (Note that these statements are only approximately correct. A line that is the locus of all mixtures given the same hue name is generally not quite a straight line, and points equally far from the origin but at different places in action space are not necessarily called equally bright.)

From a phenomenological point of view, neither of these properties of the map is surprising. If an object is illuminated with a light of varying intensity, all wavelength components of the reflected light vary in proportion to the intensity of illumination and so the ratios among the intensities of the reflected wavelength components are constant, and the map simply says that, under these conditions, the hue of the object will stay the same and its brightness will vary. But when the statement is seen in the context of action space, one is led to wonder about the physiological mechanism that yields a constant response, e.g., "yellow," when all the inputs are varying but maintaining a constant set of ratios. No physiological mechanism that performs such an operation is obvious. [One plausible mechanism performs a transformation on each of the three quantum catches that is approximately logarithmic and then performs subtractions between the transformed outputs (14, 49).]

Now consider a line running through the origin and forming equal angles with all three axes in Figure 28, and then imagine a section through the trichromatic action space that is a plane perpendicular to that line. Such a plane is represented in Figure 29. The trian-

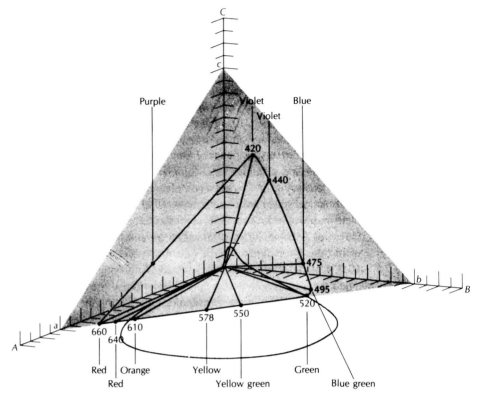

FIG. 29. A plane through trichromatic action space, showing the hue names of some of the stimuli it represents. The *slightly curved triangular line* in the *shaded plane* is the locus of the intersections of lights of all wavelengths with the plane. Therefore, it encloses a space representing the effects of all possible mixtures of wavelengths. [From Cornsweet (36).]

gularly shaped line in this plane can be called the spectral locus. It is the locus of the intersections in action space between this plane and the lines representing every wavelength in the visible spectrum. Stimuli whose actions can be plotted as points in this plane must lie within the spectral locus, and they will be called by various hue names, some of which are listed in Figure 29. To the extent that the lines of constant hue in action space are straight and run through the origin, all sections of action space that are parallel to this one can be represented by maps that differ only in magnification or scale factor, and therefore, to the extent that lines of constant hue are straight, the two-dimensional map in Figure 29 completely represents the relationships between the actions of lights on the color systems and the resulting hue names. In other words, because there are three subsystems, action space is three dimensional, but because hue names are correlated well with ratios of color system excitation, the space representing hue is only two dimensional, the dimension representing intensity being collapsed. (Similarly, to the extent that brightness is correlated with distance from the origin, the space representing brightness is one dimensional.)

If the angle of the plane in Figure 29 were changed, e.g., if the plane were made parallel to one containing two of the axes, the shape of the hue map would change correspondingly, but all the arguments above

would still apply. Furthermore, if the action space were plotted so that the three axes were not mutually perpendicular, the shape of the hue map would change, but its important properties would not. The familiar C.I.E. (Commission Internationale de l'Éclairage) diagram, extensively used to specify hues, is one of these linear transformations of a section through action space.

Now suppose that two lights of wavelengths 640 nm and 490 nm are mixed together. As the ratio of the intensities of the two components is varied, the vector in action space that represents their mixture will move in a plane defined and bounded by the 640-nm and 490-nm vectors as shown in Figure 30. To the extent that lines of constant hue are straight in action space, the hue names for all of the mixtures of 640 nm and 490 nm can be represented along a straight line in the two-dimensional hue map, the line of intersection between the plane defined by the 640-nm and 490-nm components and the arbitrarily chosen hue plane. This line, and the hue names associated with various points along it, are shown in Figure 31. If two different wavelengths are now mixed, for example 440 nm and 578 nm, there will be some ratio of their intensities for which the mixture is represented by a vector whose angle is coincident with a 640-nm + 490-nm mixture, and it is seen as the same hue, as represented by the point in Figure 31 where the two lines cross.

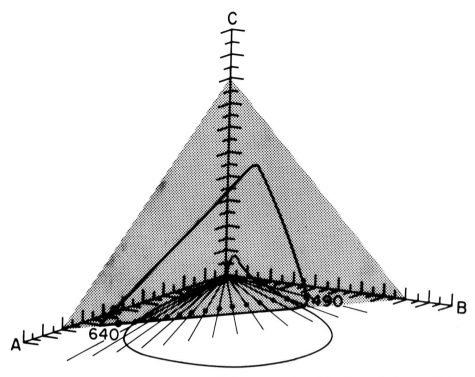

FIG. 30. A representation of the effects of mixtures of lights at 640 nm and 490 nm. As the relative intensities of the two components change, the effect of the mixtures move in a plane indicated by the *straight lines* emerging from the origin. The intersections of these lines with the *shaded plane* are indicated by *dots*, and form a straight line between the points representing 640 nm and 490 nm.

VISUAL ADAPTATION

Overview

As we pass from sunlight to shade or as we emerge from darkness to day, vision is at first difficult. But with time, our eyes adjust to the new surroundings. The adjustment of the visual system to changes in illumination is called visual adaptation. In this section we discuss the nature of this adjustment, this adaptation.

Three problems have dominated the psychophysical analysis of visual adaptation. The first problem—anatomical in nature—has been to identify the class of photoreceptors that mediates detection of lights at threshold. The second—also anatomical—has been to identify the class of photoreceptors that controls the observer's sensitivity to threshold lights. These two problems are distinct, for even though an observer may detect a signal originating in a single class of photoreceptors, sensitivity to that signal may be influenced by the adapted state of other photoreceptor classes via lateral and proximal interactions. The third problem is to model the physical and physiological mechanisms of visual adaptation. The analysis of the mechanism of adaptation stands as a central open problem in visual science. The history of the analysis is rich, and we devote more than half of our discussion to this problem.

A complete review of the research devoted to these three problems requires far more space than we can

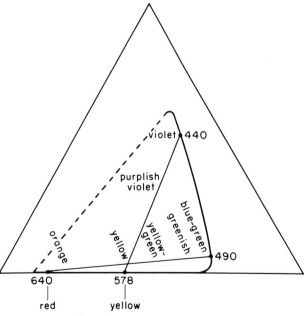

FIG. 31. The hue names of mixtures of 490-nm and 640-nm light change as the ratio of the intensities of the two components change, as indicated along the *line* between 640 nm and 490 nm. There is a particular mixture of 440-nm and 578-nm lights that will produce an identical hue, as indicated where the two straight lines cross.

allot. We limit our discussion to research conducted under scotopic viewing conditions, that is, conditions where detection depends upon a rod-initiated signal.

The organization of this section is as follows. In the next section we briefly describe the basic, experimental paradigms of psychophysical adaptation, i.e., the increment-threshold and dark-adaptation experiments. In *Identifying Neural Substrates,* this page, we review the major findings concerning the identification of the neural substrates that influence detection of weak test lights.

In *Single-Variable Theories,* p. 296, we turn to a discussion of the mechanisms of adaptation. In particular, we review the status of the hypothesis that the state of adaptation in a small region of the retina may be characterized by a single real number. Many classic theories of adaptation (e.g., refs. 9, 64, 111, 121, 130) have incorporated this assumption. Its rejection, which is likely though not yet certain, is largely responsible for the current interest in multiple channel theories of adaptation (see ref. 90).

Experimental Paradigms

Consider the following experiment: An observer centers his gaze on a large (say, 10°), uniformly illuminated field of light, called the conditioning field. The observer's threshold to a small, brief, test flash is measured. The conditioning field may be presented steadily, and the observer allowed to fully adapt, before threshold is measured. This is the equilibrium case. The experiment is then called a *light-adaptation* or *increment-threshold* experiment.

The classic increment-threshold data collected by Aguilar and Stiles (1a) under scotopic viewing conditions is shown in Figure 32. As can be seen in the figure, threshold rises as the intensity of the conditioning field rises. Threshold intensity is proportional to conditioning-field intensity over a sizable range. This part of the increment-threshold curve is generally referred to as the Weber's law region.

When the conditioning field is made to vary over time, the observer's adapted state also varies. Threshold may then be measured relative to the changing conditioning field. This is the dynamic case. A most important dynamic experiment is the measurement of threshold following the offset of a previously steady conditioning field. The experiment is then called a *dark-adaptation* or *recovery* experiment. Examples of dark-adaptation curves are shown in Figure 33.

In both the light- and dark-adaptation experiments, the conditioning field establishes the ambient illumination at the observer's eye, i.e., the action of the conditioning field—its adapting effect—is the object of study. The test light is used to probe the effect of the conditioning light upon the observer's eye; i.e., the test serves as a measuring device, and it is assumed to be too weak to disturb the state of adaptation established by the conditioning field.

Identifying Neural Substrates

Earlier in *Overview,* p. 293, we outlined three basic problems that must be solved before an adequate

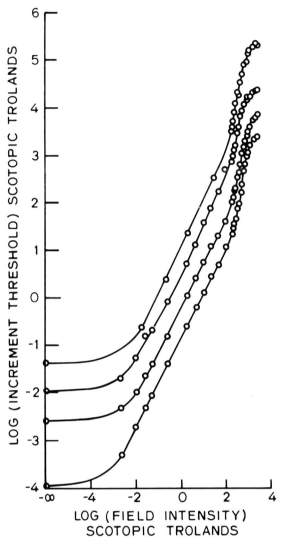

FIG. 32. Increment-threshold curves for rod-initiated detection. Test stimulus, 9° diam, 0.2 s, centered 9° from fovea. Conditioning field, 20° diam, exposed steadily. Means from four observers are shown. *Lowest curve* correctly placed with respect to both axes. Other curves displaced upwards by 0.5, 1.0, and 1.5 log units, respectively. [From Aguilar and Stiles (1a).]

understanding of scotopic adaptation may be claimed. First, the psychophysical parameters that cause detection to be mediated by a rod-initiated signal must be specified. Knowledge of these parameters can enable us to assert that the scotopic pathway has been well and truly isolated. Second, the class, or classes, of photoreceptor signals that govern the state of adaptation of the scotopic pathway must be identified, because, although detection may be initiated by rods alone, adaptation may depend on both rods and cones. Finally, the mechanisms of adaptation that determine the pathway's sensitivity must be described. The strongest proposal in this regard is the hypothesis that different states of adaptation may be described by the value of a single variable.

It is important to realize that the resolution of the last problem is logically independent of the other two.

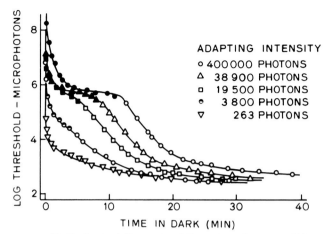

FIG. 33. Dark-adaptation curves follow adaptation to conditioning fields of various intensities. *Filled symbols* indicate thresholds where the test flash had a colored appearance [From Hecht et al. (65).]

To see why this is so, consider the following: If one rejects the hypothesis that sensitivity depends on the quantum catch of a single class of photoreceptors, one can still maintain that a single variable, computed from the quantum catch of all photoreceptors at a proximal level, governs sensitivity (69, 70). Conversely, if one accepts the hypothesis that sensitivity depends on the quantum catch of a single class of photoreceptors, the possibility remains that the state of adaptation in a small region of the retina cannot be characterized by a single real number. An important model that incorporates this feature is a version of the multiple channels model proposed by Campbell and Robson [(34); see also ref. 54]. The model assumes that any region of the retina contains many spatially overlapping, nonidentical channels, each receiving input from only one type of photoreceptor. If the channels adapt independently, sensitivity to a test flash would depend on both *1*) the receptor quantum catch and *2*) the identity of the detecting channel. Thus, no single-variable theory would suffice to describe the state of adaptation, despite the dependence of adaptation on only a single class of photoreceptors.

Because of the logical independence of these issues, we treat them in different sections. We turn now to the identification of neural substrates.

DETECTION BY RODS. Three fundamental psychophysical techniques exist for distinguishing rod-initiated detection from cone-initiated detection.

One method is to measure the observer's sensitivity to different wavelengths of a test light. Since the rods all contain a single pigment, rhodopsin, the wavelength sensitivity to test lights must be equal to the spectral sensitivity of this pigment (corrected for the stable preretinal filters of the eye).

A second method is to measure the change in the observer's threshold as the angle of incidence of the test light is varied. Stiles and Crawford (122) were the first to demonstrate that cone photoreceptors are se-

lectively sensitive to the angle of incidence of light, being maximally sensitive to light passing through the center of the pupil and progressively less sensitive as the bundle of rays pass closer to the pupil's edge. The directional sensitivity of the cones is called the Stiles-Crawford effect of the first kind (39). Rods, however, show no such directional sensitivity (i.e., for angles of incidence within the physical limits imposed by the pupil, but see ref. 48). Therefore, the presence or absence of directional sensitivity is diagnostic of detection based upon a cone- versus rod-initiated signal.

A third method is to use very weak test lights in the periphery of the eye where rods are dense and cones are sparse. Figure 33 shows an example of the way in which threshold declines in the periphery following adaptation to various conditioning fields. The two branches of the recovery curve following the intense conditioning fields have markedly different properties with respect to test-spectral sensitivity and test-directional sensitivity. The upper branch shows directional sensitivity and a spectral sensitivity quite different from rhodopsin. The lower branch shows no directional sensitivity, and test-spectral sensitivity is that of rhodopsin (appropriately corrected). For these and other reasons (see ref. 2) the upper branch is thought to be detection by cones and the lower branch detection by rods. If rod signals do not affect the sensitivity of cone-initiated pathways, the plateau of the recovery curve represents the absolute threshold of cone photoreceptors to the test light. By using a test light below the intensity level of the plateau one renders the test light invisible to cones and thereby forces detection by rods.

Use of these techniques has led to the discovery of other properties that generally, but not reliably, distinguish rod-initiated from cone-initiated detection. For example, scotopic spatial and temporal pooling is generally greater than photopic pooling (8). While these observations are of considerable interest, they are not diagnostic of rod-initiated detection, since under some adapting conditions the spatial and temporal pooling of the scotopic and photopic detection are similar. We refer the reader to Alpern (2) and Barlow (10) for a more complete review of the differences between rod-mediated and cone-mediated detection.

ADAPTATION BY RODS. A strong simplifying hypothesis for scotopic adaptation is the proposal that the quantum catch of only rods governs the state of adaptation. We call this the rod-independence hypothesis. An early and influential study by Flamant and Stiles (48) tested this hypothesis in two ways. Using a large (10°) conditioning field and a square 1° test flash, Flamant and Stiles (48) measured *1*) the action spectrum of the conditioning field for a 1 log-unit elevation of test threshold and *2*) the effect on threshold of varying the angle of incidence of the conditioning field.

The predictions of the rod-independence hypothesis are as follows. First, the action spectrum of the conditioning field must be that of rhodopsin (corrected for preretinal filters). (A methodologically superior test—used by Flamant and Stiles (48)—is to compare the action spectrum of the conditioning field with the absolute spectral sensitivity of the observer's eye for rod-initiated detection. This comparison is preferred because it obviates problems that may arise due to individual differences in preretinal absorptions.) Second, the effect of the conditioning field must be independent of the angle of incidence of the bundle of rays of the field. This follows from the rod-independence hypothesis because if *1*) adaptation is due to a signal mediated by rods, and *2*) rods show no directional sensitivity, then changes in the angle of incidence of the conditioning field should not affect threshold. Flamant and Stiles's (48) data were consistent with both of these predictions, and they concluded that under their testing conditionings scotopic adaptation was controlled by the quantum catch of the rod photoreceptors, i.e., scotopic sensitivity was independent of cones, and the rod-independence hypothesis could not be rejected.

One limitation of the validity of the rod-independence hypothesis has been reported by Makous and Boothe (92) and Makous and Peeples (93). Using stimulus conditions nearly identical to those of Flamant and Stiles (48)—most importantly a large, 10° background—Makous and Boothe (92) observed differences in the action spectrum of the conditioning field measured at high- and low-criterion levels. When the conditioning field elevated the test threshold about a log unit, or less, they confirmed Flamant and Stiles's findings of an action spectrum that coincided with test sensitivity at absolute threshold. For higher conditioning field intensities, however, which raised threshold about one-and-a-half to two log units, the action spectrum for the conditioning field deviated from test sensitivity at absolute threshold. Moreover, at high field intensities the conditioning field showed a directional sensitivity effect, a finding that was again inconsistent with the rod-independent hypothesis.

Other studies of adaptation have also shown that the independence of the scotopic pathway from the influence of cones obtains only within a limited range of experimental conditions. For example, Lennie and MacLeod (86), Blick and MacLeod (24), Frumkes and Temme (49), and Latch and Lennie (83) measured sensitivity to scotopic test lights using conditioning fields of various diameters. They found that when field diameters are large, as in the Flamant and Stiles (48) experiments, the rod-independence hypothesis cannot be rejected. For small-diameter conditioning fields, however, the action spectrum of the conditioning field differs significantly from the action spectrum for detection under rod-isolation conditions at absolute threshold. This is true even for relatively low intensity conditioning fields. This difference in spectral shape is attributed to the effect of cone photoreceptor signals on the rod-initiated detection pathway.

Lennie and MacLeod (86, 90) suggest a hypothesis to account for these findings. They point out that, in general, the sensitivity measured by a test stimulus falling on one part of the retina will depend on the conditioning-field intensity at retinal locations other than the test region (e.g., ref. 113). Therefore, the pathway that determines psychophysical sensitivity must include neural elements whose sensitivity depends, in part, on spatial pooling across the retina. The distances over which this pooling occurs are quite large, which suggests that a pooling process more extensive than simple receptor coupling is involved.

Lennie and MacLeod (86, 90) thus argue that postreceptor neural adaptation plays a role in determining psychophysical sensitivity. For postreceptor elements, large uniform fields are quite ineffective stimuli. Thus, any part played by postreceptor adaptation should be small when a large, uniform conditioning field is used. As the conditioning-field diameter is reduced toward the size of the test spot, the conditioning stimulus becomes potent for the same class of proximal neurons that are most sensitive to the test spot because of their receptive-field size. Therefore, small conditioning fields should cause relatively more adaptation than large conditioning fields at the proximal neurons that mediate detection of the test spot. Since proximal neurons receive signals from more than a single class of receptors (e.g., refs. 46, 56), sensitivity depends on more than a single class of receptors. Thus, the rod-independence hypothesis is rejected for small conditioning fields, but not necessarily for large fields.

SUMMARY. The isolation of rod-initiated detection pathways has met with considerable success. Identification of such pathways may be made from measurements of test-spectral sensitivity, test-directional sensitivity, and test-intensity levels below the cone plateau of the recovery curve.

The identification of the photoreceptor classes that control the sensitivity of rod-initiated detection pathways has proved subtle. Under certain viewing conditions (e.g., those of Flamant and Stiles, ref. 48) the hypothesis that adaptation is governed by the rod quantum catch alone has not been rejected. Variation, however, in the spatial properties of the backgrounds, or measurements with conditioning fields above one scotopic troland have led to the rejection of the hypothesis. Thus we draw the inference that cone photoreceptors may influence the sensitivity of rod-initiated detection pathways.

Single-Variable Theories

EQUIVALENT-BACKGROUND PRINCIPLE. Stiles and Crawford (121) made the following important argument in 1933. Suppose that the state of adaptation in a small patch of the retina, under steady-state adaptation to conditioning field, μ_1, may be described by a mechanism whose sensitivity is completely characterized by a single, real number. This number might represent the concentration of a chemical substance, or the number of sites available at a membrane. Threshold at this patch of the retina may be measured with a test probe, λ. The threshold value is a single, real number. If we assume that the threshold of λ is monotonically related to the real number which characterizes the state of adaptation caused by μ_1, then we may take the threshold of λ as a measure of the state of adaptation. Further, should it be the case that λ has the same threshold on conditioning field, μ_2, as on conditioning field, μ_1, we would conclude that the state of adaptation due to μ_2 was the same as that due to μ_1, i.e., μ_2 and μ_1 are equivalent backgrounds, as measured by λ.

Now, if the adapted state of this patch of retina is equivalent under μ_1 and μ_2 adaptation, then threshold to a second test, λ', must also be identical when measured on μ_1 and μ_2. If these thresholds were not identical, we would have to conclude that μ_1 and μ_2 had different adapting effects in contradiction to the measurements with λ. We call the predicted equivalence of these backgrounds (for all test flashes) the *equivalent-background* principle.

Should empirical conditions exist where μ_1 and μ_2 are equivalent with respect to a first test, λ, but not with respect to a second test, λ', we would have to reevaluate some part of our hypothesis. One difficulty may be that λ and λ' are measuring the state of adaptation of different physiological pathways, although the state of each pathway can be well described by a single variable. Alternatively, λ and λ' may be detected by the same anatomical pathway, but the single-variable hypothesis is false; that is, the state of adaptation may require more than one variable in order to be completely described.

TESTS OF EQUIVALENT-BACKGROUND PRINCIPLE. With these arguments in mind, Stiles and Crawford (121) carried out an experimental test of single-variable theories of light adaptation. They used three kinds of conditioning fields: *1*) a glare source (point of light) 6° above the observer's fixation, *2*) an annulus with inner diameter of 1° and outer diameter extending over the whole visual field, and *3*) a uniform field, also extending over the entire visual field. For each of these conditioning fields, Stiles and Crawford (121) determined the intensity required to elevate six test lights of various spatial, temporal, and spectral parameters to an equal level. This was done with both foveal and parafoveal presentation of the stimuli, and for two intensity levels of the test light.

There were measurable deviations from the equivalent-background principle of the single-variable hypothesis. The data are somewhat problematic, however, because Stiles and Crawford (121) made no attempt to isolate different visual mechanisms in their measurements. Thus failures of the equivalent-background principle of single-variable theories could have been due to either differences in the pathways being probed, or a failure of the single-variable hypothesis.

Crawford (38) later returned to the equivalent-background principle. He tested the single-variable hypothesis using experimental conditions different from those reported by Stiles and Crawford (121). Specifically, Crawford (38) extended the equivalent-background measurement to include the dynamic case.

The logic of Crawford's (38) extension, also described in Stiles and Crawford's (121) 1933 paper, is as follows. For a test, λ, threshold is measured at various intensities of a conditioning field, μ_1. Threshold recovery is then measured following adaptation to a bright conditioning field, μ_2, using this same test, λ. For each intensity of μ_1, a time during recovery from μ_2 is found such that λ threshold at that intensity of μ_1 and at that time of recovery from μ_2 were equal. This generated a set of equivalences. Each intensity of μ_1 is equivalent to some time during recovery from μ_2. On a single-variable theory, when adaptation is measured with a different test, λ', the various intensities of μ_1 must remain equivalent to the same set of times during recovery.

Crawford (121) performed such measurements with six test stimuli. His results did not reject the equivalent-background prediction. Thus, the single-variable hypothesis was consistent for equivalences between light and dark adaptation but inconsistent for the equivalences between different spatial distributions of steady-state conditioning fields (121).

Again, however, Crawford's (121) data are problematic. One problem is that fixation was not carefully controlled. (His data were taken for applied reasons during World War II.) A second problem is that the separation between rod- and cone-initiated detection is not at all clear from his measurements. Hence it is difficult to know which physiological mechanisms are being investigated.

Because of the general importance of single-variable theories, the problem was again studied by Blakemore and Rushton (22). The subject in their experiments was a rod monochromat, so the problem of isolating a rod-initiated detection pathway was solved by nature. The equivalent-background principle, derived from single-variable theories, was tested following Crawford's method of comparing increment thresholds and dark-adaptation curves. In Figure 34 we have replotted Blakemore and Rushton's (22) measurements. On the right are two increment-threshold curves, for test lights of 5' and 360' upon a 3,600'-diameter conditioning field. On the left-hand side are two recovery curves for these same test lights. The conditioning field was again the large, 3,600' field, at an intensity that Blakemore and Rushton (22) estimated to bleach "about half" of the rhodopsin in the rods.

These recovery curves illustrate an important observation emphasized by earlier writers including Craik and Vernon (37), Lythgoe (88), and Arden and Weale (6). Notice that the vertical separation between the recovery curves for the small and large test flashes grows as recovery proceeds. The increasing separation indicates that the eye is better able to integrate rod signals across the retinal surface as recovery proceeds. This increase in spatial integration is accompanied by a decrease in spatial acuity (22, 30). These observations are difficult to reconcile with any theory that supposes the photopigment concentration as the direct mechanism that limits sensitivity. Rather, some sort of neural changes appear to be involved (37, 88).

As Rushton, Barlow, and their collaborators (7, 9, 10, 110, 111, 113) point out, however, it remains possible that the nonphotochemical mechanisms are controlled by a signal whose value is determined exclusively by the photopigment concentration. Thus, while postreceptor mechanisms may be involved in the process of adaptation, they may all be driven by a single common variable. In such a circumstance, the equivalent-background experiment still measures equivalences in rhodopsin concentration (a one-dimensional variable) and thus the equivalent-background principle should still obtain.

The dotted lines in Figure 34 illustrate the test of the equivalent-background principle for these increment-threshold and recovery curves. For the 5′-flash threshold, 15 min into recovery was equal to threshold with a steady conditioning field at approximately 4 scotopic trolands. Thus the equivalent-background principle asserts that 15 min into recovery and a 4 scotopic-trolands background should generate an equal threshold for any other test. Blakemore and Rushton (22) tested this prediction for the 360′-test flash shown in the figure. The agreement here, as well as for other time and intensities, is very good.

On the basis of these (and other) observations, Rushton (111) concluded that the single-variable hypothesis could not be rejected. Using the letter G (gain) as the variable defining adaptation, he wrote:

> ... what Crawford did was to change G by bleaching [dark adaptation] and by backgrounds [increment thresholds] and to compare the organization of the G-box in the

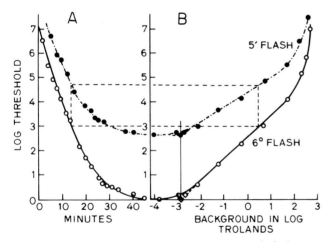

FIG. 34. *Panel A*: recovery curves for 5′ (*top*) and 6° (*bottom*) test lights following offset of 3,600′ conditioning field. *Panel B*: increment-threshold curves for the same test lights superimposed on a 3,600′ steady-background field. [From Blakemore and Rushton (22).]

two cases using different types of test ΔI. He found that when the G settings matched by one test they matched by all. Intensity and spatial integration were not independent variables that needed separate matching adjustments. All the factors that G controls are the function of a single variable (one knob).

A SPECIFIC SINGLE-VARIABLE THEORY: THE NOISE HYPOTHESIS. An important, single-variable hypothesis was studied by Barlow (7, 9). Following the suggestion of Rose (107) and de Vries (44), Barlow tested the hypothesis that threshold elevation on intense conditioning fields is due to noise in the receptor signals. According to this view, the single-variable controlling psychophysical sensitivity is the level of receptor noise. In the light-adaptation experiment the inevitable quantal fluctuations of the bleaching process generate the noise. In the dark the time-varying free opsin produced by photopigment bleaching generates the receptor noise.

In addition to tests that apply to all single-variable theories of adaptation, the receptor-noise hypothesis, together with the assumption of optimal signal-to-noise discrimination, leads to the prediction that threshold will rise as the square root of the conditioning-field intensity. This prediction is generally contradicted when long-duration, large-area test spots are used (e.g., see refs. 1a, 8). Increment-threshold curves for small, brief tests follow a different increment-threshold curve from long, large tests. The slope of this curve grows more slowly. Thus increment thresholds for small, brief stimuli can be tolerably well fit over a somewhat greater range by a curve obeying the square-root relationship than can increment-threshold curves for large, long-duration test stimuli. This has led some authors to suggest that the theory may be correct for a restricted range of test stimuli (e.g., ref. 108).

The receptor-noise hypothesis, however, as an explanatory principle is only of restricted value. For, as Stiles wrote (120):

> The reason why a uniform field raises the increment threshold is now often discussed in relation to the inevitable fluctuations in the number of light quanta from the field that are absorbed by the individual receptors, or strictly by completely summating groups of receptors. The test stimulus intensity must somewhat exceed these fluctuations, if it is to be detected. This is certainly true. But since we do not in fact see the fluctuations as such we must also suppose that somewhere in the neural chain a barrier is raised high enough to prevent the fluctuations passing into consciousness. The raising of this barrier corresponds to an increase [*sic*: decrease is meant] in the effective sensitivity of the receptors of summating receptor groups. It would seem that this is the true adaptational change. The fluctuations theory merely places a lower limit on the height of the barrier: its nature remains to be explained.

RELATED STUDIES. Further work on the problem of equivalent backgrounds was reported by Barlow and Sparrock (14) and Westheimer (139).

Barlow and Sparrock (14), working from Barlow's receptor-noise hypothesis, asked why the noise signal during dark adaptation did not appear as bright as the equivalent-background noise signal in the light-adaptation experiment. They tested the hypothesis that the brightness difference between the afterimage (7°) and real-light (28°) background that raised threshold by equal amounts was due to the stabilization of the afterimage. They measured the apparent brightness of the afterimage by matching its appearance with a stabilized annulus. The intensity of the stabilized annulus that matched the afterimage in brightness was equal to the intensity of the real-light background that raised the test threshold by the same amount as the afterimage. This provided further support for a single-variable theory but not particularly for the receptor-noise hypothesis.

Westheimer (139) examined the following important point. Suppose we perform an equivalent-background experiment with conditioning field, μ_1, and bleaching field, μ_2, that have the same spatial distribution on the retinal surface. This permits identification of intensities of μ_1 as being equivalent to times during recovery from μ_2.

Now suppose we vary the spatial distribution of μ_1 and μ_2 to a new, but common, spatial distribution using the same test light. The question posed by Westheimer (139) is: Will the set of equivalences of intensities and times—as measured with the same test λ—remain unchanged as the spatial distribution of the background is varied? The answer is no. Rather, varying the spatial distribution of the conditioning fields generates a new set of equivalences.

These observations are not inconsistent with the single-variable hypothesis. But what must be true on the single-variable hypothesis—and is so far untested—is that these new equivalences are preserved as the test flash parameters are varied. The general issue of equivalence and some potential problems in the experimental methodology of Westheimer's work is reviewed by Barlow and Sakitt [(13); see also ref. 123].

A CONSTRAINT ON SINGLE-VARIABLE THEORIES: THRESHOLD RECOVERY. Historically, the most important hypothesis to account for threshold recovery following adaptation to a conditioning field has been the effort to equate the state of adaptation with the concentration of visual pigment, rhodopsin, in the observer's rod outer segments. For a general chemical light-driven reaction, we may write that the change in concentration, s, over time, t, depends on the light intensity, I, via

$$\frac{ds}{dt} = -I\phi_1(s, x_1, x_2, \ldots, x_n) + \phi_2(s, x_1, x_2, \ldots, x_n)$$

where the x_i (i.e., $x_1, x_2, \ldots, x_n$) are variables that affect the reaction. We now know from Rushton's (109) and Weale's (134–136) studies of the bleaching of human rhodopsin in situ that pigment kinetics obey first-order equations quite well. Thus

$$\frac{ds}{dt} = -I\phi_1(s) + \phi_2(s)$$

Consider the hypothesis that sensitivity depends monotonically only on the instantaneous pigment concentration in the observer's eye, s. Following equilibrium bleaching by a conditioning field, s will vary as

$$\int_{s_0}^{s} \frac{ds}{\phi_2(s)} = t - t_0$$

Letting F be the (monotonic) indefinite integral of ϕ_2, it follows that

$$s = F\sum{}^1[t - (t_0 - F(s_0))] \qquad (1)$$

Thus, this hypothesis and first-order kinetics of bleaching lead to the conclusion that all recovery curves following the offset of a conditioning field must follow the same time course, up to displacement with respect to the time axis by an amount $t_0 - F(s_0)$ (Eq. 1).

This argument was noted by Winsor and Clark (143) as well as Lythgoe (88), Crawford (38), and Stiles (120). Figure 35 replots Winsor and Clark's (143) measurements of scotopic recovery to a 1.3°, 20-ms test following adaptation to three levels of a large conditioning field. Clearly, no sliding of these curves along the time axis will bring their rod branches into coincidence.

Furthermore, recall that Figure 33 replots the results of Hecht et al. (65). Again, it can be seen that no horizontal displacement of these curves will bring the rod branches into coincidence.

Finally, we note that Pugh (100, 101), in a recent study of rod dark adaptation and rhodopsin regeneration in situ has shown that rod dark-adaptation curves, following adaptation to different intensity conditioning lights, follow different time courses. In Figures 36A and 36B we replot Pugh's data showing the relationship between the time constant of the best-

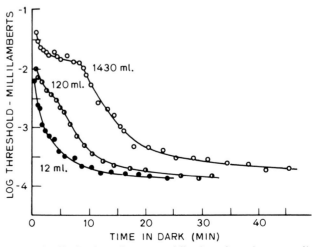

FIG. 35. Dark-adaptation curves following adaptation to conditioning fields of various intensities. [From Winsor and Clark (143).]

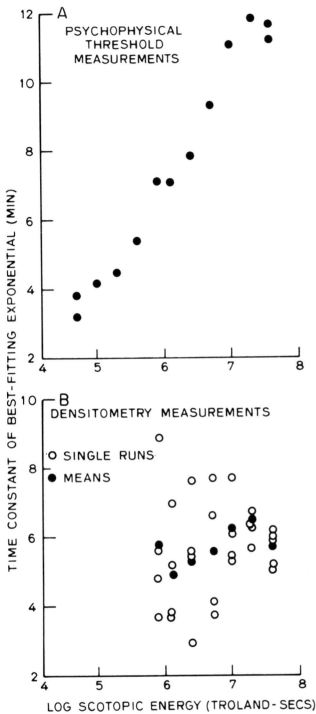

FIG. 36. Time constant of best-fitting exponential curve to *A*: psychophysical threshold recovery during dark adaptation, and *B*: rhodopsin regeneration in the living human eye. Both are plotted as a function of energy in the conditioning field. *Open symbols* in *B* are individual runs, *filled symbols* are the arithmetic means of individual runs. [Data from Pugh (100, 101).]

fitting exponential curve to threshold recovery (Fig. 36*A*) and rhodopsin regeneration (Fig. 36*B*) as a function of conditioning-field energy. Notice that the time course of rhodopsin regeneration is approximately constant, independent of bleaching energy. Threshold

recovery, however, proceeds more slowly following more intense bleaches.

Winsor and Clark (143) concluded from the failure of their prediction of a single shaped curve that either *1*) first-order kinetics equations were false, or *2*) sensitivity depended on variables other than the fraction of bleached pigment. Since no objective measurements of rhodopsin kinetics were then available, and Wald's (128, 129) work had led them to believe that rhodopsin kinetics would not be first order, Winsor and Clark (143) argued that *1*) and not *2*) should be rejected.

Twenty years after Winsor and Clark's (143) experiments, Rushton (109) and Weale (134) accomplished the difficult feat of measuring human rhodopsin in situ. From their measurements it became clear that rhodopsin density did follow first-order pigment kinetics following equilibrium adaptation. Thus, since *1*) is true within measurement error, it follows that *2*), the dependence of threshold solely upon rhodopsin concentration, must be rejected.

Notice that the objectionable aspect of the hypothesis is the identification of bleached rhodopsin as the controlling factor. The results do not allow us to reject all single-variable theories. However, Winsor and Clark's (143) arguments demand that if sensitivity depends on a single substance, that substance cannot obey first-order pigment kinetics. It is possible, however, that there exists a controlling substance, *S*, and that its concentration (*s*) depends on at least two variables. In such a case, the time course of recovery for this substance would have the functional form

$$s = H[\psi_1(t), \psi_2(t)]$$

where ψ_1 and ψ_2 are the two variables on which the concentration, *s*, depends. This single-variable theory—where the controlling variable's recovery depends on two variables—is the simplest form to which we must advance.

SUMMARY. The time course of dark adaptation, at one time thought to be identified with rhodopsin concentration, depends on more than a single variable. If a single substance is found whose concentration is perfectly correlated with the sensitivity of rod-initiated pathways, that material's concentration must depend on the effect of at least two variables (120, 143). We use the term *substance* broadly to include variables such as membrane sites.

Concluding Comment

The single-variable hypothesis tested by the equivalent background postulated the existence of some unnamed substance, or site, whose value completely characterizes the state of adaptation. The classic view of adaptation as a process controlled by the concentration of photopigment—whether Hecht's (64) photochemical depletion, Wald's (130) compartments, Rushton's (111) gain-box, or Barlow's (9) dark noise—is currently being questioned. A search for new substrates and mechanisms must follow. The advantage of testing the equivalent-background principle is that its failure would signify the failure of all single-variable theories. Hence, no single substance or site could suffice to describe the state of adaptation. If the equivalent-background principle were accepted over a wide range of experimental conditions, however, the hope of identifying a single controlling substance would increase.

NOTE ADDED IN PROOF

Since this chapter was completed, new developments have suggested answers to both of the psychophysical puzzles mentioned in *Concluding Comment*, p. 300. Publishing logistics forbid a thorough discussion of these developments—the reader is referred instead to the references at the end of this note. However, the highlights can be briefly outlined.

First, it now appears that the nearly unanimous failure to detect foveal interference fringes above 60 cycles/deg has been a matter of psychophysical methodology rather than retinal physiology. Using a refined interferometer, D. R. Williams (personal communication) has recently shown that spatial frequencies at least as high as 130 cycles/deg can definitely be detected in the foveola. The appearance of gratings at these very high frequencies seems entirely consistent with aliasing by the cones, whose inner segments in the foveola approximate a spatially regular hexagonal lattice. [Fig. 18 in this chapter shows an array of foveal outer segments. Miller and Bernard (3A) have recently presented a convincing optical argument that the image-sampling properties of photoreceptors should be analyzed on the assumption that the effective aperture of the receptors is located midway along their inner segments. Miller (2A) and Borwein et al. (1A) have shown that in the rod-free central fovea the spatial arrangement of the inner segments is much more regular than that of the outer segments. Thus our Fig. 18 suggests more spatial disorder than is apparently present in the effective foveal image sampling array.]

Second, it now appears that aliasing outside the fovea in normal vision is forestalled by spatial disorder in the photoreceptor array. Nagel (4A) pointed out that the consequences of image sampling by a spatially irregular array, such as the extrafoveal cones, are determined by the Fourier power spectrum of the array. Mathematically, the key fact is that the power spectrum of any image after sampling by a random array is its original power spectrum convolved with that of the sampling array. Subsequently Yellott (5A) computed the power spectra of sections of rhesus cones ranging across the entire retina. These spectra reveal that throughout the extrafoveal retina the cones provide a form of optimal random sampling—spatial frequencies above the aliasing cutoff implied by local cone density are not aliased back to discrete lower frequencies as would happen with spatially regular sampling arrays, but instead they are scattered into broadband spatial noise at all orientations. On the other hand, spatial frequencies below the nominal aliasing cutoff (which could have been recovered with no distortion by the same number of cones arranged in a regular lattice according to the classical sampling theorem) are transmitted with minimal noise. These twin goals are accomplished by a spatial arrangement based on constrained random placement [Yellott (6A)].

Overall, it now appears that in normal photopic vision aliasing is prevented in the fovea by the optics of the eye, which bandlimit the retinal image to 60 cycles/deg, and outside the fovea by an optimal spatial disorder in the cone mosaic.

1A. BORWEIN, B., D. BORWEIN, J. MEDEIROS, AND J. W. McGOWAN. The ultrastructure of monkey foveal photoreceptors, with special reference to the structure, shape, size, and spacing of the foveal cones. *Am. J. Anat.* 159: 125–146, 1980.

2A. MILLER, W. H. Intraocular filters. In: *Handbook of Sensory Physiology. Invertebrate Photoreceptors*, edited by H. Autrum. Berlin: Springer-Verlag, 1979, vol. 7, pt. 6A.

3A. MILLER, W. H., AND G. D. BERNARD. Averaging over the foveal receptor aperture curtails aliasing. *Vision Res.* In press, 1983.

4A. NAGEL, D. C. Spatial sampling in the retina. *Invest. Ophthalmol.* 20, Suppl. 3: 123, 1981.

5A. YELLOTT, J. I., JR. Spectral consequences of photoreceptor sampling in the rhesus retina. *Science* 221: 382–385, 1983.

6A. YELLOTT, J. I., JR. Nonhomogeneous Poisson disks model the photoreceptor mosaic. *Invest. Ophthalmol.* 24, Suppl. 3: 145, 1983.

NOTE: The complete list of references for this chapter and its *Appendix* starts on p. 313.

Appendix: Fourier transforms and shift-invariant linear operators

CONTENTS

THIS APPENDIX OUTLINES the basic mathematical ideas underlying the kind of Fourier analytic treatment of retinal imagery given earlier in VISUAL ACUITY, p. 260. Broadly speaking the idea is that inputs to the eye can be thought of as functions [i.e., $f(x,y)$ represents the light intensity in the object scene at spatial point (x,y)]; associated with each input f is an equivalent function, t_f (the *Fourier transform* of f), which describes f as a weighted sum of sinusoidal components. The effect of passing any input through the optics of the eye is then represented by an operator, $\bigcirc$, that transforms each input function, $f(x,y)$, into an output function, $\bigcirc[f(x,y)]$, corresponding to light intensity in the retinal image of f. If $\bigcirc$ satisfies two conditions (*linearity* and *shift-invariance*, both assumed to be approximately valid for the optics of the eye), its effect can be completely specified either by an associated function $o(x,y)$, called the *impulse response*, or by the Fourier transform of o, t_o, which is called the *transfer function* of $\bigcirc$. If either of these functions is known, the retinal image corresponding to any input (or equivalently, its Fourier transform) can be immediately written down. Consequently if one knows either the impulse response, $o(x,y)$, or the transfer function, t_o, of an eye, one can calculate the retinal image corresponding to any visual stimulus and thereby determine what information is actually available at the level of the photoreceptors.

The purpose of this section is to flesh out these ideas by sketching the basic mathematical steps explicitly. Fourier analytic notions have been very widely employed in physiological optics for some time, but we are not aware of any text devoted specifically to this application. Bracewell (27) is an excellent practical introduction to the transform generally, Goodman (51) and Hecht and Zajac (62) cover Fourier optics, and Lighthill (87) explains the mathematical justifi-

cation for the convenient operational calculus methods which have made the Fourier transform such a popular analytic tool.

ONE-DIMENSIONAL CASE

Although optical problems generally deal with functions of two variables, e.g., x and y, corresponding to the horizontal and vertical axes of an image plane, it is more convenient mathematically to begin with functions of a single variable. Suppose $f(x)$ is a real-valued function of a real variable x, for example, $f(x)$ might represent a light-intensity profile along the x axis of the retinal plane. The Fourier transform of f is another function, $t_f(s)$, given by the integral

$$t_f(s) = \int_{-\infty}^{\infty} e^{-i2\pi sx} f(x)\, \mathrm{d}x \qquad (A1)$$

where e is the constant 2.71828 ... and i is the imaginary unit $\sqrt{-1}$. In general $t_f(s)$ is a complex function of the real variable s: That fact can be made explicit by using the Euler relationship $e^{i\theta} = \cos\theta + i\sin\theta$ to rewrite Equation A1 in the form

$$t_f(s) = \int_{-\infty}^{\infty} f(x)\, \cos 2\pi sx\, \mathrm{d}x$$

$$- i \int_{-\infty}^{\infty} f(x)\, \sin 2\pi sx\, \mathrm{d}x \qquad (A2)$$

$$= \operatorname{Re} t_f(s) + i \operatorname{Im} t_f(s)$$

Here $\operatorname{Re} t_f(s)$ and $\operatorname{Im} t_f(s)$ are the real and imaginary parts of t_f; both are real functions of s. Recalling that any complex number $z = a + ib$ can be written in the form $z = |z|\, e^{i\,\mathrm{pha}(z)}$ [where $|z| = \sqrt{a^2 + b^2}$ and $\mathrm{pha}(z)$ is the angle through which a vector of length $|z|$ must be rotated to bring its tip into coincidence with the point (a,b)] Equation A2 can be rewritten in the form

$$t_f(s) = |t_f(s)|\, e^{i\,\mathrm{pha}\, t_f(s)} \qquad (A3)$$

Here $|t_f(s)|$ is a nonnegative real function of s, called the *amplitude spectrum* of f, and $\mathrm{pha}\, t_f(s)$ is another real function of s called the *phase spectrum* of f. The names are motivated by the roles these functions play when $f(x)$ is represented as a weighted sum of sinusoids, as we show next.

The fundamental theorem of Fourier analysis (*Fourier's inversion theorem*, e.g., ref. 87, p. 16) shows that a function f and its transform t_f contain exactly the same information, in the sense that if t_f is known, f can be recovered from the relationship

$$f(x) = \int_{-\infty}^{\infty} e^{i2\pi sx}\, t_f(s)\, \mathrm{d}s \qquad (A4)$$

If $t_f(s)$ is expressed in exponential form (i.e., Eq. A3), the inversion formula (Eq. A4) can be rewritten (after a little calculation) as

$$f(x) = \int_{-\infty}^{\infty} |t_f(s)| \cos[2\pi sx + \mathrm{pha}\, t_f(s)]\, \mathrm{d}s \qquad (A5)$$

This version shows explicitly that f can be expressed as a weighted sum of sinusoidal components: $|t_f(s)|$ $\cos[2\pi sx + \mathrm{pha}\, t_f(s)]$ is a cosine of amplitude $|t_f(s)|$ and a frequency of s cycles per unit of x. The phase term pha $t_f(s)$ means that this cosine is shifted to the left along the x axis by an amount equal to $(2\pi s)^{-1}$ pha $t_f(s)$. Consequently Equation A5 expresses the fact that the original function $f(x)$ can be thought of as a sum of cosines of various frequencies: For each frequency s, the amplitude spectrum $|t_f(s)|$ tells how much to weight the cosine term at that frequency, and pha $t_f(s)$ how much to shift it to make the entire sum (integral) equal f. [Actually, the amplitude of the cosine at frequency s is $2|t_f(s)|$ because the integral (Eq. A5) contains terms at $+s$ and $-s$; each represents the same cosine component and each has amplitude $|t_f(s)|$.] Notice that we cannot generally expect to recover a function from its amplitude spectrum alone; the phase spectrum also must be known.

Generalized Functions

It is apparent from the defining Equation A1 that many useful functions (such as the constant function $f(x) = 1$, cos x, etc.) do not actually have Fourier transforms because the necessary integration cannot be carried through. Nevertheless such functions can still be treated with Fourier analytic methods. The mathematical justification for this extension is provided by the theory of generalized functions (87), in which transforms of functions such as cos x are defined in terms of limits of sequences of transforms of functions which converge to cos x. The resulting entities are called transforms in the limit, and for most purposes can be formally manipulated in the same way as ordinary transforms, provided one exercises a little care. For example, the transform (in the limit) of cos $2\pi\phi x$ (a cosine of frequency ϕ cycles per unit of x) is a pair of impulses (Dirac delta functions) located at $s = \pm\phi$. These entities can be thought of as very tall, thin rectangular pulses—so thin that their horizontal spread can be treated as zero, even though the total area under the pulse is nonzero. [Bracewell (27) explains this concept in detail.]

Shift-Invariant Linear Operators and Convolution

Suppose $\bigcirc$ is an operator that transforms real functions into real functions; $\bigcirc$ can be thought of as a black box to which we input a function $f(x)$ and observe an output function $\bigcirc[f(x)]$. For example, if $f(x)$ is a light-intensity profile along the x axis of a visual stimulus, $\bigcirc[f(x)]$ might represent the intensity profile along the x axis in the retinal image. In this case the operator $\bigcirc$ represents the degradation of the image imposed by the optics of the eye. The symbol $\bigcirc$ is said to be a linear operator if the output corresponding to the sum of two input functions, f and g [i.e., we input $f(x) + g(x)$], is always the sum of the two outputs produced by f and g separately, i.e., $\bigcirc[f(x) + g(x)] = \bigcirc[f(x)] + \bigcirc[g(x)]$. The symbol $\bigcirc$ is said to be *shift invariant* if the output to $f(x + S)$ [i.e., $f(x)$ shifted bodily S units to the left] is the output to $f(x)$ shifted by the same amount S [i.e., if the output to $f(x)$ is $\bigcirc(x)$, then the output to $f(x + S)$ is $\bigcirc(x + S)$]. Many physically important operators are both shift invariant and linear (*SIL*), or at least satisfy both conditions closely enough for practical purposes.

The beauty of SIL operators depends on two theorems. First, if an operator is SIL it can always be represented as a *convolution*. If $\bigcirc$ is SIL, then there exists a function o such that for every input function f

$$\bigcirc[f(x)] = \int_{-\infty}^{\infty} f(x - r)o(r)\, \mathrm{d}r \qquad (A6)$$

i.e., the output to f is the convolution of f and o (denoted $f*o$). Intuitively this means that the output $\bigcirc[f(x)]$ at any point, x, is a weighted sum of the inputs at $x \pm r$, $0 \le r < \infty$, each input being weighted by a factor $o(r)$ that depends on the distance from x. Consequently the operator $\bigcirc$ is completely specified by its weighting function o. This function o is called the *impulse response* of $\bigcirc$ because when the input function is a single brief pulse of unit energy delivered at $x = 0$, the output function is exactly $o(x)$. (In optical applications, the one-dimensional impulse response is called the *linespread function*.)

The second important property of SIL operators arises from the fact that the Fourier transform of the convolution of two functions f and g is the product of the transforms of f and g alone, i.e.

$$t_{f*g}(s) = t_f(s)t_g(s)$$

Consequently from a transform standpoint the effect of applying an SIL operator $\bigcirc$ to any input f is simply to multiply the original transform t_f by the transform of the impulse response of $\bigcirc$, i.e.

$$t_{\bigcirc[f]}(s) = t_o(s)t_f(s) \qquad (A7)$$

This relationship in the transform domain enormously simplifies analysis of SIL operators, and by extension, the analysis of systems in which several such operators are applied sequentially (e.g., suppose an operator $\bigcirc_1$ is first applied to an input f, and then a second operator $\bigcirc_2$ is applied to the result, so that the final output of the system is $\bigcirc_2[\bigcirc_1[f(x)]]$. Then the Fourier transform of the output will be simply the product $t_f(s)(t_o)_1(s)(t_o)_2(s)$. It should be clear that an SIL operator $\bigcirc$ can be specified either in terms of its impulse response $o(x)$, or by the Fourier transform of $o, t_o(s)$. The latter function is called the *transfer function* of the operator. Using the fact that for any pair of complex numbers z_1, z_2 $|z_1 z_2| = |z_1||z_2|$, it follows immediately from Equation A7 that the amplitude spectrum of the output of an operator, $\bigcirc$, applied to an input, f, is the product of the amplitude spectra of the input and the impulse response, i.e.

$$|t_{\bigcirc[f]}(s)| = |t_f(s)||t_o(s)| \tag{A8}$$

The amplitude spectrum of o, i.e., $|t_o(s)|$, is called the *modulation transfer function (MTF)* of $\bigcirc$, because it specifies how the amplitude of sinusoidal modulation at each frequency in the input is altered by $\bigcirc$. If the input contains a sinusoidal component at a frequency, s, having an amplitude of A (i.e., $|t_f(s)| = A$) the output contains a sinusoidal component at frequency s having amplitude $A|t_o(s)|$. Thus if $t_o(s)$ is zero, the operator cannot transmit sinusoidal modulation at frequency s; that information is lost when f is passed through $\bigcirc$.

In general an SIL operator alters not only the amplitudes of the sinusoidal components of an input but also their phases. Writing the transform in Equation A7 in exponential form (using Eq. A3) we obtain

$$t_{\bigcirc[f]}(s) = |t_f(s)||t_o(s)|e^{i[\text{pha } t_f(s) + \text{pha } t_o(s)]} \tag{A9}$$

The interpretation of Equation A9 is that the cosinusoidal component in the input at frequency s reemerges in the output shifted to the left on the axis by an amount equal to $(2\pi s)^{-1}$ pha $t_o(s)$. Pha $t_o(s)$ can be regarded as the *phase transfer function*, analogous to MTF. If both $|t_o|$ and pha t_o are known, the operator $\bigcirc$ is completely specified, since the transfer function, $t_o(s)$, is $|t_o(s)|e^{i \text{ pha } t_o(s)}$.

EXAMPLES. Figure A1 illustrates the concepts just discussed, with special reference to the phenomenon of spurious resolution produced by defocusing (i.e., the effect demonstrated subjectively by Fig. 11). Across the figure each sequence of four panels represents successively a function, its Fourier transform (in all these cases the transform is entirely real and so can be graphed as a single function), the amplitude spectrum (which in these cases is just the absolute value of the transform graph next to it), and finally the phase spectrum. The impulse function $\delta(x)$, that is, in effect, a rectangle of unit area and zero width (i.e., the Dirac delta function mentioned earlier in this *Appen-*

dix) is represented by Sequence A. A function which provides a very good fit to the one-dimensional impulse response (i.e., the linespread function) of the human eye for a 2-min pupil as determined objectively by Campbell and Gubisch (33) is illustrated in Sequence B. The transform of this function is the transfer function of the eye. The profile of a cosine grating at 100% contrast is illustrated in Sequence C. The effect of convolving that input with the linespread function B is illustrated in Sequence D. Sequence E shows a rectangular window of width b and unit area. The convolution of this function with an input represents the effect of defocusing, i.e., the image of a point is spread over a "blur segment" (analogous to the two-dimensional blur circle) of width b. Finally, the combined effect of defocusing and line spread is illustrated in Sequence F. The transform here is the product of the transforms in Sequences B, C, and E. When the input cosine frequency ϕ falls between $1/b$ and $2/b$ the output cosine is reversed in sign so that hills in the input become valleys in the output and vice versa, as shown in the figure.

TWO-DIMENSIONAL CASE

Suppose now that f is a real-valued function of two real variables, e.g., $f(x,y)$ denotes light intensity at the spatial point (x,y). All of the Fourier analytic concepts from the one-dimensional case can readily be generalized to two (or more) dimensions. No new ideas are involved, though naturally the technical apparatus becomes somewhat more complicated. The two-dimensional Fourier transform of f is given by

$$t_f(u,v) = \int_{-\infty}^{\infty} \int_{-\infty}^{\infty} e^{-i2\pi(ux+vy)}f(x,y)\,dxdy \tag{A10}$$

which is a complex function of two real variables, u and v. The *inversion formula* becomes

$$f(x,y) = \int_{-\infty}^{\infty} \int_{-\infty}^{\infty} e^{i2\pi(ux+vy)}t_f(u,v)\,dudv \tag{A11}$$

In the same way that the one-dimensional case (Eq. A4) can be rewritten in a more informative version (Eq. A5), Equation A11 can be rewritten in a form that shows explicitly how $f(x,y)$ is composed of a weighted sum of elementary sinusoidal functions

$$f(x,y) = \int_{-\infty}^{\infty} \int_{-\infty}^{\infty} |t_f(u,v)|$$
$$\cos[2\pi(ux+vy) + \text{pha } t_f(u,v)]dudv \tag{A12}$$

Here $|t_f(u,v)|$ is again the amplitude spectrum of f, pha $t_f(u,v)$ the phase spectrum. The function $\cos[2\pi(ux + vy) + \text{pha } t_f(u,v)]$ describes a vertical cosinusoidal grating in the x,y plane [i.e., a two-dimensional function of the form $f(x,y) = \cos 2\pi\phi x$ as shown

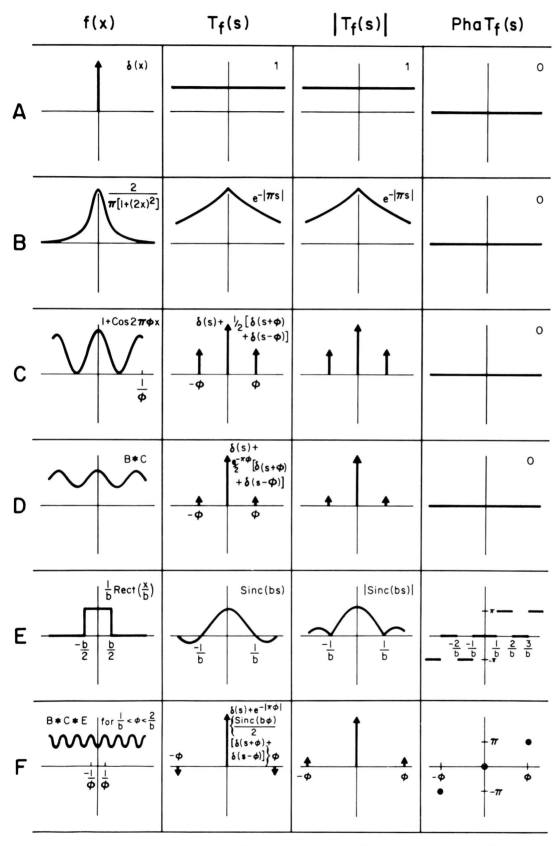

FIG. A1. Fourier analytic concepts involved in one-dimensional spurious resolution. See text for description.

earlier in Fig. 8], of frequency $\sqrt{u^2 + v^2}$, which has been rotated away from the vertical by an angle of $\tan^{-1}(v/u)$. Thus when $v = 0$ the grating is vertical; when $u = 0$ the grating is horizontal. In general, the grating $\cos[2\pi(ux + vy)]$ is perpendicular to the straight line $y = (v/u)x$. The phase term indicates how far the grating must be shifted along its axis [i.e., along the line $y = (v/u)x$]: a distance $(2\pi)^{-1}(u^2 + v^2)^{-1/2}$ pha $t_f(u,v)$ to the left. Altogether then, Equation A12 expresses the fact that $f(x,y)$ is a weighted sum of cosinusoidal gratings of various frequencies and orientations; $|t_f(u,v)|$ indicates how much to weight the cosine of frequency $\sqrt{u^2 + v^2}$ at orientation $\tan^{-1}(v/u)$, and pha $t_f(u,v)$ indicates how much to shift it, in order for the sum to reproduce f.

A two-dimensional SIL operator $\bigcirc$ is a device that transforms input functions $f(x,y)$ into output functions $\bigcirc[f(x,y)]$ and satisfies the two conditions of 1) linearity: $\bigcirc[f + g] = \bigcirc[f] + \bigcirc[g]$; and 2) shift invariance: if $\bigcirc(x,y)$ is the output to $f(x,y)$, $\bigcirc(x - a, y - b)$ is the output to $f(x - a, y - b)$ [i.e., shifting the input bodily to a new origin (a,b) shifts the output bodily to the same origin]. Such an operator can always be represented as a two-dimensional convolution

$$\bigcirc[f(x,y)] = \int_{-\infty}^{\infty} \int_{-\infty}^{\infty} f(x - x', y - y')$$
$$\cdot o(x',y') \, dx'dy' \quad \text{(A13)}$$
$$= f(x,y) * o(x,y)$$

where the function o is the impulse response of $\bigcirc$. If the input is a two-dimensional pulse of unit energy [e.g., a very tall thin cylinder of unit volume] at the origin, the output will be exactly $o(x,y)$. In optical applications o is called the *pointspread function*. The Fourier transform of o, $t_o(u,v)$, is the transfer function of $\bigcirc$. Knowledge of either the impulse response or the transfer function completely characterizes the operator $\bigcirc$ just as in the one-dimensional case, since the response to any input, f, can be determined either directly by the convolution $f * o$ or indirectly (i.e., in the transform domain) via a multiplicative relationship corresponding to Equation A7 in the one-dimensional case

$$t_{\bigcirc[f]}(u,v) = t_f(u,v)t_o(u,v) \quad \text{(A14)}$$

Taking absolute values on both sides of Equation A14 yields the two-dimensional version of Equation A8

$$|t_{\bigcirc[f]}(u,v)| = |t_f(u,v)| \, |t_o(u,v)| \quad \text{(A15)}$$

The nonnegative function $|t_o(u,v)|$ is the MTF of operator $\bigcirc$.

Relationship Between Linespread and Pointspread Functions

Suppose the linespread function of an optical system (e.g., the eye) is $o_1(x)$ [e.g., $o_1(x) = 2\pi^{-1}[1 + 2x)^2]^{-1}$,

the linespread function for the eye illustrated in Fig. A1, Sequence B]. If the system is circularly symmetric, so that rotating the object line simply rotates the original image with no change in spread, the pointspread function $o(x,y)$ (and consequently the two-dimensional transfer function) can be immediately determined. At any point in the u,v plane the two-dimensional transfer function $t_o(u,v)$ depends only on the distance from the origin $\sqrt{u^2 + v^2}$, and its value will be the one-dimensional transfer function at that distance, i.e., $t_o(u,v) = t_{o_1}(\sqrt{u^2 + v^2})$. Consequently the two-dimensional impulse response (i.e., the point spread) can be obtained by Fourier inversion

$$o(x,y) = \int_{-\infty}^{\infty} \int_{-\infty}^{\infty} e^{i2\pi(ux+vy)} t_{o_1}(\sqrt{u^2 + v^2}) \, dudv \quad \text{(A16)}$$

In the case of the linespread function in our illustration this yields the circularly symmetric pointspread function

$$o(x,y) = 2\pi^2(\pi^2 + 4\pi^2 r^2)^{-3/2} \quad \text{(A17)}$$

where $r = \sqrt{x^2 + y^2}$.

To determine the effect of defocusing we assume that each point $f(x,y)$ in the object is first convolved with a disk function of the form $D(x,y) = 4(\pi b^2)^{-1}$ for $\sqrt{x^2 + y^2} \le b/2$; $D(x,y) = 0$ elsewhere [this corresponds to a blur circle of diameter b; the factor $4(\pi b^2)^{-1}$ makes the area equal one], and the result is then convolved with the pointspread function given by Equation A17. The transform of $D(x,y)$ is

$$t_o(u,v) = \left(\frac{2}{\pi}\right) \left[\frac{J_1(\pi bq)}{bq}\right] \quad \text{(A18)}$$

where $q = \sqrt{u^2 + v^2}$, and J_1 is a Bessel function of the first kind. The graph of Equation A18 (for the case $b = 2$) is illustrated in Figure A2. Notice that this two-dimensional function has negative regions, analogous to the negative regions of its one-dimensional analog sinc (bs) (Fig. A1, Sequence E). (However, in this case the zeros are not evenly spaced along the radius.) Consequently the transfer function of a misfocused eye (i.e., the product of Eqs. A18 and A17) is also negative in the same regions of the u,v plane. This means that sinusoidal inputs with spatial frequencies in these regions will appear in the image with reversed sign, i.e., spurious resolution.

Coherent and Incoherent Illumination

The discussion so far has been carried on in terms of the "intensity" of optical images—implicitly, a quantity proportional to quanta/s per unit area incident on the image plane, or emitted from the object. We have identified an input function, $f(x,y)$, with the intensity of light in the object plane at (x,y), and an output function, $\bigcirc[f(x,y)]$, with intensity at (x,y) in the image plane. This description does not explicitly acknowledge the wave properties of light, and so one might wonder how (or whether) these are taken into account. The story, very briefly, is as follows. Fourier optics is based on scalar diffraction theory (51) in which the (monochromatic) light at a spatial point (x,y) in some plane is represented by a pair of numbers $a(x,y)$, $p(x,y)$ that correspond respectively to the amplitude and phase of a sinusoidally varying electric vector at (x,y). The expression for this vector is $a(x,y)$ $\cos[2\pi\phi t + p(x,y)]$, where t is time and ϕ is the frequency of the monochromatic light. Thus the light at (x,y) can be expressed as the real part of a complex number of the form $A(x,y) = a(x,y)e^{i[p(x,y)+2\pi\phi t]}$. The intensity of the light at (x,y) is then defined to be $|A(x,y)|^2$ [i.e., $|a(x,y)|^2$]. This quantity is proportional to quanta/s at (x,y), and consequently determines the response of any photoreceptive device (e.g., photopigments, film) in the image plane. The phase term $p(x,y)$ plays a role when the light at image point (x,y) is the sum of two or more sinusoidally varying components that may reinforce or cancel one another depending on their phase relationships. This is how the scalar diffraction model encompasses interference effects.

Now there are two cases to consider, depending on whether the light emitted from the object is coherent or incoherent. The coherent case assumes that the phases of the electric vectors at each point in the object are locked together, so that the phases $p(x,y)$ and $p(x',y')$ corresponding to any pair of object points have a difference that remains constant over time. (By definition, if there is only one object point, i.e., a point source, the light is necessarily coherent.) This can be achieved in practice by laser illumination, or (much less efficiently) by ensuring that all of the light stems from a single point source. In the incoherent case, which is the ordinary state of affairs under natural viewing conditions, the phases corresponding to different object points vary randomly and independently over time. In the image plane the coherent case allows for the possibility of stable phase relationships between contributions to $A(x,y)$ coming from many different object points, and so interference must be taken

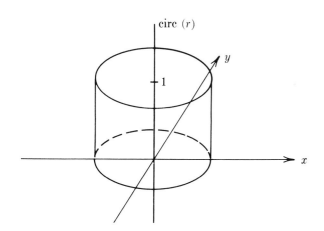

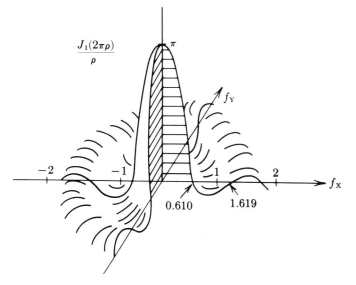

FIG. A2. Two-dimensional disk function (*top*) and its Fourier transform (*bottom*). Up to a constant factor π, the latter is the graph of Equation A18. [From Goodman (51).]

into account. In the incoherent case, on the other hand, no stable phase relationships exist between contributions stemming from different object points, and so no stable interference patterns can arise.

The two cases of coherent and incoherent illumination give rise to two different (but simply interrelated) Fourier analytic treatments. Let $A_1(x,y)$ denote the complex electric vector $a(x,y)e^{i[p(x,y)+2\pi\phi t]}$ at point (x,y) in the object plane, and $A_2(x,y)$ the electric vector at (x,y) in the image. [It is assumed that the x and y axes are parametrized so that (x,y) in the image plane is the geometrical optics image of (x,y) in the object plane, i.e., by measuring both in terms of visual angle.] And let $M(x,y)$ denote the complex impulse response produced by an object consisting of a single point source at the object point $(0,0)$. Such an object is necessarily coherent, and $M(x,y)$ is the complex response $|M(x,y)|e^{i[2\pi\phi t+\text{pha}M(x,y)]}$ representing both the amplitude and phase of the electric vector at image point (x,y) produced by a point object at $(0,0)$. Now consider an extended object consisting of many points. The quantity of interest is $|A_2(x,y)|^2$, the intensity at image point (x,y), since this determines quantum density on the photoreceptive surface in the image plane. Then it can be shown (17) that the coherent object case gives rise to the relationship

$$|A_2(x,y)|^2 = |M(x,y)*A_1(x,y)|^2 \qquad (A19)$$

[where, as usual, (*) denotes convolution], while the incoherent case gives rise to

$$|A_2(x,y)|^2 = |M(x,y)|^2*|A_1(x,y)|^2 \qquad (A20)$$

The second case is the one assumed in all of the earlier discussions. It expresses the fact that the intensity of the image (i.e., $|A_2|^2$) is the convolution of the intensity of the object $|A_1|^2$ with the intensity impulse response, $|M(x,y)|^2$. In terms of the notation used earlier, $|A_1|^2$ is the input function $f(x,y)$, $|M|^2$ is the impulse response, $o(x,y)$, and $|A_2|^2$ is the output function $\bigcirc[f(x,y)]$. So Equation A20 corresponds exactly to the earlier relationship Equation A13. Equation A19, on the other hand, describes the result expected with coherent objects, which is quite different, since in general $|M*A|^2$ is not the same as $|M|^2*|A|^2$. For example, M may be negative, but $|M|^2$ can never be. It is interesting to note that when the object is a single point (i.e., necessarily coherent) so that the appropriate expression for $|A_2(x,y)|^2$ is Equation A19, the result is $|A_2(x,y)|^2 = |M(x,y)|^2$, which is the impulse response for the incoherent case. Consequently the coherent impulse response $M(x,y)$ is never observed in isolation, even with coherent illumination.

Sampling Theorem

Suppose $f(x)$ is a function (e.g., a light-intensity profile) which we can only observe at a series of equally spaced discrete values on the x axis, i.e., we can only know $f(0)$, $f(w)$, $f(-w)$, $f(2w)$, $f(-2w)$, ..., where w is the distance between successive sample points. (This is essentially the way a one-dimensional array of equally spaced thin photoreceptors views the retinal image. A model for receptors that have appreciable width relative to the spatial periods of the input is given below.) How does such a sampling affect our ability to reconstruct the entire function f? Fourier analysis provides an elegant answer to this question in the form of the *sampling theorem*: If the Fourier transform of f vanishes for frequencies greater than some cutoff frequency (s_c) [i.e., $t_f(s) = 0$ for $|s| > s_c$], $f(x)$ can be perfectly reconstructed from a series of equally spaced sample values; $f(0)$, $f(w)$, $f(-w)$, ..., $f(nw)$, $f(-nw)$, ..., provided the sampling rate, w^{-1}, is greater than or equal to $2(s_c)$. The proof of the sampling theorem is straightforward but a bit too long to include here (see ref. 27). However, Figure A3 (from ref. 27) illustrates the underlying idea and also shows what happens when the sampling rate is too slow (i.e., less than twice the highest frequency in the input). In the frequency domain, the effect of sampling $f(x)$ at discrete intervals is to create a new function whose transform is the sum of a series of replicas of the original transform t_f. [Note: the figure uses $F(s)$ to denote the transform of $f(x)$.] These replicas are centered at 0, $1/w$, $-1/w$, ... n/w, $-n/w$, ... When the sampling rate $1/w$ is $\geq 2s_c$, these replicas do not overlap on the s axis. Consequently the replica centered at the origin provides an undistorted image of the original transform t_f, which can be used to reconstruct an undistorted image of the original function f. However, if the sampling rate is less than $2s_c$, so that the replicas on the s axis overlap, the replicas centered at higher frequencies add nonzero values to the one centered at the origin, so that it is no longer an exact image of t_f, and consequently the reconstruction process will yield a distorted version of f. This kind of distortion is known as "aliasing," because its effect is that high-frequency components in the input f reappear in the sampled version of f in the guise of low-frequency components. This can have the effect of introducing frequency components in the sampled version which were nonexistent in the original function. Consequently, in order for a sampling scheme to yield undistorted reconstructions of all potential inputs, it is essential to set the sampling rate equal to (or greater than) twice the highest frequency that will occur in any input. (It does not matter if the rate is higher than needed for some inputs, since sampling too fast does not introduce any distortion.) Figure A4 illustrates the aliasing effect.

In two dimensions, sampling consists of observing $f(x,y)$ at a set of discrete points in the x,y plane (e.g., a square lattice of the form (wn,wm), $n = 0, 1, ...,$ $m = 0, 1, ...$). In this case the optimal sampling scheme depends on the shape of the region in the u,v plane for which $t_f(u,v)$ is nonzero. The basic idea is still that f

can be exactly reconstructed from a discrete set of sample values, provided t_f vanishes outside some region, but the appropriate spacing of these samples depends on the shape of that region, and consequently the two-dimensional sampling theorem cannot be stated quite as neatly as the one-dimensional version.

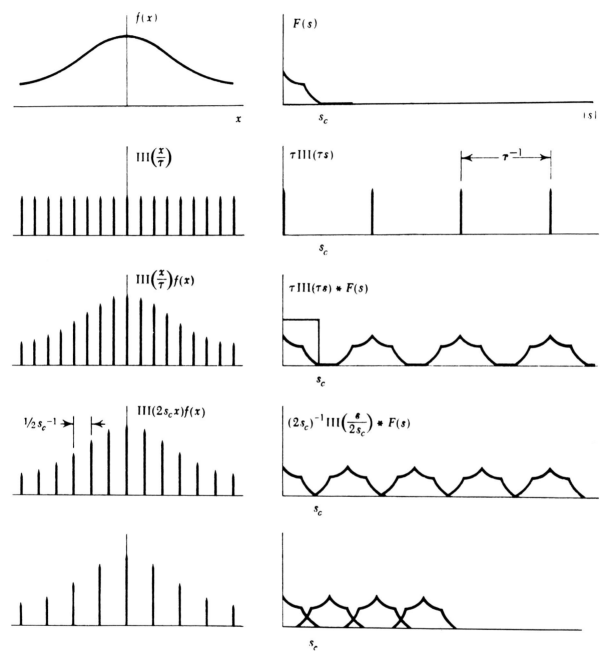

FIG. A3. Concepts involved in the one-dimensional sampling theorem; $f(x)$ is an input signal with transform $F(s)$ which vanishes for $s > s_c$. III (x/t) is an infinite row of delta functions (i.e., sample points) spaced t units apart; its transform is a row of delta functions spaced t^{-1} units apart. The *third row* shows the sampled version of f (i.e., the product $f(x)$ III (x/t)) and its transform. Note that here the sampling rate is inefficiently high: successive replicas of $F(s)$ are separated by empty intervals. The *fourth row* illustrates the optimal sampling scheme, where $t = (2s_c)^{-1}$: Here the replicas of $F(s)$ in the transform of the sampled signal are precisely adjacent. The *fifth row* shows the effect of sampling too coarsely: In the transform of the sampled signal the replicas of $F(s)$ overlap (aliasing). [From Bracewell (27). *The Fourier Transform and Its Applications* (2nd ed.), by R. Bracewell. Copyright © 1978, McGraw-Hill Book Company. Used with permission of McGraw-Hill Book Company.]

Probably the most useful exact statement can be based on the assumption that the two-dimensional transform of $f(x,y)$, i.e., $t_f(u,v)$, vanishes outside some square region in the u,v plane, i.e., $u \leq c$, $v \leq c$ [that is, the smallest square enclosing the actual nonzero region of $t_f(u,v)$]. In this case f can be exactly reconstructed by a square lattice of sample points $x = wn$, $y = wm$, with $w \leq (2c)^{-1}$ (see ref. 17).

Application to Sampling by Photoreceptors

Consider a one-dimensional retina consisting of a tightly packed line of photoreceptors, each with diameter w (e.g., an array of cones along the x axis of the retina). Suppose the input to this model retina is a function $f(x)$ (e.g., a light-intensity profile along the x axis), and that each receptor integrates the portion of f which lies directly above it and outputs that value. Thus, for example, the output of the receptor centered at the origin is $\int_{-w2/2}^{w/2} f(x)\,dx$. How much information about the input function f can be obtained from the output of the photoreceptor array? Notice that this model is not exactly the same as the case envisioned by the sampling theorem, because our receptors do not report the values of $f(x)$ at $x = 0$, $\pm w \pm 2w$, but rather the values of $\int f(x)dx$ over intervals of width w centered at $x = 0$, $\pm w$, $\pm 2w$, ... However this simply means that we are sampling the function $F(x + w/2) - F(x - w/2)$, where $F(x) = \int_{-\infty}^{x} f(y)\,dy$, and it can readily be shown that the resulting output function takes the form

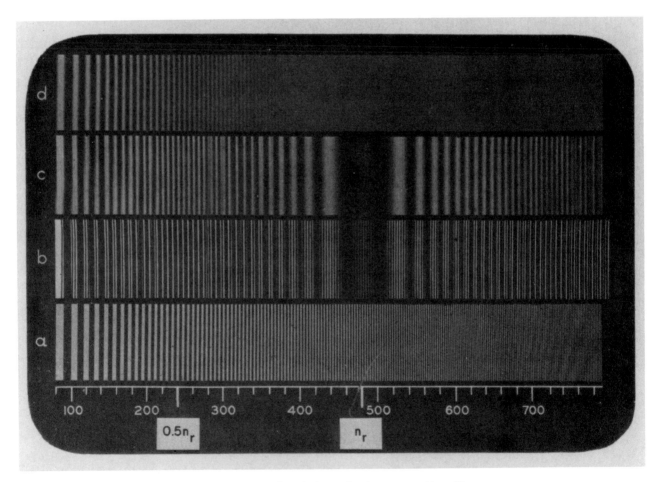

FIG. A4. One-dimensional aliasing effects. *Row a* is a linearly increasing frequency pattern. *Row b* shows the sampled appearance of pattern a viewed through a raster plate consisting of fine vertical slits spaced at a frequency equal to n_r on the scale. (This sampling rate guarantees perfect reconstruction for frequencies up to 0.5 n_r, with aliasing distortion for higher frequencies.) *Row c* shows the effect of spatially postfiltering the sampled image b (in this case by adjusting the scanning spot size in a television camera which views pattern b. The visual analogue would be lateral neural interactions at the receptors or beyond.) Notice that this removes the raster lines but does not eliminate aliasing: Frequencies higher than 0.5 n_r still appear as lower frequencies. *Row d* shows the effect of the spatial postfilter alone (i.e., on pattern a viewed without the raster plate). [From Schade (116).]

output to input $f(x)$

$$= \frac{1}{w} \, \text{comb} \left(\frac{x}{w} \right) \cdot \left[f(x) * \text{rect} \left(\frac{x}{w} \right) \right] \qquad \text{(A21)}$$

where $1/w \, \text{comb}(x/w)$ denotes a series of impulses of unit energy (i.e., a series of delta functions as in Fig. 34) spaced at $0, \pm w, \pm 2w, \ldots$, and $\text{rect}(x/w)$ is a function which equals one for $-w/2 \leq x \leq w/2$ and zero elsewhere ($*$ denotes convolution). Now the factor $1/w \, \text{comb} \left(\dfrac{x}{w} \right)$ represents a sampling scheme with sampling rate w^{-1}, and Equation A21 means that this scheme is applied to the convolution of the input f with a rectangular function of width w. The Fourier transform of this convolution is $t_f(s) \cdot w \, \text{sinc}(ws)$ [where $\text{sinc}(y) = (\sin \pi y)/\pi y$ is the function depicted in Fig. 32], and the transform of the receptor output (i.e., of Eq. A21) is

$$w \, \text{comb}(ws) * [\text{sinc}(ws) t_f(s)] \qquad \text{(A22)}$$

Thus Equation A21 tells us that the receptor output represents a sampling at rate $1/w$ of a function whose transform is essentially the product $t_f(s) \, \text{sinc}(ws)$, which has zeros at $s = \pm 1/w, \pm 2/w \ldots$ (because of the sinc factor). Beyond the first zero $\text{sinc}(ws)$ becomes negative (for a time), and so beyond this point the reproduction scheme introduces spurious resolution. Consequently we concentrate on input frequencies $<1/w$—i.e., consider the effect of the scheme on inputs with frequencies below the sampling rate. According to the sampling theorem, the sampling scheme $1/w \, \text{comb}(x/w)$ is perfect for inputs with frequencies $s < (2w)^{-1}$, and one can conclude that sinusoidal input in this range can be recovered with no frequency distortion, though the amplitude of each input frequency s will be attenuated by the factor $\text{sinc}(ws)$. For input frequencies in the range $(2w)^{-1} < s < w^{-1}$, however, sampling by receptors of width w leads to aliasing distortion in the output.

To see explicitly the form this aliasing takes, consider a cosinusoidal input with frequency ϕ, with $(2w)^{-1} < \phi < w^{-1}$. In this case the spectrum of the output of receptor sampling will contain energy at $s = w^{-1} - \phi$ (which lies in the interval $[0, (2w)^{-1}]$), and also at $s = w^{-1} + \phi$, plus all other points of the form $s = nw^{-1} \pm \phi$, $n = 0, \pm 1, \pm 2, \ldots$. This output spectrum is identical to the one that is produced by an input cosine of frequency $w^{-1} - \phi$, except that each spike in the output spectrum of $\cos[2\pi\phi x]$ is attenuated (relative to the output spectrum of $\cos[2\pi(w^{-1} - \phi)x]$) by the constant factor $\text{sinc}(w\phi)/\text{sinc}(1 - w\phi) = r(\phi)$. Consequently, the sampled output of input $\cos 2\pi\phi x$ is indistinguishable from the sampled output produced by inputting the lower frequency function $r(\phi) \cos[2\pi(w^{-1} - \phi)x]$, and any reconstruction process must confuse these two inputs.

Finally, it is natural to wonder about the effect of

shrinking receptor width while keeping the spacing between receptor centers the same, to model the effect of gaps between receptors. Specifically, suppose the width of each receptor is reduced from w to pw, $0 \leq p \leq 1$, while the spacing between receptor centers is kept at w. In this case the output is

$$\frac{1}{w} \, \text{comb} \left(\frac{x}{w} \right) \left[f(x) * \text{rect} \left(\frac{x}{pw} \right) \right] \qquad \text{(A23)}$$

which represents a sampling at rate w^{-1} of a function $\left[\text{i.e., } f(x) * \text{rect} \left(\dfrac{x}{pw} \right) \right]$ which has transform, $t_f(s) \cdot pw \, \text{sinc}(pws)$. Consequently the effect of shrinking receptor width is not to increase the effective frequency bandwidth of the system (i.e., for transmission with no harmonic distortion), since aliasing will still occur for $s > (2w)^{-1}$. However, it will increase the

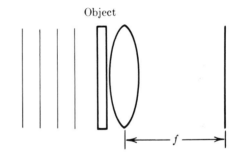

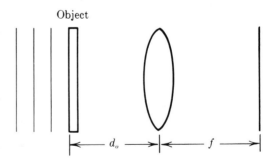

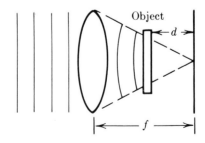

FIG. A5. Configurations for producing optical Fourier transforms. The focal length of the lens is represented by f; thin vertical lines represent the illumination (a monochromatic plane wave). [From Goodman (51).]

range between the cutoff frequency $(2w)^{-1}$ and the point (i.e., $s = (pw)^{-1}$) at which spurious resolution begins to occur.

The same ideas can be carried over to two dimensions by imagining (for the sake of convenience) square receptors with areas $(pw)^2$ centered at the points $x = 0, \pm w, \pm 2w, \ldots; y = 0, \pm w, \pm 2w, \ldots$. If each receptor integrates the portion of $f(x,y)$ directly above it, the resulting output is

$$w^{-2} \, \mathrm{comb}(x/w) \, \mathrm{comb}(y/w)$$
$$\cdot [\, f(x,y) * \mathrm{rect}(x/pw) \, \mathrm{rect}(y/pw)\,]$$

The factor outside the square brackets is a square lattice sampling scheme that provides reproduction without harmonic distortion for all two-dimensional inputs whose transforms vanish outside the square $u \le (2w)^{-1}$, $v \le (2w)^{-1}$. Consequently, if the highest spatial frequency in the input at any orientation is c, the required receptor spacing w is $(2c)^{-1}$, just as in the one-dimensional case. Any sparser sampling will lead to aliasing.

Optical Transforms and Spatial Filtering

Calculating the two-dimensional Fourier transforms of input functions corresponding to complex natural scenes (e.g., photographs of real objects) is extremely laborious, but for many purposes the same result can be obtained directly by elegant optical methods requiring no calculation at all. These methods depend on the fact that the diffraction pattern formed by an aperture is essentially the Fourier transform of that aperture (51). Three optical configurations used to compute transforms are illustrated in Figure A5. In each case the "object" is a screen whose transparency can be described by a transmission function $T(x,y)$ (which varies between zero and one) and the illumination (represented by the vertical lines to the left of the object) is assumed to be a coherent monochro-

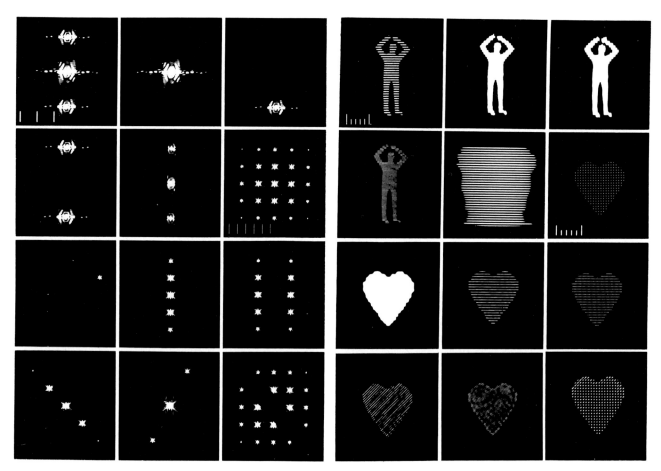

FIG. A6. Optical Fourier transforms. Each *panel* in the *left block* (three *left-hand columns*) shows the optical transform (i.e., amplitude spectrum) of the corresponding image in the *right block* (three *right-hand columns*). [From Harburn et al. (61). Reprinted from G. Harburn, C. A. Taylor, and T. R. Welberry: *Atlas of Optical Transforms*. Copyright © 1975 by G. Bell and Sons, Ltd. Used by permission of the publisher, Cornell University Press.]

matic plane wave (e.g., from a laser). All three configurations will result in an image on the screen at the right whose intensity distribution $I(x,y)$ is essentially the squared absolute value of the Fourier transform of $T(x,y)$. (That is, the image intensity will be proportional to the squared amplitude spectrum of the transmission function of the object, the proportionality constant depending on the intensity and wavelength of the light and the focal length of the lens.) A number of complex objects and their optical transforms (in effect, their amplitude spectra) are illustrated in Figure A6. The figure also shows the effects of spatial filtering, which can readily be achieved by placing a stop in the transform plane to block certain spatial frequencies, and then retransforming the image in the transform plane (i.e., by repeating the optical trans-

form process using the image in the transform plane as an object). The result is a filtered version of the original object, i.e., $T(x,y)$ minus the blocked spatial frequencies.

The same principle naturally applies to the eye, the optics of which can serve as the lens in Figure A5. This is the basis of the technique employed by Le Grand and others for circumventing the normal spatial frequency cutoff of the eye, as discussed in VISUAL ACUITY, p. 260.

We thank R. Baillargeon, N. Graham, M. Hayhoe, and D. MacLeod for helpful suggestions. Financial support from the U.S. National Institutes of Health (Grant 1-R01-EY03164-01 to B. Wandell) and the University of California, Irvine (Focused Research Project on Perception and Higher Mental Processes) is gratefully acknowledged.

REFERENCES

1. ABNEY, W., AND E. R. FESTING. Colour photometry. *Philos. Trans. R. Soc. London* 177: 423–456, 1886.
1a. AGUILAR, M., AND W. S. STILES. Saturation of the rod mechanism of the retina at high levels of stimulation. *Opt. Acta* 1: 59–64, 1954.
2. ALPERN, M. Rod vision. In: *The Assessment of Visual Function,* edited by A. M. Potts. St. Louis: Mosby, 1972.
3. ALPERN, M., AND J. MOELLER. The red and green cone visual pigments of deuteranomalous trichromacy. *J. Physiol. London* 266: 647–675, 1977.
4. ALPERN, M., AND E. N. PUGH, JR. Variation in the action spectrum of erythrolabe among deuteranopes. *J. Physiol. London* 266: 613–646, 1977.
5. ALPERN, M., AND T. WAKE. Cone pigments in human deutan colour vision defects. *J. Physiol. London* 266: 595–612, 1977.
6. ARDEN, G. B., AND R. A. WEALE. Nervous mechanisms and dark-adaptation. *J. Physiol. London* 125: 417–426, 1954.
7. BARLOW, H. B. Increment threshold at low intensities considered as signal-noise discriminations. *J. Physiol. London* 119: 69–88, 1957.
8. BARLOW, H. B. Temporal and spatial summation in human vision at different background intensities. *J. Physiol. London* 141: 337–350, 1958.
9. BARLOW, H. B. Dark-adaptation: a new hypothesis. *Vision Res.* 4: 47–58, 1964.
10. BARLOW, H. B. Dark and light adaptation: psychophysics. In: *Handbook of Sensory Physiology. Visual Psychophysics,* edited by L. Hurvich and D. Jameson. Berlin: Springer-Verlag, 1972, vol. 7, pt. 4, p. 1–28.
10a. BARLOW, H. B. Retinal and central factors in human vision limited by noise. In: *Vertebrate Photoreception,* edited by H. B. Barlow and P. Fatt. New York: Academic, 1977, p. 337–358.
11. BARLOW, H. B., C. BLAKEMORE, AND J. D. PETTIGREW. The neural mechanism of binocular depth discrimination. *J. Physiol. London* 193: 327–342, 1967.
12. BARLOW, H. B., AND P. FATT (editors). *Vertebrate Photoreception.* New York: Academic, 1977.
13. BARLOW, H. B., AND B. SAKITT. Doubts about scotopic interactions in stabilized vision. *Vision Res.* 13: 523–524, 1973.
14. BARLOW, H. B., AND J. M. B. SPARROCK. The role of after-images in dark adaptation. *Science* 144: 1309–1314, 1964.
16. BAYLOR, D. A., AND R. FETTIPLACE. Transmission from photoreceptors to ganglion cells in the retina of the turtle. In: *Vertebrate Photoreceptors,* edited by H. B. Barlow and P. Fatt. New York: Academic, 1977, p. 193–203.
17. BAYLOR, D. A., M. G. F. FUORTES, AND P. M. O'BRYAN.

Receptive fields of cones in the retina of the turtle. *J. Physiol. London* 214: 265–294, 1971.
18. BAYLOR, D. A., AND A. L. HODGKIN. Changes in time scale and sensitivity in turtle photoreceptors. *J. Physiol. London* 242: 729–758, 1974.
19. BEDFORD, R. E., AND G. WYSZECKI. Axial chromatic aberration of the eye. *J. Opt. Soc. Am.* 47: 564–565, 1957.
20. BERKLEY, M. A., F. KITTERLE, AND D. W. WATKINS. Grating visibility as a function of orientation and retinal eccentricity. *Vision Res.,* 15: 239–244, 1975.
21. BLAKEMORE, C., AND F. W. CAMPBELL. Adaptation to spatial stimuli. *J. Physiol. London* 200: 11–13, 1969.
22. BLAKEMORE, C. B., AND W. A. H. RUSHTON. Dark adaptation and increment threshold in a rod monochromat. *J. Physiol. London* 181: 612–628, 1965.
23. BLAKEMORE, C. B., AND W. A. H. RUSHTON. The rod increment threshold during dark adaptation in normal and rod monochromat. *J. Physiol. London* 181: 629–640, 1965.
24. BLICK, D. W., AND D. I. A. MACLEOD. Rod threshold: influence of neighboring cones. *Vision Res.* 18: 1611–1616, 1978.
25. BOYNTON, R. M. Ten years of research with the minimally distinct border. In: *Visual Psychophysics and Physiology,* edited by J. C. Armington, J. Krauskopf, and B. R. Wooten, New York, Academic, 1978.
26. BOYNTON, R. M., AND W. S. BARON. Sinusoidal flicker characteristics of primate cones in response to heterochromatic stimuli. *J. Opt. Soc. Am.* 65: 1091–1100, 1975.
27. BRACEWELL, R. *The Fourier Transform and its Applications* (2nd ed.). New York: McGraw-Hill, 1978.
28. BREITMEYER, B. G., AND L. GANZ. Implications of sustained and transient channels for theories of visual pattern masking, saccadic suppression, and information processing. *Psychol. Rev.* 83: 1–36, 1976.
29. BRINDLEY, G. S. *Physiology of the Retina and Visual Pathway.* Baltimore, Williams and Wilkins, 1970.
29a. BRINK, G. VAN DEN. Measurements of the geometrical aberrations of the eye. *Vision Res.* 2: 233–244, 1962.
30. BROWN, J. L., M. P. KUHNS, AND H. E. ADLER. Relation of threshold criterion to the functional receptors of the eye. *J. Opt. Soc. Am.* 47: 198–204, 1957.
31. BYRAM, G. M. The physical and photochemical basis of visual resolving power. Part III. Visual acuity and the photochemistry of the retina. *J. Opt. Soc. Am.* 34: 718–738, 1944.
32. CAMPBELL, F. W., AND D. G. GREEN. Optical and retinal factors affecting visual resolution. *J. Physiol. London* 181: 576–593, 1965.
33. CAMPBELL, F. W., AND R. W. GUBISCH. Optical quality of the

human eye. *J. Physiol. London* 186: 558–578, 1966.

34. CAMPBELL, F. W., AND J. G. ROBSON. Application of Fourier analysis to the visibility of gratings. *J. Physiol. London* 197: 551–566, 1968.

35. CARTERETTE, E. C., AND M. P. FRIEDMAN (editors). *Handbook of Perception. Biology of Perceptual Systems.* New York: Academic, 1973, vol. III.

35a. CARTERETTE, E. C., AND M. P. FRIEDMAN (editors). *Handbook of Perception. Seeing.* New York: Academic, 1975, vol. V.

36. CORNSWEET, T. N. *Visual Perception.* New York: Academic, 1970.

36a. COWAN, T. D. Some remarks on channel bandwidths for visual contrast detection. In: E. Poppel, R. Held, and J. E. Dowling. Neuronal mechanisms in visual perception. *Neurosci. Res. Program Bull.* 7, 15, 3. Cambridge, MA: MIT Press, 1977, p. 492–515.

37. CRAIK, K. J. W., AND M. D. VERNON. The nature of dark adaptation. *Br. J. Psychol.* 32: 64–81, 1941.

38. CRAWFORD, B. H. Visual adaptation in relation to brief conditioning stimuli. *Proc. R. Soc. London Ser. B* 134: 283–302, 1947.

39. CRAWFORD, B. H. The Stiles-Crawford effects and their significance in vision. In: *Handbook of Sensory Physiology. Visual Psychophysics,* edited by L. Hurvich and D. Jameson. Berlin: Springer-Verlag, 1972, vol. 7, pt. 4, p. 470–483.

40. DAVSON, H. (editor). *The Eye. Visual Function in Man.* New York: Academic, 1976, vol. 2A.

41. DAW, N. W., AND J. M. ENOCH. Contrast sensitivity, Westheimer function and Stiles-Crawford effect in a blue cone monochromat. *Vision Res.* 13: 1669–1680, 1973.

42. DE VALOIS, R. L., AND K. K. DE VALOIS. Neural coding of color. In: *Handbook of Perception. Seeing,* edited by E. C. Carterette and M. P. Friedman. New York: Academic, 1975, vol. V, p. 117–166.

44. DE VRIES, H. The quantum character of light and its bearing upon the threshold of vision, the differential sensitivity and acuity of the eye. *Physica* 10: 553–564, 1943.

45. DUKE-ELDER, S., AND D. ABRAMS. *Ophthalmic Optics and Refraction.* St. Louis: Mosby, 1970.

46. ENROTH-CUGELL, C., B. G. HERTZ, AND P. LENNIE. Convergence of rod and cone signals in the cat's retina. *J. Physiol. London* 269: 297–318, 1977.

47. FAIN, G. The threshold signal of photoreceptors. In: *Vertebrate Photoreception,* edited by H. Barlow and P. Fatt. New York: Academic, 1977.

48. FLAMANT, F., AND W. S. STILES. The directional and spectral sensitivites of the retinal rods to adapting fields of different wave-lengths. *J. Physiol. London* 107: 187–202, 1948.

49. FRUMKES, T. E., AND L. A. TEMMED. Rod-cone interaction in human-scotopic vision: II. Cones influence increment thresholds detected by rods. *Vision Res.* 17: 673–679, 1977.

50. GAZZANIGA, M. S., AND C. B. BLAKEMORE (editor). *Handbook of Psychobiology.* New York: Academic, 1975.

51. GOODMAN, J. W. *Introduction to Fourier Optics.* New York: McGraw-Hill, 1965.

52. GORRAND, J. M. Diffusion of the human retina and quality of the optics of the eye on the fovea and the peripheral retina. *Vision Res.* 8: 907–912, 1979.

53. GRAHAM, N. Visual detection of aperiodic spatial stimuli by probability summation among narrowband channels. *Vision Res.* 17: 637–652, 1977.

54. GRAHAM, N., AND J. NACHMIAS. Detection of grating patterns containing two spatial frequencies: a comparison of single-channel and multiple-channels models. *Vision Res.* 11: 251–259, 1971.

55. GRAHAM, N., AND F. RATLIFF. Quantitative theories of the integrative action of the retina. In: *Contemporary Developments in Mathematical Psychology. Measurement, Psychophysics, and Neural Information Processing,* edited by D. H. Krantz, R. C. Atkinson, R. D. Luce, and P. Suppes. San Francisco: Freeman, 1974, vol II, p. 306–371.

56. GRANIT, R. The dark adaptation of mammalian visual receptors. *Acta Physiol. Scand.* 7: 216–220, 1944.

57. GREEN, D. G. The contrast sensitivity of the colour mechanisms of the human eye. *J. Physiol. London* 196: 415–429, 1968.

58. GREEN, D. G. Regional variations in the visual acuity for interference fringes on the retina. *J. Physiol. London* 207: 351–356, 1970.

58a. GREGORY, R. L. Stereovision and isoluminence. *Proc. R. Soc. London Ser. B* 204: 467–476, 1979.

59. GUBISCH, R. W. Optical performance of the human eye. *J. Opt. Soc. Am.* 57: 407–415, 1967.

60. GUTH, S. L., N. J. DONLEY, AND R. T. MARROCCO. On luminance additivity and related topics. *Vision Res.* 9: 537–575, 1969.

61. HARBURN, G., C. A. TAYLOR, AND T. R. WELBERRY. *Atlas of Optical Transforms.* Ithaca, NY: Cornell Univ. Press, 1975.

62. HECHT, E., AND A. ZAJAC. *Optics.* Menlo Park, CA: Addison-Wesley, 1974.

63. HECHT, S. Photochemistry of visual purple. I. The kinetics of the decomposition of visual purple by light. *J. Gen. Physiol.* 3: 1–13, 1920.

64. HECHT, S. Rods, cones, and the chemical basis of vision. *Physiol. Rev.* 17: 239–290, 1937.

65. HECHT, S., C. HAIG, AND A. M. CHASE. The influence of light adaptation on subsequent dark adaptation of the eye. *J. Gen. Physiol.* 20: 831–850, 1937.

66. HELD, R., H. W. LEIBOWITZ, AND H.-L. TEUBER. *Handbook of Sensory Physiology. Perception.* Berlin: Springer-Verlag, 1978, vol. 8.

66a. HERING, E. Grundzinge des Lehre von Lichtsinn. In: *Handbuch der gesammten Augenheilkunde,* edited by A. Graefe and E. T. Saemich. Leipzig: Eugelmann, 1905, vol. 3. [Transl. L. M. Hurvich and D. Jameson. *Outlines of a Theory of the Light Sense.* Cambridge, MA: Harvard Univ. Press, 1964.]

67. HOWLAND, H. C., AND B. HOWLAND. A subjective method for the measurement of monochromatic aberrations of the eye. *J. Opt. Soc. Am.* 67: 1508–1518, 1977.

68. HUBEL, D. H., AND T. N. WIESEL. Brain mechanisms of vision. *Sci. Am.* 241: 150–162, 1979.

69. INGLING, C. R. The spectral sensitivity of the opponent-colors channel. *Vision Res.* 17: 1083–1090, 1977.

70. INGLING, C. R., AND B. H. TSOU. Orthogonal combination of three visual channels. *Vision Res.* 17: 1075–1082, 1977.

71. INGLING, C. R., B. H. P. TSOU, T. J. GAST, S. A. BURNS, J. O. EMERICK, AND L. RIESENBERG. The achromatic channel. I. The non-linearity of minimum-border and flicker matches. *Vision Res.* 18: 379–390, 1978.

72. IVANOFF, A. About the spherical aberration of the eye. *J. Opt. Soc. Am.* 46: 901–903, 1956.

73. JAMESON, D., AND L. M. HURVICH (editors). *Handbook of Sensory Physiology. Visual Psychophysics.* Berlin: Springer-Verlag, 1972, vol. 7, pt. 4.

74. KELLY, D. H. Visual contrast sensitivity. *Op. Acta* 24: 107–129, 1977.

75. KELLY, D. H. Motion and vision. II. Stabilized spatio-temporal threshold surface. *J. Opt. Soc. Am.* 69: 1340–1349, 1979.

76. KELLY, D. H. AND R. E. SAVOIE. A study of sine-wave contrast sensitivity by two psychophysical methods. *Percept. Psychophys.* 14: 313–318, 1973.

77. KELLY, D. H., AND D. VAN NORREN. Two-band model of heterochromatic flicker. *J. Opt. Soc. Am.* 67: 1081–1091, 1977.

77a. KÖNIG, A. Über den menschlichen Sehpurpur und seine Bedeutung für das Sehen. *S. B. Akad. Wiss. Berlin* 559–575, 1894.

78. KRANTZ, D. H. Measurement theory and qualitative laws in psychophysics. In: *Contemporary Developments in Mathematical Psychology. Measurement, Psychophysics, and Neural Information Processing,* edited by D. H. Krantz, R. C. Atkinson, R. D. Luce, and P. Suppes. San Francisco: Freeman, 1974, vol. II, p. 160–199.

79. KRANTZ, D. H. Color measurement and color theory. I. Rep-

resentation theorem for Grassman structures. *J. Math. Psychol.* 12: 283–303, 1975.

80. KRANTZ, D. H. Color measurement and color theory. II. Opponent colors theory. *J. Math. Psychol.* 12: 304–327, 1975.

81. KUFFLER, J. W., AND J. G. NICHOLLS. *From Neuron to Brain.* Sunderland, MA: Sinauer Assoc. 1976.

82. LAND, E. H. Color vision and the natural image. Parts I and II. *Proc. Natl. Acad. Sci. USA,* 45: 115–129, 639–644, 1959.

83. LATCH, M., AND P. LENNIE. Rod-cone interaction in light adaptation. *J. Physiol. London* 269: 517–534, 1977.

84. LE GRAND, Y. *Space and Form Vision.* Bloomington: Indiana Univ. Press, 1967.

85. LE GRAND, Y. *Light, Colour, and Vision* (2nd ed.). London: Chapman and Hall, 1968.

86. LENNIE, P., AND D. I. A. MACLEOD. Background configuration and rod threshold. *J. Physiol. London* 233: 143–156, 1973.

87. LIGHTHILL, M. J. *Introduction to Fourier Analysis and Generalized Functions.* Cambridge: Cambridge Univ. Press, 1964.

88. LYTHGOE, R. J. The mechanism of dark adaptation. *Br. J. Opthalmol.* 24: 21–43, 1940.

89. LUDVIGH, E., AND E. F. MCCARTHY. Absorption of visible light by refractive media of the human eye. *Arch. Ophthalmol.* 20: 37–51, 1938.

89a. MACADAM, D. L. *Sources of Color Science.* Cambridge, MA: MIT Press, 1970.

90. MACLEOD, D. I. A. Visual sensitivity. *Annu. Rev. Psychol.* 2: 613–645, 1978.

91. MAFFEI, L., AND F. W. CAMPBELL. Neurophysiological localization of the vertical and horizontal visual coordinates in man. *Science* 167: 386–387, 1970.

92. MAKOUS, W., AND R. BOOTHE. Cones block signals from rods. *Vision Res.* 14: 285–294, 1974.

93. MAKOUS, W., AND D. PEEBLES. Rod-cone interaction: reconciliation with Flamant and Stiles. *Vision Res.* 19: 695–698, 1979.

94. MARC, R. E., AND H. G. SPERLING. Chromatic organization of primate cones. *Science* 196: 454–456, 1977.

95. OSTERBERG, G. Topography of the layer of rods and cones in the human retina. *Acta Opthalmol. Suppl.* 6: 11–97, 1935.

96. PEARSON, D. E. *Transmission and Display of Pictorial Information.* New York: Wiley, 1975.

97. PENN, R., AND W. A. HAGINS. Kinetics of the photocurrent of retinal rods. *Biophys. J.* 12: 1073–1094, 1972.

98. POLYAK, S. L. *The Vertebrate Visual System.* Chicago: Univ. of Chicago Press, 1957.

99. POPPEL, E., R. HELD, AND J. E. DOWLING. Neuronal mechanisms in visual perception. *Neurosci. Res. Program Bull.* 7, 15, 3. Cambridge, MA: MIT Press, 1977.

100. PUGH, E. N., JR. Rhodopsin flash photolysis in man. *J. Physiol. London* 248: 393–412, 1975.

101. PUGH, E. N., JR. Rushton's paradox: rod dark adaptation after flash photolysis. *J. Physiol. London* 248: 413–431, 1975.

101a. RATLIFF, F. *Mach Bands: Quantitative Studies on Neural Networks in the Retinal.* San Francisco, CA: Holden-Day, 1965.

102. RIPPS, H., M. SHAKIB, AND E. D. MACDONALD. Peroxidase uptake by photoreceptor terminals of the skate retina. *J. Cell Biol.* 70: 86–96, 1976.

103. RIPPS, H., AND R. A. WEALE. Contrast and border phenomena. In: *The Eye. Visual Function in Man,* edited by H. Davson. New York: Academic, 1976, vol. 2A, p. 133–184.

104. RIPPS, H. AND R. A. WEALE. The visual photoreceptors. In: *The Eye. Visual Function in Man,* edited by H. Davson. New York: Academic, 1976, vol. 2A, p. 5–41.

105. ROBSON, J. G. Receptive fields: neural representations of the spatial and intensive attributes of the visual image. In: *Handbook of Perception. Seeing,* edited by E. C. Carterette and M. P. Friedman. New York: Academic, 1975, vol. 5, p. 82–116.

106. RODIECK, R. W. *The Vertebrate Retina.* San Francisco, CA: Freeman, 1973.

107. ROSE, A. The sensitivity performance of the human eye on an absolute scale. *J. Opt. Soc. Am.* 38: 196–208, 1948.

108. ROSE, A. *Vision: Human and Electronic.* New York: Plenum, 1973.

109. RUSHTON, W. A. H. The difference spectrum and the photosensitivity of rhodopsin in the living human eye. *J. Physiol. London* 134: 11–29, 1956.

110. RUSHTON, W. A. H. Bleached rhodopsin and visual adaptation. *J. Physiol. London* 181: 645–655, 1965.

111. RUSHTON, W. A. H. The Ferrier lecture. Visual adaptation. *Proc. R. Soc. London Ser. B* 162: 20–46, 1965.

112. RUSHTON, W. A. H. Review lecture: pigments and signals in colour vision. *J. Physiol. London* 220: 1–31, 1972.

113. RUSHTON, W. A. H., AND G. WESTHEIMER. The effect upon the rod threshold of bleaching neighbouring rods. *J. Physiol. London* 16: 318–329, 1962.

114. SAVOIE, R. E. The Bezold-Brucke effect and visual non-linearity. *J. Opt. Soc. Am.* 63: 1253–1261, 1973.

115. SCHADE, O. H. Optical and photoelectric analog of the eye. *J. Opt. Soc. Am.* 46: 721–739, 1956.

116. SCHADE, O. H. *Image Quality. A Comparison of Photographic and Television Systems.* Princeton, NJ: RCA Laboratories, 1975.

117. SNYDER, A. W., AND R. MENZEL (editors). *Photoreceptor Optics.* New York: Springer-Verlag, 1975.

118. SNYDER, A. W., S. B. LAUGHLIN, AND D. G. STAVENGA. Information capacity of eyes. *Vision Res.* 17: 1163–1175, 1977.

119. STABELL, U., AND B. STABELL. The effect of rod activity on colour matching functions. *Vision Res.* 15: 1119–1125, 1975.

120. STILES, W. S. *Mechanisms of Colour Vision.* New York: Academic, 1978.

121. STILES, W. S., AND B. H. CRAWFORD. Equivalent adaptation levels in localized retinal areas. In: *Report of a Joint Discussion on Vision, Physical Society of London.* London: Cambridge Univ. Press, 1932.

122. STILES, W. S., AND B. H. CRAWFORD. The luminous efficiency of rays entering the pupil at different points. *Proc. R. Soc. London Ser. B* 112: 428–450, 1939.

123. TELLER, D. Y., D. P. ANDREWS, AND H. B. BARLOW. Local adaptation in stabilized vision. *Vision Res.* 6: 701–705, 1966.

124. THOMAS, J. P. Spatial resolution and spatial interaction. In: *Handbook of Perception. Seeing,* edited by E. C. Carterette and M. P. Friedman. New York: Academic, 1975, vol. 5, p. 233–264.

126. VAN NESS, F. L., AND M. A. BOUMAN. Spatial modulation transfer in the human eye. *J. Opt. Soc. Am.* 57: 401–406, 1967.

127. WAGNER, G., AND R. M. BOYNTON. Comparison of four methods of heterochromatic photometry. *J. Opt. Soc. Am.* 62: 1508–1515, 1972.

128. WALD, G. Carotenoids and the visual cycle. *J. Gen. Physiol.* 19: 351–372, 1935.

129. WALD, G. Pigments of the bull frog retina. *Nature* 136: 382, 1935.

130. WALD, G. On the mechanism of the visual threshold and visual adaptation. *Science* 119: 887–892, 1954.

131. WALD, G. The receptors of human color vision. *Science* 145: 1007–1017, 1964.

132. WALD, G. Blue-blindness in the normal fovea. *J. Opt. Soc. Am.* 57: 1289–1301, 1967.

133. WALD, G., AND GRIFFIN, D. The change in refractive power of the human eye in dim and bright light. *J. Optical Soc. Am.* 37: 321–336, 1947.

134. WEALE, R. A. Observations on photochemical reactions in living eyes. *Br. J. Opthalmol.* 41: 461–474, 1957.

135. WEALE, R. A. Further studies of photo-chemical reactions in living human eyes. *Vision Res.* 1: 354–378, 1962.

136. WEALE, R. A. Photo-chemical changes in the dark-adapting human retina. *Vision Res.* 2: 25–33, 1962.

137. WERBLIN, F. S. Adaptation in a vertebrate retina: intracellular recording in *Necturus. J. Neurophysiol.* 34: 228–241, 1971.

138. WESTHEIMER, G. Modulation thresholds for sinusoidal light distributions on the retina. *J. Physiol. London* 152: 67–74,

1960.

139. WESTHEIMER, G. Bleached rhodopsin and retinal interaction. *J. Physiol. London* 195: 97–106, 1968.

140. WESTHEIMER, G. Visual acuity and spatial modulation thresholds. In: *Handbook of Sensory Physiology. Visual Psychophysics*, edited by D. Jameson and L. M. Hurvich. Berlin, Springer-Verlag, 1972 vol. 7, pt. 4, p. 170–187.

141. WILLIAMS, D. R., D. I. A. MacLEOD, AND M. M. HAYHOE. Punctate sensitivity of the blue-sensitive mechanism. *Vision Res.* 21: 1357–1375, 1981.

142. WILSON, H. R., AND J. R. BERGEN. A four mechanism model for threshold spatial vision. *Vision Res.* 1: 19–32, 1979.

143. WINSOR, C. P., AND A. CLARK. Dark adaptation after varying degrees of light adaptation. *Proc. Natl. Acad. Sci. USA* 22: 400–404, 1936.

144. WYSZECKI, G., AND W. S. STILES. *Color Science.* New York: Wiley, 1967.

145. YELLOTT, J. I., JR. Spectral analysis of spatial sampling by photoreceptors: topological disorder prevents aliasing. *Vision Res.* 22: 1211–1218, 1982.

146. YOUNG, T. Note on a paper by Dalton. In: *Lectures on Natural Philosophy*, (1st ed.), 1807, vol. 2, p. 315.

CHAPTER 8

The vertebrate retina

JOHN E. DOWLING | *The Biological Laboratories, Harvard University,*
Cambridge, Massachusetts

MARK W. DUBIN | *Department of Molecular, Cellular, and Developmental*
Biology, University of Colorado,
Boulder, Colorado

CHAPTER CONTENTS

THE VERTEBRATE RETINA is perhaps the most accessible part of the central nervous system. Because the retina is also organized in a highly regular fashion, it serves as a good model system for studying brain function. Synaptic contacts between retinal neurons can be visualized by electron microscopy, and the electrical activity of individual cells can be monitored by intra- and extracellular recording. Such information coupled with knowledge of retinal organization derived from light microscopic techniques permits one to propose synaptic pathways within the retina that subserve particular aspects of visual information processing. This chapter presents a unified approach to the functional organization of the vertebrate retina by discussing recent anatomical, physiological, and pharmacological studies.

All vertebrate retinas are constructed according to the same basic plan (98). Thus, a general description of the retina of any animal is sufficient to describe the retinas of all animals. Figure 1A shows the retina of the mudpuppy, *Necturus maculosa*, an amphibian that has been the subject of extensive study because of its especially large retinal cells. The retina has three nuclear (cellular) layers, interspersed with two synaptic (plexiform) layers. After passage through the optics of the eye, light enters the normally transparent retina at the ganglion cell side, penetrates through the entire retina, and is captured by the most distal retinal elements (photoreceptor outer segments). All photoreceptors have their nuclei lying in the outer nuclear layer.

The inner nuclear layer contains three other types of neuronal cell bodies: the horizontal, bipolar, and amacrine cells. The cell bodies of the remaining type, the ganglion cell, are found in the most proximal cellular layer along the inner margin of the retina. Exceptions to these normal organizational features are that displaced amacrine cells can have their cell bodies in the ganglion cell layer and that displaced ganglion cells can lie along the inner margin of the inner nuclear layer or, rarely, in the midst of the inner plexiform layer. There are, in addition, prominent glial elements (Müller cells) that extend vertically through the entire retina and have nuclei that are usually situated in the inner nuclear layer. Thus within the retina are found five major types of neuronal elements and one principal type of glial cell.

With rare exceptions (7, 47) all of the synapses of the retina are confined to the two plexiform layers. In each of these two layers the processes of three major cell types interact synaptically. Figure 1B is a drawing based on tissue prepared by the Golgi method that schematically illustrates the form of the principal cell types of the retina. Again the mudpuppy is used as the example. The receptor cells (rods and cones) provide the input to the outer plexiform layer. There they synaptically interact with the dendrites of the bipolar cells and the processes of the horizontal cells. The bipolar cells are the output neuron for the outer plexiform layer; all visual information passes from the outer to the inner plexiform layer via the bipolar cell. In contrast the horizontal cells ramify only within the outer plexiform layer. Two main subclasses of horizontal cells have been identified in many species. The A-type horizontal cells lack an axon and normally make contact with only cones as well as other horizontal and bipolar cells. The B-type horizontal cells have a large axonal arborization that usually makes contact with only rod-type photoreceptors, and a dendritic arborization in contact with cones; both arborizations also make contact with other horizontal and bipolar cells. The two ends of the B-type horizontal cell are connected by a long, thin unmyelinated axon that does

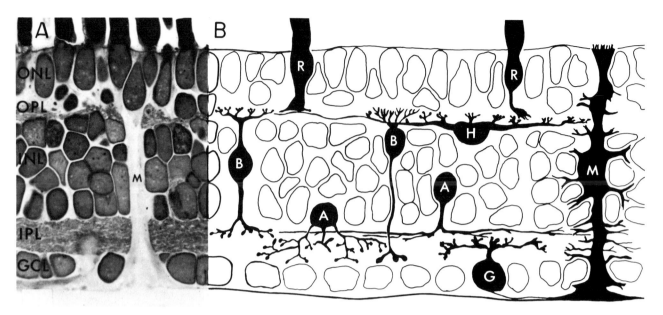

FIG. 1. *A*: light micrograph of the mudpuppy retina showing three nuclear layers, two plexiform layers, and prominent Müller (glial) cells, (M). ONL, outer nuclear layer; OPL, outer plexiform layer; INL, inner nuclear layer; IPL, inner plexiform layer; GCL, ganglion cell layer. × 345. *B*: principal cell types found in vertebrate retina, based on observations of cells in mudpuppy retina impregnated by Golgi method. R, receptors; H, horizontal cells; B, bipolar cells; A, amacrine cells; G, ganglion cells; M, Müller (glial cell). [*A*: adapted from Miller and Dowling (80); *B*: adapted from Dowling (23).]

not conduct action potentials and that is thought to electrically isolate them (91, 94). In both A- and B-type horizontal cells all points may be both pre- and postsynaptic. Thus horizontal cells are well designed to transfer information laterally in all directions in the outer plexiform layer, and the more typical designations of axonal arbor and dendrite are usually replaced by the less committal term *process*.

The inner plexiform layer is organized similarly to the outer plexiform layer. The bipolar cells provide the input to the layer where their terminals come into synaptic relationship with the dendrites of the ganglion cells and the processes of the amacrine cells. Amacrine cells have no axon and, like the horizontal cells in the outer plexiform layer, carry information laterally within the inner plexiform layer. Their extensions are also termed processes and may be both pre- and postsynaptic all along their length. The ganglion

FIG. 2. Examples of synaptic contacts observed by electron microscopy in vertebrate retinas. *A*: ribbon synapses (*arrows*) of cone receptor terminal in rhesus monkey retina. Three processes penetrate into invaginations along terminal base. Lateral processes within invagination are from horizontal cells, H; central elements are bipolar cell dendrites, B. × 38,000. *B*: ribbon synapse of bipolar teminal B (*filled arrow*), and conventional synapse of amacrine process (*open arrow*) in inner plexiform layer of chicken retina. There are usually two postsynaptic processes at ribbon synapses of bipolar terminals and one postsynaptic process at conventional synapses of amacrine cells. Note that amacrine cell process, A, is both a pre- and postsynaptic element. × 45,000. *C*: conventional synapse (*open arrow*) made by horizontal cell process, H, onto bipolar cell dendrite B, in mudpuppy retina. Note that this horizontal cell process is itself postsynaptic at ribbon synapse of receptor terminal (*filled arrow*). × 45,000. *D*: reciprocal synaptic arrangement between bipolar terminal, B, and amacrine cell process, A, in skate retina. Bipolar terminal makes contact with amacrine process at ribbon synapse (*filled arrow*); amacrine process makes conventional synapse (*open arrow*) back onto bipolar terminal. × 40,000. *E*: serial (*open arrows*) and reciprocal (*closed arrow*) synaptic arrangments between four amacrine processes (A_1 – A_4) in frog retina. Micrograph illustrates that amacrine processes may be pre- and postsynaptic along short portions of their length. × 50,000. *F*: superficial or basal contact of flat bipolar cell dendrite (FB) on base of receptor terminal (RT) in frog. Note that there is neither synaptic ribbon nor aggregation of synaptic vesicles associated with these junctions. Some membranous specializations, however, are seen along the junction along with filamentous material in junctional cleft. × 75,000. *G*: an electrical (gap) junction in inner plexiform layer of rat retina between two amacrine cell processes, A. Note that extracellular space between processes making contact is virtually obliterated at the junction. × 100,000. *H*: gap junction in inner plexiform layer of rat retina demonstrated by freeze-fracture method. Numerous tightly packed particles, 80–100 Å in diameter, are characteristic of gap junctions seen in variety of tissues. × 100,000.

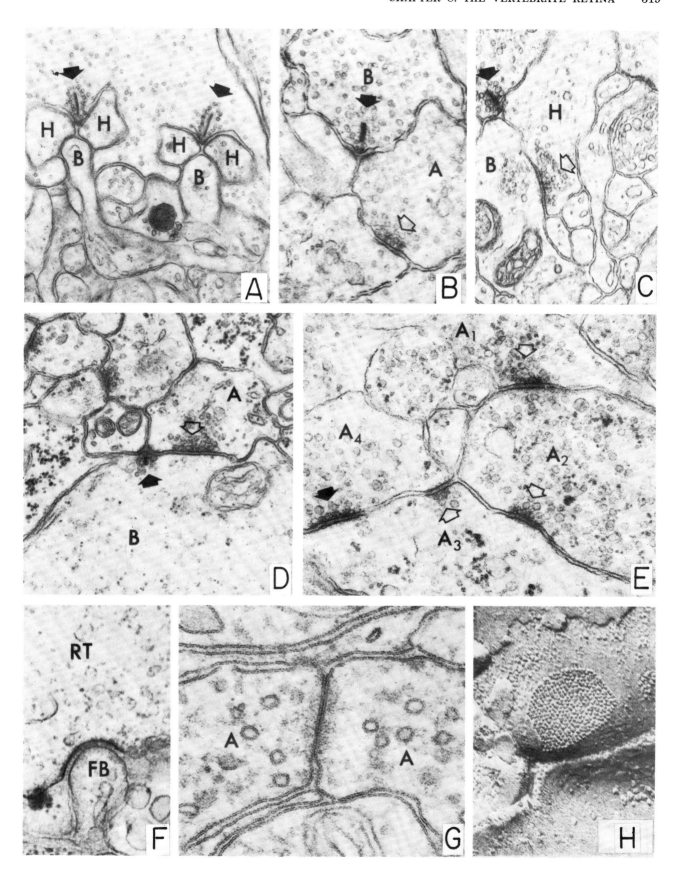

cells provide the output pathway for the inner plexiform layer as well as for the entire retina. Ganglion cell axons leave the retina at the optic nerve head (also called optic disk), where they form the optic nerve and project to other parts of the brain.

Both amacrine cells and ganglion cells are varied in form, suggesting that there are a great many subtypes of these cells. Several authors have suggested numerous subclasses of these cells in various species; however, a satisfactory subdivision based on anatomical criteria has not been generally described [see Boycott and Dowling (6)]. Physiological (see APPENDIX, p. 336, and INTRACELLULAR ACTIVITY, p. 322) and pharmacological studies (see PHARMACOLOGY OF PLEXIFORM LAYERS AND THE INTERPLEXIFORM CELL, p. 332) also suggest a variety of subclasses of these cells; correlations of anatomical, physiological, and pharmacological properties of amacrine and ganglion cells are now being explored.

SYNAPTIC ORGANIZATION

Two prominent types of contacts, believed to represent chemical synapses, have been described by electron microscopy in vertebrate retinas. These synaptic types are found in both plexiform layers. The first type, *ribbon* synapses, are characterized by an electron-dense ribbon or bar in the presynaptic cytoplasm [Fig. 2A–D; (81, 111)]. The ribbon is typically surrounded by a cluster of synaptic vesicles and is usually oriented at right angles to the presynaptic membrane. Multiple postsynaptic elements are usually observed at ribbon synapses in the retina, and electron-dense material is usually observed along the postsynaptic membranes that often give them a slightly thickened appearance (Fig. 2B). Ribbon synapses are made by the receptor terminals in the outer plexiform layer (Fig. 2A, C) and by the bipolar terminals in the inner plexiform layer [Fig. 2B, D; (25, 81)]. Thus the input neurons to the two plexiform layers make synapses of this type.

The second type of synaptic contacts observed in retinas is similar to synapses observed throughout the vertebrate brain, and therefore they have been termed *conventional* synapses [Fig. 2B–E; (25, 60)]. They are characterized by a cluster of synaptic vesicles in the presynaptic terminal close to the presumed synaptic site. Only a single postsynaptic process is observed at these synapses, and some electron-dense material is often observed on and between the pre- and postsynaptic membranes. In the retina, conventional synapses are made principally by the cells with short or no axons, i.e., the horizontal and amacrine cells (23, 25).

As noted earlier in this chapter, the processes of the horizontal and amacrine cells may be both pre- and postsynaptic. Thus both serial and reciprocal synaptic arrangements are often observed involving the processes of these elements in their respective plexiform layers (22, 60). Serial synapses are illustrated in Figure 2B, C, E, i.e., in these micrographs the amacrine or horizontal cell process that receives a synapse makes a synapse onto another element; reciprocal synapses are shown in Figure 2D, E. In these cases the amacrine cell processes that receive a synapse (either ribbon or conventional) make synapses back onto the processes that contact them.

Two other types of presumed synaptic contacts have also been observed in vertebrate retinas. The first of these, believed also to be chemical in nature, is made exclusively by the receptor cell terminals and has been termed a superficial, basal, or flat contact [Fig. 2F; (22, 72, 81)]. In mammals the basal contacts are made only by cones, but in other animals basal contacts are made by both rods and cones (22, 24). Basal contacts are found along the base of the terminal and are made with the dendrites of one subclass (flat bipolar) of bipolar cell (62, 81). At these junctions some electron-dense material on both membranes is seen as well as material within the synaptic cleft; however, neither a ribbon nor a cluster of synaptic vesicles is seen on either side of the contact. The evidence that these junctions are synaptic is twofold: 1) the only contacts made by flat bipolar cells with receptor cells are these basal junctions (62); 2) observations of cells prepared by freeze-fracture technique show that the intramembraneous particle distribution at these junctions is similar to that seen at excitatory synapses elsewhere in the nervous system (100).

Junctions that have the morphological characteristics of electrical (gap) junctions have been observed in many retinas (Fig. 2G, H). Prominent gap junctions between horizontal cells or between their processes are commonly observed (63, 137). In addition, gap junctions between photoreceptors have been found in a number of species (44, 99, 134). Presumed electrical junctions between amacrine cells have also been occasionally reported as well as between some bipolar terminals and amacrine cell processes [(46, 65, 66, 101); J. E. Dowling, unpublished observations].

Figure 3 is a summary diagram showing typical synaptic pathways observed in many retinas; for simplicity, only the chemical synapses are illustrated. Differences between species are quantitative rather than qualitative. That is, all of the synaptic arrangements illustrated here are observed in virtually all retinas. Certain retinas, however, have more of one kind of synaptic arrangement than other synaptic arrangements. This is especially true of the inner plexiform layer.

In the outer plexiform layer (*upper half*, Fig. 3) the receptor terminals make junctions with the processes of the horizontal cells and the dendrites of the bipolar cells. The flat bipolar cells (FB) are postsynaptic at basal junctions, the invaginating bipolar cells (IB) at ribbon contacts (62). As noted earlier in this section, evidence from observations of cells prepared by the freeze-fracture technique suggests that the junction

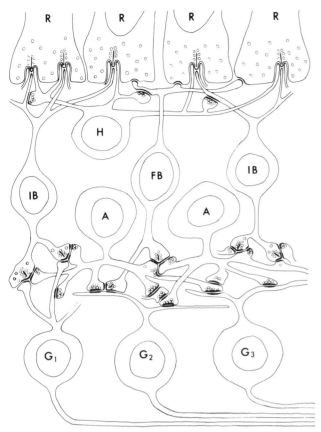

FIG. 3. Summary diagram of arrangements of synaptic contacts found in vertebrate retinas. In outer plexiform layer, processes from invaginating bipolar, IB, and horizontal, H, cells penetrate into invaginations in receptor terminals, R, and terminate near synaptic ribbons of receptors. Processes of flat bipolar cells, FB, make superficial (basal) contacts on bases of some receptor terminals. Horizontal cells make conventional synaptic contacts onto bipolar dendrites. In inner plexiform layer, bipolar terminals most commonly contact one ganglion cell, G, dendrite and one amacrine cell, A, process at the ribbon synapse (*left*), or two amacrine cell processes (*right*). When the latter arrangement predominates in a retina, numerous conventional synapses between amacrine cell processes (serial synapses) are observed. Amacrine cell synapses in all retinas make synapses back onto bipolar teminals (reciprocal synapses). Input to ganglion cells may differ in terms of proportion of bipolar and amacrine synapses. Ganglion cells may receive mainly bipolar input, G_1, an even mix of bipolar and amacrine input, G_2, or exclusively amacrine input, G_3.

between the receptor cells and flat bipolar cells has characteristics of an excitatory synapse, and that the junction between the receptor cells and the invaginating bipolar cells resembles inhibitory synapses that are observed in the brain (100).

The horizontal cells also make contact with the receptor cell terminals at the ribbon synapses. These contacts usually occur within invaginations of the receptor terminal, and often there is a precise arrangement of the processes within the invagination (81, 112). Typically, two horizontal cell processes penetrate more deeply into the invagination and lie on either side of the synaptic ribbon. The more superficially and centrally positioned processes in the invagination are

usually the dendrites of the bipolar cells [(81, 112); see also ref. 114]. What the significance of the invagination may be or what the precise arrangement of the processes within the invagination may mean is obscure. One suggestion proposes that the invagination facilitates interactions between the horizontal process and the bipolar processes or receptor cell terminal, or both (25).

Synapses made by the horizontal cells have been identified in a number of species (23, 26). These synapses are of the conventional type and are made predominantly on bipolar dendrites (Figs. 2C and 3). A horizontal cell synapse feeding back onto a receptor cell terminal has never been observed even though physiological evidence for feedback onto certain receptor cells, especially cones, has been found (3). There remains, therefore, some question about how horizontal cells interact with bipolar cells and receptor cell terminals in many retinas. The horizontal cells, however, spread processes much farther laterally in the outer plexiform layer than do the bipolar cells, and the cellular and synaptic organization of this layer does suggest that bipolar cells are not only driven directly by nearby receptors but also that they can be affected by distant receptor cells via horizontal cells (Fig. 3).

The inner plexiform layer of the retina is thicker than the outer plexiform layer in all vertebrates; more synaptic contacts per unit area are observed, and a greater variety of junctions is observed. The bipolar cell terminals make contact with amacrine cell processes and ganglion cell dendrites at ribbon synapses. Two postsynaptic elements are typically observed at these synapses. This arrangement has been termed a dyad (25); other arrangements also exist (113). The postsynaptic elements at a dyad consist of a ganglion cell dendrite and an amacrine cell process or two amacrine cell processes or, rarely, two ganglion cell dendrites. Which of these pairings predominates is species dependent.

In all retinas numerous conventional synapses made by amacrine cell processes occur in the inner plexiform layer. Amacrine cell synapses are observed on ganglion cell dendrites, on bipolar cell terminals, and on other amacrine cell processes. As noted earlier in this chapter, synapses involving the amacrine cell processes may be organized in a serial or reciprocal fashion. Such synaptic arrangements suggest the possibility of very local interactions between amacrine cell processes and the other elements within the inner plexiform layer.

Another important aspect of inner plexiform organization is sublayering. Two sublaminae (a and b) can be discerned in the cat (46, 92) and in the fish (45). Some ganglion cells ramify all of their dendrites closest to the inner nuclear layer in sublamina a, whereas most other ganglion cells ramify exclusively in sublamina b. This sublamination extends to two classes of bipolar cells that are in contact with cones in the cat. One class makes the superficial-type (flat-type) contacts in the outer plexiform layer, as previously described in this chapter. In the inner plexiform layer this cell type (a flat cone bipolar cell) terminates and makes synaptic contacts only in sublamina a. The other class invaginates its dendrites into receptor terminals at ribbon synapses made by the receptors. In the inner plexiform layer these so-called invaginating cone bipolar cells make synaptic contacts in sublamina b. Thus some ganglion cells can only be in synaptic contact with flat cone bipolar cells, while other ganglion cells can only be in contact with invaginating cone bipolar cells. Certain classes of amacrine cells also appear to be sublaminated in terms of their processes, but bipolar cells of a rod-contacting type do not necessarily fit this picture. The physiological significance of layer sublamination of the inner plexiform is discussed in INNER PLEXIFORM LAYER FUNCTIONAL ACTIVITY, p. 328.

Receptive Fields

Every neuron in the retina "sees" the world through the photoreceptor cells to which it is synaptically linked. This linkage need not be direct; for example, a ganglion cell is not in immediate synaptic contact with photoreceptor cells. Yet it can be traced back to a specific set of roughly contiguous photoreceptor cells via synaptic linkages through bipolar, horizontal, and amacrine cells. The group of receptor cells to which a retinal neuron is linked in this way "look at" an approximately circular patch of space. This region is termed the receptive field of that neuron. The receptive field of a photoreceptor cell corresponds to the region looked at by that photoreceptor cell (see later this page in INTRACELLULAR ACTIVITY for exceptions). The receptive field of the bipolar cell consists of directly overlying photoreceptor cells in contact with it and is further enlarged laterally by the horizontal cells that synapse with it; these horizontal cells are in synaptic contact with other photoreceptors. Each retinal neuron can be treated in similar fashion; indeed each neuron anywhere in the visual system can be described in terms of its receptive field. As with the bipolar cell, each neuron has some central patch of photoreceptor cells to which it is linked by a more direct pathway than other, more lateral photoreceptor cells that ultimately communicate with it. This concept of a central and a surrounding region within a neuron's receptive field has important physiological significance.

The network of synaptically linked neurons that subserve a particular cell's receptive field allows that cell to participate in processing the visual signal. Some connections are excitatory, others inhibitory; together they are organized so that complicated properties can result from the synaptic network. For example, some ganglion cells respond to objects moving in only a particular direction (1). Such properties are monitored electrophysiologically by either intra- or extracellular recordings from single cells. Thus cells are often named according to their observed physiological receptive fields. A ganglion cell like the one just mentioned is often said to have a directionally selective receptive field. In the remainder of this chapter, the results of recordings from retinal neurons are presented, and these observations are associated with the descriptions of the anatomy of these cells described earlier in this section.

INTRACELLULAR ACTIVITY

In most animals, especially mammalian species, retinal neurons are relatively small. Thus intracellular recordings are difficult, and only in a few cold-blooded animals have such recordings been made from all of the retinal cells (55, 76, 87, 132). Recordings from one or a few of the types of cells, however, have been reported for several species (91, 93, 106). The results indicate that the response characteristics of retinal cells are similar across species and that a number of generalizations can be made. The discussion here focuses on recordings from the mudpuppy (132); where relevant, results from other species are also discussed.

Typical responses from each of the neuronal types in the mudpuppy are shown in Figure 4. These responses were assigned to their respective cell types after intracellular staining with Niagara sky blue, which permits identification of perikaryon shape and location within the retina (132). [More recent intracellular staining in the retina has used dyes such as Procion yellow, which has the great advantage of diffusing throughout the cell into both dendritic and axonic processes (55, 76). Thus identification of retinal cell types after Procion yellow staining is often unequivocal.] Müller (glial) cell potentials in the mudpuppy retina have also been identified and characterized (80). Figure 4 does not illustrate the finding that in many species there is a second type of amacrine cell response that is sustained; this is in contrast to the transient amacrine cell responses shown in this figure (57, 76).

The more distal neurons (receptor, horizontal, and bipolar cells) respond to retinal stimulation with sustained potentials that are graded with intensity. Nerve impulses have never been seen associated with these responses. The neurons in the proximal retina—the amacrine cells and ganglion cells—respond with depolarizing potentials on which there are superimposed nerve impulses. The absence of impulses in cells of the distal retina is explained by the fact that these are neurons with relatively short processes that do not transmit information over long distances. Thus electrotonic spread of slow potentials is sufficient for information to reach the furthest extension of these cells. Another finding of unusual interest is that these distal neurons respond mostly with hyperpolarizing potentials. In spike-generating neurons hyperpolari-

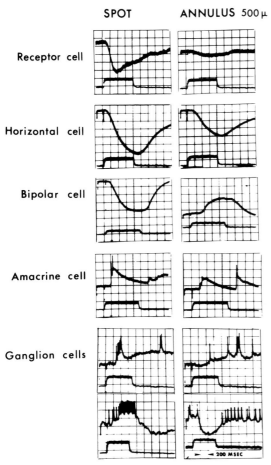

SPOT   ANNULUS 500μ

Receptor cell

Horizontal cell

Bipolar cell

Amacrine cell

Ganglion cells

FIG. 4. Intracellular recordings from neurons in mudpuppy retina. Responses elicited with a spot of light (diam approx. 100 μm) focused over electrode (*left column* of records) or with a centered annulus (radius, 500 μm; width, 100 μm).

zation is usually associated with inhibition. Here, however, no impulses are fired by the cells, and presumably excitation can be signaled by hyperpolarization of the cells. All vertebrate photoreceptor cells recorded hyperpolarize when excited by light; this appears to be compelling evidence that excitation can be signaled by hyperpolarizing potentials in the distal retina (2, 5, 120, 122).

With spot and annular stimulation it is possible to characterize the responses of each cell type and to describe its receptive-field organization. For example, receptor cells in the mudpuppy give large responses to spot illumination but only small responses when annuli are presented. Experiments using spot and annular stimuli together show only small differences when compared with spot stimulation alone. This suggests that receptors in the mudpuppy are not substantially affected by illumination of the region surrounding them. The same appears to be true for rod receptor cells in toad (11), but in turtle it has been shown that illumination of the surround can significantly depolarize cone receptors, apparently via feedback from horizontal cells (3). Evidence for feedback from horizontal

cells to receptors has been obtained also in gecko retina (61) and in the perch and goldfish (12, 54). The evidence thus far suggests that feedback from horizontal cells is more obvious in cone receptors than in rods.

In turtle and marine toads it has been shown that adjacent receptor cells electrically interact, probably via gap junctions between receptors (3, 44, 107, 108). Between cones in the turtle, the summation area has a diameter of only approximately 50 μm; the diameter of the summation area of toad and turtle rods is approximately 200 μm. Significant coupling between rods and cones in the cat also exists (91). The functional significance of receptor cell coupling is not entirely clear, although it has been suggested that such coupling may serve to average the intrinsic noise of photoreceptor cells (71).

Horizontal cells in the mudpuppy respond with large hyperpolarizing potentials to light spots that are presented over a retinal area with a diameter of several hundred micrometers. Thus both spot and annular stimulation evoke sizable potentials (Fig. 4), and when spots and annuli are presented together their effects summate. It has further been shown that horizontal cells are electrically coupled to one another, increasing their receptive-field spread (31, 56, 84). In the mudpuppy virtually all horizontal cells only hyperpolarize in response to light, regardless of stimulus intensity, wavelength, or configuration. All such horizontal cells are termed L-type (luminosity-type) cells. In other species, particularly those with color discrimination, horizontal cells may both hyperpolarize and depolarize, depending on the wavelength of the stimulus (117, 119). Such horizontal cells have been termed C-type (chromaticity-type) cells.

Two physiological types of bipolar cells have been found in the mudpuppy and in all other retinas in which bipolar cell responses have been recorded (55, 76, 106). One type has a sustained hyperpolarizing response to illumination by a central spot (Fig. 4); the other type has a depolarizing response. Annular illumination of either cell type antagonizes, or reduces, the sustained potential produced by a central spot. In the mudpuppy annular illumination does not drive the membrane potential past the resting potential of the cell, so that for one to observe the effects of the illumination of the surround, illumination by a central spot of light must be present. In other species, annular stimulation alone may polarize the cell (55, 76). In almost all species studied, however, an antagonism between the center and surround regions of the receptive field is observed at the bipolar cell level. Thus with appropriate stimulus conditions, potentials of opposite polarity may be obtained from the same bipolar cell (Fig. 4). In a few species it has been established that the flat-type cone bipolar cells are hyperpolarizing in response to illumination by a central light spot, whereas the invaginating cone bipolar cells correspond to the depolarizing bipolar cells.

In the mudpuppy, amacrine cells respond in a predominantly transient way to retinal illumination regardless of the configuration of stimulus used. The amacrine cells are the first cell types along the visual pathway to respond in a primarily transient fashion, and they usually give on- and off-responses to illumination presented anywhere within their receptive fields. Some differences between amacrine cell responses in the relative sizes of the on- and off-components are observed, and these differences usually depend on the geometry and position of stimulation used. For example, recordings from a cell that gives a large on-response to illumination by a central spot are presented in Figure 4. Annular illumination, however, evokes an off-response that is enhanced and is comparable in size to the on-response.

Nerve impulses are superimposed on the transient depolarizing responses of the amacrine cells. In the mudpuppy, however, seldom are more than two spikes observed to be riding on the transient depolarization, regardless of intensity or configuration of the stimulus. Thus it is unclear whether it is either the slow-potential response or the spikes that are the most important component for signal transmission by the amacrine cells. Further, Miller and Dacheux (78) have shown that amacrine cell spikes may be of two types, one generated within the soma and the other generated within the processes of the cell.

As noted earlier in this section, sustained amacrine cell responses have been observed in several species (57, 121). These cells may either hyperpolarize or depolarize in response to light; the response polarity may depend on wavelength (57, 121). Intracellular amacrine cell responses that have both transient and sustained components have also been observed in several species (76, 95, 121).

Two basic types of ganglion cell responses are found in the mudpuppy retina and appear to relate to the activity of one or the other of the cell types (i.e., amacrine or bipolar cells) providing input to the ganglion cells. One ganglion cell type strongly resembles the amacrine cell response, giving transient responses at both the onset and cessation of stimulation (Fig. 4). Differing amounts of on- and off-contributions may be evoked with different stimulus configurations, as is observed with amacrine cell responses. These ganglion cell responses differ from the amacrine cell responses in that the former have numerous spikes riding on the transient depolarization, and in that the number of their spikes that are fired appears to be closely related to the amount of depolarization.

The second type of ganglion cell (*bottom records*, Fig. 4) has a receptive-field organization that more closely resembles that of the bipolar cells. With central illumination a sustained slow potential and a steady discharge of spikes are evoked from the cell. With some central illumination maintained, large annular illumination hyperpolarizes the cell and inhibits firing in a sustained fashion.

OUTER PLEXIFORM LAYER FUNCTIONAL ACTIVITY

Figure 5 is a summary diagram that suggests how synaptic interactions may produce some of the potentials and certain of the receptive-field properties of outer plexiform layer neurons. The bar (*top left*) represents a flash of light that activates the receptive-field center of bipolar cell (B) at *left* as well as the overlying photoreceptor. This same flash is thus in the surround region of the receptive field of the bipolar cell (B) at *right*. As noted earlier in INTRACELLULAR ACTIVITY, p. 322, receptors respond mainly in an autonomous manner. Thus a large receptor response is observed only in the illuminated receptor. The adjacent, nonilluminated receptor shows a small response that may reflect some direct coupling between receptors.

The anatomy of both bipolar and horizontal cells suggests that they are activated by receptors (Figs. 2, 3). The scheme of Figure 5 further suggests that bipolar cells are polarized strongly in a graded, sustained fashion by direct contacts between receptor and bipolar cells (Fig. 5, *left*), and that these bipolar cell potentials are antagonized by horizontal cell contacts (Fig. 5, *right*). Evidence from their anatomy suggests that such interactions between horizontal and bipolar cells could occur at synapses of horizontal cells with

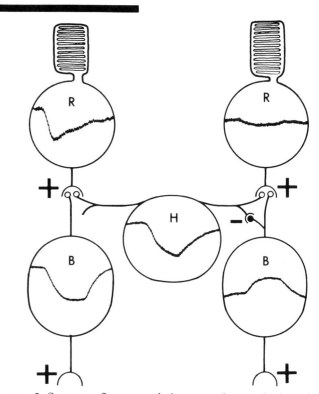

FIG. 5. Summary figure correlating synaptic organization of outer plexiform layer of retina with intracellularly recorded responses from mudpuppy retina. R, receptors; H, horizontal cell; B, bipolar cells.

bipolar cells in some species, or perhaps within invaginations of the receptor terminals, or both (34).

Because horizontal cells usually have a greater lateral extent in the outer plexiform layer than do the bipolar cells, a center-surround type of receptive-field organization is observed in the bipolar cell response. The center reponse appears mediated by the direct synapses between receptor and bipolar cells, the antagonistic surround response by the receptor-horizontal-bipolar cell pathway. In the mudpuppy a typical bipolar cell's physiologically determined receptive-field center matches closely in diameter the dendritic spread of the bipolar cells, whereas the surround response approximates the lateral spread of the horizontal cells. The only other cell type in the mudpuppy retina spreading far enough laterally to account for the antagonistic surround in the bipolar cell response is the amacrine cell, which also synaptically makes contact with the bipolar cells. Mudpuppy amacrine cells, however, respond transiently to retinal illumination at both on and off. The surround inhibition observed in the bipolar cell response is, on the other hand, graded and sustained and has the approximate form of the horizontal cell response.

Naka and colleagues (84, 88) have provided impressive evidence in favor of the hypothesis that horizontal cells form the surrounds of the bipolar cells by injecting hyperpolarizing current into catfish and dogfish horizontal cells. These investigators find that such currents mimic the effect of surround illumination in both bipolar and ganglion cells. Gershenfeld and colleagues (50), however, have provided evidence that some horizontal cells in the turtle may not contribute to the surround responses of certain of the bipolar cells.

Only bipolar cells that hyperpolarize to light presented in their receptive-field centers are illustrated in Figure 5. It must be remembered that another class, depolarizing bipolar cells, also exists. The responses of bipolar cells that depolarize in response to light in

their receptive-field center can be approximated by imagining that the two bipolar cell responses in Figure 5 are exchanged, all else remaining the same.

Given this understanding of the organization of the outer plexiform layer, a number of questions concerning retinal synaptic mechanisms naturally arise. For example, it is well established that neurons release neurotransmitters when depolarized (59). When the retina is excited with light, however, most of the distal neurons hyperpolarize. How, then, do these retinal synapses work? A clue to an answer for this question came some years ago when intracellular horizontal cell responses were first recorded and it was found that in the dark the resting potentials of horizontal cells are low (−25 to −40 mV) relative to other neurons (117). In the light, however, the cells hyperpolize to a level that is similar to the resting potential of most neurons (−60 to −80 mV). Thus horizontal cells appear to be maintained in a partially depolarized state in the dark, and light decreases this maintained depolarization. On the basis of this and other evidence it was proposed (123, 124) that photoreceptors continuously release a depolarizing transmitter in the dark and that light interrupts the flow of this transmitter.

Subsequent studies on vertebrate photoreceptors (52) showed that in the dark there is a steady inward flow of Na^+ across the plasma membrane of the outer segment; light decreases the Na^+ conductance of the outer segment, causing the cell to hyperpolarize. Thus the photoreceptors appear to be partially depolarized in the dark, a condition consistent with the idea of the release of a transmitter from receptor synapses in darkness.

An experiment that directly tests this hypothesis (33) is shown in Figure 6. It is well known that high levels of extracellular Mg^{2+} and certain other divalent cations such as Co^{2+} and Mn^{2+} block neurotransmitter release from the presynaptic terminal at chemical synapses (21, 59, 118). If photoreceptors release a transmitter in the dark, application of Mg^{2+} to the

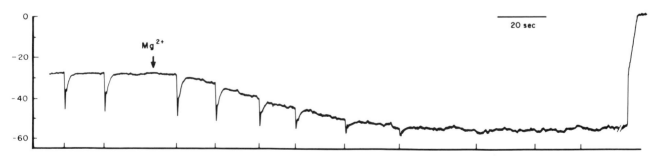

FIG. 6. Experiment showing effects of magnesium on skate horizontal cell. Ringer's solution containing magnesium was applied to retina (*arrow*); within 15–25 s the cell began to hyperpolarize. During next few minutes, cell hyperpolarized to approximately −60 mV, and light-evoked activity was lost. At end of experiment, pipette was withdrawn from cell (break in record). Rapid positive shift of potential of 55 to 60 mV confirmed increase in membrane potential in presence of high levels of magnesium. Test flash intensity and duration (0.2 s) were constant throughout both experiments. Markers along *lower trace* of each record indicate flash presentations. [From Dowling and Ripps (33).]

retina should block this release, causing horizontal cells to hyperpolarize as they do in light. That this is indeed the case is shown in Figure 6. Within a few minutes of the application of Mg^{2+} to skate retinas, horizontal cells hyperpolarized from about −25 mV to about −55 mV, and then their responses to light no longer occurred.

These and similar results strongly support the idea that receptors release transmitter in darkness and that light decreases the flow. Can the activity of the two basic types of bipolar cells in vertebrate retinas (one hyperpolarizing in response to central illumination of its receptive field, the other depolarizing) be explained on the basis of this hypothesis? The receptive fields of both types of cells are organized in such a way that surround or annular illumination antagonizes central stimulation (see Figs. 3 and 5). It has been postulated that the response to illumination by a central spot is mediated by receptor-bipolar cell junctions, whereas the surround antagonism is mediated by interactions between horizontal and bipolar cells (84, 132).

The hyperpolarizing bipolar cells exhibit increased membrane resistance during light stimulation of the center of their respective fields (90, 120); generation of these responses could thus be similar to that of horizontal cell potentials. The responses of depolarizing bipolar cells, on the other hand, provide a more difficult problem. The center response of these cells in the mudpuppy is accompanied by a decrease in membrane resistance (90, 121). If these bipolar cells also receive input to their receptive-field centers directly from receptors, then the effect of the receptor neurotransmitter to decrease conductance of the cell is implied. Thus in the light when transmitter release is decreased, an increased conductance is observed in the bipolar cell. Although this is an unconventional action for a neurotransmitter, recent experiments suggest that this does occur in neurons of frog sympathetic ganglion (127). Findings by Miller and Dacheux (79) that support these views have provided evidence that depolarizing bipolar cells are maintained in a hyperpolarized state in the dark and that hyperpolarizing bipolar cells are maintained in a depolarized state.

If these viewpoints are correct, the synapse between the receptor and the hyperpolarizing bipolar cells can be seen as an excitatory one, whereas the synapse between the receptor and the depolarizing bipolar cells is analogous to an inhibitory junction. The basal junctions made by the receptor onto the dendrites of the flat bipolar cells have certain morphological features consistent with those of excitatory synapses, whereas the junctions between receptor and invaginating bipolar cells appear more inhibitory in nature. These observations are consistent with the findings noted in INTRACELLULAR ACTIVITY, p. 322, i.e., that the flat bipolar cells in the retina are the hyperpolarizing type, whereas the invaginating bipolar cells are the depolarizing type.

Another question with regard to retinal synaptic mechanisms concerns the amount of voltage change across the presynaptic membrane that is required to alter transmitter flow, thus allowing a signal to be detected postsynaptically. The distal retinal neurons respond to light with sustained, graded potentials whose amplitudes are maximally only 20–30 mV. With dim illumination the responses of the distal retinal neurons may be only one or a fraction of a millivolt in amplitude. At other chemical synapses that have been studied, on the other hand, potential changes across the presynaptic membrane of more than 20–30 mV are required for any significant release of neurotransmitter to occur (59, 69, 118).

Some recent measurements of responses of rod receptors stimulated with lights that are near the threshold level have provided insight on this question. It has long been known that rods respond to a single quantum of light and that the perception of light requires the absorption of one quantum by 5–10 rods in a field of approximately 5,000 (53, 96). In the toad, when a field of rods is illuminated with a light that provides an average of only one quantum per receptor, a signal of approximately 1 mV is generated in each rod. When the light is dimmed to levels near the threshold, i.e., one quantum absorbed per 500 to 1,000 rods, all rods continue to see a signal because of the coupling between photoreceptors. The signal generated in any one rod, including those that capture a photon, however, is reduced significantly because of the coupling. Indeed, under these conditions the signals in all rods are so small that they cannot be detected by using present techniques. A calculation (43, 44) indicates that a potential change of no more than 50–100 μV occurs in any rod at threshold levels of illumination. These results indicate, therefore, that exceedingly small presynaptic voltages must be capable of modulating flow of synaptic transmitter at the receptor terminal. It may well be that synapses made by other retinal neurons that respond with graded potentials are also exceedingly sensitive to voltage changes.

How the photoreceptor synapse manages this high degree of voltage sensitivity is not known. The fact that photoreceptor cells are maintained in a partially depolarized state in the dark, however, provides a suggestion. It has been shown that the relation between presynaptic voltage and transmitter release is an S-shaped function. Transmitter release begins when the terminal is depolarized by 20–30 mV and is maximal when the terminal is depolarized by 50 mV or more from rest (59). If the photoreceptor has a similar voltage-release relationship, it would be at a point of significant slope of this function in the dark because the rod is depolarized by at least 30 mV under these conditions. Small, light-induced changes in the presynaptic voltage will thus have significant effects on altering transmitter flow. One reason why receptors and other retinal neurons are maintained in a partially depolarized state in the dark may relate to these considerations.

Another question concerning outer plexiform layer organization is, what function is served by the center-surround organization of bipolar cells? At least one answer to this question can be understood in terms of the phenomenon of adaptation (for general discussions of adaptation see refs. 102, 105). Intracellular recordings of the intensity-response function of a typical cone photoreceptor are shown in Figure 7. Flashes of increasing brightness were presented to the receptor, and the magnitude of the slow–potential response was measured. The figure shows a plot of the magnitude

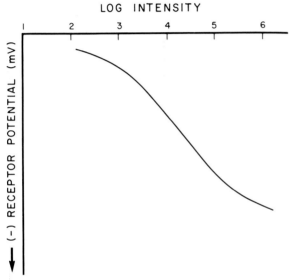

FIG. 7. Intensity-response curve of typical cone photoreceptor. Increasing numbers on log intensity scale indicate brighter stimuli. Receptor potential values are measured peak amplitudes of responses to flashed spot stimuli of approximately 2 s duration. Photoreceptor hyperpolarizes in response to light. Note that entire range of curve spans about 4 log units of illumination and that most of variation in response spans only about 3 log units of illumination. [Adapted from Werblin (129).]

of the response versus the intensity of the flash. Note that this S-shaped intensity-response curve saturates and thus operates over a limited dynamic range. That is, if a light approximately 3–4 log units brighter than the weakest light necessary to elicit a response is used, the response of the photoreceptor reaches a maximum. The range of light over which cones operate, however, is much greater than 3–4 log units. Cones function in twilight and on a bright beach; the range of intensity presented by these situations is about 10 log units. How is it, then, that the 3-to-4-log unit dynamic range of a cone photoreceptor is consistent with this 10-log unit range? The answer to this question lies in the phenomenon of adaptation. Basically, on the beach a luminous object is seen against a different level of ambient background illumination than is present at twilight. Neurons in the retina adjust to the level of background illumination by shifting their dynamic operating region as a function of that background. Much of this process goes on in the photoreceptor cells themselves (9, 32); some also occurs in the bipolar cells and elsewhere in the retinal network (86, 131). The way in which this happens in mudpuppy depolarizing bipolar cells is discussed here to illustrate this process.

The intensity-response curve of a depolarizing bipolar cell in the mudpuppy taken at three different background levels produced by an essentially diffuse illumination directed at the receptive-field surround is shown in Figure 8 (129). The 3.4 curve represents a neutral density filter of that density (log scale) interposed in the light path used to illuminate the surround. The 2.2 and 1.2 curves are taken with less dense filters interposed in the path, i.e., 1.2 represents the brightest background light falling on the surround. Note that at each background level the intensity-response curve of this cell spans a range of about 2.5 log units. The curve is shifted to the right, however, by the antagonistic

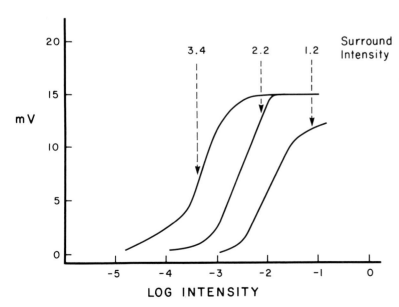

FIG. 8. Intensity-response curves for depolarizing bipolar cell in mudpuppy retina taken at three different background levels. Background levels indicated by numbers labeled Surround Intensity; 1.2 is brightest background. For each curve, steady stimulus of noted intensity (log scale) is presented in surround portion of receptive field of cell. Then, spots in center of receptive field were flashed. Intensities of those spots are shown on abscissa, and peak responses they elicited are indicated in mV on ordinate. Note that antagonistic interaction of center and surround shift operating curve of bipolar cell to the right as function of increased surround illumination. This results in midpoint of operating range falling at an intensity approximately equal to value of background illumination itself. [Adapted from Werblin (130).]

interaction of the surround and the center in such a way as to move the midpoint of the operating range of the cell to an intensity approximately equal to the background illumination. Thus at each background level illumination by a central spot of light of an intensity approximately equal to the surround illumination gives a half-maximal response in the cell. In receptive-field terms, it could be said that the antagonistic input from the horizontal cells that communicate with the surround regions is such that, for a brighter surround illumination, a brighter center illumination is necessary for the bipolar cell to even start responding. In summary, one function of the outer plexiform layer organization in some species is to bring about adaptation to the large stationary background illumination that typically falls on the retina. This allows retinal neurons, which have average dynamic ranges over only a few log units of illumination, to function in both dim and bright lights.

INNER PLEXIFORM LAYER FUNCTIONAL ACTIVITY

As already noted, in INTRACELLULAR ACTIVITY, p. 322, one major class of amacrine cells transiently responds at both the onset and cessation of illumination to light falling anywhere in their receptive field. How the sustained responses of the distal retinal cells are converted to transient responses at the level of amacrine cells is not known, but the anatomy of the synaptic complex between the bipolar cells and amacrine cells provides the basis of a suggestion. The reciprocal synapses of the amacrine cell processes made back onto the bipolar cell terminals just adjacent to the bipolar cell ribbon synapses could conceivably turn off the bipolar cell excitation locally, and a transient response in the amacrine cell could result.

Other effects of inner plexiform layer circuitry are perhaps best studied by examining ganglion cell receptive-field properties. One of the more common types of receptive fields (68) is shown in Figure 9. When the central region of the receptive field of the cell (*left*) is illuminated, the cell increases its firing rate (region represented by plus symbols). Typically the firing rate increases sharply from its maintained (unstimulated) rate at the onset of illumination and then decreases back to a firing level somewhat greater than the maintained rate. At the moment when the light is turned off, the firing rate does not immediately return to the maintained rate. Instead just after the light goes off

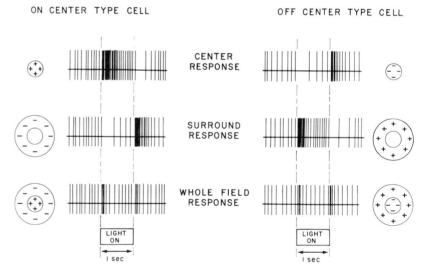

FIG. 9. Idealized response characteristics of typical center-surround type of ganglion cells. Cell at *left* is an on-center, off-surround unit; cell at *right* is an off-center, on-surround cell. For each cell, response is to various stimuli of 1 s duration. *Upper row* is response to a spot of light presented in receptive-field center. On-center cell responds with a burst of spikes at light onset and continues to fire above its unstimulated (maintained) firing rate for duration of stimulus. This cell decreases its firing rate below maintained level to a very low rate for a brief time after stimulus is turned off. This increased response at light onset is indicated by symbols (*pluses*) filling region of receptive field center (*upper left*). Response of this cell to an annular ring of light that covers surround region of receptive field is shown in *second row*. Cell responds with extra firing at light offset in this case; at light onset firing is decreased. This firing pattern is indicated by symbols (*minuses*) in region of the receptive-field surround. *Bottom row* shows that, when both center and surround regions are stimulated simultaneously by a large stimulus that covers entire receptive field, there is a weak burst of spikes both at light onset and light offset. This occurs because illumination of surround region decreases response to stimulation of receptive-field center in same way in which it brought about a decrease in maintained firing rate (*center row*). The off-center cell (*right*) has a similar response to whole-field stimulation but has a reversal of center and surround responses when compared with on-center type of cell.

the cell decreases its firing rate to less than that maintained rate. If an annulus of light is presented to the receptive-field surround region of such a cell, the opposite behavior is seen. Thus at onset of this annular stimulus the cell typically decreases its firing rate to less than the maintained rate. When the illumination of the surround is turned off, the cell undergoes a large, transient increase in firing rate. To signify that the increased response is at the moment when the light is turned off, the surround region is indicated by minus symbols. When both the center and surround are simultaneously illuminated, the response of the cell is an approximate algebraic addition of the two individual responses. At the moment when such whole-field illumination is turned on the cell responds with a burst of spikes weaker than that elicited by the central stimulus alone. This happens because the illumination of the surround, which by itself causes a decrease in the maintained firing rate, causes a similar decrease in the response of the cell to the central stimulation. An analogous interaction between the center and the surround occurs when the light is turned off. Such a receptive field is termed an *on-center*, concentric, antagonistic field (or an on-type-center-surround) receptive field. The names refer to the fact that there are concentric central regions and surrounding regions that cause opposite and antagonistic responses. The appellation on-center is needed because there are other cells that are identical, except the central region (Fig. 9, *right*) gives the off response (minus symbols) and the surround region gives the on response (plus symbols). In animals where such receptive fields occur, the two types (on-center and off-center types) are found in approximately equal numbers.

Such concentric, antagonistic, ganglion cell receptive fields can be understood in terms of the retinal circuitry in the distal retina (for reviews see refs. 77, 130, 136). Evidence from observations using light microscopy is consistent with the summary of ganglion cell activation in Figure 10. On-center ganglion cells are driven directly by depolarizing bipolar cells and off-center ganglion cells by hyperpolarizing bipolar cells. Photoreceptor, bipolar, and horizontal cells are considered to release transmitter substance tonically as a function of their polarization state. Depolarization is associated with increased transmitter release, although positive evidence for this tonic release hypothesis exists as yet only for photoreceptor cells. The way in which this all works out for on-center type of ganglion cells is shown in Figure 10. An analogous analysis holds for off-center ganglion cells. This figure shows that transmitter release from a depolarizing bipolar cell causes ganglion cell excitation. Ganglion cell firing can be understood in terms of center-surround organization of bipolar cells and the way in which that organization controls the release of bipolar cell synaptic transmitter. The reader should refer to Figure 10 for details.

The scheme of Figure 10 explains the function of concentric ganglion cells in at least some species in terms of outer plexiform layer organization; the concentric nature of the ganglion cell receptive field is postulated to be a consequence of such concentric organization in the bipolar cells that drive the ganglion cells. What then is the role of amacrine cells and inner plexiform layer organization? Many amacrine cells are very sensitive to changes in illumination. This is due in part to their transient response to prolonged stimuli. Thus if a small spot of light is moved around within the receptive field of an amacrine cell, that cell will continue to give a response as long as the spot is in motion or each time the spot is moved. A horizontal cell responds in quite a different way—hyperpolarizing to a particular level when the spot is turned on and not indicating that the spot is being moved around in its receptive field, but indicating only that it ultimately is turned off or moved out of the receptive field. In part because of the nature of amacrine cell responses, the inner plexiform layer appears to respond to dynamic (changing) spatiotemporal aspects of a given stimulus. This is in contrast to the outer plexiform layer, where the more static, spatial aspects of the stimulus are important. These differences can be seen directly in the experiment shown in Figure 11. In this experiment a test flash is centered in the receptive field of a ganglion cell. The signal that this light is flashed reaches the ganglion cell directly via bipolar cells. Surrounding the test flash is a truncated windmill that is constrained to illuminate only portions of the surround of the receptive field; the windmill may be either stationary or spinning. Signals from the windmill can reach the ganglion cell only via lateral pathways, either through the horizontal cells or the amacrine cells. The windmill delivers a constant level of illumination to the surround under all conditions, but it also generates a constant change of the pattern of illumination when it is spinning. As long as any vane of the windmill stays within the receptive field of a given horizontal cell the movement should not be reflected by that horizontal cell, which remains hyperpolarized. Further, changes in stimulation of any one horizontal cell that synapses with the central bipolar cell tend to be offset by symmetric changes in stimulation of other such horizontal cells. Thus the fact that the windmill is moving or stationary should not change the polarization of the central bipolar cell. This is exactly what is seen when recordings are made from such a bipolar cell; the outer plexiform layer treats the windmill, moving or otherwise, as if it were simply a constant background stimulus. When recordings are made from any amacrine cell underlying the windmill, however, the result is different.

An amacrine cell responds transiently as any vane of the windmill moves into or out of its receptive field. Thus the continuously moving windmill tends to cause a relatively simultaneous, constant depolarization of all of the amacrine cells in the periphery, due to the

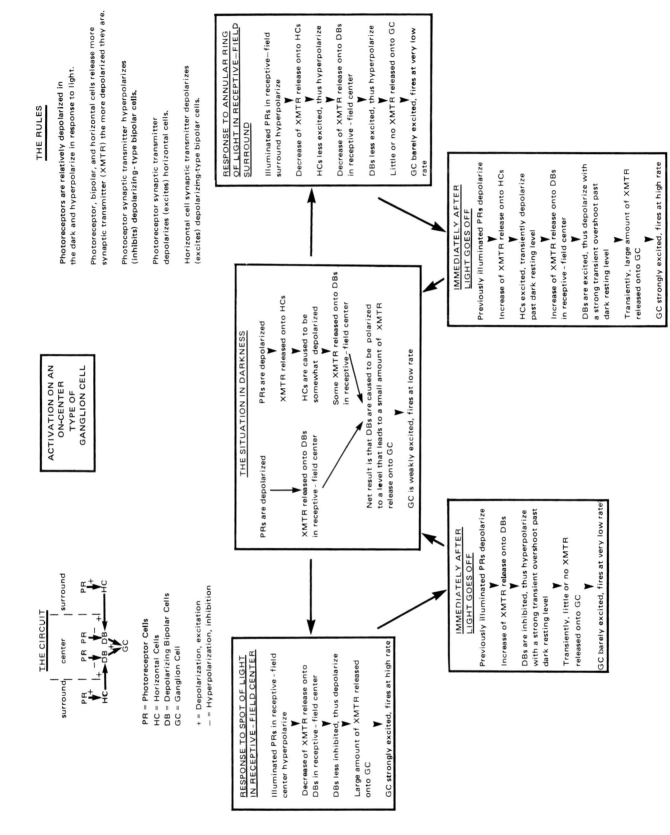

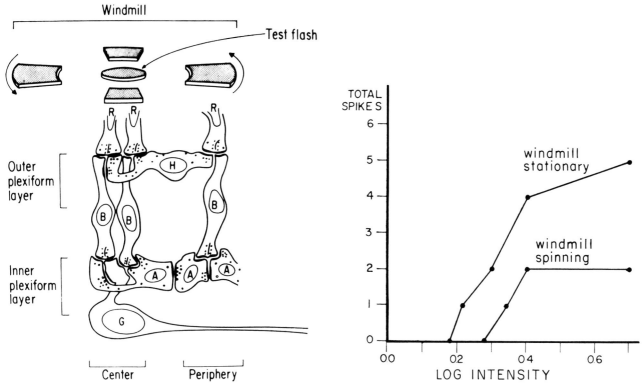

FIG. 11. Diagram (*left*) shows test spot centered in receptive field of ganglion cell and windmill vanes in surround of that cell; retinal neurons driven by these stimuli are diagrammed (*below*). Response (spikes per flash) of ganglion cell to flashes of test spot of increasing intensity is graphed at *right*. Intensity of flash (logarithmic units) is on abscissa. If test flashes are presented when windmill is spinning, ganglion cell responds less strongly than when spots are presented with windmill stationary (see two *curves*). This is taken as evidence that amacrine cells cause response of ganglion cell to be diminished. [Adapted from Werblin (129).]

addition of the repetitive, transient responses caused by the vanes. This is contrasted with a stationary windmill, which causes no continuing response in any amacrine cell. If intracellular recordings are made from a ganglion cell when the windmill spins, the cell is observed to hyperpolarize. This membrane potential movement away from spike threshold can also be seen by testing the ganglion cell with flashes of the centered spot when the windmill is stationary or moving. This is shown in Figure 11 (*right*). The curve marked windmill stationary shows the spike response of the ganglion cell to flashes of increasing intensity of the centered test spot presented when the windmill is not moving. The other curve shows that spike responses to the same range of flashes are diminished if the windmill is moving while they are presented.

The ganglion cell hyperpolarization during windmill movement must be a result of the depolarization of the amacrine cells that signal vane movement in the periphery of the receptive field. This is true because only laterally conducting pathways can bring the windmill stimulus to the ganglion cell and because the horizontal cells, which effectively treat any state of the windmill as a constant background, cannot affect the ganglion cell as a function of windmill movement. Thus the hyperpolarization and firing reduction shown in the two curves of Figure 11 are taken as evidence that at least some amacrine cells seem to antagonize (or depress) ganglion cell responsiveness as a function of spatiotemporal change within an amacrine cell receptive field. This is analogous to the way in which horizontal cells antagonize bipolar cells as a function

---

FIG. 10. Diagram showing way in which photoreceptors, horizontal cells, and depolarizing bipolar cells interact to generate center-surround responses of some types of on-center ganglion cells. Basic retinal circuitry (*upper left*) and basic (The Rules) or initial conditions (*upper right*) apply throughout. Box (*center*) describes states of various cells unstimulated in darkness. Two boxes (*left*, read in order shown by *large arrows*) indicate way in which a centered spot of light stimulates ganglion cell. Two boxes (*right*, read in order indicated by *large arrows*) indicate way in which stimulation confined to receptive-field surround of ganglion cell will affect it. Response of ganglion cell to whole-field stimulation can be approximated by appropriate conjunction of relevant parts in descriptions.

of overall illumination level. The pathway for such amacrine effects onto the ganglion cell could be direct, involving synapses of amacrine cells with ganglion cells that generate inhibitory postsynaptic potentials (IPSPs), or it could occur via negative feedback from amacrine cells to bipolar cells. It is probable that both of these pathways are used, and direct evidence for the former exists in some cases (130).

As illustrated in Figure 4, some ganglion cells respond to a stimulus of light for the length of time it is on, whereas others respond only transiently when the stimulus is turned on and off. Ganglion cells of the first type are similar to bipolar cells, while those of the second more closely resemble amacrine cells. It is likely that the former receive their inputs directly from bipolar cells, whereas the latter on-off type of ganglion cells are predominated by amacrine cell synaptic input. These on-off ganglion cells respond very well to motion, and many show complicated receptive-field properties such as those discussed later in this section (95, 128). In fact, an anatomical study in the ground squirrel shows that some ganglion cells do receive their input entirely from amacrine cells (133).

These ideas of amacrine cell function are more fully developed when we try to understand the receptive fields of many ganglion cells that are significantly more complicated than the relatively simple concentric center-surround types (for review see ref. 73). For example, independent of stimulus contrast, some ganglion cells respond to a stimulus moving in a given direction, but not in the opposite direction. Other ganglion cells have surround regions in which stimulation does not fire the cell, but in which moving stimuli reduce the response to excitatory stimulation in the center of the receptive field. Other cells respond only to bars of light in specific orientations, still others to the number of edges in their receptive field. It seems likely, therefore, that varying the amount of amacrine cell input to a ganglion cell alters its properties. There also appear to be several subtypes of amacrine cells, and varying the kind of amacrine input to a ganglion cell is also likely to alter the properties of its receptive field.

There is some direct evidence that some of these more complicated types of receptive fields involve amacrine cell pathways. In the rabbit (13–15), drugs that block synaptic transmitters that have been ascribed to amacrine cells cause ganglion cell receptive fields to simplify and lose some of their motion- or orientation-sensitive properties. Comparative observations of the anatomy of a number of species (22, 36, 38) indicate that 1) in the retinas of species where the simple, concentric type of receptive-field organization is predominant, bipolar cell terminals make numerous direct contacts with ganglion cell dendrites; in the retinas where the more complex type of receptive-field organization is predominant, relatively fewer, direct contacts between bipolar and ganglion cells occur; 2) there are significantly more amacrine synapses and

interactions between some amacrine cells and other amacrine cells in retinas with complicated receptive fields compared with retinas mainly containing the simpler type of receptive field.

Similar correlations are found when the elements at a bipolar cell synaptic dyad are quantified. When the anatomies of various species are compared, it is observed that the retinas with simple receptive-field organization (such as in the monkey and cat) have many dyad pairings consisting of one amacrine and one ganglion cell process, a relatively low number of amacrine synapses per unit area, and few serial synapses (22, 36). On the other hand the retinas with more complex receptive-field organization (such as in the frog and pigeon) have dyad pairings consisting mostly of two amacrine cell processes, abundant amacrine synapses per unit area, and many serial synapses. Retinas with numerous examples of both types of receptive fields (i.e., rabbit, ground squirrel, and mudpuppy) have approximately equal numbers of pairings of amacrine and ganglion cells and pairings of amacrine and amacrine cells associated with the dyads and intermediate numbers of amacrine synapses and serial synapses per unit area.

These ideas of amacrine function are illustrated in Figure 3. The *left side* of the figure represents a relatively simple inner plexiform layer organization; the ganglion cell G_1 receives its input mainly via direct synapses between bipolar cells and ganglion cells. The predominant pathway through the retina to cell G_1 is thus a three-neuron chain: photoreceptor cell → bipolar cell → ganglion cell. The *right side* of the figure shows a retina with ganglion cells having more complex properties. Ganglion cell G_3 receives its input mainly from amacrine cell processes that make many contacts among themselves and onto ganglion cell dendrites. Here the predominant pathway through the retina is lengthened to a four-neuron chain: photoreceptor → bipolar → amacrine → ganglion cell. The middle ganglion cell, G_2, represents an intermediate type of receptive field that has equal input from bipolar and amacrine cells. Add to this picture the idea that some synapses are inhibitory, whereas others are excitatory, and the potentially complex information processing that may occur in the inner plexiform layer is highlighted.

PHARMACOLOGY OF PLEXIFORM LAYERS AND THE INTERPLEXIFORM CELL

Identifying the specific neurotransmitters employed at the various retinal synapses has proved to be a difficult task. In the outer plexiform layer it has been shown that the acidic amino acids, aspartate and glutamate, have effects on bipolar and horizontal cells that closely mimic the effects of the receptor cell transmitter, i.e., horizontal and hyperpolarizing bipolar cells are depolarized by these agents, whereas the depolarizing bipolar cells are hyperpolarized (16, 32, 82, 83). Evidence has been provided that L-aspartate may be one receptor transmitter (135), although objections to this view have been raised (126). By use of histochemical methods, the inhibitory transmitter γ-aminobutyric acid (GABA) has been observed to be present in the outer plexiform layer and has been found to be localized in certain of the horizontal cells in goldfish (70).

In the inner plexiform layer five neurotransmitters—acetylcholine, GABA, glycine, dopamine, and an indoleamine (perhaps serotonin)—have been identified by histochemical and, in some cases, other methods (39, 51, 75, 89, 125). In addition, recent work has indicated that a number of neuropeptides are also present in this layer (10, 58, 138; B. Ehinger and K. Tornquist, unpublished observations). All of these substances have been associated with amacrine cells and their processes. It thus appears that there are pharmacologically distinct types of amacrine cells, perhaps as many as 10 to 15 types, each containing and presumably employing a different neurotransmitter. It is likely that these pharmacological types of amacrine cells make specific and different connections within the inner plexiform layer and mediate different functions. Evidence in support of this view has come from studies of the amacrine cells that accumulate (and presumably use as their neurotransmitter) either dopamine or an indoleamine (28, 41). The dopaminergic amacrines make synaptic contacts only with other amacrine cells and their processes, whereas the amacrine cells that accumulate indoleamines make connections principally with bipolar terminals. Neither of these subtypes of amacrine cells makes direct connections with ganglion cells. Those amacrine cells that make direct ganglion cell connections presumably use glycine, acetylcholine, or GABA. Figure 12 summarizes all of these findings. Although more research is needed, these results clearly imply that several pharmacological subtypes of amacrine cells make different synaptic connections and presumably produce distinct physiological effects.

In most retinas only certain amacrine cells contain dopamine (39). In two groups of animals, however, teleost fishes and New World monkeys, there is a different kind of dopaminergic neuron that had not previously been recognized (40). The perikarya of these neurons reside in the inner portion of the inner nuclear layer among the amacrine cells, and they extend processes widely in the inner plexiform layer like many amacrine cells. They differ from amacrine cells, however, in that they also extend processes to the outer plexiform layer, where they arborize extensively. Recent Golgi-stain studies have shown that this type of neuron is present in a variety of species (7, 49), so it appears to be a general feature of vertebrate retinas. Curiously, only in teleost fishes and New World monkeys do these cells contain dopamine; the transmitter used by these cells in other animals is

unknown. These neurons have been termed interplexiform cells, and their role in the retina is under active investigation at the present time, (27, 28, 30, 54).

Figure 13 shows a summary diagram of the synapses made by the interplexiform cells in the goldfish. The input to the interplexiform cells is exclusively in the inner plexiform layer, coming from amacrine cells. In the inner plexiform layer interplexiform cells themselves make synapses on amacrine cells only. In goldfish they never contact bipolar terminals or ganglion cell dendrites. In the outer plexiform layer the interplexiform cells are exclusively presynaptic. They form abundant synapses on the externally positioned horizontal cells; also they make some synapses onto bipolar dendrites. They do not make contact with receptor terminals. The interplexiform cells thus appear to provide a centrifugal pathway for information flow in the retina from inner to outer plexiform layers. All of the input to these cells is in the inner plexiform layer, whereas the output for these cells is in both plexiform layers and is especially prominent in the outer plexiform layer. Recent studies on interplexiform cells in the cat and New World monkey indicate a similar synaptic organization; i.e., input to these cells is in the inner plexiform layer and output is in both plexiform

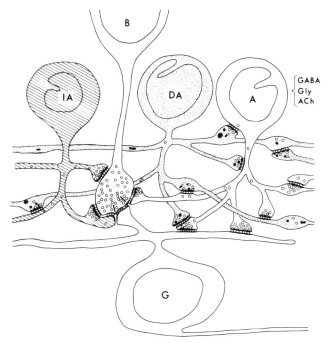

FIG. 12. Summary of amacrine cell circuitry in inner plexiform layer with attention to synaptic transmitter used by amacrine cells. Dopaminergic amacrine cells, DA, make pre- and postsynaptic contacts only with other amacrine cells. Amacrine cells that use indoleamines, IA, are pre- and postsynaptic mainly with bipolar terminals, B, although they also make some connections with amacrine cells. Connections of other amacrine cells, A, that use γ-amino butyric acid (GABA), glycine (Gly), or acetylcholine (Ach) have yet to be specifically determined, although at least some of these subclasses must provide synaptic output directly onto ganglion cells, G.

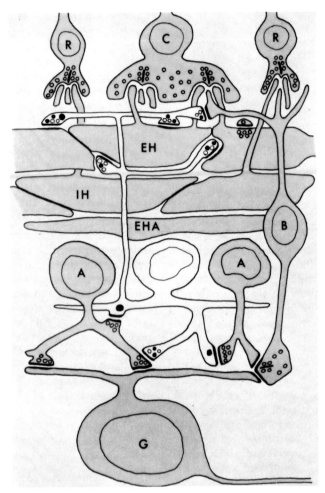

FIG. 13. Schematic diagram of synaptic connections of interplexiform cells of goldfish retina. Input to these neurons is in inner plexiform layer from amacrine cells, A. Interplexiform cell processes make synapses onto amacrine cell processes in inner plexiform layer, but never contact ganglion cells, G, or their dendrites. In outer plexiform layer, processes of interplexiform cells surround external horizontal cells, EH, making synapses on external horizontal cell perikarya and onto bipolar cell, B, dendrites. Interplexiform cell processes have never been observed as postsynaptic elements in outer plexiform layer at either rod, R, or cone, C, receptor terminals or at occasional external horizontal synapse. Also, no synapses are observed between interplexiform cell processes and elements of intermediate and internal horizontal cell layers. Intermediate (rod) horizontal cell (IH) and external horizontal cell axon process (EHA) are indicated. [From Dowling and Ehinger (28).]

layers [(67); J. E. Dowling and B. Ehinger, unpublished observations].

The physiological characteristics of the interplexiform cell have been investigated by applying dopamine to various retinal neurons while making intracellular recordings of their activity (54). The results of this work can be interpreted as follows: dopamine depolarizes horizontal cells and depresses their responsiveness to light. This results in a decrease of lateral inhibition in the outer plexiform layer, expressed in the receptor response by an alteration in wave form and in the bipolar cell by a decrease in the response to annular

illumination. In addition, dopamine appears to have a direct effect on bipolar cells, which results in a small change in the resting potential observed in the dark and an increase of responsiveness to illumination by a central spot.

It would appear, therefore, that one role of the interplexiform cells is to regulate center-surround antagonism in the outer plexiform layer. The activation of these cells depresses lateral inhibitory effects mediated by horizontal cells and enhances responsiveness of bipolar cell centers. There is less information on the role interplexiform cells may play in the inner plexiform layer. Dopamine appears to depolarize and desensitize the transient amacrine cells but not the sustained amacrine cells. It is thus conceivable that interplexiform cells could suppress lateral inhibitory effects mediated by transient amacrine cells in the inner plexiform layer.

SUMMARY

Figure 14 is a summary of much of the information currently available concerning the synaptic interactions in the retina and of how the major types of ganglion cell receptive fields may be formed. This diagram is derived from the work of a number of laboratories and focuses mainly on the physiological interactions that have been described. In this diagram excitatory (open circles) or inhibitory (closed circles) synapses are indicated. In the retina, however, this is often not easy to decide; thus a synapse indicated as excitatory means that the postsynaptic response is of the same polarity as the response in the presynaptic element. Conversely, a synapse indicated as inhibitory represents a situation where the postsynaptic response is of opposite polarity or where the postsynaptic response is diminished as a result of synaptic action. Known reciprocal interactions between two elements are also indicated (open triangles).

The first synaptic interaction in the retina occurs between the receptors themselves. This is an electrical interaction, shown here as being mediated by junctions between the receptor cell terminals. Electrical junctions between receptor cells have also been observed, however, at the level of the inner segments (20, 44). Specificity of the coupling has been reported (4)— that is, coupling between receptor cell types of the same class (rod and rod, or red cone and red cone) is strong, while coupling between different classes of receptor cells is generally very weak or not detectable (44, 107, 108), although strong rod-cone coupling exists in the cat (91). In addition, rod-rod coupling is more extensive than cone-cone coupling.

The receptor cells make chemical synapses with the bipolar and horizontal cells. The basal junctions made by the receptor cells onto the flat bipolar cells appear to be excitatory; i.e., in Figure 14 these bipolar cells (HB) hyperpolarize in response to illumination by a

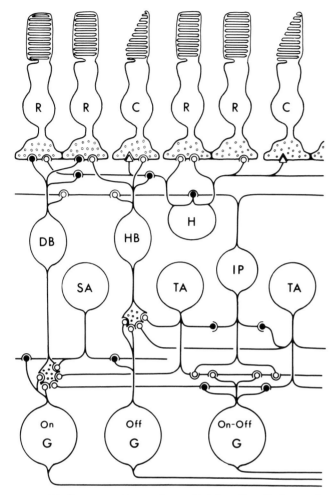

FIG. 14. Summary scheme of synaptic interactions that occur in retina and that underlie receptive-field properties of on, off, and on-off ganglion cells. Excitatory synapses (*open circles*), inhibitory junctions (*filled circles*), and reciprocal synapses (*triangles*) are indicated.

goldfish, however, the evidence previously described suggests that IP cells depress the light-evoked activity of the horizontal cells and enhance the responsiveness of the bipolar cells. Thus IP cells appear to regulate both lateral inhibitory effects mediated by horizontal cells and the strength of center-surround antagonism.

There are also electrical synapses observed in the outer plexiform and inner nuclear layers. These involve mainly the horizontal cells. In some species of animals, i.e., fishes, the junctions are between the cell perikarya; in other species the junctions are observed to be between cell processes. In all cases it appears that the electrical coupling between horizontal cells increases the receptive field of these cells, allowing the effects of the cells to be seen over a much wider area.

In the inner plexiform layer the bipolar terminals appear to make primarily excitatory contacts with ganglion cells. Ganglion cells that make contacts only with depolarizing bipolar cells are the on-center ganglion cells; those ganglion cells that make contacts with the hyperpolarizing bipolar cells are therefore the off-center bipolar cells. K.-I. Naka and colleagues (85) have further shown that the sustained amacrine cells in the catfish retina interact with the on- and off-center ganglion cells. The sustained amacrine cells provide a surround antagonism to the responses of these cells in the inner plexiform layer similar to the surround antagonism imparted by horizontal cells to bipolar cell responses in the outer plexiform layer.

On-off ganglion cells, typical of the non-center-surround cells, are more complicated. Clearly they receive substantial input from amacrine cells of the transient type, and much of this input is inhibitory. Whether they receive their excitatory input from bipolar cells or amacrine cells is unclear. Regardless of the case, it appears that the on-off ganglion cells receive substantial inhibitory input from the transient amacrine cells. This inhibitory input significantly affects the ganglion cell responses and is probably responsible for determining their complex properties. To answer the question of how these inhibitory circuits work, which presumably involves the various pharmacological subtypes of amacrine cells, requires future research.

The amacrine cells receive their input from the bipolar cells. Miller (77) has proposed that transient amacrine cells receive input from both the hyperpolarizing and depolarizing bipolar cells; the opposite polarities of response of the two cell types coupled with small latency differences could explain the transient nature of these amacrine cell responses. It might be supposed, therefore, that sustained amacrine cells receive their input from one or another of the types of bipolar cells, depending on whether the sustained amacrine cell is primarily hyperpolarizing or depolarizing. The anatomy of reciprocal synapses between bipolar cells and amacrine cells has been described; no evidence concerning the physiology for such an interaction has as yet been described. As previously noted, the feedback synapses between bipolar and amacrine

central spot. On the other hand, the ribbon contacts between receptor cells and invaginating bipolar cells appear to be inhibitory; i.e., these cells (DB) depolarize in response to illumination by a central spot. Receptor cells also drive the horizontal cells at the ribbon synapses; these junctions are excitatory. Like the receptor cells, horizontal cells mainly hyperpolarize in response to illumination. Horizontal cells (H) interact with the receptor terminals of some receptor cells, primarily cones, in a reciprocal fashion (open triangles)—that is, the horizontal cells feed back onto the receptor cells, depolarizing them.

The horizontal cells also appear to mediate the surround antagonism observed in bipolar cells. This surround antagonism in some cases may be mediated presynaptically through the receptors or by direct interactions with bipolar cell dendrites. The final chemical synaptic interaction described in the outer plexiform layer involves the interplexiform cells (IP), about whose physiology we have little knowledge. In cells may serve to enhance the transient nature of certain amacrine cell responses.

The last group of synaptic interactions in the inner plexiform layer to be considered in this chapter is that of the interplexiform cells. Some indirect evidence indicates that the interplexiform cells are driven by transient amacrine cells. Because dopamine only affects transient amacrine cells in the goldfish retina, the interplexiform cells possibly only make synapses onto the transient amacrine cells (54). What role the interplexiform cells play in the inner plexiform layer is unclear. By analogy to their role in the outer plexiform layer, they may modulate the inhibitory interactions mediated by the transient amacrine cells.

In summary, the response of the output neurons, the bipolar and ganglion cells, of the two plexiform layers of the retina is substantially shaped by inhibitory interactions mediated by the intrinsic interneurons of the plexiform layers, the horizontal and amacrine cells. These inhibitory interneurons, in turn, appear to be under the influence of another class of neuron, the interplexiform cells, which may modulate the primary inhibitory interactions within the retina. Thus there may be two levels of control exerted within each plexiform layer on the responses of the output neurons.

Finally, it should be stressed that the diagram in Figure 14, although complex, probably reflects only the simplest of interactions that occur within the retina. Ganglion cell receptive-field organization observed in many species shows a remarkable diversity and complexity that cannot yet be explained. We have come a long way in understanding this tiny piece of the brain, but much work lies ahead.

APPENDIX

Ganglion Cell Functional Terminology

Many ganglion cells are of the antagonistic, center-surround type; others require more parameters to completely describe them. This situation is well exemplified by ganglion cells in the cat, although the underlying principles clearly cross species lines. Enroth-Cugell and Robson (42) have shown that concentric on- and off-center cells could be described in terms of yet another property. Certain of the cells were found to have a line of symmetry through their center such that when a field of illumination that covered the region to one side of the line was suddenly changed to illuminate the other side, the cell would not respond. (This stimulus change does not alter the amount of light falling on the receptive field, but does change the place in the receptive field where it is presented.) This type of ganglion cell is somewhat like a horizontal cell; its response is simply a function of the net excitation in the receptive field. The line of symmetry is not unique in orientation. These ganglion cells have roughly circular receptive fields; when the stimulus is at almost any orientation passing through the center of the receptive field there is no response. Such cells have been given the noncommittal name *X-type* cells. A second type of ganglion cell always responded to a positional exchange of such a stimulus, independent of the placement of the line through the receptive field. A relatively strong response was found at all possible placements of the line about which the stimulus was exchanged. Cells of this sort have been termed *Y-type* cells. Significant subsequent experimentation [see Dubin and Cleland (37) for review] has shown that these are indeed two independent classes of cells. For example, it has been shown (17) that the responses of X-type cells to stationary spots of light centered in the receptive field are sustained in nature, whereas the responses of the Y-type cells to the same stimuli are much more transient. The X- and Y-type cells have been shown to correspond to two anatomically different classes of ganglion cells (8), and partial serial section reconstructions have suggested that the X-type ganglion cells receive predominantly bipolar cell input, whereas Y-type cells receive predominantly amacrine cell input (64). In addition, these cell types have differing patterns of central termination of their axons in the brain (18, 19, 104). The original names are no longer the only ones applied to these cells, and the various terminologies are reviewed elsewhere (37, 104). The X- and Y-type properties are superimposed on the basic on- and off-center types; thus one can find on-X, off-X, on-Y, and off-Y types of ganglion cells.

Subsequent work has shown that there are other ganglion cells in the cat retina that do not seem to conform to the properties of the classes just described. Such cells had only sporadically been observed over the years, probably because their cell bodies are extremely small and recordings from them are not easily made. Extensive studies using various search strategies and technical variations of electrode technology, however, have more fully characterized these cells (18, 19, 115, 116). A variety of evidence from observations of the anatomy and physiology of these cells suggests they compose between one-third and one-half of all cat ganglion cells. Some of these cells do not have demonstrable surrounds; others are not organized in a concentric fashion. Even the cells that are on- or off-center, antagonistic, concentric types differ from those previously described in that they have a very low maintained firing rate and respond in only a sluggish fashion to optimal stimulation. Originally all such cells that did not fit the X- or Y-type pattern were termed *W-type* cells (116). In many ways this name has become a catch-all that serves to mask the true differences among these types of receptive fields. The only feature that they all have in common is that anatomically or physiologically they are neither X- nor Y-type cells. Also, the central pattern of termination in the CNS of many of these types of cells is somewhat different from that of X- and Y-type cells. For these reasons, some workers have chosen to call these cells by a variety of names (for review see refs. 37, 103, 104). What should not be obscured by these terminology difficulties is that in all animals ganglion cells receive some diversity of input, particularly amacrine cell input, and this results in a variety of receptive-field properties. The danger of the term W-type cell is that it tends to deemphasize this basic fact; it is unlikely that a sluggish type of concentric cell is more like a directionally selective unit than it is unlike a standard X- or Y-type unit. A tendency has developed to apply to other species the classification using W, X, and Y terminology that was developed from studies in the cat. Although it is clear that X- and Y-like ganglion cells can be found in animals such as the monkey (35, 74, 110), tree shrew

(109), rabbit (13), and rat (48), care must be taken to differentiate between homology and analogy. The problem becomes more extreme with regard to so-called W-type ganglion cells in other species. Whereas such a name says what type the cell is not (namely X or Y), that is almost all that it does say. Terminology or classification schemes that would help point toward physiological and anatomical similarities across species will be more useful in the long run, especially if, as the evidence from the studies of the pharmacology of the cells suggests, there are numerous subclasses of amacrine cells that subserve these various ganglion cell types.

The authors thank Patricia Sheppard for preparation of the figures.

This work was supported in part by National Institutes of Health Grants EY-00824, EY-00811 (J. E. Dowling), and EY-00998 (M. W. Dubin).

REFERENCES

1. BARLOW, H. B., AND W. R. LEVICK. The mechanism of directionally selective units in the rabbit's retina. *J. Physiol. London* 178: 477–504, 1965.

2. BAYLOR, D. A., AND M. G. F. FUORTES. Electrical responses of single cones in the retina of the turtle. *J. Physiol. London* 207: 77–92, 1970.

3. BAYLOR, D. A., M. G. F. FUORTES, AND P. M. O'BRYAN. Receptive fields of cones in the retina of the turtle. *J. Physiol. London* 214: 256–294, 1971.

4. BAYLOR, D. A., AND A. L. HODGKIN. Detection and resolution of visual stimuli by turtle photoreceptors. *J. Physiol. London* 234: 163–198, 1973.

5. BORTOFF, A. Localization of slow potential responses in the *Necturus* retina. *Vision Res.* 4: 626–627, 1964.

6. BOYCOTT, B. B., AND J. E. DOWLING. Organization of the primate retina: light microscopy. *Philos. Trans. R. Soc. London Ser. B* 255: 109–184, 1969.

7. BOYCOTT, B. B., J. E. DOWLING, S. K. FISHER, H. KOLB, AND A. M. LATIES. Interplexiform cells of the mammalian retina and their comparison with catecholamine-containing retinal cells. *Proc. R. Soc. London Ser. B* 191: 353–368, 1975.

8. BOYCOTT, B. B., AND H. WÄSSLE. The morphological types of ganglion cells of the domestic cat's retina. *J. Physiol. London* 240: 397–419, 1974.

9. BOYNTON, R. M., AND D. N. WHITTEN. Visual adaptation in monkey cones: recordings of late receptor potentials. *Science* 170: 1423–1426, 1970.

10. BRECHA, N., H. J. KARTEN, AND C. LAVERACK. Enkephalin-containing amacrine cells in the avian retina: immunohistochemical localization. *Proc. Natl. Acad. Sci. USA* 76: 3010–3014, 1979.

11. BROWN, J. E., AND L. H. PINTO. Ionic mechanism for the photoreceptor potential of the retina of *Bufo marinus. J. Physiol. London* 236: 575–591, 1974.

12. BURKHARDT, D. A. Responses and receptive-field organization of cones in perch retinas. *J. Neurophysiol.* 40: 53–62, 1977.

13. CALDWELL, J. H., AND N. W. DAW. New properties of rabbit retinal ganglion cells. *J. Physiol. London* 276: 257–276, 1978.

14. CALDWELL, J. H., AND N. W. DAW. Effects of picrotoxin and strychnine on rabbit retinal ganglion cells: changes in centre surround receptive fields. *J. Physiol. London* 276: 299–310, 1978.

15. CALDWELL, J. H., N. W. DAW, AND H. J. WYATT. Effects of picrotoxin and strychnine on rabbit retinal ganglion cells: lateral interactions for cells with more complex receptive fields. *J. Physiol. London* 276: 277–298, 1978.

16. CERVETTO, L., AND E. F. MACNICHOL, JR. Inactivation of horizontal cells in turtle retina by glutamate and aspartate. *Science* 178: 767–768, 1972.

17. CLELAND, B. G., M. W. DUBIN, AND W. R. LEVICK. Sustained and transient neurones in the cat's retina and lateral geniculate nucleus. *J. Physiol. London* 217: 473–496, 1971.

18. CLELAND, B. G., AND W. R. LEVICK. Brisk and sluggish concentrically organized ganglion cells in the cat's retina. *J. Physiol. London* 240: 421–456, 1974.

19. CLELAND, B. G., AND W. R. LEVICK. Properties of rarely encountered types of ganglion cells in the cat's retina and an overall classification. *J. Physiol. London* 240: 457–492, 1974.

20. CUSTER, N. V. Structurally specialized contacts between the photoreceptors of the retina of the axolotl. *J. Comp. Neurol.* 151: 35–56, 1973.

21. DEL CASTILLO, J., AND B. KATZ. The effects of magnesium on the activity of motor nerve endings. *J. Physiol. London* 124: 553–559, 1954.

22. DOWLING, J. E. Synaptic organization of the frog retina: an electron microscopic analysis comparing the retinas of frogs and primates. *Proc. R. Soc. London Ser. B* 170: 205–228, 1968.

23. DOWLING, J. E. Organization of vertebrate retinas. *Invest. Ophthalmol.* 9: 655–680, 1970.

24. DOWLING, J. E. Synaptic arrangements in the vertebrate retina: the photoreceptor synapse. In: *Synaptic Transmission and Neuronal Interaction*, edited by M. V. L. Bennett. New York: Raven, 1974, p. 87–101.

25. DOWLING, J. E., AND B. B. BOYCOTT. Organization of the primate retina: electron microscopy. *Proc. R. Soc. London Ser. B* 166: 80–111, 1966.

26. DOWLING, J. E., J. E. BROWN, AND D. MAJOR. Synapses of horizontal cells in rabbit and cat retinas. *Science* 153: 1639–41, 1966.

27. DOWLING, J. E., AND B. EHINGER. Synaptic organization of the interplexiform cells of the goldfish retina. *Science* 188: 270–273, 1975.

28. DOWLING, J. E., AND B. EHINGER. The interplexiform cell system. I. Synapses of the dopaminergic neurons of the goldfish retina. *Proc. R. Soc. London Ser. B* 201: 7–26, 1978.

29. DOWLING, J. E., AND B. EHINGER. Synaptic organization of the dopaminergic neurons in the rabbit retina. *J. Comp. Neurol.* 180: 203–220, 1978.

30. DOWLING, J. E., B. EHINGER, AND W. HEDDEN. The interplexiform cell: a new type of retinal neuron. *Invest. Ophthalmol.* 15: 916–926, 1976.

31. DOWLING, J. E., AND H. RIPPS. S-potentials in the skate retina: intracellular recordings during light and dark adaptation. *J. Gen. Physiol.* 58: 163–189, 1971.

32. DOWLING, J. E., AND H. RIPPS. Adaptation in skate photoreceptors. *J. Gen. Physiol.* 60: 698–719, 1972.

33. DOWLING J. E., AND H. RIPPS. Neurotransmission in the distal retina: the effect of magnesium on horizontal cell activity. *Nature London* 242: 101–103, 1973.

34. DOWLING, J. E., AND F. S. WERBLIN. Organization of the retina of the mudpuppy, *Necturus maculosus.* I. Synaptic structure. *J. Neurophysiol.* 32: 315–338, 1969.

35. DREHER, B., Y. FUKADA, AND R. W. RODIECK. Identification, classification and anatomical segregation of cells with X-like and Y-like properties in the lateral geniculate nucleus of old-world primates. *J. Physiol. London* 258: 433–452, 1976.

36. DUBIN, M. The inner plexiform layer of the vertebrate retina: a quantitative and comparative electron microscopic analysis. *J. Comp. Neurol.* 140: 479–505, 1970.

37. DUBIN, M. W., AND B. G. CLELAND. Organization of visual inputs to interneurons of lateral geniculate nucleus of the cat. *J. Neurophysiol.* 40: 410–427, 1977.

38. DUBIN, M. W., AND L. TURNER. Anatomy of the retina of the mink. *J. Comp. Neurol.* 173: 275–288, 1977.

39. EHINGER, B. Biogenic monoamines as transmitters in the retina. In: *Transmitters in the Visual Process*, edited by S. L.

Bonting. New York: Pergamon, 1976, p. 145–163.

40. EHINGER, B., B. FALCK, AND A. M. LATIES. Adrenergic neurons in teleost retina. *Z. Zellforsch. Mikrosk. Anat.* 97: 285–297, 1969.

41. EHINGER, B., AND I. HOLMGREN. Electron microscopy of the indoleamine-accumulating neurons in the retina of the rabbit. *Cell Tissue Res.* 197: 175–194, 1979.

42. ENROTH-CUGELL, C., AND J. G. ROBSON. The contrast sensitivity of retinal ganglion cells of the cat. *J. Physiol. London* 187: 517–552, 1966.

43. FAIN, G. L. Quantum sensitivity of rods in the toad retina. *Science* 187: 838–841, 1975.

44. FAIN, G. L., G. H. GOLD, AND J. E. DOWLING. Receptor coupling in the toad retina. *Cold Spring Harbor Symp. Quant. Biol.* 40: 547–561, 1976.

45. FAMIGLIETTI, E. V., JR., A. KANEKO, AND M. TACHIBANA. Neuronal architecture of on and off pathways to ganglion cells in carp retina. *Science* 198: 1267–1269, 1977.

46. FAMIGLIETTI, E. V., JR., AND H. KOLB. Structural basis for on- and off-center responses in retinal ganglion cells. *Science* 194: 193–195, 1976.

47. FISHER, S. K. A somato-somatic synapse between amacrine and bipolar cells in the cat retina. *Brain Res.* 43: 587–590, 1972.

48. FUKUDA, Y., M. SUGITANI, AND K. IWAMA. Flash-evoked responses of two types of principal cells of the rat lateral geniculate nucleus. *Brain Res.* 113: 188–196, 1973.

49. GALLEGO, A. Horizontal and amacrine cells in the mammal's retina. *Vision Res. Suppl.* 3: 33–50, 1971.

50. GERSCHENFELD, H. M., AND M. PICCOLINO. Pharmacology of the connections of cones and L-horizontal cells in vertebrate retina. In: *The Neurosciences, Fourth Study Program*, edited by F. O. Schmitt and F. G. Worden. Cambridge, MA: MIT Press, 1979, p. 213–226.

51. GRAHAM, L. T., JR. Comparative aspects of neurotransmitters in the retina. In: *The Eye, Comparative Physiology*, edited by H. Davson and L. T. Graham, Jr. New York: Academic, 1974, vol. 6, p. 283–342.

52. HAGINS, W. Excitation in vertebrate photoreceptors. In: *The Neurosciences, Fourth Study Program*, edited by F. O. Schmitt and F. G. Worden. Cambridge, MA: MIT Press, 1979. p. 183–191.

53. HECHT, S., S. SHLAER, AND M. H. PIRENNE. Energy, quanta, and vision. *J. Gen. Physiol.* 25: 819–840, 1942.

54. HEDDEN, W. L., AND J. E. DOWLING. The interplexiform cell system. II. Effects of dopamine on goldfish retinal neurones. *Proc. R. Soc. London Ser. B* 201: 27–55, 1978.

55. KANEKO, A. Physiological and morphological identification of horizontal, bipolar, and amacrine cells in goldfish retina. *J. Physiol. London* 207: 623–633, 1970.

56. KANEKO, A. Electrical connexions betweeen horizontal cells in the dogfish retina. *J. Physiol. London* 213: 95–105, 1971.

57. KANEKO, A. Physiological studies of single retinal cells and their morphological identification. *Vision Res. Suppl.* 3: 17–26, 1971.

58. KARTEN, H. J., AND N. BRECHA. Localisation of substance P immunoreactivity in amacrine cells of the retina. *Nature London* 283: 87–88, 1980.

59. KATZ, B., AND R. MILEDI. A study of synaptic transmission in the absence of nerve impulses. *J. Physiol. London* 192: 407–436, 1967.

60. KIDD, M. Electron microscopy of the inner plexiform layer of the retina in the cat and the pigeon. *J. Anat.* 96: 179–88, 1962.

61. KLEINSCHMIDT, J., AND J. E. DOWLING. Intracellular recordings from gecko photoreceptors during light and dark adaptation. *J. Gen. Physiol.* 66: 617–648, 1975.

62. KOLB, H. Organization of the outer plexiform layer of the primate retina: electron microscopy of Golgi-impregnated cells. *Philos. Trans. R. Soc. London Ser. B* 258: 261–283, 1970.

63. KOLB, H. The organization of the outer plexiform layer in the retina of the cat: electron microscopic observations. *J. Neurocytol.* 6: 131–153, 1977.

64. KOLB, H. The inner plexiform layer in the retina of the cat:

electron microscopic observations. *J. Neurocytol.* 8: 295–329, 1979.

65. KOLB, H., AND E. V. FAMIGLIETTI, JR. Rod and cone pathways in the inner plexiform layer of cat retina. *Science* 186: 47–49, 1974.

66. KOLB, H., AND E.V. FAMIGLIETTI, JR. Rod and cone pathways in the retina of the cat. *Invest. Ophthalmol.* 15: 935–946, 1976.

67. KOLB, H., AND R. WEST. Synaptic connections of the interplexiform cell in the retina of the cat. *J. Neurocytol.* 6: 155–170, 1977.

68. KUFFLER, S. W. Discharge patterns and functional organization of mammalian retina. *J. Neurophysiol.* 16: 37–68, 1953.

69. KUSANO, K. Influence of ionic environment on the relationship between pre- and postsynaptic potentials. *J. Neurobiol.* 1: 435–457, 1970.

70. LAM, D. M. K. Synaptic chemistry of identified cells in the vertebrate retina. *Cold Spring Harbor Symp. Quant. Biol.* 40: 571–579, 1975.

71. LAMB, T. D., AND E. J. SIMON. The relation between intercellular coupling and electrical noise in turtle photoreceptors. *J. Physiol. London* 263: 257–286, 1976.

72. LASANSKY, A. Basal junctions at synaptic endings of turtle visual cells. *J. Cell Biol.* 40: 577–581, 1969.

73. LEVICK, W. R. Receptive fields of retinal ganglion cells. In: *Physiology of Photoreceptor Organs*, edited by M. G. F. Fuortes. Berlin: Springer-Verlag, 1972, p. 531–566.

74. MARROCCO, R. T. Sustained and transient cells in monkey lateral geniculate nucleus: conduction velocities and response properties. *J. Neurophysiol.* 39: 340–353, 1976.

75. MASLAND, R. H., AND C. J. LIVINGSTONE. Effect of stimulation with light on synthesis and release of acetylcholine by an isolated mammalian retina. *J. Neurophysiol.* 39: 1210–1219, 1976.

76. MATSUMOTO, N., AND K.-I. NAKA. Identification of intracellular responses in the frog retina. *Brain Res.* 42: 59–71, 1972.

77. MILLER, R. F. The neuronal basis of ganglion-cell receptive-field organization and the physiology of amacrine cells. In: *The Neurosciences, Fourth Study Program*, edited by F. O. Schmitt and F. G. Worden. Cambridge, MA: MIT Press, 1979, p. 227–245.

78. MILLER, R. F., AND R. F. DACHEUX. Dendritic and somatic spikes in mudpuppy amacrine cells: Identification and TTX sensitivity. *Brain Res.* 104: 157–162, 1976.

79. MILLER, R. F., AND R. F. DACHEUX. Synaptic organization and ionic basis of on and off channels in mudpuppy retina. III. A model of ganglion cell receptive field organization based on chloride-free experiments. *J. Gen. Physiol.* 67: 679–690, 1976.

80. MILLER, R. F., AND J. E. DOWLING. Intracellular responses of the Müller (glial) cells of mudpuppy retina: their relation to b-wave of the electroretinogram. *J. Neurophysiol.* 33: 323–341, 1970.

81. MISSOTTEN, L. *The Ultrastructure of the Retina.* Brussels, Belgium: Arscia Uitgaven N. V., 1965.

82. MURAKAMI, M., K. OHTSU, AND T. OHTSUKA. Effects of chemicals on receptors and horizontal cells in the retina. *J. Physiol. London* 227: 899–913, 1972.

83. MURAKAMI, M., T. OHTSUKA, AND H. SHIMAZAKI. Effects of aspartate and glutamate on the bipolar cells in the carp retina. *Vision Res.* 15: 456–458, 1975.

84. NAKA, K.-I. The horizontal cells. *Vision Res.* 12: 573–588, 1972.

85. NAKA, K.-I. Neuronal circuitry in the catfish retina. *Invest. Ophthalmol.* 15: 926–935, 1976.

86. NAKA, K.-I., R. Y. CHAN, AND S. YASUI. Adaptation in catfish retina. *J. Neurophysiol.* 42: 441–454, 1979.

87. NAKA, K.-I., AND T. OHTSUKA. Morphological and functional identifications of catfish retinal neurons. II. Morphological identification. *J. Neurophysiol.* 38: 72–91, 1975.

88. NAKA, K.-I., AND P. WITKOVSKY. Dogfish ganglion cell discharge resulting from extrinsic polarization of the horizontal cells. *J. Physiol. London* 223: 449–460, 1972.

89. NEAL, M. J. Acetylcholine as a retinal transmitter substance. In: *Transmitters in the Visual Process*, edited by S. L. Bonting.

New York: Pergamon, 1976, p. 127–143.

90. NELSON, R. A comparison of electrical properties of neurons in *Necturus* retina. *J. Neurophysiol.* 36: 519–535, 1973.

91. NELSON, R. Cat cones have rod input: a comparison of the response properties of cones and horizontal cell bodies in the retina of the cat. *J. Comp. Neurol.* 172: 109–136, 1977.

92. NELSON, R., E. V. FAMIGLIETTI, JR., AND H. KOLB. Intracellular staining reveals different levels of stratification for on- and off-center ganglion cells in cat retina. *J. Neurophysiol.* 41: 472–483, 1978.

93. NELSON, R., H. KOLB, E. V. FAMIGLIETTI, JR., AND P. GOURAS. Neural responses in the rod and cone systems of the cat retina: intracellular records and procion stains. *Invest. Ophthalmol.* 15: 946–953, 1976.

94. NELSON, R., A. V. LUTZOW, H. KOLB, AND P. GOURAS. Horizontal cells in cat retina with independent dendritic systems. *Science* 189: 137–139, 1975.

95. NORTON, A. L., H. SPEKREIJSE, H. G. WAGNER, AND M. L. WOLBARSHT. Responses to directional stimuli in retinal preganglionic units. *J. Physiol. London* 206: 93–107, 1970.

96. PIRENNE, M. H. Absolute thresholds and quantum effects. In: *The Eye. Visual Process,* edited by H. Davson. New York: Academic, 1962, vol. 2, p. 123–140.

97. POLYAK, S. L. *The Retina.* Chicago, IL: Chicago Univ. Press, 1941.

98. RAMÓN Y CAJAL, S. *Structure of the Retina* (1911), transl. by S. A. Thorpe. Springfield, IL: Thomas, 1972.

99. RAVIOLA, E., AND N. B. GILULA. Gap junctions between photoreceptor cells in the vertebrate retina. *Proc. Natl. Acad. Sci. USA* 70: 1677–1681, 1973.

100. RAVIOLA, E., AND N. B. GILULA. Intramembrane organization of specialized contacts in the outer plexiform layer of the retina. *J. Cell Biol.* 65: 192–222, 1975.

101. RAVIOLA, G., AND E. RAVIOLA. Light and electron microscopic observations on the inner plexiform layer of the rabbit retina. *Am. J. Anat.* 120: 403–426, 1967.

102. RODIECK, R. W. *The Vertebrate Retina: Principles of Structure and Function.* San Francisco: Freeman, 1973. (Biology Ser.)

103. RODIECK, R. W. Visual pathways. *Annu. Rev. Neurosci.* 2: 193–225, 1979.

104. ROWE, M. H., AND J. STONE. Naming of neurons. Classification and naming of cat retinal ganglion cells. *Brain Behav. Evol.* 14: 185–216, 1977.

105. RUSHTON, W. A. H. Visual adaptation. *Proc. R. Soc. London Ser. B* 162: 20–45, 1965.

106. SCHWARTZ, E. A. Responses of bipolar cells in the retina of the turtle. *J. Physiol. London* 236: 211–224, 1974.

107. SCHWARTZ, E. A. Cones excite rods in the retina of the turtle. *J. Physiol. London* 246: 639–651, 1975.

108. SCHWARTZ, E. A. Rod-rod interaction in the retina of the turtle. *J. Physiol. London* 246: 617–638, 1975.

109. SHERMAN, S. M., T. T. NORTON, AND V. A. CASAGRANDE. X- and Y-like cells in the lateral geniculate nucleus of the tree shrew (*Tupaia glis*). *Brain Res.* 93: 152–157, 1975.

110. SHERMAN, S. M., J. R. WILSON, J. H. KAAS, AND S. V. WEBB. X- and Y-cells in the dorsal lateral geniculate nucleus of the owl monkey (*Aotus trivirgatus*). *Science* 192: 475–476, 1976.

111. SJOSTRAND, F. S. Ultrastructure of retinal rod synapses of the guinea pig eye as revealed by three-dimensional reconstructions from serial sections. *J. Ultrastruct. Res.* 2: 122–170, 1958.

112. STELL, W. K. Correlation of retinal cytoarchitecture and ultrastructure in Golgi preparations. *Anat. Rec.* 153: 389–397, 1965.

113. STELL, W. K. The morphological organization of the vertebrate retina. In: *Physiology of Photoreceptor Organs,* edited by M. G. F. Fuortes. Berlin: Springer-Verlag, 1972, p. 111–214.

114. STELL, W. K. Functional polarization of horizontal cell dendrites in goldfish retina. *Invest. Ophthal.* 15: 895–908, 1976.

115. STONE, J., AND Y. FUKUDA. Properties of cat retinal ganglion cells: a comparison of W-cells with X- and Y-cells. *J. Neurophysiol.* 37: 722–748, 1974.

116. STONE, J., AND K.-P. HOFFMAN. Very slow-conducting ganglion cells in the cat's retina: a major, new functional type? *Brain Res.* 43: 610–616, 1972.

117. SVAETICHIN, G., AND E. F. MACNICHOL, JR. Retinal mechanisms for chromatic and achromatic vision. *Ann. NY Acad. Sci.* 72: 385–404, 1958.

118. TAKEUCHI, A., AND N. TAKEUCHI. Electrical changes in pre- and postsynaptic axons of the giant synapse of *Loligo. J. Gen. Physiol.* 45: 1181–1193, 1962.

119. TOMITA, T. Electrical activity in the vertebrate retina. *J. Opt. Soc. Am.* 53: 49–57, 1963.

120. TOMITA, T. Electrical activity of vertebrate photoreceptors. *Q. Rev. Biophys.* 3: 179–222, 1970.

121. TOYODA, J. E., H. HASHIMOTO, AND K. OHTSU. Bipolar-amacrine transmission in the carp retina. *Vision Res.* 13: 295–307, 1973.

122. TOYODA, J., H. NOSAKI, AND T. TOMITA. Light-induced resistance changes in single photoreceptors of *Necturus* and *Gecko. Vision Res.* 9: 453–463, 1969.

123. TRIFONOV, Y. A. Study of synaptic transmission between photoreceptors and horizontal cells using electrical stimulation of the retina. *Biophysics USSR* 13: 809–817, 1968.

124. TRIFONOV, Y. A., AND A. L. BYZOV. The response of the cells generating S-potential on the current passed through the eye-cup of the turtle. *Biophysics USSR* 10: 673–680, 1965.

125. VOADEN, M. J. Gamma-aminobutyric acid and glycine as retinal neurotransmitters. In: *Transmitters in the Visual Process,* edited by S. L. Bonting. New York: Pergamon, 1976, p. 107–125.

126. WALOGA, G., AND W. L. PAK. Horizontal cell potentials: dependence on external sodium ion concentration. *Science* 191: 964, 1976.

127. WEIGHT, F. F. Synaptic potentials resulting from conductance decreases. In: *Synaptic Transmission & Neuronal Interaction,* edited by M. V. L. Bennett. New York: Raven, 1974, vol. 28, p. 141–152. (Soc. Gen. Physiol. Ser.)

128. WERBLIN, F. S. Response of retinal cells to moving spots: intracellular recordings in *Necturus maculosus. J. Neurophysiol.* 33: 342–350, 1970.

129. WERBLIN, F. S. Organization of the vertebrate retina: receptive fields and sensitivity control. In: *The Eye, Comparative Physiology,* edited by H. Davson and L. T. Graham, Jr. New York: Academic, 1974, vol. 6, p. 257–282.

130. WERBLIN, F. S. Integrative pathways in local circuits between slow potential cells in the retina. In: *The Neurosciences, Fourth Study Program,* edited by F. O. Schmitt and F. G. Worden. Cambridge, MA: MIT Press, 1979, p. 193–211.

131. WERBLIN, F. S., AND D. COPENHAGEN. Control of retinal sensitivity: III. Lateral interactions at the inner plexiform layer. *J. Gen. Physiol.* 63: 88–110, 1974.

132. WERBLIN, F. S., AND J. E. DOWLING. Organization of the retina of the mudpuppy, *Necturus maculosus.* II. Intracellular recording. *J. Neurophysiol.* 32: 339–355, 1969.

133. WEST, R. W., AND J. E. DOWLING. Synapses onto different morphological types of retinal ganglion cells. *Science* 178: 510–512, 1972.

134. WITKOVSKY, P., M. SHAKIB, AND H. RIPPS. Interreceptor junctions in the teleost retina. *Invest. Ophthalmol.* 13: 996–1009, 1974.

135. WU, S. M., AND J. E. DOWLING. L-aspartate: evidence for a role in cone photoreceptor synaptic transmission in the carp retina. *Proc. Natl. Acad. Sci. USA* 75: 5205–5209, 1978.

136. WUNK, D. F., AND F. S. WERBLIN. Synaptic inputs to ganglion cells in the tiger salamander retina. *J. Gen. Physiol.* 73: 265–286, 1979.

137. YAMADA, E., AND T. ISHIKAWA. The fine structure of the horizontal cells in some vertebrate retinae. *Cold Spring Harbor Symp. Quant. Biol.* 30: 383–392, 1965.

138. YAMADA, T., D. MARSHAK, S. BASINGER, J. WALSH, J. MORLEY, AND W. STELL. Somatostatin-like immunoreactivity in the retina. *Proc. Natl. Acad. Sci. USA* 77: 1691–1695, 1980.

Processing of visual information within the retinostriate system

P. O. BISHOP | *Department of Physiology, John Curtin School of Medical Research, Australian National University, Canberra City, Australia*

CHAPTER CONTENTS

THE YEAR 1959 WAS, in a sense, a watershed in the history of visual neurophysiology, and Bartley's chapter (15a), "Central mechanisms of vision," published that year in the first edition of the *Handbook of Physiology*, came at the end of an era. The chapter was largely concerned with the interpretation of multiunit field potentials recorded at different levels in the visual pathway in response to electrical stimulation variously applied to the optic nerve, tract, or radiation. Up to that time much of the interest in the visual system had centered around the analysis of fiber size and conduction velocity groups in the optic nerve and tract and the significance of fiber size for the function of the visual centers in the brain (24, 25, 36, 40). By 1959, however, the technique for single-unit recording in the central nervous system and the concept of a receptive field were both well established, yet neither the technique nor the concept was considered in that *Handbook* chapter.

In 1952 Jung and his colleagues (15b, 189a) reported the first single-unit recording in the visual cortex using diffuse light stimulation. In the same year Talbot and Kuffler (366a) made an important technical advance by developing a multibeam ophthalmoscope for stimulating and recording from single retinal ganglion cells in the cat's eye. The importance of the technical advance was that, except for the introduction of the microelectrode, the eye was intact and its optics preserved so that small, flashing spots of light could be focused on the retina. Using this technique Kuffler (210b, 211) discovered that the receptive fields of cat ganglion cells were spatially organized, and the observations he made at that time have provided the foundation for all subsequent receptive-field studies.

The year 1959 saw the appearance of a radical new outlook in visual neurophysiology, exemplified in particular by the publication of two papers: one by Hubel and Wiesel (167), the first in the long collaboration; the other by Lettvin and his colleagues (224). The title of the paper by Lettvin et al. (224), "What the frog's eye tells the frog's brain," and the speculations it contained undoubtedly caught the imagination of the time. They expressed the new outlook somewhat in the form of a manifesto:

> We decided then how we ought to work. First, we should find a way of recording from single myelinated and unmyelinated fibers in the intact optic nerve. Second, we should present the frog with as wide a range of visible stimuli as we could, not only spots of light but things he would be disposed to eat, other things from which he would flee, sundry geometrical figures, stationary and moving about, etc. From the variety of stimuli we should then try to discover what common features were abstracted by whatever groups of fibers we could find in the optic nerve. Third, we should seek the anatomical basis for the grouping.

In 1959 Hubel and Wiesel (167) were the first to report upon the receptive fields of single cells in the visual cortex and to analyze their spatial organization. They also took the important step of using as stimuli both moving objects and patterns of light projected on a screen in front of the cat. The stimulus features important for striate neurons were found to be straight lines, bars, and edges whose orientation and, usually, direction of movement were characteristic and critical for the cell (167, 169).

Among the stimuli used by Lettvin et al. (224) were silhouettes of different size and shape, cut out of matte white, gray, or black paper, moved over a matte white, gray, or black background, and seen by reflected light. This emphasis on the use of stimuli that mimic those occurring under natural conditions led away from flashing spots of light on the retina toward the movement of objects on a tangent screen in front of the animal. There was a shift of attention from image space to object space. Years later Bishop and Henry (34) described the revolutionary effect of the new outlook in the following terms:

> It was as though the investigators had turned their backs on the retina to look in the direction of the tangent screen so as to put themselves, as observers, in the same place as the animal, and to see for themselves what the single neuron was reporting. This shift in the investigators' attention had powerful psychological advantages. In ordinary life it is obvious that we think of the visual world in terms of object space and not in terms of retinal images and almost without exception the concepts of psychophysics are framed in terms of object space.

Another important aspect of the new approach was the emphasis that Lettvin et al. (224a) placed on the correlation between morphological and functional cell types. They made vivid suggestions of possible correlations between the functional cell classes of frog retinal ganglion cells and the various morphological types that Cajal (57a) had described in Golgi preparations.

Something of the new outlook had already been expressed by Barlow (12a) as early as 1953 in a paper that also describes "on-off" retinal ganglion cells in the frog as having receptive fields with an inhibitory surround. Referring to observations that any small moving object will evoke feeding responses from the frog, Barlow (12a) comments that "'on-off' units seem to possess the whole of the discriminatory mechanism needed to account for this rather simple behavior. The receptive field of an 'on-off' unit would be nicely filled by the image of a fly at 2 in. distance and it is difficult to avoid the conclusion that the 'on-off' units are matched to this stimulus and act as 'fly detectors'." It was not surprising therefore that Barlow and colleagues (14) were among the first to exploit the new approach at the level of the ganglion cells in the retina. Out of these studies came the concept of the single cell as a feature detector. The rather naturalistic language used by Lettvin and his colleagues to describe the operations of visual neurons was replaced by one more descriptive of the relevant observations made on the single cells and their probable importance in the visual life of the animal. The particular stimulus feature that brought out the strongest response from the neuron was referred to by Barlow et al. (14) as the "trigger feature."

By 1965 Hubel and Wiesel (171) had elaborated the hierarchical concept of the operation of the visual cortex, a concept that was to play such a dominant role in vision research over the next decade or so. According to this theory the processing of visual information was to be seen in the successive transformations of the receptive-field properties of cells from simple to complex types in the striate cortex and then through lower-order and higher-order hypercomplex neurons in the prestriate cortex. The transformations from simple to higher-order hypercomplex cells involved the repetition of a sequence whereby increased stimulus specificity at one level was followed by generalization for the same specific stimulus at the next level. So dramatic were the advances between the years 1959 and 1965 that it seemed as though an understanding of the mechanisms of pattern discrimination was at last within grasp.

By 1965, however, there were also beginning to appear new ideas and techniques that were to undermine the hierarchical concept. One of the first to emerge was the idea that Fourier analysis could be used to understand how spatial signals are transmitted and transformed by the nervous system. The possibility of applying Fourier methods to visual information processing led Enroth-Cugell and Robson (105) to devise tests for the linearity of the spatial summation of excitation within the receptive fields of retinal ganglion cells. Out of this approach came the unexpected observation that the well-known on-center and off-center concentrically organized cell types could be divided into two classes, X and Y, according to whether the summation was linear or nonlinear. Since that time the further application of Fourier methods has influenced visual neurophysiology relatively little whereas they have had a major impact on visual psychophysics. Nevertheless, the recognition of the X/Y dichotomy coupled with the earlier ideas of feature extraction led, in due course, to the discovery that cat retinal ganglion cells were of quite diverse types. The discrimination and detailed description of the various cell types, particularly at the hands of Cleland and Levick and Stone and their respective colleagues (see RETINAL GANGLION CELL CLASSIFICATION, p. 344), brought about a further revolution in our outlook. The subsequent recognition that the activity of the different cell types is relayed largely in parallel through the lateral geniculate nucleus to the visual cortex has led in recent years to the development of parallel processing models (223, 355). While it is clear that the original hierarchical model of Hubel and Wiesel (171) is no longer tenable, any parallel processing model must obviously incorporate the operation of hierarchical mechanisms.

At the same time as the physiological discoveries just described were being made, the introduction of a succession of powerful new histological procedures was also bringing about a revolution in our understanding of the structural organization of the visual system. The introduction in 1967 of the Fink-Heimer method (111) for the selective silver impregnation of degenerating axons and terminals was soon followed by the use of anterograde axoplasmic transport of radioactively labeled amino acids (77, 217) and the retrograde axonal transport of horseradish peroxidase (209, 219). More recently introduced methods include the use of radioactively labeled deoxyglucose (347) for determining relative levels of neuronal activity in conscious animals under different conditions of sensory stimulation. By offering a fairly ready answer to problems that could not have been solved by purely physiological methods, the application of these new histo-

logical procedures has tended to redirect neurophysiological experiments more and more toward structural analysis, particularly with respect to the neuronal connections within and between the various brain centers. This neuroanatomical bias, as well as the quickening pace at which new knowledge is being acquired, has temporarily discouraged consideration of the general functional properties of the various levels in the visual pathway. The current emphasis in research on central visual mechanisms is toward a combined approach using single-unit recording in association with the newer histological procedures. The present chapter reflects this current emphasis.

In a recent analysis of visual information processing, Marr (252) has argued that a system as complex as a nervous system must be analyzed and understood at several different levels. He distinguished four important levels of description. The lowest level is concerned with the basic elements of the system (neurons and synapses) and how they work. The second level is the study of particular neuronal mechanisms made up of assemblies of the basic components. The third level is that of the algorithm, the scheme by which the various neuronal mechanisms are applied to solve a particular computation, and finally the top level contains the theory of the computation. Each of the four levels of description must have its place in the eventual understanding of perceptual information processing by the visual system, but the present account of the retinostriate system is largely restricted to Marr's second level of description. Only in this way has it been possible to keep the account within reasonable bounds. Even so, further limitations were needed. It was decided to restrict the account to the domestic cat and the macaque monkey and only to call upon data from other species and other animals where none were specifically available from these two.

In the last few years there have been many valuable reviews covering various aspects of the material discussed in the present chapter (8, 29, 53, 179, 223, 301, 304, 330, 342, 355, 381).

RETINOSTRIATE PATHWAY

The essential elements in the retinostriate pathway are the same in carnivores and primates, as shown in the semidiagrammatic plan view of the human system in Figure 1. Though the elements are the same in cat, monkey, and man, there are, of course, morphological differences. The brief introductory account that follows refers to the human retinostriate system. There are effectively two mirror-symmetrical retinostriate systems, one for each cerebral hemisphere. Optic nerve fibers from the nasal retina of one eye cross in the optic chiasma to join with fibers from the temporal retina of the other eye to form an optic tract that, in due course, relays through the lateral geniculate nucleus before projecting to the striate cortex in the

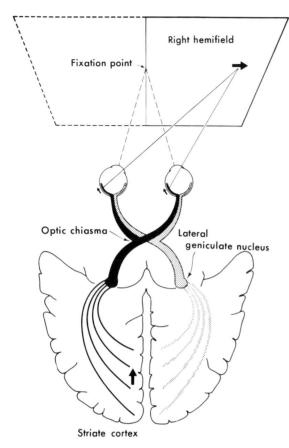

FIG. 1. Human retinostriate system, which consists, in effect, of two mirror-symmetrical retinostriate systems, one for each cerebral hemisphere. Optic nerve fibers from nasal retina of one eye cross in optic chiasma to join with fibers from temporal retina of other eye to form an optic tract that, in due course, relays through lateral geniculate nucleus before projecting to striate cortex in occipital lobe of one cerebral hemisphere. Vertical through fixation point (center of gaze) separates visual field into two hemifields, *left* and *right*. As a result of decussation of optic nerve fibers at chiasma, right visual hemifield is represented in left striate cortex (*solid pathway*) and vice versa for left hemifield (*dotted pathway*). *Solid arrows*: projection of hemifield onto striate cortex, center of gaze being represented posteriorly and horizontal periphery of hemifield anteriorly.

occipital lobe of one cerebral hemisphere. The vertical through the fixation point (center of gaze) separates the visual field into two hemifields, left and right. As a result of the decussation of optic nerve fibers at the chiasma, the right visual hemifield is represented in the left striate cortex (solid pathway) and vice versa for the left hemifield (dotted pathway). The projection of the hemifield onto the striate cortex is topographic, as indicated by the solid arrows, the center of gaze being represented posteriorly and the horizontal periphery of the hemifield anteriorly.

There are a number of different central visual pathways, but they all begin with the retinal ganglion cells and the axons of these cells that form the optic nerves and tracts. It is very convenient to take up the account of the central visual pathways at the level of the retinal

ganglion cells, because all the visual information that passes from the eye to the brain is funneled along the axons of these cells. The retinostriate pathway is only one of a number of central visual pathways. For the purposes of the present chapter it is taken to include not only the lateral geniculate nucleus, as illustrated in Figure 1, but also other thalamic regions, such as the pulvinar, that not only receive a direct retinal input but also relay it directly to the striate cortex. Though the present account ends with the striate cortex, this is not the end of the visual pathway. The axons that leave the striate cortex make their way to a number of different destinations that include several other areas in the visual cortex.

RETINA

Cat Retina

RETINAL GANGLION CELL CLASSIFICATION. A brief historical outline will assist the reader to appreciate the nature of the controversy that continues to be associated with the classification of retinal ganglion cells.

The idea of a receptive field as a basis for the organization of a sensory system is due to Adrian (1) as a result of his studies of single afferent nerve fibers from skin receptors. However, it was not till 1938 that Hartline (148) provided the first definition of the receptive field of a visual neuron based on single-unit recording. He isolated single-nerve fiber activity from small bundles dissected free from the anterior surface of the frog retina. The receptive field was defined as the area of the frog retina that had to be illuminated in order to obtain a response from a given fiber (149). Only much later did Kuffler (211) describe, for the first time, the antagonistic center-surround receptive-field organization characteristic of ganglion cells in the mammalian retina. His observations on the cat retina were, however, restricted to what have since been called concentric units, two general classes of cell being distinguished: 1) on-center, off-surround that increased their discharge when a light was turned on the center, and 2) off-center, on-surround that increased their discharge when a light was turned off the center.

Since the early observations of Hartline and Kuffler a great diversity of retinal ganglion cell types has been discovered, beginning with the discrimination by Enroth-Cugell and Robson (105) of two classes of ganglion cells in the cat retina that were independent of the on-center/off-center dichotomy. The stimulus for this work, however, was not the possibility of discovering new cell classes but rather the possibility of applying Fourier methods to the visual system in the way that they had already been successfully applied to electronic systems. Since it is only within the limits of linearity that the techniques of Fourier analysis and synthesis can be applied, Enroth-Cugell and Robson (105) devised tests for the linearity of spatial summation within the receptive fields of ganglion cells. Recording from optic tract axons, they divided ganglion cells into X and Y types on the basis of their responses to drifting sinusoidal gratings at the highest spatial frequencies capable of eliciting a response. The X-cells always showed a modulation of firing at the drift frequency, while the Y-cells showed an unmodulated increase in the mean discharge. A number of cells of both types were also distinguished by the presence or absence of a null position for a stationary grating of low spatial frequency at which the introduction or removal of the pattern yielded no significant response. Figure 2 shows the difference in the behavior of X- and Y-cells to the introduction and withdrawal of a stationary sinusoidal grating located at different spatial positions (phase angles) with respect to the center of the receptive field (vertical dashed line). For the X-cell (Fig. 2A) there were two positions of the grating at which the effects of changes in luminance over one-half of the receptive field exactly balanced the effects from the changes over the other half. For the two positions at which the cell failed to respond (null positions) the grating lay with odd-symmetry about the center of the receptive field. The phase angles of the two null positions are 180° apart, showing that the null position is independent of the sign of the grating contrast. Furthermore, it was shown that neither the existence nor the phase angle of a null position depends upon the mean luminance of the grating. By contrast the Y-cell (Fig. 2B) responded at all the phase angles with large increases in firing frequency both when the grating was introduced and when it was withdrawn.

Both the tests described check for linearity but under rather different conditions. With the simultaneous presentation of increments and decrements of light in different parts of the receptive field, X-cells pool excitation and inhibition linearly both within the center and the surround components. For the case of exactly concentric center and surround components the null output is due to the cancellation of signals within the one receptive-field region (e.g., center) and not to the cancellation of center signals by opposite surround signals. With Y-cells cancellation of the effects of increments and decrements does not occur and a null position cannot be found. With the drifting grating test a high spatial frequency is used so as to activate selectively the spatially fine nonlinear mechanisms of Y-cells. Enroth-Cugell and Robson probably used the drifting grating test for rapid screening and the null test for the definitive characterization of a cell. Since then most investigators have relied on some variant of the null test, and recently Hochstein and Shapley (161) have strengthened the original qualitative test by devising a nonlinearity index. They measured contrast sensitivity as a function of spatial phase for the different Fourier components in the averaged neural responses to alternating phase (contrast reversal) sinusoidal gratings. There was a significant second harmonic component in the responses from Y-cells

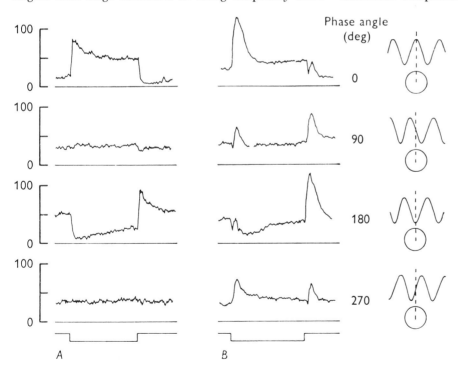

FIG. 2. Responses of cat retinal ganglion cells to introduction and withdrawal of a stationary sinusoidal grating pattern. A: off-center X-cell; spatial frequency 0.13 cycles/deg. B: off-center Y-cell; spatial frequency 0.16 cycles/deg. Contrast (0.32) was turned off and on at 0.45 Hz, as indicated by square waves (downward deflection, off). Length of zero line, duration of 2 s; ordinate, spikes/s. *Right*: sketches showing phase angle of pattern, i.e., angular position (in deg) of (cosine) grating relative to midpoint of receptive-field center (*dashed line*). [From Enroth-Cugell and Robson (105).]

that was spatial-phase insensitive. The nonlinearity index was defined as the maximum value for various spatial frequencies of the ratio of the sensitivity for the second-harmonic component to that for the fundamental component for various spatial phases. The X-cells always had a nonlinearity index that was less than 1, whereas for Y-cells it was always greater than 1.

Following an earlier report by Gouras (135) working on the monkey retina (see RECEPTIVE FIELDS OF RETINAL GANGLION CELLS, p. 354), a number of investigators (69, 74, 117, 312) began describing various new classes of cells in the cat retina using methods quite distinct from those of Enroth-Cugell and Robson (105). Initially the concentrically organized center-surround types of ganglion cells described by Kuffler (211) were divided into only two classes, largely on the basis of their responses to maintained stimuli as well as their conduction velocities. In particular Cleland et al. (69, 74) divided the cells into sustained- and transient-response types as the result of the application of a battery of simple tests based on the responses to standing contrast, fine grating patterns, size and speed of contrasting targets, and the presence or absence of a periphery effect. Although none of these studies tested for linearity of spatial summation, the two classes were, at that time, regarded as being equivalent to the X/Y (linear/nonlinear) subdivision of Enroth-Cugell and Robson (105). The terms *sustained* and *transient* were, however, retained by Cleland and Levick as providing a more descriptive designation of the classes than the X/Y terminology.

At about the time of these observations Stone and Hoffmann (360) also reported the presence in the cat retina of a further population of ganglion cells that have distinctive receptive-field properties differing from the familiar center-surround pattern and that have very slowly conducting axons, thereby confirming earlier brief reports of similar cat ganglion cell types (303, 356). This was a major advance: although ganglion cells with unusual properties of this kind had previously been described in other species, particularly the rabbit (15, 233), the general belief at that time was that they were not to be found in the cat and monkey retina. The two ganglion cell response types referred to as sustained and transient had by then been accepted by Stone and Hoffmann (360) as equivalent to the X/Y subdivision, but these investigators effectively discarded the linearity criterion for ganglion cell classification by using conduction velocity as a basis for selecting a label for the new group of very slowly conducting cells. The term W-cell was chosen so that the alphabetical sequence W,X,Y follows the axonal conduction velocities of the three cell types. Except for only one cell, all the W-type ganglion cells described by Stone and Hoffmann (360) in their initial account had nonconcentrically organized receptive fields and it was only subsequently that Stone and Fukuda (358) and Levick and Cleland (236) reported

that the very slowly conducting cell group also included a proportion as large as 60% having concentrically organized center-surround receptive fields. Stone and Fukuda (358) termed these concentrically organized cells *tonic* and *phasic*, respectively, depending on the nature of their responses to maintained stimulation.

These observations prompted Cleland and Levick (71, 72) to reexamine the ganglion cell classes they had already described. They were then able to subdivide both the transient and sustained classes into brisk and sluggish varieties not only on the basis of their responsiveness to visual stimuli and other features but also from the latencies of their antidromic responses to optic tract stimulation. The four classes that Cleland and Levick (71) defined in this way were called *brisk-sustained*, *brisk-transient*, *sluggish-sustained*, and *sluggish-transient*, the latter two types being equivalent to the tonic and phasic groups of Stone and Fukuda (358). At the same time Stone and Fukuda (358) and Cleland and Levick (72) both published detailed accounts of the rarely encountered cell types with nonconcentrically organized receptive fields. Though based on quite separate investigations and despite the differing terminologies that were used, the two accounts proved to be in close accord. Since then Cleland and Levick have continued to regard the concentrically organized sluggish-sustained and sluggish-transient cell types as quite distinct from the more rarely encountered nonconcentric cells, and the obvious heterogeneity of the rarely encountered cell types has caused them to continue to treat each type separately. Though also recognizing the heterogeneity of the W-cell class, Stone and many others have nevertheless found it convenient to use the W-label not only for the rarely encountered nonconcentric cells but also for the concentrically organized tonic (sluggish-sustained) and phasic (sluggish-transient) cell types.

Both the terminologies thus outlined have their drawbacks. The terminology used by Cleland and Levick, though logically consistent, lacks the apparent simplicity of the X, Y, W scheme, and it is doubtless the apparent simplicity of the latter scheme that has led to its widespread adoption at the present time. However, the X, Y, W scheme can be seriously criticized on at least two grounds. The terms X and Y can refer to two quite different classifying criteria, principally conduction velocity on the one hand and linear/nonlinear spatial summation on the other. Furthermore the W-cell class includes cells as diverse as those with concentrically and nonconcentrically organized receptive fields. The difficulties associated with the two terminologies have recently been brought to a head by the linearity tests that Levick and Thibos (238) have applied to the various types of cells with concentrically organized receptive fields. Using a modified form of Hochstein and Shapley's (161) nonlinearity index they have found, with only a rare exception, that the brisk-sustained and brisk-transient response types do correspond to the X/Y types of Enroth-Cugell and Robson (105). However, both the sluggish-sustained and sluggish-transient classes were mixed populations of X and Y types. In other words, some sluggish-sustained cells were linear (X) and some were nonlinear (Y), and the sluggish-transient cells were similarly mixed. While the sample tested so far is too small to establish the generality of these observations with any certainty, these results clearly establish the ambiguity inherent in the X, Y, W terminology. As they are most commonly used, the labels X and Y refer to the linearity or otherwise of spatial summation and, on this basis, some cells can belong to both X and W categories. It is only on the basis of the conduction velocity of their axons that cat retinal ganglion cells can be classified into the X, Y, and W categories of Stone and Fukuda (358), these being then equivalent to the t_1 and t_2 conduction velocity groups of Bishop and McLeod (40) and the t_3 of Bishop et al. (25).

It is remarkable that, despite the differing terminologies, the various observations that have been made on the properties of the retinal ganglion cell in the cat are nevertheless in close general accord. Table 1 shows the equivalences that can be established between the various terminologies. At the time of writing it is not clear how the difficulties outlined will be resolved.

PROPERTIES OF CAT RETINAL GANGLION CELLS. *Cells with concentric receptive fields: brisk and sluggish types.* The distinction between the four concentrically organized receptive-field types (brisk-sustained, brisk-transient, sluggish-sustained, sluggish-transient) was based on applying a battery of tests (71), one of which depended on the extent to which the response was sustained when the stimulus was kept steadily on the center (standing contrast). The brisk-sluggish dichotomy was based mainly on the general responsiveness of the cells. Both of the brisk cell types have a strong but irregular maintained discharge, rather higher in brisk-sustained (~40/s) than in brisk-transient (~20/s) cells, whereas with sluggish cells of both kinds the maintained discharge rarely rises above 10/s. In response to standing contrast the discharge from a brisk-sustained cell rises rapidly to a sharp peak and then falls back to a sustained level clearly above the prestimulus level. By contrast, in sluggish-sustained cells the initial peak is smaller, sometimes rises much more gradually, and may be absent altogether, but the firing during the sustained part of the response is characteristically very regular. Brisk-transient cells respond to standing contrast with a particularly vigorous initial peak of firing that soon falls back to the prestimulus level. With sluggish-transient cells the peak response is weaker and the prestimulus level of firing is resumed rather more rapidly. Taken in isolation, however, these responses to standing contrast are not always a reliable guide to cell classification, particularly in the case of the two transient cell classes that can be difficult to distinguish on this basis alone.

Other features, however, assist in making the distinction between the cell classes. At any given retinal eccentricity brisk-transient cells have receptive-field center sizes that are larger than those of brisk-sustained cells by a factor of 2 or 3 and are without any overlap between them (70). Center sizes for both brisk types are smallest at the area centralis and increase hyperbolically with retinal eccentricity such that diameters have doubled at an eccentricity of 4°. At the area centralis, the center diameter for brisk-sustained cells is as small as 0.25°, corresponding to a spatial cutoff frequency of about 9.5 cycles/deg. An important observation is that within any local area of retina,

TABLE 1. *Classification of Ganglion Cells in Cat Retina*

Receptive-Field Organization	Tested for Linearity (X) and Nonlinearity (Y)		Not Tested for Linearity (X) or Nonlinearity (Y)			
	Enroth-Cugell and Robson (105)*	Levick and Thibos (238)	Cleland and Dubin and Levick (69, 71, 72)	Stone et al. (162a, 358, 360)		Conduction velocity group (24, 25, 36, 40)
Concentric	Either Y or X	Y	Brisk-transient		Y	t_1
		X	Brisk-sustained		X	t_2
		Either Y or X	Sluggish-transient	Phasic	W	t_3
		Either Y or X	Sluggish-sustained	Tonic		
Nonconcentric	Not tested	Not tested	Local-edge-detector	Phasic on-off center (excited-by-contrast)		
			Direction-selective	Direction-selective (a) on-center (b) on-off center		
			Edge-inhibitory off-center	Suppressed-by-contrast		
			Uniformity detector	Suppressed-by-contrast		
			Color-coded	Color-coded		

* Reference numbers in parentheses.

ganglion cells of the same brisk kind are closely matched for center diameters, and it is only when cells of different classes are considered that a sizable range of concentric receptive-field center sizes develops, the upper and lower bounds being determined by the brisk-transient and brisk-sustained cells, respectively. The receptive-field center sizes of sluggish-concentric cells also increase with increasing retinal eccentricity, but at any given eccentricity they are usually larger than the brisk-sustained centers and overlap those of brisk-transient cells. In addition the local scatter of center sizes for the sluggish cells is greater than that of either of the brisk cell types.

Usually brisk-transient cells have a prominent periphery (shift) effect that is usually weak or absent with brisk-sustained cells and absent in sluggish cells, whether they are sustained or transient. The periphery effect is an asynchronous augmentation of the maintained discharge to large-area visual stimulation well outside the conventional receptive field.

Finally, significant differences in the conduction velocities need to be considered. Although there is general agreement in the literature concerning the relative conduction velocities of the various cell types, the absolute velocities that have been reported differ somewhat, depending on the methods used and the assumptions that have been made. Because the intra-retinal fibers are unmyelinated, their conduction velocity is much slower than the myelinated extraretinal fibers. According to Cleland and Levick's (71) estimates for the extraretinal fibers, the axons of the brisk-transient cells have a mean velocity of 52 m/s compared to mean velocities of 14 and 8 m/s for the brisk-sustained and sluggish cells, respectively.

Rarely encountered cat retinal ganglion cells. The conduction velocity of the axons of all the rarely encountered retinal ganglion cell types in the cat fall into the t_3 velocity range (mean ~8m/s). None of the five or six cell types that have been described have the concentric center-surround receptive-field organization that is characteristic of the brisk cells (60, 72, 73, 204, 233, 303, 311, 358, 360, 398).

Local-edge-detector (excited-by-contrast, on-off-center-phasic-W). Local-edge-detector cells have an on-off center and a silent inhibitory surround. They have a low- or zero-maintained discharge and an encounter rate of <5%. Whereas stimulation of the surround is without any excitatory effect, it nevertheless reduces or abolishes an excitatory response from the center. The effective stimulus for these cells is an edge of either contrast presented or moved in the center without encroaching on the surround. Hence the edge must be of a restricted length (i.e., local).

Direction-selective. Direction-selective cells respond to a certain direction of movement, are independent of contrast, and are completely unresponsive to movement in the opposite direction. Based on the responses to stationary flashing spots, Stone and Fukuda (358) have described two varieties (on-off and

on), whereas Cleland and Levick report only one (on-off). The recorded samples are not large enough to determine if there is clustering of the preferred axes of direction selectivity (283). Their encounter rate is about 1% (72, 358).

Suppressed-by-contrast (uniformity detector, edge-inhibitory off-center). Suppressed-by-contrast cells have a brisk-maintained discharge that is suppressed by all forms of visual stimulation. Cleland and Levick (72) made a distinction between two types: uniformity detectors and edge-inhibitory off-center types. The latter type resembled the uniformity detectors with respect to small targets, but with large targets they appeared to have a triple concentric receptive-field organization with a central inhibitory region, stimulation of which led to a sustained reduction of both the maintained discharge and the excitatory responses from the inner (off-excitatory) and outer (on-excitatory) annular surrounds. In response to an edge they found that uniformity detectors were only transiently inhibited, whereas with edge-inhibitory off-center cells the inhibition was well sustained. Rowe and Stone (311) were, however, unable to confirm the distinction between the two cell types, regarding both as equivalent to the suppressed-by-contrast cells that were first described in the cat retina by Rodieck (303).

Color-coded. Color-coded cells have opponent color responses with an on-response for blue light and off-responses for green and red lights. They have an encounter rate of less than 1%.

MORPHOLOGICAL CLASSES OF RETINAL GANGLION CELLS. Using Golgi-stained whole-mount preparations, Boycott and Wässle (45) described three distinctive morphological types of ganglion cell in the cat retina. They differ in their dendritic branching patterns, their dendritic field dimensions, and their cell body sizes (Fig. 3). Alpha cells have a large cell body (diam ~30 μm) and a large dendritic tree whose diameter increases from 200 μm in the central area to about 1,000 μm in peripheral retina. Beta cells (Fig. 3C–E) have a medium-sized cell body (~20 μm) and a small, bushy dendritic tree that is significantly smaller than the dendritic fields of other ganglion cell types at comparable eccentricities, being only 25 μm in the central area and 300 μm in the periphery. Gamma cells (Fig. 3F) have the smallest cell bodies (<16 μm) but have large, sparsely branched dendritic trees as big as those of α-cells. At every retinal location there is a broad scatter of γ-cell dendritic field sizes ranging from 300 to 800 μm in diameter. For the various cells, axon size corresponds to cell body size. The α-cells have the largest axons and γ-cells the finest. The δ-cells (Fig. 3G) are a further, rarely encountered, type of retinal ganglion cell (45).

RETINAL DISTRIBUTION OF RETINAL GANGLION CELL TYPES. Because of their bias toward large cell bodies and large axons, encounter rates in electrophysiologi-

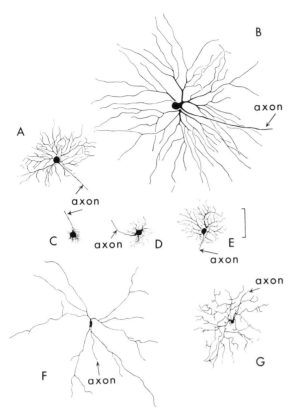

FIG. 3. Golgi-stained ganglion cells from flat mounts of the cat's retina as seen in plan view. *A,B*: α-cells, *C–E*: β-cells; *F*: γ-cell. *G*: δ-cell. Cells *A,C,F* were located 1.2 mm from center of area centralis; *D,G* at 2.9 and 2.8 mm, respectively; *B,E* at 10.0 mm. All are shown at same magnification: calibration bar (near *E*) = 100 μm. [From Levick (234) as adapted from Boycott and Wässle (45).]

cluded on the grounds that they are displaced amacrine cells, the total ganglion cell count reduces to about 160,000, of which about 52% are β-cells and 45% are γ-cells, the relative proportions of the two cell types being much the same over the retina (184, 383).

Famiglietti and Kolb (108) have subdivided the α- and β-cell classes (their classes I and II) into two populations based on the level of branching of their dendrites in the inner plexiform layer of the retina, one with dendritic fields in the outer one-third of the layer and the other with fields in the inner two-thirds. Nelson and colleagues (269) have identified the cells having dendrites in the outer third of the inner plexiform layer as having off-center receptive fields, whereas those with branching in the inner two-thirds are on-center. Recently it has been shown that the α- and β-cell classes are each equally represented in the two populations (384, 386). Furthermore the on-and-off β-cells form independent mosaics to cover the retina homogeneously with their dendritic trees (387). Systematic physiological exploration of the retina has also found that the brisk ganglion cell types possess on-center and off-center receptive fields with equal frequency (71).

MORPHOLOGICAL CORRELATES OF FUNCTIONAL CLASSES OF CAT RETINAL GANGLION CELLS. Considerable progress has been made in correlating morphological types of retinal ganglion with functional classes, particularly in the cat retina. Alpha cells have been unequivocally identified as the morphological correlate of the physiological brisk-transient class (75, 385). In addition there is, at any eccentricity, a good correspondence between the size of the dendritic tree of α-cells and the receptive-field center size of brisk-transient cells. There is also good reason to regard the β-cells as the morphological correlate of brisk-sustained cells (71, 200, 234, 287, 358). It is worth noting that β-cells have the smallest dendritic trees of any morphological type and brisk-sustained the smallest receptive-field center sizes (0.2°–1.3°) (70, 71, 358). By exclusion, the remaining physiological classes (concentric receptive fields of the sluggish kind and the rarely encountered nonconcentric receptive fields) may be associated with γ-cells (and possibly with δ-cells).

RESPONSE LATENCIES AND CONDUCTION VELOCITIES OF CAT GANGLION CELL AXONS. There has long been considerable interest in the discrimination of conduction velocity groupings in the optic nerve and tract. In the older literature (24, 25, 36, 40) attempts were made to discern conduction velocity groups in the compound action potentials produced by electrical stimulation of the optic nerve or tract. The velocity groupings were of interest at that time because of the physiological consequences they might have for brain centers farther along the visual pathway rather than for the possibility that they might reflect different response properties of the parent cell bodies. In recent years, however, interest has shifted toward the use of single-

cal recordings are a poor guide to the spatial distribution and relative frequencies of the three cell classes. Histological evidence indicates that all ganglion cells have their peak density at the central area, the densities decreasing monotonically toward the periphery (183, 184, 350, 353). The relative proportions of cells in the three classes is approximately constant over most of the retina, so that the distribution maps for the various classes are similar to the total density map (Fig. 4). The α-cell proportion is about 3%–5% except in the central area, where the proportion is only about 2%. There is still a measure of controversy concerning the relative distribution of the β- and γ-cells. There may be a relative increase in the proportion of γ-cells toward the retinal periphery and of β-cells in the central region (287), but Hughes (184) has concluded that the distribution maps for ganglion cells in each of the three modes of soma diameter spectra are similar in form and resemble that of the total neuron density map. A proportion of neurons in the γ-mode both survive sectioning of the optic nerve, which causes retrograde degeneration of true ganglion cells (351), and also fail to fill by retrograde transport of horseradish peroxidase from either optic nerve or superior colliculus injections (184, 383). If these cells are ex-

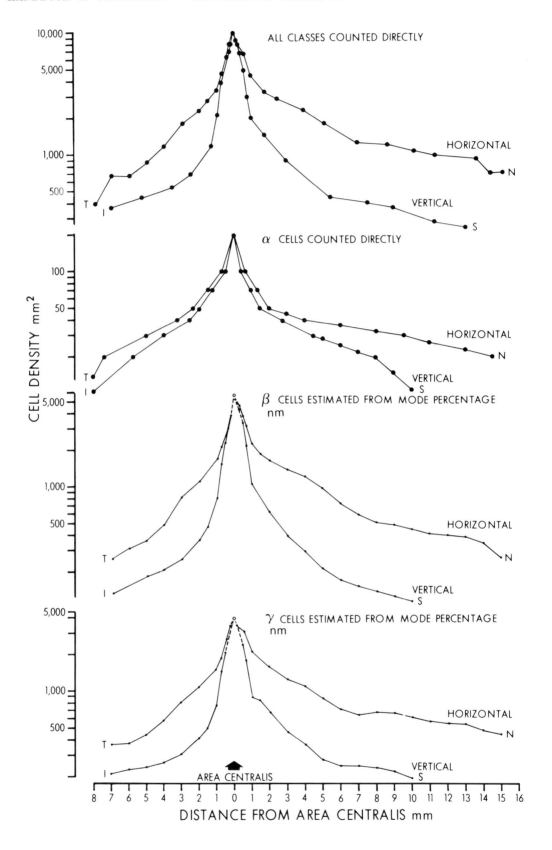

unit antidromic response latencies to electrical stimulation of the optic nerve or optic tract as a guide to retinal ganglion cell type (69, 71, 72, 117, 118, 204, 205, 236, 310, 358, 360). The sites most commonly used for stimulation are the optic chiasma (OX) and optic tract (OT), and the single-unit responses are recorded at the bodies of the ganglion cells.

In latency tests of the kind referred to, the overlap between response latency groupings are minimal when a long conduction pathway is used, when each of the fibers in the pathway has the same length and each retains its conduction properties unchanged throughout that length, and when only a single stimulus site is used. Unfortunately, with antidromic activation of ganglion cells, many factors operate to relax these constraints. Whereas the extraretinal fibers are myelinated, the intraretinal fibers are unmyelinated and of varying path length depending upon the retinal locations of their cell bodies. Attempts to increase the path length by stimulating centrally beyond the lateral geniculate nucleus must face the problem of axonal branching and possible change in fiber caliber. Even within the optic nerve and tract, fibers may undertake a tortuous path and suffer irregular variations in their caliber. In addition, changes in the site of stimulation may occur with increase in stimulus strength, and there may be uncertain variations in the time taken for the development of propagated impulses at different stimulus sites. The conversion of latency data into conduction velocities usually confers no advantage for the assessment of cell type, because of the uncertainty regarding conduction distance.

Figure 5A shows the distribution of response latencies to optic chiasm stimulation for three ganglion cell groupings: Y, brisk-transient; X, brisk-sustained; W, sluggish and nonconcentric types (310). The cells were recorded in four preparations over a fairly wide range of retinal eccentricities in each case. Response latency increases with increasing distance of the ganglion cell body from the optic disk and much of the overlap of latency values for the three groupings in Figure 5A is due to the pooling of data recorded at widely different retinal eccentricities. Over a more-restricted range of eccentricities there is usually a clear separation be-

tween the brisk-transient and brisk-sustained latency populations and a much-reduced overlap between the brisk-sustained group and that of the remaining cell types. Thus at any particular eccentricity the brisk-transient cells form a short-latency population, brisk-sustained cells an intermediate-latency population, and the sluggish and nonconcentric types a long-latency group. At the area centralis there is a marked local increase in latency for the brisk-transient and brisk-sustained cells that is not found for the remaining cell classes. This local increase in latency presumably reflects finer caliber fibers for these cells.

Although the slowly conducting sluggish and nonconcentric cells show different distributions of conduction latencies associated with receptive-field type, there is, nevertheless, a considerable scatter of latencies within a given class and a substantial overlap between the different classes. Color-coded cells have the shortest mean latency and local edge detectors the longest. The mean sluggish-sustained latency was consistently shorter than that of sluggish-transient cells, the latter units having a particularly wide scatter of latencies, 4.9 to 33 ms to optic tract stimulation (204).

It is not possible to assign cells unambiguously to a particular receptive-field type solely on the basis of conduction latency values.

CROSSED AND UNCROSSED PATHWAYS IN CAT. According to the classic description of the nasotemporal partition of the retina, cells to the temporal side of a sharp vertical line through the center of the area centralis have axons that remain uncrossed at the optic chiasm, whereas the axons of those on the nasal side of the line cross to the opposite cerebral hemisphere. By both anatomical (351) and physiological (206, 207, 357) methods it has, however, been shown that the line separating cells with crossed and cells with uncrossed axons is not sharp. Instead, there are bands straddling the vertical midline, within which crossed and uncrossed cells intermingle, the width of the bands and their spatial alignment with respect to the vertical midline of the retina varying from one ganglion cell class to another. The nature of the intermingling of crossed and uncrossed cells is illustrated

---

FIG. 4. Distribution of cat retinal ganglion cell types as function of horizontal and vertical distance from area centralis. *T*: temporal; *N*: nasal; *I*: inferior; *S*: superior. *Top* two curves show total ganglion cell densities as a function of eccentricity. *Lower* three pairs of curves show distributions of α-, β-, and γ-cell types, either counted directly (α) or based on β- and γ-modes (m) of the Nissl-stained (n) soma diameter spectra. Relative peak densities of β_n- and γ_n-modes were estimated from horseradish peroxidase filling from superior colliculus. The β- and γ-modes can be regarded as only a guide to class cell densities, not only because of cross-modal class contamination but also because the γ_n-mode contains a class of displaced amacrine cells. Density profiles for all three cell-diameter modes are very similar in form and resemble that of total neuronal density map. Hence the relative densities of various cell types are much the same at all eccentricities. [From Hughes (184).]

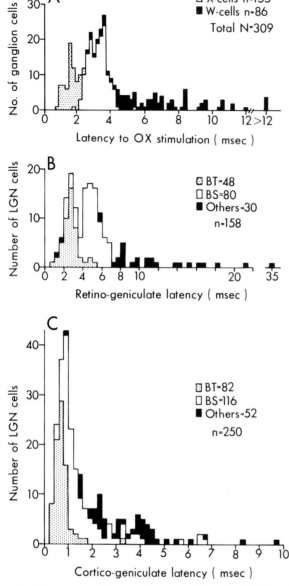

FIG. 5. *A*: frequency histogram of response latencies of different types of cat retinal ganglion cells (X,Y,W) following antidromic electrical stimulation from optic chiasm (OX). Y, brisk-transient; X, brisk-sustained; W, sluggish and nonconcentric types. Cells were recorded in four preparations, in each case, over a fairly wide range of retinal eccentricities. *B*: frequency histogram of response latencies of different types of cells in dorsal nucleus of lateral geniculate body (LGNd) of cat following electrical stimulation of retina by an electrode located near center of receptive field of particular LGNd cell. BT, brisk-transient class; BS, brisk-sustained. *C*: frequency histogram of responses of cat LGNd cells following antidromic activation from visual cortex. Height of each column in all three histograms (*A,B,C*) represents total cell count for a particular latency value. [*A*: from Rowe and Stone (310); *B,C*: from Cleland et al. (73).]

in Figure 6. The histograms *A* and *C* were made by recording the number of receptive fields of crossed and uncrossed brisk-sustained (Fig. 6*A*) and brisk-tran-

sient (Fig. 6*C*) ganglion cells in a succession of narrow vertical strips across the visual field of the left eye in a series of cats. The crossed and uncrossed destinations of the axons were determined by antidromic activation of the cells, using stimulating electrodes located in the two optic tracts. The trend within the region of crossed-uncrossed overlap is more readily seen by plotting the percentage of cells having crossed axons (open circles) as a function of the horizontal coordinate (azimuth) of receptive-field position and similarly with respect to cells with uncrossed axons (filled circles). It is important to distinguish between azimuth values in the visual field and the corresponding retinal locations. Negative azimuth values in the visual field correspond to temporal locations in the right eye and nasal locations in the left eye, the relations being opposite for positive azimuths. For the brisk-sustained cells the plot in Figure 6*B* reveals that the region of transition from 100% crossed to 0% crossed takes place over a band about 2° wide and similarly for the uncrossed cells. The region of transition is approximately symmetrical about the 50% point, which by definition coincides with zero azimuth, the vertical midline of the retina.

The transition pattern for brisk-transient cells (Fig. 6*D*) is distinctly different. On passing from nasal to temporal on the retina, the percentage of crossed cells starts falling from 100% at about the same negative azimuth value as for the brisk-sustained cells. However, the decline from 100% crossed is more gradual and tails off in an asymmetrical fashion to reach 0% at about 16° azimuth into the temporal retina. Thus the position where 50% of the brisk-transient cells are crossed comes to lie about 2° on the temporal side of the vertical midline of the retina (Fig. 6*D*). The location into the temporal retina at which crossed brisk-transient cells cease to be found (16°) approximately corresponds to the largest azimuth value into the "wrong" hemifield for the receptive fields of cells recorded in the part of the medial interlaminar nucleus where it adjoins the dorsal nucleus of the lateral geniculate body (LGNd) (203, 314, 318).

The pattern of the crossed-uncrossed overlap for the sluggish-sustained cells is approximately the same as that of the brisk-transient cells described. The pattern for the remaining cells (sluggish-transient, local-edge-detector, direction-selective) showed a predominance of crossed cells over the full extent of the temporal retina so that, for these cells, crossed axons came not only from all the cells in the nasal retina but also from a majority of cells in the temporal retina. By contrast, cells with uncrossed axons were located no more than 1° into the nasal retina.

From the preceding account it can be seen that there are at least three distinct patterns of crossed-uncrossed overlap shown by *1*) brisk-sustained cells, *2*) brisk-transient and sluggish-sustained cells, and *3*) sluggish-transient, local-edge-detector and direction-selective cells. For each of these patterns, the temporal

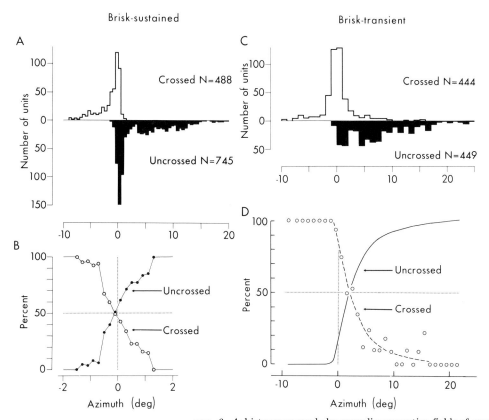

FIG. 6. *A*: histograms made by recording receptive fields of crossed and uncrossed brisk-sustained retinal ganglion cells in a succession of narrow vertical strips across visual field of left eye of cat. Retinal azimuth (horizontal eccentricity) inferred from positions of receptive fields on a frontal screen. Antidromic activation of cells (accomplished by stimulating electrodes located in the two optic tracts) determined crossed and uncrossed destinations of axons. Pooled data from 30 cats. *B*: data in *A* expressed as percentages of crossed (*open circles*), and uncrossed (*filled circles*) ganglion cells. Zero azimuth (*dotted line*) coincides with center of band of crossed-uncrossed overlap of brisk-sustained cells. The two complementary curves have been drawn to illustrate symmetry of transition on either side of line of zero azimuth. Abscissa scale magnified to 5 times that of *A*. *C*: same as *A* for brisk-transient retinal ganglion cells. Pooled data from 30 cats. *D*: data in *C* expressed as percentages of crossed (*open circles*) and uncrossed (*continuous line*) ganglion cells. Zero azimuth same as for *B*. Position where 50% of brisk-transient cells are crossed lies about 2° into temporal retina from that of brisk-sustained system. [Adapted from Kirk et al. (207) and Levick (235).]

extent of the locations of cells with crossed axons differs widely, but cells with uncrossed axons are never located more than 0.5° to 1° into the nasal retina irrespective of cell class.

The crossed-uncrossed overlap for brisk-sustained cells is of importance in relation to theories of binocular depth discrimination (27, 29, 41), since it is required for the neural coding of retinal image disparities of objects in midline vision at depths behind or in front of the fixation point. In addition Levick (235) has argued that the brisk-transient overlap is used in binocular depth discrimination for monitoring a frontal plane much closer to the cat than the fixation plane.

CENTRAL DISTRIBUTION OF OPTIC NERVE FIBERS IN CAT. A number of detailed systematic studies of the distribution of optic nerve fibers in the cat have been conducted using the silver impregnation of degener-

ating axons and terminals following removal of an eye (121, 218, 345). The newer axoplasmic transport methods have been used to study the retinal input to particular central regions but have not so far been applied in the same systematic way as in the earlier studies referred to. Using anterograde labeling with tritiated amino acids Berman and Jones (20) noted that the following regions received a direct retinal input: the suprachiasmatic nuclei of the hypothalamus, dorsal and ventral lateral geniculate nuclei, medial interlaminar nucleus, perigeniculate nucleus, pulvinar, nuclei of the optic tract and accessory optic tract, olivary nucleus, pretectum, and superior colliculus. The retinal inputs to those regions that subsequently provide a direct relay to the striate cortex are considered in detail later on (see RETINAL INPUT TO DORSAL LGN NEURONS, p. 364, *Medial Interlaminar Nucleus*, p. 369, and ZONES DEFINED BY AFFERENT INPUTS, p. 371).

Monkey Retina

RECEPTIVE FIELDS OF RETINAL GANGLION CELLS. In 1960 Hubel and Wiesel (168) reported that the retinal ganglion cells in the monkey could be divided not only into the on- and off-center varieties described by Kuffler (211) in the cat retina but also into spectrally-opponent and nonopponent categories. Subsequently Wiesel and Hubel (392) divided neurons in the macaque monkey lateral geniculate body into four cell types (I to IV) on the basis of their degree of spatial and spectral opponency and their laminar segregation. Since it was later found that the properties of these various cell types had remained relatively unaffected by their passage through the lateral geniculate nucleus, the same cell type numbers have come to be applied to their retinal ganglion cell counterparts. The earlier observations on the ganglion cells of the retina were confirmed by Gouras (134, 135), who also reported that the cells with spectrally opponent properties had sustained responses (tonic) and slow conduction velocities, while spectrally nonopponent cells had transient responses (phasic) and fast conduction velocities. Since 1975 (88) considerable clarification has been achieved with respect to the variety of cells and their properties (84–86, 88–93, 101, 253, 324, 325).

In addition to the four cell types, corresponding to those originally described by Wiesel and Hubel (392) as occurring in the macaque LGNd, two further types of retinal ganglion cells (types V and VI) have now been recognized (84–86). As in the cat retina, the monkey ganglion cell receptive fields may be either concentrically or nonconcentrically organized and have spatial summation properties that resemble either the X- or the Y-cell systems (Table 2). But whereas color-coded cells are rarely encountered in the cat retina, monkey ganglion cells commonly have the added complication, mainly confined to the X-cells, of showing opponent-color responses to stimuli of different wavelengths. The linearity of the X-cells and the nonlinearity of the Y-cells has been established by methods similar to those used by Enroth-Cugell and Robson (105) in the cat, namely by means of the null test to alternating contrast and by the nature of the responses to drifting gratings (84, 92). The so-called atypical cells (types II, V, and VI) lack the center-surround organization that is found in types I, III, and IV, and they have other affinities with the rarely encountered ganglion cell types in the cat (86, 324). The relative encounter rates of the different cell types in variously recorded samples were type I, 60%–70%; types III and IV, 20%–30%; and the atypical cells, 5%–10% (87). On the basis of experience in the cat, it is possible that the atypical cells may form a much larger fraction of the total cell population than is indicated by these encounter rates, particularly as these cells are thought to have small cell bodies and fine axons.

CONCENTRICALLY ORGANIZED RECEPTIVE FIELDS. *Type I (spectrally opponent, X-cells).* In addition to linear spatial summation (X type), type I cells have small receptive fields, a high level of spontaneous activity and, usually, long conduction latencies. They have a concentric receptive-field organization and show both spatial- and spectral-opponent properties. Signals from only one cone type usually mediate the center responses, while signals from one or two other cone types mediate surround responses. About 80% of the neurons show a red vs. green opponency of the type red-center, green-surround or vice versa. Not infrequently they receive additional signals from blue-sensitive cones in their surround which result in red vs. green-blue (cyan) and green vs. red-blue (magenta) varieties. The remaining cells always receive opponent signals from all three cone types in a blue vs. red-green (yellow) arrangement. The red-green and blue-yellow opponent cells can also be divided into on-center and off-center classes such as red on-center, green off-surround; red off-center, green on-surround; and so on, giving rise to an additional range of distinct subtypes.

Type I cells can be further divided into two classes, depending upon whether the spectral opponency is evident or concealed. In about 25% of these cells the

TABLE 2. *Classification of Ganglion Cells in Macaque Retina*

Class No.	Receptive-Field Organization	Linear (X) Nonlinear (Y)	Response Properties
I	Concentric	X	Spectrally opponent (either evident or concealed) and spatially opponent
II	Nonconcentric	X	Spectrally opponent but not spatially opponent
III	Concentric	Y	Broad-band, spectrally nonopponent
IV	Concentric	Y	Broad-band, spectrally opponent
Va	Nonconcentric	Y	On-off cells lacking a surround
Vb	Nonconcentric	Y	On-off cells with silent surround
VI	Nonconcentric	Not tested	Motion-sensitive inhibition

Data from de Monasterio (84, 86, 87).

spectral opponency is concealed by reason of a remarkably weak surround antagonism. Unless the center sensitivity is selectively depressed, the responses mimic those of spectrally nonopponent cells and show neither spectral nor spatial opponency. This phenomenon is more frequently found in extrafoveal than in foveal neurons, and in red-center rather than in green-center neurons. It has not been found in blue-center cells.

The relative encounter rate of type I cells decreases from about 85% in the central 1° to about 35% at 40° eccentricity. They have the smallest receptive-field center size of any cell at a given eccentricity, typically less than 0.02°, and this shows little variation with distance from the fovea. Nearly all blue-center cells are on-center, whereas red- and green-center cells show a rather even distribution of their on- and off-center varieties.

Types III and IV (Y-cells). In addition to their nonlinear spatial summation, types III and IV cells have large receptive fields, a comparatively low level of spontaneous activity, and, usually, short conduction latencies. Both cell types are Y-like, having nonlinear spatial summation across their receptive fields. These two cell types appear to represent varieties within a single continuum with type III cells being more frequently encountered toward the peripheral regions of the retina and type IV cells more frequently in the central region (93). Within the central 30° to 40° these Y-cells have, on the average, conduction times about twice as short and receptive-field centers two to four times as large as those of the red-green opponent cells in the X group.

Type III (broad-band, spectrally nonopponent). Type III cells have antagonistic center and surround mechanisms receiving input from the same cone types (almost exclusively red- and green-sensitive) and thus show spectrally nonopponent responses, i.e., they respond to changes in stimulus luminance independent of wavelength. They have spatial- but not spectral-opponent properties. Because more than one cone type mediates their center and surround, these cells also have a broad-band spectral sensitivity. However, the strength of the signals from the green-sensitive cones in the surround decreases with decreasing retinal eccentricity. Toward the fovea, type III cells come to have responses intermediate between perifoveal type III cells, whose surrounds receive a rather similar input from both cone types, and the predominantly foveal type IV cells, whose surrounds appear to lack input from green-sensitive cones, thereby giving them a rudimentary form of spectral opponency.

Type IV (broad-band, spectrally opponent). Type IV cells are much less frequently encountered than type III cells and, in some respects, their response properties resemble those of type I. They have center and surround mechanisms with different spectral sensitivities and thus show spectrally opponent responses. However, unlike type I cells, they receive input from

two or three different cone types with center and surround responses being partly mediated by the same type or types of cone. In most cells signals from one of the two or three cone types mediating the center are absent from the responses from the surround, the typical arrangement being red-green center, red surround. All type IV cells are on-center. There seem to be no off-centers.

NONCONCENTRICALLY ORGANIZED RECEPTIVE FIELDS. About 10% of the cells encountered in the macaque retina have receptive fields that lack a center-surround organization (86). These cells have a diffuse extrafoveal distribution and are less frequently found in the foveal region. Their conduction latencies to optic tract stimulation overlap those of cells in types I, III, and IV that have a center-surround organization. Three types have been distinguished—types II, V, and VI (86)—but they do not form a functional class.

Type II cells (X-cells, spectrally opponent). Type II cells have spectral and spatial properties similar to those of the type II cells described by Wiesel and Hubel (392) in the monkey lateral geniculate nucleus. These cells have wavelength-dependent responses that are abolished by white light stimuli, showing that the spectrally opponent mechanisms have similar or identical spatial distributions and response latencies. The opponent responses are cone specific, i.e., they are mediated by spectrally different types of cone. Most cells receive input from all three types of cone, commonly in a blue vs. yellow arrangement, and they lack a rod input. Type II cells have a high spontaneous activity, and their receptive fields are similar in size to the overall dimensions of the fields of spectrally opponent cells. Type II cells are found predominantly in the central retina though rarely in the fovea. They have a linear spatial summation over the receptive field and have conduction latencies that are intermediate between those of type I and types III and IV.

Type V cells (Y-cells). The common characteristic of the type V cells is their transient on-off responses to incremental stimuli. Two subgroups can be distinguished depending particularly on the presence or absence of a silent (inhibitory) surround.

Type Va. Type Va cells have very transient on-off responses, show no spontaneous activity, and lack an antagonistic or inhibitory surround. Usually the on-responses are mediated by input from red cones and the off-responses by input from green cones. They appear not to have an input from blue cones. The spatial distribution of the mechanisms generating on-responses and off-responses are approximately coextensive. They were encountered at retinal depths more sclerad than those of other spike-generating neurons and they could not be antidromically driven from the optic tract or more central structures. They had nonlinear spatial summation.

Type Vb. Type Vb cells have a silent surround whose activation suppresses both the maintained activity and the changes in cell firing produced by concurrent stimulation of the central on-off region, whereas isolated stimulation of the surround typically fails to generate cell firing. Incremental stimulation of the central region produces either a transient increase in cell firing ("excitatory" on-off cells) or a transient decrease in cell firing ("inhibitory" on-off cells). Like type Va cells they receive input from green- and red-sensitive cones but not blue-sensitive cones. They have nonlinear spatial summation and can be antidromically activated from both the LGNd and the superior colliculus with comparatively long conduction latencies.

Type VI cells. Relatively little is known about the type VI cells. They have a high maintained activity that is predominantly inhibited by moving stimuli but remains unaffected by stationary flashing stimuli. They had comparatively short conduction latencies to optic tract stimulation, but no reliable antidromic responses could be elicited from either the LGN or superior colliculus. Their spatial summation properties have not been tested.

MORPHOLOGICAL CORRELATES OF FUNCTIONAL GANGLION CELL CLASSES IN MONKEY RETINA. It is not so far possible to identify the morphological correlates of the functional classes of ganglion cells in the monkey retina. Detailed studies have been made of the retinal ganglion cells in the monkey (44, 295) but, being based on vertical sections, they are not directly applicable to the whole-mount preparations that have proved so valuable for the correlations in the cat. Boycott and Dowling (44) confirmed the presence of midget ganglion cells originally observed by Polyak (295) and also described five other types that they classified into diffuse and stratified ganglion cells according to the level at which their dendrites branch within the inner plexiform layer. Both Polyak (295) and Boycott and Dowling (44) agree that all varieties of ganglion cells, with the possible exception of the giant ganglion cell, are present in every region of the retina from the central foveal region to the far periphery. Whereas whole-mount preparations of the monkey retina have been prepared (52, 350, 361, 380), the pileup of ganglion cells just outside the fovea, up to seven layers deep, makes impracticable the same kinds of density measurements that have been carried out in the cat. Out to 5° from the fovea the ganglion cells are small (8–10 μm diam), uniform in size, and form a closely spaced mosaic. Cell body size increases with eccentricity but there is apparently no clear indication, in any part of the retina, of more than one mode in the distribution of sizes. There is disagreement regarding the presence of giant ganglion cells comparable to the α-cells in the cat retina. Polyak (295) and Bunt et al. (52) reported ganglion cells 30 μm in diameter, but these were not observed by Stone (350) or by Boycott and Dowling (44).

CONDUCTION PROPERTIES OF MONKEY RETINAL GANGLION CELL AXONS. The conduction properties of monkey retinal ganglion cell axons have been much less studied than those in the cat. Classifying the majority of the ganglion cells as either color-opponent or broad-band, Schiller and Malpeli (324) estimated the mean conduction velocities for the fibers between the optic chiasm and lateral geniculate nucleus to be 12.9 m/s and 22.1 m/s, respectively, for the two categories, although the distributions overlapped substantially. The corresponding velocities for the intraretinal unmyelinated fibers were 0.9 m/s and 1.3 m/s, respectively. Since conduction velocity remained essentially constant with retinal eccentricity, Schiller and Malpeli (324) concluded that the mean diameter of the intraretinal axons also remained the same over the retina. The distributions of the response latencies of ganglion cells to optic tract stimulation observed by de Monasterio (84) agree well with the optic chiasm latencies reported by Schiller and Malpeli (324), if one assumes that the type I and the combined types III and IV of the former are to be respectively equated with the color-opponent and broad-band categories of the latter. The mean latency of the type I cells was 9.44 ms, while that for the combined types III and IV group was 5.65 ms. With respect to their conduction properties de Monasterio did not distinguish between type III and type IV: both had relatively short response latencies to optic tract stimulation. By contrast only the type IIIy subtype of Dreher et al. (101) had a short response latency, the latency of the type IIIx subtype being similar to that of type I cells. The number of cells that have so far been examined in the remaining cell categories are too few for any firm conclusions to be drawn about their conduction properties, but the latency values that are available for types II, Vb, and VI indicate that they fall entirely within the latency distribution of the type I units (86).

CROSSED AND UNCROSSED PATHWAYS IN MONKEY. There is anatomical (52, 361) and physiological (84, 292) evidence for a vertical median strip of retina in which the ganglion cells project both ipsilaterally and contralaterally. By observing the pattern of ganglion-cell degeneration in retinal whole-mount preparations of monkeys in each of whom an optic tract had been sectioned 6–12 months previously, Stone et al. (361) observed that ipsilaterally and contralaterally projecting ganglion cells intermingle along a vertically oriented median strip about 1° wide and centered on the fovea. A similar observation was made by Bunt et al. (52) following injections of horseradish peroxidase (HRP) into the macaque LGN. Almost every cell in the contralateral nasal retina was labeled and, in addition, labeled ganglion cells were found in the contralateral temporal retina up to 0.5° from the vertical midline. Apart from an occasional extrafoveal labeled ganglion cell as far as 2° from the vertical midline in the otherwise unlabeled hemiretinas, there was none of the very broad overlap of different classes of ganglion cells to be found in the cat retina. Although the overlap in the monkey is restricted to a very narrow band that straddles the vertical midline, it is, nevertheless, more than ample to account for the distribution of preferred retinal image disparities that Poggio and Fischer (292) found for tuned excitatory and tuned inhibitory neurons in monkey cortical areas 17 and 18. Cowey and Perry (78) found no labeled cells in the so-called wrong half of the macaque retina after injections of HRP into the superior colliculus.

CENTRAL DISTRIBUTION OF OPTIC FIBERS IN MONKEY. Hendrickson et al. (155) traced the distribution of optic nerve fibers in the macaque monkey using silver impregnation techniques for demonstrating degenerating axons and terminals. In addition the distribution of normal fibers was studied by the autoradiographic method following injection of tritiated leucine into the vitreous cavity. Their results are summarized in Figure 7. The following sites of termination were found: pregeniculate nucleus, dorsal lateral geniculate nucleus, lateral terminal nucleus of the accessory optic tract, pretectal nucleus, nucleus olivaris,

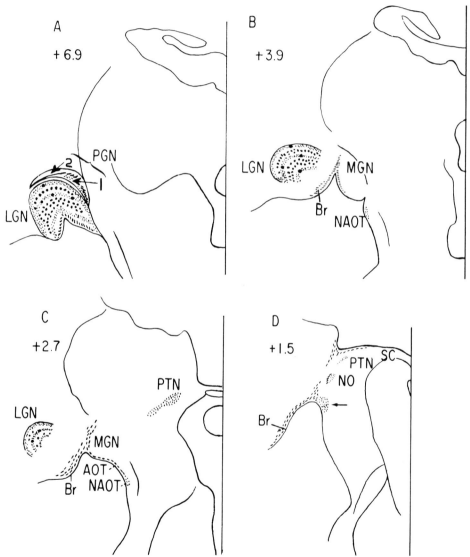

FIG. 7. *A-D*: location of optic nerve axons and terminals in coronal sections of contralateral hemisphere of *Macaca mulatta*. Composite drawings based on degeneration patterns revealed by Nauta methods following eye enucleation and from autoradiographs following vitreal injection of tritiated leucine. Brain section numbers (+6.9, etc.) are mm anterior to interaural plane. *Small dots*, terminal degeneration; *large dots* and *dashes*, degenerating fiber bundles; *PGN*, pregeniculate nucleus with subdivisions (1, 2); *LGN*, dorsal lateral geniculate nucleus; *MGN*, medial geniculate nucleus; *PTN*, pretectal nucleus; *NAOT*, lateral terminal nucleus of accessory optic tract; *NO*, nucleus olivaris; *AOT*, posterior accessory optic tract; *Br*, brachium of superior colliculus; *SC*, superior colliculus. [From Hendrickson et al. (155).]

and superior colliculus. In addition they found bilateral terminals in a region just medial to the LGN that they regarded as equivalent to the parageniculate nucleus of Polyak (296). The parageniculate nucleus of Polyak (296) is probably equivalent to the inferior pulvinar nucleus of later authors (see *Extrageniculate Visual Thalamus in Monkey*, p. 377). Hendrickson et al. (155) made no mention of a direct retinal input to the hypothalamus in the macaque monkey. Further consideration is given in this chapter only to those regions of direct retinal input that subsequently also provide a direct relay to the striate cortex.

Central distribution of retinal ganglion cell types. Only scattered information is so far available concerning the central distribution of the axons of the various retinal ganglion cell types in the monkey retina, and even this is limited to the LGNd and superior colliculus. Whereas most, if not all, retinal ganglion cell types project to the LGNd (52), a fraction of the noncolor-opponent cells, both with and without a center-surround organization, also project to the superior colliculus (85, 324, 325). Cell types I, II, III, IV, and Vb have all been antidromically activated by stimulation of the LGNd (84, 86, 325) and cells with properties similar to types I to IV have been recorded in the LGNd (101, 325, 392), but so far not types V and VI. Only types III and Vb have been shown to project to the superior colliculus, and types Va and VI have not so far been antidromically driven by stimulation of either the LGNd or the superior colliculus (86). Thus the retinogeniculate projection carries both chromatic and achromatic information, whereas the retinocollicular projection appears to be restricted to achromatic information.

VISUAL THALAMUS

The pathway through the dorsal lateral geniculate nucleus (LGNd) is the major thalamocortical system transmitting visual information from the retina to the visual cortex. However, the concept of a single direct visual pathway bringing information to the visual cortex via the LGNd and having this information further processed only via corticocortical connections from striate to prestriate, and then to inferotemporal cortices, has been much modified in recent years. It now appears that each modality of sensation has multiple pathways in the central nervous system. Even within the geniculostriate system there are multiple, largely independent pathways related to the different classes of retinal ganglion cells. In addition, information from the retina can reach the visual cortex via extrageniculate routes. In the so-called second visual system the pathway from the retina goes first to the superior colliculus and pretectum and then, via the posterior thalamic complex, to mainly extrastriate visual areas (138, 329). Whereas the direct geniculostriate system appears to mediate fine-grained pattern analysis, the colliculocortical system seems to be mainly concerned

with orientation toward visual stimuli and the control of eye movements (94, 131, 262, 326). This colliculocortical system lies outside the scope of the present chapter and is not considered further here.

There is now, however, good evidence for a direct extrageniculate retinothalamic projection to the striate and extrastriate cortex in both cat and monkey. Using silver impregnation methods for degenerating axons following removal of an eye, Campos-Ortega et al. (64) have shown that there is a direct bilateral retinal input to the inferior pulvinar nucleus in both macaque monkey and baboon. Using both axon degeneration and autoradiographic methods in the macaque monkey, Hendrickson et al. (155) also reported a direct bilateral retinal input to a region just medial to the LGN that presumably corresponds to the inferior pulvinar nucleus, although these authors did not give a name to the region. These observations need to be confirmed and extended, particularly since there is now clear-cut evidence for a direct retinopulvinar projection in the cat (20, 21). In contrast to the retinopulvinar projection, much detailed information is now available concerning the reciprocal connections between the posterior thalamic complex and cortex in both the macaque monkey (18, 275, 276, 298, 375) and cat (21, 139, 378).

Cat Dorsal Lateral Geniculate Nucleus (LGN)

MORPHOLOGY OF DORSAL LGN AND ASSOCIATED NUCLEI. The mammalian visual thalamus comprises essentially the lateral geniculate complex and the lateralis posterior-pulvinar complex. The general organization of the dorsal lateral geniculate nucleus (LGNd) and adjacent nuclei in the cat are shown in Figure 8. Figure 8A shows the LGNd as it appears in a Nissl-stained parasagittal section taken approximately through the middle of the mediolateral extent of the nucleus. The semidiagrammatic coronal section in Figure 8B, taken through the middle of anteroposterior extent of the nucleus, has been labeled according to the A, C system of Guillery [(144); see *Laminar organization of dorsal LGN*, p. 359]. The optic tract fibers approach the LGNd from below, partially surrounding the ventral lateral geniculate nucleus (LGNv). The cat LGNv is generally regarded as homologous with the primate pregeniculate nucleus (PGN in Fig. 7A), but the latter seems more likely to be homologous with the perigeniculate nucleus in the cat (PGN in Fig. 8B; see *Perigeniculate Nucleus and Nucleus Reticularis Thalami*, p. 370). Despite their close proximity, the ventral and dorsal lateral geniculate nuclei have quite different embryological origins. The ventral nucleus differentiates from the anlage of the ventral diencephalon, whereas the dorsal nucleus derives from the dorsal diencephalon (66). The LGNv receives a bilateral retinal input but does not project to the cerebral cortex. Since the LGNv does not project to the cerebral cortex it may be regarded as lying

Cat LGN

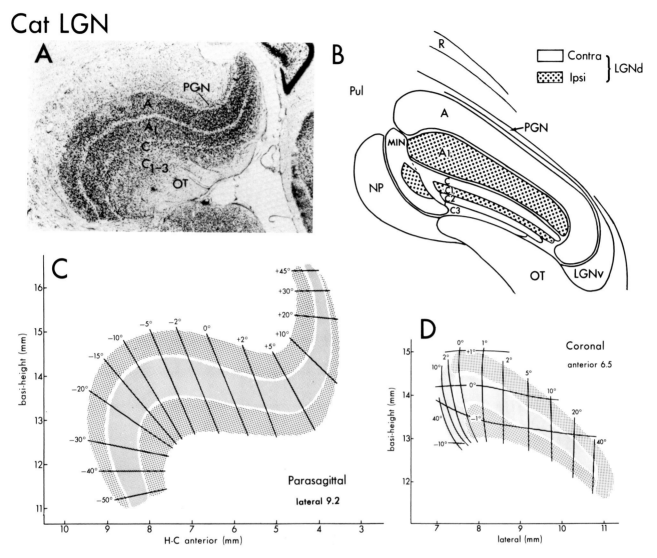

FIG. 8. Lateral geniculate nucleus in cat. *A*: Nissl-stained parasagittal section through middle of mediolateral extent of dorsal lateral geniculate nucleus (LGNd). *A, A₁, C, C₁–C₃,* cell laminae of dorsal lateral geniculate nucleus; *PGN,* perigeniculate nucleus; *OT,* optic tract. *B*: semidiagrammatic coronal section through middle of the anteroposterior extent of LGNd showing laminar distribution of crossed and uncrossed optic nerve fibers. *LGNv,* ventral lateral geniculate nucleus; *MIN,* medial interlaminar nucleus; *R,* reticular nucleus; *NP,* posterior nucleus; *Pul,* pulvinar. *C*: projection map of a parasagittal section through middle of LGNd (lateral 9.2) showing pattern of isoelevation lines; *D*: projection map of a coronal section through middle of the LGNd (anterior 6.5) showing pattern of isoazimuth and isoelevation lines. Isoelevation values are marked as + or − to distinguish them from isoazimuth lines (unmarked). [*C, D*: from Sanderson (314).]

outside the scope of the present chapter (cf. ref. 349). The LGNv extends dorsally and medially over lamina A as a thin mantle of cells, and as it does so it splits into two thin sheets—one, the perigeniculate nucleus (PGN in Fig. 8*B*), fairly closely applied to lamina A; and the other, the reticular nucleus (R), some little distance above the lamina. Closely applied to the medial aspect of the LGNd is the medial interlaminar nucleus (MIN; cf. ref. 368), which receives a second direct retinotopic projection. Although the MIN is a general feature among carnivores it appears not to have a homologous structure in other mammals.

Immediately adjacent to the MIN on its medial side is the lateralis posterior-pulvinar complex that can be differentiated into three main divisions—a tectorecipient zone, a corticorecipient zone, and a retinal and pretectal recipient zone (139). These aspects of the visual thalamus are discussed when the extrageniculate visual pathways are considered. The posterior nucleus (NP in Fig. 8*B*) belongs to the corticorecipient zone, whereas the pulvinar (Pul) forms the retinal and pretectal recipient zone.

Laminar organization of dorsal LGN. In a wide range of mammals ipsilateral retinogeniculate terminals are segregated from the contralateral. In many species, however, particularly those with well-developed binocular vision, such as the carnivores and primates, the terminals project to separate cell layers that are segregated from each other by narrow zones almost devoid of cells. In the cat LGNd it is possible to distinguish as many as six (A,C system, ref. 160) or seven (A,M,B system, ref. 107) layers. The two main laminae, A and A_1, have the same labels in the two systems. The difference between the six- and the seven-layer schemes concerns lamina C. The extra lamina in the A,M,B scheme comes about by splitting the C-lamina of Hickey and Guillery (160) into dorsal and ventral layers called M and B_o, respectively. Thereafter layers C_1, C_2, and C_3 have their counterparts in B_1, B_2, and B_3. Three geniculate layers receive a contralateral innervation (A, C, and C_2), while only two (A_1 and C_1) receive an ipsilateral input. Layers A and A_1 are reasonably closely matched as regards size and structure and they can be regarded as providing a functionally matched pair of pathways to the cortex. Although layers C and C_1 also receive afferents from the contralateral and ipsilateral eyes, respectively, they do not form a matched pair as do A and A_1. Lamina C is not homogeneous. The dorsal part of lamina C (layer M) is characterized by a concentration of large cells, and it is closely associated with the overlying A-laminae in terms of its retinal input and output projections. By contrast the ventral part of lamina C (B_o) is made up of small cells with properties and connections similar to those of the underlying C-laminae. Laminae C_1–C_3 all contain small cells, C_1 getting an input from the ipsilateral eye and C_2 from the contralateral eye. Lamina C_3 has yet to be shown to receive a retinal input. The dorsal part of lamina C receives a significant coarse-fibered retinogeniculate input, whereas those to the remaining C laminae are all fine. Lamina C_1 contains only small cells. This difference between laminae C and C_1 means that the geniculate relay for axons from the temporal retina is not the same as that from the nasal retina. The remaining two laminae, C_2 and C_3, both contain small cells.

COORDINATE SYSTEM FOR VISUAL-FIELD PROJECTIONS. In all mammals the contralateral half of the total visual field is represented in each lateral geniculate nucleus. In order to describe this representation a suitable coordinate system is needed for specifying direction in visual space. For all the early animal studies the coordinate system employed was the same as that used in human clinical perimetry. In this spherical polar coordinate system (Fig. 9B) the polar axis passes through the fixation point (F), in line with the visual axis. Where the primary aim is to determine the extent or outer limits of the visual field, this coordinate system is appropriate both in clinical practice and in experimental neurology. Bishop and co-workers (38) have discussed the relative advantages of

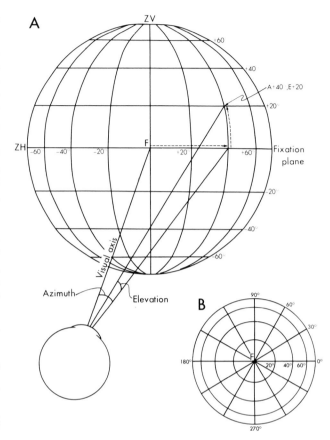

FIG. 9. Spherical polar coordinate systems for defining visual direction relative to visual axis and fixation point (F). A: coordinate system most suitable for mapping projection of visual field onto visual centers in brain. Polar axis passes vertically through nodal point of eye, at right angles to fixation plane. Visual direction expressed by two angles, azimuth (A) and elevation (E). ZV, zero vertical; ZH, zero horizontal (fixation plane). B: coordinate system used for human perimetry. Polar axis coincident with visual axis.

several alternative coordinate systems. The system they introduced (Fig. 9A) is now generally accepted for neurophysiological studies and is used in this chapter. It has the advantage that, in the central visual field, it is rectilinear and both coordinates are equivalent in terms of actual distances on the retina. In these respects it resembles the Amsler chart used for clinical examination of central vision. In this system the polar axis passes through the fixation point (F) at right angles to the fixation plane, and visual direction is specified in terms of two angles, azimuth (A) and elevation (E). Azimuth is the angle in the fixation plane between the visual axis and the projection of the line of sight onto the fixation plane (positive to the right, negative to the left). A line of sight is the line passing through any given point in the visual field and the nodal point of the eye. Elevation is the angle between a given line of sight and the fixation plane (positive upward, negative downward). In this system the zero horizontal (ZH, elevation = 0°) coincides with the fixation plane and the zero vertical (ZV, azimuth = 0°) is the meridian through the fixation point.

VISUAL-FIELD PROJECTION INTO DORSAL LGN. *General principles.* The representation of the visual field in the lateral geniculate nucleus is topological with an orderly projection of the contralateral visual hemifield via one eye or the other into alternating laminae. The successive laminae are stacked in visuotopic register so that there is a direct continuity of visual-field representation across the layers. Thus a single point in the visual field projects to the LGNd as a line, called a *projection line* by Bishop and colleagues (39). A projection line passes through the nucleus from one margin to another through all the layers and more or less perpendicular to them as shown by the isoelevation lines in Figure 8C. The family of projection lines representing points along a line in the visual field determines a surface in the LGN that also passes through the nucleus from the most ventral to the most dorsal layers. In other words a line in the visual field is represented as a surface in the LGNd. Thus a projection line in the LGNd can be defined by the intersection of isoazimuth and isoelevation surfaces as illustrated in Figure 10. The projection of the whole of the visual field into the LGNd can then be represented by two intersecting families of surface: one for azimuth and one for elevation. Thus a frontoparallel surface in the visual field is represented as a volume in the LGNd. The nature of the representation of the visual field in the LGNd indicates that one of the basic functions of the laminar organization is to bring into precise visuotopic alignment input from the contralateral hemiretina of one eye and the ipsilateral hemiretina of the other eye as a step toward the binocular integration of the visual input. In a sense, depth in space is represented along projection lines, since cells lying along these lines in adjacent laminae project in

common onto single cells in the striate cortex to form the basis of a neural mechanism for depth discrimination [see *Projection subunit ("column"),* this page].

Visual-field projection into cat dorsal LGN. The concepts outlined above have been developed by Bishop and colleagues (39), who showed that visual directions of constant elevation or azimuth are projected into the LGNd of the cat as surfaces that are approximately planar. Thus in the cat LGNd a parasagittal section is approximately a plane of isoazimuth (Fig. 8C) and, at least in the region of central visual-field representation, a coronal section is roughly a plane of isoelevation (Fig. 8D). The parasagittal section in Figure 8C corresponds to the 5° isoazimuth plane indicated by the corresponding projection line in Figure 8D. The vertical lines in Figure 8D are isoazimuth lines and the horizontal lines are isoelevation lines.

The midline in the visual field (zero vertical meridian) is represented medially in the LGNd (Fig. 8B, D) where the full complement of laminae abut the lateral margin of the medial interlaminar nucleus (MIN). The periphery of the contralateral hemifield is represented at the lateral margin of the nucleus where the layers of contralateral input extend beyond the layers of ipsilateral input. The segment of the nucleus with a full complement of laminae represents the binocular visual field and the smaller segment beyond about azimuth 45° represents the monocular field. Thus the extent of the binocular visual field in the cat is only 80° to 90°, which is nevertheless probably the most extensive binocular field of vision in a nonprimate mammal.

Projection subunit ("column"). When an electrode penetration through the LGNd cuts across projection lines there is a systematic shift in receptive-field position during the course of the penetration as well as a random scatter about the mean line of the systematic shift. As a result of an analysis of the random scatter in receptive-field position, Sanderson (315) introduced the concept of a projection column as the LGNd volume containing 90% of all the cells that have receptive fields with a common visual direction. The diagram in Figure 11B shows that the volume distribution of these cells in the LGNd is columnar, leading to the name *projection column.* The term *projection subunit* is, however, preferred in order to avoid confusion with the morphological concept of a column such as the ocular dominance columns in the visual cortex. In the region of the LGNd devoted to central vision the subunits have a circular cross section about 1 mm in diameter (315). This corresponds to a range of receptive-field positions of about ± 1.6° of azimuth. The central axis of the subunit is the projection line for the given visual direction. The LGNd can be considered as consisting of a large series of overlapping subunits, the members of each population having a common receptive-field position. The subunits are not spatially discrete but show a continuous distribution from one

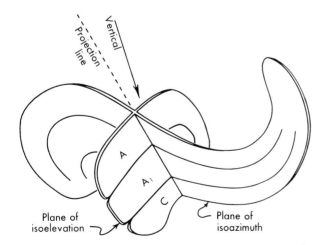

FIG. 10. Semischematic perspective drawing showing planes of isoazimuth and isoelevation in dorsal lateral geniculate nucleus (LGNd) of cat. The two planes intersect along a projection line, which is defined by column of geniculate cells whose receptive fields have a common direction in visual field. The LGNd planes are viewed from a point posterior, medial, and slightly above the nucleus. A, A₁, C, main LGNd cell laminae. [Adapted from Bioshop et al. (39).]

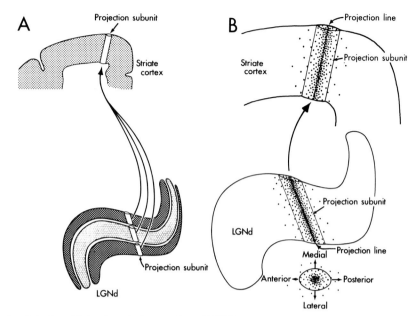

FIG. 11. *A*: relationship between a projection subunit in dorsal lateral geniculate nucleus (LGNd) and a projection (position) subunit in striate cortex. *B*: parasagittal section through LGNd showing distribution of cells in a projection subunit, the column in LGNd that contains 90% of all cells whose receptive fields have a common visual direction. Projection line is axis of a projection subunit. Diagram of cross section of a projection column is shown immediately below outline of LGNd. Cortical projection (position) subunit gets its input from a corresponding subunit in LGNd. [Adapted from Sanderson (315).]

subunit to the next, each extensively interpenetrating its neighbors and being only partially shifted with respect to them. Bishop (28) has developed a similar concept ("position subunit") for cells in the striate cortex. Superimposed on the progressive topographical representation of the visual field on the striate cortex there is also a localized monocular receptive-field position scatter. The suggestion has been made (28, 315) that the monocular segments of the projection subunits in the LGNd come together to form the position or projection subunits in the striate cortex (Fig. 11). If the pairing of ipsilateral and contralateral inputs to cells in the cortical subunit reflects the random receptive-field scatter in the LGNd subunits, then the two receptive fields of a binocularly activated cortical cell will more often than not fail to occupy corresponding visual-field positions. They will have a disparity distribution about the same size as the random scatter of receptive fields in the geniculate subunit. Receptive-field position disparities have been used as a key element in the neural theory for binocular depth discrimination (13, 189, 273).

MORPHOLOGICAL CLASSIFICATION OF GENICULATE NEURONS. The cells in the LGNd have been classified on the basis of cell size as revealed by the Nissl stain, cellular morphology as seen with Golgi methods, cortical projection using retrograde transport, and the presence of cytoplasmic laminated bodies. Following Guillery's original classification (140, 145), four cell types are now generally recognized (110, 125, 165, 226). Figure 12 shows representative examples of the three major cell types to be seen in Golgi preparations of the A-laminae of the cat LGNd (140, 145). The cells are numbered according to their class—1, 2, or 3. Lamina A is at the top of the figure and lamina A$_1$ at the bottom, the parallel dotted lines representing the interlaminar zone. Classes 1 and 2 are relay cells and class 3 cells are possibly interneurons. These original observations of Guillery have formed the basis of most subsequent classifications of LGNd neurons.

Class 1. Class 1 cells are large (20–40 μm in diam) multipolar neurons whose large dendritic trees do not respect laminar boundaries and are free of appendages except for an occasional spine. They receive their retinal input by simple axodendritic synapses. Class 1 cells are found in the A-laminae, in the magnocellular part of lamina C, and in the MIN.

Class 2. Class 2 cells are medium sized (15–25 μm in diam) with dendrites that generally do not cross laminar borders. Some of these cells contain laminated bodies (123, 193, 226). Laminated bodies are cytoplasmic organelles whose characteristic laminar stucture becomes evident under the electron microscope (263, 365). The dendrites of class 2 cells bear prominent grapelike appendages (glomeruli) close to their primary branching points. With the exception of the corticogeniculate terminals, these encapsulated synaptic zones or glomeruli (Fig. 13*B*) are thought to include all the vesicle-containing profiles in the LGNd (109), namely axon terminals of both retinal (RLP) and nonretinal (RSD) fibers as well as interneuron cell (I) axonal endings and dendritic terminals. The latter two endings are equivalent to Guillery's types F1 and

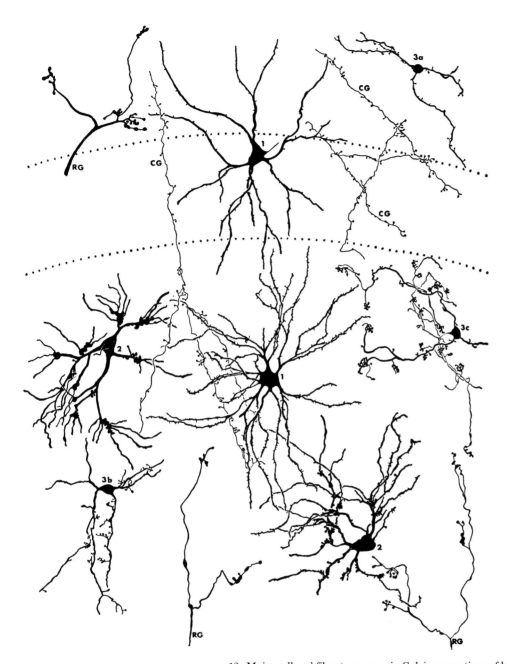

FIG. 12. Major cell and fiber types seen in Golgi preparations of laminae A and A₁ of dorsal lateral geniculate nucleus of the cat. *Top,* lamina A; *bottom,* lamina A₁; *dotted lines,* region of interlaminar plexus between laminae A and A₁. Not all of the elements have been drawn to the same scale. Cells labeled 1, 2, and 3 according to class; *RG,* retinogeniculate fibers; *CG,* corticogeniculate fibers. [From Guillery (145).]

F2, respectively (142). The principal constituents of the glomerulus are often only one retinal fiber synaptic knob, a number of interneuron dendrites, and, finally, dendritic spines coming from geniculocortical relay cells (P). The dendrites of the interneurons contain flat (pleomorphic) vesicles and form symmetrical synapses with the dendrites of relay cells as well as with the dendrites of other interneurons (109). The retinogeniculate terminal, the interneuron dendrites, and the geniculocortical relay cell enter into a triadic re-

lationship in which the optic tract synapses are presynaptic to the vesicle-containing interneuron dendrites that are, in turn, presynaptic to the relay cell dendrite. Class 2 cells are found in the A-laminae, in lamina C, and in the MIN.

Class 3 (277, 370, 371). Class 3 cells have small cell bodies (10–25 μm in diam) and fine, wavy, and tortuous dendrites with frequent clusters of complex stalked appendages along them. These appendages probably form the presynaptic elements of dendrodendritic synapses. The interneuron dendritic terminals are the only elements in the LGNd that synapse on others of their own kind, and are postsynaptic to all types of identified axons (109). There are probably no axoaxonic synapses in the dorsal layers of the LGNd, since in these layers the interneuron dendrites appear to be the only postsynaptic processes that contain synaptic vesicles. Retrograde transport of markers injected into the visual cortex indicate that no more than about 20% of the cells in both the A- and the C-laminae are interneurons (123, 226, 242).

Class 4. Class 4 cells have an intermediate soma size and fairly appendage-free dendritic tree, usually oriented in a plane parallel to the laminae. These cells are found in laminae C_1–C_3 and probably represent the morphological correlate of the sluggish and nonconcentric physiological cell classes.

Correspondence with functional cell classes. There is, as yet, no generally accepted correlation between morphological cell classes and physiological types. LeVay and Ferster (110, 226) have proposed that the morphological class 1 cells are brisk-transient (Y) cells, class 2 cells are brisk-sustained (X) cells, and class 3 cells are interneurons. However, they did not consider intermediate or unclassified morphological types that Guillery (140) found made up a significant proportion of his Golgi-impregnated cells. In addition Friedlander et al. (116) have recorded from single LGNd cells and made intracellular injections of HRP. They report that class 1 morphological characteristics were associated with Y-cells (brisk-transient) and class 3 with X-cells (brisk-sustained) and that class 2 structural traits were seen in both physiological types. Physiological evidence indicates that less than 10% of the cells in the LGNd have mixed X- and Y-properties (69, 73, 346, 397), so that the morphological characteristics of the various cells, as presently understood, are not sufficiently distinctive to be a reliable guide to their physiological properties. Nevertheless, it seems that the large- and medium-sized cells in the A-laminae and in the magnocellular portion of lamina C are to be equated with brisk-transient (Y) and brisk-sustained (X) cells, respectively, whereas the small cells in the parvocellular portions of the C-laminae can be equated with the sluggish and nonconcentric cell types.

RETINAL INPUT TO DORSAL LGN NEURONS. Each type of lateral geniculate neuron appears to be innervated by retinal ganglion cells of essentially the same type without significant cross talk between pathways. Hence the laminar distribution of the different cell types in the LGNd give a good indication of the distribution of the axon terminals of the various kinds of retinal ganglion cells. So far only electrophysiological encounter rates are available as an indicator of the relative frequency of the different cell types in the various laminae in the LGNd (73, 397). There is general agreement that all the cells in the A-laminae have concentrically organized receptive fields. Brisk-sustained cells are much the most common in the A-laminae, forming between 70% and 80% of the cells encountered in lamina A and between 50% and 60% of the cells in A_1. Most of the remaining cells are brisk-transient cells, but Cleland et al. (73) have reported that between 3% and 5% of the cells in the A-laminae are the sluggish-sustained type. Taking into account electrode bias, it is probable that an even greater proportion of the cells in the A-laminae are of the brisk-sustained type. All types of cell were encountered in the C-lamina, although most of the cells were either brisk-transient (43%) or sluggish (41%) cell types, and only a very small proportion (5%) were brisk-sustained neurons. Furthermore, most of the brisk-transient (Y) and brisk-sustained (X) were to be found in the large-celled dorsal part of the C-lamina (397). The cells in the small-celled ventral part of the C-lamina and in the remaining C-laminae were mainly of the sluggish cell types with a few color-coding, suppressed-by-contrast, and local-edge-detector cells (73, 75a, 397, 398).

While electrophysiological recording from geniculate neurons can provide good evidence for the termination of axons of the various retinal ganglion cell types, microelectrode bias can make cell encounter rates a rather unsatisfactory guide to the relative frequency of the different inputs. Since there is a good correlation between functional ganglion cell class and morphological class, a much more reliable estimate of the relative frequencies of the various terminals can be obtained by the method of retrograde axonal transport of horseradish peroxidase (383). After HRP injections into the LGNd, and subsequent counterstaining of the retinal whole-mount preparation with cresyl violet, it has been possible to show that all retinal α-cells and all β-cells show retrograde filling with HRP so that their numbers are therefore reliable. Similarly it has been possible to label all α-cells and some 90% of the γ-cells from the superior colliculus. Hence, by axonal branching, all α-cells innervate both the LGNd and the superior colliculus (SC). While all β-cells project to the LGNd, only 10% of them send axon collaterals to the SC. All γ-cells project to the SC and about 50% also project to the LGNd (383). The above analysis indicates that the axonal branching of optic tract fibers is much more widespread than had previously been suspected.

NEURONAL CIRCUITRY IN DORSAL LGN. The excitatory and inhibitory interactions in the LGNd indicate that the integrative functions and transfer properties of the relay cells are determined by a multiplicity of inhibitory interactions that are always of the postsynaptic type (cf. refs. 53, 342). Most of our knowledge of these mechanisms has been obtained from the cat (73, 103, 194, 274, 279, 313) but also from the rat (54–56, 240, 241, 331, 362, 363). Relatively little is known about intrinsic geniculate circuitry in the monkey. In Figure

13A Dubin and Cleland (103) summarize the circuits involved in these integrative interactions. Two relay cells (open circles) are shown receiving direct excitatory retinal inputs as well as inhibitory interneuronal inputs. A given retinal ganglion cell axon can innervate more than one relay cell. There are two types of interneurons (filled circles): the one on the *right* in Figure 13A is placed level with the relay cells to indicate its location within the geniculate laminae. These cells get direct excitatory retinogeniculate and corticogeniculate inputs, but note that they do not receive a recurrent collateral from the LGNd relay cells (3). The position of the other interneuron (*left*) above the relay cells indicates its location in the perigeniculate nucleus immediately above geniculate lamina A. Thus part of the inhibitory mechanisms controlling LGNd transmission is located outside the main nuclear complex. Both types of interneuron are shown making synapses on LGNd relay cells and there is much evidence to suggest that these synapses are inhibitory (cf. refs. 103, 342). Other aspects of the structure and connections of the LGNd are summarized in Burke and Coles' (53) diagram (Fig. 13B) using the terminology of Burke and Sefton (54) and Guillery (142). Three types of axon terminals are shown: excit-

atory retinogeniculate axons (RLP, round vesicles, large terminals, pale mitochondria), excitatory corticogeniculate axons (RSD, round vesicles, small terminals, dark mitochondria), and intrageniculate axons (F). Both F1- and F2-terminals contain flat (pleomorphic) vesicles and are presumed to be inhibitory. Axons are shown as single lines, ordinary dendrites (D) as broad elements, and presynaptic dendrites as narrow elements, except that their synaptic contacts are enlarged (F2). The essential element in the glomerulus is the "triad" (*bottom center* in Fig. 13) in which the optic nerve terminal is presynaptic to both relay cell dendrite and presynpatic dendrite; the latter is also presynaptic to the relay cell dendrite.

From a functional point of view LGNd neurons consist of two major cell types: principal cells (P-cells) that relay retinal inputs to the visual cortex, and intrinsic cells (I-cells) whose axons ramify within the LGNd. The distinction between these two cell types was first established by Burke and Sefton (54-56, 331) working in the rat LGNd, and the two types have subsequently been identified in the cat LGNd (194, 274, 279, 313). In response to a single shock applied to the optic tract, P-cells are characterized by a single spike followed by a prolonged inhibitory phase, and

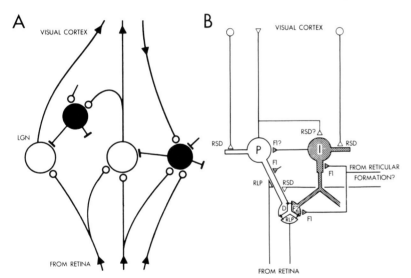

FIG. 13. *A*: principles of organization of dorsal lateral geniculate nucleus (LGNd). Relay cells (*open circles*) are shown receiving direct, excitatory retinal inputs as well as inhibitory interneuronal inputs. Interneurons (*filled circles*) of both types are depicted. An intrageniculate interneuron (*right*) is placed at same level as relay cells to indicate its position within geniculate laminae. Direct retinal inputs as well as proposed cortical afferent input are shown as being excitatory to such interneurons. A perigeniculate interneuron (*left*) is placed above the other cells, indicative of its position just above geniculate lamina A. Recurrent collateral and other, presently undefined, inputs are shown exciting such interneurons. *B*: diagram of LGNd illustrating interneuronal connections and connections from visual cortex and reticular formation on a principal cell (P) and an interneuron (I). RLP (round vesicles, large terminals, pale mitochondria, retinogeniculate axon) and RSD (round vesicles, small terminals, dark mitochondria, corticogeniculate axon) terminals contain round vesicles that are presumed to be excitatory. Intrageniculate axon terminals F1 and F2 contain flat (pleomorphic) vesicles, presumed to be inhibitory. *Single lines*, axons; *broad* elements, dendrites (D); *narrower* elements, presynaptic dendrites, except that their synaptic contacts are enlarged (F2). *Bottom center*, "triad," in which optic nerve terminal is presynaptic to both relay cell dendrite and presynaptic dendrite; the latter is also presynaptic to relay cell dendrite. [*A*: from Dubin and Cleland (103); *B*: from Burke and Cole (53).]

the same occurs when the cells are antidromically activated by a single shock given to the ipsilateral visual cortex. By contrast, I-cells respond with a high-frequency burst of spikes when single shocks are applied to either the optic tract or visual cortex. The phase of suppression following the initiation of the single spike in P-cells lasts from 20 to 100 ms corresponding to a prolonged inhibitory postsynaptic potential (IPSP). The response of I-cells is characterized by a long-lasting excitatory postsynaptic potential (EPSP) of 20–80 ms, on which are superimposed the burst of 3–10 spikes at a mean rate of 130/s. The numerical values given above differ somewhat between reports.

Using in vitro slices of cat LGNd Ogawa et al. (274) encountered P-cells 13.5 times more frequently than I-cells. This I-cell encounter rate is rather less than might be expected on the basis of the frequency of unlabeled cells following retrograde axonal transport of markers injected into the visual cortex. On the basis of the latter procedure approximately 20% of the LGNd cells are probably interneurons (123). Sakakura (313) also regarded as I-cells about 20% of the cells he encountered in the cat LGNd. Somewhat at odds with the above account, other investigators (73, 103) failed to observe in cat LGNd neurons that gave a long repetitive discharge following single shocks applied to the retina comparable to the responses seen in rat I-cells. The latter authors specifically draw attention to the brief, high-frequency discharge ("clustered firing") that they believe can occasionally occur in principal cells following electrical stimulation of the retina.

Despite the differing reports referred to, Dubin and Cleland (103) have provided other evidence for the presence of intrageniculate interneurons. The cells they identified as intrageniculate interneurons responded transsynaptically to stimulation of the visual cortex with a characteristic burst of spikes in which the latency of the earliest spike was variable and was influenced by the strength of the stimulus. The intrageniculate interneurons also received a direct monosynaptic retinal input as determined by recording simultaneously from such interneurons and from the retinal ganglion cells that provide excitatory input to them. Dubin and Cleland (103) also distinguished intrageniculate interneurons as a class separate from those responsible for recurrent (feedback) inhibition. Recurrent inhibition is mediated by cells lying outside the LGNd in the perigeniculate nucleus (see *Perigeniculate Nucleus and Nucleus Reticularis Thalami*, p. 370). The perigeniculate cells receive axon collaterals from LGNd relay cells and feedback onto the relay cells. Apparently direct ganglion cell inhibition (feedforward) is mediated only by the intrageniculate interneurons. It is possible that still other types of inhibitory interactions exist in the LGNd than those described here. In particular no functional correlate has so far been found for the dendrodendritic synapses originally described by Famiglietti (106).

In their responses to visual stimuli, intrageniculate interneurons are indistinguishable from relay cells (103). They have a center-surround receptive-field organization and can be subdivided into brisk or sluggish and sustained or transient categories. By contrast perigeniculate interneurons are generally binocularly innervated, give on-off responses to small spot stimulation throughout their large (5° diam) nonconcentric receptive fields, and respond well to rapid movements of large targets. Their large, poorly structured receptive fields of mixed on-off type suggest a high degree of convergence from the axon collaterals of LGNd relay cells.

Thus two kinds of inhibitory interneurons have been described in relation to the LGNd, one intrinsic to the main nuclear complex and the other located outside the complex in the perigeniculate nucleus. Perigeniculate neurons have very generalized diffuse receptive fields; intrageniculate interneurons have smaller, more precise, concentric receptive fields. The generalized pathway of the perigeniculate interneurons involving convergence of axon collaterals from relay cells and divergence of their axon terminals in laminae A and A_1 (see *Perigeniculate Nucleus and Nucleus Reticularis Thalami*, p. 370.) seems ideal for mediating such diverse effects as those involved in arousal phenomena, sleep, and wakefulness. On the other hand, intrageniculate neurons, with their small, well-organized receptive fields appear better suited for highly specific spatial interactions such as those involved in the mechanisms for binocular depth discrimination. In the latter respect it seems that the corticofugal influence impinging on the intrageniculate neuronal circuits is likely to come from simple cells in lamina 6. As Harvey (151) has pointed out, corticofugal simple cells, especially in area 17, are very specific in their stimulus requirements, and there would be a great deal of redundancy if such cells projected onto a diffuse inhibitory network. On the other hand the visual properties of corticofugal complex cells seem appropriate for participation in the diffuse nonspecific inhibitory pathway mediated by perigeniculate neurons.

FUNCTIONAL PROPERTIES OF CAT LATERAL GENICU-LATE NEURONS. Most studies of the properties of LGNd neurons have been confined to the geniculocortical relay cells [for references see Dubin and Cleland (103)] and these have shown that the main response patterns of the relay cells differ little from those in their afferent fibers. In general the spontaneous activity is reduced in the geniculocortical pathway and the responses become more phasic than in the optic nerve, but the characteristic receptive-field properties of retinal ganglion cells are by and large preserved. This is a consequence of the highly selective excitatory connections between retinal afferents and geniculate relay cells. From recordings made simultaneously from these relay cells and their ganglion cell inputs (68, 69, 237) it has been shown that the relay cells receive their major excitatory input from only one to a maximum of six retinal ganglion cells of the same center type, i.e., on-center or off-center. Furthermore brisk-sustained and brisk-transient inputs rarely converge onto the same relay cell. Judging by the conduction velocities of the cells concerned, these observations were made on the brisk cell classes, and it is not known whether the observations would also apply to the uncommonly encountered concentric and nonconcentric cell types. However, even these uncommonly encountered cells probably have a comparably restricted retinal input, since their receptive-field properties also closely resemble those of their ganglion cell afferents. Probably all the retinal ganglion cell classes project to the LGNd and, with the sole exception of direction-selective cells, representatives of all the cell classes have now been observed in the LGNd (73, 397). Not only is there separation of the afferents from the two eyes but also some cell classes are segregated to specific layers in the LGNd. Further, the classes seem to remain distinct and separated as they are relayed to the visual cortex (397). However, these parallel channels are coupled to each other by powerful inhibitory interconnections (see NEURONAL CIRCUITRY IN DORSAL LGN, p. 364).

Detailed studies of the relay cells in the LGNd have been largely confined to the brisk cell classes in the A-laminae. The center sizes of the receptive fields of these cells cover approximately the same range as those of corresponding retinal ganglion cells. The only additional feature to be found in the LGNd cells appears to be the suppressive field that forms an annular zone beyond the limits of the conventional antagonistic surround (237). Stimulation of the sup-

pressive field produces only inhibitory effects on the responses elicited by simultaneous stimulation of center or surround.

GENICULOCORTICAL CONDUCTION PROPERTIES OF CAT DORSAL LGN NEURONS. Figure 5B shows the distribution of the orthodromic retinogeniculate response latencies of LGNd neurons to local electrical stimulation of the retina (73). The stimulating electrodes were applied to the retinal surface in the vicinity of the ganglion cells providing the LGN cell's excitatory input. The distribution of retinogeniculate latencies is similar to the distribution of antidromic latencies of retinal ganglion cells (Fig. 5A) following electrical stimulation of the optic chiasma (OX) if allowance is made both for the increased conduction distance and for the added synaptic discharge delay in the retinogeniculate experiments. The similarity of histograms A and B in Figure 5 indicates that the response properties of geniculate neurons closely resemble those of their afferent ganglion cells. The similarity also illustrates the close agreement that exists between the cell classification of Rowe and Stone (310) used for the retinal ganglion cells in histogram A, and that of Cleland et al. (73), used for the geniculate neurons in histogram B, despite the differing terminologies.

In Figure 14 the orthodromic retinogeniculate latencies have been plotted against the antidromic corticogeniculate latencies for 115 LGNd cells, the two latencies being recorded from the same cell in each case (73). Geniculate neurons with a fast input from the retina tend to have fast axons to the visual cortex and correspondingly for the medium-speed and slow inputs. Lacking information about the respective conduction distances it is not possible to compare con-

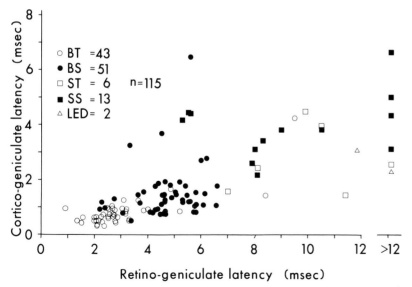

FIG. 14. Scatter diagram of antidromic corticogeniculate latency against orthodromic retinogeniculate latency for 115 dorsal lateral geniculate nucleus (LGNd) cells. BT, brisk-transient cells; BS, brisk-sustained cells; ST, sluggish-transient cells; SS, sluggish-sustained cells; LED, local-edge-detector cells. [From Cleland et al. (73).]

duction velocities in the retinogeniculate and geniculocortical pathways. The addition of the retinogeniculate and geniculocortical latencies suggests that an action potential from a brisk-transient retinal ganglion cell might arrive at the cortex in about 3.5 ms, an action potential from a brisk-sustained cell in about 6 ms, and one from a ganglion with a slowly conducting axon in about 14 ms, although this last value would be much more variable than the other two. The above estimates for brisk-transient and brisk-sustained cells are in good agreement with those obtained by Lee et al. (221), who made simultaneous recordings from a cortical cell and a ganglion cell that excited it.

PROJECTIONS FROM GENICULATE LAMINAE TO CORTEX. The projections of the LGN to the visual cortex of the cat have been studied by a variety of anatomical techniques: the anterograde degeneration method (122), the anterograde transport method (227), the retrograde degeneration method (272), and the retrograde transport method (125, 165, 226, 242). (For a more complete list of references see ref. 123.) There is general agreement that the cat LGNd projects to areas 17, 18, and 19 and to the suprasylvian regions, but not all parts of the nucleus project to each cortical area. In addition Geisert (123) has used a double-tracer technique to show that several cortical areas share inputs from individual geniculate neurons. The relay cells in the A-laminae project to cortical area 17 or to area 18 but not elsewhere. Ten per cent of the cells project to both area 17 and 18 by axons that branch, 70% of the neurons project to area 17 only, less than 1% project to area 18 only, and approximately 20% of the cells are probably interneurons (123). The great majority of the cells in the A-laminae are those that project only to area 17 and they are almost certainly brisk-sustained (X) cells, whereas those that project to area 18 and those that project to both area 17 and 18 are probably brisk-transient (Y) cells.

The cortical projections of the cells in the C-laminae are still not well understood and quantitative data concerning the projections of the various cell types in these laminae are not available. Probably all the cell types in the C-laminae project to areas 17, 18, and 19. The cells in the parvocellular portions of the C-laminae provide the major input to area 19 but they also contribute, with decreasing frequency, to areas 18 and 17 in that order. Probably the large and medium-sized cells in the magnocellular portion also contribute to area 19 (123). For the purposes of quantitative analysis, Geisert (123) grouped all the C-laminae together. He found that 80% of the cells project to areas 17 and 18, and since 60% of the cells of the C-laminae were labeled following injections of area 19, many of the cells that project to area 19 must also project to area 17 or to area 18, and some cells must project to all three areas by branching axons.

INTRAGENICULATE ORGANIZATION OF CORTICOGENICULATE AFFERENTS. In both cat (125, 372, 377, 378)

and monkey (16, 164, 247) there are precise reciprocal topographical geniculocortical and corticogeniculate projections. There may be at least as many axons projecting from the visual cortex back to the LGNd as there are relay cell axons running to the cortex (141, 143). In the cat the corticofugal fibers (125, 141, 143, 372, 377, 378) originate from pyramidal cells in layer VI of area 17, 18, and 19 and traverse all the LGNd laminae, running parallel to the projection lines across the nucleus. Along their course across the nucleus they form multiple synapses, partially en passant and usually on the shafts of dendrites outside the synaptic glomeruli of both relay cells and interneurons (109). Rarely the corticofugal axon terminals may participate in the synaptic complex within the glomeruli. The corticofugal terminals contain spherical vesicles and form asymmetrical synapses and are presumably excitatory to both relay cells and interneurons. In the macaque monkey, also, fibers projecting to the LGNd originate in layer VI of area 17 from small to medium-sized pyramidal cells. The upper half of layer VI projects to the parvocellular layers of the LGNd and the lower part to the magnocellular layers [Fig. 23; (247)].

It is only recently that specific information has become available concerning the properties of the lamina VI cells that project to the LGNd (150, 151) and this is discussed in EXTRASTRIATE PROJECTIONS FROM CAT STRIATE CELL LAMINAE, p. 383.

NASOTEMPORAL OVERLAP: CENTRAL PROJECTION OF IPSILATERAL VISUAL HEMIFIELD. At the medial margin of the A-laminae, cells are recorded having receptive fields with center points located across the vertical midline up to about 1.5° into the ipsilateral hemifield [Fig. 15A; (203, 318)]. The receptive-field locations plotted in Figure 15A and B were from cells recorded in the left LGNd and MIN, respectively, the open circles being the receptive fields for the left eye and the filled circles the fields for the right eye. In Figure 15A only receptive fields located in the left ("wrong") hemifield have been plotted. Presumably most of these cells would be innervated by brisk-sustained retinal ganglion cells located in a narrow vertical strip of retina either to the nasal side of the midline in the ipsilateral eye or to the temporal side in the contralateral eye. The cells in the A-laminae having receptive fields in the "wrong" hemifield project to area 17 along its border with area 18 in the region of the representation of the zero vertical meridian (273).

In the rather vaguely defined region where the C-lamina of the main nucleus abuts the lateral margin of the MIN, a region that includes parts of both nuclei, there are cells having receptive fields whose center points are located up to 15° into the ipsilateral visual hemifield along a band covering the full vertical extent of the field (203, 314, 318). All these cells are innervated by brisk-transient ganglion cells located in the temporal retina of the contralateral eye (Fig. 15B,

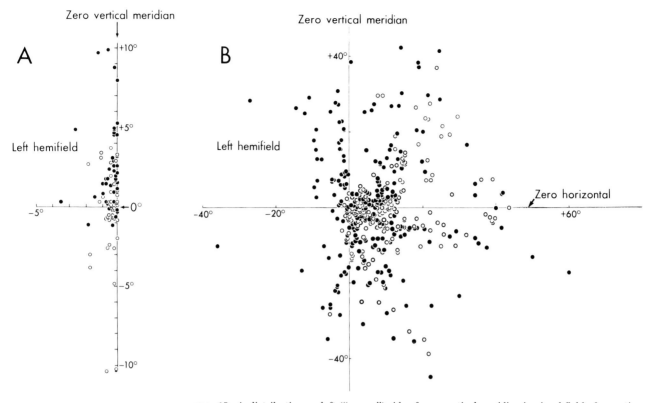

FIG. 15. *A*: distribution on left ("wrong") side of zero vertical meridian in visual field of receptive-field center points of cells recorded in laminae A and A₁ in the left dorsal lateral geniculate nucleus (LGNd) of cat. *Filled circles*, cells with input from contralateral eye; *open circles*, cells with input from ipsilateral eye. Standard deviation of distribution, 0.76°; standard deviation of error in determination of zero vertical meridian, 0.50°. *B*: distribution in visual field of the receptive-field center points of cells recorded in left medial interlaminar nucleus (MIN) in 28 cats. *Filled* and *open circles* as in *A*. Note that cells with their receptive fields in left ("wrong") hemifield have their input almost exclusively from temporal retina of contralateral eye. [*A*: from Sanderson and Sherman (318); *B*: from Sanderson (314).]

filled circles). The cortical projection of these C-laminae and MIN cells is still uncertain. Presumably some project to area 18 along the border with area 17 and others to the lateral border of area 19.

Nothing is known about the central projections of the sluggish concentric and slowly conducting nonconcentric ganglion cells in the temporal retina whose axons cross to the opposite side in the optic chiasma.

Medial Interlaminar Nucleus

The medial interlaminar nucleus (MIN) lies just medial to the main geniculate laminae and is usually regarded as a subdivision of the dorsal lateral geniculate nucleus. It receives a direct retinal input (144, 152, 218) and projects to the visual cortex (248, 308). Although no lamination is evident in Nissl-stained sections, experimental techniques indicate that the MIN has hidden lamination. There are at least two laminae, one for each eye (Fig. 8*B*). Using autoradiography following intravitreal eye injections of tritiated proline, Kratz et al. (208) have shown that the smaller, ipsilaterally innervated portion of the nucleus is immediately adjacent to the medial margins of the C-laminae and

that the larger, contralateral portion is wrapped around the medial aspect of the ipsilateral portion. The projection of the visual field into the MIN is a mirror image of that into the LGNd, the midline of the visual field being represented laterally and the periphery medially (26, 203, 314, 333). The projection lines appear to be continuous across the junction between the LGNd and the MIN [Fig. 8*D*; (203, 314)]. The ipsilateral projection has a visuotopic map covering the same extent of the visual field as for the A-laminae, but the contralateral map, like the most medial part of the C-laminae, also includes a representation of the ipsilateral hemifield as a result of decussating fibers from the temporal retina of the contralateral eye (see NASOTEMPORAL OVERLAP. . ., p. 368).

The retinal input to the MIN seems largely confined to brisk-transient fibers (102, 256, 286), but there are also brisk-sustained, sluggish, and local-edge-detector cells (102). The great majority of MIN cells belong to Guillery's class 1, but there are some smaller cell types that contain laminated bodies and could therefore be class 2 cells (123, 226). Presumably these two cell types are to be equated with brisk-transient and brisk-sustained cells, respectively.

There is general agreement that the MIN projects to both cortical areas 17 and 18. The type 2 cells project to area 17 and the type 1 mainly to area 18 with some projecting to both areas 17 and 18 by a collateral branching system (123). Gilbert and Kelly (125) failed to observe a projection to area 19, but others (123, 165) have found one.

Perigeniculate Nucleus and Nucleus Reticularis Thalami

As mentioned above, the perigeniculate nucleus is regarded as a specialized part of the nucleus reticularis thalami. It is closely applied to the anterior and dorsal surfaces of the LGNd and separated by a cell-free zone from the more dorsally located, scattered cells of the reticular nucleus (Fig. 8B). Recent observations indicate that these two nuclei have a much more intimate and complex relationship to the LGNd than has hitherto been suspected, but the details of their afferent and efferent connections are still in dispute. For details regarding the responses of perigeniculate neurons to visual stimuli see NEURONAL CIRCUITRY IN DORSAL LGN, p. 364.

There is anatomical (20, 218) and physiological (327) evidence that the perigeniculate neurons receive a direct retinal input. Schmielau (327) found that a large proportion of perigeniculate cells responded to electrical stimulation of either optic nerve with latencies that indicate that they receive a monosynaptic input from the retinal ganglion cells of both eyes. Furthermore the latencies to optic chiasm stimulation (1.0–1.5 ms) also indicated that the retinal input was of the brisk-transient (Y) type. The longer latencies that Schmielau (327) observed for cells in the nucleus reticularis thalami suggested that they are mainly innervated polysynaptically from the optic tract, possibly from axon collaterals of LGNd relay cells. Ahlsén et al. (3) found that the LGNd principal cells do issue collaterals, but to the perigeniculate nucleus and not to the reticular nucleus of the thalamus. After identified LGNd principal cells had been stained by intracellular injections of HRP, most of their axons could be shown to issue collaterals that branched within the perigeniculate region over a rather extensive area (about 0.5 mm × 0.5 mm) in register with the visual-field projection subunit ("column") of the injected cell. Both transient and sustained cells gave axon collaterals. With one exception there was no axon collateral observed within the borders of the LGNd, but even this cell had its main branching in the perigeniculate zone. In addition, intracellular injection of perigeniculate cells showed that they project back to both laminae A and A₁ where their terminal branches diverge extensively (2).

In contrast to Schmielau (327), Dubin and Cleland (103) found that perigeniculate neurons responded to electrical stimulation at the optic disk with a spike latency that was approximately one synaptic delay longer than the latency of brisk-transient LGNd relay cells, suggesting that the perigeniculate neurons were excited by axon collaterals from these relay cells. The reason for the discrepancy between the above two sets of observations is not clear. It should be noted that because only the latency of the earliest spike was taken into consideration, and because bursts of spikes were elicited by the stimulus, Dubin and Cleland (103) could not rule out an additional input from recurrent collaterals from brisk-sustained cells.

The perigeniculate nucleus also receives a direct corticofugal input from areas 17 and 18 (199, 377, 378), the cortical cells of origin being pyramidal cells in lamina 6 (125, 372). However, Dubin and Cleland's (103) observation concerning the response latency to electrical stimulation of the visual cortex does not decide between orthodromic activation either by corticofugal afferents or by collaterals from antidromically discharged geniculocortical relay cells. Either way the evidence is that the perigeniculate and reticular cells do not project directly to the visual cortex and are only transsynaptically activated by cortical stimulation. The nucleus reticularis thalami also receives an input from the mesencephalic reticular formation that is mainly inhibitory (327).

Neurons of the perigeniculate and reticular nuclei are identified as interneurons both because they respond to stimulation of the visual cortex by a transsynaptically elicited burst of spikes and because each spike, and especially the late ones, show a high degree of latency scatter. The effect of stimulation of perigeniculate neurons appears to be a rather diffuse, generalized inhibition of LGNd relay cells that is, nevertheless, still confined to the projection column of the cells concerned. The inhibitory feedback mechanism via axon collaterals onto perigeniculate neurons could form the basis of the corresponding inhibitory receptive fields responsible for binocular inhibition in the LGNd (316, 317, 341). Harvey (151) has also made the interesting suggestion that it is the complex cells in cortical lamina 6 that innervate the perigeniculate neurons, since the visual properties of the efferent complex cells seem appropriate for participation in the diffuse, nonspecific inhibitory pathways mediated by perigeniculate neurons. This corticofugal feedback mechanism would act to reinforce the effects of the perigeniculate pathway.

In order to explain the facilitatory or disinhibitory effect that mesencephalic reticular formation stimulation has upon LGNd relay cells (343) Schmielau (327) has suggested that nucleus reticularis thalami interneurons are inhibitory to perigeniculate interneurons.

Extrageniculate Visual Thalamus

Analysis of the extrageniculate visual thalamus is complicated by both the differing criteria used to demarcate subdivisions and the differing names applied to these subdivisions. The present account of the extrageniculate visual thalamus in the cat uses the terminology of Graybiel and Berson (139). As these authors point out, it is difficult to draw reliable borders of subdivisions solely on the basis of cytoarchitectonic criteria. Though their terminological framework follows the classic architectonic studies of Rioch (300) and of Ingram et al. (187), Graybiel and Berson (139) have introduced modifications in the light of recent studies of the afferent and efferent connections and the histochemistry of the region (see EXTRAGENICULATE VISUAL THALAMUS IN CAT, this page). The study of Niimi and Kuwahara (271) is also closely related to Rioch's but, in an attempt to apply a standard nomenclature to cat, monkey, and man, these authors reclassified the lateralis posterior-pulvinar complex in the cat according to the naming system used in primates (inferior, medial, lateral, and oral pulvinar). As indicated in Table 3 the lateralis posterior-pulvinar complex of Graybiel and Berson (139) is contained within the posterior nuclear group of Niimi and Kuwahara (271). The latter authors also describe a lateral nuclear group composed of two subdivisions: a dorsal lateral nucleus and a posterior lateral nucleus. These two nuclei are respectively equivalent to the nucleus lateralis dorsalis and to the nucleus lateralis intermedius of Graybiel and Berson (139), neither of which forms part of the visual thalamus. The intermediate nucleus has reciprocal connections with areas 5 and 7 of the parietal cortex.

The extrageniculate visual thalamus is much less well known in the monkey than it is in the cat. The commonly recognized nuclei of the pulvinar region in the monkey are still those based on cytoarchitectonic criteria, and subdivisions based on afferent and efferent connections and histochemical methods have yet to be adequately identified. Only the inferior pulvinar and lateral pulvinar nuclei appear to be involved in projections to the striate and prestriate cortex, and

these nuclei receive inputs from the retina (64, 155), colliculus (17), and visual cortex (63, 275).

EXTRAGENICULATE VISUAL THALAMUS IN CAT. In the cat the extrageniculate visual thalamus is represented mainly by the pulvinar and nuclei of the lateral thalamic group. Following earlier anterograde degeneration studies (138) and the use of axoplasmic transport methods (21), Graybiel and Berson (139) have now identified the visual thalamic subdivisions histochemically by their differing contents of acetylthiocholinesterase. They describe the caudal part of the lateral thalamic region as being divided into two main subdivisions: the lateralis posterior-pulvinar complex, which receives the extrageniculate visual input, and the complex comprising the nucleus lateralis medialis and suprageniculatus, which receives fiber projections from the auditory association cortex and the deep layers of the superior colliculus.

ZONES DEFINED BY AFFERENT INPUTS. Within the lateralis posterior-pulvinar complex four discrete afferent inputs terminate in a series of nonoverlapping slabs that in cross section form stripes oriented roughly at right angles to the dorsal aspect of the thalamus. Figure 16 illustrates the principal visual zones as they appear when individually delimited by experimental demonstration of their respective afferent connections. The anterolateral marginal zone of the pulvinar receives a bilateral fiber projection from the retina (Fig. 16A) and also a sparse input from the striate cortex (21). Updyke (378), however, failed to observe any input to this region from area 17. By retrograde labeling with HRP Kawamura et al. (198) have shown that the retinal ganglion cells projecting to the pulvinar are all of medium to small size (8–22 μm). Thus, although the retinopulvinar projection appears continuous with the MIN (Fig. 16A), the cells of origin in the retina are different, since the pulvinar lacks an input from the brisk-transient class. The large remainder of the pulvinar receives a dense projection from the pretectum (Fig. 16B). Just medial to the pulvinar the lateral part of the nucleus lateralis posterior (LPℓ) and the nucleus posterior of Rioch (NP) together form a bandlike zone that forms a dense descending projection from the striate cortex (Fig. 16C) and to a lesser extent from areas 18 and 19. Along the medial side of the LPℓ-NP zone is an elongated, gently curving band receiving input from the superior colliculus.

PROJECTIONS TO VISUAL CORTEX. Most of the input zones described in the preceding subsection could be identified on the basis of ascending as well as descending (reciprocal) corticofugal connections. Thus the corticorecipient zone (LPℓ-NP) projects to areas 17 and 18, the projection being concentrated at the 17/18 border corresponding to the representation of the zero vertical meridian (125). Rosenquist et al. (309) report subcortical afferents to area 17 from the medial inter

TABLE 3. *Extrageniculate Visual Thalamus in Cat*

Lateralis Posterior-Pulvinar Complex of Graybiel and Berson (139)*	Visual Subdivisions of Posterior Nuclear Group of Niimi and Kuwahara (271)*
1. Tectorecipient zone Nucleus lateralis posterior pars medialis (L Pm)	(Medial part) Medial pulvinar nucleus (PM)
2. Corticorecipient zone a. Nucleus lateralis posterior pars lateralis (LPℓ)	(Lateral part)
b. Posterior nucleus (NP)	Inferior pulvinar nucleus (equivalent to posterior nucleus)
3. Retinal and pretectal recipient zone Pulvinar (Pul)	Lateral pulvinar (PL)

* Reference numbers in parentheses.

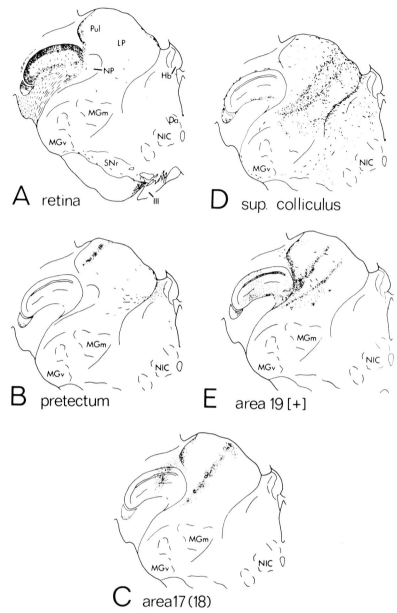

FIG. 16. *A–E*: Chartings of transverse sections through cat's lateral posterior-pulvinar complex illustrate zones of termination of afferent fibers from indicated regions. Chartings based on anterograde autoradiographic experiments. *Da*, nucleus of Darkschewitsch; *Hb*, habenular nuclear complex; *LP*, nucleus lateralis posterior; *MGm*, medial geniculate body, magnocellular division; *MGv*, medial geniculate body, ventral division; *NIC*, interstitial nucleus of Cajal; *NP*, nucleus posterior of Rioch; *Pul*, pulvinar; *SNr*, substantia nigra, pars reticulata; *III*, oculomotor nerve. [From Berson and Graybiel (21).]

laminar nucleus (MIN) and the LPℓ-NP zone as terminating in cortical lamina 1 (Fig. 23). By contrast area 19 receives a projection from both the corticorecipient zone (LPℓ-NP) and the pretectorecipient zone (Pul). Since retinal axons do not terminate in the LPℓ-NP zone, there is a direct retinoextrageniculate thalamic relay to area 19 but not to areas 17 and 18. Any relay to areas 17 and 18 through the LPℓ-NP zone is presumably via connections from either the LGN complex or the pulvinar.

RETINOTOPIC ORGANIZATION. Each of the slablike zones in the lateralis posterior-pulvinar complex is retinotopically organized (197, 378). In particular the LPℓ-NP zone contains a retinotopic representation of the visual field that is an approximate mirror image of the representation in the MIN. Using orthograde axoplasmic transport of tritiated amino acids injected at various sites in area 17, Updyke (378) has shown that the lower visual field is represented rostrolaterally and the upper visual field caudomedially in LPℓ-NP zone. The zero vertical meridian is represented medially and the lateral periphery of the visual field is represented along the border of the LPℓ-NP zone with the pulvinar nucleus and MIN. Furthermore the projections from areas 17, 18, and 19 all terminate in retinotopic register within this region.

The histological observations concerning the visuotopic organization of the LPℓ-NP zone are essentially similar to the neurophysiological reports of Kinston, Vadas, and Bishop (203) and of Mason (257). In plotting the projection of the visual field onto the posterior nucleus Kinston et al. (203) noted that the representation was largely limited to the lower hemifield, penetrating only 5° to 10° into the upper hemifield. From Mason's (257) observations (Fig. 17) and the anatomical data noted above, it is now clear that the full visual hemifield is projected onto the corticorecipient zone (LPℓ-NP) as a whole, the upper hemifield being largely confined to the LPℓ nucleus. It seems that the representation of the zero horizontal roughly corre-

sponds to the junction between the LPℓ and NP nuclei and that of the zero vertical meridian with the boundary between the cortico- and tectorecipient zone. Observations along these lines led Updyke (378) to regard the corticorecipient region as a single functional zone called by him the lateral division of the lateralis posterior complex (LPℓ). Many cells in the posterior nucleus had receptive fields well into the ipsilateral visual hemifield up to about 10° from the vertical midline (203).

The pulvinar nucleus also contains a retinotopic representation of the visual field (378). The lower visual field is represented rostrally in the nucleus and the upper visual field caudally. The zero vertical meridian is represented at the lateral edge of the nucleus, and azimuths out to 45° or 50° are represented in the pulvinar adjacent to its border with the LPℓ-NP zone.

LATERALIS POSTERIOR-PULVINAR CELL PROPERTIES. The properties of cells in the lateral posterior-pulvinar

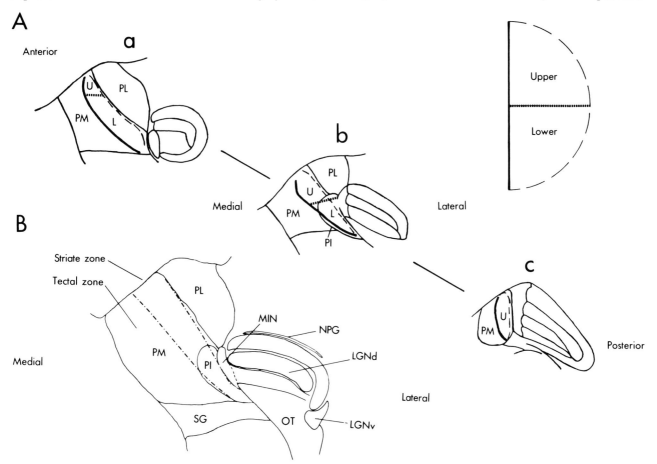

FIG. 17. *A*: visuotopic organization of striate recipient zone within feline pulvinar complex. *Heavy line*, zero vertical meridian; *dotted line*, zero horizontal; *dashed line*, peripheral extent of visual field; *U* and *L*, upper and lower visual field, respectively. *B*: nuclei constituting cat's visual thalamus in transverse section showing lateral and posterior nuclear groups and lateral geniculate complex. *PI*, inferior pulvinar; *PM*, medial pulvinar; *PL*, lateral pulvinar; *SG*, suprageniculate nucleus; *LGNd*, dorsal lateral geniculate nucleus; *LGNv*, ventral lateral geniculate nucleus; *MIN*, medial interlaminar nucleus; *NPG*, perigeniculate nucleus; *OT*, optic tract. Nomenclature from Niimi and Kuwahara (271). [From Mason (257).]

complex have so far been relatively little studied (129, 130, 203, 257, 364). The majority of the cells respond to visual stimulation but have large, rather diffuse receptive fields with no clear-cut spatial organization, and many of the cells are binocularly activated. It is worth noting that the distribution of receptive fields over the midline into the ipsilateral hemifield is perhaps even more extreme than is the case of cells in the MIN (203). Commonly the cells respond well to moving stimuli, though rarely to slow velocities (less than 5°/s), and many show some degree of selectivity for stimulus characteristics including, particularly, direction of stimulus movement and, to a lesser extent, stimulus orientation.

Macaque Lateral Geniculate Nucleus

MORPHOLOGY OF LGN. The lateral geniculate nucleus (LGN) of anthropoid primates is usually described as consisting of six layers separated by sparsely celled interlaminar zones. A ventral pair of magnocellular layers mostly contain large cells, and four dorsal parvocellular layers are comprised primarily of small neurons (66, 67). These layers are referred to by numbers, starting from the magnocellular layer closest to the optic tract (layer 1) and proceeding toward the optic radiation (Fig. 18). An alternative nomenclature has been introduced by Kaas and his colleagues (190, 191) based on the location of the layers and their cell type (Fig. 18). Two major advantages are claimed for the new system. Unlike the numerical system that is based solely on position, it identifies homologous layers in different species of primates. In addition it distinguishes layers from sublayers. Kaas et al. (190, 191) argue that the basic primate LGN pattern consists of two parvocellular (PE and PI) layers, two magnocellular (ME and MI) layers, and a pair of poorly developed and variable superficial (SE and SI) layers. The individual layers are named according to their relative positions in the nucleus. Thus the external magnocellular layer, ME, lies ventral to the internal magnocellular layer, MI, and similarly for the other layers. In the rhesus monkey, the two parvocellular layers subdivide in the posterior part of the nucleus (central visual-field representation) to give the appearance of four layers or leaflets. The two magnocellular layers correspond to layers 1 and 2 in the numbered system and the four parvocellular layers to layers 3–6. The numbered system does not take account of the superficial (S) layers. Each of the geniculate layers receives an input from one eye only, layers 1, 4, and 6 from the contralateral eye and layers 2, 3, and 5 from the ipsilateral eye. It is not known why a reversal of eye of input should occur between the dorsal four layers and the ventral four. Of the two superficial layers, the one (SI) adjacent to the ME layer receives a direct retinal input from the contralateral eye and the other (SE) adjacent to the optic tract receives input from the ipsilateral eye.

Neglecting the two thin superficial (S) layers, the

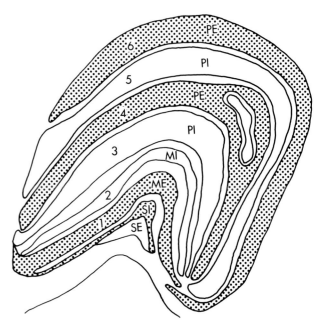

FIG. 18. Laminar organization of lateral geniculate nucleus of rhesus monkey (*Macaca mulatta*) as seen in transverse section showing two systems of laminar nomenclature (numbers and letters). Medial at *left*; lateral at *right*. Laminae receiving an input from the contralateral eye are *stippled*, those with an input from the ipsilateral eye are not. *SE, SI,* layer S (superficial) external and internal; *ME, MI,* external and internal magnocellular layers; *PE, PI,* parvocellular layers. [Adapted from Kaas et al. (191).]

rhesus LGN can be shown to consist of three distinct regions containing 6, 4, and 2 cell laminae, respectively, the transitions between the regions being well defined. The binocular visual field is represented in the first two regions, whereas the absolute monocular area corresponds to the portion of the LGN that consists of only two layers. The full complement of six layers is to be found only in the posterior third of the nucleus. Rostral to azimuth 17°, corresponding to the projection of the optic disk, layer 4 ends and the remnant of layer 5 fuses with layer 3 leaving only two parvocellular (3 and 6) and two magnocellular (1 and 2) layers. This location, corresponding to the peripheral extent of the input from the ipsilateral eye and hence of the projection of the binocular field, indicates that the rhesus monkey has about 130° to 140° of binocular vision. Finally, rostral to about azimuths 65°, corresponding to the monocular crescent area, layers 2 and 3 terminate leaving only layers 1 and 6. The location of the monocular crescent projection at the inferior-medial part of the anterior pole of the nucleus results in its receiving the brunt of the incoming optic tract fibers. Thus the monocular portion of the LGN is much broken up by optic tract fiber bundles, whereas most of the binocular portion is spared this disruption.

Since leaflets are only found in the greatly thickened part of the parvocellular mass that represents central and paracentral vision, it appears that the formation of leaflets in some primates is directly related to the thickening of the parvocellular mass. In at least some primates the ganglion cells that project to the magnocellular layers of the LGN appear to be fairly evenly distributed across the retina, while those related to the parvocellular layers appear to be concentrated in the central retina. Since the lateral geniculate layers remain in register, this difference in the retinal distribution of input systems means that the parvocellular layers must thicken relative to the magnocellular layers in the portions of the lateral geniculate nucleus related to central vision.

VISUAL-FIELD PROJECTION INTO LGN. Despite the greater morphological complexity of the macaque LGN, the detailed study of Malpeli and Baker (251) shows that the same general principles apply to the visual-field projection in the monkey as for the cat. A detailed description of the projection in the monkey LGN is beyond the scope of this chapter, but some aspects of the maps are shown in Figure 19. Figure 19*B* shows a semischematic projection of the right visual hemifield (*A*) onto the dorsal surface of layer 6 of the left LGN, the surface being distorted to lie in a plane. The projection of the zero horizontal divides the LGN along its plane of symmetry into a medial-superior half having negative elevations and a lateral-inferior half having positive elevations. Other aspects of the arrangement of isoelevation (solid lines) and isoazimuth (broken lines) projection lines are shown in the coronal section (Fig. 19*C*, *left*) taken at Horsley-Clarke (HC) coordinates anterior 7.0 and the parasagittal section (Fig. 19*C*, *right*) taken at HC lateral 12.0. Since the projection of the visual field into the LGN is continuous across the laminae, the lamination pattern and ocular dominance distribution have not been included in these constructions.

FUNCTIONAL PROPERTIES OF MACAQUE LATERAL GENICULATE NEURONS. In the various studies that have been made of the functional properties of the neurons in the macaque LGNd (80, 95–97, 101, 210, 222, 254, 284, 325, 392) the cells have been classified in various ways, either according to their spectral sensitivities or to the spatial organization of their receptive fields. Based on the responses to monochromatic flashes covering a large retinal area, De Valois et al. (96, 97) distinguished four color-opponent and two nonopponent cell types (reviewed in ref. 95). Since this classification takes no account of the spatial organization of the receptive fields, it does not include the distinctions made by Wiesel and Hubel (392) nor does it recognize differences in response properties between parvo- and magnocellular layers. On the other hand, there are strong grounds for accepting the classification of Wiesel and Hubel (392), at least as a basis for further development. They classified macaque LGN cells into four main types depending upon their receptive-field properties as revealed by spectrally and spatially distinct stimuli. The main features of the cell types are as follows: type I has an antagonistic center-surround organization, the center and surround having different spectral sensitivities; type II lacks a center-surround organization but has color-opponent properties with a neutral point at about 500 nm across the whole of the receptive field; type III has a center-surround organization, but both spatial components have the same spectral sensitivity; type IV cells are all on-center with a phasic response that is suppressed by a steady red light in the surround, i.e., the off-surround has a bias toward red. Types I and II were found exclusively in the dorsal parvocellular layers, type IV in the ventral magnocellular layers, and type III in both. Encounter rates for the different cell types in the nucleus as a whole cannot be estimated from Wiesel and Hubel's data because their electrodes did not always penetrate as deeply as the magnocellular layers. Of the cells encountered in the parvocellular layers 77% were type I, 7% type II, and 16% type III. The encounter rates for the magnocellular layers were type III, 68%, and type IV, 32%.

More recently the same four cell classes have again been distinguished in the LGNd by Dreher et al. (101) and, in addition, by de Monasterio (84, 86) in the ganglion cell layer of the macaque retina (see RECEPTIVE FIELDS OF RETINAL GANGLION CELLS, p. 354). Both studies have shown that the four classes have the same general properties as those described by Wiesel and Hubel (392). Available evidence also suggests that the retinal ganglion cell types V and VI described by de Monasterio (86) have an input to the LGNd, but recordings have yet to be made from them.

As well as categorizing the LGNd neurons into types I to IV, Dreher et al. (101) also distinguished them as either X-like or Y-like on the basis of their responses to stationary spots, to fast-moving wands and to moving gratings, and by their latencies to optic chiasm stimulation. The cells were referred to as X-like or Y-like because the stimuli they used did not test for linearity of spatial summation as in the original Enroth-Cugell and Robson (105) methods. All type I and type II cells had X-like properties and all type IV had Y-like properties, whereas type III consisted of two subtypes, one (IIIx) being X-like and the other (IIIy), Y-like. No X-like cell had a response latency to optic chiasm stimulation shorter than 1.7 ms and no Y-like cell had a latency longer than 1.6 ms. Hence the retinal input to X-like cells is slowly conducting and that to Y-like cells faster conducting, the two groups presumably being respectively equivalent to the tonic and phasic ganglion cell types described by Gouras (134, 135).

It should be recalled that de Monasterio (84, 86) categorized macaque retinal ganglion cells as X or Y using tests for the linearity of spatial summation similar to those of Enroth-Cugell and Robson (105). Nevertheless, there is excellent agreement between his X/Y classifications of macaque retinal ganglion cells and the X-like and Y-like categories that Dreher et al. (101) found for LGNd cells, the one exception being the X-like type III subtype of Dreher et al. By contrast

Monkey LGN

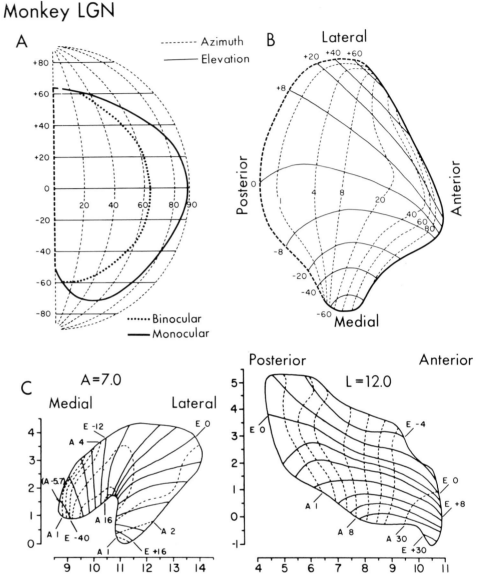

FIG. 19. Projection of visual field onto macaque lateral geniculate nucleus (LGN). *A, B:* semischematic view of right visual hemifield (*A*) and its projection onto dorsal surface of layer 6 of left LGN (*B*) using spherical polar coordinate system of Fig. 9*A.* Surface of LGN is distorted to lie in a plane, distortion being mainly in anteroposterior direction. *Thin broken lines,* azimuths; *solid lines,* elevations. Scales in degrees, positive values above zero horizontal, negative values below it. *Thick broken lines* and *solid lines,* perimeter of right monocular hemifield; they correspond in both drawings. *Heavy dotted line* in *A,* outer limit of right binocular hemifield. *C:* coronal (A = 7.0) and parasagittal (L = 12.0) sections through macaque LGN. *Broken lines,* isoazimuth; *solid lines,* isoelevation. Only a few isoazimuth (A) and isoelevation (E) lines are labeled and their angular values in degrees indicated (e.g., A 1, A 8 ... and E − 4, E 0 ... etc.). Horsley-Clarke coordinate scales in mm. The coronal section is approximately at middle of anteroposterior extent of nucleus (cf. parasagittal section at L = 12.0) and parasagittal section is just lateral to middle of mediolateral extent (cf. coronal section at A = 7.0). [Adapted from Malpeli and Baker (251).]

de Monasterio (84) did not discriminate any type III subtypes but found them all to be in the Y-class. He did, however, observe that about 6% of the type III neurons had surround responses too weak to be detected in the the absence of light adaptation of the center. The weakness of the surround in these cells resulted in the responses being more sustained (and

hence X-like) than those typical of the general run of type III cells. These observations are relevant in the present context because de Monasterio also concluded that spatial summation in the center mechanism of type III cells as a class was relatively linear and that the nonlinear (or Y) property of these cells was dependent upon the surround. It is possible that the X-like type III cells described by Dreher et al. may have been Y-cells with concealed spatial opponency rather than true X-cells. This explanation must, however, face the difficulty that all type IIIx geniculate cells had a response latency to optic chiasm stimulation greater than 1.7 ms and hence characteristic of X-cells.

On grounds that the type IIIx subtype was X-like, Dreher et al., (101) concluded that only X-like cells (types I, II, and IIIx) are to be found in the parvocellular layers and Y-like (types IIIy and IV) cells in the magnocellular layers. If the type IIIx cells are indeed Y-cells with concealed spatial opponency, it would to some degree invalidate the view that the anatomical segregation of the X- and Y-cells in the monkey LGNd constitutes a major difference with the cat where the two classes are not segregated in this way. Whether this is so or not, it is still the case that, as in the cat, the main response patterns of the monkey LGNd relay cells differ little from those of their afferent fibers. The characteristic receptive-field properties of monkey retinal ganglion cells are by and large preserved in their passage through the LGNd.

Schiller and Malpeli (325) observed a difference between the dorsal and ventral pairs of parvocellular laminae in that there was a segregation of on- and off-center cells, the on-center type being more common in the dorsal two laminae and the off-center type more common in the ventral pair. These observations have not so far been confirmed, and Schiller and Malpeli put forward a number of reasons why they have not been noted in earlier studies.

In summary, there is general agreement that the cells in the parvocellular layers are predominantly color opponent, respond in a sustained fashion, have slowly conducting axons, and are activated from the retina by slowly conducting axons. In contrast, cells in the magnocellular layers have broad-band properties, respond transiently to stationary stimuli, have rapidly conducting axons, and are activated from the retina by rapidly conducting axons.

GENICULOCORTICAL CONDUCTION PROPERTIES OF MONKEY DORSAL LGN NEURONS. Optic tract conduction velocities are appreciably slower in the monkey than they are in the cat, but the data are not available to make comparable estimates for the optic radiation. By recording response latencies of LGNd neurons to optic chiasm and visual cortex stimulation, Schiller and Malpeli (325) showed that the magnocellular layers receive rapidly conducting axons from the retina and conduct rapidly to the cortex. By contrast, the input to the parvocellular layers is from more slowly conducting axons and the axons of these cells also conduct more slowly. These observations parallel those that have been made in the cat. Published data (324, 325) suggest that impulses traveling in the fast-conducting group (mostly spectrally nonopponent) might take about 6.5 ms to travel from retina to cortex, whereas impulses in the slower-conducting group (mostly spectrally opponent) would take about 12 ms. These values are appreciably longer than the comparable values in the cat.

Macaque Pregeniculate Nucleus

Relatively little is known about the anatomical connections and function of the pregeniculate nucleus in the monkey. Following Polyak (296), the pregeniculate nucleus of primates is generally regarded as homologous with the ventral lateral geniculate nucleus of other species (cf. ref. 11), but it seems, in the light of its location and connections, more likely that, for the cat at least, the homology is with the perigeniculate nucleus (PGN, see Fig. 8B) and thalamic reticular nucleus (R in Fig. 8B). The macaque pregeniculate nucleus forms a cap covering the LGN dorsally (Fig. 7) so that the geniculocortical and corticogeniculate fibers pass through it on their way to and from the visual cortex as they do in the cat. It is divisible into two laminae, an inner and an outer, but, while appearing as two laminae in frontal sections, the pregeniculate would better be considered as being formed from the inner lamina only, the outer lamina being identical with that region of the reticular nucleus of the thalamus situated lateral and dorsal to the LGN (11). The inner lamina receives a direct retinotopically organized input from the retina (155), whereas the outer lamina has reciprocal connections with the visual cortex (65, 153) and pretectum (19).

The function of the monkey pregeniculate nucleus is largely unknown. Büttner and Fuchs (57) had the impression that the perigeniculate cells in the monkey were binocularly activated by visual stimuli as they are in the cat. In addition the majority of units exhibited a clear change in activity with all eye saccades in the dark. Hence the monkey PGN receives an oculomotor input as well as an input from the retina. However, the saccade-related unit discharges appear to occur too long after the movement either to participate in saccadic suppression or to aid in differentiating those movements of the retinal image due to eye movements from those due to movements of the visual world per se.

Extrageniculate Visual Thalamus in Monkey

Rezak and Benevento (298) have redefined some of the pulvinar subdivisions in the macaque monkey on the basis of their afferent and efferent connections rather than by the former emphasis on their cytoarchitectonic features. In particular they have distinguished three separate regions (PLα, PLβ, and PLγ) in the lateral pulvinar (PL). Region PLα is located ventrolaterally immediately adjacent to the inferior pulvinar. The inferior pulvinar (PI) and the immediately adjacent part of the lateral pulvinar (PLα) have parallel topographic projections to the visual cortex (18, 276, 298) that are reciprocal with corticothalamic projections (63, 275, 298). The remaining portions of the lateral pulvinar (PLβ and PLγ) overlying the PLα and the medial pulvinar do not project to area 17.

The inferior pulvinar receives a direct bilateral retinal input along its lateroventral margin adjacent to the LGNd. The ipsilateral retinal projection lies dorsal to the contralateral; there appears to be little or no binocular overlap (64). In addition the inferior pulvinar receives overlapping visuotopically organized projections both from the superficial cell layer of superior colliculus (17) and from the visual cortex (63, 247, 275). The superficial cell layer of the superior colliculus also has a direct retinal input. The visuotopic organization is such that the vertical meridian is located along the lateral margin of the nucleus where it adjoins the LGNd. The zero horizontal cuts through the nucleus with the upper contralateral quadrant of the visual field located ventrally and the lower quadrant located dorsally.

The adjacent lateral pulvinar (PLα) also has a visuotopic input from the visual cortex, but not from the superior colliculus, and is thus distinguished from the remainder of the lateral pulvinar. The latter has an input from the pretectum and deep layers of the superior colliculus. The visuotopic organization in PLα is apparently such that it mirrors the one found in the inferior pulvinar with the mutual border between the two regions containing the representation of the zero vertical meridian.

Pulvinar-cortical projections. In contrast to the LGNd, which projects only to the striate cortex, both pulvinar regions (PI and PLα) project to both areas 17 and 18, the two projections being retinotopically organized and existing in parallel with those from the LGNd. Also in contrast to the projection from the LGNd, those from PI and PLα terminate in the striate cortex mainly in layer 1 but also in layers 2 and 3. The distribution of terminals in layer 1 is continuous but of variable density, whereas the distribution in layers 2 and 3 occurs in definite patches with a center-to-center periodicity of about 600 μm. Area 18 in the macaque has no direct projection from the LGNd but receives a greater density of pulvinar terminals than does area 17. In area 18 the pulvinar terminals are found in layer 4, the lower portion of layer 3, and layer 1. Once again there are alternating zones of dense and sparse accumulations of terminals, the center-to-center distances being much greater and more variable than those in area 17. The geniculate input to area 17 also occurs in patches (176) that appear to extend through all layers of the cortex from pia to white matter (202). These represent the ocular dominance columns where the banding corresponds to a segregation of the input from the two eyes. Since the pulvinar neurons are mainly binocular, it seems unlikely that their input to areas 17 and 18 would be organized into regions of ocular dominance even though the width of an LGNd ocular dominance column is similar to that reported for pulvinar afferents in area 17. Since similar discontinuities in terminal labeling occur in other cortical pathways, this pattern probably reflects some fundamental aspect of cortical organization not restricted to ocular dominance.

Corticopulvinar projection. Both areas 17 and 18 have topographic projections back to both pulvinar regions PI and PLα (63, 275). The cells of origin of the efferent axons are layer 5 pyramidal cells (247, 276), which in area 17 are concentrated in lamina 5B and only to a much lesser extent in lamina 5A. By contrast, in area 18 the pyramidal cells of origin are mostly in layer 5A immediately under the granule cells in layer 4.

VISUAL CORTEX

Cat Striate Cortex (Area 17)

RETINOTOPIC ORGANIZATION. Figure 20 shows the dorsal and medial aspects of the left cerebral hemisphere of the cat's brain indicating the pattern of gyri and sulci related to the main visual areas (Fig. 21D). The unique character and extent of area 17 have been distinguished by cytoarchitectonic studies (47, 59, 119, 122, 246, 278, 282, 319), by the pattern of afferent and efferent connections (see LAMINAR TERMINATIONS OF AXONS AFFERENT TO CAT STRIATE CORTEX, p. 381), and by electrophysiological methods (22, 169, 171, 192, 366, 376).

Much the most detailed study of the retinotopic organization of the cat striate cortex is that of Tusa et al. (376). They demonstrated a single representation of the entire contralateral visual hemifield that corresponds closely to the cytoarchitectonically defined area 17. The spherical polar coordinate system used by Tusa et al. (376) to describe the topography of area 17 is the same as that illustrated in Figure 9A. The perimeter chart in Figure 21A shows the extent of the monocular (thick solid line) and binocular (dotted line) visual-field representation in cat area 17. The meridians (solid lines) in Figure 21A are lines of isoazimuth and the parallels (dotted lines) are lines of isoelevation. It should be noted that there are no horizontal meridians. The location and extent of area 17 on the surface of the cat's brain is shown in Figure 21B, C, D. From the crown of the lateral (marginal) gyrus, where it shares with area 18 the representation of the zero meridian (zero vertical, ZV), area 17 extends down the interhemispheric surface to the superior bank of the splenial sulcus. The area centralis is represented at Horsley-Clarke coordinates posterior 4.5 mm (range 3.5–5.5 mm), lateral 2 mm (195), set by the intersection of the representations of the zero vertical (ZV) and zero horizontal (ZH) (Fig. 21B, C). The lower zero vertical is represented rostrally, whereas the representation of the upper zero vertical extends caudally along the posterior lateral gyrus onto the tentorial surface and finally into the posterior portion of the splenial sulcus. The lower visual field is

Cat

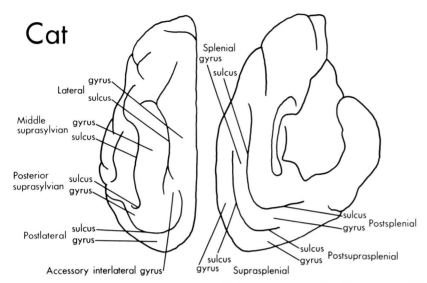

FIG. 20. Pattern of gyri and sulci associated with visual parts of cat cerebral cortex showing plan (*left*) and medial (*right*) aspects of left hemisphere.

represented rostral to and the upper visual field caudal to the zero horizontal. The most peripheral parts of the lower and upper visual field are represented deep within the superior bank of the splenial sulcus along its anterior, middle, and posterior portions.

Tusa et al. (376) paid particular attention to the nature of the areas bordering area 17. On the dorsal convexity of the brain (Fig. 21*D*) area 17 is contiguous with area 18. Area 20b abuts the representation of the upper visual field in the posterior portion of the splenial sulcus. The status of the area immediately adjacent to area 17 in the anterior portion of the splenial sulcus is still controversial. On the basis of cytoarchitectonics it has been called area 19 (282), but Sanides and Hoffmann (319) failed to find any resemblance to areas 18 or 19 and called it a prostriate area. Kalia and Whitteridge (192) found this area to be retinotopically organized and called it the splenial visual area, but Tusa et al. (376) were unable to excite the cells with any visual stimuli.

Area 17 contains the most extensive representation of the visual field of any of the visual areas so far mapped in the cortex. It extends out along the zero horizontal to the 90° azimuth and to the upper and lower 50° elevations along the zero vertical (Fig. 21*A*). Only the 10° segment of the visual field adjacent to the zero vertical is accessible on the dorsal surface of the brain and the peripheral 60° of the visual field is buried in the splenial sulcus.

Tulsa et al. (376) found that receptive-field centers appeared to extend about 1.5° into the ipsilateral hemifield throughout the extent of the zero vertical. This spread over the vertical midline is represented in Figure 21*B* by the $-1\frac{1}{2}°$ isoazimuth line lateral to the zero vertical (ZV). Uncertainty regarding the exact position of the zero vertical makes it difficult to decide whether this overlap represents the cortical counterpart of the crossed-uncrossed overlap of retinal gan-

glion cells (see CROSSED AND UNCROSSED PATHWAYS IN CAT, p. 351).

CORTICAL MAGNIFICATION FACTOR. The retinotopic organization found in area 17, where all adjacent points in the visual field are represented by adjacent points in the cortex, is referred to as a *first-order transformation* of the visual hemifield (9). In a first-order transformation the only deformations of the original perimetry chart as it is represented on the cortex are local stretching and twisting. Proportionately more striate cortex is devoted to the representation of the central rather than the peripheral visual field. Daniel and Whitteridge (82) used the concept of a magnification factor to quantify the distortions in the visual-field representation. This concept is considered in more detail in relation to the monkey striate cortex and only a brief outline is given here. With respect to the cortex the magnification factor is best expressed in mm^2 of cortex per degree^2 of visual space. At the cortical representation of the area centralis in the cat, Tusa et al. (376) found the peak magnification factor to be 3.6 mm^2/deg^2, with 50% of the cortical area devoted to the central 10°. In the cat there seems to be a direct correspondence between the change in retinal ganglion cell density with eccentricity and the changes in LGNd and cortical magnification factors with eccentricity. By contrast the macaque has a proportionately larger amount of striate cortex devoted to the central visual field (peak magnification factor 42 mm^2/deg^2) with 90% of the cortical area devoted to the central 10°. In the monkey the area devoted to the central visual field is much larger than would be expected on the basis of the spatial distribution of retinal ganglion cell densities (see Fig. 35).

LAMINAR DIFFERENTIATION OF STRIATE CORTEX. Some years ago Garey (119) and Billings-Gagliardi et al. (23) reviewed the more commonly encountered

Cat

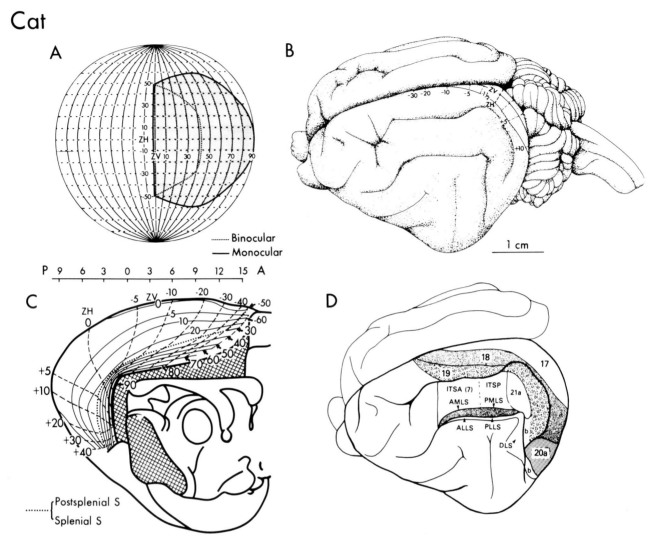

FIG. 21. Semischematic view of right visual hemifield (*A*) and its projection onto left cerebral hemisphere of cat (*B–D*). Spherical polar coordinate system of Fig. 9*A. A–C: thin solid lines,* azimuths (meridians); *broken lines,* elevations (parallels). *ZH,* zero horizontal (*dashed line*); *ZV,* zero vertical (*solid line*). Scales are in degrees, positive values above zero horizontal, negative below. *Thick solid lines* in *A,* perimeter of right monocular hemifield; *dotted line,* outer limit of right binocular hemifield. *B:* perspective drawing showing extent of representation of visual field on exposed dorsal surface of area 17. The 1-cm bar refers only to *B* and *D. C:* topographic representation in area 17 on medial surface of left cerebral hemisphere with cingulate gyrus removed. Upper *cross-hatched* area shows portion of cortex normally hidden by cingulate gyrus. The Horsley-Clarke scale PA (posterior, anterior) is in mm and refers only to drawing *C. Dotted line,* upper edge of splenial and postsplenial sulci. *D:* perspective drawing showing various visual areas on exposed outer surface of cerebral cortex. Lettered designations, divisions of lateral suprasylvian cortex according to Tusa et al. (375a). [*A–C:* adapted from Tusa et al. (376); *D:* from Sprague et al. (349a).]

lamination schemes for the striate cortex in the cat and monkey. Figure 22 summarizes these reviews with some modifications based on more recent information. The two commonly used lamination schemes for area 17 in the cat are those of O'Leary (278) (modified by Lund et al., ref. 246) and Otsuka and Hassler (282). The key differences between these two schemes concern the designation of the upper and lower borders of lamina 4. Following O'Leary (278), Lund et al. (246) have placed the upper border of lamina 4 on a level with the cell bodies of O'Leary's border pyramidal

neurons, the cell bodies being assigned to lamina 3. Otsuka and Hassler (282) seem to have placed the boundary between laminae 3 and 4 at a rather higher level. As regards the lower boundary of lamina 4, O'Leary (278) suggested that a discrete sublamina (5A) exists between the lower margin of lamina 4B and the upper edge of lamina 5B with its large pyramidal cells. The principal cells in sublamina 5A are small to medium pyramids with recurrent axons ending in profuse arborizations in laminae 3 and 2. Otsuka and Hassler (282) did not differentiate this sublamina

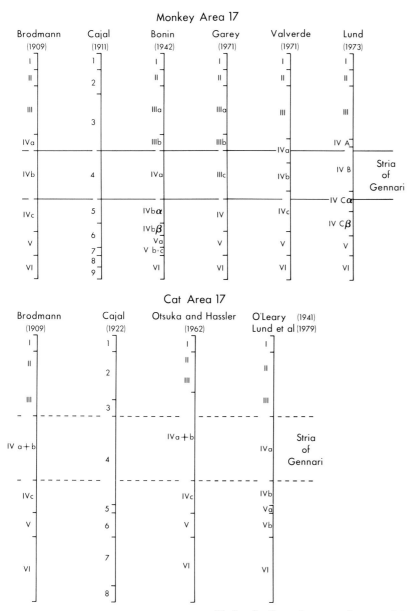

FIG. 22. Lamination schemes and nomenclature of laminae of area 17 of the cat and monkey according to various authors. [Adapted from Garey (119).]

and apparently included it within their lamina 4C. The lamination scheme used in the present review is that of Lund et al. [cf. Fig. 23; (246).]

The total thickness of area 17 of the cat is between 1.75 and 2 mm. Immediately below the pia lies layer 1, a zone almost free of cell bodies and composed mainly of the terminal arborizations of the apical dendrites of underlying pyramidal cells and the terminals of axons afferent to the striate area. Laminae 2 and 3 are difficult to separate and are commonly considered together. They are composed mainly of small pyramidal cells, the cell bodies increasing in size with increasing depth from the cortical surface. Lamina 4 is characterized by the presence of spiny stellate cells, but there are, in addition, both pyramidal neurons and stellate neurons with smooth or sparsely spined den-

drites. The lamina has two subdivisions: a lower portion (4B) having smaller, more closely packed neurons, and an upper region (4A) where the cells are more widely separated and where there is a concentration of horizontally orientated fibers. Lamina 5A has been referred to above. The cell bodies of the largest pyramidal neurons of the cat visual cortex lie at the boundary of laminae 5A and 5B. These cells and the smaller pyramidal neurons in lamina 5B have well-developed apical dendrites that reach to lamina 1. The pyramidal neurons of lamina 6 of the cat are small and medium in size, with none of the very large pyramids that are to be found in monkey lamina 6.

LAMINAR TERMINATIONS OF AXONS AFFERENT TO CAT STRIATE CORTEX. The terminations of geniculocortical

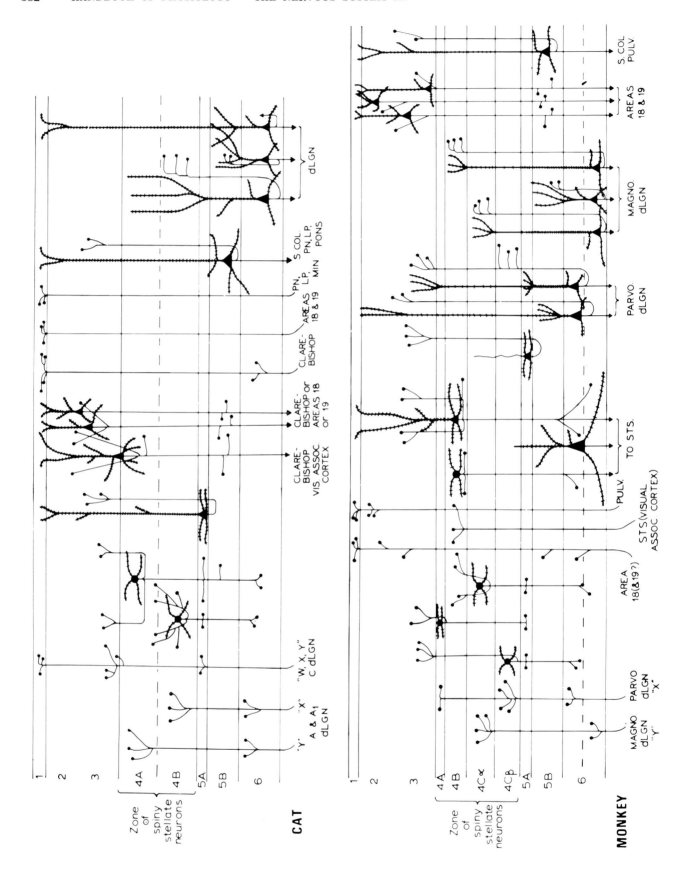

axons in the cat striate cortex have been explored in some detail (50, 110, 122, 126, 227, 246, 395). The dorsal geniculate laminae, which contain a mixture of brisk-sustained (X) and brisk-transient (Y) cells, project to layers 4 and 6 in the striate cortex (Fig. 23). The finer axons of the smaller slowly conducting brisk-sustained cells terminate in the lower portion of lamina 4 (Fig. 23, lamina 4B) among closely packed small spiny stellate cells. By contrast the terminals of the coarser axons of the larger, fast-conducting, brisk-transient cells distribute to the upper portion of lamina 4 (lamina 4A) among more widely spread and somewhat larger spiny stellate neurons and may, in addition, extend a short distance into lamina 3. No afferents arborize in both sublayers of lamina 4, the inputs to this layer from the two geniculate cell types being segregated, at least on their arrival in the cortex. Most afferents of both types give off collaterals to the upper half of lamina 6. Apparently there are no axons that exclusively innervate layer 6. The great majority of geniculocortical axon terminals synapse on dendritic spines and apparently all are excitatory to their target cells. The terminals of both the fast- and the slowly conducting axons in layers 4 and 6 synapse on cells in the simple family and, in addition, the fast-conducting axons innervate complex cells in lamina 6. The simple cells in lamina 6 project directly back to the LGNd and it has been proposed that the lamina 6 complex cells project to the perigeniculate nucleus (151).

The axons supplying layer 4A have a wide lateral spread in the cortex (up to 2 mm) with rich arbors grouped into patches separated by terminal-free gaps. The patches presumably correspond to ocular dominance columns driven by one eye, the intervening gaps to columns driven by the other eye.

Ferster and LeVay (110) concluded that the lateral geniculate neurons in laminae C_1–C_3, which presumably correspond to Guillery's type 4 cells, send extremely fine axons to terminate in the upper part of layer 1 after giving off collaterals to the upper part of layer 5 (5A) and sometimes also to the lower part of layer 3. In contrast to layer 4, which receives its principal, if not its entire afferent innervation from the LGNd, layer 1 receives fibers from various sources, including the LGN, the pulvinar, the MIN, the posterior nucleus, area 18, and other cortical areas.

EXTRASTRIATE PROJECTIONS FROM CAT STRIATE CELL LAMINAE. Figure 23, from Lund et al. (246), summarizes some of the main extrastriate projections of the various striate cell laminae (7, 125, 163, 188, 250, 334, 372). Laminae 2 and 3 project to other cortical areas, including areas 18 and 19, the medial bank of the

lateral suprasylvian sulcus (Clare-Bishop area), and, via the corpus callosum, areas 18 and 19 in the opposite visual cortex. Both the cells projecting to the Clare-Bishop area and those projecting to the opposite visual cortex are located mainly in lamina 3 and include particularly the large border pyramidal cells at the boundary of laminae 3 and 4 (115). The axons of the border pyramids issue collaterals to lamina 5B on their way out of the cortex into the white matter. The pyramidal neurons in lamina 5B project to the superior colliculus, pulvinar (nucleus lateralis posterior pars lateralis and nucleus posterior), pontine nuclei, and other subcortical destinations. Albus and Donate-Oliver (7) have recently found that some lamina 5 complex cells can be antidromically driven from the pons. The cells in lamina 5A seem to serve principally as intrinsic relay neurons projecting to the upper cortical laminae. The cells in lamina 6 are efferent to the LGNd.

Almost all the corticotectal neurons are complex cells. They have fast-conducting axons, are broadly tuned for stimulus orientation, are responsive to a wide range of stimulus velocities, and have large binocular receptive fields (151). Some of these cells respond equally well to both small moving spots and elongated stimuli, while others respond only to stimuli of restricted length (cf. ref. 285). Both types are highly direction selective.

The corticothalamic cells in lamina 6 can be either of the simple or complex type. They are, however, most commonly simple, with slowly conducting axons, are almost always direction selective, and have about half their number with binocular receptive fields. Their response latency to antidromic optic radiation stimulation is in accord with the orthodromic latencies of intrageniculate interneurons obtained after electrical stimulation of the visual cortex (cf. refs. 73, 103).

Harvey (151) has suggested that there may be at least three subgroups within the corticothalamic cells: lamina 5 complex cells projecting to the pulvinar complex, possibly by collaterals from corticotectal axons; lamina 6 complex cells projecting to the perigeniculate nucleus; and finally, lamina 6 simple cells innervating interneurons intrinsic to the LGNd. He has pointed out that corticofugal simple cells, especially in area 17, are very specific in their stimulus requirements and that there would be a great deal of redundancy if such cells projected onto a diffuse inhibitory network. Rather, they are more likely to be involved in the precise, retinotopically organized inhibitory pathways mediated in part by the interneurons intrinsic to the LGNd. Schmielau and Singer (328, 342) have proposed that the corticogeniculate projection is concerned with the control of binocular interactions in the LGNd.

FIG. 23. Diagrams summarizing details of afferent and efferent relationships and intrinsic spinous neuron relays of cat and monkey visual cortex, area 17. [From Lund et al. (246).]

Their proposal requires that a disparity-sensitive cell in the visual cortex, which is optimally excited by an appropriate stimulus presented to the two eyes, should facilitate transmission through the LGNd by suppressing binocular inhibition in the corresponding LGNd projection subunit (column) as well as by facilitating the particular neurons in laminae A and A_1 that provide the excitatory binocular input to the cortical cell in question.

A number of large-field, binocular complex cells in lamina 6 appear to project to the LGNd (151). However, their fast-conducting axons and short latencies to optic radiation stimulation make it unlikely that they innervate interneurons intrinsic to the LGNd. Instead, Harvey (151) has suggested that they innervate perigeniculate neurons. The visual properties of efferent complex cells seem appropriate for participation in the diffuse, nonspecific inhibitory pathways mediated by perigeniculate neurons (103, 342).

Unlike the corticotectal and corticothalamic projections, the lamina 3 cells projecting through the corpus callosum form a heterogeneous group, all major receptive-field classes being represented (151). The cells are encountered within about 1 mm to either side of the 17/18 border zone, with their receptive-field centers close to the vertical midline and responding best to stimuli moving toward the ipsilateral hemifield. By contrast, the cells innervated by the corticofugal axons are mostly complex and B cells and, unlike the corticofugal cells, can be found in all cortical layers though still mostly in laminae 2 + 3. They are encountered up to 3 mm into area 18 and can have receptive fields up to 9° into the contralateral and 8° into the ipsilateral hemifields. Thus all the corticofugal cells have receptive fields close to the midline, whereas the cells they innervate in the opposite visual cortex can have receptive fields up to 8° into the hemifield ipsilateral to them. The cell receiving the callosal input could therefore have highly disparate receptive fields, with disparities large enough to account for the relatively large qualitative depth estimates to be found in coarse stereopsis [(29); cf. refs. 33, 151].

CLASSIFICATION OF NEURONS IN CAT STRIATE CORTEX. *Historical perspective.* In 1962 Hubel and Wiesel (169) published their observations both on the properties of cells in the cat striate cortex and on the functional architecture of the visual cortex. These observations had an immediate determining effect on the direction of research in visual neurophysiology and they have formed the basis for all subsequent studies on the visual cortex. Hubel and Wiesel (169) discriminated striate cells into two main categories, simple and complex, and their descriptions contain most of the features of these tw) cell types as we know them today. However, Hubel and Wiesel used mainly hand-held stimuli to make their cell classifications, and their descriptions are couched in largely qualitative terms. Furthermore, many of the cell properties are only briefly mentioned. In attempting to develop these pioneer observations toward a more explicit and quantitative account, it was inevitable that major differences would arise in the way that subsequent investigators characterized the cell classes. Quantitative methods, particularly those involving averaging procedures, may reveal receptive-field properties that are either difficult to interpret or not in evidence at all if only hand methods are used. The problem regarding the reliance to be placed on hand methods as opposed to quantitative procedures is further aggravated by the variety of quantitative procedures adopted by different investigators. Continuing differences in the way cells are classified make it difficult to achieve a consensus not only with respect to the discrimination of subclasses within the two broad categories of simple and complex cells but also in regard to the recognition of cell classes that cannot easily be accommodated within these two categories.

Hubel and Wiesel (169) defined simple cells by mapping their receptive fields with stationary flashing stimuli. The receptive fields of these cells could be subdivided into spatially separate on and off areas when tested with a stationary flashing bar of a given orientation, the optimal orientation varying from cell to cell. The two common types of receptive-field arrangements were a central excitatory region flanked on either side by regions of the opposite type, or two regions of the opposite type arranged side by side. Wider slits gave an increasingly stronger response up to the full width of an on or off subdivision short of invading an adjoining antagonistic region. Hence there was spatial summation of responses within each subregion, mutual antagonism between subregions, and little or no response when the entire receptive field was stimulated with diffuse light.

Hubel and Wiesel (169) introduced the concept of a complex cell not to describe a single well-defined class but rather groups of cells that did not obey the principle of summation within and mutual antagonism between the subregions in their receptive fields. In general the receptive fields of complex cells could not be subdivided into spatially separate on-and-off areas, the cells responding with only mixed (on-off) discharges throughout the field. The stimuli that were most effective in activating cells with simple fields—slits, edges, and dark bars—were also the most effective for cells with complex fields, and the stimulus orientation was also critical. For complex cells there was spatial summation of responses along the line of the optimal stimulus orientation but not to any extent at right angles to the orientation. The optimal width of a bar stimulus was always much less than the width of the complex cell receptive field, but it was effective wherever it was placed in the field, provided the orientation was appropriate.

Hubel and Wiesel (169) recognized that moving stimuli were generally more effective than stationary flashing patterns, the responses of simple cells being characteristically different from those of complex cells. Of the 233 cells they regarded as simple, 117 were classified as such, though with less certainty, purely on the basis of their responses to moving stimuli. The latter group included cells that gave an inadequate or no response to stationary flashing stimuli, and presumably also, cells that exhibited only a single on or off zone without any additional zone or zones. More recently other investigators (34, 104, 185, 337, 339, 344) have repeatedly observed a substantial group of cells in the striate cortex that cannot be classified on the basis of their responses to hand-held stationary flashing stimuli, either because the responses are inadequate or because they are absent altogether. There seems to be fairly general agreement that, when tested with hand-held stationary stimuli, between 30% and 40% of striate cells fall into this category, and many of them are simple-cell–like in their responses to moving stimuli.

Cells having receptive fields of the hypercomplex type were first described by Hubel and Wiesel (171) in areas 18 and 19 of the cat visual cortex. They recognized two types of hypercomplex cell (a lower order and a higher order), but the feature distinguishing both types as hypercomplex was the same: they responded best to short optimally oriented bars or edges and the extension of these stimuli beyond their optimal length reduced or suppressed the response. This *stopped-end* characteristic of hypercomplex cells indicated the presence in the receptive fields of inhibitory areas located beyond the ends of the central excitatory region along the line of the optimal stimulus orientation. The main additional feature distinguishing higher-order hypercomplex cells from those of the lower order was a dual orientation specificity, enabling them to respond to two sets of stimuli with orientations 90° apart. No further descriptions of the higher-order cells have, however, appeared since the original account. Cells of the lower order were subsequently observed in the striate cortex of both cat and monkey (173) and their presence in area 17 has been repeatedly confirmed (cf. ref. 195 for further references). Detailed quantitative observations on the properties of hypercomplex cells have only recently become available [(37, 124, 195, 280, 281, 306, 339, 340); see also *The hypercomplex property,* p. 387].

The poor responses of many striate cells to stationary flashing stimuli led Pettigrew, Nikara, and Bishop (289) to develop quantitative criteria for distinguishing simple and complex cells on the basis of their responses to moving stimuli and, since dark bars were not available at that time, only the responses to light bars were examined. The classifying criteria were later extended to include responses to moving light and dark edges (31, 132). Simple cells may respond only to one type of edge (light or dark) and then only in one direction of movement, or they may respond only to one edge in each direction. Alternatively, when the cell responds to both types of edge, the discharge

regions are small and generally spatially offset or separated. By contrast, complex cells nearly always respond to both light and dark edges over relatively large overlapping regions either in one or, more usually, in both directions of edge movement.

Recently Kulikowski, Bishop, and Kato (213, 215) have further extended the range of stimuli beyond those used in the earlier studies mentioned to include not only stationary flashing and moving bars that were both brighter and darker than the background but also stationary flashing and drifting sinusoidal gratings. The relationship between the responses to these stimuli is described in *Recent analysis of the simple/ complex cell classification,* p. 387.

Nonorientation-sensitive cells. The great majority of cells in the cat striate cortex are stimulus-orientation sensitive. The occurrence of nonorientation-sensitive cells in the cat striate cortex has, however, been repeatedly reported (189), but in an encounter rate too low to permit a systematic study of their properties. Two types of nonorientation-sensitive units have been described, one having a concentric receptive-field organization resembling that of LGNd neurons and the other having complex on-off responses to a stationary flashing spot with no obvious center-surround type of organization. Since cells with these properties are to be found in subcortical nuclei there is always the possibility that the electrode is recording from axons afferent to the cortex. Many of these units have, however, been regarded as striate cells on the basis of the cell-type extracellular wave form of their spikes and the fact that they are discharged from both eyes. In addition many of these cells fail to respond to electrical stimulation of the optic radiation above relatively low stimulus repetition rates indicating that the activation is transsynaptic (158). Intracellular recording and marking techniques will probably be required to demonstrate with certainty whether these cells are cortical.

LATER SCHEMES FOR CLASSIFYING STRIATE CELLS. There is now general agreement that the great majority of orientation-sensitive cells can be readily classified as simple or complex and that all nonoriented cells are excluded from these two categories. It is also generally agreed that cells otherwise classified as simple or complex may show varying degrees of end-zone inhibition. Simple-type cells with end-zone inibition have been referred to as hypercomplex I and the complex-type as hypercomplex II (34, 100). It is convenient, therefore, to regard both simple and hypercomplex I cells as belonging to the simple family and complex and hypercomplex II cells as belonging to the complex family (195, 306). Without departing from the classification scheme just outlined, Henry (156) has, however, proposed an alternative nomenclature that avoids the connotation of a hierarchical organization inherent in the simple/complex terminology and allows for the naming of additional cell classes as these are discriminated. According to this nomenclature, simple and complex cells are referred to by their initial letters S and C, respectively. The use of the subscript H indicates the presence of the hypercomplex property. Insofar as they possess the hypercomplex property, S_H and C_H cells may be regarded as equivalent to hypercomplex I and II cells mentioned above, though the level of end-zone inhibition that warrants the addition of the H-subscript (48, 158) appears to be rather greater than that recognized by other authors with respect to cells referred to as hypercomplex [(195); see *The hypercomplex property*, p. 387.]. Henry (156) applied the letter A to a class of cell originally described by Hubel and Wiesel (169) and classified by them as complex. These cells, rarely encountered in area 17, have receptive fields that can be subdivided into on and off areas but, unlike simple cells, there appears to be relatively little antagonism between the areas so that the response at on and off depends upon the polarity of an edge and not upon its precise location within the receptive field. Subsequently Henry et al. (159) used the letter B to refer to cells having properties intermediate between those of simple and complex cells (see *Intermediate-type cells,* this page).

Recently classification schemes other than those described above have been put forward and Tables 4 and 5 attempt a comparison between the various proposals. The following cell types have response properties that particularly occasion difficulty with respect to classification.

1. Cells that either fail to respond or give only an indefinite response to a stationary flashing stimulus.

2. Cells that have only a single response region, either on or off, to a stationary flashing stimulus.

3. Cells with response properties intermediate between those in the simple and complex categories.

4. Cells with the hypercomplex property.

Responses to stationary stimuli. As seen in Table 4, Singer et al. (344) placed the cell types described in paragraphs 1 and 2 above in their classes IV and I, respectively, but, depending upon the nature of their responses to moving stimuli, most authors (e.g., refs. 158, 169, 195, 288, 339) have regarded these cells as either simple or complex. It is important to appreciate that the data in Table 4 are largely based on qualitative observations and that the number of cells responding inadequately to stationary flashing stimuli would have been considerably reduced had quantitative averaging methods been used. The latter methods are, however, both technically demanding and time consuming, and data involving their detailed systematic use have yet to be published (see *Recent analysis of the simple/complex cell classification,* p. 387).

Sillito (339) subdivided the simple cell class into his groups 1 and 2. The cells in group 1 had the classic simple cell properties as defined by Hubel and Wiesel (169). Provided their properties were otherwise like those of classic simple cells, cells of the types in paragraphs 1 and 2 above were categorized by Sillito (339) as group 2 simple cells. Like those in group 1, the direction selectivity of group 2 cells was significantly reduced by the iontophoretic application of the γ-aminobutyric acid (GABA) antagonist bicuculline, in this respect differentiating them from the classic type of complex cell. By contrast Gilbert (124) placed cells of the types in paragraphs 1 and 2 in his *standard complex* category.

Intermediate-type cells (159, 214). Cells with properties intermediate between those in the simple and complex categories have been called *B-cells* by Henry et al. (159). Like simple cells, B-cells usually have little or no spontaneous activity, have small receptive fields, and are commonly direction selective and sharply orientation tuned, but they lack the spatially separate on and off regions that characterize the receptive fields of simple cells. Like complex cells, B-cells give a mixed on-off response over the whole receptive field when tested with a stationary flashing bar. Like both simple and complex cells, B-cells can also be end stopped, the hypercomplex B subgroup being referred to as B_H. The general properties of these cells puts them in the complex rather than the simple family (Table 5).

TABLE 4. *Distribution of Cell Classes in Cat Striate Cortex in Response to Hand-Held Stationary Flashing Light*

	Kato, Bishop, and Orban (195)* Percentage Distribution					Singer et al. (344)*	
	Simple family		Complex family				
	Simple	Hyper-complex I	Complex	Hyper-complex II	Distribution, %	Cell class	Distribution, %
Clear "on", with no or only an indefinite separated "off", or clear "off", with no or only an indefinite separated "on"	17	16	0	0	33	I	22
Both clear "on" and clear "off" but spatially offset or separated	15	12	0	0	27	II	44
Mixed "on"-"off"	0	0	13	12	25	III	20
No response or too indefinite to be helpful	6	5	2	2	15	IV	14
Totals, %	38	33	15	14	100		100

* Reference numbers in parentheses.

TABLE 5. *Classifications of Orientation-Sensitive Cells in Cat Striate Cortex*

Henry et al. (158)*	Kato et al. (195) Kulikowski et al. (215)			Sillito (339)	Gilbert (124)
S and S$_H$	Simple family	Simple and hypercomplex I	Clearly defined and spatially separated "on" and "off" subdivisions	Simple group 1	Simple
			Simple-like responses to moving stimuli but no response, an indefinite response or a single response region (either "on" or "off") to a stationary flashing stimulus	Simple group 2	Standard complex
B	Complex family		B	Complex type 1	
B$_H$			B$_H$	Hypercomplex cells in cortical layers 2 and 3	
C			Complex	Complex type 2	
C$_H$			Hypercomplex II	Complex type 3	Special complex

* Reference numbers in parentheses.

A group of intermediate-type cells, called *silent periodic cells,* have been discriminated (214) that have the same general properties as B-cells but also show characteristic responses to gratings. Nonlinear spatial summation is indicated by the absence of a null position to a stationary flashing grating (105), a spatial periodicity is revealed by a modulated discharge to drifting gratings, and these cells have a spatial frequency tuning curve that is very sharp.

The hypercomplex property. The preparation of a length-response curve is the decisive test for a hypercomplex cell. Figure 24 shows typical length-response curves for a hypercomplex I (*A*) and for a simple cell (*B*), indicating how the strength of the end inhibition is estimated in each case. Most observers (124, 306, 320, 396) consider that the percentage of end-zone inhibition in end-stopped cells covers the full range from 0 to 100%, although Kato, Bishop, and Orban (195) found that cells rarely had end inhibition between 15% and 40% (Fig. 25*B*), suggesting a distinction between end-free and end-stopped cells. Based on qualitative testing, the degree of inhibition required for a cell to be classed as hypercomplex varies among observers from being just reliably detectable (195) to being sufficient to suppress the excitatory response either totally or almost totally (158). Kato, Bishop, and Orban (195) found that the level of end inhibition that could be reliably detected by ear was about 40% on the basis of subsequent quantitative checks. It should also be borne in mind that cells almost totally suppressed to qualitative observation may be much less so when averaging methods are used.

The hypercomplex property has now been subjected to detailed quantitative examination (37, 124, 195, 280, 281, 306). This property appears to be very largely, if not completely, independent of the simple/complex classification. In both the simple and complex families end-stopped cells are encountered almost as commonly as end-free cells. Cells with the shortest optimal stimulus length tend to have the strongest end-zone inhibition (Fig. 25*A*). End-inhibitory areas are probably always present at both ends of the discharge region. The inhibition is both stimulus-orientation and stimulus-position dependent, being maximal both when the orientation is the same as the orientation that is optimal for the excitatory region and when the stimulus lies precisely along the line of the most responsive part of the discharge center and just beyond its lateral border. Spatial summation of end inhibition takes place along the line of the optimal orientation. End inhibition is usually nondirectional even when the discharge region is itself completely direction selective.

Recent analysis of the simple/complex cell classification. Kulikowski et al. (213, 215) have applied to each of a series of striate cells the full range of stimuli and quantitative test procedures in common use by the various investigators. They found good general agreement between the main receptive-field subregions revealed by stationary flashing bars and those given by light and dark bars moving at optimal velocities. On the other hand, moving light and dark bars generally revealed more subregions in the receptive fields of simple cells than were evident from the response profiles to a stationary flashing bar, particularly when the receptive field had many subregions. A detailed relationship was also established between the responses to narrow moving bars, which were both brighter and darker than the background, and the responses to moving light and dark edges. Hubel and

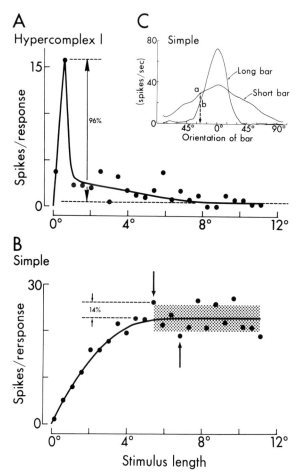

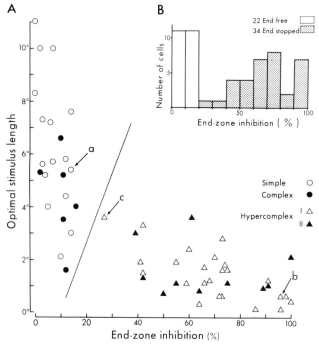

FIG. 24. *A*: length-response curve from a hypercomplex I cell showing 96% end-zone inhibition. *B*: length-response curve from a simple cell showing considerable response variability. *Stippled band* indicates ± 1 SD of response variability to either side of mean plateau level. Response indicated by *upward-pointing arrow* is approximately 28% below response indicated by *downward-pointing arrow*. *C*: short and long bar stimulus orientation tuning curves from a simple cell showing how a length-response curve recorded with the bar sufficiently away from the optimal (here 25°) can resemble the type of length-response curve that is obtained from a hypercomplex cell [From Kato, Bishop, and Orban (195).]

Wiesel (169) clearly recognized the essential feature of simple cells when they stressed that the receptive fields consist of separate subregions having spatial summation within the mutual antagonism (inhibition) between the subregions. As described in relation to Figure 26, the responses to moving light and dark edges provide a rapid guide to spatial summation across the width of a subregion and the possible subtractive (antagonistic) effect of the next subregion in sequence. The most rigorous test for linear spatial summation is, however, the null-position test of Enroth-Cugell and Robson (105). This test is passed by the majority of simple cells provided the stimuli are reasonably close to optimal [cf. Fig. 28; (213, 266)]. Even the few simple cells that fail to show a complete null response are relatively linear by comparison to complex cells. As a further indication that simple cells

operate linearly, Kulikowski and Bishop (213) showed that the inverse Fourier transform of a cell's spatial frequency tuning curve gives a reasonably good fit to the response profile to moving lines and edges (Fig. 29; cf. also refs. 10, 266). By the reverse procedure, the spatial frequency tuning curves of simple cells can be satisfactorily predicted from their spatial response profiles (213). In contrast to simple cells, complex cells lack the spatial organization of simple cells and exhibit marked nonlinearities of spatial summation (267).

Kulikowski et al. (215) concluded that the use of light and dark bars (lines) and edges moving at about their optimal velocity is not merely an equivalent or alternative way of discrminating one striate cell type from another but is a simpler, faster, and more reliable way than the use of a stationary flashing bar.

Alternative complex cell classifications. On the basis of their receptive-field characteristics, their distribution in terms of cortical layers, and the effect of iontophoretically applied bicuculline on their direction selectivity, Sillito (339) described three types of complex cell in the cat striate cortex: types 1, 2, and 3, respectively. The type 1 complex cell that was found mainly in cortical layer 3 probably corresponds to the B-cell described in *Intermediate-type cells,* p. 386, whereas the hypercomplex cell that Sillito and Versiani (340) observed as occurring in cortical layers 2 and 3 appears to be equivalent to a B_H-cell. Direction selectivity in simple and type 1 complex cells appears

FIG. 25. *A*: optimal stimulus length plotted as function of end-zone inhibition. *a*, Simple cell with the largest response variability shown in Fig. 24*B*; *b*, hypercomplex I cell in Fig. 24*A*. With the exception of cell *c*, all cells classified as hypercomplex had end-zone inhibition of about 40% or more. *B*: distribution of various levels of end-zone inhibition. [From Kato, Bishop, and Orban (195).]

to depend upon a GABA-mediated postsynaptic inhibitory input, since the selectivity is either greatly reduced or eliminated locally by the iontophoretic application of the GABA antagonist bicuculline (339). On the other hand, the direction selectivity of hypercomplex cells in layers 2 and 3 was unaffected by bicuculline (339).

Sillito (339) made the distinction between complex cell types 2 and 3 largely because the type 3 cell had a rather higher resting discharge (8–30 impulses/s) that was suppressed by stimuli moving in the nonpreferred direction. As well as having a lower resting discharge (2–20 impulses/s), the type 2 complex cell generally gave a small, excitatory response to stimuli moving in the nonpreferred direction. The great majority of the type 3 cells could be classified as hypercomplex on the grounds of a preference for stimulus length and most were recorded in layer 5. The type 2 complex cell was found in both the superficial layers of the cortex and layer 5, with the majority in layer 5. There seems little doubt that the complex cells of Kato, Bishop, and Orban (195) and the C-cells of Henry et al. (158) are the same as Sillito's type 2 complex cell (339). The type 3 complex cell is probably equivalent to the completely direction-selective hypercomplex II cell (37) and possibly also the C_H-cell (158). The observation that a driven background discharge in completely directional hypercomplex II cells is suppressed by stimulus movement in the nonpreferred direction (37) is in keeping with a similar block in type 3 complex cells when an artificially high resting discharge is produced by the iontophoretic application of D,L-homocysteic acid (339a).

Sillito (339) has suggested that type 3 complex cells are to be equated with the layer 5 corticotectal cells described by Palmer and Rosenquist (285). There are, however, strong arguments for believing that the Palmer and Rosenquist corticotectal cells are mostly type 2 complex cells that are not completely direction selective (37).

Gilbert (124) distinguished two types of complex cell, standard and special. As mentioned above the majority of cells in the standard complex category would probably be classified by both Kato, Bishop, and Orban (195) and Henry et al. (158) as belonging to the simple family (S and S_H). One of the main features distinguishing Gilbert's cell types concerns the length of the receptive-field discharge region. The length of this region was determined by testing the cell's response to the movement of a short, light bar centered at different positions along the axis of the optimal stimulus orientation. Both simple and standard complex cells showed spatial summation along the line of the optimal orientation up to the full length of the discharge region. In other words, the length of the receptive field corresponded to that of the shortest slit that could elicit the maximal response. Special complex cells had the general attributes that characterize complex cells but, in addition, they had the salient property that their response to a moving bar increased only over a narrow range of bar lengths, becoming maximal for bars that were much shorter than the length of the discharge region. These units continued to fire to a short moving slit wherever it was centered along the orientation axis, provided it was within the responsive portion of the field. Orban, Kato, and Bishop (280) have argued that this property of special complex cells may be found in hypercomplex I cells and, much more commonly, in hypercomplex II cells, and is to be attributed to a spatial overlap between discharge region excitation and end-zone inhibition. Particularly in hypercomplex II cells, the length summation required for excitation is much less than that required to produce an inhibitory effect. On this view Gilbert's special complex cell is probably equivalent to the hypercomplex II cell (280, 281). There are, however, additional differences between Gilbert's classifications and those of Orban, Kato, and Bishop (280) and of Henry et al. (158).

PROPERTIES OF CELL TYPES IN CAT STRIATE CORTEX. Figure 26 compares the responses of two cells, one in the simple family (A) and the other in the complex (B), to light and dark bars, both stationary (Aa,b and Ba) and moving (Ac,d and Bb), as well as to moving light and dark edges (Ae and Bc). The cell in column A was a hypercomplex I cell recorded in lamina 4 and the cell in column B a complex cell recorded in lamina 5 farther down along the same electrode penetration. The responses to the light bar (open histograms) and to the dark bar (filled histograms) were recorded separately and only subsequently combined, the regions common to both responses being dotted. The responses for each cell are in accurate vertical alignment after correcting for the response latency for the moving stimuli.

In response to stationary stimuli the cell in Figure 26A shows two main, equally responsive (but antagonistic) subregions positioned side by side in the center, with the possible addition of very weak subregions located farther out on either side of the central pair, the four subregions making an off/on/off/on sequence. The presence of one, and possibly the other, weak subregion is confirmed by the responses to moving light and dark bars. For a cell to show linearity of spatial summation, the response to a moving edge should approximate the integral of the response to movement of the corresponding bar. Thus the response to an edge should grow and reach its peak after passing over most of the region that responds to the bar and only begin to decline as it enters the next antagonistic subregion. In keeping with these concepts, the peaks of the responses to the two edges in Figure 26A (part e) lie each near the junction between antagonistic bar responses. Furthermore, provided the responses to moving bars are reasonably strong, the number of response regions to an edge is, in general, one less than the number responding to a bar.

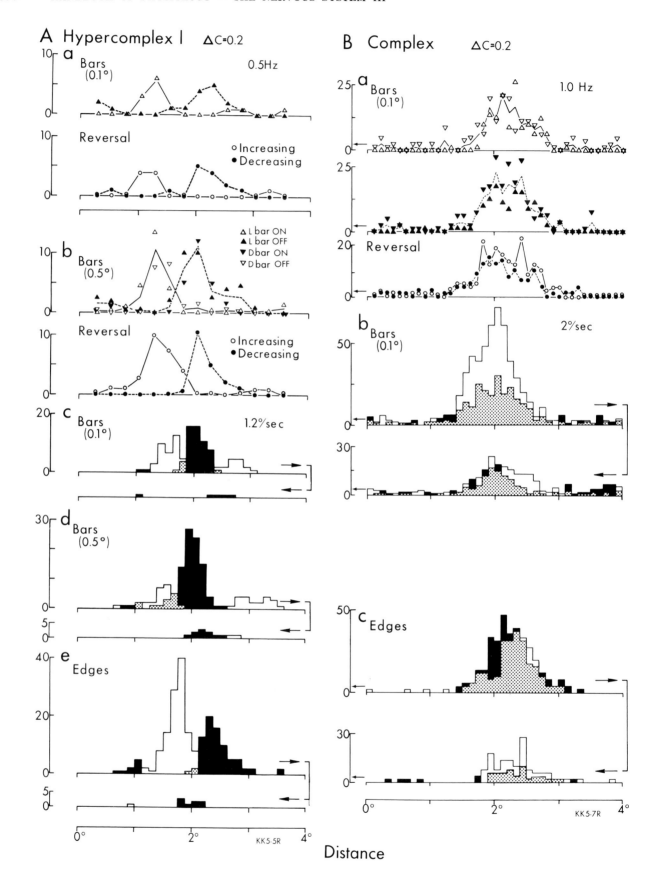

Distance

The complex cell (Fig. 26B) responded transiently to stimulus onset, offset, and reversal at all positions across the receptive field. A similarly complete overlap is to be seen in response to moving light and dark bars and edges. There was no consistent evidence of receptive-field subregions responding preferentially to one rather than another type of stationary or moving stimulus.

Detailed quantitative information is available concerning the properties of simple and complex cells (cf. particularly refs. 31, 32, 104, 124, 169, 171, 195, 213, 215, 232, 288, 306, 339, 396) but not as yet in relation to B-cells (214). Many of the receptive-field properties change with visual-field eccentricity (396). Cells have larger receptive fields, less orientation selectivity, and higher preferred-stimulus speeds with increasing eccentricity, although these changes are more pronounced for complex than for simple cells. The numerical values given in the following account refer to cells with receptive fields within about 5° of the center of gaze.

Spontaneous activity. The level of spontaneous activity of cells in the simple family (mean 0.4 spikes/s, range 0–3) is much the same in all layers in the striate cortex. By contrast, cells in the complex family located deep to layer 4 have a higher resting discharge (mean 12 spikes/s, range 4–23) than those superficial to that layer (mean 1.7 spikes/s, range 0–5).

Orientation specificity (62, 146, 157, 232, 270, 307). The general shape of the orientation-response curves (orientation tuning curves) is the same for both simple and complex cells, and the curves for individual cells are the same whether moving or stationary bar stimuli are used. The curves are bell shaped (Fig. 27) and are usually slightly asymmetrical with respect to the optimal orientation. The half-widths at half-height of the tuning curves for simple cells have a mean value of 17° (range 7°–33°) while that for complex cells is 28° (range 9°–54°). Despite their sensitivity to stimulus length, hypercomplex I cells are almost as sharply tuned as simple cells and similarly for hypercomplex II cells and complex cells. For cells in the simple family the orientation tuning curves progressively sharpen as stimulus lengthens (Fig. 24C), whereas for cells in the complex family the tuning curves seem relatively unaffected by changes in stimulus length. The optimal orientation varies from cell to cell, covering the full range of orientations fairly uniformly, with possibly a

slight preference for the vertical and the horizontal. The optimal orientations for the two eyes of binocularly activated single cells vary widely from cell to cell over a range of nearly ± 20°, but the two curves for any given cell are always closely matched for sharpness (Fig. 27).

Ocular dominance. Cells in the simple family tend to be dominated by one eye or the other with relatively few cells driven equally by the two eyes. By contrast the tendency is for B-cells and complex cells to be equally discharged from both eyes. The simple cells that are discharged by only one eye or the other are, however, only apparently monocular, since they are virtually all significantly influenced by the nondominant eye (196).

Direction selectivity (37, 104a, 132, 133, 147, 339). The selectivity for the direction of stimulus motion can be expressed as a percentage calculated from the response ratio: (preferred minus nonpreferred)/preferred. In response to a narrow light bar many cells in the simple family are completely direction selective and more than 80% have a response in the preferred direction that is greater than twice that in the nonpreferred direction (>50% direction selective). Simple family cells that respond equally in the two directions are rarely encountered. Hypercomplex II cells have a distribution of the degree of direction selectivity similar to that of simple cells, more than half of the cells being completely (100%) direction selective. The completely direction-selective hypercomplex II cells have a high level of spontaneous firing that is inhibited by stimulus motion in the nonpreferred direction. By contrast, direction selectivity in complex cells is fairly evenly distributed: as many cells responding equally in both directions as cells responding to only one direction and not the other. The properties and mechanism of direction selectivity in both simple and complex cells are discussed in detail by Goodwin and Henry (132) and Bishop and Goodwin and others (37, 133). Unlike simple cells, complex cells, particularly those deep to layer 4, are responsive to randomly textured "visual noise" and in many cases the preferred directions for motion of noise and of an optimally oriented bar stimulus are dissimilar (147).

Inhibitory sidebands (32, 37, 195, 337, 396). Although simple and hypercomplex I cells have little or no spontaneous activity, a maintained discharge can be produced by various forms of repetitive stimulation.

FIG. 26. Comparison of responses of a hypercomplex I cell (A) and a complex cell (B) to light and dark bars, both stationary flashing (Aa, Ab, Ba) and moving (Ac, Ad, Bb), as well as to moving light and dark edges (Ae, Bc). Stationary bars (0.1° or 0.5° wide) were flashed at indicated frequencies either on or off (*filled* and *open triangles*) or reversed in contrast (*filled* and *open circles*), change in contrast being the same in each case (Δc = 0.2). Keys to symbols same for both cells. Hypercomplex I cell has an antisymmetrical response profile. Responses to light bar (*open histograms*) and to dark bar (*filled histograms*) were recorded separately and only subsequently combined, regions common to both responses being *dotted.* Responses for each cell in accurate vertical alignment after correcting for response latency for moving stimuli. [From Kulikowski, Bishop, and Kato (215).]

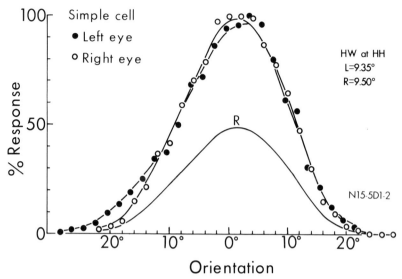

FIG. 27. Monocular stimulus orientation tuning curves for each of the two eyes from a binocular simple cell in striate cortex of cat. Curve (R) for right eye has been normalized to same height as the curve for left eye. The abscissa zero is arbitrarily located so that curves are approximately symmetrical about it. HW at HH: half-width at half-height of tuning curves of left (L) and right (R) eye. [From Bishop (27a).]

When this is done, movement of a light bar over the receptive fields of these cells displays regions of inhibition to one or, more frequently, to both sides of the discharge region in the preferred direction of stimulus motion. In addition B-cells nearly always show evidence of side-band inhibition though, more commonly than in simple cells, on only one side of the discharge region (R. M. Camarda, E. Peterhans, and P. O. Bishop, unpublished observations). By contrast, complex and hypercomplex II cells rarely, if ever, show any clear evidence of side-band inhibition comparable to that seen in simple cells. The exact mechanism underlying the inhibition has yet to be determined. Undoubtedly a major component in the inhibition is the antagonistic action of an off area to either side of a centrally located on area (and vice versa for a moving dark bar), but there appears to be a more widespread but purely inhibitory component as well.

LAMINAR DISTRIBUTION OF CELL TYPES IN CAT STRIATE CORTEX. A number of studies have been made of the laminar distribution of the different cell types in the cat striate cortex (124, 158, 169, 195, 201, 232, 339). It is difficult to make a comparison between these reports, principally because of the different schemes that have been used for the classification of the cells but also because of differences in the interpretation of laminar boundaries. Certain trends are, however, clearly evident, particularly when cells located near the boundaries of the layers are excluded from consideration. The following brief outline concerns only orientation-sensitive cells. It uses a cell classification along the lines of Henry et al. (158) and Kulikowski, Bishop, and Kato (215) and calls upon unpublished data (R. M. Camarda, E. Peterhans, and P. O. Bishop,

unpublished observations) as well as those available in the literature and cited at the beginning of this subsection. All cell types are to be found in laminae 2 + 3, with hypercomplex I, simple, B-cells, and the remaining cell types in the complex family encountered in that order of decreasing frequency. The cells in lamina 4 are virtually confined to the simple family, with simple and hypercomplex I cells about equally represented. By contrast, only cells in the complex family are encountered in layer 5, the most common being B-cells and hypercomplex II cells. In lamina 6 the great majority are simple cells with an occasional hypercomplex I and B-cell. Thus cells in the simple family are much more widely distributed than those in the complex family. Simple family cells are found in laminae 2, 3, 4, and 6, whereas cells in the complex family are largely confined to layers 3 and 5.

NEURAL CIRCUITS IN CAT STRIATE CORTEX. Although details are slowly becoming available concerning the neural circuits intrinsic to the striate cortex (48–50, 126, 158, 201, 239, 299, 344, 373, 374, 388, 389) a proper understanding of the neural mechanisms in the cortex is still remote. The different classification schemes that are used with respect to the morphological and to the functional cell types to be found in the cortex and among their geniculocortical afferents, the differing criteria used for classifying cell types with the same name, and the variety of cortical lamination schemes, all make it difficult to correlate data coming from different laboratories. A number of generalities, however, seem to be emerging. Thalamocortical axons synapse in layer 4 with pyramidal cells whose somata occur in layers 3 to 6 inclusive, with layer 4 spiny stellate cells and with several types of layer 4 nonspiny or sparsely spined stellate cells. White (389) has concluded that every cortical neuron type with a dendrite in layer 4 receives some portion of its input directly from the thalamus. It might then be supposed that thalamocortical projections to layers 1 and 6 also terminate on dendrites irrespective of their cell type of origin. If so, then neurons throughout the full thickness of the neocortex receive input from the thalamus. All thalamocortical afferents are probably excitatory to their target cells and inhibition is probably always di- or polysynaptic (239, 374, 388). Spiny stellate cells are thought to be excitatory and aspinous, and sparsely spinous stellates inhibitory (299).

It appears that all physiologically identified cortical cell types can be mono-, di-, or polysynaptically activated from the thalamus (48–50). As expected, cells with latencies to electrical stimulation of the afferent pathway indicative of a monosynaptic drive occur in the region of termination of LGNd axons (i.e., in laminae 6, 4, and the 3/4 border) while cells with latencies suggestive of an indirect activation congregate in laminae 2, 3, and 5. The morphological evidence of a widespread thalamic input to cells whose somata lie outside the laminae of termination of LGNd axons indicates that these cells may be directly influenced from the thalamus though not necessarily monosynaptically driven, at least when tested by electrical stimulation of the afferent pathway. Some cells of both simple and complex type can be driven by electrical stimulation of either fast or slowly conducting axons. However, nearly all complex and B-cells receive their input from brisk-transient (Y) LGNd cells. Hypercomplex I cells with marked end-zone inhibition (S_H) and most nonoriented cells are driven from brisk-sustained (X) LGNd cells, whereas the remaining cells in the simple family are driven in almost equal numbers by the two kinds of afferent cells. It seems likely, both from their location in the striate cortex and from the direct evidence of Lee et al. (221), that simple cells are the primary destinations of both brisk-transient and brisk-sustained afferent cells. However, it has not so far been possible to discriminate two groups of simple cells that might reflect the distinctive properties of the two kinds of afferent cells. It is still not possible to make any general correlations between morphological and functional cell types in the striate cortex, but complex cells are probably nearly always pyramidal, whereas simple cells can be either stellate or pyramidal (126).

SPATIAL FREQUENCY ANALYSIS. Over the past 15 years or so, there have developed two different approaches to an understanding of the operation of the visual system. One approach, based on the pioneering work of Lettvin et al. (224) and Hubel and Wiesel (169), has tended to regard the visual cortex as concerned with the extraction of certain elementary features from the visual scene. This approach has concentrated attention on the spatial organization of cortical cell receptive fields, and lines and edges have come to be regarded as the elementary features extracted by simple cells. The descriptions of the receptive-field characteristics and response properties of cortical neurons given in this chapter have been largely couched in these terms. The alternative approach is based on the application of spatial frequency (Fourier) methods (105) leading to the idea that the visual cortex operates as a spatial frequency analyzer, representing visual patterns in terms of their Fourier components (61, 76, 127, 249, 293). The idea of the visual cortex as a spatial frequency analyzer has yet to be clearly formulated in terms of neural structure and function (301, 330, 332) and further consideration of the concept lies beyond the scope of this chapter. It was this notion, however, that led to the introduction of sinusoidal grating stimuli and directed the attention of the early investigators, rather exclusively, toward defining the spatial frequency selectivity of cortical cells rather than toward the use of the techniques of Fourier analysis as a way of studying the operational characteristics of these cells. In the latter regard, it is only recently that attempts have been made to bring the two approaches together by examining the relationship between a cell's spatial frequency selectivity and its response profiles to line and edge stimuli (10, 212, 213, 266).

The only requirement that must be satisfied, or approximately satisfied, before Fourier analysis can be applied is linear summation over the cell's receptive field. The tests for linearity of spatial summation devised by Enroth-Cugell and Robson (105) for retinal ganglion cells have also been applied to cortical cells (10, 213, 266, 267). To drifting sinusoidal gratings, cells in the simple family give a response that is modulated in synchrony with the passage of the bars of the grating across their receptive fields and the response continues to be modulated at the highest spatial frequencies to which the cells respond (Fig. 28A). To a stationary flashing sinusoidal grating placed at different phase positions across their receptive fields these cells also respond with a complete sinusoidal profile, the on-responses forming one half-period and the off-responses the other half-period (Fig. 28B). There are two null phases, 180° apart, at which the grating elicits no response, and this occurs whether the same change in contrast is achieved by turning the grating on and off (Fig. 28B, part a) or by using contrast reversal (Fig. 28B, part b). By these responses to sinusoidal gratings, the majority of simple cells indicate that they sum inputs from different parts of their receptive fields linearly. A minority of simple cells have significant nonlinearities of spatial summation, though not to a degree sufficient to warrant their exclusion from the simple family. By contrast Movshon et al. (267) have shown that complex cells in the cat's striate cortex exhibit gross nonlinearities when tested with sinusoidal grating stimuli. Their responses to moving gratings of all but the lowest spatial frequencies are usually dominated by a component that is not modulated by

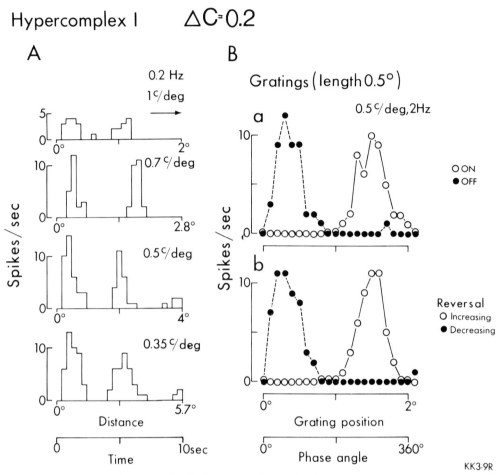

FIG. 28. *A*: histograms of average responses from a hypercomplex I cell in cat striate cortex to sinusoidal gratings of four different spatial frequencies drifting over receptive field at a constant rate (0.2 Hz) in preferred direction. Response is modulated in synchrony with passage of bars of grating up to highest spatial frequency to which cell responds. *B*: responses from same cell as in *A* to a stationary flashing sinusoidal grating (0.5 cycles/deg) placed at different phase positions across receptive field. Grating was flashed at 2 Hz either on and off (*a*) at each position or reversed in contrast (*b*), the change in contrast being the same in each case (ΔC = 0.2). In both cases there are two null phases, 180° apart, at which the grating elicits no response. [From Kulikowski and Bishop (213).]

the passage of the bars of the grating across the receptive field. Furthermore they give responses to temporally modulated stationary gratings that vary little in amplitude or wave form as the spatial phase of the grating is varied.

Spatial frequency selectivity (10, 186, 213, 249, 268). Spatial frequency tuning curves can be prepared in various ways. The selectivity of the cells can be measured with sinusoidal gratings drifting either at a constant velocity or at a constant temporal frequency and expressed in terms of either response amplitude or contrast sensitivity. The temporal frequency of a grating refers to its rate of movement expressed as the number of cycles of the grating that pass a given point in one second. Contrast sensitivity is the inverse of the contrast of the grating that just elicits a detectable response. When an arbitrary stimulus is presented to the receptive field of a cell, it passes over the field with all its spatial frequency components moving at the

same velocity. Hence a constant-velocity tuning curve is probably a more fundamental indication of the cell's spatial filtering properties than a constant-temporal-frequency tuning curve. In practice, however, both methods of stimulation and both measures of response give very similar tuning curves in all cases. The bandwidth of the tuning curve (full breadth at half-maximal amplitude) is usually given by the ratio of the upper and lower spatial frequencies either at half-sensitivity or half-response amplitude expressed in octaves. For one octave the ratio is 2:1 (decimal log unit 0.3). For simple cells with receptive fields within 5° of the area centralis the mean optimal spatial frequency is about 0.9 cycles/deg (range 0.3–2.5) and the mean bandwidth is about 1.45 octaves (range 0.9–2.0). Simple and complex cells in area 17 do not differ in their distributions of preferred spatial frequency, although complex cells are, on the average, slightly less selective for spatial frequencies than simple cells (268).

Fourier transformations. If simple cells have linear spatial summation, the inverse Fourier transform of the spatial frequency tuning curve should predict the spatial response (receptive-field profile). Several such comparisons have been made (10, 266), though in only one series (212, 213) were both the tuning curves and the response profiles obtained with moving stimuli. To light and dark bars moving at the optimal velocity, the response profiles of most simple cells can be classified as either spatially symmetrical (with a dominant central response flanked by antagonistic responses) or antisymmetrical (with two equal, or nearly equal, antagonistic responses and smaller antagonistic responses on each side). Figure 29 illustrates the response profiles (histograms) to moving bars (a) and edges (b) recorded from three simple cells (A, B, and C), the profiles above and below the base lines being to light and dark bars, respectively, and similarly for

the responses to edges. The bars, 0.1° wide, are regarded as approximating a line stimulus. The smooth curves superimposed on the response histograms to the moving bars are the inverse Fourier transforms of the respective spatial frequency (contrast sensitivity) tuning curves (Ac, Bc, and Cc). The tuning curves were obtained with drifting sinusoidal gratings and, in each case, contrast sensitivity for the optimal spatial frequency has been normalized to one. The smooth curves superimposed on the response histograms to edges are integrals of the predicted responses to bars. The bar responses from cell A are well fitted by an antisymmetrical profile (sinusoidal Fourier transform), while those of cells B and C, recorded within 0.1 mm of one another along the same electrode track, are equally well fitted by symmetrical and antisymmetrical profiles, respectively.

Good quantitative agreement is achieved when the

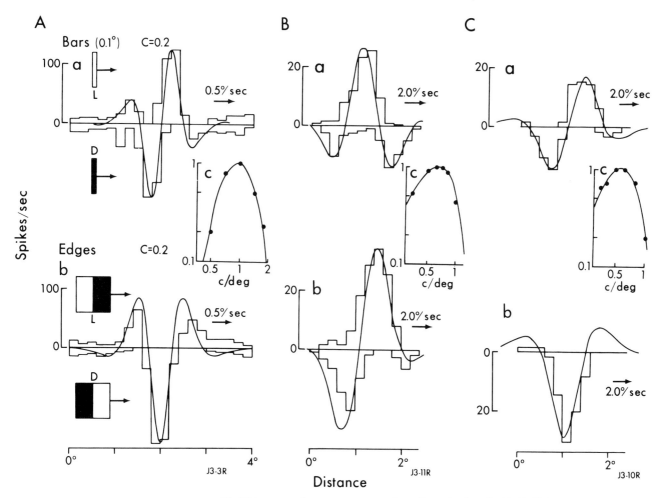

FIG. 29. Histograms of average responses from three simple cells (*A, B, C*) in cat striate cortex to moving bars (*a*) and edges (*b*) showing predictability of these responses from inverse Fourier transformation (*continuous lines*) of respective contrast sensitivity tuning curves (*c*). Shapes of these tuning curves were chosen to produce best fit to data points, thereby testing predictability of responses to bars and edges (essential for proper classification of simple cells). However, fitted tuning curves are not greatly different from ideal Gaussian functions for tuning curves with medium and narrow bandwidths (<1.5 octaves). Cell *A* is fitted best by an antisymmetrical profile (sinusoidal Fourier transform), whereas cells *B* and *C* are a pair fitted with symmetrical and antisymmetrical profiles, respectively. Contrast (C) = 0.2. [From Kulikowski and Bishop (212).]

comparisons are between tuning curves and response profiles obtained with moving stimuli in both cases, and a somewhat reduced agreement when the response profile is to a stationary flashing bar (213). Kulikowski and Bishop (213) also found reasonable agreement between spatial frequency tuning curves recorded experimentally and those predicted by the Fourier transform of the response profiles to moving and stationary stimuli. Thus the responses to lines by cells with symmetrical and antisymmetrical receptive fields represent the respective cosine and sine components of the inverse Fourier transform of the spatial frequency tuning curves. Kulikowski and King-Smith (216) made the same observation when evaluating line and edge detectors in psychophysical experiments. For simple cells operating within their linear range, the descriptions of the responses to lines and edges are mathematically equivalent to those expressed in terms of sinusoidal gratings. Spatial summation in simple cells is, however, linear only over a restricted range of stimuli reasonably close to optimal. Responses to nonoptimal stimulus orientations and nonpreferred directions and velocities of stimulus movement are not predicted by linear analysis. Finally, the success of

Fourier analysis argues neither for nor against the concept of the visual cortex as a Fourier analyzer.

FUNCTIONAL ARCHITECTURE OF CAT STRIATE CORTEX. *Spatial organization of receptive-field position.* The visual field is mapped onto the striate cortex with the preservation of topological order, but the representation does not have a continuous nonoverlapping one-to-one correspondence with the visual field. As with the LGNd [see *Projection subunit ("column")*, p. 361] there is a local monocular receptive-field position scatter superimposed on the progressive topological representation. Figure 30 shows plots of the contralateral receptive-field positions for cells recorded along the course of long, oblique microelectrode penetrations through area 17 postlateral gyrus. In Figure 30C, the path of the electrode used for recording the cells in Figure 30A and B is shown passing anteroposteriorly through successive coronal sections of the postlateral gyrus. The outlines (Fig. 30A) and locations of the centers (Fig. 30B) of the receptive fields are shown in relation to the area centralis (a.c.) in numbered sequence (from 1 to 45) as the cells were recorded. For small displacements of the electrode, less than about

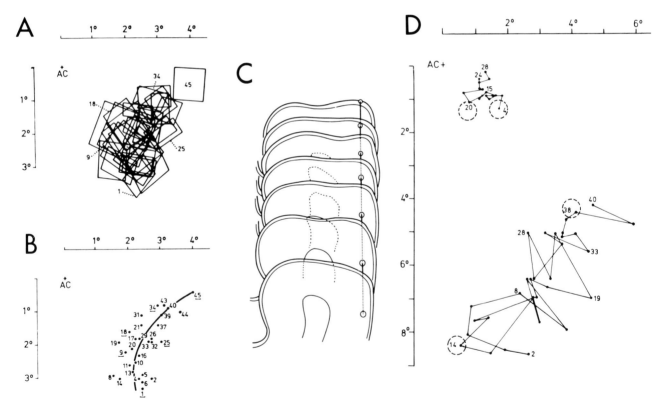

FIG. 30. Tangential microelectrode penetrations through left postlateral gyrus in cat. *A, B, C* from one experiment; *D* from another. Receptive fields (*A*) and receptive-field centers (*B*) in lower right hemifield are from cells recorded along microelectrode track shown in coronal histological sections through postlateral gyrus (*C*). *Line* in *B*, mean receptive-field position (drawn by hand); AC, projection of area centralis. *D*: centers of two series of receptive fields, one close to area centralis, the other farther away, recorded from cells along two further tangential electrode penetrations. [Adapted by Bishop (28) from Albus (4).]

200 μm, the receptive fields are scattered randomly about a mean position and it is only with longer tangential penetrations that a change in mean receptive-field position becomes apparent. The full length of the electrode penetration in Figure 30C was 3 mm and this produced a change in mean receptive-field position (full line in Fig. 30B) of the order of 3°–4°, directed mainly upward and laterally in the visual field. Two further electrode penetrations are shown in Figure 30D, giving two clusters of receptive fields, one close to the area centralis and the other farther away. By confining his analysis to cells recorded within 100 μm of one another, Albus (4) found that, for receptive fields with eccentricities less than 1.5° from the area centralis, the scatter about the mean receptive-field position had a standard deviation of 0.35°.

Creutzfeldt et al. (79) also obtained an estimate of the receptive-field position scatter by making a series of vertical electrode penetrations each as nearly parallel to the radial fiber bundles as possible. For recording sites up to about 5° eccentric, they found that the scatter about the mean position during a single electrode penetration had a standard deviation of 0.91° with maximum values about ±2°. Besides being independent of eye dominance, the magnitude of the scatter is independent of recording depth in the cortex, being the same for the various cell layers in the cortex. The magnitude of the scatter appears to increase continuously with eccentricity: there are no locations in the cortex where there is little or no scatter.

Bishop (28) has linked the monocular receptive-field position scatter described above with the position disparities for the two receptive fields of binocularly activated striate neurons. Receptive-field position disparity provides the basis of a neural mechanism for binocular depth discrimination (29).

Position subunit in cortex. By analogy with the LGNd projection subunit [see *Projection subunit ("column")*, p. 361] the term *position subunit* [Bishop (28); cf. spatial subunit of Albus ref. 4] refers to the linear tangential extent of the cortical volume that contains all the cells with a common receptive-field position. The width of a position subunit at a given eccentricity is given by the product of the total scatter of the receptive fields of cells recorded along a single vertical electrode penetration at that eccentricity and the magnification factor expressed in terms of millimeters of cortex per degree of visual field (82). Receptive-field scatter and magnification factor are inversely related (with increasing eccentricity, receptive-field scatter increases and magnification factor decreases), so that the width of the position subunit tends to remain constant (4, 178). By using the values given above for the receptive-field scatter at central (SD 0.35°) and paracentral (SD 0.91°) regions, and by taking the magnification factors for the two locations as 1.7 and 0.66 mm/deg (4), the width of the position subunit for the two regions is about the same, namely 2.4 mm.

Like the LGNd, the striate cortex can also be considered as consisting of a large series of overlapping subunits with the members of each population having a common receptive-field position. As with the "partially shifted reciprocal overlap" concept of Lorente de Nó (243), the subunits are not spatially discrete but show a continuous distribution from one subunit to the next, each extensively interpenetrating its neighbors and only partially shifted with respect to them.

Spatial organization of optimal stimulus orientation. Within the striate cortex, the spatial organization of the preferred stimulus orientations of neurons has much in common with that of their receptive-field positions discussed above. Electrode penetrations tangential to the cell layers reveal a surprisingly ordered and systematic spatial organization of preferred orientations that change continuously with horizontal position but show occasional sharp discontinuities (5, 177). Superimposed on this progressive change in optimal orientation there is, however, in the cat at least, a considerable variability that is difficult to reconcile with a system of discrete orientation columns (see *Orientation "columns,"* p. 398).

Using long oblique electrode penetrations crossing the cortical layers in a nearly tangential fashion, Albus (5) gathered a series of 89 instances in which he recorded from two cells simultaneously with the same electrode. He found differences in preferred orientation for the two cells ranging up to 30° or more. When these observations are corrected for the incyclorotation of the eyes due to anesthesia and paralysis of the extraocular muscles under the conditions of Albus' experiments, the orientation differences would still have been 20° or more (cf. Bishop, ref. 28). Estimates of the optimal stimulus orientation scatter at a single locus in the cortex have been obtained by Lee et al. (220) by making a series of vertical electrode penetrations along the line of the radial fiber bundles coupled with suitable controls for eye drift. For five penetrations in which the electrode angle was histologically demonstrated to be no more than 5° from the line of the fiber bundles, and along each of which eight or more cells were analyzed, the standard deviation of the neuronal optimal orientation ranged between ±8.5° and ±21.2°. Thus the range of optimal stimulus orientations to be expected in depth at a single cortical locus would be at least ±20°. The variability appears to be independent cell classification, ocular dominance, and depth within the cortex, occurring equally in all cell layers.

As with receptive-field position scatter, Bishop (28) has also linked the optimal orientation scatter described above with the orientation disparities between the two receptive fields of binocularly activated striate neurons and has discussed the role in binocular vision of the selectivities of these cells for differing orientation disparities [cf. Nelson, Kato, and Bishop (270)].

Orientation subunit. By analogy with the position

subunit, but differing from the definition proposed by Albus (5), an orientation subunit is here defined as the linear tangential extent of the cortical volume that contains all the cells having the same preferred orientation (cf. Bishop, ref. 28). Since the full range of preferred orientations is repeatedly represented over the whole striate cortex, there will be a great many subunits having the same preferred orientation. The width of an orientation subunit is given by the product of the orientation factor and the total scatter of the preferred orientations at a given cortical locus. The orientation factor is defined as the rate of change of preferred orientation parallel to the cortical surface and expressed in terms of millimeters of cortex per 180° change in preferred orientation. Albus (5) found that a cortical distance of 900 μm was needed to encompass a full 180° change in preferred orientation. Taking the orientation scatter as 20° (±10° of the mean preferred orientation), the width of the orientation subunit is 100 μm, $\frac{1}{24}$ the width of a position subunit.

Columnar organization. The view is now widely current that the basic unit of operation in the neocortex is a vertically arranged group of cells—the minicolumn of Mountcastle (265)—heavily interconnected in the vertical axis running across the cortical layers and sparsely connected horizontally (264, 265). This columnar concept was first applied to the visual cortex by Hubel and Wiesel (169, 170) and has subsequently been extensively developed by them (179). In the cat striate cortex, along vertical microelectrode penetrations parallel to the radial fiber bundles and perpendicular to the cortical laminae, Hubel and Wiesel (169, 170) observed that successively recorded cells all had very similar preferred stimulus orientations. These and subsequent recordings (172) also indicated that besides being grouped according to preferred stimulus orientation, cells in the striate cortex are grouped by ocular dominance into regions of ipsilateral, contralateral, and mixed dominance. Hubel and Wiesel (170, 173) put forward the idea that the visual cortex is subdivided into at least two independent systems of discrete regions or columns extending vertically from surface to white matter. In one system the columns contain cells with a common preferred stimulus orientation whereas, in the other system, the cells are aggregated into columns according to eye preference, the boundaries of the two systems being apparently independent of one another. Hubel and Wiesel (173) used the term *column* to refer to a "discrete aggregation of cells, each aggregation being separated from its neighbours by vertical walls that intersect the surface (or a given layer) in a mosaic."

Later observations led Hubel and Wiesel (177) to replace the concept of columns by one of thin parallel slabs. However, they failed to observe any random variations in the preferred orientations of neighboring cells and, while recognizing the possibility that orientation may vary continuously with horizontal position, they have, nevertheless, continued to favor the idea of orientation columns as discrete aggregates of cells, each having the form of a slab with walls perpendicular to the surface and with the cells in it all having virtually the same preferred orientation (179). They consider that the slabs are about 50 μm thick and that, in moving from one slab to the next, a horizontally directed electrode will record a stepwise shift in the preferred orientation of the cells of about 10°. The anatomical evidence for orientation columns, so far available only for the monkey, is discussed next.

Orientation "columns". The weight of evidence is against the idea of orientation slabs as discrete entities. On the contrary, the indication is that there is a steady drift or progression in the preferred orientation with movement through the cortex and, superimposed on the drift, a random variation in the orientations of neighboring cells. Thus the spatial organization of preferred orientations resembles the partially shifted reciprocal overlap that characterizes the representation of spatial position in the cortex. There is, however, a basic difference between the representations of spatial position and preferred orientation (28). In keeping with the concept of a projection line in the LGNd (see VISUAL-FIELD PROJECTION INTO DORSAL LGN, p. 361), the central axis of a position subunit can be regarded as the representation in the cortex of a given visual direction or position in the visual field. In this sense each direction in the visual field has only a single representation in the striate cortex, but a given preferred orientation is rerepresented over and over again through the cortex. The progressive change in preferred orientation provides each cortical subregion with a full range of orientations. However, it is not physically possible to sustain a continuously progressive change in preferred orientations in all directions horizontally through the cortex. There must be frequent local modifications of this pattern so that small subregions having the same mean preferred orientation come to lie side by side or form extended twisting strips. Occasionally also there are abrupt changes in the mean preferred orientation. In all probability the orientation slabs seen in tangential sections as swirling stripes with many bifurcations and blind endings (182) represent the closest approximation that it is possible for the cortex to achieve to an organization whereby preferred orientation changes progressively in all directions parallel to the surface (28).

The ideas concerning the spatial organization of the preferred orientation are illustrated in Figure 31. Figure 31*A* is a scale diagram of part of the postlateral gyrus in the cat showing hypothetical and actual cell positions projected onto the cortical surface and identified there by short lines that also indicate each cell's preferred orientation. The locations of 43 cells recorded along three anteroposteriorly directed electrode tracks in the one preparation have been indicated in the figure by placing filled circles on the particular orientation lines. The electrode tracks are

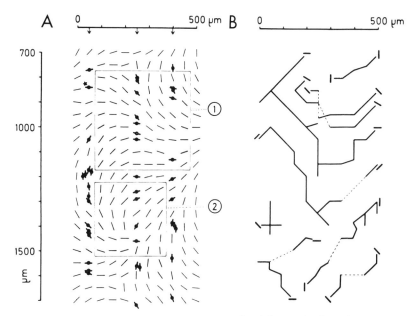

FIG. 31. Spatial organization of orientation domain. *A*: plan view of an extended surface of postlateral gyrus in cat. Striate cells were recorded along three tangential electrode tracks indicated by *arrows* from the scale at *top*. The 43 cell positions (*filled circles*) are projected onto surface and their preferred stimulus orientation in each case indicated by a *line*. Area (orientation matrix) selected is 1 mm long in anteroposterior direction and 0.5 mm wide in mediolateral direction. Gaps between experimentally recorded cells have been filled in with hypothetical neurons located at regular spacings of 50 μm, each preferred orientation being set 10° different from that of preceding cell. The interpolation procedure started at the second experimentally recorded neuron (*star*) and proceeded always toward next experimentally recorded cell from left to right and from top to bottom. Squares labeled ① and ② are arbitrarily selected regions, one with a side length of 400 μm, the other of 300 μm, in which full range, or nearly the full range, of preferred orientations is represented, although not to an equal degree. *B*: positions of cells having same preferred orientation and not more than 50 μm apart as shown in *A* are connected by continuous lines. Broken lines interconnect cells between 50 and 100 μm apart. Orientation represented by each isoorientation line is indicated at one or both ends of line. [From Albus (5).]

indicated by the arrows on the horizontal scale at the top of the figure. The gaps between the experimentally recorded cells have been filled in with hypothetical neurons interpolated at regular spacings of 50 μm, the preferred orientation of each cell being 10° different from that of the preceding cell. The interpolation procedure started at the second experimentally recorded neuron (marked by an asterisk) and proceeded always toward the next experimentally recorded cell from left to right and from up to down.

Although the above interpolations were made according to a fixed schedule, Albus (5) noted that, for much of the cortical surface, cells having a similar preferred orientation are grouped together in regions that appear in cross section as bands. The courses of these bands in Figure 31*A* are shown in Figure 31*B* by lines that connect orientations within ±5° of one another. These isoorientation lines spread across the cortical surface in various directions indicating the presence of bands of a finite length and of a width that does not exceed 100 μm. Furthermore, the continuous change in preferred orientation with horizontal position guarantees that as many orientations as possible are represented in a given area or volume. The two squares labeled with circled numbers 1 and 2 in Figure

31*A* are arbitrarily selected regions, one with a side-length of 400 μm and the other of 300 μm, in which the full range, or nearly the full range, of preferred orientations is represented, although not to an equal degree.

Ocular-dominance columns. The early observations by Hubel and Wiesel (172) that cells in the cat striate cortex responding preferentially to stimulation of one or the other eye are grouped together in columns that extend vertically through all the cortical layers has since been amply confirmed by anatomical (126, 229, 230, 335), physiological (6, 230), and combined anatomical and physiological (336) methods.

Although most cells in the cat striate cortex, even in layer 4, are binocularly driven, those that are nearly equally driven by the two eyes tend to occur in groups between cells strongly dominated by one eye or the other. Thus the eye preference of cells encountered along electrode penetrations tangential to layer 4 varies periodically. There is a gradual progressive shift in ocular dominance, with binocular cells interposed between patches of monocularly driven cells. The cortical distance over which the cells are dominated by input from the same eye is about 350 μm. The groupings are found in all cortical layers. Hence the spatial distribution of the afferents from the LGNd determines the eye preference not only of the cells in layer 4 but also, by virtue of secondary connections, of cells in the other layers that lie directly above and below them.

The physiological observations described have been shown to have an anatomical basis in a segregation of the geniculocortical afferents that is most readily evident in layer 4. Shatz et al. (335) used transneuronal transport of intraocularly injected radioactive labels to identify the set of thalamocortical afferents from the injected eye. When large portions of the fourth layer of ipsilateral area 17 were subsequently reconstructed from serial parasagittal sections, patches of label representing the injected eye were seen to be organized into a system of irregular bands roughly 0.5 mm wide separated by gaps of similar width but containing less label. Thus afferents, particularly those representing the contralateral eye, were present within the gaps, suggesting that the two eyes share a good deal of common territory even in the fourth layer. In surface view the columns have the shape of bands or patches about 500 μm wide that alternate with each other to form a rather constant overall pattern in area 17. The bands run mediolaterally and perpendicular to the anatomical 17-18 border. In the cortex representing both the central and the peripheral visual fields the combined size of a left and right eye band is about 1 mm.

In cats it has proved possible to reconstruct the entire terminal arborization of single geniculocortical afferents by anterograde transport of horseradish peroxidase, either bulk-injected into the optic radiation close to the visual cortex (110) or by direct injection into individual axons (126). Single afferent arborizations are broken up into clumps of terminal-bearing branches, about 0.5 mm across, separated by terminal-free gaps of about the same size. The clumps are regarded as corresponding to a number of ocular dominance columns for the same eye, the gaps, to the intervening columns for the other eye.

Shatz and Stryker (336) have used a combination of techniques in the one cat preparation to confirm the anatomical basis for the physiologically recorded ocular dominance columns. They injected one eye with radioactive label. Then, after allowing sufficient time for transneuronal transport, they used long microelectrode penetrations to mark with electrolytic lesions points of transition between groups of cells dominated by one eye and those dominated by the other. A good correspondence was found between the locations of cells dominated by the injected eye and the patches of radioactively labeled geniculocortical afferents.

In the kitten (229, 230), as in the monkey (180, 297), geniculocortical afferents serving the two eyes are initially intermingled within layer 4. Thereafter the adult pattern emerges by a progressive segregation of the two sets of afferents. Segregation begins during the third week of life in the kitten and does not attain its adult extent until after the sixth week. Hence the rearrangement of the axonal arbors in normal development takes place during the critical period when the visual cortex and its afferents are susceptible to the effects of monocular deprivation (391).

Functional architecture: summary. If one looks at reasonably wide areas of the striate cortex, the striking feature of the spatial organizations of receptive-field position, of preferred stimulus orientation, and of ocular dominance is their systematic and highly ordered nature. A block of tissue 1 mm square on the surface has within it all the cells needed to analyze the region of the visual field that projects to it, examining the region for light-dark contours of all orientations and with both eyes. The size of the spatial subunit ensures that the cells representing each of the visual directions that project to the 1-mm block are scattered throughout the whole of its extent. The full 180° range of preferred orientations is covered within a millimeter of cortex and, since each ocular dominance column is about 0.5 mm wide, this distance also takes care of the columns for both eyes. The regions of visual cortex subserving either a full range of orientations or both eyes are referred to by Hubel and Wiesel (178) as *hypercolumns.*

SERIAL AND PARALLEL PROCESSING IN VISUAL CORTEX. In their original hierarchical scheme Hubel and Wiesel (169, 171) proposed that both within area 17 and between areas 17 and 18 there might be a serially organized elaboration of visual information. Simple cells in area 17 were regarded as receiving the bulk of the direct input from the LGNd, relaying the information first within area 17 to complex cells and thence to the complex and hypercomplex cells in area 18. This serial scheme is no longer tenable, and in recent years considerable attention has been directed, particularly by Stone (352) and his colleagues, toward the idea of parallel processing of visual information. The separate relay in the LGNd of fast- and slowly conducting visual afferents (359) and the correlation of complex and simple cells in the striate cortex with fast- and slowly conducting axons, respectively, (162) led Stone (352) to suggest that simple and complex cells did not represent sequential stages in the visual process; rather they represent the separate and parallel terminations of the X- and Y-cell systems, respectively. There is much evidence in favor of this idea: the observation that simple and complex cells may both be activated monosynaptically from the LGNd has subsequently been confirmed (48, 344, 354) and some complex cells respond to stimuli that do not excite simple cells (147). Morphological and physiological evidence indicates that there are at least three separate pathways that convey different but presumably complementary aspects of information from the retina through the thalamus to the cortex, the three pathways ending separately in different regions in the cortical laminae. Most simple cells show linear spatial summation (10, 213, 266) and it is assumed that they get their excitatory input largely, if not entirely, from linear X-cells.

As Stone (352) observed, hierarchical and parallel processing mechanisms are not mutually exclusive, and it is likely that the cortex uses both parallel and serial mechanisms to process the input from the thalamus. Although cells in the striate cortex that are known to receive either an X- or a Y-input, but not both, may be at the beginning of hierarchical processing sequences for their respective inputs, these processing sequences must sooner or later, either in the striate cortex or elsewhere, combine to produce a complete representation of visual space. There is already much evidence of interaction between the parallel pathways not only in the LGNd but also after their arrival in the cortex. Morphological evidence suggests that neurons throughout the full thickness of the cortex receive an input directly from the thalamus (389), and physiological evidence indicates that no cell class receives exclusively a mono-, di-, or polysynaptic input from the thalamus (48). Furthermore many of the stimulus specificities shown by simple cells could result from an indirect inhibitory input from nonlinear Y-cells and it is possible that the minority of simple cells that show a measure of nonlinear spatial summation might have a significant Y-cell component in their input. Although the nonlinear spatial summation shown by complex cells could result from a purely nonlinear Y-cell input, it could also be the case that complex cells might combine the outputs either of linear X-cells or of simple cells (or of both) in a nonlinear manner (267).

The question of hierarchical and parallel mechanisms in the visual system has been the subject of two recent extensive reviews (223, 355).

Monkey Striate Cortex

Figure 32 shows the lateral and medial aspects of the left cerebral hemisphere of the macaque brain indicating the pattern of gyri and sulci related to the main visual areas. The striate cortex is partly exposed on the smooth outer surface (operculum, number 1 in Fig. 33C) of the occipital lobe and partly buried on the inner side of the hemisphere. It takes up almost the entire occipital lobe, being sharply separated from the rest of the hemisphere by the lunate sulcus and the inferior occipital sulcus. Although the lunate sulcus runs continuously from the lateral to the medial surface of the hemisphere, it is known laterally as the lunate sulcus and medially as the parietooccipital sulcus (Fig. 32). Figure 33 shows the exposed part of the striate cortex to be bounded by the 17-18 border (Fig. 33A, dashed line), extending to within a millimeter or so of the lunate sulcus and a slightly greater distance above the inferior occipital sulcus (see Fig. 32). Medially, the striate cortex bends around onto the inner surface of the hemisphere to become concealed within

Macaca

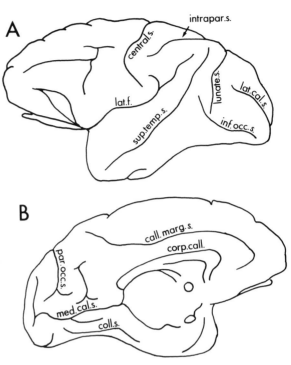

FIG. 32. Pattern of sulci associated with, or surrounding, visual parts of left hemisphere of macaque monkey cerebral cortex. *A*: lateral; *B*: medial. The following sulci are labeled: central, intraparietal, superior temporal, lunate, lateral calcarine, inferior occipital, parietooccipital, medial calcarine, collateral, and callosomarginal (cingulate). Lateral fissure and corpus callosum are also labeled.

the medial calcarine sulcus except at the posterior pole along the ascending and descending arms of the medial calcarine sulcus. The dotted line in Figure 33A shows the extent of the striate cortex that is folded back under the medial part of the operculum (1 in Fig. 33C) to form the roof (2 in Fig. 33C) of the calcarine fissure. The parasagittal sections (Fig. 33C–E), corresponding respectively to the oblique lines in Figure 33A, show that at both its superior and inferior margins the buried triangular region of cortex curves back to form a third and even deeper level (3 in Fig. 33C), occupying the same triangular area as the second, but consisting of two separate leaves. Where the two leaves meet, they turn anteriorly and form the banks of the stem of the calcarine fissure. Medially the roof of the fissure is broad and the stem short, but laterally the roof becomes progressively narrower and the stem longer (Fig. 33C–E).

RETINOTOPIC ORGANIZATION. The complexly folded nature of the macaque striate cortex makes the preparation of a retinotopic projection map a difficult task, and one comparable to that available for the cat (376) has not so far been attempted. However, the projection maps of Talbot and Marshall (367) and Daniel and Whitteridge (82) provide the main features of retino-

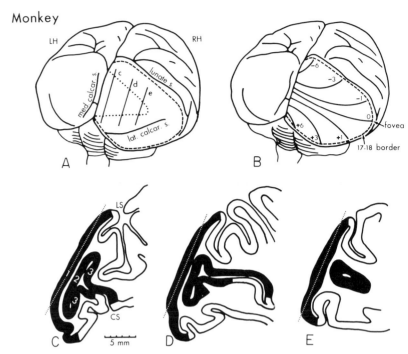

Monkey

FIG. 33. Topography of striate cortex in the macaque monkey. *A*: posterolateral view of brain showing area 17–area 18 border (*broken line*) and extent of roof of buried calcarine sulcus (*dotted line*). Three *oblique lines* indicate levels of parasagittal sections shown at *c*, *d*, and *e*. *B*: same view, with representation of zero horizontal (0) and of the parallels 1°, 3°, and 6° above (+) and below (−) zero horizontal. Fovea is represented laterally where zero horizontal meets the area 17–area 18 border (zero vertical meridian). *C–E*: parasagittal sections (medial to lateral) to show extent of area 17 (*black*). Three levels of cortex lie in parallel planes: *1*, operculum; *2*, roof of calcarine sulcus; *3*, leaves joining roof to stem. Stem of sulcus is oriented perpendicular to other levels. *Dotted white lines*, approximate planes of tangential sections used for reconstructed patterns of ocular dominance columns in Fig. 38*B* and Fig. 39. *LS*, lunate sulcus; *CS*, calcarine sulcus. [From LeVay et al. (228).]

topic organization. The whole of the contralateral visual hemifield is represented in the striate cortex, the smooth outer surface (operculum) containing the representation of the most central parts of the field. The fovea is represented laterally just anterior to the end of the lateral calcarine sulcus (Fig. 33*A* and *B*) and the zero horizontal runs medially, reaching an azimuth value of about 8° at the midline where it turns round the medial edge of the hemisphere. The zero horizontal then runs laterally again, roughly across the middle of the roof of the medial calcarine sulcus, before turning anteriorly at the lateral end of the sulcus and running along the blind lateral end of the stem. Thus the monocular temporal crescent of the visual field lies entirely within the stem of the sulcus. The zero vertical meridian is represented by the 17-18 border (dashed line in Figure 33*A* and *B*): above the fixation point it runs downward and medially above the inferior occipital sulcus and below the fixation point it courses upward and medially just behind the lunate sulcus. The parallels illustrated (Fig. 33*B*) are at elevations 1°, 3°, and 6° above (+) and below (−) the zero horizontal in the visual field.

LAMINAR DIFFERENTIATION AND NEURONAL ORGANI-ZATION OF MACAQUE STRIATE CORTEX. Various lami-

nation schemes that have been proposed for the macaque area 17 are shown in Figure 22 (cf. refs. 23 and 119). The lamination scheme of Lund (244), based on that of Brodmann (46, 47), is now widely accepted as the standard. Figure 34 shows this scheme applied to two sections of the perimacula area 17 of *Macaca mulatta*, one Nissl-stained (*A*) and the other a Golgi "rapid" preparation (*B*). The principal advantage of the Brodmann-Lund scheme is that it restricts the main geniculate afferent endings to lamina 4 rather than spreading them across both layers 3 and 4 as in von Bonin's scheme (43). In general the layering in the Brodmann-Lund scheme is clearly visible in Nissl-stained material (Fig. 34*A*) without reliance on information from the Golgi method. Its only disadvantage seems to be some ambiguity in determining the exact boundary between laminae 3 and 4A. In Nissl-stained material the central region of lamina 4A is sometimes seen as a prominent band of neurons (Figure 34*A*), but the upper limit of the lamina can be clearly seen only in Golgi rapid preparations (Fig. 34*B*).

The following account of the laminar differentiation and neuronal organization of the macaque striate cortex is based on the studies of J. S. Lund and her collaborators (244–247). On the basis of the arrangement of the dendritic branches, cortical neurons have

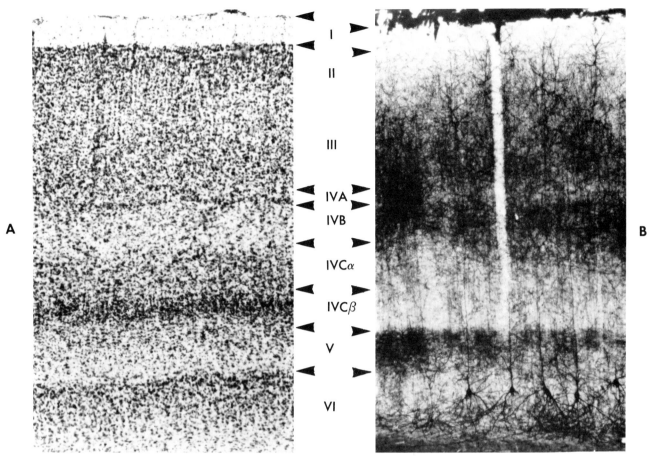

FIG. 34. *A*: Nissl-stained section of area 17 of *Macaca mulatta* from the perimacular area of occipital operculum. Average depth in this area from pia to white matter in frozen sections is 1,700 μm; average thickness for lamina 1 = 100 μm, lamina 2 + 3 = 650 μm, lamina 4A = 70 μm, lamina 4B = 150 μm, lamina 4Cα = 140 μm, lamina 4Cβ = 140 μm, lamina 5 = 210 μm, lamina 6 = 240 μm. *B*: Golgi rapid preparation of perimacular area 17. Large pyramidal cells of Meynert can be seen in lamina 6. [From Lund (244).]

been grouped into two main varieties, pyramidal cells and stellate cells. Pyramidal cells have a pyramid-shaped cell body with a single apical dendrite directed toward the cortical surface and several dendrites characteristically arising from the base of the pyramid and spreading in a radial fashion. The axon of a pyramidal cell usually descends to the subcortical white matter to project either to another cortical site or to a subcortical nucleus. Stellate cell dendrites arise round the circumference of the cell body in a star-shaped fashion and the axon ramifies locally to form intracortical connections. Stellate cells have been subdivided into those that have small spines arising from their dendrites and those that do not (225, 244). Spinous stellate cells are found only in the divisions of lamina 4 and, though probably most cells in lamina 4 receive a thalamic input (83, 227, 389), the spinous stellate cells seem to be the primary target for those thalamic axons that terminate in this layer. Stellate cells with aspinous or sparsely spinous dendrites are to be found in all laminae. Pyramidal neuron cell bodies occur in all

laminae except 1 and 4C. Extrastriate projecting cells include pyramidal cells of all sizes in laminae 2, 3, 4B, 5B, and 6. Large spiny stellate cells in lamina 4B almost certainly also give rise to extrastriate projecting axons (Fig. 23).

Laminar characteristics. The diagrams in Figure 23 summarize the details of the afferent and efferent relays of the spine-bearing neuron types in area 17 of the cat and monkey. The following outline describes the characteristics of the various laminae in the macaque monkey.

Lamina 1. Lamina 1 is a narrow lamina consisting mainly of fiber terminals and the terminal branches of apical dendrites. The fiber terminals are from the thalamic projection and from axon collaterals of pyramidal and stellate cells located mainly in laminae 2 and 3. The thalamic terminals form a horizontally oriented axon plexus. The terminal branches of the apical dendrites are from pyramidal cells in deeper laminae. The few scattered neurons are stellate cells with smooth or sparsely spined dendrites. The axons of these cells distribute within the lamina or project downward into layers 2 and 3, with an occasional collateral reaching the axon plexus of lamina 4B.

Laminae 2 and 3. Laminae 2 and 3 merge gradually into one another, the lower border of lamina 3 being marked by the start of the arborization of axon trunks rising from neurons in the lower cortical layers. The laminae contain pyramidal neurons and aspinous or sparsely spined stellate cells but no spinous stellate cells. The axons of the pyramidal cells have extrastriate connections that are mainly with other cortical visual areas, but there are, in addition, axon collaterals that distribute either to the same upper laminae as the dendritic fields of the cells or to lamina 5B (Fig. 23).

Lamina 4A. Lamina 4A, located immediately above the stria of Gennari, contains both spinous and aspinous or sparsely spinous stellate cells as well as pyramidal cell somata. The spinous dendrites of the stellate cells are confined to the lamina, but the basal dendrites of the pyramidal cells turn down into lamina 4B and their apical dendrites pass up to branch within layer 3. Lamina 4A receives a direct projection from the parvocellular LGNd composed of collaterals from the axons that also supply lamina 4Cβ. These axons, on entering lamina 4A, turn and run horizontally within the lamina. The spinous stellate neurons have axons that distribute collaterals within their own dendritic field and within the lower half of lamina 3; in addition an axon trunk descends to collateralize within lamina 5A with usually a fine axon branch reaching lamina 6.

Lamina 4B. Lamina 4B contains both pyramidal neurons and spinous stellates. It is identified by a dense horizontally oriented plexus—the stria of Gennari and Vicq-d'Azyr or the outer stripe of Baillarger (Fig. 34B)—composed of the axon collaterals from various sources: from pyramidal and stellate neurons lying within the lamina, from neurons in the more superficial laminae, and from the spinous stellate neurons of lamina 4Cα. This fiber band includes both lamina 4B and the upper half of lamina 4Cα. It has a sharp upper boundary coincident with the upper limit of lamina 4B and grades off with a less sharply defined lower border about the middle of lamina 4Cα.

Lamina 4B has no direct input from the thalamus. The pyramidal neurons, with basal dendritic field in lamina 4B and apical dendrites aborizing in lamina 3 and above, distribute axon collaterals to lamina 3 and to the horizontal fiber band of lamina 4B. The descending axon projection of spiny stellates and pyramidal neurons appears to be mainly to lamina 6. There is a reciprocal extrastriate connection to the superior temporal sulcus (STS in Fig. 23).

Lamina 4Cα. Lamina 4Cα contains stellate neurons with spinous dendrites as well as stellate forms with smooth or sparsely spinous dendrites but no pyramidal cells. However, the apical dendrites arising from pyramidal cell bodies in laminae 5 and 6 start to bear side branches in this lamina, and the apical dendrites

of the largest pyramidal cells in lamina 5 become profusely spinous for the first time as they enter and pass through this layer. Lamina 4Cα receives a direct input from the magnocellular (Y-type) LGNd. As well as ramifying widely within lamina 4Cα, the axons of the spinous stellates project mainly to lamina 4B, which does not receive a direct thalamic input, and also to lamina 5A.

Lamina 4Cβ. Like lamina 4Cα, lamina 4Cβ has both spinous and aspinous or sparsely spinous stellate cells but no pyramidal cells. On entering the lamina the apical dendrites of lower pyramidal cells undergo a marked reduction in the number of spines on their surface, and often a reduction in the diameter of the dendritic shaft. Lamina 4Cβ receives a direct input from the parvocellular (X-type) LGNd. The spinous stellate neurons send a strong recurrent projection to lamina 3, distribute local collaterals within 4C, and send a less-developed projection to laminae 5A and 6. The rising axon trunks to lamina 3 bypass the main recipient lamina for the magnocellular (Y-type) geniculate input (lamina 4Cα) as well as its second relay station (lamina 4B) before reaching their destination in layer 3.

Lamina 5. The prominent feature of lamina 5 is the band of horizontally oriented axons with sharply defined upper and lower limits—the inner stripe of Baillarger. The axons are collaterals derived from pyramidal cells of all laminae and axons of stellate neurons, at least of laminae 4, 5, and 6. There are two distinct sublaminae, 5A and 5B. Pyramidal neurons in lamina 5A have a basal dendritic field confined to layer 5A and a very fine unbranched apical dendrite that bears few spines and comes to an end in lamina 4C. These cells have recurrent axons that ascend unbranched to arborize in laminae 3 and 2. The large pyramidal neurons in lamina 5B have a very extensive basal field of dendrites spreading exclusively in lamina 5 and a stout apical dendrite that ascends toward the pia mater to branch profusely in lamina 3. These dendritic branches then extend upward to spread horizontally in lamina 1. The apical dendrite is virtually spine-free until it reaches lamina 4Cα but then bears numerous spines throughout the rest of its extent. The pyramidal neurons in layer 5B project to the superior colliculus and inferior pulvinar nucleus, possibly in many cases by collateral axon branches to both pulvinar and colliculus. In many cases also, the axons of these pyramidal cells give off collaterals within lamina 5 and a main collateral trunk that ascends unbranched to arborize terminally within layers 3 and 2.

Lamina 6. Lamina 6 contains both pyramidal neurons and stellate neurons with sparsely spined dendrites. In the upper half of the lamina the cells are tightly packed, the great majority being small to medium sized, but occasional very large pyramidal neuron cell bodies are found. The lower half of the lamina contains loosely packed small to medium-sized pyramidal and stellate cell bodies. The population of very large pyramidal neurons project to the superior temporal sulcus (STS) of the temporal lobe, and lamina 6, like lamina 4B, receives a reciprocal projection from the same region. The upper half of lamina 6 receives an input from the parvocellular laminae in the LGNd and the pyramidal neurons in this half of lamina 6 relay back to the same LGNd laminae. The lower half of lamina 6 has a similarly reciprocal relation with the magnocellular laminae in the LGNd. The pyramidal cells in the two halves of the lamina have distinctive apical dendritic arborizations and recurrent axonal feedback into the different laminae above them (Fig. 23). The dendritic arborizations and recurrent axon collaterals of the pyramidal cells in the upper half of lamina 6 associate these cells with those cortical laminae above them that are particularly related to the parvocellular laminae in the LGNd. In a similar manner pyramidal cells in the lower half of the laminae have an association with those cortical layers above them that are particularly related to the magnocellular geniculate laminae. Thus, in addition to the direct input, lamina 6 also appears to receive an indirect input from the LGNd via the laminae above it, the information from the parvo- and magnocellular geniculate laminae remaining segregated to some extent in passing between the different sets of laminae in the cortical depth.

EXTRASTRIATE LAMINAR CONNECTIONS. *Subcortical connections with dorsal LGN.* There is general agreement that, in the monkey, all afferents from the LGNd project exclusively to the striate cortex (122, 154, 395). These projections are retinotopically organized and do not extend to any cortical layer superficial to lamina 4A. Studies by Hubel and Wiesel (174), confirmed by Garey and Powell (122) and Polley (294), have demonstrated that after lesions of the dorsal layers of the lateral geniculate nucleus, two bands of terminal degeneration appear located in Brodmann laminae 4a and 4c, respectively, and separated by the intact stria of Gennari. Subsequently Hubel and Wiesel (176) and Lund (244) found that the upper band of geniculocortical terminals extends quite high into Brodmann's lamina 4a. By placing small lesions in different parts of the LGNd and studying the disposition of the degenerating axon terminals in the cortex, Hubel and Wiesel (176) also determined the laminar distribution of the geniculocortical fibers. After lesions in the dorsal (parvocellular) layers, terminal degeneration was found mainly in cortical layer 4Cβ and some in 4A, while lesions in the ventral (magnocellular) layers caused degeneration in lamina 4Cα (Fig. 23). Autoradiographic techniques have also shown a projection from the parvocellular layers of the LGNd to the upper part of lamina 6 and from the magnocellular layers to the lower part of lamina 6 [Fig. 23; (154)]. It is not known whether the population of nonconcentric rarely encountered retinal ganglion cells that project to the LGNd subsequently also project to the cortex.

On the assumption that X-like cells are found only in the parvocellular layers of the monkey LGNd and Y-like cells only in the magnocellular layers (101, 325, 338), X-like cells project to layers 4Cβ, 4A, and 6, while Y-like cells project to layer 4Cα and layer 6. Thus, although the cat LGNd appears to be more diverse than the monkey LGNd both in terms of its cellular morphology and cortical projections, the projection to the striate cortex has a basic similarity in the two animals.

The projection to the LGNd (16, 154, 164) arises from small- to medium-sized pyramidal cells in lamina 6, those projecting to the parvocellular laminae lying in the upper half of the layer and those projecting to the magnocellular laminae in the lower half (154, 245, 247).

Other subcortical connections. Apart from the LGNd, the striate area has a number of other subcortical connections. These include the inferior pulvinar (PI) and the immediately adjacent part of the lateral pulvinar (PLα) whose parallel topographic projections to area 17 terminate mainly in lamina 1 but also in laminae 2 and 3 (18, 276, 298). The reciprocal topographic corticopulvinar projections come from pyramidal cells in layer 5, mainly 5B (247, 276). Layer 5 pyramidal cells also project to the superior colliculus (247).

Corticocortical connections. The striate cortex is extensively interconnected with other cortical regions. The pyramidal cells that project to extrastriate visual regions, areas 18 and 19, are primarily in the superficial cortical layers 2 and 3 (114, 255, 348). Interconnection with the opposite striate cortex via the corpus callosum is limited to the 17-18 border region, including particularly the group of conspicuous large pyramidal cells in the deep part of layer 3 that are regarded as being the origin of commissural fibers (115, 120, 128, 399–401). Reciprocal connections from extrastriate visual areas terminate mainly in the superficial layers 1, 2, and 3 but also in layers 5 and 6 (369). Axons from the opposite striate cortex project mainly to layers 2 and 3.

Pyramidal cells in layers 4B and 6 project to the superior temporal sulcus (STS) (247, 401, 402) and both these laminae receive a reciprocal projection from the same region (247).

PROPERTIES OF RECEPTIVE FIELDS OF CELLS IN MONKEY STRIATE CORTEX. Beginning with the pioneering study of Hubel and Wiesel (173) there have been many investigations of the properties of the receptive fields of cells in the monkey striate cortex (51, 98, 99, 112, 136, 137, 210a, 258–261, 290–292, 320–323) but, despite these efforts, considerable confusion exists on almost every aspect of these properties.

Apart from the inherent complexities of cortical organization, there are many other reasons for the confusion. The various investigations have, with one or two exceptions, used only qualitative methods. In addition, some have studied the spatial properties of the receptive fields without giving much attention to color coding or particularly taking care to avoid confounding luminance and color variations in the stimuli. Others have studied color coding, varying luminance and color independently of each other, but have largely neglected the spatial properties of the fields. In the latter respect the small size of many of the receptive fields in the monkey striate cortex has added to the difficulty of characterizing their spatial properties. Considerable uncertainty exists concerning the extent to which information about color and luminance contrast occupy the same channels in the striate cortex or are kept apart in different groups of opponent-color and opponent-contrast cortical cells. Most cortical cells respond to luminance contrast, and color opponency, so characteristic of geniculate cells, is not obvious. Cortical cells commonly do not appear to be excited by one part of the spectrum and inhibited by another, as are those in the lateral geniculate nucleus; they respond best to midspectral or white-light stimulation and do not show overt color opponency.

Although the cell classifications used in various investigations have all been based on those of Hubel and Wiesel (173), the criteria used for assigning cells to the various classes have differed from one study to the next, leading to widely different encounter rates for the different cell types, a circumstance certain to have been aggravated by varying experimental procedures and microelectrode types. Further work is needed to determine the extent to which the properties of the cells vary with eccentricity from the cortical region subserving central vision. Finally, the adoption of different lamination schemes for the striate cortex has led to confusion concerning the distribution of the various cell types among the different layers.

CELL CLASSIFICATION. Hubel and Wiesel (173) found that most cells in the monkey striate cortex could be categorized as simple, complex, or hypercomplex with properties very similar to those they had previously described in the cat. On the average, however, the receptive fields of the cells were smaller and a small proportion of the cells were color coded. In addition, units lacking orientation specificity were encountered much more commonly in the monkey than in the cat. The units lacking orientation specificity mostly had receptive fields like those of geniculate cells, but some had responses that differed from those found in the geniculate nucleus.

General overview. Since 1968 most investigators have grouped the cells in the monkey striate cortex into two major categories: oriented neurons sensitive to the spatial orientation of the stimulus, and nonoriented neurons that respond more or less equally to a stimulus at any orientation. On the basis of their chromatic properties, the cells in each of these two categories can be further segregated into luminosity and color-coded groups. Most investigators have found that, whereas the great majority of cells respond to luminance contrast, some of these cells are also color coded in that they show characteristically different responses to different portions of the visible spectrum. Thus color-coded cells respond better to certain monochromatic lights than to white light and have action spectra whose peaks are displaced laterally from the peak of the photopic spectral sensitivity curve of the macaque monkey. Noncolor cells, on the other hand, respond best to white light and have action spectra with a broad peak in the middle of the visible spectrum. Only a very small minority, possibly as little as 3% (137), respond almost exclusively to color and not to luminance contrast. In the early studies, fewer than 10% of the cells were found to be color coded. Later investigations have, however, yielded estimates as high as 50% or more (98, 99, 136, 137, 290). Out of keeping with the generalization that only a small minority of cells are almost exclusively color coded are the observations of Michael (258–261), who found that a large number of cells of all types, oriented and nonoriented, responded only to monochromatic stimuli and not to white light in any form (see *Color coding in nonoriented cells*, p. 407).

Following Hubel and Wiesel (173), all subsequent investigators have noted the common occurrence in the monkey striate cortex of units lacking orientation specificity, although the reported encounter rates have varied widely from 6% (173) to 41% (290). There has, however, always been difficulty in deciding whether or not some at least of these nonoriented units are lateral geniculate axon terminals, especially those with a concentric center-surround organization similar to that of the common type of lateral geniculate neurons. The only investigators to use electrical stimulation of the geniculocortical axons to settle this issue have been Bullier and Henry (51). Largely reflecting the different classification criteria, the encounter rates for the different cell types, both oriented and nonoriented, have also varied widely from one study to another. Some investigators (98, 136, 173, 290) have reported a low proportion of simple cells (5%–10%) and relatively large numbers of complex cells (40%–50%). By contrast Bullier and Henry (51) found an encounter rate of 42% for S (simple) cells and only a relatively small percentage (20%) for C and B cells (equivalent to Hubel and Wiesel's complex cell with a uniform receptive field). Although it has been known for some time in the cat that both the simple and complex cell types can show end-zone inhibition with increasing stimulus length (34, 100, 195), in only two studies of the monkey striate cortex (51, 320) has the hypercomplex property been reported in neuron types other than the classic complex cell. The B-cell category, recently introduced by Bullier and Henry (51), has yet to find general acceptance. Though B-cells have properties intermediate between those of the simple and complex types, they are classified in the complex family. The class III cells of Dow (98) would probably be regarded as B-cells.

Taking into account the various types of hypercomplex cell, Bullier and Henry (51) reported encounter rates of 49% for cells in the simple family, 20% for the complex family, and 31% for the nonoriented group. These encounter rates give a simple/complex cell ratio of 71:29, similar to that commonly reported in the cat (195). Presumably the large increase in nonoriented cells found in the macaque striate cortex, particularly in layer 4, is the physiological counterpart of the anatomical observations of Rockel et al. (302). By comparison with subprimate mammalian species, Rockel et al. (302) found that in certain primates including the macaque monkey and man there was a marked increase in the number of cells in the binocular part of area 17, the increase being particularly marked in layer 4.

It is only recently that the cortical lamination scheme of Lund (244) has come into wide general use. By using different schemes both for physiological cell classification and for cortical lamination, it is not surprising that the laminar distribution of the various physiological cell types have differed considerably from one study to another.

Nonoriented cells. A variety of different types of nonoriented cells have been described. Much the most common type, called uniform neurons by Poggio et al. (290), has receptive fields composed of a single, roughly circular, activating region from which responses can be evoked with moving stimuli and, usually, also with stationary flashes. Stationary flashes restricted to the activating regions evoke on-, off-, or, less frequently, on-off responses in different cells. Except for a commonly encountered off-discharge from the surrounds of cells that give a composite on-off response from the central activating region (51), firing can rarely be elicited from the surrounds of the receptive fields of nonoriented cells. By contrast, a large proportion of nonoriented cells exhibit a silent inhibitory surround, so that these cells give either no response or a reduced response to stimuli several times larger than the activating center.

Using electrical stimulation of the optic radiation, Bullier and Henry (51) were able to distinguish afferent geniculate axons from striate neurons, thereby confirming the presence of cortical neurons lacking orientation sensitivity. Considering units that responded with an on- or an off-discharge to stationary flashing stimuli restricted to the field center and with the opposite kind of discharge to stimuli in the surround, Bullier and Henry (51) found that virtually all of these concentrically organized units were geniculate axons.

Color coding in nonoriented cells. A large proportion of the nonoriented cells are color-coded either of the spectrally tuned or of the spectrally opponent types. All the tuned neurons and most of the opponent cells have a single activating region. Spectrally tuned neurons respond in the same manner to different wavelengths, but over a narrower range than luminosity neurons, their maximal sensitivity being shifted toward one or the other end of the visible spectrum.

By contrast spectrally opponent cells are either excited or inhibited by long wavelengths and respond in the opposite manner to short wavelengths. The opponent cells have a single activating region in which the two opponent systems are spatially coextensive.

The status of the so-called dual-opponent, color-coded cells with concentric receptive fields is somewhat uncertain. These are cells with both a color-opponent and a spatially opponent center-surround organization. Michael (258) reported a large population of these dual-opponent cells with concentric receptive fields as having a red-green opponent-color system in the field center and the opposite organization in the surround. The units were always monocular and confined to cortical layer 4. Other investigators (173, 290) have observed a very occasional concentric neuron with properties consistent with a dual-opponent organization, but apparently no one, other than Michael, has so far reported cells in the monkey striate cortex in which the dual opponency has been directly observed. Electrical stimulation of the geniculocortical axons has yet to be used to demonstrate that the dual-opponent concentric units are cortical cells. On the other hand, double opponent-color cells have so far not been reported in the monkey geniculate.

Oriented cells. Monkey striate cells with orientation-specific responses can be categorized into the same simple, complex, and B-cell classes as those described above for the cat, and all three cell types can exhibit the hypercomplex property of end-zone inhibition. Except for color coding, the general properties of these cell types (51, 98, 290, 291, 320) appear to be essentially the same as those in the cat and there is also a basic similarity with respect to the distribution of the cell types among the cortical laminae. In addition it appears that no cell type is exclusively identified with a monosynaptic, disynaptic, or polysynaptic input from the thalamus. Using electrical stimulation at two selected sites in the optic radiation, Bullier and Henry (51) found that there were many types of potential first-order neurons and that most cell types had representatives in the three ordinal groupings referred to above.

Color coding in oriented cells. Probably the majority of simple cells in the monkey striate cortex are color coded, being both spectrally opponent as well as spatially opponent (98, 259, 290). There are two common types of color-coded simple cell: those with bipartite receptive fields in which the two spatial-field components have different spectral sensitivities for excitation, and those with a central strip that responds to lights toward one end of the spectrum and is flanked on both sides by antagonistic regions responding to lights toward the other end. Some of these cells appear to have a dual-opponent organization in which the central region has a red-blue (290) or red-green (259) opponent-color system and antagonistic flanks of the reverse opponent arrangement. Complex cells appear to be much less commonly color coded than simple cells, being either of the tuned or opponent types (260,

290). All the color-coded cells that Bullier and Henry (51) found had an input that came exclusively from the parvocellular layers of the LGNd. By contrast, cells in both the simple and complex families could be driven from the magnocellular layers in the geniculate nucleus.

FUNCTIONAL ARCHITECTURE OF MONKEY STRIATE COR-TEX. Although the visual field is represented in the striate cortex in what is commonly called a "point-to-point" manner, there are various distortions in the orderliness of the arrangement.

Magnification factor. Whereas the amount of retinal surface devoted to a square degree of visual field is approximately constant, this is far from being the case in the striate cortex. The amount of cortical surface devoted to the foveal region is relatively very large and falls off progressively as eccentricity increases. This variation in magnification was first systematically analyzed by Daniel and Whitteridge (82). They defined the magnification factor in terms of the linear extent of the cortex concerned with each degree of visual field (mm cortex/deg visual field). The concept of a magnification factor can, of course, be applied to any level in the visual pathway, and a more signif-

icant measure of magnification is the number of neurons at a particular level per square degree of visual field (39, 305). The data presently available for the retina (305), LGNd (251), and striate cortex (82) now make it possible to compare the change in magnification factor with eccentricity at these three levels in terms either of cell densities or of measures that approximate cell densities (Fig. 35).

The calculations used for Figure 35 assume that all radial eccentricities equidistant from the center of the fovea have the same magnification factor. While this is approximately true, there are, nevertheless, at the various levels in the visual pathway, factors operating to impair the radial symmetry. Thus the falloff in retinal ganglion cell densities with eccentricity is not completely radially symmetrical. The values used in Figure 35 are the average ganglion cell densities along nasal and temporal retinal horizontals. These values are greater than those along superior and inferior meridians (390). There is a further complication with retinal ganglion cell densities. At eccentricities of less than 10° ganglion cell densities cannot be directly related to eccentricity because of the low density close to the fovea and the heaping-up that occurs for a few degrees beyond about 3°. On the assumption that near

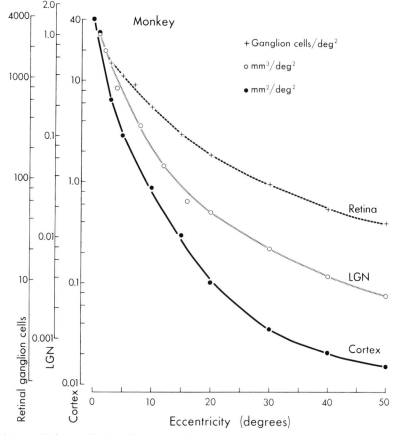

FIG. 35. Retinal, lateral geniculate (LGN), and striate cortical magnification factors as a function of visual eccentricity in macaque monkey. The three curves have been normalized with respect to their ordinate values at 0° eccentricity. [Data for retinal curve from Rolls and Cowey (305); for LGN curve from Malpeli and Baker (251); for striate cortex from Daniel and Whitteridge (82).]

the fovea the ratio of ganglion cell to cone is about one, Rolls and Cowey (305) took cone density as a measure of ganglion cell density within 7° of the center of the fovea. The LGNd also presents the problem of differences in cell densities between the parvo- and magnocellular layers as well as regional differences in the relative extents of these laminae. There are further complications at the level of the cortex. The number of cells in the thickness of the neocortex underlying unit area of cortical surface is remarkably constant throughout the whole of its extent, except in the binocular part of area 17 in certain primates, including the macaque monkey and man, where there are approximately 2.5 times as many neurons (302). Most of this increase in cell number occurs in layer 4 where it is coupled with an increase in cell density. However, the increase in cell number appears to be uniform throughout the binocular part of area 17 so that, within this part, surface area still remains a fairly reliable measure of mean cell density. Despite the uniformity of cell number per unit surface area, the presence of ocular-dominance columns in the binocular part of area 17 leads to local modifications of the magnification factor (see *Representation of visual fields in layer 4C*, p. 414).

The three curves in Figure 35 have been normalized with respect to their ordinate values at 0° eccentricity. Malpeli and Baker (251) concluded that the LGNd accounts for a large part of the change in central magnification relative to peripheral magnification that occurs between retina and visual cortex. Thus for the retina in Figure 35 the ratio of the magnification at 0° eccentricity (about 4,000 ganglion cells/deg^2) to magnification at 50° (about 40 cells/deg^2) is about 100:1, while the ratios for the LGNd and cortex at these two eccentricities are 530 and 2,710, respectively. In proceeding along the retinocortical pathway there is an increasingly great expansion of neural apparatus devoted to the central visual field as compared with the periphery. Magnification seems to vary with eccentricity in such a way as to keep the cell density and thickness of the cortex uniform (178, 302). Instead of being heaped up in the region representing central vision, the cortex is spread out to just the amount needed to preserve uniformity.

Spatial organization of receptive-field position. Subject to the distortions brought about by the variation in the magnification factor with eccentricity, the visual field is represented in a continuously progressive topographic manner throughout the striate cortex. As in the cat (169), however, this detailed topographic representation does not hold at the microscopic level. Along cortical electrode penetrations extending vertically from surface to white matter, the receptive fields of successively recorded cells are not precisely superimposed: there is not only some variation in field size but also a certain amount of apparently random scatter in position. The variation in field position from cell to cell is small enough so that the fields overlap but

large enough so that the area covered is about 2 to 4 times that of the average receptive field for the particular cortical location (173, 178). Hubel and Wiesel (179) refer to the area collectively covered by the receptive fields of cells encountered along any one vertical penetration as the *aggregate field* for the particular cortical locus. The concept of an aggregate field is somewhat analogous to the position subunit discussed above in connection with the cat striate cortex (see *Position subunit in cortex*, p. 397).

With horizontal electrode penetrations parallel to the cortical surface two factors modify the gradual overall drift in receptive-field position in the direction dictated by the topographic map of the visual field on the cortex. Over distances small compared to the width of an ocular-dominance column (400 μm) the random scattering of the receptive fields dominates the recording but, as the penetration proceeds, a clear progression through the visual field becomes evident. This progression is, however, modified in turn by the alternation of the left- and right-eye ocular-dominance columns. The alternation leads to small intermittent backward and forward displacements in the receptive-field positions when the direction of the electrode penetration is across the line of the columns (see *Representation of visual fields in layer 4C*, p. 414). It is, however, only in layer 4C that the precision of the representation is sufficient to permit the detection of these displacements. In the face of these distorting factors, it requires a traverse of 1–2 mm horizontally through the cortex to produce a drift equal to the size of the aggregate field, the displacement of the receptive fields being then sufficient to bring them into an entirely new terrain. Both receptive-field size and magnification factor increase in parallel fashion with eccentricity (Fig. 36) and this is true also for receptive-field position scatter. These relationships seem to hold throughout the striate cortex so that, like the spatial subunit in the cat striate cortex, the span of cortex corresponding to the local receptive-field size plus scatter seems to be constant irrespective of the cortical region. The receptive-field size plus associated scatter varies tremendously over the cortex, but so does the visual-field area corresponding to 1 mm of cortex. As Hubel and Wiesel (178) remark, the degree to which these are matched is striking and surely no accident.

Orientation "columns". As in the cat, preferred stimulus orientation in the monkey has a highly ordered and systematic spatial organization (173, 177, 179, 182). Cells recorded along an electrode penetration perpendicular to the cortical surface tend to favor the same stimulus orientation, but as yet no quantitative estimates have been made of the scatter about the mean preferred orientation for a given penetration. In horizontal or oblique penetrations successively recorded cells show regular clockwise or anticlockwise progressions of preferred orientations over distances of up to several millimeters (Fig. 37). The orderly sequences are, however, often terminated by sudden

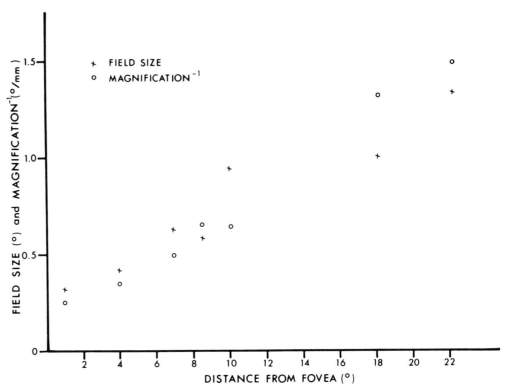

FIG. 36. Graph of average receptive-field size (*crosses*) and magnification⁻¹ in deg/mm (*circles*) against eccentricity for 5 striate cortical locations. Points for 4°, 8°, 18°, and 22° were from one monkey; point for 1° from a second. Receptive-field size was determined by averaging fields at each eccentricity, estimating size from (length × width)$^{0.5}$. [From Hubel and Wiesel (178).]

unpredictable changes in the direction of the orientation shifts.

Hubel and Wiesel (179) favor the view that the monkey striate cortex is subdivided by vertical partitions into columns or slender slabs in each of which all the cells have the same preferred orientation. According to this view there are stepwise shifts in preferred orientation of about 10° in going from one slab to the next with horizontal movement along the cortex, although Hubel and Wiesel (177) were unable to exclude the possibility that orientation may vary continuously. In this connection they specifically considered the possibility of a local random variation in preferred orientation but failed to find any evidence in support of such a proposition. However, a number of technical considerations need attention and quantitative studies must be undertaken before a determination can be made concerning the extent of any preferred orientation scatter in the monkey striate cortex (28). Whether or not the slabs are discrete, the notion of a hypercolumn as the horizontal extent of the cortex (roughly about 1 mm) that is needed to cover the full 180° rotation remains valid. Furthermore the rate of change of orientation with distance along the cortex seems to be independent of eccentricity from the fovea.

The introduction of the 2-deoxyglucose autoradiographic method (202, 347) has provided a striking anatomical confirmation that stimulus orientation is represented in the monkey cortex in a systematic and highly organized manner (181, 182). An anesthetized monkey was given an injection of [^{14}C]2-deoxyglucose and then visually stimulated for 45 min with a large array of moving vertical stripes, with both eyes open. The autoradiographs of the striate cortex showed vertical bands of label extending through the full thickness of the cortex. The pattern seen in tangential sections (Fig. 38A) was complex, consisting of swirling stripes with many bifurcations and blind endings, but with occasional more regular regions where the stripes were roughly parallel. The interstripe distance was rather constant at 570 μm over the cortex. Such an interstripe distance was to be expected if about 1 mm along the cortex corresponds to 180° rotation and the spatial organization of preferred orientation is similar to that seen in the cat (Fig. 31). Taking into account the range of orientations over which a given cell responds, the presentation of a stimulus at any one orientation will activate cells to a greater or lesser extent over a considerable fraction of area 17. In fact, if the whole visual field is stimulated with parallel lines of a given orientation, activation of patches or stripes covering about 50% of the whole striate cortex would be expected (220), leading to an interstripe distance of about half a hypercolumn (i.e., about 500 μm). While confirming the highly ordered representation of preferred orientation in the monkey striate

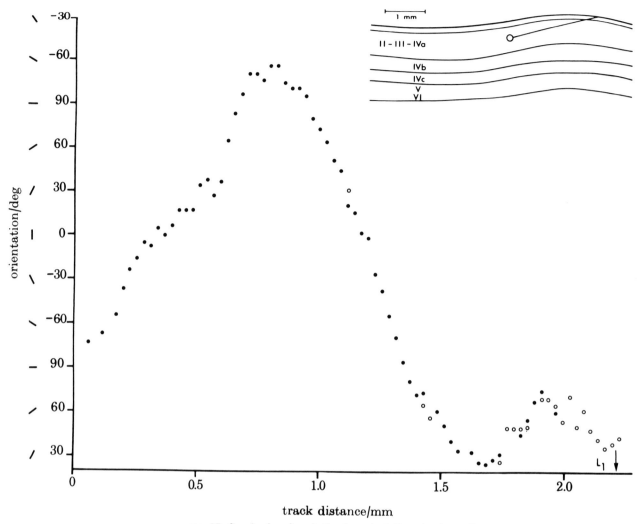

FIG. 37. Graph of preferred stimulus orientation of striate cells vs. electrode track distance for an oblique penetration restricted to layers 2 and 3 (*inset*) in monkey cortex. *Filled circles*, cells dominated by right eye; *open circles*, by left eye. Several reversals in direction of rotation occur, with two very long, almost linear, sequences followed by two short ones. Right eye was dominant until almost end of the sequence. [From Hubel and Wiesel (179).]

cortex, the 2-deoxyglucose method leaves unresolved the question whether orientation is represented in a discrete (i.e., columnar) or a continuous manner. There is, unfortunately, a tendency in the literature to use the terms *columns* and *hypercolumns* interchangeably.

Ocular-dominance columns. Ocular-dominance columns in the striate cortex are much more clearly defined physiologically in the macaque monkey (173) than they are in the cat (169, 172). In the monkey the cells encountered along an electrode penetration perpendicular to the cortical surface nearly always respond preferentially to the same eye. In a horizontal or oblique penetration there is an alternation of eye dominance, apparently quite independent of changes in preferred orientation: first one eye dominates, then the two become roughly equal, and finally the other eye dominates, a complete cycle occurring roughly

every 800 μm. Within layer 4C the rigid anatomical segregation of the geniculocortical afferents representing each eye (176, 228, 393) is reflected physiologically in the marked monocularity of the fourth-layer cortical neurons (173). In tangential penetrations along layer 4C there is an abrupt shift in eye dominance, within 50 μm or less, as the electrode passes from one ocular-dominance column to the next. Above and below layer 4C the transitions are less sharp, though generally still within 100 μm. The cells outside layer 4C are likely to be binocular, but they still prefer the eye that dominates the monocular 4C region below or above them along the same radial line, i.e., in the same column. Thus the striate cortex is subdivided into ocular-dominance regions that extend through the full thickness of the cortex, each with a cross-sectional width of about 400 μm and with walls perpendicular to the cortical surface and to the layers. One complete

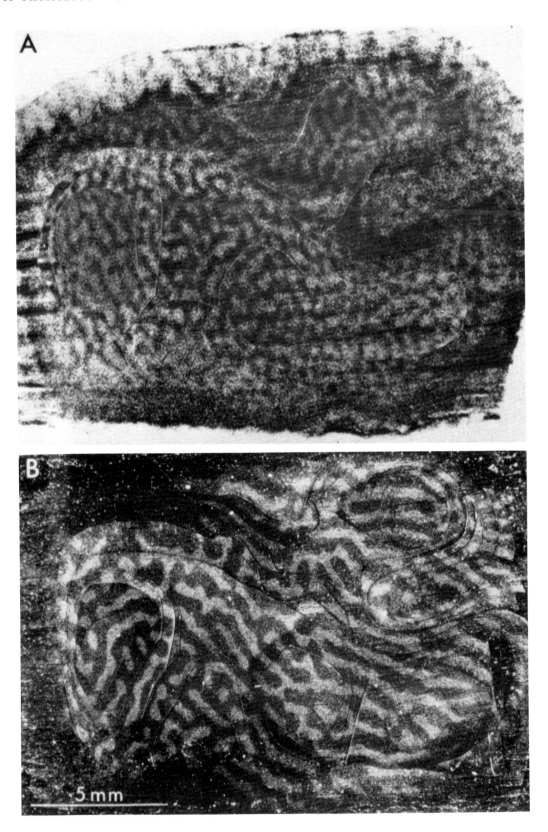

set of left- and right-eye columns has been termed a hypercolumn (178).

It is the marked segregation of the geniculocortical afferents representing each eye that makes it possible to visualize the ocular-dominance columns anatomically. In this respect they differ profoundly from the orientation columns that depend upon complex intracortical circuits. Four independent anatomical methods have shown the eye-dominance system to have the form of parallel, vertically disposed sheets. In the first method, Hubel and Wiesel (174, 176) made small lesions confined to a single geniculate layer resulting in degeneration of the axon terminals in layer 4C in the striate cortex. The degenerating terminals were selectively stained by the Wiitanen modification (394) of the Nauta-Fink-Heimer method and shown to occur in discrete regular patches with gaps between. In two further methods, transneuronal autoradiography following eye injection of labeled material was used in one (180, 393), and a reduced silver stain in the other (228). Finally, Kennedy et al. (202a) made use of the increased uptake of intravenously injected 2-deoxyglucose by active cells and the inability of these cells to get rid of the metabolic end product of the deoxyglucose.

In tangential sections through layer 4C (Fig. 38B) the ocular-dominance columns appear as a set of fairly regular stripes with varying numbers of cross linkages, bifurcations, and blind endings. In contrast to the methods that depend upon the staining of the geniculocortical axon terminals, the deoxyglucose procedure reveals the entire column from layer 1 down to layer 6 rather than just the part in layers 4A and C. To establish that the stripes seen in anatomical preparations are the basis of the physiologically defined columns, LeVay et al. (228, 231) used a combination of techniques in the macaque monkey. Oblique electrode penetrations were made down to layer 4C, making lesions each time the electrode tip crossed from a region dominated by one eye to a region dominated by the other. When the brain was later sectioned tangentially and stained by the reduced-silver method, the lesions were found exactly on the borders of labeled bands. In later experiments (231) the autoradiographic method was combined with terminal physiological recording, and again points of transition in

ocular dominance coincided with the borders of labeled bands.

Using the reduced-silver method and combining those parts of serial tangential sections that passed through layer 4C (dotted line in Fig. 33C–E), it has been possible to reconstruct the ocular-dominance columns over the entire exposed surface of the macaque monkey's occipital lobe (the operculum), representing a region of visual field that extends from the fovea out to about 8° or 9° (228). In Figure 39 alternate stripes have been inked in to show the twofold nature of the subdivisions. The dark stripes represent the projections of one eye onto layer 4C and the light stripes the projections from the other eye. Although not illustrated in Figure 39, the reconstruction was also carried into the calcarine fissure, representing the peripheral visual field. A conspicuous feature of the anatomical stripes is the constancy of their width, about 400 μm, from the fovea out almost as far as the monocular crescent. The most orderly part of the pattern is at the 17-18 border, which the columns always meet more or less at right angles. Over most of the smooth outer surface of the cortex (Fig. 39) the columns run along curves corresponding to isoelevation lines (horizontals) in the visual field (cf. Fig. 33B). Broken line F-ZH in Figure 39 corresponds to the zero horizontal in the visual field. The doubling of the visual-field representation brought about by the parcellation of the striate cortex into left- and right-eye ocular-dominance columns requires halving of the overall magnification factor across the width of a given column if the magnification is to be the same along or across the corresponding hypercolumn (see next subsection, p. 414). LeVay et al. (228) have suggested that the disposition of the columns along the representation of horizontal lines in the visual field may be connected with the mechanisms for stereoscopic vision. The monocular crescent, which is represented in the lateral part of the stem of the calcarine fissure, is free from columns.

In order to establish the nature of the spatial relationships between the preferred orientation and ocular-dominance columns, Hubel et al. (182) examined the same striate region in a monkey after injecting one eye with [³H]proline two weeks before the deoxyglucose experiment in which the anesthetized monkey,

---

FIG. 38. *A*: reconstructed pattern of orientation columns in macaque striate cortex viewed face-on. Reconstruction made from deoxyglucose autoradiographs by cutting tangential sections through exposed part of left occipital cortex and mounting the parts of each section that passed through layer 6. *B*: reconstructed pattern of ocular-dominance columns in the same region as *A*, made from autoradiographs of [³H]proline sections following injection of right eye; dark-field photographs. Both reconstructions *A* and *B* based on the same series of tangential sections, every third section being set aside for transneuronal labeling with tritium. For *B*, parts of each autoradiograph that passed through layer 4C were cut and mounted. [From Hubel et al. (182).]

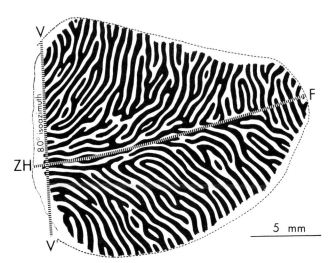

FIG. 39. Reconstruction of ocular-dominance columns over whole of exposed part of striate cortex in right occipital lobe of a macaque monkey, as shown also in Fig. 33. Reconstruction prepared from set of serial sections roughly tangential to exposed surface of lobe and stained by reduced silver method of Liesegang (228). In diagram, every other column has been inked in, *dark stripes* corresponding to one eye and the *light stripes* to the other. *F*, representation of fovea on cortex; *broken line VFV'*, area 17- area 18 border, representing vertical midline; *ZH*, zero horizontal drawn by eye along path of confluence of stripes as they stream in from *VF* and *V'F*. Line *VV'* at medial edge of lobe indicates where cortex bends over abruptly to continue as a buried fold. Line approximates the 8° isoazimuth. [Adapted from Hubel and Freeman (166).]

with both eyes open, was stimulated with a large array of moving vertical stripes. Two sets of autoradiographs of tangential sections through layer 4C were prepared, the deoxyglucose in one set having been removed by prolonged washing. A comparison between the two sets of columns in the same area showed no clear relationship between the two, and in particular no marked tendency for them to run parallel to one another or to be orthogonal. In Figure 40 the vertical orientation columns in Fig. 38*A* have been traced as thick lines and the ocular-dominance columns in Figure 38*B* as thin lines. The angles of intersection of the lines show a distribution that is not obviously different from that expected for any two randomly superimposed sets of lines.

Representation of visual fields in layer 4C. Reference has already been made to the local distortions in the cortical magnification factor produced by the presence of ocular-dominance columns best exemplified by the precision of the representation of the visual field in layer 4C. With horizontal electrode penetrations along this layer, but across the ocular-dominance columns, the alternation of the left- and right-eye columns leads to intermittent forward and backward displacements in receptive-field position (179). Across one column there is a small progression of receptive-field positions in a direction predicted by the topographic map of the visual field. Then, as the border of the column is crossed, there is an abrupt discontinuity in receptive-field position, the receptive fields sud-

denly jumping back in the visual field through a distance equal to about half that crossed in the preceding column, when the other eye was used. This pattern is repeated over successive columns so that the visual field is traversed completely in each eye, but, as Hubel and Wiesel (179) have described it, in an intermittent "two steps forward and one step back" fashion, in which each eye must take its turn. By contrast, when the electrode penetration is along the line of an ocular-dominance column, the progression of receptive-field positions continues without interruption provided the electrode remains within the same column.

The double representation of the visual field in neighboring ocular-dominance columns described above has associated with it a local modification of the cortical magnification factor such that the magnification (mm cortex/deg visual field) across the width of a given column is only half that for an equal distance along its length (179). This means that the overall magnification factor for the combined width of neighboring left- and right-eye columns is the same as that for an equal distance along their length, thereby making the magnification factor independent of direction along the cortex over distances that are large compared with the width of a column.

The lamina 4 increase in cell number in the binocular part of area 17 over that found in the monocular part [(302); see *Magnification factor*, p. 408] seems to be required by the pronounced segregation of the ocular-dominance columns whereby a given region in the visual field has a double representation in neighboring left- and right-eye columns. This interpretation, however, encounters the difficulty that the same increase in cell number is to be found in area 17 of both

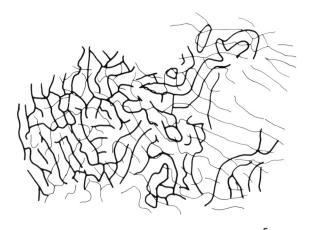

FIG. 40. Comparison of patterns of orientation and ocular-dominance columns in same area of striate cortex in same monkey. Orientation columns from Fig. 38*A* have been traced as *thick lines*, left-eye ocular-dominance columns from Fig. 38*B* as *thin lines*. Average widths of the hypercolumns are 770 μm for ocular dominance, 570 μm for orientation. Angles of intersection of two sets of columns show a distribution not obviously different from that expected for any two randomly superimposed sets of lines. [From Hubel et al. (182).]

squirrel and macaque monkeys (302), but ocular-dominance columns have not been shown with histological techniques in the squirrel monkey (154).

Development of ocular-dominance columns. Segregation of left- and right-eye afferents to the macaque striate cortex begins in utero (297). At 1 wk postnatally the afferents within the fourth layer still overlap extensively with each other (231). By 3 wk, segregation is nearly complete, but there is still a slight overlap at the borders of the columns. By 6 wk the afferents are fully segregated, and physiologically the ocular-dominance columns have their mature organization. The process of columnar development, in the monkey at least, does not seem to require visual experience. Physiologically, binocularly deprived monkeys show an even more pronounced segregation according to eye preference than is seen in normal animals (231).

Functional architecture: summary. While it is no surprise that the spatial organization of receptive-field position, of preferred-stimulus orientation, and of ocular dominance should be even more systematic and highly ordered in the monkey than it is in the cat, it is perhaps surprising that the pattern of the organization should be so similar in the two animals. In the monkey, the width of an ocular-dominance hypercolumn is about 800 μm, divided equally between the two eyes. This may be compared with a hypercolumn width of about 500 μm to cover the full 180° range of preferred orientations. A movement of 1–2 mm horizontally through the cortex over most of the striate area is accompanied by a movement of receptive fields through the visual field about equal in size to the local aggregate receptive field. Thus a block of tissue 1–2 mm square on the surface contains several hypercolumns of both kinds and presumably, therefore, all the neural machinery needed to subserve an aggregate receptive field. The magnification factor seems to vary with eccentricity in such a way as to keep the striate cortex uniform in both thickness and cell density over most of its extent.

BINOCULAR VISION

Most of the cells in the striate cortex can be independently driven from both eyes, and Hubel and Wiesel (167, 169) were the first to observe that binocularly activated neurons have two receptive fields, one for each eye. Recent observations indicate that, both in the cat (196) and in the monkey (292), virtually all the cells encountered in the striate cortex are either discharged or influenced by stimulation of either eye. The two receptive fields of a cortical cell are in approximately corresponding positions in the contralateral hemifield and both have the same, or nearly the

same, highly specific stimulus requirements. The selectivities of cells in the visual cortex for small disparities in the retinal images in the two eyes have been extensively studied in the cat (13, 35, 42, 81, 113, 189, 196, 270, 273, 289, 382) and in the monkey (175, 292), leading to the development of a detailed neurophysiological theory for binocular single vision and depth discrimination (27, 33). A description of the experimental observations and an analysis of the proposed neural mechanisms for stereoscopic depth perception lie outside the scope of the present chapter, but recent reviews by Bishop (29, 30) are available elsewhere.

CONCLUSION

In this chapter the account of the processing of visual information within the retinostriate system deals with only a limited aspect of the topic and keeps strictly within the bounds set by the retinal ganglion cells on the one hand and the striate cortex on the other. It has been concerned with neural elements and local neural circuits. Little has been said about the larger-scale cooperative interactions between these local neural mechanisms that are ultimately responsible for visual pattern recognition. It would require another chapter to outline the more global aspects of the visual information processing accomplished at each of the successive levels along the way from the retina to the cerebral cortex. Even so, available knowledge would still not take us far toward an understanding of the brain mechanisms by which we discriminate the visual forms of everyday life.

The account has, of course, been limited to the cat and monkey. At the various levels in the visual pathway each animal has been discussed separately, the aim being to avoid confusion about which of the two animals is referred to in a particular observation. The procedure was not intended as a way of comparing the visual systems in the two species. In the event, however, it has provided an ideal basis for a detailed comparison between the two animals. The antecedents of the carnivores and primates probably diverged from the placental mammalian stock during the Eocene epoch some 50 million years ago and have developed independently since that time. It is truly remarkable that, despite their independent development, the retinostriate visual system in the two animals should resemble one another so closely.

I wish to thank my colleagues Dr. B. G. Cleland, Dr. G. H. Henry, Dr. A. Hughes, and Dr. W. R. Levick for much helpful discussion. I am grateful to K. Collins for his skilled assistance in preparing many of the figures and to J. Livingstone and E. M. McNaughton for considerable secretarial assistance.

REFERENCES

1. ADRIAN, E. D. *The Basis of Sensation. The Action of Sense Organs.* London: Christophers, 1928.

2. AHLSÉN, G., AND S. LINDSTRÖM. Axonal branching of functionally identified neurones in the lateral geniculate body of the

cat. *Neurosci. Lett. Suppl.* 1: 156, 1978.

3. AHLSÉN, G., S. LINDSTRÖM, AND E. SYBIRSKA. Subcortical axon collaterals of principal cells in the lateral geniculate body of the cat. *Brain Res.* 156: 106–109, 1978.

4. ALBUS, K. A quantitative study of the projection area of the central and the paracentral visual field in area 17 of the cat. I. The precision of topography. *Exp. Brain Res.* 24: 159–179, 1975.

5. ALBUS, K. A quantitative study of the projection area of the central and the paracentral visual field in area 17 of the cat. II. The spatial organization of the orientation domain. *Exp. Brain Res.* 24: 181–202, 1975.

6. ALBUS, K. Predominance of monocularly driven cells in the projection area of the central visual field in cat's striate cortex. *Brain Res.* 89: 341–347, 1975.

7. ALBUS, K., AND F. DONATE-OLIVER. Cells of origin of the occipito-pontine projection in the cat: functional properties and intracortical location. *Exp. Brain Res.* 28: 167–174, 1977.

8. ALLMAN, J. Evolution of the visual system in the early primates. In: *Progress in Psychobiology and Physiological Psychology*, edited by J. M. Sprague and A. N. Epstein. New York: Academic, 1977, vol. 7, p. 1–53.

9. ALLMAN, J. M., AND J. H. KAAS. The organization of the second visual area (V II) in the owl monkey: a second order transformation of the visual hemifield. *Brain Res.* 76: 247–265, 1974.

10. ANDREWS, B. W., AND D. A. POLLEN. Relationship between spatial frequency selectivity and receptive field profile of simple cells. *J. Physiol. London* 287: 163–176, 1979.

11. BABB, R. S. The pregeniculate nucleus of the monkey (*Macaca mulatta*). I. A study at the light microscopy level. *J. Comp. Neurol.* 190: 651–672, 1980.

12. BABB, R. S. The pregeniculate nucleus of the monkey (*Macaca mulatta*). II. A study at the electron microscopic level. *J. Comp. Neurol.* 190: 673–697, 1980.

12a. BARLOW, H. B. Summation and inhibition in the frog's retina. *J. Physiol. London* 119: 69–88, 1953.

13. BARLOW, H. B., C. BLAKEMORE, AND J. D. PETTIGREW. The neural mechanisms of binocular depth discrimination. *J. Physiol. London* 193: 327–342, 1967.

14. BARLOW, H. B., R. M. HILL, AND W. R. LEVICK. Retinal ganglion cells responding selectively to direction and speed of image motion in the rabbit. *J. Physiol. London* 173: 377–407, 1964.

15. BARLOW, H. B., AND W. R. LEVICK. The mechanism of directionally selective units in rabbit's retina. *J. Physiol. London* 178: 447–504, 1965.

15a. BARTLEY, S. H. Central mechanisms of vision. In: *Handbook of Physiology. Neurophysiology*, edited by J. Field and H. W. Magoun. Washington, DC: Am. Physiol. Soc., 1959, sect. 1, vol. I, chapt. 30, p. 713–740.

15b. BAUMGARTEN, R. VON, AND R. JUNG. Microelectrode studies on the visual cortex. *Rev. Neurol.* 87: 151–155, 1952.

16. BENEVENTO, L. A., AND J. H. FALLON. The projection of occipital cortex to the dorsal lateral geniculate in the rhesus monkey (*Macaca mulatta*). *Exp. Neurol.* 46: 409–417, 1975.

17. BENEVENTO, L. A., AND J. FALLON. The ascending projections of the superior colliculus in the rhesus monkey (*Macaca mulatta*). *J. Comp. Neurol.* 160: 339–362, 1975.

18. BENEVENTO, L. A., AND M. REZAK. The cortical projections of the inferior pulvinar and adjacent lateral pulvinar in the rhesus monkey (*Macaca mulatta*): an autoradiographic study. *Brain Res.* 108: 1–24, 1976.

19. BENEVENTO, L. A., M. REZAK, AND R. SANTOS-ANDERSON. An autoradiographic study of the projections of the pretectum in the rhesus monkey (*Macaca mulatta*): evidence for sensorimotor links to the thalamus and oculomotor nuclei. *Brain Res.* 127: 197–218, 1977.

20. BERMAN, N., AND E. G. JONES. A retino-pulvinar projection in the cat. *Brain Res.* 134: 237–248, 1977.

21. BERSON, D. M., AND A. M. GRAYBIEL. Parallel thalamic zones in the LP-pulvinar complex of the cat identified by their afferent and efferent connections. *Brain Res.* 147: 139–148, 1978.

22. BILGE, M., A. BINGLE, K. N. SENEVIRATNE, AND D. WHITTERIDGE. A map of the visual cortex in the cat. *J. Physiol. London* 191: 116P–118P, 1967.

23. BILLINGS-GAGLIARDI, S., V. CHAN-PALAY, AND S. L. PALAY. A review of lamination in area 17 of the visual cortex of *Macaca mulatta*. *J. Neurocytol.* 3: 619–629, 1974.

24. BISHOP, G. H., AND M. H. CLARE. Organization and distribution of fibers in the optic tract of the cat. *J. Comp. Neurol.* 103: 269–304, 1955.

25. BISHOP, G. H., M. H. CLARE, AND W. M. LANDAU. Further analysis of fiber groups in the optic tract of the cat. *Exp. Neurol.* 24: 386–399, 1969.

26. BISHOP, P. O. The nature of the representation of the visual fields in the lateral geniculate nucleus. *Proc. Aust. Assoc. Neurol.* 3: 15–25, 1965.

27. BISHOP, P. O. Neurophysiology of binocular single vision and stereopsis. In: *Handbook of Sensory Physiology. Central Processing of Visual Information*, edited by R. Jung. Berlin: Springer-Verlag, 1973, Vol. 7, pt. 3A, p. 255–304.

27a. BISHOP, P. O. Orientation and position disparities in stereopsis. In: *Frontiers in Visual Science*, edited by S. J. Cool and E. L. Smith III. New York: Springer-Verlag, 1978, p. 336–350.

28. BISHOP, P. O. Stereopsis and the random element in the organization of the striate cortex. *Proc. R. Soc. London Ser. B* 204: 415–434, 1979.

29. BISHOP, P. O. Binocular vision. In: *Adler's Physiology of the Eye. Clinical Application* (7th ed.), edited by R. A. Moses. St. Louis, MO: Mosby, 1981, p. 575–649.

30. BISHOP, P. O. Neural mechanisms for binocular depth discrimination. In: *Advances in Physiological Sciences. Sensory Functions*, edited by E. Grastyan and P. Molnar. Oxford: Pergamon, 1981, vol. 16, p. 441–449.

31. BISHOP, P. O., J. S. COOMBS, AND G. H. HENRY. Responses to visual contours: spatio-temporal aspects of excitation in the receptive fields of simple striate neurones. *J. Physiol. London* 219: 625–657, 1971.

32. BISHOP, P. O., J. S. COOMBS, AND G. H. HENRY. Receptive fields of simple cells in the cat striate cortex. *J. Physiol. London* 231: 31–60, 1973.

33. BISHOP, P. O., AND G. H. HENRY. Spatial vision. *Annu. Rev. Psychol.* 22: 119–160, 1971.

34. BISHOP, P. O., AND G. H. HENRY. Striate neurons: receptive field concepts. *Invest. Ophthalmol.* 11: 346–354, 1972.

35. BISHOP, P. O., G. H. HENRY, AND C. J. SMITH. Binocular interaction fields of single units in the cat striate cortex. *J. Physiol. London* 216: 39–68, 1971.

36. BISHOP, P. O., D. JEREMY, AND J. W. LANCE. The optic nerve. Properties of a central tract. *J. Physiol. London* 121: 415–432, 1953.

37. BISHOP, P. O., H. KATO, AND G. A. ORBAN. Direction-selective cells in complex family in cat striate cortex. *J. Neurophysiol.* 43: 1266–1283, 1980.

38. BISHOP, P. O., W. KOZAK, AND G. J. VAKKUR. Some quantitative aspects of the cat's eye: axis and plane of reference, visual field co-ordinates and optics. *J. Physiol. London* 163: 466–502, 1962.

39. BISHOP, P. O., W. KOZAK, W. R. LEVICK, AND G. J. VAKKUR. The determination of the projection of the visual field on to the lateral geniculate nucleus in the cat. *J. Physiol. London* 163: 503–539, 1962.

40. BISHOP, P. O., AND J. G. McLEOD. Nature of potentials associated with synaptic transmission in lateral geniculate of cat. *J. Neurophysiol.* 17: 387–414, 1954.

41. BLAKEMORE, C. Binocular depth discrimination and the nasotemporal division. *J. Physiol. London* 205: 471–497, 1969.

42. BLAKEMORE, C., A. FIORENTINI, AND L. MAFFEI. A second neural mechanism of binocular depth discrimination. *J. Physiol. London* 226: 725–740, 1972.

43. Bonin, G. von. The striate area of primates. *J. Comp. Neurol.* 77: 405–429, 1942.

44. Boycott, B. B., and J. E. Dowling. Organization of the primate retina: light microscopy. *Philos. Trans. R. Soc. London Ser. B* 255: 109–184, 1969.

45. Boycott, B. B., and H. Wässle. The morphological types of ganglion cells of the domestic cat's retina. *J. Physiol. London* 240: 397–419, 1974.

46. Brodmann, K. Beiträge zur histologischen Lokalisation der Grosshirnrinde. Dritte Mitteilung: die Rinderfelder der niederen Affen. *J. Psychol. Neurol. Leipzig* 4: 177–226, 1905.

47. Brodmann, K. *Vergleichende Lokalisationslehre der Grosshirnrinde in ihren Prinzipien dargestellt auf Grund des Zellenbaues.* Leipzig: Barth, 1909, p. 324.

48. Bullier, J., and G. H. Henry. Ordinal position of neurons in cat striate cortex. *J. Neurophysiol.* 42: 1251–1263, 1979.

49. Bullier, J., and G. H. Henry. Neural path taken by afferent streams in striate cortex of the cat. *J. Neurophysiol.* 42: 1264–1270, 1979.

50. Bullier, J., and G. H. Henry. Laminar distribution of first-order neurons and afferent terminals in cat striate cortex. *J. Neurophysiol.* 42: 1271–1281, 1979.

51. Bullier, J., and G. H. Henry. Ordinal position and afferent input of neurons in monkey striate cortex. *J. Comp. Neurol.* 193: 913–935, 1980.

52. Bunt, A. H., A. E. Hendrickson, J. S. Lund, R. D. Lund, and A. F. Fuchs. Monkey retinal ganglion cells: morphometric analysis and tracing of axonal projections, with a consideration of the peroxidase technique. *J. Comp. Neurol.* 164: 265–286, 1975.

53. Burke, W., and A. M. Cole. Extraretinal influences on the lateral geniculate nucleus. *Rev. Physiol. Biochem. Pharmacol.* 80: 105–166, 1978.

54. Burke, W., and A. J. Sefton. Discharge patterns of principal cells and interneurones in lateral geniculate nucleus of rat. *J. Physiol. London* 187: 201–212, 1966.

55. Burke, W., and A. J. Sefton. Recovery of responsiveness of cells of lateral geniculate nucleus of rat. *J. Physiol. London* 187: 213–229, 1966.

56. Burke, W., and A. J. Sefton. Inhibitory mechanisms in lateral geniculate nucleus of rat. *J. Physiol. London* 187: 231–246, 1966.

57. Büttner, V., and A. F. Fuchs. Influence of saccadic eye movements on unit activity in simian lateral geniculate and pregeniculate nuclei. *J. Neurophysiol.* 36: 127–141, 1973.

57a. Cajal, S. R. y. La rétine des vertébrés. *Cellule* 9: 17–257, 1893.

58. Cajal, S. R. y. *Histologie due système nerveux de l'homme et des vertébrés.* Paris: Maloine, 1911, Tome 2. (Repr. 1955, Madrid: CSIC, Instituto Ramón y Cajal.)

59. Cajal, S. R. y. Studien über die Sehrinde der Katze. *J. Psychol. Neurol. Leipzig* 29: 161–181, 1922.

60. Caldwell, J. H., and N. W. Daw. New properties of rabbit retinal ganglion cells. *J. Physiol. London* 276: 257–276, 1978.

61. Campbell, F. W., and J. G. Robson. Application of Fourier analysis to the visibility of gratings. *J. Physiol. London* 197: 551–566, 1968.

62. Campbell, F. W., B. G. Cleland, G. F. Cooper, and C. Enroth-Cugell. The angular selectivity of visual cortical cells to moving gratings. *J. Physiol. London* 198: 237–250, 1968.

63. Campos-Ortega, J. A., and W. R. Hayhow. On the organization of the visual cortical projection to the pulvinar in *Macaca mulatta. Brain Behav. Evol.* 6: 394–423, 1972.

64. Campos-Ortega, J. A., W. R. Hayhow, and P. F. de V. Clüver. A note on the problem of retinal projections to the inferior pulvinar nucleus of primates. *Brain Res.* 22: 126–130, 1970.

65. Campos-Ortega, J. A., W. R. Hayhow, and P. F. de V. Clüver. The descending projections from the cortical visual fields of *Macaca mulatta* with particular reference to the question of a cortico-lateral geniculate-pathway. *Brain Behav. Evol.* 3: 368–414, 1970.

66. Clark, W. E. LeGros. A morphological study of the lateral geniculate body. *Br. J. Ophthalmol.* 16: 264–284, 1932.

67. Clark, W. E. LeGros, and G. G. Penman. The projection of the retina in the lateral geniculate body. *Proc. R. Soc. London Ser. B* 114: 291–313, 1934.

68. Cleland, B. G., M. W. Dubin, and W. R. Levick. Simultaneous recording of input and output of lateral geniculate neurones. *Nature London New Biol.* 231: 191–192, 1971.

69. Cleland, B. G., M. W. Dubin, and W. R. Levick. Sustained and transient neurones in the cat's retina and lateral geniculate nucleus. *J. Physiol. London* 217: 473–496, 1971.

70. Cleland, B. G., T. H. Harding, and U. Tulunay-Keesey. Visual resolution and receptive field size: examinations of two kinds of cat retinal ganglion cell. *Science* 205: 1015–1017, 1979.

71. Cleland, B. G., and W. R. Levick. Brisk and sluggish concentrically organized ganglion cells in the cat's retina. *J. Physiol. London* 240: 421–456, 1974.

72. Cleland, B. G., and W. R. Levick. Properties of rarely encountered types of ganglion cells in the cat's retina and an overall classification. *J. Physiol. London* 240: 457–492, 1974.

73. Cleland, B. G., W. R. Levick, R. Morstyn, and H. G. Wagner. Lateral geniculate relay of slowly conducting retinal afferents to cat visual cortex. *J. Physiol. London* 255: 299–320, 1976.

74. Cleland, B. G., W. R. Levick, and K. J. Sanderson. Properties of sustained and transient ganglion cells in the cat retina. *J. Physiol. London* 228: 649–680, 1973.

75. Cleland, B. G., W. R. Levick, and H. Wässle. Physiological identification of a morphological class of cat retinal ganglion cells. *J. Physiol. London* 248: 151–171, 1975.

75a. Cleland, B. G., R. Morstyn, H. G. Wagner, and W. R. Levick. Long-latency retinal input to lateral geniculate neurones of the cat. *Brain Res.* 91: 306–310, 1975.

76. Cooper, G. F., and J. G. Robson. Successive transformations of spatial information in the visual system. In: *IEE/NPL Conference on Pattern Recognition. IEE Conf. Publ. London* 42: 134–143, 1968.

77. Cowan, W. M., D. I. Gottlieb, A. E. Hendrickson, J. L. Price, and T. A. Woolsey. The autoradiographic demonstration of axonal connections in the central nervous system. *Brain Res.* 37: 21–51, 1972.

78. Cowey, A., and V. H. Perry. The projection of the fovea to the superior colliculus in rhesus monkeys. *Neuroscience* 5: 53–62, 1980.

79. Creutzfeldt, O., G. M. Innocenti, and D. Brooks. Vertical organization in the visual cortex (area 17) in the cat. *Exp. Brain Res.* 21: 315–336, 1974.

80. Creutzfeldt, O. D., B. B. Lee, and A. Elepfandt. A quantitative study of chromatic organization and receptive fields of cells in the lateral geniculate body of the rhesus monkey. *Exp. Brain Res.* 35: 527–545, 1979.

81. Cynader, M., and D. Regan. Neurones in cat parastriate cortex sensitive to the direction of motion in three-dimensional space. *J. Physiol. London* 274: 549–569, 1978.

82. Daniel, P. M., and D. Whitteridge. The representation of the visual field on the cerebral cortex in monkeys. *J. Physiol. London* 159: 203–221, 1961.

83. Davis, T. L., and P. Sterling. Microcircuitry of cat visual cortex: classification of neurons in layer IV of area 17, and identification of the patterns of lateral geniculate input. *J. Comp. Neurol.* 188: 599–628, 1979.

84. De Monasterio, F. M. Properties of concentrically organized X and Y ganglion cells of macaque retina. *J. Neurophysiol.* 41: 1394–1417, 1978.

85. De Monasterio, F. M. Center and surround mechanisms of opponent-color X and Y ganglion cells of retina of macaques. *J. Neurophysiol.* 41: 1418–1434, 1978.

86. De Monasterio, F. M. Properties of ganglion cells with atypical receptive-field organization in retina of macaques. *J. Neurophysiol.* 41: 1435–1449, 1978.

87. De Monasterio, F. M. Functional properties and presumed

roles of retinal ganglion cells of the monkey. In: *Advances in Physiological Sciences. Regulatory Functions of the CNS: Subsystems*, edited by J. Szentagothai, J. Hamori, and M. Palkovits. Oxford: Academic, 1981, vol. 2, p. 261–270.

88. DE MONASTERIO, F. M., AND P. GOURAS. Functional properties of ganglion cells of the rhesus monkey retina. *J. Physiol. London* 251: 167–196, 1975.

89. DE MONASTERIO, F. M., AND P. GOURAS. Responses of macaque ganglion cells to far violet lights. *Vision Res.* 17: 1147–1156, 1977.

90. DE MONASTERIO, F. M., P. GOURAS, AND D. J. TOLHURST. Trichromatic colour opponency in ganglion cells of the rhesus monkey retina. *J. Physiol. London* 251: 197–216, 1975.

91. DE MONASTERIO, F. M., P. GOURAS, AND D. J. TOLHURST. Concealed colour opponency in ganglion cells of the rhesus monkey retina. *J. Physiol. London* 251: 217–229, 1975.

92. DE MONASTERIO, F. M., P. GOURAS, AND D. J. TOLHURST. Spatial summation, response pattern and conduction velocity of ganglion cells of the rhesus monkey retina. *Vision Res.* 16, 674–678, 1976.

93. DE MONASTERIO, F. M., AND S. J. SCHEIN. Protan-like spectral sensitivity of foveal Y ganglion cells of the retina of macaque monkeys. *J. Physiol. London* 299: 385–396, 1980.

94. DENNY-BROWN, D., AND R. A. CHAMBERS. Physiological aspects of visual perception. I. Functional aspects of visual cortex. *Arch. Neurol. Chicago* 33: 219–227, 1976.

95. DE VALOIS, R. L. Central mechanisms of color vision. In: *Handbook of Sensory Physiology. Central Processing of Visual Information*, edited by R. Jung. Berlin: Springer-Verlag, 1973, vol. 7, pt. 3A, p. 209–253.

96. DE VALOIS, R. L., I. ABRAMOV, AND G. H. JACOBS. Analysis of response patterns of LGN cells. *J. Opt. Soc. Am.* 56: 966–977, 1966.

97. DE VALOIS, R. L., I. ABRAMOV, AND W. R. MEAD. Single cell analysis of wavelength discrimination at the lateral geniculate nucleus in the macaque. *J. Neurophysiol.* 30: 415–433, 1967.

98. DOW, B. M. Functional classes of cells and their laminar distribution in monkey visual cortex. *J. Neurophysiol.* 37: 927–946, 1974.

99. DOW, B. M., AND P. GOURAS. Color and spatial specificity of single units in rhesus monkey foveal striate cortex. *J. Neurophysiol.* 36: 79–100, 1973.

100. DREHER, B. Hypercomplex cells in the cat's striate cortex. *Invest. Ophthalmol.* 11: 355–356, 1972.

101. DREHER, B., Y. FUKADA, AND R. W. RODIECK. Identification, classification and anatomical segregation of cells with X-like and Y-like properties in the lateral geniculate nucleus of old-world primates. *J. Physiol. London* 258: 433–452, 1976.

102. DREHER, B., AND A. J. SEFTON. Properties of neurons in cat's dorsal lateral geniculate nucleus: a comparison between medial interlaminar and laminated parts of the nucleus. *J. Comp. Neurol.* 183: 47–64, 1979.

103. DUBIN, M. W., AND B. G. CLELAND. Organization of visual inputs to interneurons of lateral geniculate nucleus of the cat. *J. Neurophysiol.* 40: 410–427, 1977.

104. EMERSON, R. C., AND G. L. GERSTEIN. Simple striate neurons in the cat. I. Comparison of responses to moving and stationary stimuli. *J. Neurophysiol.* 40: 119–135, 1977.

105. ENROTH-CUGELL, C., AND J. G. ROBSON. The contrast sensitivity of retinal ganglion cells of the cat. *J. Physiol. London* 187: 517–552, 1966.

106. FAMIGLIETTI, E. V., JR. Dendro-dendritic synapses in the lateral geniculate nucleus of the cat. *Brain Res.* 20: 181–191, 1970.

107. FAMIGLIETTI, E. V., JR. Another look at lateral geniculate lamination in the cat. *Neurosci. Abstr.* 1: 41, 1975.

108. FAMIGLIETTI, E. V., JR., AND H. KOLB. Structural basis for on- and off-center responses in retinal ganglion cells. *Science* 194: 193–195, 1976.

109. FAMIGLIETTI, E. V., JR., AND A. PETERS. The synaptic glomerulus and the intrinsic neuron in the dorsal lateral geniculate nucleus of the cat. *J. Comp. Neurol.* 144: 285–334, 1972.

110. FERSTER, D., AND S. LEVAY. The axonal arborizations of lateral geniculate neurons in the striate cortex of the cat. *J. Comp. Neurol.* 182: 923–944, 1978.

111. FINK, R. P., AND L. HEIMER. Two methods for selective impregnation of degenerating axons and their synaptic endings in the central nervous system. *Brain Res.* 4: 369–374, 1967.

112. FINLAY, B. L., P. H. SCHILLER, AND S. F. VOLMAN. Quantitative studies of single-cell properties in monkey striate cortex. IV. Corticotectal cells. *J. Neurophysiol.* 39: 1352–1361, 1976.

113. FISCHER, B., AND J. KRÜGER. Disparity tuning and binocularity of single neurons in cat visual cortex. *Exp. Brain Res.* 35: 1–8, 1979.

114. FISKEN, R. A., L. J. GAREY, AND T. P. S. POWELL. Patterns of degeneration after intrinsic lesions of the visual cortex (area 17) of the monkey. *Brain Res.* 53: 208–213, 1973.

115. FISKEN, R. A., L. J. GAREY, AND T. P. S. POWELL. The intrinsic, association and commissural connections of area 17 of the visual cortex. *Philos. Trans. R. Soc. London Ser. B* 272: 487–536, 1975.

116. FRIEDLANDER, M. J., C. S. LIN, AND S. M. SHERMAN. Structure of physiologically identified X and Y cells in the cat's lateral geniculate nucleus. *Science* 204: 1114–1117, 1979.

117. FUKADA, Y. Receptive field organization of cat optic nerve fibers with special reference to conduction velocity. *Vision Res.* 11: 209–226, 1971.

118. FUKUDA, Y., AND J. STONE. Retinal distribution and central projections of Y-, X-, and W-cells of the cat's retina. *J. Neurophysiol.* 37: 749–772, 1974.

119. GAREY, L. J. A light and electron microscopic study of the visual cortex of the cat and monkey. *Proc. R. Soc. London Ser. B* 179: 21–40, 1971.

120. GAREY, L. J., E. G. JONES, AND T. P. S. POWELL. Interrelationships of striate and extrastriate cortex with the primary relay sites of the visual pathway. *J. Neurol. Neurosurg. Psychiatry* 31: 135–157, 1968.

121. GAREY, L. J., AND T. P. S. POWELL. The projection of the retina in the cat. *J. Anat.* 102: 189–222, 1968.

122. GAREY, L. J., AND T. P. S. POWELL. An experimental study of the termination of the lateral geniculo-cortical pathway in the cat and monkey. *Proc. R. Soc. London Ser. B* 179: 41–63, 1971.

123. GEISERT, E. E., JR. Cortical projections of the lateral geniculate nucleus in the cat. *J. Comp. Neurol.* 190: 793–812, 1980.

124. GILBERT, C. D. Laminar differences in receptive field properties of cells in cat primary visual cortex. *J. Physiol. London* 268: 391–421, 1977.

125. GILBERT, C. D., AND J. P. KELLY. The projections of cells in different layers of the cat's visual cortex. *J. Comp. Neurol.* 163: 81–106, 1975.

126. GILBERT, C. D., AND T. N. WIESEL. Morphology and intracortical projections of functionally characterised neurones in the cat visual cortex. *Nature London* 280: 120–125, 1979.

127. GLEZER, V. D., V. A. IVANOFF, AND T. A. TSHERBACH. Investigation of complex and hypercomplex receptive fields of visual cortex of the cat as spatial frequency filters. *Vision Res.* 13: 1875–1904, 1973.

128. GLICKSTEIN, M., AND D. WHITTERIDGE. Degeneration of layer III pyramidal cells in area 18 following destruction of callosal input. *Anat. Rec.* 178: 362–363, 1974.

129. GODFRAIND, J.-M., M. MEULDERS, AND C. VERAART. Visual receptive fields of neurons in pulvinar, nucleus lateralis posterior and nucleus suprageniculatus thalami of the cat. *Brain Res.* 15: 552–555, 1969.

130. GODFRAIND, J.-M., M. MEULDERS, AND C. VERAART. Visual properties of neurons in pulvinar, nucleus lateralis posterior and nucleus suprageniculatus thalami in the cat. I. Qualitative investigation. *Brain Res.* 44: 503–526, 1972.

131. GOLDBERG, M. E., AND R. H. WURTZ. Activity of superior colliculus in behaving monkey. II. Effect of attention on neuronal responses. *J. Neurophysiol.* 35: 560–574, 1972.

132. GOODWIN, A. W., AND G. H. HENRY. Direction selectivity of complex cells in a comparison with simple cells. *J. Neurophysiol.* 38: 1524–1540, 1975.

133. GOODWIN, A. W., G. H. HENRY, AND P. O. BISHOP. Direction selectivity of simple striate cells: properties and mechanism. *J. Neurophysiol.* 38: 1500–1523, 1975.

134. GOURAS, P. Identification of cone mechanisms of monkey ganglion cells. *J. Physiol. London* 199: 533–547, 1968.

135. GOURAS, P. Antidromic responses of orthodromically identified ganglion cells in monkey retina. *J. Physiol. London* 204: 407–419, 1969.

136. GOURAS, P. Opponent-colour cells in different layers of foveal striate cortex. *J. Physiol. London* 238: 583–602, 1974.

137. GOURAS, P., AND J. KRÜGER. Responses of cells in foveal visual cortex of the monkey to pure color contrast. *J. Neurophysiol.* 42: 850–860, 1979.

138. GRAYBIEL, A. M. Some extrageniculate visual pathways in the cat. *Invest. Ophthalmol.* 11: 322–331, 1972.

139. GRAYBIEL, A. M., AND D. M. BERSON. Histochemical identification and afferent connections of subdivisions in the lateralis posterior-pulvinar complex and related thalamic nuclei in the cat. *Neuroscience* 5: 1175–1238, 1980.

140. GUILLERY, R. W. A study of Golgi preparations from the dorsal lateral geniculate nucleus of the adult cat. *J. Comp. Neurol.* 128: 21–50, 1966.

141. GUILLERY, R. W. Patterns of fiber degeneration in the dorsal lateral geniculate nucleus of the cat following lesions in the visual cortex. *J. Comp. Neurol.* 130: 197–222, 1967.

142. GUILLERY, R. W. The organization of synaptic interconnections in the laminae of the dorsal lateral geniculate nucleus of the cat. *Z. Zellforsch. Mikrosk. Anat.* 96: 1–38, 1969.

143. GUILLERY, R. W. A quantitative study of synaptic interconnections in the dorsal lateral geniculate nucleus of the cat. *Z. Zellforsch. Mikrosk. Anat.* 96: 39–48, 1969.

144. GUILLERY, R. W. The laminar distribution of retinal fibers in the dorsal lateral geniculate nucleus of the cat: a new interpretation. *J. Comp. Neurol.* 138: 339–368, 1970.

145. GUILLERY, R. W. Patterns of synaptic interconnections in the dorsal lateral geniculate nucleus of cat and monkey: a brief review. *Vision Res. Suppl.* 3: 211–227, 1971.

146. HAMMOND, P., AND D. P. ANDREWS. Orientation tuning of cells in area 17 and 18 of the cat's visual cortex. *Exp. Brain Res.* 31: 341–351, 1978.

147. HAMMOND, P., AND D. M. MACKAY. Differential responsiveness of simple and complex cells in cat striate cortex to visual texture. *Exp. Brain Res.* 30: 275–296, 1977.

148. HARTLINE, H. K. The response of single optic nerve fibers of the vertebrate eye to illumination of the retina. *Am. J. Physiol.* 121: 400–415, 1938.

149. HARTLINE, H. K. The receptive fields of optic nerve fibers. *Am. J. Physiol.* 130: 690–699, 1940.

150. HARVEY, A. R. Characteristics of corticothalamic neurons in area 17 of the cat. *Neurosci. Lett.* 7: 177–181, 1978.

151. HARVEY, A. R. A physiological analysis of subcortical and commissural projections of areas 17 and 18 of the cat. *J. Physiol. London* 302: 507–534, 1980.

152. HAYHOW, W. R. The cytoarchitecture of the lateral geniculate body in the cat in relation to the distribution of crossed and uncrossed optic fibers. *J. Comp. Neurol.* 110: 1–64, 1958.

153. HENDRICKSON, A. The pregeniculate nucleus in the monkey. *Anat. Rec.* 175: 341, 1973.

154. HENDRICKSON, A. E., J. R. WILSON, AND M. P. OGREN. The neuroanatomical organization of pathways between the dorsal lateral geniculate nucleus and visual cortex in Old World and New World primates. *J. Comp. Neurol.* 182: 123–136, 1978.

155. HENDRICKSON, A., M. E. WILSON, AND M. J. TOYNE. The distribution of optic nerve fibers in *Macaca mulatta*. *Brain Res.* 23: 425–427, 1970.

156. HENRY, G. H. Receptive field classes of cells in the striate cortex of the cat. *Brain Res.* 133: 1–28, 1977.

157. HENRY, G. H., B. DREHER, AND P. O. BISHOP. Orientation specificity of cells in the cat striate cortex. *J. Neurophysiol.* 37: 1394–1409, 1974.

158. HENRY, G. H., A. R. HARVEY, AND J. S. LUND. The afferent connections and laminar distribution of cells in the cat striate cortex. *J. Comp. Neurol.* 187: 725–744, 1979.

159. HENRY, G. H., J. S. LUND, AND A. R. HARVEY. Cells of the striate cortex projecting to the Clare-Bishop area of the cat. *Brain Res.* 151: 154–158, 1978.

160. HICKEY, T. L., AND R. W. GUILLERY. An autoradiographic study of retinogeniculate pathways in the cat and the fox. *J. Comp. Neurol.* 156: 239–254, 1974.

161. HOCHSTEIN, S., AND R. M. SHAPLEY. Quantitative analysis of retinal ganglion cell classifications. *J. Physiol. London* 262: 237–264, 1976.

162. HOFFMAN, K.-P., AND J. STONE. Conduction velocity of afferents to cat visual cortex: a correlation with cortical receptive field properties. *Brain Res.* 32: 460–466, 1971.

162a. HOFFMANN, K.-P., J. STONE, AND S. M. SHERMAN. Relay of receptive-field properties in dorsal lateral geniculate nucleus of the cat. *J. Neurophysiol.* 35: 518–531, 1972.

163. HOLLÄNDER, H. On the origin of the corticotectal projections in the cat. *Exp. Brain Res.* 21: 433–439, 1974.

164. HOLLÄNDER, H., AND L. MARTINEZ-MILLÁN. Autoradiographic evidence for a topographically organized projection from the striate cortex to the lateral geniculate nucleus in the rhesus monkey (*Macaca mulatta*). *Brain Res.* 100: 407–411, 1975.

165. HOLLÄNDER, H., AND H. VANEGAS. The projection from the lateral geniculate nucleus onto the visual cortex in the cat. A quantitative study with horseradish peroxidase. *J. Comp. Neurol.* 173: 519–536, 1977.

166. HUBEL, D. H., AND D. C. FREEMAN. Projection into the visual field of ocular dominance columns in macaque monkey. *Brain Res.* 122: 336–343, 1977.

167. HUBEL, D. H., AND T. N. WIESEL. Receptive fields of single neurones in the cat's striate cortex. *J. Physiol. London* 148: 574–591, 1959.

168. HUBEL, D. H., AND T. N. WIESEL. Receptive fields of optic nerve fibres in the spider monkey. *J. Physiol. London* 154: 572–580, 1960.

169. HUBEL, D. H., AND T. N. WIESEL. Receptive fields, binocular interaction and functional architecture in the cat's visual cortex. *J. Physiol. London* 160: 106–154, 1962.

170. HUBEL, D. H., AND T. N. WIESEL. Shape and arrangement of columns in cat's striate cortex. *J. Physiol. London* 165: 559–568, 1963.

171. HUBEL, D. H., AND T. N. WIESEL. Receptive fields and functional architecture in two nonstriate visual areas (18 and 19) of the cat. *J. Neurophysiol.* 28: 229–289, 1965.

172. HUBEL, D. H., AND T. N. WIESEL. Binocular interaction in striate cortex of kittens reared with artificial squint. *J. Neurophysiol.* 28: 1041–1059, 1965.

173. HUBEL, D. H., AND T. N. WIESEL. Receptive fields and functional architecture of monkey striate cortex. *J. Physiol. London* 195: 215–243, 1968.

174. HUBEL, D. H., AND T. N. WIESEL. Anatomical demonstration of columns in the monkey striate cortex. *Nature London* 221: 747–750, 1969.

175. HUBEL, D. H., AND T. N. WIESEL. Cells sensitive to binocular depth in area 18 of the macaque monkey cortex. *Nature London* 225: 41–42, 1970.

176. HUBEL, D. H., AND T. N. WIESEL. Laminar and columnar distribution of geniculo-cortical fibers in the macaque monkey. *J. Comp. Neurol.* 146: 421–450, 1972.

177. HUBEL, D. H., AND T. N. WIESEL. Sequence regularity and geometry of orientation columns in the monkey striate cortex. *J. Comp. Neurol.* 158: 267–294, 1974.

178. HUBEL, D. H., AND T. N. WIESEL. Uniformity of monkey striate cortex: a parallel relationship between field size, scatter and magnification factor. *J. Comp. Neurol.* 158: 295–306, 1974.

179. HUBEL, D. H., AND T. N. WIESEL. Functional architecture of macaque visual cortex. *Proc. R. Soc. London Ser. B* 198: 1–59, 1977.

180. HUBEL, D. H., T. N. WIESEL, AND S. LEVAY. Plasticity of ocular dominance columns in monkey striate cortex. *Philos. Trans. R. Soc. London Ser. B* 278: 377–409, 1977.

181. HUBEL, D. H., T. N. WIESEL, AND M. P. STRYKER. Orientation columns in macaque monkey visual cortex demonstrated by the 2-deoxyglucose autoradiographic technique. *Nature London* 269: 328–330, 1977.

182. HUBEL, D. H., T. N. WIESEL, AND M. P. STRYKER. Anatomical demonstration of orientation columns in macaque monkey. *J. Comp. Neurol.* 177: 361–380, 1978.

183. HUGHES, A. A quantitative analysis of the cat retinal ganglion cell topography. *J. Comp. Neurol.* 163: 107–128, 1975.

184. HUGHES, A. Population magnitudes and distribution of the major model classes of cat retinal ganglion cell as estimated from HRP filling and a systematic survey of the soma diameter spectra for classical neurones. *J. Comp. Neurol.* 197: 303–339, 1981.

185. IKEDA, H., AND M. J. WRIGHT. Evidence of "sustained" and "transient" neurones in the cat's visual cortex. *Vision Res.* 14: 133–136, 1974.

186. IKEDA, H., AND M. J. WRIGHT. Spatial and temporal properties of "sustained" and "transient" neurones in area 17 of the cat's visual cortex. *Exp. Brain Res.* 22: 363–383, 1975.

187. INGRAM, W. R., F. I. HANNETT, AND S. W. RANSON. The topography of the nuclei of the diencephalon of the cat. *J. Comp. Neurol.* 55: 333–394, 1932.

188. INNOCENTI, G. M., AND L. FIORE. Morphological correlates of visual transformation in the corpus callosum. *Neurosci. Lett.* 2: 245–252, 1976.

189. JOSHUA, D. E., AND P. O. BISHOP. Binocular single vision and depth discrimination. Receptive field disparities for central and peripheral vision and binocular interaction on peripheral single units in cat striate cortex. *Exp. Brain Res.* 10: 389–416, 1970.

189a.JUNG, R., R. VON BAUMGARTEN, AND G. BAUMGARTNER. Mikroableitungen von einzelnen Nervenzellen im optischen Cortex der Katze: Die lichtaktivierten B-Neurone. *Arch. Psychiatr. Nervenkr.* 189: 521–539, 1952.

190. KAAS, J. H., R. W. GUILLERY, AND J. M. ALLMAN. Some principles of organization in the dorsal lateral geniculate nucleus. *Brain Behav. Evol.* 6: 253–299, 1972.

191. KAAS, J. H., M. F. HUERTA, J. T. WEBER, AND J. K. HARTING. Patterns of retinal terminations and laminar organization of the lateral geniculate nucleus of primates. *J. Comp. Neurol.* 182: 517–554, 1978.

192. KALIA, M., AND D. WHITTERIDGE. The visual area in the splenial sulcus of the cat. *J. Physiol. London* 232: 275–283, 1973.

193. KALIL, R., AND J. WORDEN. Cytoplasmic laminated bodies in the lateral geniculate nucleus of normal and dark reared cats. *J. Comp. Neurol.* 178: 469–486, 1978.

194. KATO, H. Types of neurons in the sliced LGB of cat. *Brain Res.* 66: 332–336, 1974.

195. KATO, H., P. O. BISHOP, AND G. A. ORBAN. Hypercomplex and simple/complex cell classifications in cat striate cortex. *J. Neurophysiol.* 41: 1071–1095, 1978.

196. KATO, H., P. O. BISHOP, AND G. A. ORBAN. Binocular interaction on monocularly discharged lateral geniculate and striate neurons in the cat. *J. Neurophysiol.* 46: 932–951, 1981.

197. KAWAMURA, S. Topical organization of the extra geniculate visual system in the cat. *Exp. Neurol.* 45: 451–461, 1974.

198. KAWAMURA, S., N. FUKUSHIMA, AND S. HATTORI. Topographical origin and ganglion cell types of the retino-pulvinar projection in the cat. *Brain Res.* 173: 419–429, 1979.

199. KAWAMURA, S., J. M. SPRAGUE, AND K. NIIMI. Corticofugal projections from the visual cortices to the thalamus, pretectum and superior colliculus in the cat. *J. Comp. Neurol.* 158: 339–362, 1974.

200. KELLY, J. P., AND C. D. GILBERT. The projection of different morphological types of ganglion cells in the cat retina. *J. Comp. Neurol.* 163: 65–80, 1975.

201. KELLY, J. P., AND D. C. VAN ESSEN. Cell structure and function in the visual cortex of the cat. *J. Physiol. London* 238: 515–547, 1974.

202. KENNEDY, C., M. H. DES ROSIERS, O. SAKURADA, M. SHINOHARA, M. REIVICH, J. W. JEHLE, AND L. SOKOLOFF. Metabolic mapping of the primary visual system of the monkey by means of the autoradiographic [^{14}C]deoxyglucose technique. *Proc. Natl. Acad. Sci. USA* 73: 4230–4234, 1976.

202a.KENNEDY, C., M. DES ROSIERS, L. SOKOLOFF, M. REIVICH, AND J. JEHLE. The ocular dominance columns of the striate cortex as studied by the deoxyglucose method for measurement of local cerebral glucose utilization. *Trans. Am. Neurol. Assoc.* 100: 74–77, 1975.

203. KINSTON, W. J., M. A. VADAS, AND P. O. BISHOP. Multiple projection of the visual field to the medial portion of the dorsal lateral geniculate nucleus and the adjacent nuclei of the thalamus of the cat. *J. Comp. Neurol.* 136: 295–316, 1969.

204. KIRK, D. L., B. G. CLELAND, AND W. R. LEVICK. Axonal conduction latencies of cat retinal ganglion cells. *J. Neurophysiol.* 38: 1395–1402, 1975.

205. KIRK, D. L., B. G. CLELAND, H. WÄSSLE, AND W. R. LEVICK. Axonal conduction latencies of cat retinal ganglion cells in central and peripheral retina. *Exp. Brain Res.* 23: 85–90, 1975.

206. KIRK, D. L., W. R. LEVICK, AND B. G. CLELAND. The crossed or uncrossed destination of axons of sluggish-concentric and non-concentric cat retinal ganglion cells, with an overall synthesis of the visual field representation. *Vision Res.* 16: 233–236, 1976.

207. KIRK, D. L., W. R. LEVICK, B. G. CLELAND, AND H. WÄSSLE. Crossed and uncrossed representation of the visual field by brisk-sustained and brisk-transient cat retinal ganglion cells. *Vision Res.* 16: 225–231, 1976.

208. KRATZ, K. E., S. V. WEBB, AND S. M. SHERMAN. Effects of early monocular lid suture upon neurons in the cat's medial interlaminar nucleus. *J. Comp. Neurol.* 181: 615–626, 1978.

209. KRISTENSSON, K., AND Y. OLSSON. Retrograde axonal transport of protein. *Brain Res.* 29: 363–365, 1971.

210. KRÜGER, J. Stimulus dependent colour specificity of monkey lateral geniculate neurones. *Exp. Brain Res.* 30: 297–311, 1977.

210a.KRÜGER, J., AND P. GOURAS. Spectral selectivity of cells and its dependence on slit length in monkey visual cortex. *J. Neurophysiol.* 43: 1055–1069, 1980.

210b.KUFFLER, S. W. Neurons in the retina: Organization, inhibition and excitation problems. *Cold Spring Harbor Symp. Quant. Biol.* 17: 281–292, 1952.

211. KUFFLER, S. W. Discharge patterns and functional organization of mammalian retina. *J. Neurophysiol.* 16: 37–68, 1953.

212. KULIKOWSKI, J. J., AND P. O. BISHOP. Fourier analysis and spatial representation in the visual cortex. *Experientia* 37: 160–163, 1981.

213. KULIKOWSKI, J. J., AND P. O. BISHOP. Linear analysis of the responses of simple cells in the cat visual cortex. *Exp. Brain Res.* 44: 386–400, 1981.

214. KULIKOWSKI, J. J., AND P. O. BISHOP. Silent periodic cells in the cat striate cortex. *Vision Res.* 22: 191–200, 1982.

215. KULIKOWSKI, J. J., P. O. BISHOP, AND H. KATO. Spatial arrangements of responses by cells in the visual cortex to light and dark bars and edges. *Exp. Brain Res.* 44: 371–385, 1981.

216. KULIKOWSKI, J. J., AND P. E. KING-SMITH. Spatial arrangement of the line, edge and grating detectors revealed by subthreshold summation. *Vision Res.* 13: 1455–1478, 1973.

217. LASEK, R., B. S. JOSEPH, AND D. G. WHITLOCK. Evaluation of a radioautographic neuroanatomical tracing method. *Brain Res.* 8: 319–336, 1968.

218. LATIES, A. M., AND J. M. SPRAGUE. The projection of optic fibers to the visual centers in the cat. *J. Comp. Neurol.* 127: 35–70, 1966.

219. LaVAIL, J. H., AND M. M. LaVAIL. Retrograde axonal transport in the central nervous system. *Science* 176: 1416–1417, 1972.

220. LEE, B. B., K. ALBUS, P. HEGGELUND, M. J. HULME, AND O. D. CREUTZFELDT. The depth distribution of optimal stimulus orientations for neurones in cat area 17. *Exp. Brain Res.* 27: 301–314, 1977.

221. LEE, B. B., B. G. CLELAND, AND O. D. CREUTZFELDT. The retinal input to cells in area 17 of the cat's cortex. *Exp. Brain Res.* 30: 527–538, 1977.

222. LEE, B. B., O. D. CREUTZFELDT, AND A. ELEPFANDT. The

responses of magno- and parvocellular cells of the monkey's lateral geniculate body to moving stimuli. *Exp. Brain Res.* 35: 547-557, 1979.

223. LENNIE, P. Parallel visual pathways: a review. *Vision Res.* 20: 561-594, 1980.

224. LETTVIN, J. Y., H. R. MATURANA, W. S. MCCULLOCH, AND W. H. PITTS. What the frog's eye tells the frog's brain. *Proc. IRE* 47: 1940-1951, 1959.

224a.LETTVIN, J. Y., H. R. MATURANA, W. H. PITTS, AND W. S. MCCULLOCH. Two remarks on the visual system of the frog. In: *Sensory Communication. Contributions to the Symposium on Principles of Sensory Communication*, edited by W. A. Rosenblith. New York: Wiley, 1961, p. 757-776.

225. LEVAY, S. Synaptic patterns in the visual cortex of the cat and monkey. Electron microscopy of Golgi preparations. *J. Comp. Neurol.* 150: 53-86, 1973.

226. LEVAY, S., AND D. FERSTER. Relay cell classes in the lateral geniculate nucleus of the cat and the effects of visual deprivation. *J. Comp. Neurol.* 172: 563-584, 1977.

227. LEVAY, S., AND C. D. GILBERT. Laminar patterns of geniculocortical projection in the cat. *Brain Res.* 113: 1-19, 1976.

228. LEVAY, S., D. H. HUBEL, AND T. N. WIESEL. The pattern of ocular dominance columns in macaque visual cortex revealed by a reduced silver stain. *J. Comp. Neurol.* 159: 559-576, 1975.

229. LEVAY, S., AND M. P. STRYKER. The development of ocular dominance columns in the cat. *Soc. Neurosci. Symp.* 4: 83-98, 1979.

230. LEVAY, S., M. P. STRYKER, AND C. J. SHATZ. Ocular dominance columns and their development in layer IV of the cat's visual cortex: a quantitative study. *J. Comp. Neurol.* 179: 223-244, 1978.

231. LEVAY, S., T. N. WIESEL, AND D. H. HUBEL. The development of ocular dominance columns in normal and visually deprived monkeys. *J. Comp. Neurol.* 191: 1-51, 1980.

232. LEVENTHAL, A. G., AND H. V. B. HIRSCH. Receptive-field properties of neurons in different laminae of visual cortex of the cat. *J. Neurophysiol.* 41: 948-962, 1978.

233. LEVICK, W. R. Receptive fields and trigger features of ganglion cells in the visual streak of the rabbit's retina. *J. Physiol. London* 188: 285-307, 1967.

234. LEVICK, W. R. Form and function of cat retinal ganglion cells. *Nature London* 254: 659-662, 1975.

235. LEVICK, W. R. Participation of brisk-transient retinal ganglion cells in binocular vision—an hypothesis. *Proc. Aust. Physiol. Pharmacol. Soc.* 8: 9-16, 1977.

236. LEVICK, W. R., AND B. G. CLELAND. Receptive fields of cat retinal ganglion cells having slowly conducting axons. *Brain Res.* 74: 156-160, 1974.

237. LEVICK, W. R., B. G. CLELAND, AND M. W. DUBIN. Lateral geniculate neurones of cat: retinal inputs and physiology. *Invest. Ophthalmol.* 11: 302-311, 1972.

238. LEVICK, W. R., AND L. N. THIBOS. X/Y analysis of sluggish-concentric retinal ganglion cells of the cat. *Exp. Brain Res.* 41: A5, 1980.

239. LI, CH.-L., A. ORTIZ-GALVIN, S. N. CHOU, AND S. Y. HOWARD. Cortical intracellular potentials in response to stimulation of lateral geniculate body. *J. Neurophysiol.* 23: 592-601, 1960.

240. LIEBERMAN, A. R. Neurons with presynaptic perikarya and presynaptic dendrites in the rat lateral geniculate nucleus. *Brain Res.* 59: 35-59, 1973.

241. LIEBERMAN, A. R., AND K. E. WEBSTER. Aspects of the synaptic organization of intrinsic neurons in the dorsal lateral geniculate nucleus. An ultrastructural study of the normal and of the experimentally deafferented nucleus in the rat. *J. Neurocytol.* 3: 677-710, 1974.

242. LIN, C. S., K. E. KRATZ, AND S. M. SHERMAN. Percentage of relay cells in the cat's lateral geniculate nucleus. *Brain Res.* 131: 167-173, 1977.

243. LORENTE DE NÓ, R. Studies on the structure of the cerebral cortex. II. Continuation of the study of the ammonic system. *J. Psychol. Neurol. Leipzig* 46: 113-177, 1934.

244. LUND, J. S. Organization of neurons in the visual cortex, area 17, of the monkey (*Macaca mulatta*). *J. Comp. Neurol.* 147: 455-496, 1973.

245. LUND, J. S., AND R. G. BOOTHE. Interlaminar connections and pyramidal neuron organization in the visual cortex, area 17, of the macaque monkey. *J. Comp. Neurol.* 159: 305-334, 1975.

246. LUND, J. S., G. H. HENRY, C. L. MACQUEEN, AND A. R. HARVEY. Anatomical organization of the primary visual cortex (area 17) of the cat. A comparison with area 17 of the macaque monkey. *J. Comp. Neurol.* 184: 599-618, 1979.

247. LUND, J. S., R. D. LUND, A. E. HENDRICKSON, A. H. BUNT, AND A. F. FUCHS. The origin of efferent pathways from the primary visual cortex, area 17, of the macaque monkey as shown by retrograde transport of horseradish peroxidase. *J. Comp. Neurol.* 164: 287-304, 1975.

248. MACIEWICZ, R. J. Thalamic afferents to areas 17, 18 and 19 of cat cortex traced with horseradish peroxidase. *Brain Res.* 84: 308-312, 1975.

249. MAFFEI, L., AND A. FIORENTINI. The visual cortex as a spatial frequency analyzer. *Vision Res.* 13: 1255-1268, 1973.

250. MAGALHÃES-CASTRO, H. H., P. E. S. SARAIVA, AND B. MAGALHÃES-CASTRO. Identification of corticotectal cells of the visual cortex of cats by means of horseradish peroxidase. *Brain Res.* 83: 474-479, 1975.

251. MALPELI, J. G., AND F. H. BAKER. The representation of the visual field in the lateral geniculate nucleus of *Macaca mulatta*. *J. Comp. Neurol.* 161: 569-594, 1975.

252. MARR, D. Visual information processing: the structure and creation of visual representations. *Philos. Trans. R. Soc. London Ser. B* 290: 199-218, 1980.

253. MARROCCO, R. T. Sustained and transient cells in monkey lateral geniculate nucleus: conduction velocities and response properties. *J. Neurophysiol.* 39: 340-353, 1976.

254. MARROCCO, R. T., AND J. B. BROWN. Correlation of receptive field properties of monkey LGN cells with the conduction velocity of retinal afferent input. *Brain Res.* 92: 137-144, 1975.

255. MARTINEZ-MILLÁN, L., AND H. HOLLÄNDER. Cortico-cortical projections from striate cortex of squirrel monkey (*Saimiri sciureus*). A radioautographic study. *Brain Res.* 83: 405-417, 1975.

256. MASON, R. Cell properties in the medial interlaminar nucleus of the cat's lateral geniculate complex in relation to the transient/sustained classification. *Exp. Brain Res.* 22: 327-329, 1975.

257. MASON, R. Functional organization in the cat's pulvinar complex. *Exp. Brain Res.* 31: 51-66, 1978.

258. MICHAEL, C. R. Color vision mechanisms in monkey striate cortex: dual-opponent cells with concentric receptive fields. *J. Neurophysiol.* 41: 572-588, 1978.

259. MICHAEL, C. R. Color vision mechanisms in monkey striate cortex: simple cells with dual opponent color receptive fields. *J. Neurophysiol.* 41: 1233-1249, 1978.

260. MICHAEL, C. R. Color-sensitive complex cells in monkey striate cortex. *J. Neurophysiol.* 41: 1250-1266, 1978.

261. MICHAEL, C. R. Color-sensitive hypercomplex cells in monkey striate cortex. *J. Neurophysiol.* 42: 726-744, 1979.

262. MOHLER, C. W., AND R. H. WURTZ. Role of striate cortex and superior colliculus in visual guidance of saccadic eye movements in monkeys. *J. Neurophysiol.* 40: 74-94, 1977.

263. MORALES, R., D. DUNCAN, AND R. REHMET. A distinctive laminated cytoplasmic body in the lateral geniculate neurons of the cat. *J. Ultrastruct. Res.* 10: 116-123, 1964.

264. MOUNTCASTLE, V. B. Modality and topographic properties of single neurons of cat's somatic sensory cortex. *J. Neurophysiol.* 20: 408-434, 1957.

265. MOUNTCASTLE, V. B. An organizing principal for cerebral function: the unit module and the distributed system. In: *The Mindful Brain: Cortical Organization and the Group-Selective Theory of Higher Brain Function*, edited by G. M. Edelman and V. B. Mountcastle. Cambridge, MA: MIT Press, 1978, p. 7-50.

266. MOVSHON, J. A., I. D. THOMPSON, AND D. J. TOLHURST. Spatial summation in the receptive fields of simple cells in the cat's striate cortex. *J. Physiol. London* 283: 53-77, 1978.

267. MOVSHON, J. A., I. D. THOMPSON, AND D. J. TOLHURST.

Receptive field organization of complex cells in the cat's striate cortex. *J. Physiol. London* 283: 79–99, 1978.

268. MOVSHON, J. A., I. D. THOMPSON, AND D. J. TOLHURST. Spatial and temporal contrast sensitivity of neurones in areas 17 and 18 of the cat's visual cortex. *J. Physiol. London* 283: 101–120, 1978.

269. NELSON, R., E. V. FAMIGLIETTI, JR., AND H. KOLB. Intracellular staining reveals different levels of stratification for on- and off-center ganglion cells in cat retina. *J. Neurophysiol.* 41: 472–483, 1978.

270. NELSON, J. I., H. KATO, AND P. O. BISHOP. Discrimination of orientation and position disparities by binocularly activated neurons in cat striate cortex. *J. Neurophysiol.* 40: 260–283, 1977.

271. NIIMI, K., AND E. KUWAHARA. The dorsal thalamus of the cat and comparison with monkey and man. *J. Hirnforsch* 14: 303–325, 1973.

272. NIIMI, K., AND J. M. SPRAGUE. Thalamo-cortical organization of the visual system in the cat. *J. Comp. Neurol.* 138: 219–250, 1970.

273. NIKARA, T., P. O. BISHOP, AND J. D. PETTIGREW. Analysis of retinal correspondence by studying receptive fields of binocular single units in cat striate cortex. *Exp. Brain Res.* 6: 353–372, 1968.

274. OGAWA, T., S. ITO, AND H. KATO. P-cells and I-cells in in vitro slices of the lateral geniculate nucleus of the cat. *Tohoku J. Exp. Med.* 130: 359–368, 1980.

275. OGREN, M. P., AND A. E. HENDRICKSON. Pathways between striate cortex and subcortical regions in *Macaca mulatta* and *Saimiri sciureus*: evidence for a reciprocal pulvinar connection. *Exp. Neurol.* 53: 780–800, 1976.

276. OGREN, M. P., AND A. E. HENDRICKSON. The distribution of pulvinar terminals in visual areas 17 and 18 of the monkey. *Brain Res.* 137: 343–350, 1977.

277. O'LEARY, J. L. A structural analysis of the lateral geniculate nucleus of the cat. *J. Comp. Neurol.* 73: 405–430, 1940.

278. O'LEARY, J. L. Structure of the area striata of the cat. *J. Comp. Neurol.* 75: 131–164, 1941.

279. ONO, T., AND W. K. NOELL. Characteristics of P- and I-cells of cat's lateral geniculate body. *Vision Res.* 13: 639–646, 1973.

280. ORBAN, G. A., H. KATO, AND P. O. BISHOP. End-zone region in receptive fields of hypercomplex and other striate neurons in the cat. *J. Neurophysiol.* 42: 818–832, 1979.

281. ORBAN, G. A., H. KATO, AND P. O. BISHOP. Dimensions and properties of end-zone inhibitory areas in receptive fields of hypercomplex cells in cat striate cortex. *J. Neurophysiol.* 42: 833–849, 1979.

282. OTSUKA, R., AND R. HASSLER. Über Aufbau und Gliederung der corticalen Sehsphäre bei der Katze. *Arch. Psychiatr. Nervenkr.* 203: 212–234, 1962.

283. OYSTER, C. W. The analysis of image motion by the rabbit retina. *J. Physiol. London* 199: 613–635, 1968.

284. PADMOS, P., AND D. V. NORREN. Cone systems interaction in single neurons of the lateral geniculate nucleus of the macaque. *Vision Res.* 15: 617–619, 1975.

285. PALMER, L. A., AND A. C. ROSENQUIST. Visual receptive fields of single striate cortical units projecting to the superior colliculus in the cat. *Brain Res.* 67: 27–42, 1974.

286. PALMER, L. A., A. C. ROSENQUIST, AND R. TUSA. Visual receptive fields in the lam LGNd, MIN and PN of the cat. *Neurosci. Abstr.* 1: 54, 1975.

287. PEICHL, L., AND H. WÄSSLE. Size, scatter and coverage of ganglion cell receptive field centres in the cat retina. *J. Physiol. London* 291: 117–141, 1979.

288. PETTIGREW, J. D., T. NIKARA, AND P. O. BISHOP. Responses to moving slits by single units in cat striate cortex. *Exp. Brain Res.* 6: 373–390, 1968.

289. PETTIGREW, J. D., T. NIKARA, AND P. O. BISHOP. Binocular interaction on single units in cat striate cortex: simultaneous stimulation by single moving slit with receptive fields in correspondence. *Exp. Brain Res.* 6: 391–410, 1968.

290. POGGIO, G. F., F. H. BAKER, R. J. W. MANSFIELD, A. SILLITO, AND P. GRIGG. Spatial and chromatic properties of neurons

subserving foveal and parafoveal vision in rhesus monkey. *Brain Res.* 100: 25–59, 1975.

291. POGGIO, G. F., R. W. DOTY, JR., AND W. H. TALBOT. Foveal striate cortex of behaving monkey: single-neuron responses to square-wave gratings during fixation of gaze. *J. Neurophysiol.* 40: 1369–1391, 1977.

292. POGGIO, G. F., AND B. FISCHER. Binocular interaction and depth sensitivity in striate and prestriate cortex of behaving rhesus monkey. *J. Neurophysiol.* 40: 1392–1405, 1977.

293. POLLEN, D. A., J. R. LEE, AND J. H. TAYLOR. How does the striate cortex begin the reconstruction of the visual world? *Science* 173: 74–77, 1971.

294. POLLEY, E. H. Intracortical distribution of lateral geniculate axons in cat and monkey. *Anat. Rec.* 169: 404, 1971.

295. POLYAK, S. *The Retina.* Chicago, IL: Univ. of Chicago Press, 1941.

296. POLYAK, S. *The Vertebrate Visual System.* Chicago, IL: Univ. of Chicago Press, 1957.

297. RAKIC, P. Prenatal genesis of connections subserving ocular dominance in the rhesus monkey. *Nature London* 261: 467–471, 1976.

298. REZAK, M., AND L. A. BENEVENTO. A comparison of the organization of the projections of the dorsal lateral geniculate nucleus, the inferior pulvinar and adjacent lateral pulvinar to primary visual cortex (area 17) in the macaque monkey. *Brain Res.* 167: 19–40, 1979.

299. RIBAK, C. E. Aspinous and sparsely-spinous stellate neurons in the visual cortex of rats contain glutamic decarboxylase. *J. Neurocytol.* 7: 461–478, 1978.

300. RIOCH, D. M. Studies on the diencephalon of carnivora I. The nuclear configuration of the thalamus, epithalamus, and hypothalamus of the dog and cat. *J. Comp. Neurol.* 49: 1–119, 1929.

301. ROBSON, J. G. Receptive fields: neural representation of the spatial and intensive attributes of the visual image. In: *Handbook of Perception*, edited by E. C. Carterette and M. P. Friedman. New York: Academic, 1975, vol. 5, p. 81–112.

302. ROCKEL, A. J., R. W. HIORNS, AND T. P. S. POWELL. The basic uniformity in structure of the neocortex. *Brain* 103: 221–244, 1980.

303. RODIECK, R. W. Receptive fields in the cat retina: a new type. *Science* 157: 90–92, 1967.

304. RODIECK, R. W. Visual pathways. *Annu. Rev. Neurosci.* 2: 193–225, 1979.

305. ROLLS, E. T., AND A. COWEY. Topography of the retina and striate cortex and its relationship to visual acuity in rhesus monkeys and squirrel monkeys. *Exp. Brain Res.* 10: 298–310, 1970.

306. ROSE, D. Responses of single units in cat visual cortex to moving bars of light as a function of bar length. *J. Physiol. London* 271: 1–23, 1977.

307. ROSE, D., AND C. BLAKEMORE. An analysis of orientation selectivity in cat's visual cortex. *Exp. Brain Res.* 20: 1–17, 1974.

308. ROSENQUIST, A. C., S. B. EDWARDS, AND L. A. PALMER. An autoradiographic study of the projections of the dorsal lateral geniculate nucleus and posterior nucleus in the cat. *Brain Res.* 80: 71–93, 1974.

309. ROSENQUIST, A. C., L. A. PALMER, S. B. EDWARDS, AND R. J. TUSA. Thalamic efferents to visual cortical in the cat. *Neurosci. Abstr.* 1: 53, 1975.

310. ROWE, M. H., AND J. STONE. Conduction velocity groupings among axons of cat retinal ganglion cells, and their relationship to retinal topography. *Exp. Brain Res.* 25: 339–357, 1976.

311. ROWE, M. H., AND J. STONE. Properties of ganglion cells in the visual streak of the cat's retina. *J. Comp. Neurol.* 169: 99–126, 1976.

312. SAITO, H., T. SHIMAHARA, AND Y. FUKUDA. Phasic and tonic responses in the cat optic nerve fibers—stimulus-response relation. *Tohoku J. Exp. Med.* 104: 313–323, 1971.

313. SAKAKURA, H. Spontaneous and evoked unitary activities of cat lateral geniculate neurons in sleep and wakefulness. *Jpn. J. Physiol.* 18: 23–42, 1968.

314. SANDERSON, K. J. The projection of the visual field to the

lateral geniculate and medial interlaminar nuclei in the cat. *J. Comp. Neurol.* 143: 101–118, 1971.

315. SANDERSON, K. J. Visual field projection column and magnification factors in the lateral geniculate nucleus of the cat. *Exp. Brain Res.* 13: 159–177, 1971.

316. SANDERSON, K. J., P. O. BISHOP, AND I. DARIAN-SMITH. The properties of the binocular receptive fields of lateral geniculate neurons. *Exp. Brain. Res.* 13: 178–207, 1971.

317. SANDERSON, K. J., I. DARIAN-SMITH, AND P. O. BISHOP. Binocular corresponding receptive fields of single units in the cat lateral geniculate nucleus. *Vision Res.* 9: 1297–1303, 1969.

318. SANDERSON, K. J., AND S. M. SHERMAN. Nasotemporal overlap in visual field projected to lateral geniculate nucleus in the cat. *J. Neurophysiol.* 34: 453–466, 1971.

319. SANIDES, F., AND J. HOFFMANN. Cyto- and myeloarchitecture of the visual cortex of the cat and of the surrounding integration cortices. *J. Hirnforsch.* 11: 79–104, 1969.

320. SCHILLER, P. H., B. L. FINLAY, AND S. F. VOLMAN. Quantitative studies of single-cell properties in monkey striate cortex. I. Spatiotemporal organization of receptive fields. *J. Neurophysiol.* 39: 1288–1319, 1976.

321. SCHILLER, P. H., B. L. FINLAY, AND S. F. VOLMAN. Quantitative studies of single-cell properties in monkey striate cortex. II. Orientation specificity and ocular dominance. *J. Neurophysiol.* 39: 1320–1333, 1976.

322. SCHILLER, P. H., B. L. FINLAY, AND S. F. VOLMAN. Quantitative studies of single-cell properties in monkey striate cortex. III. Spatial frequency. *J. Neurophysiol.* 39: 1334–1351, 1976.

323. SCHILLER, P. H., B. L. FINLAY, AND S. F. VOLMAN. Quantitative studies of single-cell properties in monkey striate cortex. V. Multivariate statistical analyses and models. *J. Neurophysiol.* 39: 1362–1374, 1976.

324. SCHILLER, P. H., AND J. G. MALPELI. Properties and tectal projections of monkey retinal ganglion cells. *J. Neurophysiol.* 40: 428–445, 1977.

325. SCHILLER, P. H., AND J. G. MALPELI. Functional specificity of lateral geniculate nucleus laminae of the rhesus monkey. *J. Neurophysiol.* 41: 788–797, 1978.

326. SCHILLER, P. H., AND M. STRYKER. Single-unit recording and stimulation in superior colliculus of the alert rhesus monkey. *J. Neurophysiol.* 35: 915–924, 1972.

327. SCHMIELAU, F. Integration of visual and non visual information in nucleus reticularis thalami of the cat. In: *Developmental Neurobiology of Vision*, edited by R. D. Freeman. New York: Plenum, 1979, p. 205–226.

328. SCHMIELAU, F., AND W. SINGER. The role of visual cortex for binocular interactions in the cat lateral geniculate nucleus. *Brain Res.* 120: 354–361, 1977.

329. SCHNEIDER, G. E. Two visual systems. *Science* 163: 895–902, 1969.

330. SCHWARTZ, E. L. Computational anatomy and functional architecture of striate cortex: a spatial mapping approach to perceptual coding. *Vision Res.* 20: 645–669, 1980.

331. SEFTON, A. J., AND W. BURKE. Reverberatory inhibitory circuits in the lateral geniculate nucleus of the rat. *Nature London* 205: 1325–1326, 1965.

332. SEKULER, R. Spatial vision. *Annu. Rev. Psychol.* 25: 195–232, 1974.

333. SENEVIRATUE, K. N., AND D. WHITTERIDGE. Visual evoked responses in the lateral geniculate nucleus. *Electroencephalogr. Clin. Neurophysiol.* 14: 785, 1962.

334. SHATZ, C. J. Anatomy of interhemispheric connections in the visual system of Boston Siamese and ordinary cats. *J. Comp. Neurol.* 173: 497–518, 1977.

335. SHATZ, C. J., S. LINDSTRÖM, AND T. N. WIESEL. The distribution of afferents representing the right and left eyes in the cat's visual cortex. *Brain Res.* 131: 103–116, 1977.

336. SHATZ, C. J., AND M. P. STRYKER. Ocular dominance in layer IV of the cat's visual cortex and the effects of monocular deprivation. *J. Physiol. London* 281: 267–283, 1978.

337. SHERMAN, S. M., D. W. WATKINS, AND J. R. WILSON. Further differences in receptive field properties of simple and complex cells in cat striate cortex. *Vision Res.* 16: 919–927, 1976.

338. SHERMAN, S. M., J. R. WILSON, J. H. KAAS, AND S. V. WEBB. X- and Y-cells in the dorsal lateral geniculate nucleus of the owl monkey (*Aotus trivirgatus*). *Science* 192: 475–477, 1976.

339. SILLITO, A. M. Inhibitory processes underlying the directional specificity of simple, complex and hypercomplex cells in the cat's visual cortex. *J. Physiol. London* 271: 699–720, 1977.

340. SILLITO, A. M., AND V. VERSIANI. The contribution of excitatory and inhibitory inputs to the length preference of hypercomplex cells in layers II and III of the cat's striate cortex. *J. Physiol. London* 273: 775–790, 1977.

341. SINGER, W. Inhibitory binocular interaction in the lateral geniculate body of the cat. *Brain Res.* 18: 165–170, 1970.

342. SINGER, W. Control of thalamic transmission by corticofugal and ascending reticular pathways in the visual system. *Physiol. Rev.* 57: 386–420, 1977.

343. SINGER, W., AND U. DRÄGER. Postsynaptic potentials in relay neurons of cat lateral geniculate nucleus after stimulation of the mesencephalic reticular formation. *Brain Res.* 41: 214–220, 1972.

344. SINGER, W., F. TRETTER, AND M. CYNADER. Organization of cat striate cortex: a correlation of receptive-field properties with afferent and efferent connections. *J. Neurophysiol.* 38: 1080–1098, 1975.

345. SINGLETON, M. C., AND T. L. PEELE. Distribution of optic fibers in the cat. *J. Comp. Neurol.* 125: 303–328, 1965.

346. SO, Y. T., AND R. M. SHAPLEY. Spatial properties of X and Y cells in the lateral geniculate nucleus of the cat and conduction velocities of their inputs. *Exp. Brain Res.* 36: 533–550, 1979.

347. SOKOLOFF, L., M. REIVICH, C. KENNEDY, M. H. DES ROSIERS, C. S. PATLAK, K. D. PETTIGREW, O. SAKURADA, AND M. SHINOHARA. The [^{14}C]deoxyglucose method for the measurement of local cerebral glucose utilization: theory, procedure, and normal values in the conscious and anesthetized albino rat. *J. Neurochem.* 28: 897–916, 1977.

348. SPATZ, W. B., J. TIGGES, AND M. TIGGES. Subcortical projections, cortical associations, and some intrinsic interlaminar connections of the striate cortex in the squirrel monkey (*Saimiri*). *J. Comp. Neurol.* 140: 155–174, 1970.

349. SPEAR, P. D., D. C. SMITH, AND L. L. WILLIAMS. Visual receptive-field properties of single neurons in cat's ventral lateral geniculate nucleus. *J. Neurophysiol.* 40: 390–409, 1977.

349a.SPRAGUE, J. M., J. L. LEVY, A. DiBERARDINO, AND G. BERLUCCHI. Visual cortical areas mediating form discrimination in the cat. *J. Comp. Neurol.* 172: 441–488, 1977.

350. STONE, J. A quantitative analysis of the distribution of ganglion cells in the cat's retina. *J. Comp. Neurol.* 124: 337–352, 1965.

351. STONE, J. The naso-temporal division of the cat's retina. *J. Comp. Neurol.* 126: 585–600, 1966.

352. STONE, J. Morphology and physiology of the geniculocortical synapse in the cat: The question of parallel input to the striate cortex. *Invest. Ophthal.* 11: 338–346, 1972.

353. STONE, J. The number and distribution of ganglion cells in the cat's retina. *J. Comp. Neurol.* 180: 753–772, 1978.

354. STONE, J., AND B. DREHER. Projection of X- and Y-cells of the cat's lateral geniculate nucleus to areas 17 and 18 of visual cortex. *J. Neurophysiol.* 36: 551–567, 1973.

355. STONE, J., B. DREHER, AND A. LEVENTHAL. Hierarchical and parallel mechanisms in the organization of visual cortex. *Brain Res. Rev.* 1: 345–394, 1979.

356. STONE, J., AND M. FABIAN. Specialized receptive fields of the cat's retina. *Science* 152: 1277–1279, 1966.

357. STONE, J., AND Y. FUKUDA. The naso-temporal division of the cat's retina re-examined in terms of Y-, X- and W-cells. *J. Comp. Neurol.* 155: 377–394, 1974.

358. STONE, J., AND Y. FUKUDA. Properties of cat retinal ganglion cells: a comparison of W-cells with X- and Y-cells. *J. Neurophysiol.* 37: 722–748, 1974.

359. STONE, J., AND K.-P. HOFFMANN. Conduction velocity as a parameter in the organisation of the afferent relay in the cat's lateral geniculate nucleus. *Brain Res.* 32: 454–459, 1971.

360. STONE, J., AND K.-P. HOFFMANN. Very slow-conducting ganglion cells in the cat's retina: a major, new functional type? *Brain Res.* 43: 610–616, 1972.

361. STONE, J., J. LEICESTER, AND S. M. SHERMAN. The naso-temporal division of the monkey's retina. *J. Comp. Neurol.* 150: 333–348, 1973.

362. SUMITOMO, I., AND K. IWAMA. Some properties of intrinsic neurons of the dorsal lateral geniculate of the rat. *Jpn. J. Physiol.* 27: 717–730, 1977.

363. SUMITOMO, I., M. NAKAMURA, AND K. IWAMA. Location and function of the so-called interneurons of rat lateral geniculate body. *Exp. Neurol.* 51: 110–123, 1976.

364. SUZUKI, H., AND H. KATO. Neurons with visual properties in the posterior group of the thalamic nuclei. *Exp. Neurol.* 23: 353–365, 1969.

365. SZLACHTA, H. L., AND R. E. HABEL. Inclusions resembling Negri bodies in the brains of non-rabid cats. *Cornell Vet.* 43: 207–216, 1953.

366. TALBOT, S. A. Arrangement of visual field on cat's cortex. *Am. J. Physiol.* 129: P477–P478, 1940.

366a. TALBOT, S. A., AND S. W. KUFFLER. A multibeam ophthalmoscope for the study of retinal physiology. *J. Opt. Soc. Am.* 42: 931–936, 1952.

367. TALBOT, S. A., AND W. H. MARSHALL. Physiological studies on neural mechanisms of visual localization and discrimination. *Am. J. Ophthalmol.* 24: 1255–1264, 1941.

368. THUMA, B. D. Studies on the diencephalon of the cat. I. The cyto-architecture of the corpus geniculatum laterale. *J. Comp. Neurol.* 46: 173–199, 1928.

369. TIGGES, J., M. TIGGES, AND A. A. PERACHIO. Complementary laminar termination of afferents to area 17 originating in area 18 and in the lateral geniculate nucleus in squirrel monkey. *J. Comp. Neurol.* 176: 87–100, 1977.

370. TÖMBÖL, T. Short axon neurons and their synaptic relations in the specific thalamic nuclei. *Brain Res.* 3: 307–326, 1967.

371. TÖMBÖL, T. Two types of short axon (Golgi 2nd) interneurones in the specific thalamic nuclei. *Acta. Morphol. Acad. Sci. Hung.* 17: 285–297, 1969.

372. TÖMBÖL, T., F. HAJDU, AND GY. SOMOGYI. Identification of the Golgi picture of the layer VI cortico-geniculate projection neurons. *Exp. Brain Res.* 24: 107–110, 1975.

373. TOYAMA, K., K. MAEKAWA, AND T. TAKEDA. An analysis of neuronal circuitry for two types of visual cortical neurones classified on the basis of their responses to photic stimuli. *Brain Res.* 61: 395–399, 1973.

374. TOYAMA, K., K. MATSUNAMI, T. OHNO, AND S. TOKASHIKI. An intracellular study of neuronal organization in the visual cortex. *Exp. Brain Res.* 21: 45–66, 1974.

375. TROJANOWSKI, J. Q., AND S. JACOBSON. Areal and laminar distribution of some pulvinar cortical efferents in rhesus monkey. *J. Comp. Neurol.* 169: 371–391, 1976.

375a. TUSA, R. J., L. A. PALMER, AND A. C. ROSENQUIST. The retinotopic organization of the visual cortex in the cat (Abstract). *Neurosci. Abstr.* 1: 52, 1975.

376. TUSA, R. J., L. A. PALMER, AND A. C. ROSENQUIST. The retinotopic organization of area 17 (striate cortex) in the cat. *J. Comp. Neurol.* 177: 213–236, 1978.

377. UPDYKE, B. V. The patterns of projection of cortical areas 17, 18 and 19 onto the laminae of the dorsal lateral geniculate nucleus of the cat. *J. Comp. Neurol.* 163: 377–396, 1975.

378. UPDYKE, B. V. Topographic organization of the projections from cortical areas 17, 18 and 19 onto the thalamus, pretectum and superior colliculus in the cat. *J. Comp. Neurol.* 173: 81–122, 1977.

379. VALVERDE, F. Short axon neuronal subsystems in the visual cortex of the monkey. *Int. J. Neurosci.* 1: 181–197, 1971.

380. VAN BUREN, J. M. *The Retinal Ganglion Cell Layer.* Springfield, IL: Thomas, 1963.

381. VAN ESSEN, D. C. Visual areas of the mammalian cerebral cortex. *Annu. Rev. Neurosci.* 2: 227–263, 1979.

382. VON DER HEYDT, R., CS. ADORJANI, P. HÄNNY, AND G. BAUMGARTNER. Disparity sensitivity and receptive field incongruity of units in the cat striate cortex. *Exp. Brain Res.* 31: 523–545, 1978.

383. WÄSSLE, H., AND R.-B. ILLING. The retinal projection to the superior colliculus in the cat: a quantitative study with HRP. *J. Comp. Neurol.* 190: 333–356, 1980.

384. WÄSSLE, H., B. B. BOYCOTT, AND R.-B. ILLING. Morphology and mosaic of on- and off-beta cells in the cat retina and some functional considerations. *Proc. R. Soc. London Ser. B* 212: 177–195, 1981.

385. WÄSSLE, H., W. R. LEVICK, AND B. G. CLELAND. The distribution of the alpha type of ganglion cells in the cat's retina. *J. Comp. Neurol.* 159: 419–438, 1975.

386. WÄSSLE, H., L. PEICHL, AND B. B. BOYCOTT. Morphology and topography of on- and off-alpha cells in the cat retina. *Proc. R. Soc. London Ser. B* 212: 157–175, 1981.

387. WÄSSLE, H., AND H. J. REIMANN. The mosaic of nerve cells in the mammalian retina. *Proc. R. Soc. London Ser. B* 200: 441–461, 1978.

388. WATANABE, S., M. KONISHI, AND O. D. CREUTZFELDT. Postsynaptic potentials in the cat's visual cortex following electrical stimulation of the afferent pathway. *Exp. Brain Res.* 1: 272–283, 1966.

389. WHITE, E. L. Thalamocortical synaptic relations: a review with emphasis on the projections of specific thalamic nuclei to the primary sensory areas of the neocortex. *Brain Res. Rev.* 1: 275–311, 1979.

390. WHITTERIDGE, D. Geometrical relations between the retina and the visual cortex. In: *Mathematics and Computer Science in Biology and Medicine.* London: Medical Research Council, 1965, p. 269–277.

391. WIESEL, T. N., AND D. H. HUBEL. Single-cell responses in striate cortex of kittens deprived of vision in one eye. *J. Neurophysiol.* 26: 1003–1017, 1963.

392. WIESEL, T. N., AND D. H. HUBEL. Spatial and chromatic interactions in the lateral geniculate body of the rhesus monkey. *J. Neurophysiol.* 29: 1115–1156, 1966.

393. WIESEL, T. N., D. H. HUBEL, AND D. M. K. LAM. Autoradiographic demonstration of ocular-dominance columns in monkey striate cortex by means of transneuronal transport. *Brain Res.* 79: 273–279, 1974.

394. WIITANEN, J. T. Selective silver impregnation of degenerating axons and axon terminals in the central nervous system of the monkey (*Macaca mulatta*). *Brain Res.* 14: 546–548, 1969.

395. WILSON, M. E., AND B. G. CRAGG. Projections from the lateral geniculate nucleus in the cat and monkey. *J. Anat.* 101: 677–692, 1967.

396. WILSON, J. R., AND S. M. SHERMAN. Receptive-field characteristics of neurons in cat striate cortex: changes with visual field eccentricity. *J. Neurophysiol.* 39: 512–533, 1976.

397. WILSON, P. D., M. H. ROWE, AND J. STONE. Properties of relay cells in the cat's lateral geniculate nucleus: a comparison of W-cells with X- and Y-cells. *J. Neurophysiol.* 39: 1193–1209, 1976.

398. WILSON, P. D., AND J. STONE. Evidence of W-cell input to the cat's visual cortex via the C laminae of the lateral geniculate nucleus. *Brain Res.* 92: 472–478, 1975.

399. WINFIELD, D. A., K. C. GATTER, AND T. P. S. POWELL. Certain connections of the visual cortex of the monkey shown by the use of horseradish peroxidase. *Brain Res.* 92: 456–461, 1975.

400. WONG-RILEY, M. T. T. Demonstration of geniculocortical and callosal projection neurons in the squirrel monkey by means of retrograde axonal transport of horseradish peroxidase. *Brain Res.* 79: 267–272, 1974.

401. ZEKI, S. M. Interhemispheric connections of prestriate cortex in the monkey. *Brain Res.* 19: 63–75, 1970.

402. ZEKI, S. M. Functional organization of a visual area in the posterior bank of the superior temporal sulcus. *J. Physiol. London* 236: 549–573, 1974.

403. ZEKI, S. M. Cells responding to changing image size and disparity in the cortex of the rhesus monkey. *J. Physiol. London* 242: 827–841, 1974.

CHAPTER 10

Neural mechanisms of color vision

RUSSELL L. DE VALOIS | *Department of Psychology, University of California, Berkeley, California*

GERALD H. JACOBS | *Department of Psychology, University of California, Santa Barbara, California*

CHAPTER CONTENTS

ONE OF THE CURIOSITIES of color vision is that the term itself is somewhat misleading. This comes about in the following way. Visual stimuli in adjacent regions (or in one region in adjacent time periods) can vary in two independent ways: in intensity (number of photons striking each unit area of the retina) and in wavelength (energy level of each photon). Perceptual brightness variations are in general related to intensity differences in the stimulus, and color variations to wavelength differences. Color vision, however, does not mean vision based on wavelength variations as opposed to intensity variations in the stimulus. In fact, every animal, regardless of whether it has color vision, utilizes wavelength as well as intensity differences in the visual environment. Rather, what is meant (or should be meant) by saying that an individual has color vision is that he or she has the ability to respond *independently* to wavelength and to intensity differences. For single photoreceptors, for some animals most of the time, and for most animals some of the time, wavelength and intensity differences are confounded: both are responded to, but they are not distinguished from each other.

The absorbance curves of visual pigments are never flat across the electromagnetic spectrum. Thus for a single receptor a shift in wavelength of a light stimulus, with no change in the number of photons, will produce a change in absorption. The same thing will happen if there is a change in the number of photons with no change in wavelength. There is no way for the receptor to distinguish between a change in absorbance resulting from either a change in the intensity or the wavelength of the stimulus. Quite the same holds in an animal whose retina contains only a single receptor type or in an animal with multiple receptor types under conditions where only one receptor type is functional. The same would also be true for an animal with multiple receptor types but with no neural mechanism for differentiating among the receptors. Clearly what is required for color vision is a system of multiple receptor types plus a neural mechanism for determining the relative activity rates of the receptors. Only this comparison permits the differentiation of wavelength from intensity changes in the light stimulus. Since the presence of a differential response to different wavelengths tells nothing by itself about the presence or the nature of color vision, the question that must be asked is whether there is a differential response to different wavelengths that is invariant with changes in the intensity or that operates even if the various stimuli are equated to produce equal overall effects on the photopigments.

Color vision is present in many different animals, from insects to primates. Among the fishes, birds, and reptiles, for instance, some species have superb color vision. Of the mammalian species it appears that only the primates have excellent color vision, although the ability is probably not completely absent in any mammals. Cats, for instance, which for a long time were thought to be completely color blind, turn out to have color vision of a rudimentary sort (18), so restricted that it may play little role in the normal behavior of the animal.

Color vision presumably evolved independently in the different phyletic groups, since the basic mechanisms appear to differ considerably among animal species. For instance, it is clear that among the primates the receptor basis for color discrimination is the presence of different photopigments distributed in different classes of cones; on the other hand, some birds have multiple types of colored oil droplets in front of the receptors, as well as multiple types of photopigments (9), and so have different mechanisms of receptor selectivity as well as possibly different dimensionality of their color space. Even in animals without retinal oil droplets, the actual photopigments present in different cones vary considerably from species to species. With this great diversity, there is some question concerning the extent to which information about the color vision of birds, for instance, can tell us about the underlying basis for human color vision. It is for this reason that we restrict ourselves in this chapter mainly to the visual organization in primates (especially the macaque monkeys and human beings).

Even among the primates there is considerable diversity in color vision in different species. In particular, the New World primates appear to differ considerably from Old World primates (38). No Old World primate that has been studied has been found to have color vision significantly different from that of humans (although the data base is rather small). On the other hand, many of the various species of South American monkeys that have been studied are different from macaques and humans in various aspects of their color vision. One does not have to turn to different species of animals, however, to find diversity in color vision. It is well known that there are considerable variations in color vision among people. In almost 10% of human males color vision diverges significantly enough from the norm for these people to be considered color defective. Even among so-called color normal individuals, color vision is not present under all circumstances. In particular, color discrimination is excellent for foveal stimuli but becomes increasingly poor as the stimuli are displaced toward the periphery of the retina. And even with central vision, color vision is only present under reasonably high intensities of light.

Perhaps the question should be raised of why the ability to discriminate wavelength from intensity differences (that is, color vision) is not universal among animals; why does it vary so much from one species to another and even within a single species under different circumstances? The basic problem is that, given the nature of visual photopigments, there is very little information present about wavelength differences relative to the information present with respect to intensity differences. To discriminate wavelength differences in the stimulus, therefore, requires a large photon catch by the photoreceptors. This can only be accomplished at moderate and high levels of luminance, that is, under mesopic and photopic conditions. Even then, to extract the small amount of information about color differences present in the stimulus requires summation over considerable periods of time and over spatial regions containing a considerable number of photoreceptors.

The points raised in the previous paragraph are shown in Figures 1 and 2. Figure 2A depicts a useful stimulus for study of color discrimination, a pure-color grating consisting of interlaced red and green bars equated for luminance. (Luminance is a photometric specification of light in which the spectral energy distribution of a stimulus is weighted according to the spectral sensitivity of the observer.) The only differences across space in this stimulus are in the wavelengths of the light, not in the amount of light captured by the receptors. If this interlaced red and green grating is phase-shifted by 90° so that the peaks and troughs, rather than being out of phase, now coincide (Fig. 2B), the grating pattern now varies in luminance but not in wavelength content. In this case the only spatial variations are in the number of photons striking the retina, rather than in their wavelength. It is instructive to compare the information present in the output of the two long-wavelength receptors in the human eye with respect to these two stimuli. Since the pigments in these receptors absorb across the whole visible spectrum, both receptor types will respond to both the red and green gratings, but to a slightly different extent (Fig. 1). Next consider the results of summing and differencing the receptor outputs for these stimuli. The sum of the receptor signals, in the case of the color grating (Fig. 2C), and the difference between them, in the case of the luminance grating (Fig. 2F), yield a zero output. Rather, the information about color is present in the differential output of the two receptors (Fig. 2E), and information about luminance is in the sum of the receptor outputs (Fig. 2D). Luminance differences can, therefore, be utilized at much lower light levels, and the information need not be integrated over nearly as much space and time. Because of the small amount of color information present in the differential output of the light receptors, we can utilize color information only under bright-light conditions. Consequently, animals that are primarily nocturnal in habit (as are most mammals) would obtain very little advantage from the presence of a color vision system.

Perhaps a second reason why highly developed color vision is not the rule is that it is expensive in terms of

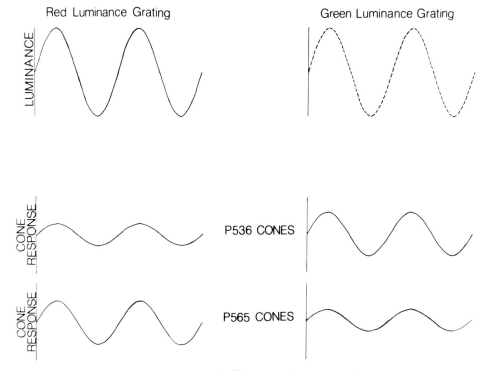

FIG. 1. Diagrammatic representation of luminance profiles of two gratings modulated around some mean level, and of the responses of each of the two long-wavelength cone populations (P536 and P565) to these gratings. The abscissa is distance along the retina. Because of their broad sensitivities, each cone type responds to each of the gratings, but to differing extents.

the number of neural elements required. To extract useful information about both the color and intensity differences involves at least a doubling of the neural pathways relative to that required if only the confounded (intensity and wavelength) information is to be used. In the case of the trichromatic animal, the neural pathway may well have to be tripled in complexity.

A third reason why perhaps only a minority of animals have extremely good color vision, and even then only under limited conditions, is that information concerning both intensity and wavelength is often redundant: objects usually differ from their backgrounds both in intensity and in wavelength. Most objects can be seen perfectly well in black-and-white photographs in which only intensity variations are present. Although pure-color–varying stimuli cannot be created as readily, if that were done one could also see perfectly well if only color variations were present in a scene, a condition that is approximated in many cartoons. Nonetheless, it is useful to have independent information about intensity and wavelength differences—that is, to have color vision—particularly in the identification of objects, rather than just in the perception of their presence or absence.

In this chapter the physiological mechanisms thought to underlie color vision are described. This general topic has been the subject of a number of recent reviews (2–4, 26, 33, 37) in which numerous references to earlier work can be found. Information about the basic features of human color perception is presented elsewhere [e.g., Graham (52) and the chapter by Yellott, Wandell, and Cornsweet in this *Handbook*].

PHOTOPIGMENTS

The absorption of photons by a photopigment constitutes the initial active step in the processing of information about color vision, so it is hardly surprising that understanding the operation of cone pigments has been a persistent goal of those interested in color vision. Major attention has been focused on establishing the spectral absorbance characteristics of these pigments and on measuring the dynamics of their operation. These tasks have been difficult, primarily because the cone pigments have been proved to be remarkably resistant to extraction from retinas and thus to study with standard spectrophotometric methods. Consequently, much of what is known about cone pigments comes from measurements that are indirect and, therefore, have necessarily involved some debatable assumptions.

Spectral Absorbance Characteristics

With regard to the spectral absorbance characteristics of the cone pigments, three questions require

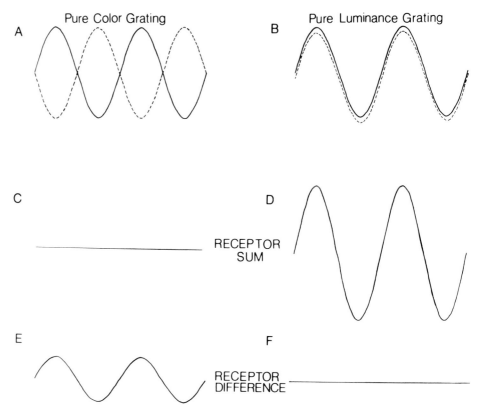

FIG. 2. The red and green gratings shown in Figure 1 are combined in each of two phase angles. *A*: gratings combined out of phase to form a pure-color grating; luminance is constant throughout, and the only variation is in dominant wavelength. *B*: gratings combined in phase to form a pure-luminance grating; wavelength is constant throughout, and the only variation is in luminance. *C–F*: results of adding and subtracting receptor responses (shown in Fig. 1) to pure-color and pure-luminance patterns. If receptor outputs are summed, there is no net response to the color grating, *C*, but a large response to the luminance grating, *D*. Differencing the receptor outputs yields no output for the luminance grating, *F*, but a small output for the color grating, *E*. Thus it can be seen that luminance information is carried by the receptor sums and color information by the receptor differences. Note also that the color response, *E*, is considerably smaller than the luminance response, *D*, even though the wavelengths chosen in Figure 1 were such as to produce about the maximum differentiation between the P536 and the P565 cones. Any smaller wavelength difference would leave the luminance response the same size but would decrease the color response.

answers: *1)* How many classes of cone pigments are there? *2)* What are the spectral locations at which they absorb light maximally? *3)* What are the shapes of their absorbance spectra? A number of different behavioral, physiological, and biochemical procedures have been brought to bear on these problems.

The methods involved in assessing spectral absorbance characteristics are sufficiently well known so that only brief comments need be made here. There is a long history involving the use of a variety of psychophysical methods to obtain indications of the spectral absorbance characteristics of the cone pigments [reviewed by Abramov (2) and De Valois (32)]. The major problem in this endeavor is that the cone pigments show considerable overlap in their spectral absorbance, so that any spectral stimulus will likely affect more than one of the cone pigments. One of the principal techniques to circumvent this difficulty has been to use intense chromatic adaptation in an at-tempt to suppress the effects of one (or two) cone pigment systems. The argument is that chromatic light will primarily desensitize one of the pigment systems, leaving the others more or less isolated. The use of color-defective observers, whose photopigment complements may already be naturally reduced, has proved to be a definite asset in this procedure. An analogue of this procedure has also been extensively used in physiological experiments in which the responses of a cell or a group of cells are compared both with and without concurrent chromatic adaptation of the eye. Some of the difficulties associated with this argument have recently been discussed by Sirovich and Abramov (106).

A somewhat more direct approach to defining the spectral characteristics of the cone pigments is use of retinal densitometry, in which a light of known composition is beamed into the eye and the difference between it and that of the light reflected back out of the eye gives a measure of pigment absorbance (102). Used in conjunction with chromatic adaptation, this technique has also yielded estimates of the spectral properties of the cone pigments.

Finally, perhaps the conceptually most straightforward technique to assess the spectral properties of cone pigments involves the in situ measurement of the pigment in single photoreceptors. This approach, microspectrophotometry (MSP), has been put to use in various forms over the past decade and a half. Although simple in principle, MSP faces formidable technical problems, most deriving from the restricted dimensions of typical cone photoreceptors and the limited amount of photopigment they contain (84).

The question of the number of distinct classes into which the cone pigments can be placed requires only a short response. Although the long history of the study of color vision is studded with theories postulating various numbers of photopigments and receptors, there is currently no serious evidence to suggest that the retinas of humans and other Old World primates contain either more or less than three classes of cone pigments located in three separate receptor types. For many other vertebrate species the picture is considerably less certain.

SPECTRAL ABSORBANCE PEAKS. Whereas the question of the number of cone pigment classes can be dispatched with certainty, the issue of the location of their spectral absorbance peaks (λ_{max}) cannot. From a large number of psychophysical studies done on humans, the consensus is that the three spectral locations of peak absorbance are at about 440 nm, somewhere between 530 and 540 nm, and in the range from 560 to 580 nm [these studies are summarized in Abramov (2) and in Jameson (74)].

The most direct way to establish these peak locations would be by using MSP. After the initial measurement made on the cones of humans and macaque monkeys in the early 1960s (19, 87), it was widely assumed that a large body of accurate measurements would soon be forthcoming. Unfortunately, this did not occur, and several years later one of the pioneers in this area, Liebman (84), delivered the pessimistic conclusion that the MSP data on primate cones could not be considered accurate to better than 20 or 30 nm. Recently, however, Bowmaker et al. (10) have reported some new MSP measurements made on rhesus monkey cones with the use of a methodology that they believe permits the specification of λ_{max} of the cone pigments much more precisely.

Bowmaker et al. (10) measured the absorbance characteristics of 82 cones. These investigators found no instance where a single cone contained more than one class of cone pigment. Of the cones they measured, 42 had λ_{max} between 530 and 540 nm, while the other 40 receptors showed peaks between 560 and 570 nm. The λ_{max} locations for these two groups are at 536 ± 3.5 and 565 ± 2.5 nm (mean and standard deviation).

Surprisingly, no cones were found to contain a photopigment with peak sensitivity in the short wavelengths. In view of other evidence indicating that this monkey is a trichromat, as well as a lot of physiological evidence pointing to the presence of a short-wavelength photopigment, the failure to find the short-wavelength cones probably reflects some experimental problems and is not an indication that they are in fact absent (although they are certainly less numerous than the other two cone types). At any rate, the measurements of the two long-wavelength pigment classes seem to represent the best current estimates of the absorbance peaks for these classes of cone pigments. Since most of the psychophysical studies (2, 74), as well as earlier MSP studies [see Bowmaker et al. (10)], indicate that the short-wavelength photopigment absorbs maximally at about 440 nm, we will assume that the cone pigments found in the retinas of humans and Old World monkeys have λ_{max} at 440, 536, and 565 nm. These spectra are shown in Figure 3. We will term the cones containing these three pigments the P440, P536, and P565 cones, respectively. We have elsewhere referred to these as the S, M, and L cones, respectively (37). They most certainly should not be called by the misleading names of blue, green, and red cones, for the many reasons enumerated elsewhere [see De Valois and De Valois (37)].

Given the difficulty of establishing with certainty the λ_{max} for the cone pigments, it might appear premature to raise the possibility of significant variations in these spectra within a given species. Nevertheless, there is evidence for some real variation in the location of λ_{max} for various photopigments. For example, Bowmaker and co-workers (11) have shown that the λ_{max} for frog rhodopsin may vary over a range of 8 nm among samples obtained from different individuals. A variation of similar magnitude has been postulated by Alpern and Pugh (5) from psychophysical estimates of the long-wavelength photopigment of humans. And, although Bowmaker et al. (10) found no evidence for significant variations between rhesus monkeys in the measurements just referred to, there is an indication in their data that those cones having an average λ_{max} at 536 nm may in fact reflect two different populations within a given animal, one sample of cones showing an average peak at about 534 nm and the other having a peak at about 542 nm. It is probably too soon to make much of any of these indications of variation in the location of peak absorbance within a pigment class. Nevertheless, since formal models of color vision are typically based on mechanisms whose spectral absorbance colors are precisely specified, these variations may represent an issue on which color theory does not yet accurately reflect what is to be found in real retinas.

SHAPE OF ABSORBANCE FUNCTIONS OF PHOTOPIGMENTS. Actual measurements of the shapes of pigment absorbance spectra assume relevance for color

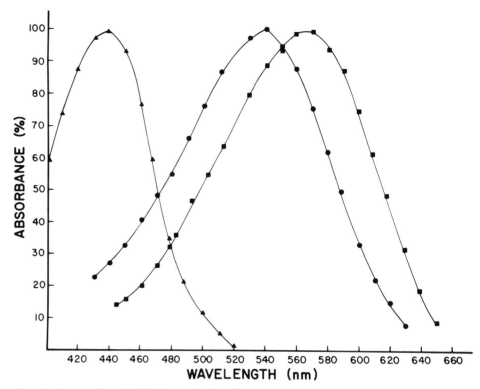

FIG. 3. Spectral absorbance curves for primate cone pigments. Each curve is plotted as percentage of maximal absorbance. Curve and data points for P440 generated from a Dartnall nomogram. Curves and data points for the two long-wavelength photopigments (P536 and P565) from Bowmaker et al. (10).

vision to the extent that these functions differ one from another. Visual photopigments in different animal groups are based on either retinal or dehydroretinal. A fundamental simplification emerged when Dartnall (24) presented evidence that the absorbance functions for all retinal-based visual pigments have the same shape when plotted in quantal terms against the frequency of the light. This being the case, knowledge of the λ_{max} value and access to a nomogram that Dartnall published specified the shape of the pigment spectra. Later it was shown that, although the same principle held, a different nomogram was required to deal with the spectra for these pigments based on dehydroretinal (16, 93). Although the spectra for many photopigments are well fitted by these nomograms, it has become clear that many are not. In particular, those pigments having longer λ_{max} often have absorbance spectra that are distinctly narrower than that predicted by the earlier nomograms. Ebrey and Honig (47) have suggested that the bandwidth of photopigment absorbance functions decreases linearly as a function of increasing values of λ_{max}. Because this decrease is a gradual one, these authors (47) provide as a close approximation a set of three nomograms, each appropriate for a different restricted range of λ_{max} values.

Because it has potential importance for the physiology of color vision, it is worth reminding the reader

that in addition to the main absorbance peak, visual pigments show a secondary absorbance hump (the β-peak) displaced toward the shorter wavelengths and having considerably lower absorbance. The β-peak is broadly centered at a wavelength approximately two-thirds of that of the main peak. Thus, if the main peak is located at a sufficiently long wavelength so that the β-peak is not shielded by one of the prereceptor filters (such as the lens or macular pigment), this secondary peak may absorb light and contribute to visual responses. We note later (see *Spectrally opponent cells*, p. 436) an instance where this appears to occur.

Univariance of Photopigment Response

About two out of every three absorbed quanta result in the bleaching of visual pigment (25). The absorbance spectrum for a photopigment expresses only the relative probability that light will bleach the photopigment as a function of its wavelength. Every photon absorbed, however, has exactly the same effect, regardless of its wavelength. The photopigment response, therefore, depends only on the total number of photopigment molecules bleached and not on the particular wavelength involved. Photopigments are therefore frequently described as behaving univariantly. It should be noted that whereas the photopigment responds univariantly (and thus a single class of photopigment cannot by itself underlie color vision), the photoreceptor containing that pigment may not behave univariantly. One way this can occur is by interactions between receptors containing different types of photopigment (see *Cone Responses*, this page).

RECEPTORS

*Prevalence and Retinal Distribution
of Different Cone Types*

Although there has been some controversy on cone types, it now appears, as already noted, that each cone contains only one of the three types of cone pigment (10). Until recently, information about the retinal distribution of receptors containing different cone pigments and their relative prevalence came exclusively from psychophysical experiments. Some direct information about these questions has recently become available through the use of a histochemical marking procedure. Using the light-stimulated reduction of nitroblue tetrazolium chloride and choosing spectral lights to maximally stimulate one or another of the different cone types, Marc and Sperling (86) examined the distribution of these cones in the baboon retina. At retinal locations beyond about 5° from the fovea they found that about 13% of the cones contained P440, about 33% contained P565, while the remainder (54%) contained P536. The P440 cones were distributed regularly, whereas the other two classes appeared random in distribution. Application of the same technique to the center of the fovea shows that about 3%–4% of the cones there contain P440, while the proportions of cones containing P536 and P565 are probably about 63% and 33%, respectively. The prevalence of the different cone types (particularly the small number of P440 cones) and the relative distributions in the fovea and the parafovea for baboon retina correspond at least qualitatively with what has been concluded from psychophysical experiments on the human retina (86).

Cone Responses

Vertebrate cones undergo a hyperpolarizing change in response to an increase in the amount of light falling on the outer segment and a depolarization in response to a light decrement (113). (This is not to imply that the magnitudes and time courses are necessarily the same in the responses to increments and decrements). As in other neurons, transmitter is released from the photoreceptor in response to depolarization of the cell (see the chapter by Dowling and Dubin in this *Handbook*). The magnitude of the cone hyperpolarization is directly proportional to the intensity of the light delivered in a brief flash, up to a point where the light intensity achieves a value roughly half that required to saturate the cone response. Above that point, the intensity-response relationship deviates from linearity,

and for bright flashes the cone response becomes saturated (48).

Among the recent discoveries about retinal organization, one of the most surprising is the degree to which signal interactions occur at the very earliest stages in the system. Baylor et al. (7) found that cones in the turtle retina were functionally coupled so that the occurrence of a voltage change in one cone was followed by a change of similar sign in its cone neighbors. In the turtle this synergistic effect spreads across about five cones and it appears to occur only among cones containing the same class of photopigment. These synergistic interactions seem to be mediated via gap junctions interposed between photoreceptor terminals. As yet there is no direct physiological evidence for such signal averaging among adjacent cones in the primate, but there is anatomical evidence for gap junctions both between cones and between cones and rods in the monkey retina (99).

On the basis of anatomical studies Polyak (98) fostered the notion that some foveal cones have private pathways through the retina, where they eventually provide the sole input to a single ganglion cell (although his own observations of horizontal cells interconnecting receptors contradicted this view). To the extent that neighboring receptors are interconnected by gap junctions, then even the center regions of the receptive fields (RF) of midget ganglion cells that receive input from the forveal region should indicate the influence of several cones. Measurement of the size of the RF center of cells in monkey retina indicates that this is probably true (27). Of course, the additional existence of RF surrounds makes even more unlikely, if that is possible, the idea of private cone pathways. These surrounds probably originate partially by virtue of lateral interactions made at the photoreceptor terminals.

Horizontal Cell Feedback

Color vision must be produced through the interaction of signals originating from cells containing different classes of photopigments. Where does this first occur in the visual system? The answer, surprisingly, appears to be in the photoreceptors themselves. In addition to the synergistic interactions among cones in the turtle retina noted in *Cone Responses*, this page, the response of a single cone to a large spot of light may include a depolarizing component (49). This depolarizing component has been shown to result from feedback onto the receptor's synaptic region from the horizontal cells. The horizontal cells that generate this feedback signal receive inputs from two classes of cones in the turtle—a strong input from cones containing P620, and a weaker input from the P520 cones. Because of this arrangement, the state of polarization of a particular cone depends jointly on the spectral and spatial characteristics of the stimulating light (49). Consider the responses obtained from a P520 cone illustrated in Figure 4. These represent the responses to an annulus of light centered on the cone from which the records were obtained. A red annulus generates a horizontal cell signal, which results in a large depolarization in the P520 cone (the direct effect of light on a photoreceptor, one should remember, is hyperpolarization). A green annulus, however, produces only minor antagonistic feedback from the horizontal cell, so the response is a hyperpolarization, presumably due to light from the annulus that scatters onto the P520 cone. These two stimuli were not set up to be equiluminant for the turtle, but it seems clear that responses to these two wavelengths would remain antagonistic even if they had been. That is, the signal generated by this turtle photoreceptor could form the informational basis for color vision. Whether or not it does is not known. Nor is it known whether similar kinds of processes occur in all vertebrate retinas, particularly among the primates. Nevertheless, an interaction potentially useful for color vision can take place at the synaptic region of the photoreceptors themselves. To the extent that this occurs, the principle of univariance may apply to the photopigments, not to the photoreceptors.

Much more is known about the physiology and anatomy of photoreceptors than is relevant here (see the chapter by Dowling and Dubin in this *Handbook*). From the standpoint of color vision the story still has considerable uncertainties, because those species in which color vision is best understood have not been widely studied anatomically or physiologically, and vice versa. At present, some reasonable surmises about primate receptors would include the following: *1*) the cones each contain one of three classes of photopigment whose peaks are at about 440 nm, 536 nm, and 565 nm, respectively; *2*) the three cone types do not occur in equal proportions and the distributions of these three classes vary across the retinal surface; *3*) neighboring cones containing the same type of photopigment are synergistically linked through interreceptor contacts; *4*) the cones are probably subjected to a modifying feedback from the horizontal cells, a condition that would alter the spectral characteristics of the cone output.

OUTER PLEXIFORM LAYER

Horizontal Cells

Clearly one of the most significant discoveries about the physiology of color vision was Svaetichin's (109) finding that some neural elements in the fish retina showed chromatically opponent responses, depolarizing to some stimulus wavelengths and hyperpolarizing to others. Figure 5 reproduces some examples of such responses. It took some time before it became clear that the generators of these responses were the horizontal cells (75) and not the cones, as Svaetichin (109) initially thought, or any of the several other candidates that had been suggested at various times [reviewed by Brindley (17)]. The significance of the discovery of such response patterns was considerable. It demonstrated that antagonistic interactions between the outputs from different photopigment classes take place at

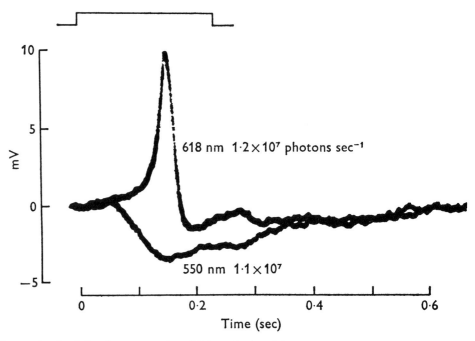

FIG. 4. Responses of a P520 turtle cone to stimulation from an annulus of 618 nm (*top*) and from an annulus of 550 nm (*bottom*). Stimulus duration is indicated by the marker bar at the top. Response is the change from resting potential of the photoreceptor. [Adapted from Fuortes et al. (49).]

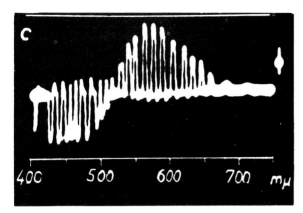

FIG. 5. Example of S potentials recorded from fish retina. Potentials were recorded from a small micropipette electrode inserted into a horizontal cell. Each vertical trace shows magnitude of change from resting membrane potential when the retina was in darkness. Each trace is the response to a single test wavelength. Note that these graded potentials are in the hyperpolarizing direction (upward) to long wavelengths and depolarizing direction (downward signals) to short wavelengths. [From Svaetichin and MacNichol (110).]

an early stage in the visual system. Furthermore, this discovery made it apparent that information about color vision is transmitted as the output of opponent interactions and not along independent pathways with narrow spectral tuning—this despite the fact that in writing a chapter in the first edition of this *Handbook*, Granit [(56), p. 704] could conclude that Svaetichin's observations "confirm the demonstration of dominators and narrow-banded modulators in this eye."

Since the horizontal cells represent the first location where chromatic opponency is clearly present, it would be obviously useful to know how these patterns are produced. Unfortunately, the anatomical and physiological organization underlying chromatically opponent responses from horizontal cells has been vigorously studied only in turtles (50) and in cyprinid fishes (94, 104, 107). On the other hand, the functional significance of chromatically opponent responses has been most thoroughly investigated in the monkey, but only at higher levels in the system. Since there are great interspecies differences in organization of the retina, it is not at all certain that the results from fishes and turtles can be applied to the primate visual system. That fact should be kept firmly in mind while considering the following illustrative example.

Figure 6 (*top*) shows spectral response curves for two classes of chromatically opponent horizontal cells (C-cells) and one class of nonopponent horizontal cell (L-cell) in the turtle retina (50). For example, chromatically opponent red/green (R/G) cells hyperpolarize maximally to lights of about 550 nm (but have a subsidiary peak at about 450 nm) and show maximal depolarization to lights of about 650 nm. These cells sum inputs from photoreceptors over a large retinal region without apparent regard to the spatial distribution of the stimulus light.

Fuortes and Simon (50) used a variety of chromatic adaptation conditions and different spatial configurations of stimuli in an attempt to determine how these response patterns are built up from the receptor responses. The model they arrive at is also sketched in Figure 6 (*bottom*), which shows the connections among the four classes of cones (three cone types containing a single photopigment and a double cone whose two outer segments contain different classes of photopigments) and three classes of horizontal cells, all in the turtle retina. Each chromatically opponent cell type receives direct inputs from only one type of cone. In the case of the R/G cell, the major direct input is from the P520 cone, which accounts for most of the hyperpolarization seen to this part of the spectrum. The depolarizing responses to the long wavelengths given by the R/G cell arise from an antagonistic feedback of the L-horizontal cells (which are mostly driven by P620 cones) onto the P520 cone. In addition, there are some modifying interactions, including inputs to the R/G horizontal cell from the Y/B horizontal cell, the latter accounting for the additional peak shown by the R/G cell in the short wavelengths (Fig. 6). The essential point, which also applies to the work on retinas of fishes (107), is that a substantial range of interactions is required to account for the chromatically opponent response properties of cells, even at these very early stages in the visual system.

Bipolar Cells

As we have seen, at least in the turtle, information is fed back from the horizontal cells to the photoreceptors. It is also fed forward by the horizontal cells to influence the bipolar cells (76, 105). Beyond this, however, almost nothing that has clear relevance for color vision is known about the physiology of the bipolar cells. Some bipolar cells do show chromatically opponent responses both in fishes (76) and in turtle (105). Bipolar cells are also found that display strong spatial effects, with RFs that have full-fledged center-surround organizations. The surround antagonism is believed to be mediated by the horizontal-bipolar cell connections (76, 105).

GANGLION CELLS AND LATERAL GENICULATE CELLS

Whereas successful recordings from single cells in the distal portions of the retina constitute a relatively recent chapter in retinal electrophysiology, the ability to record from retinal ganglion cells (54, 55) and cells in the lateral geniculate nucleus (LGN) has a longer history. In terms of the processing of color information there are probably few differences between the capacities of monkey ganglion cells and cells in the LGN (88). Consequently we consider these results together.

In keeping with the general theme of this chapter, our focus is on the primate; however, significant results from two other representative species known to have

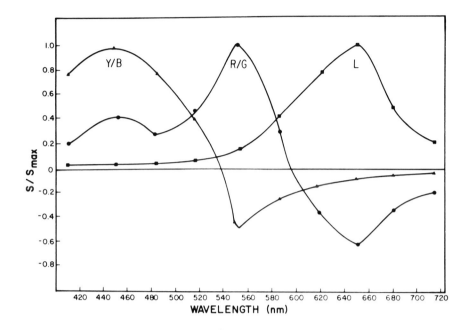

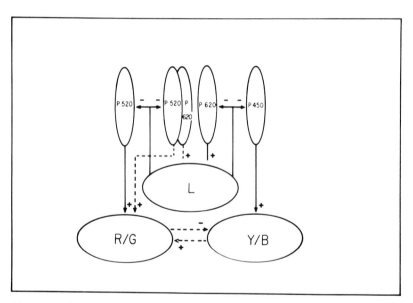

FIG. 6. Horizontal cell responses in turtle retina. *Top*: spectral response curves for C-cells (B/Y, blue/yellow, and R/G, red/green) and L-cells. *Bottom*: wiring diagram illustrating the kinds of interactions believed necessary to account for responses of horizontal cells. Vertical ovals represent classes of cones found in this retina. Pluses and minuses (+, −) indicate transmission with and without inversion of polarity. Basic connections responsible for the main properties of the cells are shown by *solid lines; dashed lines* represent the modifying interactions. [Adapted from Fuortes and Simon (50).]

color vision, goldfish and ground squirrel, have also received quite a bit of attention. Much of this work has been reviewed previously (2, 26), but some additional results have appeared since then (8, 59, 63, 91, 114).

The most striking characteristic of the responses of primate ganglion and LGN cells is their spectral opponency to stimuli that are large with respect to their

receptive fields: for most of the cells, lights of certain wavelengths produce increases in firing rate while other wavelengths produce decreases. These spectrally opponent responses are most striking to pure-color stimuli, that is, stimuli equated for luminance and varying only in wavelength. Some cells, for instance, show an increase in activity when the wavelength of the light is shifted toward longer wavelengths and show a decrease in activity with a shift toward shorter wavelengths; other cells show the reverse response (see Fig. 7 for an example of the responses of such a cell).

That these cells show differential responses to different wavelengths equated for luminance is prima facie evidence that they are carrying color information. This conclusion is reinforced by the fact that the cells described would fire when the light was shifted toward

long wavelengths, whether the long-wavelength light was somewhat higher or lower in luminance than the initial stimulus. Activity in these cells would be inhibited by a shift toward shorter wavelengths regardless of the relative luminances of the lights over a considerable range. This point is illustrated in Figure 8, which shows the responses of a +G/−R cell to an alternation between a yellow and a red light. It can be seen that the cell fires to the yellow and inhibits to the red when they are of equal luminance and when the red is brighter or dimmer than the yellow.

In addition to these spectrally opponent cells, at these levels other cells are found that respond with increases in firing rate to increments of light irrespective of wavelength, and with decreases in firing rate to decrements, or vice versa. These cells have been termed spectrally nonopponent for that reason. To equal-luminance wavelength shifts the nonopponent cells show little or no change in firing rate and are thus not involved in color processing (35).

Spectral Properties

SPECTRAL RESPONSE PATTERNS. Before directly considering the spectral response patterns of ganglion and LGN cells, perhaps brief attention should be directed to the question of the general nature of such response categories. In single-unit recording experiments an attempt is usually made to place each cell into one of several classes. This categorization process can be more or less arbitrary, but given the complexity of cell responses and the myriad of variables that determine the response, it is inevitably arbitrary to some degree. At the same time, the number of response classes can be expected to escalate as the number of stimulus dimensions and other experimental manipulations increases. However, even when using apparently the same experimental procedures, different experimenters would very likely come up with different sets of response categories. Hughes (71) has recently reminded us that taxonomists are sometimes categorized as "splitters or lumpers" according to the extent to which they divide the animal kingdom. So too it would appear to be with visual physiologists concerned with the classification of cell responses.

Although all of this may seem trivially obvious, once defined, a set of response categories tends to achieve an independent status, quite beyond the context in which it was initially devised. For example, a particular response category is sometimes described as wrong or inadequate because it does not account for the behavior of cells in a new test situation, even though the conditions may be markedly different from those used for the initial categorization. This problem, however, is probably not any more or less serious in the physiology of color vision than in other areas of sensory physiology. The disagreements over the appropriate categorizations of the response properties of cells in area 17 of the cat cortex may well be a case in point [cf. Henry (64)].

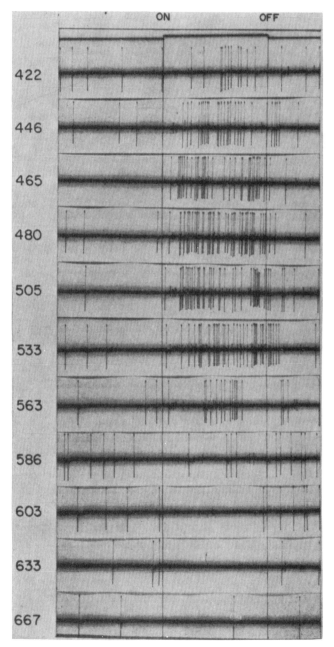

FIG. 7. Responses of a +G/−R spectrally opponent LGN cell to light of various wavelengths. A line is drawn through superimposed records at *left* to indicate time of light onset; the line at *right* marks light offset (1-s duration). Numbers at *left*: wavelength (in nm) of each light stimulus. [From De Valois, Abramov, and Jacobs (34).]

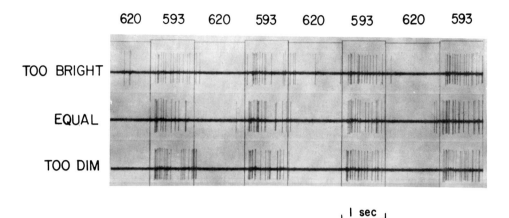

FIG. 8. Responses of a +G/−R lateral geniculate nucleus cell to shifts back and forth between two lights of 620 and 593 nm. *Middle record*: the two wavelengths are of equal luminance. *Top record*: 593-nm light had the same luminance as in the middle record; 620-nm light was 0.5 log units brighter than in middle record. *Bottom record*: 593-nm light had the same luminance as in the middle record; 620-nm light was 0.5 log units dimmer than in middle record. It can be seen that the cell fires to the 593-nm light and inhibits to the 620-nm light despite wide variations in their relative luminances. [From De Valois et al. (35).]

Primate ganglion and LGN cells are of many varieties, at least in terms of the spectral locations of peak excitatory and inhibitory responses. Some cells fire to very long wavelengths and inhibit to the middle of the spectrum, whereas other cells fire to very short wavelengths and inhibit to the longer wavelengths. Both the spectral locations of the response peaks and the locations where cell responses cross from excitation to inhibition span a considerable range. Nevertheless, in considering the multimodal distribution of peak excitatory and inhibitory loci of a population of cells and the distribution of their crossovers from excitation to inhibition, De Valois, Abramov, and Jacobs (34) concluded that these spectrally opponent cells could be grouped into four categories. Those cells that fired to the very long wavelengths (that we see as red) and inhibited maximally in that part of the spectrum we see as green were termed +R/−G cells; a class of cells showing a reversal of this response pattern was called +G/−R. Together these two classes comprise the R/G system. Other cells show maximum excitation in the yellow part of the spectrum, cross to inhibition roughly in the green, and have their maximum inhibition in the blue. These cells were called +Y/−B, and they in turn had a mirror-image pair, the +B/−Y cells. Together these make up the Y/B system. In addition, there are spectrally nonopponent cells that either fire to all wavelengths across the spectrum or are inhibited by all wavelengths. These were called +Wh/−Bl (white excitatory, black inhibitory) and +Bl/−Wh, respectively. Figure 9 shows the average responses of the four types of spectrally opponent cells.

The categorization of cells into four opponent cell classes is based on the responses of these cells to large stimuli and represents an attempt to "lump" these obviously very diverse cells into as few categories as seem reasonable. But as our previous discussion sug-

gests, the number of response classes needed to categorize monkey cells also depends on the stimulus conditions under which they are examined. For example, De Monasterio and Gouras (27) concluded that if both the spatial and spectral dimensions of the stimulus are varied, 26 different classes are required to account for the response properties of rhesus monkey ganglion cells. Of these, the cells falling into 23 different classes would appear to possess the requisite properties needed to be potentially useful for color vision.

CONE INPUTS TO INDIVIDUAL CELLS. The categorization of cells just described was based on their responses to spectral stimuli and to increments and decrements of light in which the stimuli were large with respect to the size of the receptive field of the cell. The categorization, as well as the terminology used, does not refer to nor does it carry any implications about the possible cone inputs to the various cell types. It is important to recognize that this is a separable and distinct problem from that of response categories. Although both issues are of obvious interest, they are unfortunately often confounded in the literature.

Spectrally opponent cells. It is obvious that the spectrally opponent cells must be receiving excitatory inputs from some receptor type or types and inhibitory inputs from other type or types of receptors. The particular combinations of cones that feed into the various opponent cell types is a point of interest and one of some dispute. The principal tool used to establish this is chromatic adaptation. The use of this technique rests on the basic assumption that all or most of the adaptation occurs at the receptor (outer segment) level. Because the absorbance curves of the cone pigments overlap considerably (see Fig. 3), any chromatic adaptation condition will inevitably affect

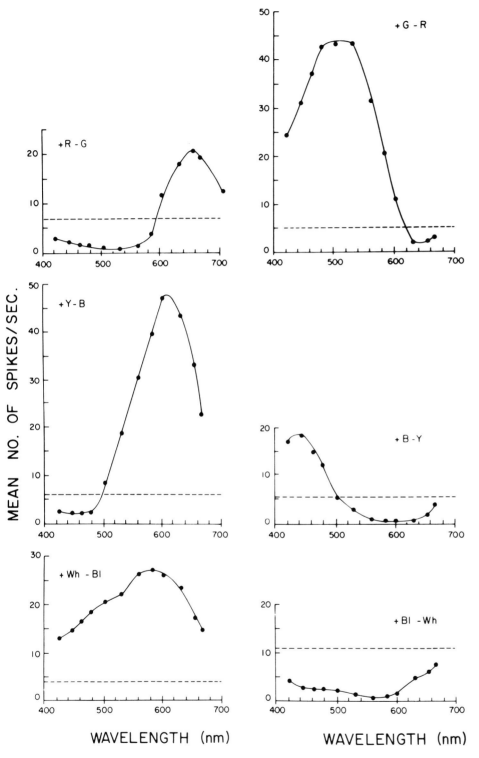

FIG. 9. Plots of average firing rates of a large sample of cells of each of the six lateral geniculate nucleus cell types. Stimuli were 0.7 log unit incremental flashes of monochromatic light, 1 s in duration, covering the entire receptive field. *Horizontal dashed lines*, average maintained discharge rates of these cells, as measured in the 1-s interval before each stimulus. *Top* and *middle panels*: results from spectrally opponent cells; *bottom panels*: results from spectrally nonopponent cells. Note that these are responses to increments of light; in response to decremental flashes of any wavelength the +Bl/−Wh cells would fire and the +Wh/−Bl cells would inhibit. [Adapted from De Valois, Abramov, and Jacobs (34).]

more than one receptor type. Nevertheless, to the extent that the spectral sensitivities of the cone types differ, one cone system will be more desensitized by a light of an appropriately chosen wavelength than will the other, and so this procedure can be used to essentially isolate one cone type. An example of the application of this procedure to examine the inputs to a +G/−R cell can be seen in Figure 10. Insofar as the inputs from the different cone types are spatially segregated in the receptive fields of spectrally opponent cells, this separation can also be utilized as an aid in the identification of cone inputs to later cells.

The results of studies of the inputs to the +R/−G or the +G/−R cell are fairly clear cut—these cells appear to receive excitatory inputs from the P565 cones and inhibitory inputs from the P536 cones, or vice versa (1, 27, 39, 117).

An occasional R/G cell is found that responds in the same direction (either excitatory or inhibitory) to light from both ends of the spectrum and in the opposite direction to lights from the middle wavelengths. Some of these cells have been shown to represent a P536 vs. P565 opponency with a short-wavelength component due to absorbance by the β- band of the P565 pigment

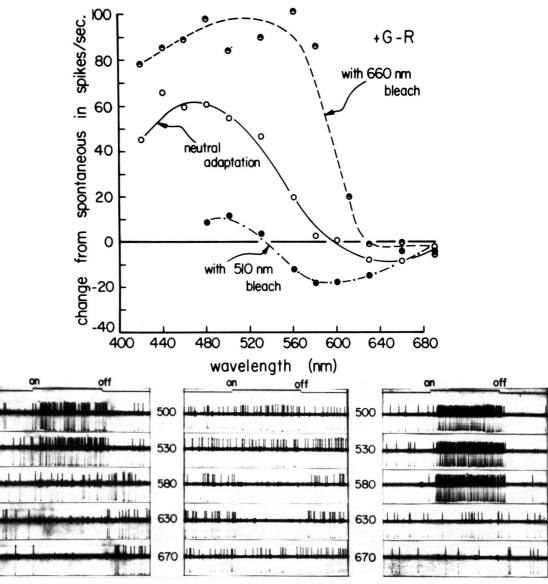

FIG. 10. Chromatic adaptation experiment with a +G/−R cell. *Bottom left*, responses of the cell under neutral (white light) adaptation conditions: to 1-s flashes of light covering the entire receptive field, the cell fires to short wavelengths (maximally at about 500 nm) and inhibits to long wavelengths. Data plotted as *open circles* in graph at *top*. With a 510-nm bleach (*bottom center* and *closed circles* at *top*) inhibition increases and the point of maximum inhibition is shifted to shorter wavelengths. With 660-nm bleach (*bottom right* and *half-closed circles* at *top*) amount of excitation is greater and maximum is shifted toward longer wavelengths. It is clear that responses under neutral adaptation conditions are the result of algebraic addition of separate excitatory and inhibitory components, from P536 and P565 cones, respectively. [From De Valois (31).]

(27). This organization may underlie those instances where the response to short-wavelength light has some of the properties more typically associated with responses to long-wavelength light—for example, the common observation that the short-wavelength portion of the spectrum has a pronounced reddish appearance.

The application of these same procedures of cone isolation to the study of the Y/B cells does not lead to such a satisfactory, simple conclusion. From studies of this type of cell under various conditions of chromatic adaptation, it has been variously contended that the pigment systems involved in establishing this chromatic opponency are P440 vs. P536 (51, 117), P440 vs. P565 (1, 30), P440 vs. P536 + P565 (29), and P565 vs. P440 + P536 (96). These findings can be alternately interpreted as indicating either that there is no single arrangement of cone inputs feeding into all the Y/B cells or that the Y/B cells do not constitute a single response category.

Spectrally nonopponent cells. Although the cone inputs to the spectrally nonopponent ganglion and LGN cells have not been widely investigated, it is clear that these cells receive inputs predominantly from the two long-wavelength cones [(51); see Fig. 11]. The principal interaction between the cone types feeding into these cells, however, is that of summation of their outputs rather than the differencing of their outputs, as is the case with the spectrally opponent cells. There is some dispute in the literature with respect to whether all these cells should in fact be termed spectrally nonopponent. It has been shown (28, 95), with the use of intense chromatic adaptation, that for some units there are also some inhibitory interactions underlying the cells' responses. Because many LGN nonopponent cells show their peak sensitivity at wavelengths longer than 565 nm (the peak of the longest wavelength cone pigment), further evidence may be inferred for the presence of inhibitory interactions at some level.

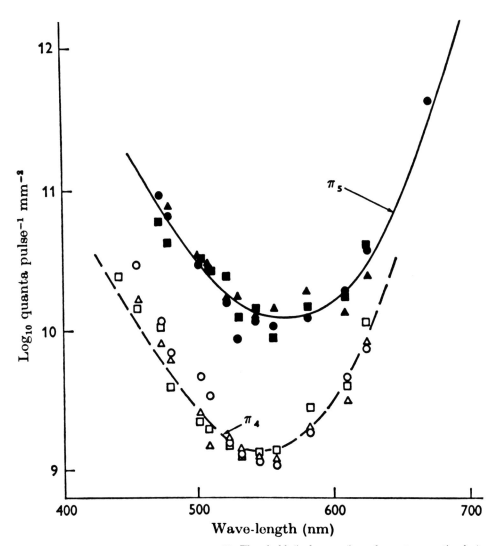

FIG. 11. Threshold (in log number of quanta per stimulus) sensitivity curves for nonopponent ganglion cells in monkey in the presence of intense red (*open* symbols) and intense blue (*closed* symbols) adaptation. [From Gouras (51).]

Despite the fact that intense chromatic adaptation reveals the presence of inhibitory interactions in some spectrally nonopponent cells, these cells do actually respond in the same direction to light of all wavelengths under normal viewing conditions. That is, the spectral opponency of these cells is relatively minor and is masked, except under the atypical conditions of intense chromatic adaptation, by the overall summation across cone types. These cells can, therefore, not be conveying much (if any) useful color information. Given the complexity of interactions within the retina, it would not be surprising to find that all of the cells in the pathway show some degree of opponent interactions under some stimulus conditions.

The discussions here and in *Spectrally opponent cells*, p. 436, aim to show that all of the spectrally opponent and nonopponent ganglion and LGN cells receive inputs from multiple-cone types. None receive input from only a single-cone type; most have input from two varieties, and some foveally related cells receive inputs from all three cone classes (27, 29). In this latter case the typical arrangement is for one class of cone to provide input to the center of the receptive field, while the other two provide an opposite (in sign) input to a surround region. This kind of response pattern has been referred to as *trichromatic* (29). However, it is important to note that these cells were not tested to determine whether they were in fact trichromatic as opposed to being only dichromatic; the authors failed to distinguish trichromacy from the presence of inputs from three cone pigment classes. Whether these three inputs have been neurally contrasted at some distal locations so as to achieve a trichromatic property is not known, but it is unlikely. It is probable that lights of only two different wavelengths (one producing excitation, one producing inhibition in the cell) would have to be mixed to match the cell's responses to any light; this would make it dichromatic (despite its three cone inputs). The terms *trichromatic* and *dichromatic* have operationally defined meanings in color vision (see the chapter by Yellot, Wandell, and Cornsweet in this *Handbook*) and should be reserved for specific instances where those properties are in fact present.

Given the evidence that all of the various cells in the pathway are either summing or differencing the outputs of more than one cone type, theories of color vision based on separate projection of the different receptor types to the cortex (82, 100) are not supported, and in fact are refuted, by the physiological evidence.

Spatial Properties

The two preceding subsections mainly described investigations utilizing stimuli that cover the whole RF of the cell, the conditions for obtaining the optimum chromatic responses. On the other hand, if more spatially discrete stimuli are used, other properties of the cells are seen. In particular, the inputs of the various cone types to different portions of the RF are found to be spatially nonhomogeneous.

DISTRIBUTION OF CONE TYPES. A very common pattern of cone inputs into single ganglion and LGN cells is one in which one cone type feeds in from the center of the RF and another cone type feeds in from the RF surround in an antagonistic fashion [the type I cell of Wiesel and Hubel (117); see also refs. 27 and 81]. For example, the P565 cones may provide an excitatory input to the RF center, while the P536 cones provide an inhibitory input to the RF surround, or vice versa.

In a minority of cells [the type II cells of Wiesel and Hubel (117)] there may be uniform, spatially overlapping distributions of antagonistic cone inputs. There is reason, however, to suppose that the inputs to the type I cells are also overlapping (90), as is the case with comparable cells in the goldfish retina (116), but with the surround and center inputs having different spatial extents [see De Valois and De Valois (37) for a discussion on this point]. Since both the type I and type II cells have overlapping centers and surrounds, it is not certain whether they are separate classes or just two ends of a continuum. There have also been reports (27) of cells in which one cone type feeds into the RF center, whereas two other cone types feed into the surround in an antagonistic fashion.

RECEPTIVE-FIELD ORGANIZATION. The spatial distribution of cone inputs to a cell is often confused with the cell's RF organization; it is critical to distinguish between these two concepts. The receptive field of a cell (60) refers to those receptors that activate a given cell, and the receptive-field organization of a cell refers to the types of responses elicited by stimulation of the different spatial regions within the RF. For example, a cell's RF might consist of an excitatory region of a certain extent plus an inhibitory surround (as revealed by mapping with a luminance increment). Whether these excitatory and inhibitory responses originate in rods or cones, or from one type of cone as against another, is quite a different question.

In an earlier part of this section, DISTRIBUTION OF CONE TYPES, this page, we considered the distribution of cone inputs into ganglion and LGN cells; here we examine the organization of the cells' RFs—how they respond to various spatial stimuli.

Considering color vision in its broadest sense, we find two discrete dimensions of concern—variations in luminance and variations in wavelength. Stimuli varying along one or the other of these two dimensions produce different responses in one cone type compared to another. Stimuli varying just in luminance drive the three cone types in common; an increase in luminance produces a hyperpolarization of all the receptors, and a decrement in luminance produces a depolarization of all the receptors. So a variation in pure luminance, whether of white or monochromatic light, affects all the receptors in the same direction. On the other hand, a pure chromatic light, varying not in luminance but just in wavelength, produces opposite responses in the different cone types.

To illustrate this point, consider how the P536 and P565 cones respond to a shift from a 560-nm light to a 600-nm light of equal luminance. This change in pure color will produce an increase in photon capture for the P565 cones and a decrease for the P536 cones. The P565 cones will, therefore, hyperpolarize and the P536 cones depolarize. A pure-color shift in the opposite spectral direction would, of course, produce just the opposite changes—depolarization of the P565 cones and hyperpolarization of the P536 cones. On the other hand, an increase in the luminance of either of these two lights without a change in wavelength would hyperpolarize both the P565 and the P536 cones. In sum, a pure-color shift produces opposite responses from the different cone types, whereas a luminance change produces the same response from the various cone types. (Of course, most natural stimuli vary in both luminance and color, in which case a combination of the two types of responses would be produced. Nonetheless, stimuli can be usefully parceled out into the two separate components, chromatic variations and luminance variations.)

To continue the example under discussion, consider now a ganglion or LGN cell to which P565 and P536 cones are connected in opposite fashion [Wiesel and Hubel's type I cells (117)]. If the stimulus is a luminance variation, the receptors will be driven in common, and the opposite cone inputs will have antagonistic effects on the LGN cell. Since one cone type is feeding into the surround, this will result in a receptive-field organization consisting of an excitatory center and inhibitory surround in response to a luminance increment (see Fig. 12). On the other hand, when the same cell is stimulated with a change in pure color, the stimulus will drive the two cone types in opposite directions. Since the cones in turn influence the LGN cell's responsiveness in opposite directions, they will be synergistic in their responses to the color change. In response to such a color change, then, the RF does not consist of an antagonistic center and surround, but rather a synergistic center and surround or, in other words, a uniform RF (see Fig. 12).

In dealing with cells that are spectrally nonopponent and respond only to luminance variations (as, for instance, most of the cells in the cat visual system), one can describe the RF organization without specifying the nature of the stimulus (which in most phys-

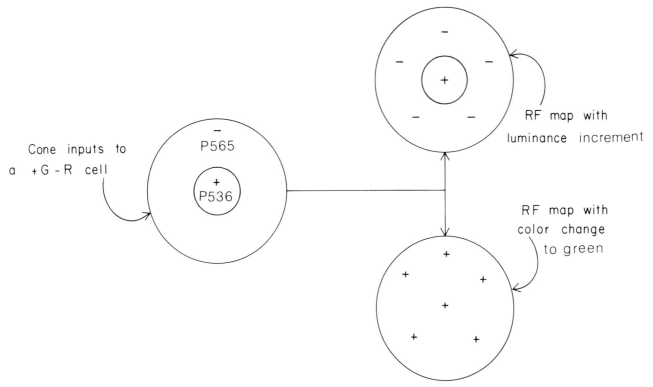

FIG. 12. Map of cone input and maps of receptive field (RF) for a spectrally opponent cell that also shows spatial opponency. *Left*: cone inputs from the two long-wavelength cones feed into this cell in opposite directions, and into the center and surround, respectively. Such a cell responds to both luminance and color changes but with entirely different receptive field maps for the two types of stimuli. *Top right*: when mapped with a luminance change, the cell shows a spatial antagonism between center and surround. *Bottom right*: mapped with a color change, the cell shows center-surround synergism, firing everywhere in the field to a shift toward green, and inhibiting everywhere to a shift toward red. [From De Valois and De Valois (37).]

iological studies is implicitly assumed to be a luminance increment). But in the case of cells that respond to both luminance and color changes, as is true for the vast majority of primate ganglion and LGN cells, it is meaningless to talk of *the* RF organization of the cell. Each cell has two quite different RF organizations: an antagonistic center-surround organization in response to luminance increments or decrements, and a synergistic center-surround in response to color changes.

The consequence of the fact that ganglion and LGN cells have these quite different RF organizations for luminance and color-varying stimuli is seen in the different types of responses the cells show to these types of stimuli (42, 43, 81). Consider the responses of a +G/−R cell to incremental stimuli of various sizes centered on the cell's RF. As the width of the stimulus is expanded to cover more and more of the center of the RF, one sees an increase in response; with still further increases in width the response decreases as the stimulus starts to invade the antagonistic surround. On the other hand, in response to stimuli of different widths, which vary only in their wavelength content, this same cell shows an increase in response with increasing width all the way to the total extent of the RF (43). That this relation holds not just for an occasional cell but across the whole population of LGN opponent cells is shown in Figure 13.

One can think of this organization of inputs to the primate ganglion and LGN cells as a multiplexing of color and luminance information. That is, although

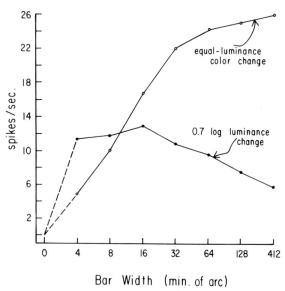

FIG. 13. Averaged responses of 23 spectrally opponent lateral geniculate nucleus cells, including cells from each of the opponent cell classes to luminance and color lines of various widths, centered on the receptive field. Luminance responses are those given to a log unit change of 0.7 in luminance of a white light, either an increment or a decrement depending on type of cell. Color responses are those given to an equal-luminance change in color, from a wavelength that inhibited the cell to one that excited it. [From De Valois et al. (43).]

there are some cells carrying only luminance information (the spectrally nonopponent cells) and perhaps some carrying only color information [the type II cells of Wiesel and Hubel (117)], most of these cells are carrying both luminance and color information, but over different spatial frequency bands. Considered in terms of the spatial frequencies of the stimuli (see SPATIAL AND TEMPORAL PROPERTIES, p. 449, and the chapter by Yellott, Wandell, and Cornsweet in this *Handbook*), the same cells are carrying luminance information at medium and high spatial frequencies, and color information at low and medium spatial frequencies.

CORTICAL CELLS

Area 17

Perhaps nowhere in the literature on the physiology of color vision is there greater confusion than with respect to the processing of color information in area 17 of the primate cortex. There have been a number of studies (6, 44, 45, 69, 92, 97, 112, 117) of the responses of cells in the striate cortex to chromatic stimuli, and about as many different accounts of the nature of the cortical organization. Rather than simply recounting these studies, it is more worthwhile to examine the reasons why this story appears complicated and confused.

Unquestionably the principal difficulty encountered in trying to understand this literature is the lack of agreement among investigators on the criteria to be used for deciding that a particular unit is a color cell or is involved with color processing. This difficulty does not occur with respect to other types of stimuli—orientation tuning of cortical cells, for instance. It is clear what is meant by orientation selectivity: a cell that responds to elongated stimuli of some orientations but not others, as opposed to cells that respond to stimuli independent of their orientation. Since the stimuli for testing orientational selectivity are well defined and agreed upon, the interpretation of the resulting responses is not in dispute, so no significant contradictions appear in the literature on orientation tuning of cells in visual cortex. The situation is quite different for color. Individual investigators differ widely in their definitions of color selectivity; as a result there is almost no overlap in the type of tests that have been used. Furthermore, many tests are actually inadequate to the questions the experimenters are attempting to answer.

A basic source of confusion is the confounding of color and luminance variations in the stimuli used in most of these studies, although, as noted in the preceding section, p. 433, the possession of color vision means the ability to discriminate between luminance and color variations. Despite this, virtually all of the studies of color properties of cortical cells have used monochromatic stimuli that are superimposed on a continuously present background; these spots have, therefore, a different color as well as a higher luminance than the background. That is, they vary from the background in both color and luminance. Whether a cell's response to such a stimulus is due to the color difference or to the luminance difference is completely indeterminate. Clearly the appropriate stimuli are those in which the luminance and color components can be separately varied.

Various other indirect strategies have often been used to establish that a cell is color selective. One such indirect method consists of attempting to find cortical cells that have properties similar to those of color cells at earlier locations in the visual pathway. But, of course, if the cortical cells important for color vision have properties different from those of the LGN cells, such methods may be quite inappropriate.

Many of the studies of the cortex have not been concerned with the properties of the color processing in the cortex but rather with the more elementary question of the extent to which the cells in area 17 are processing color information at all. The origin of this concern is that in the first major investigation of the monkey visual cortex it was reported that only a small percentage (perhaps 10% of all cells) were "color coded" [see Hubel and Wiesel (69)]. This finding was paradoxical for several reasons: *1*) the vast majority of cells earlier in the pathway signal information about stimulus color (see GANGLION CELLS AND LATERAL GENICULATE CELLS, p. 433; *2*) the principal cells of the LGN all project to the striate cortex; and *3*) the major input to the striate cortex is from the LGN. To find that only a tiny portion of cortical cells were involved with color processing was, then, quite unexpected.

Because Hubel and Wiesel (69) used flashes of monochromatic light as stimuli, they were always presenting changes in both luminance and color. They apparently defined as *color-coded* those cells that responded to only a restricted spectral range, or that gave spectrally opponent responses. All of the more recent investigators of monkey cortex have found higher percentages of cells involved in processing of color information (44, 45, 97, 119). It is not clear to what extent this change reflects differences in stimulus conditions or differences in the criteria for categorization, or simply reflects a more thorough investigation of the chromatic response properties of cortical cells.

Only infrequently have pure-color stimuli been used to study cells in the cortex [(112); L. G. Thorell, unpublished observations]. Such stimuli were used to determine whether cells were transmitting color information by observation of the actual abilities of these cells to discriminate among pure chromatic stimuli. In these studies about 80% of all cells in the foveal projection region of area 17 were found to be involved in color processing, a percentage very close to that found among LGN cells.

A major transformation in the processing of color information takes place in the retina at those levels where spectrally opponent interactions are set up. There seems to be no further modification through the LGN. An important question is the extent to which further changes take place in the cortex. Whereas there are many differences between the properties of LGN and cortical cells, there is little evidence that changes in the purely chromatic aspects are involved. Rather, as we see later in this subsection, the transformation principally involves the spatial response properties of the cells.

Although we do not know what transformations in color information, if any, occur within the cortex, one can imagine several that might take place. As we have seen, LGN cells respond both to luminance and chromatic variations (although with different spatial characteristics in the two cases). It is entirely conceivable, although perhaps not necessary, that at some level in the cortex the chromatic and luminance information are represented by separate neural events. Another possible transformation in area 17 would be a further narrowing of the spectral response bands of cells. The receptors have broad spectral response patterns. Through opponent interactions the ganglion and LGN cells achieve a higher degree of color selectivity, roughly corresponding to the broad categories of the color names *blue, green, yellow,* and *red* (34). It is possible that a further narrowing of the spectral bandwidths of single cells occurs at some later point. That is, there might be cells that respond just to very narrow spectral regions, such as just to the deep reds or just to the reddish oranges, for instance. While there have been reports of cells in the cortex with such narrow spectral tuning (6, 119), there is no compelling reason to think that these cells are in fact any narrower in their spectral tuning than many spectrally opponent LGN cells, if one considers only the excitatory half of the responses. Since cortical cells typically have very low maintained discharge rates, the inhibitory half of the response would not be obvious. To distinguish, as Yates (119) does, between narrow-band and opponent cells is in any case surely in error. Since the receptors are all broadly tuned and all the chromatic interactions at locations prior to the cortex are opponent in nature, the color-specific cortical cells must be opponent color cells. If they have still narrower tuning than do LGN cells, it must be because of an additional opponent interaction there, not because of an absence of one.

The further cortical processing of information about stimulus color that does appear to take place is with respect to the spatial properties of the cells. It is doubtless no accident that the same statement can be made with respect to information about stimulus luminance; there again, the principal activity that seems to take place in area 17 is a drastic modification of the spatial characteristics of the information being carried about luminance variations. Since we have much more information about the spatial response properties of cells with respect to luminance, perhaps it would be well to review briefly this information and then point out the parallels between that process and the transformations that may occur in the color domain.

There are two striking differences between the responses of the geniculate and cortical cells. One is that most cortical cells have orientation tuning. Cortical cells respond only to a certain range of orientations of elongated light stimuli, whereas cells earlier in the pathway have radially symmetrical RFs and therefore respond equally well to stimuli of all orientations (67, 68).

The second characteristic of cortical cells, not as widely publicized but probably equally important, is that they have much narrower spatial tuning than do cells earlier in the pathway. This narrowing is a consequence of the much stronger RF surrounds of cortical cells than of ganglion and LGN cells (67, 68). The difference between the spatial tuning of cells in the LGN and the cortex can be most clearly seen in their responses to grating patterns of different spatial frequencies. The LGN cells respond to a wide range of spatial frequencies. They have a very broad spatial bandwidth, showing a sharp, high-frequency attenuation but much more gradual low-frequency attenuation. The location of the high-frequency attenuation is related to the size of the center of the RF, while the low-frequency attenuation is produced by the presence of an antagonistic surround. Since the antagonistic surrounds of LGN cells are relatively weak, the low-frequency attenuation is gradual. Cells in the striate cortex are much more narrowly tuned, showing sharp attenuation to both low and high frequencies (20, 85). This more abrupt cutoff in sensitivity to the low spatial frequencies is produced by more powerful antagonistic surrounds and, in the case of many cells, the presence of additional sidebands or flanks within their RFs. That is, in addition to a central excitatory region and two antagonistic flanks, for instance, a cell may have an additional pair of excitatory regions.

In a section of the cortex within which all the cells receive inputs from the same portion of the visual field, cells tuned to every orientation are found in adjacent orientation columns. Within a given orientation column are cells tuned to each of a wide range of different spatial frequencies. The physiological evidence, then, is completely consistent with the suggestion of Campbell and Robson (21) of visual information being processed by multiple spatial frequency channels. The overall behavioral contrast sensitivity function is clearly not a reflection of *the* tuning curve of the cortical cells, as implied by some (e.g., the chapter by Yellott, Wandell, and Cornsweet in this *Handbook*), but is some sort of envelope of the sensitivities of narrow-band cortical cells tuned to each of many different spatial frequencies.

If the spatial response properties of cells are studied with purely chromatic stimuli, LGN cells show a sharp high spatial frequency attenuation (although characteristically at somewhat lower frequencies than the same cells show to luminance variations). On the other hand, they show virtually no attenuation at all at low spatial frequencies (J. Ready, H. von Blanckensee, and R. L. De Valois, unpublished observations). As discussed in GANGLION CELLS AND LATERAL GENICULATE CELLS, p. 433, this result is due to the fact that with pure-color–stimuli LGN cells do not have an antagonistic but rather a synergistic center-surround organization. When examined with the same pure-color stimuli, most cortical cells also show narrow spatial tuning in the color domain, just as they do in the luminance domain [(112); L. G. Thorell, unpublished observations]. Figure 14 shows the spatial tuning for pure-color stimuli of a typical cortical cell. Note that it is much more narrowly tuned than the whole behavioral function (the psychophysically determined contrast sensitivity function) which is also shown. The cortical cell typically shows low-frequency attenuation, which is not seen in the LGN cell response to pure-color stimuli. This is because cortical cells, in contrast to LGN cells, have a powerful antagonistic center-surround organization in the color as well as in the luminance domain. (This is equivalent to saying that they have a double-opponent organization.) Again, there are cortical cells tuned to each of a wide range of different spatial frequencies. If examined with purely chromatic stimuli these cells also show orientation selectivity, indeed much the same as is found with luminance variations (see Fig. 15). Thus, in the color domain as in the luminance domain, cortical cells acquire a high selectivity for stimuli of a particular orientation and a particular spatial frequency, whereas LGN cells respond over a wide range of spatial frequencies and orientations, as shown in Figure 16.

Without specifically noting it, we have dealt thus far primarily with the simple cells found in the striate cortex. Some additional comments are required because cells having rather different response properties are also found in the striate cortex. In their well-known studies of visual cortex, Hubel and Wiesel (68) distinguished two main cell types—simple cells and complex cells—primarily on the basis of their spatial response properties. On the other hand, another difference between these cell types that is not widely recognized, and indeed is not directly noted by Hubel and Wiesel (68), is that cat and monkey complex cells respond identically both to black bars and to white bars positioned in exactly the same RF location. In contrast to simple cells, then, complex cells are not color specific with respect to black/white stimuli. Many complex cells are also not color specific with respect to spectral stimuli, either, although they will in fact respond to pure-color changes such as those illustrated in Figure 2 (see also ref. 32). Because of this, the color properties of such cells would go unrecognized by those who use as stimuli only flashes of light that vary in both color and luminance from their backgrounds. That is, if a

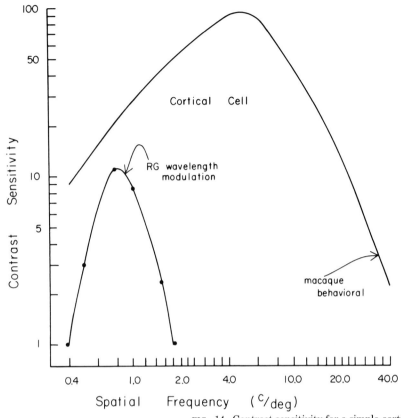

FIG. 14. Contrast sensitivity for a simple cortical cell, responding to red/green pure-color gratings. Note that the cell shows sharp low and high spatial frequency attenuation. It is much more narrowly tuned than the overall monkey behavioral contrast sensitivity function, also shown.

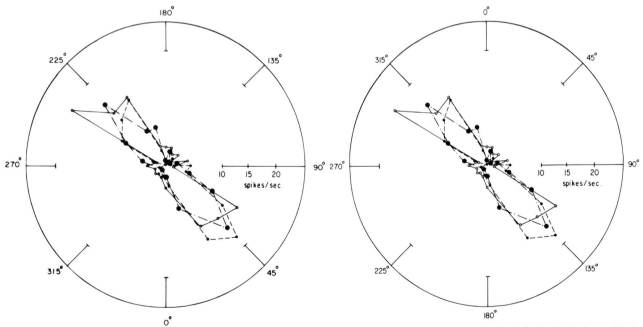

FIG. 15. Responses of a macaque striate cortex cell to white, *small filled circles*, black, *large filled hexagons*, and red-on-green, *small open circles*, pure-color bars moved across the cells' receptive field at various orientations. In this polar plot, number of spikes to bars of each orientation are shown by distance out and along that radius. (R. L. De Valois, E. W. Yund, and N. K. Hepler, unpublished data.)

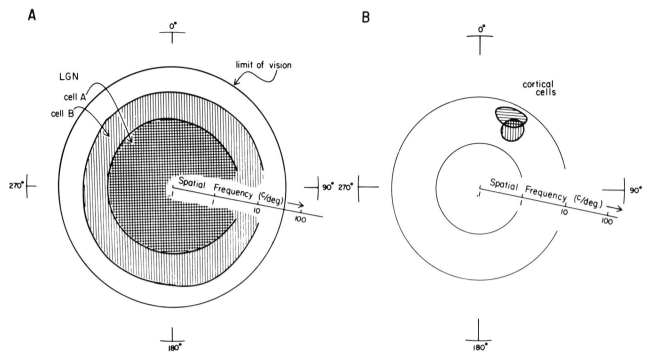

FIG. 16. Polar plots of combined orientation and spatial-frequency selectivity of typical lateral geniculate nucleus (LGN) cells (*A*) and cortical cells (*B*). In these figures spatial frequency increases from center outward, and various orientations are the radii around the circle. It can be seen that, in response to gratings of various spatial frequencies and orientations, LGN cells respond to a disk-shaped region in this orientation frequency space, since they respond to any orientation and to all spatial frequencies up to some cutoff point (chosen as that frequency at which response drops to half-maximum). The cortical cells, on the other hand, have both orientation and frequency selectivity and respond to stimuli only within a small region in this orientation frequency space. Two neighboring cortical cells are shown, each with the same orientation selectivity but with different spatial frequency selectivities. The limit of vision is the highest spatial frequency that the animal can discriminate under these conditions. [From De Valois et al. (36).]

cell fires both to a red flash and to a green flash, it is usually assumed to be unconcerned about color; i.e., it is thought to be comparable to the spectrally nonopponent cells in the LGN and retina. The implicit assumption underlying this conclusion is that if a cell responds to a luminance increment and to a change to red, and also to a luminance increment and a change to green, then it must be the luminance increment that is producing the response. The alternative possibility (which is in fact often the case) is that the cell has responded to the color change but that it is not specific with regard to wavelength content. The very small portion of complex cells that were classed as responding to color in the initial studies of monkey cortex (69) probably reflects the method of testing more closely than it does the actual number of complex cells involved in color vision.

The overall role in vision played by complex cells is in every respect more difficult to fathom than that of the simple cells; complex cells are indeed well named. It could be that the type of color response shown by these cells, along with their lack of color specificity, reflects the fact that complex cells are designed to respond to the spatial features of a stimulus independ-

ent of the particular luminance or color changes that define the stimulus shape. That is, such cells may use color variations to detect the presence and spatial characteristics of a stimulus but are unconcerned about the particular colors involved (32). The utilization of color information in this way should hardly be surprising, since one of the purposes of color vision is to provide an informative device to aid in the identification of the shapes of stimuli.

Cortical Processing of Color
Information: Beyond Striate Cortex

Several distinct regions of visually related cortex, each with retinotopic mapping, have been anatomically identified. With area 17 termed V1, these later regions have been called V2 through V6 (121, 123). Physiological studies of the regions beyond area 17 are still in their infancy, but mainly as a result of the studies of Zeki (121, 123) the dim outlines of a pattern can be seen. The later cortical regions appear to be specialized, as previous levels were not, for just one or another aspect of vision. The posterior bank of the superior temporal sulcus may be concerned principally with movement; perhaps V2 is concerned with stereopsis (70) and V4 (121, 123) and a region in the superior temporal sulcus (122) with color. Although many further experiments will be required to completely understand this organization, the initial studies of Zeki have provided an important introduction to the question of what happens next to color information.

That cortical area V4 is in fact importantly involved with color processing can be concluded from three findings of Zeki: one is that a large proportion of these cells are color selective, although the proportion so identified has declined somewhat over time, from 100% (121) to 55% (123). Another is the presence of a very strong columnar organization based on color selectivity; in one column all the cells might fire only to red patterns, in another only to blue, and so on. Finally, indirect evidence that these cells are centrally involved with color vision comes from the observation that V4 cells in general seem not to be very selective for other stimulus properties such as form or movement, which are so critical to cells in other visual areas.

Most cells in V4 (121, 123) respond to monochromatic lights over only a limited spectral range. The spectral bandwidths of these cells are reported to be narrower than those in earlier portions of the pathway. To firmly establish this would require a series of investigations using exactly the same experimental techniques at each level. There are so many experimental variables that affect such measures (particularly the adaptation conditions and the extent to which color changes and luminance changes are confounded) that it is hazardous to compare the results from different investigations.

Finally, it is interesting to note that in the clinical literature over the years there have been occasional reports of what is usually termed color agnosia (79), an inability to identify the color of objects. This condition is associated with cortical damage that would appear to involve areas anterior and lateral to the striate cortex. It is entirely possible that V4 might be the region involved in these cases, although the anatomical localization to date does not unambiguously implicate it. One interesting feature of at least some color agnosias is that the patient may retain color discrimination while losing the ability to identify colors on an absolute basis. As noted in *Area 17*, p. 442, this is just the property that many complex cells have.

PHYSIOLOGY AND COLOR VISION

For more than a century the field of color vision has provided fertile ground for theorists. Of the innumerable "theories of color vision," the most dominant varieties are typified by the Young-Helmholtz theory of three color receptors with independent pathways to some central area of indeterminate character, on the one hand, and on the other by Hering theory of three opponent pairs of receptors (or later elements). It is time to move beyond such theories and the disputes that have swirled around them.

From the perspective of present knowledge of the physiology underlying color vision, it is clear that Helmholtz (61) and Hering (65) and their respective followers were largely talking to each other in different languages. Each was emphasizing a different aspect of vision; the opposing positions were based for the most part on different kinds of experiments that yielded information about different levels of the system. In the main, Helmholtz was right about the visual receptors, or at least the photopigments. We do, in fact, have three different cone types, as he postulated, or as Young (120) postulated and Helmholtz (61) finally accepted, whereas Hering (65) was mainly right about the nature of the central processing, which is based entirely on excitatory-inhibitory (i.e., opponent) interactions, as we have seen. Of course, if we wished to be less magnanimous, we could be led by the same facts to the conclusion that Hering was mainly wrong about the receptors, which do not respond to different spectral regions in an opposing way (but note Fig. 4), while Helmholtz was even more wrong about the nature of the central path, which contains no channels from the individual receptor types to the brain, as has been made abundantly clear.

One reason, then, for burying the dispute and the discussions of Young-Helmholtz vs. Hering-type models of color vision is the fact that these are really not opposing theories but are consonant in the sense that they can be thought of as descriptions of the activity at different neural levels.

A more cogent reason for attempting to end such controversy is that both of these theories are oversimplifications of how the system operates. Most visual theories postulate, in effect, a single stage at which a complete process of analysis takes place. But we now know that multiple stages are involved in the operation of the visual system, multiple synaptic levels at each of which the information is modified in some way. Consequently, any single-stage model provides far too simple an explanation of the actual process. One reason for the complexities of the actual visual system, as opposed to the models that are often built to explain them, may be that most theorists have only been concerned with explaining one set of facts at a time. Thus theorists about color vision usually concern themselves just with color vision and ignore other aspects of vision. Other theorists may try to understand rod vs. cone vision, ignoring other aspects of vision. The problem with this approach is that the visual system does not consist of a dozen independent systems, one extracting color information, another black/white information, another dealing with movement, and so on. Rather, at precortical stages at least, there is a single integrated system that accomplishes all of these tasks simultaneously, with a severe limitation (at the level of the ganglion cell and optic nerve in particular) on the number of cells involved. For instance, the reciprocal relation between the color and luminance systems in their spatial and temporal properties [(78); and see discussion in *Contrast sensitivity*, p. 449] is hard to understand except in the context of the economy of simultaneously transmitting color and luminance information down the same channels.

Before leaving the topic of color theory, it ought to be noted that we have given Helmholtz more than his due by saying that he was right about the receptors, and Hering slightly more than his due by saying that he was right about the central processing of color information. In truth, Helmholtz was not entirely right about the receptors and Hering [even in a modernized form, i.e., Hurvich and Jameson (72)] was not entirely right about the central processing of color information. The three color receptors in the Helmholtz-type theory are either explicitly or implicitly based on the notion of fairly nonoverlapping receptor types, in which the activation of a particular receptor signals a particular color; hence they are often referred to as red, green, and blue cones. This is largely true as far as the P440 cones are concerned, and it is perhaps forgivable to call them blue cones; they appear to signal blue and to be involved in very little else. The two long-wavelength receptors, however, are almost completely overlapping in their spectral sensitivities (both peak in the greenish-yellow part of the spectrum), and, in addition to their multiple color interactions, are involved in signaling black/white, movement, and every other dimension we perceive. The activation of the middle-wavelength receptor does not in any sense signal green, nor the activation of the long-wavelength receptor, red. Indeed, in experiments in which human subjects have reported what they see under experimental conditions where there is good reason to think that their vision is almost completely dependent on a single receptor type, they have reported a very saturated color when the P440 cones alone are stimulated, but with stimulation of either of the other cone types by themselves, a very desaturated, almost white, color (17). As has been discussed elsewhere (37), a great number of people have befuddled themselves about various aspects of color vision by thinking of the two long-wavelength cone types as green and red receptors.

Hering's model of opponent pairs certainly comes closer than the Young-Helmholtz theory to accommodating the facts of color vision in general; even his positing of the process in the receptors is more nearly correct than appeared possible just a few years ago. This is certainly true for the black/white system; as we noted earlier, receptors do respond to black/white variations in the stimuli, with opposite responses of hyperpolarization and depolarization with respect to the polarization level produced by the mean light level at the time. The red/green and yellow/blue opponent color systems, of course, involve not just processes within a single receptor but rather interactions between the receptors. Even that process, however, seems to take place to some extent right at the receptor level. And, as Hurvich and Jameson (65) have pointed out, Hering did locate the opponent interactions later than the photopigment level. Nevertheless, the complete symmetry among these three opponent systems that is a characteristic of the Hering-type theories does not in fact hold. Not only do the white/black systems differ drastically in their mode of operation from the red/green and yellow/blue systems, but they are not independent of them in the early part of the pathway. There is also increasing evidence that the red/green and yellow/blue systems operate in basically different modes. We discuss both of these matters in *Red/Green vs. Yellow/Blue Systems*, p. 453.

Relation of Physiology to Color Vision

The ultimate goal of visual physiology and visual perception is to achieve an understanding of visual behavior in terms of the underlying anatomy and physiology. In the case of color vision, as for other aspects of vision, that understanding is still a distant goal but one toward which considerable progress has been made in the last two decades.

COLOR MIXING. Many studies of color vision have involved color mixing (see the chapter by Yellott, Wandell, and Cornsweet in this *Handbook*). The central fact demonstrated by such experiments is that human color vision is trichromatic: only the relative proportions of three fixed-spectral lights need be varied in order to match exactly the appearance of any other light. This basic three-dimensionality of human color vision has long been postulated to be so limited by the presence of only three cone pigments. This is, in fact, the case (see PHOTOPIGMENTS, p. 427). Metameric colors (those lights of different spectral composition that appear identical) undoubtedly are indistinguishable because they have the same effects on the three cone pigments. That being so, no later changes that might take place within the visual pathway can destroy the identity.

Rods can contribute to color vision under mesopic stimulus conditions when both rods and cones are active. There is little evidence, however, that they contribute in the independent fashion that would make peripheral color vision tetrachromatic (22). Such a lack of independence might occur if the rods were to feed equally into both sides of all spectrally opponent channels, or if they were to feed only into the black/white system. In both of these cases, their effect would be to desaturate the color; this in fact is what usually occurs. Thus colors appear more saturated when seen foveally (where no rods are present) than when viewed slightly peripherally (where rods are numerous). Similarly, colors appear more saturated when viewed early in dark adaptation at a time when the cones have reached their maximum sensitivity but rods are still desensitized (83).

On other occasions, however, rods do not play this "negative" role in color vision, but rather a positive one. In these situations it appears that colors are being discriminated by the comparison of the output of cones with those of rods, rather than by the usual comparison of two or more cone outputs (89). An occasional opponent cell found in monkey (96) and in ground squirrel (114) appears to be differencing rod and cone outputs. This latter situation would provide a physiological explanation for the "positive" role of rods in color vision, but it leaves open the difficulty of reconciling this with the usual desaturating effect of rod activity.

COLOR SPACE. The three-dimensionality of color mixing is reflected in the three-dimensional character of color space, in which various colors differ from one another in hue, saturation, and lightness. (Hue refers to the percept of various color qualities such as red, green; saturation is the perceptual dimension varying from pure colors through the pastel shades to gray; all these colors can vary in lightness from very bright to dark.) Many of the facts of color mixing and the perceptual relations between colors can be represented geometrically by a double conical shape: lightness forms the main axis, the various hues of the spectrum being arranged in a circle around the perimeter, and saturation is represented by the distance from the central axis to the perimeter, the maximum saturation occurring at middle lightness levels.

As has been discussed in more detail elsewhere (37), such a three-dimensional color space can, to a first approximation, be related to the activity rates of the three opponent mechanisms, the black/white opponent cells providing the lightness axis and the firing rates of the red/green and yellow/blue spectrally opponent cells defining the other two axes. In this scheme the hue, saturation, and lightness of visual objects are encoded by the relative firing rates of the cells of these three varieties of opponent pairs.

HUE AND SATURATION DISCRIMINATION. Discrimination of wavelength is not equally acute at all spectral locations. This fact would be represented in the double-cone model of color space by a nonuniform spacing of wavelengths corresponding to the various colors around the circle. The classic wavelength discrimination curve, with its two minima at about 490 and 590 nm, can be readily thought of as consisting of two separate components; the good discrimination around 590 nm would be attributable to the red/green system and that around 490 nm to the yellow/blue system. In fact, a direct test of this idea showed that the red/green cells show best discrimination around 590 nm and are much poorer at other spectral locations, whereas cells in the yellow/blue system show best discrimination around 490 nm (35). In each case the discrimination is best in those spectral regions where

the responses of the cells are changing most rapidly from excitation to inhibition with changes in wavelength.

A direct physiological correlate of saturation variations is seen in the fact that the extent to which a spectrally opponent cell fires to a light of a particular wavelength depends on the purity of the light. For instance, the degree to which a +R/−G cell responds to various equiluminant lights made of varying proportions of 650-nm and white light (that is, varying from high to low purity) is directly related to the amount of red in the mixture (41).

These comparisons would suggest that to a first approximation, hue is encoded by which types of spectrally opponent cells are more active in any situation, and saturation is determined by the extent of spectrally opponent as compared to nonopponent cell activity (2, 4, 33, 37).

SPATIAL AND TEMPORAL PROPERTIES. *Contrast sensitivity.* Insofar as the visual system is linear, the response to any complex stimulus should be predictable from the Fourier spectrum of the stimulus and the contrast sensitivity of the observer (sensitivity to sine waves of different frequencies: see the chapter by Yellott, Wandell, and Cornsweet in this *Handbook*). In 1972 Kelly (77) provided an elegant demonstration that this was true in the temporal domain by showing that the results from many different experiments in the classic flicker literature could all be predicted from the temporal contrast sensitivity functions of normal observers. There is now considerable psychophysical and physiological evidence that this holds also in the case of spatial patterns, as suggested first by Campbell and Robson (21). It is therefore of interest to examine the nature of the color contrast sensitivity function, and to attempt to relate it to various classic problems of color vision.

Psychophysical studies (53, 66) have shown that human observers have different contrast sensitivities when tested with color-varying gratings as compared to luminance-varying gratings (i.e., the patterns illustrated in Fig. 2). As shown in Figure 17, the sensitivity to luminance-varying gratings peaks in the middle spatial frequencies, with an attenuation to both high and low spatial frequencies. In the case of red/green pure-color gratings, however, the sensitivity peaks at lower spatial frequencies, shows a lower high-frequency cutoff point, and exhibits no low-frequency attenuation at all (at least within the spatial range tested). With blue/yellow gratings, the high-frequency cutoff is located at still lower spatial frequencies.

Similar experiments carried out with pure-color vs. luminance flicker (78) show that much the same holds in the temporal domain. The fact that we are more sensitive to high-frequency luminance flicker than to high-frequency color flicker is, of course, the basis for heterochromatic flicker photometry.

Another way to state these findings (and to under-

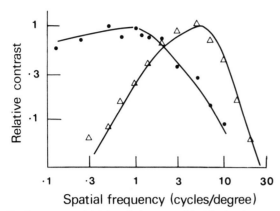

FIG. 17. Contrast sensitivities of a human subject for luminance-modulated (△) and red/green color-modulated (●) gratings of the kind diagramed in Figure 2. Note that humans are sensitive over different spatial frequency bands with these two types of stimuli. [Adapted from Granger and Heurtley (53).]

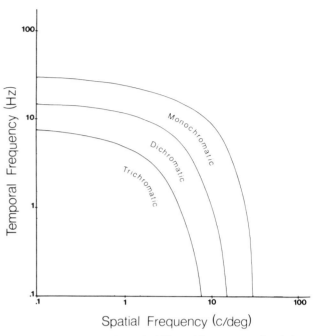

FIG. 18. Representation of ability of humans to discriminate chromatic stimuli of various spatial and temporal frequency ranges. At low spatial and temporal frequencies trichromatic color vision is present; at higher spatial and temporal frequencies, the yellow/blue system drops out and only dichromatic vision is present; at the highest spatial and temporal frequencies the red/green system drops out as well, and only monochromatic color vision is present.

line their significance) is to note that we are totally lacking in color discrimination with high spatial and high temporal frequency stimulation. Over an intermediate spatial and temporal frequency range we are tritanopic dichromats, having just red/green color vision, and we can make trichromatic color discriminations only among lower frequency stimuli. This is shown diagrammatically in Figure 18.

Although the retinal projections to superior colliculus are doubtless of great importance for visual behavior, it would appear that the geniculostriate path carries the critical information used for visual perception. While the cortical transformation of visual information appears to be critically important for perception, very little information is probably lost in the process. Therefore, what information arrives at the cortex determines the limits of visual sensitivity: what does not get to the cortex is lost to perception, and what does is seen by the observer.

The relevance of this to the spatial and temporal characteristics of vision is as follows. Ganglion and LGN cells have quite different RF structures if they are mapped with luminance as against pure-color stimuli (see Fig. 19). The center-surround antagonism to luminance variations in LGN cells (discussed in *Spatial Properties*, p. 440) produces a maximum sensitivity to middle spatial frequencies with an attenuation of sensitivity to lower and higher spatial frequencies. Thus, since virtually all LGN cells show this low-frequency attenuation, and since these cells provide the sole input to the cortex, the cortical input is perforce depressed at the lower spatial frequencies.

The absence of a center-surround antagonism in the color domain among LGN cells means that these cells do transmit low spatial frequency color information with respect to color variations. The large RFs these cells have with a center-surround synergism for color-varying stimuli also means, however, that they are insensitive to high spatial frequencies. The yellow/blue geniculate cells have even larger RFs on the

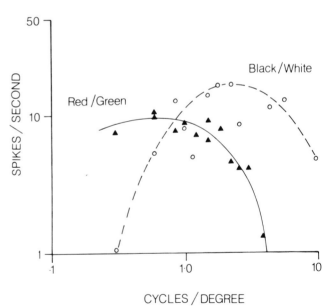

FIG. 19. Response of a spectrally opponent lateral geniculate nucleus cell to pure-luminance (○) and pure-color (▲) gratings of various spatial frequencies, which were drifted across the cells' receptive field. The cell responds to the two types of stimulus patterns over different spatial frequency ranges. (Based on unpublished data from H. von Blanckensee.)

average than do the red/green cells, and thus have lower high-frequency cutoff points. Therefore, red/green color information, yellow/blue color information, and luminance information arrive at the cortex over somewhat different spatial frequency bands.

It has been pointed out (43) that the different RF structures LGN cells have for color and luminance patterns can also account for the differing temporal contrast sensitivities for color and luminance stimuli, given that there are slight latency differences in the responses of center and surround mechanisms. The argument is as follows. At low temporal frequencies the latency difference between the center and surround would be insignificant, and the RF organizations shown in Figure 12 would hold. There should thus be high sensitivity to color and low sensitivity to luminance at these low frequencies, as indeed there is. But as the temporal frequency is increased, the center and surround responses should increasingly shift in relative phase. That is, the center-surround antagonism shown to luminance stimuli would gradually shift to center-surround synergism, with a resulting increase in sensitivity to these middle frequencies. This same phase shift, however, that converts the luminance RF from antagonism to synergism will of course also convert the color RF from synergism to antagonism, with a resulting loss in sensitivity to the middle temporal frequencies. This shift would explain Kelly's (78) finding that color and luminance sensitivities change in opposite directions with changes in temporal frequency. It would also account for our greatest sensitivity to color changes at low temporal frequencies and luminance changes at middle frequencies. Just such latency shifts producing opposite color and luminance effects have been reported (124).

Successive and simultaneous color interactions. The colors seen at a given location in space depend partly on the stimuli that have been at that location previously and partly on the stimuli present in neighboring regions. These effects have classically been known as successive and simultaneous color interactions, respectively (52).

The most familiar type of color interaction is color contrast—a displacement (in color space) of the color of a given region away from that of adjacent regions. Thus, a long-wavelength light may appear still redder if it has been preceded by a green light (successive contrast), or if it is seen against a green background (simultaneous contrast). The interactions in the opposite direction, in which the colors appear more similar to each other, are less well recognized but may be even more common and thus of greater importance for color vision. For example, a red stimulus on a green background often appears yellower, not redder. Similarly, rapidly alternated red and green lights merge into an unchanging yellow rather than becoming more dissimilar, as in color contrast. This direction of change has been termed *similitude*, as opposed to *contrast* (37). The critical factors determining whether contrast or similitude occurs appear to be the spatial and temporal frequencies involved: contrast effects occur at low to middle temporal and spatial frequen-

cies, while higher temporal and spatial frequencies produce similitude effects. This point is elaborated later in this subsection. Helson (62) showed that the interactions changed continuously from brightness contrast to similitude as line width was varied. The same doubtless holds for color interactions, but in each case it is likely that spatial frequency rather than line width is the crucial dimension.

Although it is probably more informative to consider these successive and simultaneous interactions in the larger context of spatial and temporal vision, they deserve separate consideration, since they are historically important concepts. All but simultaneous color contrast effects can be largely accounted for on the basis of precortical processes.

Successive contrast effects can be readily seen in the activity of individual spectrally opponent LGN cells (40); a +R/−G cell fires more to a 650-nm light if the RF of the cell has been previously exposed to a green light for some time. Two processes are probably involved in this effect: differential chromatic adaptation of the underlying receptors (the preceding green light would adapt the P536 cones slightly more than the P565 cones), and a neural rebound effect (the cell fires at the offset of the green light just as if the red light had gone out, even if the retina is left in total darkness).

The opposite type of interaction, successive similitude, has a physiological counterpart in the progressive decrease in firing rate of a +R/−G cell as the flicker rate of a red/green alternating stimulus is increased.

Simultaneous color-contrast effects cannot be accounted for on the basis of the spatial organization of ganglion and LGN cells, but they do follow from the narrow spatial frequency tuning for color patterns or double-opponent organization seen in many area 17 cells [(69, 92); L. G. Thorell, unpublished observations]. Contrast effects are related to the presence of an antagonistic center-surround RF organization (see the chapter by Yellott, Wandell, and Cornsweet in this *Handbook*). Such center-surround antagonism is seen in the luminance but not in the color domain at the LGN level. It occurs in the color domain, however, at the level of the simple cortical cells (as described in *Area 17*, p. 442).

Simultaneous similitude effects may be indicated in the decreasingly small responses a spectrally opponent LGN cell gives to a colored stimulus as its size is decreased (43). Similitude effects are related to the RF center size which, as pointed out in *Spatial Properties*, p. 440, is very large for LGN cells responding to chromatic stimuli.

In general, one can predict similitude and contrast effects from the spatial and temporal contrast sensitivity functions. Consider luminance variations. A uniform inspection pattern in a classic contrast experiment is similar to a half-cycle of a very low spatial frequency pattern. The contrast sensitivity to very low frequencies is modest. As the spatial frequency is increased, contrast sensitivity rises. The black/white bars now appear more different from each other (more contrasting) than at lower spatial frequencies. This is a shift in the direction of contrast. At still higher frequencies, however, the contrast sensitivity falls below that seen at the low spatial frequency end. This would be a change in the direction of similitude. The same argument holds in the case of color-varying stimuli.

Because the spatial and temporal contrast sensitivity functions are different for luminance-varying and color-varying patterns, whether simultaneous or successive interactions occur in any given situation depends on the nature of the stimuli. For instance, the transition from similitude to contrast occurs at a much higher spatial frequency in the case of luminance-modulated patterns (producing brightness changes) than in the case of color-modulated patterns. Patterns of some dimensions will therefore produce color similitude but brightness contrast, e.g., the patterns shown in Schober and Munker (103).

Borders and edges. A related problem is that of the role played by color and luminance variations, respectively, in determining perceptual contours or borders between objects (and in determining the corresponding temporal transitions as well). As was first examined by Koffka (80) and studied quantitatively by Boynton and his colleagues (12, 13), luminance differences play a much more important role in determining a sharp border between two areas than do pure-color differences. A minimally distinct border between two colored areas occurs when they are equated for luminance. Juxtaposed patches of equiluminant red and green will have a fairly sharp border between them, but blue/yellow color variations are almost totally ineffective in producing a border at all: the colors tend to flow together [see Tansley and Boynton (111)]. Similar relations hold among luminance, red/green, and blue/yellow lights in the extent to which they support sharp temporal transitions as well (14).

These borders or edge phenomena can also be deduced from the spatial and temporal contrast sensitivity for color- and luminance-varying patterns described in the preceding subsection and thus ultimately from the differing RF organizations of ganglion and LGN cells for these patterns [see De Valois and Pease (42)]. The physical presence of sharp edges or borders is determined by high spatial frequencies, and sharp temporal transitions by the presence of high temporal frequencies, in the stimulus. Thus a spatial sine-wave grating consists of very blurred bars with fuzzy borders. The addition of (the appropriate) higher spatial harmonics turns a sine-wave grating into a square-wave grating, with sharp edges and borders. Since we are most sensitive to high spatial (and temporal) frequencies for luminance-varying patterns, but have some high-frequency attenuation for red/green and even more for blue/yellow color-varying patterns

(see Fig. 18), one can readily account for Tansley and Boynton's findings. Since we are quite insensitive to high spatial frequencies with yellow/blue color variations, such patterns yield only very blurred borders.

That color variations made relatively little contribution to sharp borders or edges should not lead one to dismiss the importance of color for vision. Most of our visual activity (except for tasks like reading) consists not of making out fine detail but of discriminating and identifying large visual objects in a visually noisy environment. Low spatial frequency information, carried most effectively by color variations, may well be more important for this major visual task than high spatial frequency information, which is signaled most effectively by luminance variations.

PROBLEMS AND UNKNOWNS

The principal features of the proposed neural basis of color vision include three independent receptor types containing three different photopigments whose outputs are processed by an opponent organization that sums and differences these outputs in different neural channels. This is close to the type of organization postulated by Hurvich and Jameson (72), building on Hering's (65) ideas. There are, however, some major deviations from this picture. One of the principal complications is that the red/green, yellow/blue, and black/white opponent systems are not a matched trio, but rather have quite different properties.

Black/White System

We have pointed out that the opponent organization of the black/white system in a very real way occurs in the receptors, as Hering originally postulated rather than at later levels, as holds for the spectrally opponent systems. That is, the receptors respond to momentary increases and decreases in light with graded changes, depolarizing to light decrements and hyperpolarizing to light increments. The site and nature of the initial opponent interactions then are different for the black/white system than for the red/green and yellow/blue systems.

The spatial and temporal properties of the black/white and the spectrally opponent systems are also markedly different, and thus they display different contrast effects. The nonopponent cells have a center-surround antagonism (and thus a double-opponent organization) early in the pathway—weak at ganglion and LGN levels, then strong at the cortex. The spectrally opponent cells show a center-surround antagonism in the color domain for the first time at the cortex. The consequence of this difference is that we are most sensitive to luminance variations over the middle and high spatial and temporal frequencies, but most sensitive to color variations at low and middle spatial and temporal frequencies.

Finally, it should be pointed out again that the

TABLE 1. *Some Differences Between the P440 and P536/P565 Cones*

Property	References
Many fewer P440 cones than other cone types	Marc and Sperling (86)
Low foveal density of P440 cones	Marc and Sperling (86)
Weber fraction for P440 cones much higher than for P535 and P565 cones	Stiles (108)
Peak absolute sensitivity of P440 cones low relative to that of P535 and P565 cones	Rodieck (101)
Spatial and temporal contrast sensitivity lower and shifted to lower frequencies for the P440 cones	Green (57, 58) and Boynton and Whitten (15)
P440 cones contribute little to luminance	Vos and Walraven (115)
P440 cones make no contribution to perception of sharp chromatic borders	Tansley and Boynton (111)

nonopponent cell pathway (perhaps 20%–30% of all cells in the LGN) makes up only a part of the black/white system. Much of the luminance information is carried by the spectrally opponent cells, perhaps to be disentangled from the color information at later cortical levels.

Red/Green vs. Yellow/Blue System

Opponent-color theorists frequently treat the red/green and the yellow/blue systems as being symmetrical color systems of similar nature. The anatomical and physiological evidence, however, suggests that this is not so—that there are some fundamental differences between the two sets of color systems. Most of the differences revolve around or are consequences of the peculiarities of the P440 cones with respect to the two long-wavelength cones. A number of these differences are summarized in Table 1. In several respects the P440 cones resemble rods more than they do cones—in particular, in their virtual absence from the fovea and in their sluggish temporal responsivity. Indeed, phenomenologists have noted that objects seen at scotopic light levels have a bluish cast, and this has

led some to speculate that the short-wavelength photoreceptors were in fact rods (118). Although this notion is no longer tenable, the rodlike behavior of the short-wavelength cones still presents a puzzle.

The red/green system differences the output of two cone types that are similar in their properties, that overlap in absorbance across much of the spectrum, and that occur with about the same prevalence and with about the same retinal distributions. The red/green opponent cell pairs are very numerous in the visual pathway; indeed, one investigator [Michael (92)] finds only red/green cells in the visual cortex. There is agreement on the cone inputs to the red/green cells. Finally, there is good agreement between the way the red/green cells at the LGN respond to various stimuli and the correlated visual behavior one can reasonably attribute to the red/green system.

In almost every one of these respects, the yellow/blue system differs. The yellow/blue cells are differencing the outputs of entirely different cone types, insofar as the P440 cones provide one input to these cells. The absorbance curves of the P440 cone and either of the two other cone types show little spectral overlap, and they have quite different retinal distributions. Furthermore, the physiology of the yellow/blue system is replete with unknowns and disagreements. It is not clear that only one cell type is in fact involved (see *Spectral Properties*, p. 435). And, finally, the relative paucity of such cells at levels up to and including area 17 of the cortex relative to the numbers of red/green cells is not consonant with the major contributions that this system makes to color perception. For instance, while the total activity rates of different opponent-cell–types in response to lights of different wavelengths agree well with the color-naming behavior of normal observers (34), this relation breaks down at short wavelengths. There is also a report (27) that the P440 cones feed only into the RF centers of yellow/blue cells, which would indicate a lack of symmetry within the yellow/blue system that is not seen in the red/green opponent pairs. In short, the yellow/blue and red/green opponent systems have many differences, and the nature and organization of the yellow/blue system is simply not at all well understood at the present time.

REFERENCES

1. ABRAMOV, I. Further analysis of the responses of LGN cells. *J. Opt. Soc. Am.* 58: 574–579, 1968.
2. ABRAMOV, I. Retinal mechanisms of colour vision. In: *Handbook of Sensory Physiology. Physiology of Photoreceptor Organs,* edited by M. G. Fuortes. Berlin: Springer-Verlag, 1972, vol. 7, pt. 2, p. 567–607.
3. ABRAMOV, I., AND J. GORDON. Seeing. In: *Handbook of Perception. Biology of Perception Systems,* edited by E. C. Carterette and M. P. Friedman. New York: Academic, 1973, vol. 3, p. 359–406.
4. ABRAMOV, I., AND J. GORDON. Vision. In: *Handbook of Perception. Biology of Perception Systems,* edited by E. C. Car-

terette and M. P. Friedman. New York: Academic, 1973, vol. 3, p. 327–357.
5. ALPERN, M., AND E. N. PUGH, JR. Variation in the action spectrum of erythrolabe among deuteranopes. *J. Physiol. London* 266: 613–646, 1977.
6. ANDERSON, V. O., B. BUCHMANN, AND M. A. LENNOX-BUCHTHAL. Single cortical units with narrow spectral sensitivity in monkey *Cercocebus torquatex atys. Vision Res.* 2: 295–307, 1962.
7. BAYLOR, D. A., M. G. F. FUORTES, AND D. M. O'BRYAN. Receptive fields of cones in the retina of the turtle. *J. Physiol. London* 214:265–294, 1971.

8. BEAUCHAMP, R. D., AND J. V. LOVASIK. Blue mechanism response of single goldfish optic fibers. *J. Neurophysiol.* 36: 925–939, 1973.

9. BOWMAKER, J. K. The visual pigments, oil droplets and spectral sensitivity of the pigeon. *Vision Res.* 17: 1129–1138, 1977.

10. BOWMAKER, J. K., H. J. A. DARTNALL, J. N. LYTHOGOE, AND J. D. MOLLON. The visual pigments of rods and cones in the rhesus monkey (*Macaca mulatta*). *J. Physiol. London* 274: 329–348, 1978.

11. BOWMAKER, J. K., E. R. LOEW, AND P. A. LIEBMAN. Variation in the λ_{max} of rhodopsin from individual rods. *Vision Res.* 15: 997–1003, 1975.

12. BOYNTON, R. M. Implications of the minimally distinct border. *J. Opt. Soc. Am.* 63: 1037–1043, 1973.

13. BOYNTON, R. M., AND P. K. KAISER. Vision: the additivity law made to work for heterochromatic photometry with bipartite fields. *Science* 161: 366–368, 1968.

14. BOYNTON, R. M., AND P. K. KAISER. Temporal analog of the minimally-distinct border. *Vision Res.* 18: 110–112, 1978.

15. BOYNTON, R. M., AND D. N. WHITTEN. Selective chromatic adaptation in primate photoreceptors. *Vision Res.* 12: 855–874, 1972.

16. BRIDGES, C. D. B. Spectroscopic properties of porphyropsins. *Vision Res.* 7: 349–367, 1967.

17. BRINDLEY, G. S. *Physiology of the Retina and Visual Pathway.* Baltimore, MD: Williams & Wilkins, 1970.

18. BROWN, J. L., F. D. SHIVELEY, R. G. LA MOTTE, AND J. A. SECHZER. Color discrimination in the cat. *J. Comp. Physiol. Psychol.* 84: 531–544, 1973.

19. BROWN, W. B., AND G. WALD. Visual pigments in single rods and cones of the human retina. *Science* 144: 45–52, 1964.

20. CAMPBELL, F. W., G. F. COOPER, AND C. ENROTH-CUGELL. The spatial selectivity of the visual cells of the cat. *J. Physiol. London* 203: 223–235, 1969.

21. CAMPBELL, F. W., AND J. G. ROBSON. Application of Fourier analysis to the visibility of gratings. *J. Physiol. London* 197: 551–566, 1968.

22. CLARKE, F. J. J. Further studies of extrafoveal colour metrics. *Optica Acta* 10: 257–284, 1963.

24. DARTNALL, H. J. A. The interpretation of spectral sensitivity curves. *Br. Med. Bull.* 9: 24–30, 1953.

25. DARTNALL, H. J. A. Photosensitivity. In: *Handbook of Sensory Physiology. Photochemistry of Vision,* edited by H. J. Dartnall. Berlin: Springer-Verlag, 1972, vol. 7, pt. 1, p. 122–145.

26. DAW, N. W. Neurophysiology of color vision. *Physiol. Rev.* 53: 571–611, 1973.

27. DE MONASTERIO, F. M., AND P. GOURAS. Functional properties of ganglion cells of the rhesus monkey retina. *J. Physiol. London* 251: 167–195, 1975.

28. DE MONASTERIO, F. M., P. GOURAS, AND D. J. TOLHURST. Concealed colour opponency in ganglion cells of the rhesus monkey retina. *J. Physiol. London* 251: 217–229, 1975.

29. DE MONASTERIO, F. M., P. GOURAS, AND D. J. TOLHURST. Trichromatic colour opponency in ganglion cells of the rhesus monkey retina. *J. Physiol. London* 251: 197–216, 1975.

30. DE VALOIS, R. L. Analysis and coding of color vision in the primate visual system. *Cold Spring Harbor Symp. Quant. Biol.* 30: 567–579, 1965.

31. DE VALOIS, R. L. Physiological basis of color vision. In: *Tagungsbericht Internationale Farbtagung COLOR 69 Stockholm, 1969.*

32. DE VALOIS, R. L. Processing of intensity and wavelength information by the visual system. *Invest. Ophthalmol.* 11: 417–426, 1972.

33. DE VALOIS, R. L. Central mechanisms of color vision. In: *Handbook of Sensory Physiology. Central Processing of Vision Information,* edited by R. Jung. Berlin: Springer-Verlag, 1973, vol. 7, pt 3A, p. 209–253.

34. DE VALOIS, R. L., I. ABRAMOV, AND G. H. JACOBS. Analysis of response patterns of LGN cells. *J. Opt. Soc. Am.* 56: 966–977, 1966.

35. DE VALOIS, R. L., I. ABRAMOV, AND W. R. MEAD. Single cell analysis of wavelength discrimination at the lateral geniculate nucleus in the macaque. *J. Neurophysiol.* 30: 415–433, 1967.

36. DE VALOIS, R. L., D. G. ALBRECHT, AND L. G. THORELL. Spatial tuning of LGN and cortical cells in monkey visual system. In: *Spatial Contrast,* edited by H. Spekreijse and H. van der Tweel. Amsterdam: North Holland, 1976, p. 60–63.

37. DE VALOIS, R. L., AND K. K. DE VALOIS. Neural coding of color. In: *Handbook of Perception. Seeing,* edited by E. C. Carterette and M. P. Friedman. New York: Academic, 1975, vol. 5, p. 117–166.

38. DE VALOIS, R. L., AND G. H. JACOBS. Vision. In: *Behavior of Nonhuman Primates,* edited by A. M. Schrier and F. Stollnitz. New York: Academic, 1971, vol. 3, p. 107–157.

39. DE VALOIS, R. L., G. H. JACOBS, AND A. E. JONES. Responses of single cells in primate red-green color vision system. *Optik Stuttgart* 20: 87–98, 1963.

40. DE VALOIS, R. L., AND A. E. JONES. Single-cell analysis of the organization of the primate color-vision system. In: *The Visual System: Neurophysiology and Psychophysics,* edited by R. Jung and K. Kornhuber. Berlin: Springer-Verlag, 1961, p. 178–191.

41. DE VALOIS, R. L., AND R. T. MARROCCO. Single cell analysis of saturation discrimination in the macaque. *Vision Res.* 13: 701–711, 1973.

42. DE VALOIS, R. L., AND P. L. PEASE. Contours and contrast: responses of monkey lateral geniculate nucleus cells to luminance and color figures. *Science* 171: 694–696, 1971.

43. DE VALOIS, R. L., D. M. SNODDERLY, E. W. YUND, AND N. K. HEPLER. Responses of macaque lateral geniculate cells to luminance and color figures. *Sensory Processes* 1: 244–259, 1977.

44. DOW, B. M. Functional classes of cells and their laminar distribution in monkey visual cortex. *J. Neurophysiol.* 37: 927–946, 1974.

45. DOW, B. M., AND P. GOURAS. Color and spatial specificity of single units in rhesus monkey foveal striate cortex. *J. Neurophysiol.* 36: 79–100, 1973.

47. EBREY, T. G., AND B. HONIG. New wavelength dependent visual pigment nomograms. *Vision Res.* 17: 147–151, 1977.

48. FAIN, G. L., AND J. E. DOWLING. Intracellular recordings from single rods and cones in the mudpuppy retina. *Science* 180: 1178–1180, 1973.

49. FUORTES, M. G. F., E. A. SCHWARTZ, AND E. J. SIMON. Colour-dependence of cone responses in the turtle retina. *J. Physiol. London* 234: 199–216, 1973.

50. FUORTES, M. G. F., AND E. J. SIMON. Interactions leading to horizontal cell responses in the turtle retina. *J. Physiol. London* 240: 177–198, 1974.

51. GOURAS, P. Identification of cone mechanisms in monkey ganglion cells. *J. Physiol. London* 199: 533–547, 1968.

52. GRAHAM, C. H. (editor). *Vision and Visual Perception.* New York: Wiley, 1965.

53. GRANGER, E. M., AND J. C. HEURTLEY. Visual chromaticity-modulation transfer function. *J. Opt. Soc. Am.* 63: 1173–1174, 1973.

54. GRANIT, R. *Sensory Mechanisms of the Retina.* London: Oxford Univ. Press, 1947.

55. GRANIT, R. *Receptors and Sensory Perception.* New Haven, CT: Yale Univ. Press, 1955.

56. GRANIT, R. Neural activity in the retina. In: *Handbook of Physiology. Neurophysiology.* Washington, DC: Am. Physiol. Soc., 1959, sect. 1, vol. I, chapt. 21, p. 693–712.

57. GREEN, D. G. The contrast sensitivity of the colour mechanisms of the human eye. *J. Physiol. London* 196: 415–429, 1968.

58. GREEN, D. G. Sinusoidal flicker characteristics of the color-sensitive mechanisms of the eye. *Vision Res.* 9: 591–601, 1969.

59. GUR, M., AND R. L. PURPLE. Retinal ganglion cell activity in the ground squirrel under halothane anesthesia. *Vision Res.* 18: 1–14, 1978.

60. HARTLINE, H. K. The response of single optic nerve fibers of the vertebrate eye to illumination of the retina. *Am. J. Physiol.*

121: 400–415, 1938.

61. HELMHOLTZ, H. VON. *Handbook of Physiological Optics* (1909), transl. by J. P. C. Southall. Rochester, NY: Optical Soc. Am., 1924, vol. 2.

62. HELSON, H. Studies of anomalous contrast and assimilation. *J. Opt. Soc. Am.* 53: 179–184, 1963.

63. HEMILA, S., T. REUTER, AND K. VIRTANEN. The evolution of colour-opponent neurones and colour vision. *Vision Res.* 16: 1359–1362, 1976.

64. HENRY, G. H. Receptive field classes of cells in the striate cortex of the cat. *Brain Res.* 133: 1–28, 1977.

65. HERING, E. *Outlines of a Theory of the Light Sense* (1920), transl. by L. M. Hurvich and D. Jameson. Cambridge, MA.: Harvard Univ. Press, 1964.

66. HORST, G. J. C. VAN DER, AND M. A. BOUMAN. Spatiotemporal chromaticity discrimination. *J. Opt. Soc. Am.* 59: 1482–1488, 1969.

67. HUBEL, D. H., AND T. N. WIESEL. Receptive fields of single neurones in the cat's striate cortex. *J. Physiol. London* 148: 574–591, 1959.

68. HUBEL, D. H., AND T. N. WIESEL. Receptive fields, binocular interaction and functional architecture in the cat's visual cortex. *J. Physiol. London* 160: 106–154, 1962.

69. HUBEL, D. H., AND T. N. WIESEL. Receptive fields and functional architecture of monkey striate cortex. *J. Physiol. London* 195: 215–243, 1968.

70. HUBEL, D. H., AND T. N. WIESEL. Stereoscopic vision in macaque monkey. *Nature London* 225: 41–42, 1970.

71. HUGHES, A. The topography of vision in mammals of contrasting life style: comparative optics and retinal organization. In: *Handbook of Sensory Physiology. The Visual System in Vertebrates,* edited by F. Crescitelli. Berlin: Springer-Verlag, 1977, vol. 7, pt. 5, p. 613–756.

72. HURVICH, L. M., AND D. JAMESON. An opponent-process theory of color vision. *Psychol. Rev.* 64: 384–404, 1957.

73. HURVICH, L. M., AND D. JAMESON. Introduction. In: *Outlines of a Theory of the Light Sense* (1920), by E. Hering, transl. by L. M. Hurvich and D. Jameson. Cambridge, MA.: Harvard Univ. Press, 1964.

74. JAMESON, D. Theoretical issues of color vision. In: *Handbook of Sensory Physiology. Visual Psychophysics,* edited by D. Jameson and L. M. Hurvich. Berlin: Springer-Verlag, 1972, vol. 7, pt. 4, p. 381–412.

75. KANEKO, A. Physiological and morphological identification of horizontal, bipolar and amacrine cells in goldfish retina. *J. Physiol. London* 207: 623–633, 1970.

76. KANEKO, A. Receptive field organization of bipolar and amacrine cells in the goldfish retina. *J. Physiol. London* 235: 113–153, 1973.

77. KELLY, D. H. FLICKER. *Handbook of Sensory Physiology. Visual Psychophysics.* edited by D. Jameson and L. M. Hurvich. Berlin: Springer-Verlag, 1972, vol. 7, pt. 4, p. 273–302.

78. KELLY, D. H. Luminous and chromatic flickering patterns have opposite effects. *Science* 188: 371–372, 1975.

79. KINSBOURNE, M., AND E. K. WARRINGTON. Observations on colour agnosia. *J. Neurol. Neurosurg. Psychiatry* 27: 296–299, 1964.

80. KOFFKA, K. *Principles of Gestalt Psychology.* New York: Harcourt, Brace, 1935.

81. KRUGER, L. Stimulus dependent colour specificity of monkey lateral geniculate neurones. *Exp. Brain Res.* 30: 297–311, 1977.

82. LAND, E. H., AND J. J. MCCANN. Lightness and retinex theory. *J. Opt. Soc. Am.* 61: 1–11, 1971.

83. LIE, I. Dark adaptation and the photochromatic interval. *Doc. Ophthalmol.* 17: 411–510, 1963.

84. LIEBMAN, P. A. Microspectrophotometry of photoreceptors. In: *Handbook of Sensory Physiology. Photochemistry of Vision,* edited by H. J. Dartnall. Berlin: Springer-Verlag, 1972, vol. 7, pt. 1, p. 482–528.

85. MAFFEI, L., AND A. FIORENTINI. The visual cortex as a frequency analyser. *Vision Res.* 13: 1255–1267, 1973.

86. MARC, R. E., AND H. G. SPERLING. Chromatic organization of primate cones. *Science* 196: 454–456, 1977.

87. MARKS, W. B., W. H. DOBELLE, AND E. F. MACNICHOL, JR. Visual pigments of single primate cones. *Science* 143: 1181–1182, 1964.

88. MARROCCO, R. T. Responses of monkey optic tract fibers to monochromatic lights. *Vision Res.* 12: 1167–1174, 1972.

89. MCKEE, S. P., J. J. MCCANN, AND J. L. BENTON. Color vision from rod and long-wave cone interactions: conditions in which rods contribute to multicolored images. *Vision Res.* 17: 175–185, 1977.

90. MEAD, W. R. Analysis of the Receptive Field Organization of Macaque Lateral Geniculate Nucleus Cells. Bloomington: Indiana Univ., 1967. Dissertation.

91. MICHAEL, C. R. Opponent-color and opponent-contrast cells in lateral geniculate nucleus of the ground squirrel. *J. Neurophysiol.* 36: 536–550, 1973.

92. MICHAEL, C. R. Color vision mechanisms in monkey striate cortex: dual-opponent cells with concentric receptive fields. *J. Neurophysiol.* 41: 572–588, 1978.

93. MUNZ, R. W., AND S. A. SCHWANZARA. A nomogram for retinene-based visual pigments. *Vision Res.* 14: 1237–1244, 1967.

94. NAKA, K. I., AND W. A. H. RUSHTON. An attempt to analyse colour reception by electrophysiology. *J. Physiol. London* 185: 555–586, 1966.

95. PADMOS, P., AND D. VAN NORREN. Cone systems interaction in single neurons of the lateral geniculate nucleus of the macaque. *Vision Res.* 15: 617–619, 1975.

96. PEASE, P. L. Spectral Properties of Monkey Lateral Geniculate Cells. Berkeley: Univ. of California, 1975. Dissertation.

97. POGGIO, G. F., F. H. BAKER, R. J. W. MANSFIELD, A. SILLITO, AND P. GRIGG. Spatial and chromatic properties of neurones subserving foveal and parafoveal vision in rhesus monkey. *Brain Res.* 100: 25–59, 1975.

98. POLYAK, S. L. *The Retina.* Chicago, IL: Univ. of Chicago Press, 1941.

99. RAVIOLA, E. Intercellular junctions in outer plexiform layer. *Invest. Ophthalmol.* 15(11): 881–894, 1976.

100. REGAN, D. An evoked potential correlate of colour: evoked potential findings and single-cell speculations. *Vision Res.* 13: 1933–1941, 1973.

101. RODIECK, R. W. *The Vertebrate Retina: Principles of Structure and Function.* San Francisco, CA: Freeman, 1973.

102. RUSHTON, W. A. H. Visual pigments in man. In: *Handbook of Sensory Physiology. Photochemistry of Vision,* edited by H. J. Dartnall. Berlin: Springer-Verlag, 1972, vol. 7, pt. 1, p. 364–394.

103. SCHOBER, H., AND H. MUNKER. Untersuchungen zu den Ubertragungseigenschaften des Gesichtssinns fur die Farbinformation. *Vision Res.* 7: 1015–1026, 1967.

104. SCHOLES, J. H. Colour receptors, and their synaptic connexions in the retina of a cyprinid fish. *Philos. Trans. R. Soc. London Ser. B* 270: 61–118, 1975.

105. SCHWARTZ, E. A. Responses of bipolar cells in the retina of the turtle. *J. Physiol. London* 236: 211–224, 1974.

106. SIROVICH, L., AND I. ABRAMOV. Photopigments and pseudopigments. *Vision Res.* 1: 5–16, 1977.

107. STELL, W. K., AND D. O. LIGHTFOOT. Color-specific interconnections of cones and horizontal cells in the retina of the goldfish. *J. Comp. Neurol.* 159: 473–502, 1975.

108. STILES, W. S. Increment thresholds and the mechanisms of color vision. *Doc. Ophthalmol.* 3: 138–165, 1949.

109. SVAETICHIN, G. The cone action potential. *Acta Physiol. Scand. Suppl.* 106: 565–600, 1953.

110. SVAETICHIN, G., AND E. F. MACNICHOL, JR. Retinal mechanisms for chromatic and achromatic vision. *Ann. NY Acad. Sci.* 74: 385–404, 1958.

111. TANSLEY, B. W., AND R. M. BOYNTON. Chromatic border perception: the role of red- and green-sensitive cones. *Vision Res.* 18: 683–698, 1978.

112. THORELL, L. G., D. G. ALBRECHT, AND R. L. DE VALOIS.

Spatial tuning properties of macaque cortical cells to pure color and luminance stimuli. *Invest. Ophthalmol. Suppl.* 17: 195, 1978.

113. TOMITA, T. Electrophysiological study of the mechanism subserving color coding in fish retina. *Cold Spring Harbor Symp. Quant. Biol.* 30: 559–566, 1965.

114. TONG, L. Contrast Sensitive and Color Opponent Optic Tract Fibers in the Mexican Ground Squirrel: Evidence for Rod (502 max) Input. Ann Arbor: Univ. of Michigan, 1977. Ph.D. dissertation.

115. VOS, J. J., AND P. L. WALRAVEN. On the derivation of the foveal receptor primaries. *Vision Res.* 11: 799–818, 1971.

116. WAGNER, H. G., E. G. MacNICHOL, JR., AND M. L. WOLBARSHT. Functional basis for "on"-center and "off"-center receptive fields in the retina. *J. Opt. Soc. Am.* 53: 66–70, 1963.

117. WIESEL, T. N., AND D. H. HUBEL. Spatial and chromatic interactions in the lateral geniculate body of the rhesus monkey. *J. Neurophysiol.* 29: 1115–1156, 1966.

118. WILLMER, E. N. *Retinal Structure and Colour Vision.* Cambridge, MA: Cambridge Univ. Press, 1946.

119. YATES, T. Chromatic information processing in the foveal projection (area striata) of unanesthetized primate. *Vision Res.* 14: 163–173, 1974.

120. YOUNG, T. On the theory of light and colours. *Philos. Trans. R. Soc. London* 12–49, 1802.

121. ZEKI, S. M. Colour coding in rhesus monkey prestriate cortex. *Brain Res.* 53: 422–427, 1973.

122. ZEKI, S. M. Colour coding in the superior temporal sulcus of rhesus monkey visual cortex. *Proc. R. Soc. London Ser. B* 197: 195–223, 1977.

123. ZEKI, S. M. Uniformity and diversity of structure and function in rhesus monkey prestriate visual cortex. *J. Physiol. London* 277: 273–290, 1978.

124. ZRENNER, E., AND P. GOURAS. Retinal ganglion cells lose color opponency at high flicker rates. *Invest. Ophthalmol. Suppl.* 17: 130, 1978.

CHAPTER 11

The superior colliculus and visual function

PETER H. SCHILLER | *Department of Psychology, Massachusetts Institute of Technology, Cambridge, Massachusetts*

CHAPTER CONTENTS

THE DORSAL SURFACE OF THE MIDBRAIN consists of four small domes, the quadrigeminal bodies. In mammals the anterior two are called the superior colliculi; in submammalian species they are generally referred to as the optic tecta or the optic lobes. This brain region is our central topic. I begin with its anatomy and then examine its functional properties as revealed by electrical recording, stimulation, ablation, and de-

velopmental studies. In the past decade all of these approaches have yielded significant new information about midbrain visuomotor function; these advances are partly attributable to the development of new techniques and partly to the refinement of old ones. Recent anatomical studies have made extensive use of autoradiographic and retrograde transport tracing methods to clarify the neural connections of the superior colliculus. By beginning work with alert animals, neurophysiologists were able to relate the properties of single cells in the superior colliculus to behavior. Unanesthetized animals have also been used in stimulation experiments; with the introduction of microstimulation methods it became possible to combine recording and stimulation of small selected regions in the colliculus. Investigators examining the behavioral effects of superior colliculus ablation have developed several new methods for controlling and assessing behavior and have paired them with accurate measurements of eye movement, head orientation, and locomotion. Developmental studies have produced a great variety of new paradigms for the systematic manipulation of environmental influences on the growing organism.

This chapter does not provide a comprehensive review of all the work on this subject, which is very extensive indeed, but deals in a selective way with current findings that contribute to our understanding of the organization and function of the mammalian superior colliculus. For earlier reviews on the topic the reader is referred to Ingle and Sprague and others (117, 231) and to Sparks and Pollack (221).

ANATOMY OF SUPERIOR COLLICULUS

Methods

The results described in this section are based on both neuroanatomical and electroanatomical methods. Neuroanatomical studies have examined three aspects of collicular organization—its intrinsic structure, its inputs, and its outputs. Several methods are available for the study of each of these. Intrinsic organization can be determined: by selective staining for either cell bodies or fibers; by various modifications of the well-known Golgi method, which stains all or most of the processes of a relatively small number of neurons in the tissue under study; and by electron microscopy, which reveals synaptic relationships among cells. For the study of the inputs and outputs of the colliculus, anatomists have relied on both retrograde and anterograde transport methods by using horseradish peroxidase and radioactively labeled amino acids. These methods are described in more detail in the chapter by Jones in this *Handbook*.

Electroanatomical studies are predominantly concerned with the manner in which visual, auditory, and somatosensory space is represented in the colliculus. These studies use electrical recording techniques. For this kind of work the animals are paralyzed and anesthetized to prevent body and eye movements. The superior colliculus is systematically explored with microelectrodes, and at each site determination is made of the area in visual space where a stimulus evokes maximal activity. This is typically done by presenting visual stimuli on a screen or hemisphere facing the animal. The spatial organization of the auditory and somatosensory representation in the colliculus can also be determined through the use of acoustic and somatic stimuli.

Intrinsic Organization

The anterior roof of the midbrain is a laminated structure, the upper layers of which are concerned with the analysis of visual information. In the lower layers input from other sense organs converge, and output commands are generated that are believed to contribute to the control of orientation and eye movement. Among all the projections to this structure the visual input is the most conspicuous. However, the relative number of retinal ganglion cells that project to the colliculus decreases significantly in higher mammals and coincides with the progressive elaboration of the geniculostriate system in the course of evolution. Structurally the consequences of this are apparent: the relative amount of brain tissue devoted to the tectal and geniculostriate systems is strikingly different in lower and higher vertebrates. Figure 1 shows the brains of the toad, the rabbit, and the monkey. Each superior colliculus is marked by an arrow. The relative amounts of brain tissue relegated to the colliculus and to cortex are quite different in each of these three species. In the toad the colliculus is almost as large as the telencephalon, while in the monkey the colliculus appears miniscule in comparison with the cortical mantle. Calculation of the volume ratios of the superior colliculus (stratum griseum superficiale) and the lateral geniculate nucleus, the main thalamic relay nucleus to the cortex for vision, provides a more specific comparison. This yields the following ratios for a few mammals: hamster, 3:1; rat, 2:1; rhesus monkey, 1:8. The dramatic changes wrought by evolution are also reflected in the functional characteristics of

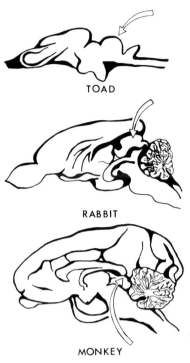

FIG. 1. Sagittal sections of toad, rabbit, and monkey brain. *Arrows,* location of superior colliculi. Note the significant difference among these three species in the relative amount of brain tissue devoted to telencephalon and to colliculus.

these systems. In nonmammalian vertebrates, such as fishes and amphibians, the dorsal region of the optic tectum is the main center for visual pattern analysis. By contrast, in higher mammals this function appears to have been largely assumed by the cerebral cortex; the superior colliculus, however, remains a nicely laminated structure as shown in Figure 2. This figure represents a frontal section through the superior colliculus of the cat; the section was stained for Nissl substance with cresyl violet. While it is functionally convenient to divide the superior colliculus into two general areas, an upper and a lower division, it is clear that numerous laminae exist. Three dorsal laminae form the upper region: I, stratum zonale; II, stratum griseum superficiale; and III, stratum opticum; these can be further divided into sublaminae as shown in the figure. These laminae process visual information. The lower region of the superior colliculus can be divided into four laminae: IV, stratum griseum intermediale; V, stratum lemnisci; VI, stratum griseum profundum; and VII, stratum album profundum. Taken together, these laminae show an alternation between cell-rich and fiber-rich layers. Thus, laminae II, IV, and VI predominantly contain cells, and laminae I, III, V, and VII contain fibers and neuropils.

While the laminar organization of the superior colliculus has remained well defined throughout the evolution of vertebrate species, the cellular organization of this structure has undergone significant changes. In fishes, amphibians, and reptiles the Golgi method reveals a great variety of distinct cell types in the optic tectum. Figure 3 demonstrates the cellular organization of the frog optic tectum; it shows an abundance of pyramidal cells with extensive basal and apical dendritic arborizations that allow these cells to sample inputs within several laminae. By contrast, in mammals we do not see such extensive dendritic arbors in the cells of the colliculus (117, 137, 262). This is seen in Figure 4, which illustrates the cell types in the cat's superior colliculus and the absence of pyramidal cells. Although a variety of cell types may be discerned, the dendrites of these cells either remain within the lamina where their cell bodies are located or extend only into the adjacent layers. This suggests that there may be some degree of independence among the laminae (117).

Studies of the synaptic organization of the superficial laminae with the aid of the electron microscope show that collicular cells make numerous dendrodendritic synaptic contacts with each other (144, 145, 241, 242). The retinal and cortical axons terminating in the colliculus make two types of contacts: the first of these occurs on the dendrites of collicular cells; the second makes junctions with those regions where the dendrodendritic contacts occur. These contacts are largely devoid of synaptic vesicles. The three types of connections noted so far (including dendrodendritic) comprise about 90% of the synaptic contacts seen in the cat (241). The remaining contacts are probably intrin-

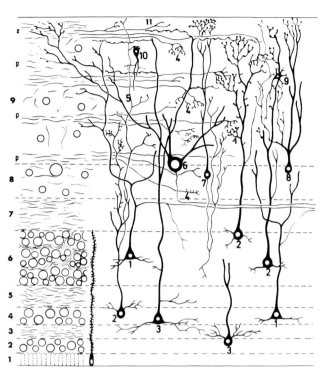

FIG. 3. Representative types of neurons in frog optic tectum shown in a combined cytoarchitectonic diagram obtained from staining with hematoxylin-eosin and reduced silver. Numerals at extreme *left* indicate the different layers; z, stratum zonale; p, plexiform sheets in layer 9. Golgi picture begins with a truncated ependymoglial cell. Numerals at *right*: 1, large pyramidal neuron with type 1 dendritic arborization pattern; 2 and 3, large pear-shaped neurons with type 2 and 3 dendritic arborization patterns, respectively; 4, optic terminals; 5, ascending axon; 6, large ganglionic neuron; 7, small pear-shaped neuron with descending axon; 8, small pear-shaped neuron with a beaded axonlike process; 9, stellate neuron; 10, amacrine cell; 11, assumed endings of diencephalic afferent fibers. [From Székely et al. (257).]

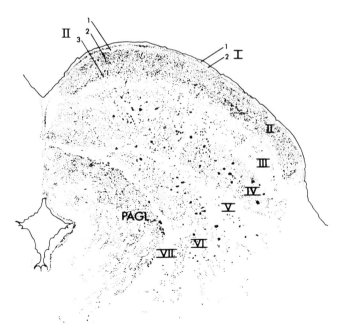

FIG. 2. Projection drawing of a transverse section through superior colliculus of the cat (cresyl violet stain) to show development of laminae. $I_{1,2}$, sublaminae of stratum zonale; $II_{1,2,3}$, sublaminae of stratum griseum superficiale; III, stratum opticum; IV, stratum griseum intermediale; V, stratum lemnisci; VI, stratum griseum profundum; VII, stratum album profundum; PAGL, periaquiductal gray, pars lateralis. [From Kanaseki and Sprague (125).]

sic connections from axonal collaterals of other collicular cells. The functional significance of this organization is not clear.

Inputs to Superior Colliculus

The complexity of the superior colliculus becomes evident when one begins to examine its inputs and outputs. These are numerous enough to give pause to any investigator whose aim is to understand the detailed function of this structure. To ease the reader's task of coming to terms with this maze of connections, I am retaining as much as possible the somewhat simplified division into upper and lower regions.

UPPER REGION INPUTS. The upper region of the superior colliculus (laminae I, II, and III in Fig. 2), as already noted, appears to be involved in visual analysis of inputs from other visual structures (4, 12, 63, 64, 79, 87, 92, 125, 128, 138, 241, 242, 271). The two most notable inputs are topographically organized projections from the retina and from the visual cortex. The density of the telencephalic input varies with the

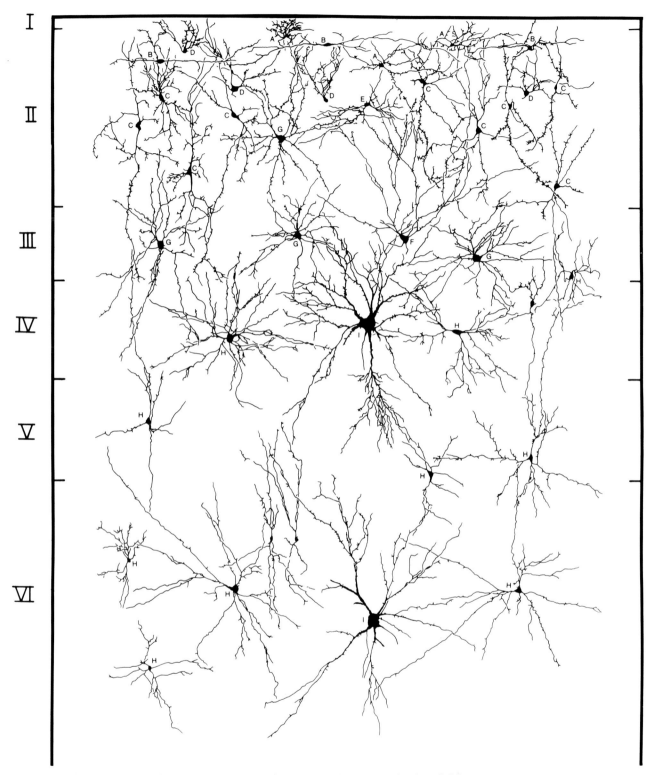

FIG. 4. Cell types in cat superior colliculus. Superior colliculus is divisible into two laminar divisions based on cell types seen in Golgi-stained material. Superficial division (I, II, and upper portion of III) is characterized by neurons with vertically elongated (narrow-field vertical cells, C) or horizontally elongated (horizontal cells, B) dendritic fields or by dendritic fields eccentrically distributed about the cell body (piriform cells, D; wide-field vertical cells, F; inverted ganglion cells, E). The cat is unusual in apparently lacking marginal cells but having small stellate granule cells, A, in upper part of its superficial division. Stellate cells, G, are rarely seen in the middle of superficial division but become increasingly more frequent in its deep portion as it becomes transitional with deep division. Neurons of deep division (lower portion of III, IV, V, VI) are predominantly small- and medium-sized stellate multipolar neurons, H, with occasional large or massive stellate neurons, I, usually in middle regions of layers IV and VI. (Courtesy of T. P. Langer.)

species. Thus, in nonmammalian forms, the projection from the telencephalon to the colliculus is sparse because the cortex and related structures are relatively small. In higher mammals, by contrast, this projection is often more extensive than that from the retina. A third significant projection to this upper region of the superior colliculus is from the parabigeminal nucleus. This small structure seen in most vertebrates is located on the lateral margin of the lower midbrain, ventral to the brachium of the inferior colliculus, and it receives a heavy projection from the upper collicular laminae and projects back to them. This nucleus also has a retinotopic organization (215).

Retinotopic distribution of visual inputs. The density of receptors across the retina and their relative convergence on retinal ganglion cells is fairly uniform in some species. Such animals can be expected to have similar sensitivity and acuity for visual stimuli in various parts of the visual field. By contrast, many fishes, birds, and mammals possess a more specialized retina, where a central region is densely packed with receptors and associated ganglion cells. The result is better acuity in that part of the visual field sampled by this region. In primates this area is called the fovea. There are two important consequences of this specialization. One is that when high acuity is restricted to such a small retinal area, it becomes necessary for the gaze to be directed precisely toward objects of interest and importance in the world. I deal with this aspect of vision in detail later, for it forms an important aspect of collicular function. The second consequence of note is that the development of the specialized, foveate retina requires, at higher visual centers, more brain area to be devoted to central than to peripheral vision.

The retinal surface is represented in an orderly, topographic fashion on the collicular surface. The relative representation of the various regions of the visual field, however, depends on the degree of retinal specialization. Figure 5 shows three maps of the retinal projection—for mouse, rabbit, and cat. It can be seen that in the mouse, which is an animal with a relatively uniform retinal distribution of ganglion cells, the topographic layout of the superior colliculus is also relatively uniform. On the other hand, in the cat much more of the colliculus is allocated for central than for peripheral vision.

How the visual projections become arranged during development in the superior colliculus so as to provide topographic transformations is not fully understood. Several interesting problems are associated with this question, and one of these merits further examination. From Figure 5 it can be seen that in each map the length of the vertical coordinate lines per degree of visual angle is greater than the length of the corresponding horizontal lines. The coordinate transform is particularly evident in the rabbit. In this species the distribution of retinal ganglion cells is nonuniform; ganglion cells are stacked more densely within the visual streak than above and below it. By contrast, in

the superior colliculus the density of axon terminals and the distribution of cells are relatively uniform. Therefore, to accommodate the dense input from the visual streak, more space has to be relegated to this region in the colliculus. It might appear that this is not the case, since in the central area of visual response the vertical coordinate lines are longer than the horizontal coordinate lines. Examination of corresponding areas for horizontal and vertical regions near the central meridians shows, however, that much more area is allocated for the visual streak. How could one explain the distortion seen along the two principal meridians in the colliculus? Assuming that in the course of development the peripheral retinal fibers are constrained to terminate around the margin of the superior colliculus, the observed collicular topography is readily explainable. On the *left* side of Figure 6 are drawn polar isograms for the retina (*top*) and corresponding density distributions of rabbit retinal ganglion cells for the horizontal and vertical meridians (*bottom*). The stippled regions represent the visual streak. The diagrams of Figure 6, *right*, show how the retinal fibers are distributed on the surface of the tectum. In the retinal region representing the far periphery the fiber density is the same at all locations (the area falling outside of line 1 in all parts of Fig. 6); therefore the space allocated is the same in all peripheral segments of the colliculus. Toward the center the retinal fibers terminating in the colliculus need more space along the horizontal than along the vertical meridian. To accommodate area to this the isograms become more oval in shape (lines 2 and 3, Fig. 6, *top right*). Transformation of the polar coordinates to a rectilinear coordinate system makes it clear that in the central area of the visual field representation the vertical meridian coordinate lines are elongated relative to the horizontal lines (Fig. 6, *bottom right*).

The consequences of this transformation, which has been extensively studied in the cat by McIlwain (154–156), are interesting. If the retina is exposed to a circular patch of light, which activates a circular patch of retinal ganglion cells (as shown by the black patch in Fig. 6), the axon terminals of these cells in the colliculus will activate an oval area. Conversely, a circular patch of cells on the collicular surface "sees" an oval area in space with its long axis parallel to the horizontal meridian (scheme represented in Fig. 6, *bottom right*).

Selectivity of retinal ganglion cell projections. These observations bring us to the second point about the retinal projection to the superior colliculus. It has by now been amply demonstrated that in the retina of most vertebrates several different types of retinal ganglion cells can be discerned (see the chapter by Dowling and Dubin in this *Handbook* and PHYSIOLOGICAL STUDIES OF INPUTS TO SUPERIOR COLLICULUS, p. 487). These classes of cells are not equally distributed across the retinal surface, and they project differentially to the rest of the brain (32, 41, 48, 75, 98, 204, 247, 264).

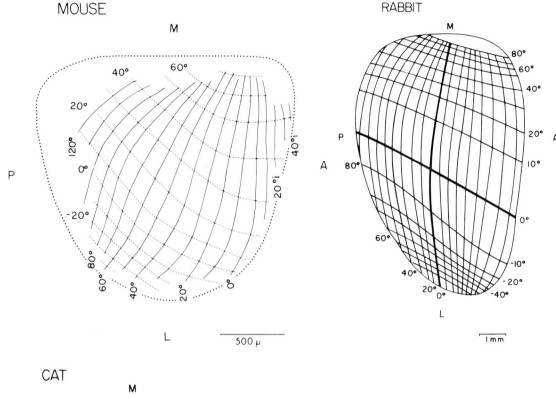

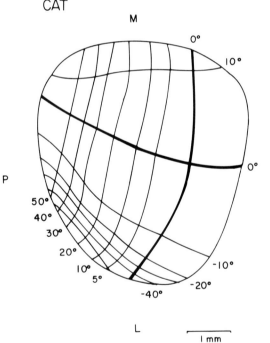

FIG. 5. Topographic layout of visual field on surface of superior colliculus of mouse, rabbit, and cat. Derivation of 0° vertical meridian is different in each of these maps. In the mouse map the 0° vertical meridian is the vertical plane that intersects the projection of the long axis of the mouse's head. In the rabbit map the 0° vertical meridian intersects the perpendicular to the long axis of the head, which passes through the corneal vertex. In the cat map the 0° vertical meridian intersects the projection line of area centralis. In all three maps the 0° horizontal meridian intersects each of the described projection lines in the horizontal plane. Horizontal meridians run in the antero-posterior direction. The maps represent the contralateral retinal projection. A, anterior; P, posterior; M, medial; L, lateral. [Mouse data from Dräger and Hubel (44); rabbit data from Hughes (108); cat diagram courtesy of H. Sherk from data of Berman and Cynader (21) and Feldon et al. (53).]

Recent examination of cat retinal ganglion cells by Boycott and Wässle (28), using the Golgi method, yielded three classes: the α-cells, which are the largest, with a mean perikaryal diameter of about 33 μm; the β-cells, which measure 20 μm; and the γ-cells, with a mean diameter of 14 μm. Retrograde labeling of cat ganglion cells by horseradish peroxidase injection into the superior colliculus has shown that it is the small

γ-like cells that constitute the major input to this structure (132, 147). These small cells do not show an increase in density in central retina comparable to that of the β-cells.

Convergence of the input from the two eyes. The third point to be made about the retinal input to the superior colliculus pertains to the convergence of projections from the two eyes. In many lower species the

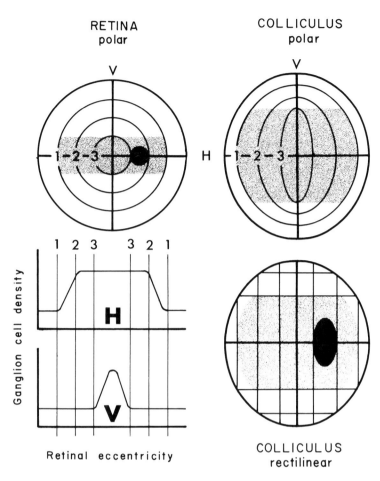

RETINA
polar

COLLICULUS
polar

Ganglion cell density

1 2 3   3 2 1

H

V

Retinal eccentricity

COLLICULUS
rectilinear

FIG. 6. Retinotectal transformation. *Top left*: polar isograms for retinal surface of rabbit. The 0° vertical meridian intersects the perpendicular to the long axis of the head, which passes through the corneal vertex. The 0° horizontal meridian intersects the projection line in the horizontal plane. Stippled area, visual streak. *Bottom left*: approximate density distribution of retinal ganglion cells along horizontal, H, and vertical, V, meridians. *Top right*: collicular topography, polar coordinates. Stippled area, visual streak. *Bottom right*: collicular topography, rectilinear coordinates; transformation of circular spot on retina (*black disk*) is shown in colliculus by *black oval area*. [*Bottom left*, data from Hughes (108).]

lateral position of the eyes is such that there is little binocular overlap of the two visual fields. In carnivores, and to a still greater degree in primates, the two visual fields overlap, thus providing the possibility for viewing large portions of the visual field with both eyes. A change in the central connections parallels this shift. Whereas in animals with small binocular overlap the optic nerves are mostly crossed, in higher mammals with a great deal of binocular vision there are almost as many uncrossed as crossed fibers at the optic chiasm. Thus in cats, monkeys, and humans the fibers from the nasal hemiretinas project to contralateral sites and the fibers from the temporal hemiretinas project to ipsilateral sites. A complicating factor is that in some species the degree to which fibers projecting to a given structure remain crossed or uncrossed depends upon the class of retinal ganglion cells involved. In the cat, for example, the projections to the geniculostriate systems are about 55% crossed and 45% uncrossed (142), while the retinotectal projections are much more heavily crossed than uncrossed (see Fig. 7).

Figure 7 shows the pattern of projections from the retina to the superior colliculus in three species—the rabbit, the cat, and the monkey. In all three of these examples the right eye was injected with labeled amino acids. The distribution of the labeled optic nerve terminals from this eye shows that the projection in the rabbit is predominantly crossed. In the cat there is an increase in the size of the ipsilateral pathway to the colliculus, whereas in the monkey the numbers of crossed and uncrossed fibers are almost equal. One other fact is notable in Figure 7: the label often appears to be bunched in little groups or puffs, suggesting some degree of separation of the inputs to the superior colliculus from the two eyes. These puffs actually form bands that look rather like cortical ocular dominance columns. This has been reported by Hubel et al. (104) for the monkey and by Graybiel (80) for the cat. Since the dendritic arborization of superior colliculus cells is often quite extensive, most of these cells could receive projections from both eyes in spite of this banding. Single-unit recordings show, in fact, that most cells within the area of binocular vision seem to be sensitive to light stimulation of either eye (see PHYSIOLOGY OF SUPERIOR COLLICULUS: ELECTRICAL RECORDING STUDIES, p. 467).

The story of the convergence of inputs from the two eyes to the colliculus is actually somewhat more complicated, because most cells in the visual cortex that make axonal terminations within the colliculus can be activated from either eye (57, 177). Therefore the

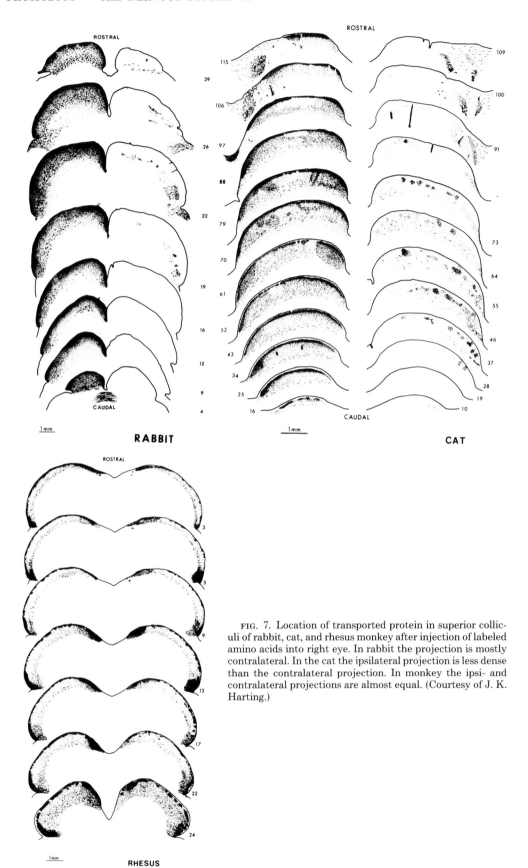

FIG. 7. Location of transported protein in superior colliculi of rabbit, cat, and rhesus monkey after injection of labeled amino acids into right eye. In rabbit the projection is mostly contralateral. In the cat the ipsilateral projection is less dense than the contralateral projection. In monkey the ipsi- and contralateral projections are almost equal. (Courtesy of J. K. Harting.)

input from the two eyes to single cells in the colliculus may take two routes: i.e., convergence from the retinal ganglion cells of the two eyes, and input from binocular cortical cells. The role of the cortical input on the binocularity of collicular cells has been determined experimentally by selectively disrupting the corticotectal projection or by selectively depriving animals of binocular vision. The results of these manipulations are discussed later (see *Cortical Input*, p. 488, and *Effect of Selective Rearing on Collicular Functions*, p. 495).

LOWER REGION INPUTS. The inputs to the deeper layers of the superior colliculus originate from several brain sites. There are projections from both auditory and somatosensory areas, cortical as well as subcortical. The auditory inputs come from auditory cortex and from the region of the inferior colliculus. The somatosensory input originates in the somatosensory cortex and the spinal trigeminal nucleus. The auditory and somatosensory regions in the colliculus are topographically represented and are in some form of congruence with the visual input (45, 240, 259). As with other inputs, the density of the projection is species dependent. Thus in some rodents the auditory as well as the somatosensory areas are extensive; in primates they seem to be somewhat less pronounced.

Several other regions of the cortex project to the superior colliculus, as shown for the cat in Figure 8. A general progression is evident for these inputs, such that increasingly deeper regions of the colliculus receive projections from cortical regions arranged posteroanteriorly. Thus Brodmann area 17 in Figure 8 projects to the stratum opticum most heavily, just below the retinal input, and overlaps with it to some degree. Inputs from areas 18 and 19 are lower. Progressively deeper regions are innervated by parietal and frontal areas. Among these are the axons from the frontal eye fields, a little-understood area, parts of which appear to be related to the control of eye movement (24, 25, 193, 276). This area appears to be reciprocally connected with the colliculus: the deep collicular cells project to several dorsal thalamic nuclei, which in turn project to the frontal eye fields (88a).

Subcortical areas projecting to the deeper layers of the superior colliculus are the pretectal complex, the ventral lateral geniculate nucleus, the mesencephalic reticular formation, the red nucleus, substantia nigra, cerebellum, and spinal cord (4, 11, 29, 78, 79, 85, 159, 160, 171, 172, 181, 185, 186, 232).

Outputs of Superior Colliculus

The observation that the upper regions of the superior colliculus are related to the analysis of visual information is further supported by the fact that most of its neurons project to other visual areas (5, 76, 88). Most pronounced are the projections to the pulvinar

and the parabigeminal nucleus. Other extensive projections are to the ventral nucleus of the lateral geniculate body and the pretectum, whereas the dorsal lateral geniculate body receives a smaller input from the superior colliculus. The axons of cells in the upper layers also ramify in other collicular laminae, thereby providing for a flow of neural activity that can be either downward or upward within the superior colliculus. According to Graham (76) the middle cellular layer (stratum griseum intermediale), although it also projects to the pretectum, makes mostly intrinsic connections within the colliculus. Another notable pathway reciprocally interconnects the deeper laminae between the two sides of the colliculus via the intertectal commissure (46).

The deep layers of the tectum, primarily stratum griseum profundum, give rise mostly to descending pathways (1, 19, 67, 76, 86, 88, 126, 127, 183, 195). Two major descending pathways originate from the deeper regions of the monkey and cat colliculus: one is an ipsilateral tract, the other a contralateral tract, and both terminate mainly in the brain stem. The targets of the ipsilateral pathway are the mesencephalic reticular formation, the dorsal-lateral pontine gray, the nucleus reticularis pontis oralis, the capsule of the inferior colliculus, and the cuneiform nucleus (76, 86). The crossed pathway (classically the predorsal bundle or tectospinal tract) terminates most heavily in the pontine tegmentum. Other target sites include the medial accessory nucleus of the inferior olivary complex and a projection to central gray immediately below the colliculus (46).

Since the superior colliculus has often been implicated in the regulation of body and head orientation and eye movement (see sections PHYSIOLOGY OF SUPERIOR COLLICULUS, p. 467 and p. 480) there has been considerable interest in assessing just how closely connected it is to motor regions that contain neurons innervating eye muscles or the muscles of the neck. Recent studies suggest that there are profuse projections to regions that in turn are intimately linked with the motor apparatus of the extraocular muscles. Thus the paramedian pontine reticular formation, which receives extensive input from the superior colliculus, is known to project to the ipsilateral abducens nucleus, whose neurons innervate the lateral rectus muscle (81, 95). This nucleus also has connections with the third cranial nerve nuclei, which innervate four of the six extraocular muscles. Some direct connections between the superior colliculus and oculomotor nuclei have also been reported, although the pathway is a small one (47, 86). These observations are supported by electrophysiological studies (77, 179, 180, 182, 184).

Table 1 provides an outline of the inputs and outputs of the superior colliculus as seen in higher mammals. The functional significance of some of these multiple pathways into and out of the colliculus are clarified in the section on control of eye movement to

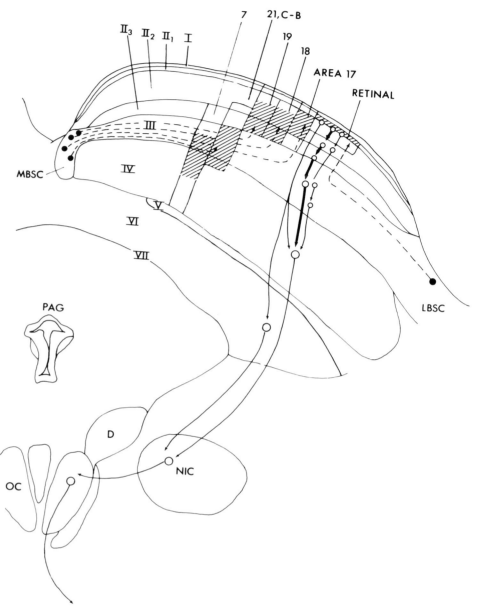

FIG. 8. Schematic drawing of cat superior colliculus showing possible neuronal linkages in visuo-motor transform. *Thick arrows*, major path; *boxes* outline representative slices of terminal fields from optic (retinal) tract and corticotectal tracts from areas 17, 18, 19, 21,C-B, and 7; *shaded areas*, major foci of degeneration after lesions to these areas. MBSC, medial brachium of superior colliculus; LBSC, lateral brachium of superior colliculus; NIC, interstitial nucleus of Cajal and adjacent reticular formation; C-B, Clare-Bishop area; D, nucleus of Darkshevitch; OC, oculomotor nuclei; PAG, peri-aquiductal gray matter. Roman numerals represent the seven collicular laminae. [From Ingle and Sprague (117).]

be dealt with in the next two sections of this chapter, p. 467 and p. 480.

Summary

The mammalian superior colliculus is a laminated structure. The upper laminae receive extensive inputs from the retina, the visual cortex, and the parabigeminal nucleus. These upper laminae project to several other sites involved in vision: the parabigeminal nucleus, the lateral geniculate nucleus, the pretectum, the pulvinar, and the nucleus of the optic tract. The deeper layers of the colliculus in most species receive input from visual, auditory, and somatosensory systems and project extensively to brain stem regions associated with motor control. The inputs to these deeper regions come from many cortical areas and from several subcortical centers. The descending outputs of the deep tectum innervate the paramedian pontine reticular formation on both sides of the brain,

TABLE 1. *Afferents and Efferents of Mammalian Superior Colliculus*

Inputs	Outputs
Retina	Pulvinar
Ventral lateral geniculate nucleus	Lateral geniculate nucleus
Occipital cortex	Pretectum
Parietal cortex	Posterior nuclear group
Temporal cortex	Suprageniculate nucleus
Frontal cortex	Intralaminar thalamic nuclei
Parabigeminal nucleus	Reticular formation
Reticular formation	Pontine nuclei
Substantia nigra	Parabigeminal nucleus
Cerebellum	Inferior olive
Periaquiductal gray	Oculomotor complex
Inferior colliculus	Central gray
Spinal cord	

the inferior olivary complex, the capsule of the inferior colliculus, and the cuneiform nucleus. Several investigators have also reported a direct pathway to the abducens nucleus. Intrinsic connections provide links among the laminae and between the left and right colliculi.

PHYSIOLOGY OF SUPERIOR COLLICULUS: ELECTRICAL RECORDING STUDIES

Methods

Three types of electrical signals can be recorded from active neurons in the central nervous system: *1)* electric potentials generated by the activity of many neurons and axon terminals in the region of the electrode tip, *2)* the activity of single cells as monitored extracellularly, and *3)* the activity of single cells as assessed intracellularly. The last of these methods is difficult, and it has not been applied with much success in the superior colliculus.

The method most widely used for studying the superior colliculus during the past decade has been the extracellular recording of single cells. This work has been done predominantly in paralyzed animals by using the procedures that were described briefly in *Methods*, p. 457. Recent developments have made it possible to undertake recordings from behaving, fully alert animals. If permitted to do so, alert animals move their heads and eyes constantly. Since single cells in the colliculus are activated from very small portions of the visual field, maintaining appropriate spatial control of visual stimuli is impossible without some forms of restraint of movement. It is relatively simple to restrain head movements by using surgically implanted skull bolts attached to a rigid frame. Eye movements can be eliminated surgically or pharmacologically, or they can be minimized by training the animal to maintain visual fixation on a small target. Given a stable retinal position, controlled stimuli can be localized to the specific portions of the retina from which the cell can be activated. Systematic changes in

stimulus variables can then yield a description of the response properties of these cells; these variables include stimulus size, shape, wavelength, movement direction, and stimulus velocity. The simplest observations to be made consist of noting the temporal sequence of single-cell discharges relative to stimulus presentation. Such data can be displayed in the form of individual or cumulative records and enable one to specify in more quantitative terms the response properties of cells to sensory stimuli.

A novel behavioral training procedure for bringing eye movements under experimental control has been developed by Wurtz (273). Animals are deprived of water and are taught to press a lever that activates a small spot of light in front of them. After a varying period of time the light is dimmed. If the animal releases the lever at this time, he is rewarded with a drop of water. Since the stimulus change is barely perceptible, the animal must keep his eyes on the target. Thus, while the animal's foveal gaze is centered on the stimulus, by using another set of stimuli the experimenter can explore the receptive fields of cells he is recording from. This method also enables the investigator to induce the animal to make specific eye movements: the stimulus to be discriminated can be presented successively in various locations, and the animal will saccade to these new target locations.

Several methods are available for the monitoring of eye movements. The electrooculogram (EOG) has been used extensively for this purpose. Four silver–silver-chloride electrodes are implanted around the orbit or are taped on the skin. Because the eye behaves like a dipole and generates a different voltage across each pair of electrodes as it moves, eye movements in the horizontal and vertical planes can be determined. This is a simple, inexpensive, and reliable method, but it has two shortcomings: the gain of the signal varies, particularly as a function of illumination level; and the base line, even with the best of electrodes, tends to drift.

Because of the limitations of the EOG several other methods have also been devised, the most successful being the implanted coil method introduced by D. A. Robinson (187). A fine multistrand wire is looped around the eyeball, and its terminals are brought out to a plug attached to the skull. The animal, whose head is restrained by skull screws of some sort, is placed in the center of two pairs of large coils; these are used to generate a magnetic field, within which the position of the eye coil is detected by use of phase-lock amplifiers. These signals are converted, as in the case of EOG, into records of horizontal and vertical eye movement. The stability of the recording permits another training paradigm for the control of eye movement; this method involves operant conditioning (218), and the animal is simply rewarded for looking at a target. A window discriminator is used on the eye movement record, and thirsty animals can be made to learn to fixate on a light spot by being periodically reinforced with drops of water for keeping their eyes on the target.

Surgical procedures for eye immobilization involve the transection of the third, fourth, and sixth cranial nerves, which innervate the extraocular muscles (203). Typically only one eye is immobilized; the other eye retains its normal ocular motility, which can be monitored by using implanted EOG electrodes or an eye coil. The receptive fields of collicular cells can be studied through the immobilized eye, and eye movements can be assessed through the normal eye.

Recordings from Paralyzed Animals

In the next two subsections I first examine the sensory properties of collicular cells in various species as assessed in paralyzed animals and then discuss results that disclose the eye- and head-movement–related activity of collicular cells in behaving, alert animals.

SUPERFICIAL LAMINAE. A large series of investigations in several mammalian species has shown that in the superficial laminae of the superior colliculus *1)* cells respond almost exclusively to visual stimuli and *2)* selectivity of response varies considerably among the species (3, 6, 21, 22, 27, 36–38, 44, 45, 52, 57, 60, 61, 72, 73, 82–84, 89, 91, 97–99, 101, 102, 108–110, 120, 122–124, 133, 136, 150–152, 154–158, 162–165, 169, 182, 197, 218–220, 234, 235, 238, 240, 243, 245, 249–251, 258, 259, 261, 263, 267, 272).

The receptive-field characteristics of neurons within the superficial laminae of the cat colliculus have been studied in most detail, with a yield of considerable quantitative data. Several aspects of receptive fields have been examined, including receptive-field size and shape, contrast specificity, directional selectivity, sensitivity for stimulus shape and orientation, ocular dominance, selectivity for velocity of stimulus movement, and wavelength specificity.

Most collicular cells in stratum griseum superficiale and stratum opticum of the cat respond vigorously to small stimuli that are either flashed into the receptive field or moved across it (21, 72, 73, 99, 157, 241, 243). Responses are largely independent of stimulus contrast; white or black spots are equally effective on a gray background. Small stimuli elicit better responses than large ones; the optimal stimulus size is often smaller than the activating region of the receptive field.

The most striking property is that about 75% of cells in these two layers are selective for the direction of stimulus movement. An example of such a cell, as recorded by McIlwain and Buser (157), appears in Figure 9A. The cell responds both when the stimulus of small stationary spots appears and when it goes off, as indicated by the plus or minus signs. Stimulus movement across the receptive field produces the best response to right upward motion and no response in the opposite direction. Examination of a large sample

of such cells disclosed another interesting fact: selectivity for the various directions of movement in space is not represented uniformly in the colliculus. Figure 9B demonstrates this; these data show that the majority of cells respond preferentially to movement in the visual field that is in the direction away from the vertical meridian.

Among the various species studied, the extent to which directional selectivity is represented in the colliculus varies considerably. In frog, rabbit, mouse, tree shrew, and monkey this property is rare (3, 38, 45, 83, 108, 117, 245, 261). This may be considered surprising for the rabbit, since a high percentage of its retinal ganglion cells show directional selectivity (16, 108, 175). In the pigeon colliculus, estimates of directionally selective cells range from 20% to 60% (60, 122); in hamsters the range is from 11% to 56% (43, 54, 259). Published accounts of direction preference distributions in the pigeon and the hamster are not consistent enough to permit any generalizations. Some investigators found in the pigeon tectum a preference for horizontal (as opposed to vertical) movement in space relative to the animal's position, with about an equal number of cells preferring forward (nasal) and backward movement (122). Other investigators, however, found preference for forward movement in the pigeon (60). In the hamster preference for forward and upward movements has been reported (43, 259). These preferences appear to be different from what has been found in the cat.

Given the fact that directional selectivity in the colliculus is prominent in some species, one may speculate about the function of this property. Directionally selective cells may accomplish several tasks, two of which are enumerated.

1. To stabilize the eye with respect to the world when the animal's head is in motion. Basically, stabilization is accomplished by the vestibuloocular reflex. To keep the eye stable while the animal moves, this reflex must have a gain of 1.0. If the gain is significantly different, retinal slip will result. The reflex is controlled by a visual feedback system, and it has been shown that the wearing of prisms or lenses can modify the gain of the vestibuloocular reflex (118, 166, 190, 191). In the rabbit's retina one class of directionally selective cells appears to be involved in the stabilization of the eyes with respect to the world (34, 174, 176). These cells have as their main target sites the terminal nuclei and the nucleus of the optic tract, which in turn project to other brain sites involved in control of eye movement (35, 36). Since direction-selective cells do not appear to project to the colliculus, it is unlikely that this structure is concerned with the regulation of the vestibuloocular reflex.

2. To enable the animal to orient toward (or away from) visual targets. Orientation with respect to visual targets is particularly important in appetitive behavior. Animals that have to move through space to obtain food objects must have information about the

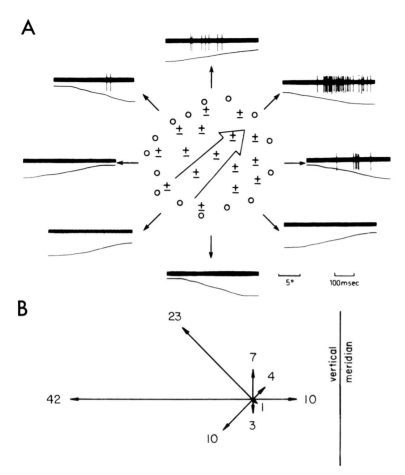

A

B

FIG. 9. *A*: directionally selective unit in superior colliculus. *Upper trace,* microelectrode recording; *lower trace,* potentiometer recording of mirror movements indicating time course of moving light spot; *solid arrows,* direction of stimulus movement; ±, on-off response to flashed light spot; ○, no response to light spot; *large open arrow,* preferred direction. *B*: distribution of direction-selective neurons in cat superior colliculus. Number at end of each *arrow* gives percentage of cells in total sample of 317 cells that responded best in direction shown by *arrow*. Relative length of each line is proportional to percentage of cells represented by that line. Pooled data from left and right colliculi are computed in terms of directions relative to vertical meridian; directional preferences of majority of cells are for movement away from vertical meridian. [*A*: from McIlwain and Buser (157). *B*: data from results of Berman and Cynader (21), Gordon and Gummow (73), and Sterling and Wickelgren (243).]

motion and position of such stimuli, and their motion relative to the visual background should be readily detectable. Recent neurophysiological studies in pigeons have shown that relative motion of small stimuli against patterned backgrounds is a potent stimulus for many collicular cells (61). Directional selectivity appears prominent among predatory animals and those animals that feed extensively on small food objects, the food in both cases being acquired while the animal moves about. By contrast, the frog strikes at small, stationary targets and does this while motionless; behavioral experiments indicate that the frog cannot compute movement of a stimulus (112, 114).

In the pigeon the predominance of directional cells along the horizontal axis may be linked to the extensive head movements of this animal during feeding. In the cat it may be inferred that the high percentage of directional cells for movement away from the vertical meridian has the function of triggering head and eye movements that bring moving targets into the field of central vision. These inferences must be regarded as rather speculative, since it has by no means been established what the function of these directionally selective cells might be. Ablation of area 17 in the cat significantly reduces directional selectivity in the superior colliculus (see PHYSIOLOGICAL STUDIES OF INPUTS TO SUPERIOR COLLICULUS, p. 487) without dis-

cernible deficits in tracking. It is clear that firmer hypotheses will have to await more extensive research on this problem.

Another interesting property of collicular cells pertains to the region of binocular representation, where most of them can be activated through either eye. In cat and monkey the visual fields of the two eyes overlap extensively, and the majority of cells in the superior colliculus are binocular. In species having little binocular overlap most cells are monocular (117, 164, 165). The distribution of ocular dominance in the cat is shown in Figure 10.

Cells in the stratum griseum superficiale and stratum opticum of the rhesus monkey show less selectivity for direction of movement than most other species. There is only a small degree of variation in the data gathered by different investigators (38, 68, 151, 203). Selectivity for discrimination of stimulus shape or for orientation is also absent in the monkey superior colliculus. The cells are fairly specific for stimulus size, however, preferring small stimuli to large ones, as in most other species. An example of this in Figure 11*A* shows that increasing stimulus size yields spatial summation up to a point, after which further increase in stimulus size produces inhibition and hence fewer responses. This is a generally observed phenomenon found in many collicular cells in mammals (21, 204,

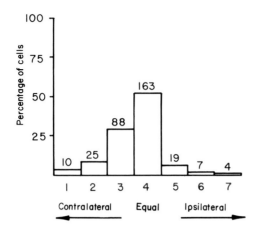

FIG. 10. Distribution of ocular dominance of cells in cat superior colliculus. Total number of cells, 316. Numeral above each bar, number of cells per category. Cells in group 1 can be activated only through the contralateral eye, cells in group 4 are equally driven by either eye, and cells in group 7 are activated only by the ipsilateral eye. Groups 2, 3, 5, and 6 represent in-between gradations. [Data from Berman and Cynader (21), Gordon and Gummow (73), and Sterling and Wickelgren (243). Groupings 1–7 from Hubel and Wiesel (105).]

241). Figure 11B shows response curves for stimuli of different sizes in the cat.

Figure 11A shows several other significant properties of collicular cells. The response is transient, a brief burst being given when the stimulus comes on and when it goes off. The response is independent of contrast, for bursts are produced to both light increment and light decrement. When a dark spot is used on a light background, the response profile is similar to the one shown in Figure 11A. The activating region is uniform, unlike that which one finds in the retina and the lateral geniculate nucleus; a small spot of light, when flashed, produces on- and off-responses throughout the activating region of the receptive field (as in Fig. 9A). In most species the size of the activating region varies as a function of retinal eccentricity and recording depth. Near the fovea the smallest fields in the monkey may span 0.125°, whereas 20°–30° out they may become 4°–6° in diameter. Cells in the stratum opticum have larger fields than in the stratum griseum superficiale. Curiously, the optimal stimulus size is not the same as the activating region of the receptive field. Generally, stimuli smaller than the size

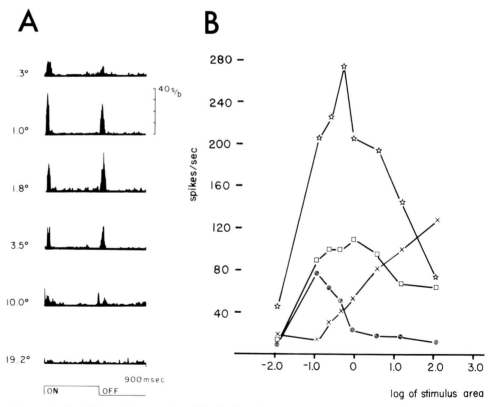

FIG. 11. A: histograms obtained from a single cell in monkey superior colliculus showing response to stimuli of varying diameters. Stimulus duration, 500 ms, presented once every 1,300 ms, 25 times per histogram. Response field, 18° from fovea; s/b, number of spikes per bin. B: response frequency as a function of stimulus size for four superior colliculus cells in cat superior colliculus. Each data point represents average of 12 repeated stimulus presentations obtained in a randomized order for each cell. [A: from Schiller and Koerner (203); B: data from H. Sherk, unpublished observations.]

of the activating region are optimal. This is particularly evident in the cells below the superficial gray layer.

The rhesus monkey has excellent color vision, and this capacity is subserved by color-selective cells, which are abundant in the retina and in the lateral geniculate nucleus. This kind of information does not appear to be processed in the superior colliculus of this species, for the cells here do not respond selectively to various wavelengths (151). On the other hand, color-selective responses have been reported in squirrel monkeys (272).

INTERMEDIATE AND DEEP LAMINAE. The receptive fields of cells in the deeper collicular laminae tend to be much larger than those found in the superficial regions. In the ground squirrel, characteristics similar to those observed in the visual cortex have been reported (163, 165); some cells are orientation specific and have complex and hypercomplex attributes. Such cells have also been found in the tree shrew superior colliculus (3). Orientation-specific cells have not been reported in rat, cat, and monkey.

In the deeper layers of the superior colliculus of paralyzed animals most cells show a significant response decrement with repeated stimulation; this is not the case in the superficial laminae (38, 102). A rest period of a few minutes restores cell responsivity. The vigor of the discharge declines rapidly for most cells in the deeper laminae within three to ten repetitions of the same stimulus at rates of 0.3–2.0 Hz. The activity can be reinstated by alteration of the stimulus as well as by rest. If the stimulus is significantly modified in shape, size, or wavelength, the response is again increased, apparently even when the new stimulus is one that is not readily discriminable from the old one by collicular cells. These findings suggest that the mechanisms for the observed habituation does not reside entirely within the colliculus. Instead, it is likely that inputs from other structures take a significant role in establishing habituation.

The second interesting observation about the deeper colliculus is that in addition to activation with visual stimuli, many cells respond to somatic and acoustic input (44, 72, 235, 240). The majority of cells are activated selectively through only one modality, but some cells are bimodal and even trimodal.

Studies investigating the topographic representations of the various modalities have shown an interesting relationship among them. Gordon (72) has demonstrated, for example, that collicular auditory cells are spatially selective. The location of the auditory stimulus that elicits the optimal response is closely aligned with the location of the visual receptive field of the neuron. With respect to the somatosensory representation, a similar relationship has been observed by Stein et al. (240), as shown in Figure 12, where the somatosensory fields are superimposed on the map of the visual field.

A convergence of sensory modalities in the lower layer of the superior colliculus is also evident in rodents. Of particular interest in these animals is the extensive representation of vibrissae. Figure 13 demonstrates this arrangement (44). The vibrissae of the

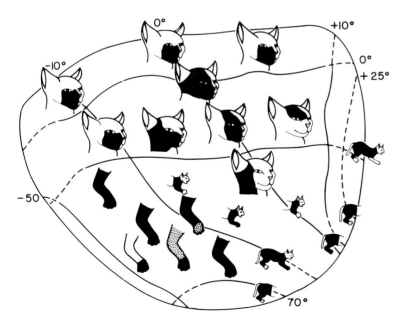

FIG. 12. Representation of different body sections in cat superior colliculus. Coordinates are shown for a map of the visual field of the colliculus and is turned so that the anterior region faces the top of the figure. Note that a disproportionately large area is devoted to the trigeminal and forelimb representations. [From Stein et al. (240).]

mouse are shown and numbered under B. The layout of these vibrissae on the tectum appear under A. Part C shows the map of the visual field, which has already appeared in more detail in Figure 5. Examination of Figure 13A might suggest to the reader that the region subserving the vibrissae is not quite congruent with the topographic map of the visual field. A study of their arrangement led Dräger and Hubel (43) to a most interesting conclusion. They say: "The place of the somatosensory projection in the tectum is thus determined by the way in which particular tactile body parts are seen from the eye, and is logically dependent on the visual projection to the tectal layers above rather than on the innervation density of the tactile periphery." This organization stands in striking contrast with what is seen in the somatosensory cortex, where the amount of tissue allocated for each vibrissa is directly proportional to peripheral innervation density (141).

The organization of the deeper tectal layers shows considerable variation among species; this applies both to the extent to which various modalities are represented and how their topography is arranged in relation to the map of the visual field. One of the more interesting specializations was noted recently by Terashima and Goris (258) in the pit viper, an animal which has infrared receptors. The infrared-sensitive facial pit is mapped onto the superior colliculus to represent the external world topographically. This map is largely congruent with the map of the visual field, although some differences in magnification and fine detail have been reported (89).

The arrangement of the various maps of sensory response in the colliculus raises interesting questions about the functional significance of this property. It is tempting to conjecture that such sensory convergence has the function of providing the organism with an integrated view of the external world. Input through

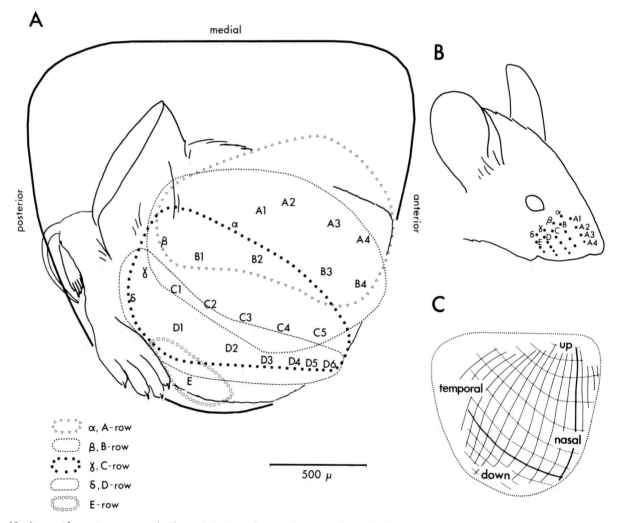

FIG. 13. A: map of somatosensory projection onto tectum of mouse. Letters refer to vibrissae, using notations shown in B; they indicate centers of tectal areas in which responses were recorded. *Ovals*, five overlapping regions within which the five rows of whiskers were represented. B: vibrissae. C: visual topography. [From Dräger and Hubel (44).]

the various modalities provides a unified cue about the location of stimuli in the external world, so that the animal may orient toward (or away from) them. This function could be well served in animals in which the relationships among the sensory modalities remain invariant with respect to each other. This would certainly be the case in those species that exhibit little or no head and eye movements. But in those animals with extensive ocular motility, the significance of topographically aligned convergence is not as easy to comprehend, for the external world in such animals would be congruent only while the head and eye are straight ahead. Thus a dual input from one location through two modalities would activate the same collicular region when the eyes are centered in orbit but would activate two different regions when the eyes are deviated, despite the same source of stimulus. One solution to this problem would be to eliminate inputs from nonvisual sensory modalities in animals that have pronounced ocular motility. This may indeed be what happened in the rhesus monkey, where single-unit recordings have uncovered only a small number of cells sensitive to auditory and somesthetic stimuli. On the other hand, Updyke (261) reported that in the cebus monkey auditory and somatosensory responses in the deeper layers were common. The second solution would be to develop a means of computing the differences between the positions of the eye, head, and body (see PHYSIOLOGY OF SUPERIOR COLLICULUS: STIMULATION STUDIES, p. 480). The third solution to the problem would be to render the spatial organization of the nonvisual modalities less specific, so that small ocular displacements would not cause a significant misalignment among the various sensory representations. It is true that the somatosensory and auditory fields in the colliculus are typically large, so that in species that can deviate their eyes only a relatively few degrees from straight ahead, the topographic representation of the world on the superior colliculus is not significantly affected.

Recordings from Alert Animals

Most of the work with alert animals has been performed on monkeys. This subsection is therefore devoted predominantly to examination of the results obtained in these animals.

SUPERFICIAL LAMINAE. The basic receptive-field properties of monkey collicular cells in the superficial laminae are similar to those observed in the paralyzed, anesthetized animal (68, 69, 203, 277). Recent studies by Goldberg and Wurtz and Mohler (69, 277) have disclosed an important hitherto unobserved property common to some of these cells: their activity is partially contingent upon the relevance of the stimulus for the monkey as evaluated from observation of subsequent eye movements. To study this phenomenon, which has been given the name "the enhancement effect," Wurtz and his collaborators trained monkeys either to fixate on a visual target or to perform a saccadic eye movement to a second target (see *Methods*, p. 467). In the first task the monkey fixated the target and had to discriminate a small decrement in light intensity by releasing a hand lever. Correct detection resulted in a reward of water. In the second task the monkey fixated the target stimulus, which after a short period was extinguished only to reappear somewhere else in the visual field. In this case the monkey's task was to move his eyes to the new location and again to release the lever when the target dimmed. The basic procedure was to record from cells in the superior colliculus and to examine the discharge properties of these cells when a stimulus was presented in their receptive fields. The responses could then be examined under three conditions: *1*) when the monkey performed no eye movements; *2*) when he performed a saccade to the target that was placed into the receptive field; and *3*) when he performed a saccade to the target that was placed into a different region of the visual field. Examples of single-cell activity under these three conditions appear in Figure 14. Response to the visual stimulus was significantly enhanced when a saccade was performed to the target presented in the receptive field of the cell.

The initiation of a saccadic eye movement to a visual target in this situation takes about 200 ms. By contrast the latency of light-evoked response is 35–60 ms. Because of this it is safe to conclude that the response observed was due to the visual stimulus and was not an artifact of motor activity. Some degree of enhanced visual response was observed in 40% of the cells in the superficial laminae but was absent in cells located in the top 0.25 mm of tissue, which is the location where retinal fibers terminate most heavily.

Wurtz and Mohler (277) also examined the time course of the enhancement effect by presenting brief probe flashes at various times relative to saccade onset. They found that cell excitability begins 200–300 ms before saccade onset, increases until the saccade is initiated, and persists for a short time thereafter. (The time course of this increased excitability is similar to that of the eye movement cells of the intermediate layers discussed in INTERMEDIATE AND DEEP LAMINAE, p. 471.) Because of this response they suggested that enhancement in the superficial laminae is brought about as a result of a faciliatatory input from lower laminae. In another study, Wurtz and Mohler (276) reported work on recordings from the visual cortex as well as from the frontal eye fields. They found no enhancement effect in area 17, but they did find it in the frontal eye fields. Cells in this area, however, have significantly longer latencies for the visual response than do the cells in the colliculus. Therefore these investigators felt that the frontal eye fields were not likely to be contributory to the collicular enhancement effect. These findings do not, of course, exclude the possibility that other cortical areas have a significant role in this phenomenon.

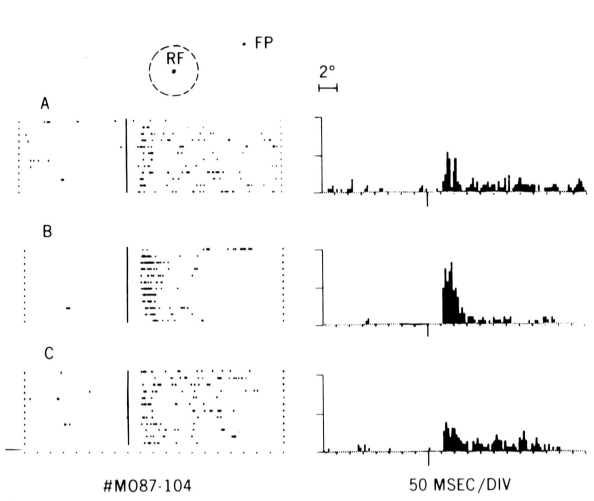

FIG. 14. Selective enhancement of on-response of a cell in monkey superior colliculus. Histograms on the *right* constructed from same cell discharges as displayed in rasters on *left*. Bin width, 8 ms; vertical scale, height of a bin if a cell discharged at 250 spikes/s per trial. Vertical scale line below histogram, stimulus onset; time between dots along abscissa on both rasters and histograms, 50 ms. *A*: cell discharge to receptive-field stimulus, RF; *dashed circle*, excitatory central region of receptive field while the monkey was looking at fixation point, FP. *B*: increased response associated with saccades to receptive-field stimulus; average latency after stimulus onset, 250 ms. *C*: saccades to a control stimulus, CON, in contralateral visual field; no enhancement. [From Wurtz and Mohler (276).]

INTERMEDIATE AND DEEP LAMINAE. Recordings in the adult monkey and cat have shown that in the intermediate and deep layers of the superior colliculus the principal feature of single cells is their discharge activity associated with eye movements. Before we examine the response characteristics of these cells in detail, it is necessary to first discuss some of the basic properties of eye movements and their neural control.

In higher mammals and man several distinct types of eye movements have been discerned. These fall into two general categories: conjugate eye movements and vergence movements. The direction of movement of the two eyes is the same during conjugate eye movements and is in opposition on the horizontal plane for vergence movements. Having these types of move-

ments enables the system to keep the two foveae on targets anywhere in three-dimensional space. Conjugate eye movements are of two basic types: pursuit movements and saccadic movements. The function of the pursuit eye movement system is to keep the fovea on target when either the head or the target is in motion. Under such conditions the object is tracked as a result of smooth, progressive displacement of the two eyes in orbit. The saccadic system is one that enables the observer to acquire targets for foveal viewing (265). This is accomplished by rapid, high-velocity ballistic displacements of the eye from one position to another.

Ocular motility in most higher mammals is brought about by six extraocular muscles for each eye; these are innervated by the axons of three cranial nuclei: the abducens (sixth cranial nerve), which innervates the lateral rectus muscle; the trochlear (fourth), which innervates the superior oblique muscle; and the oculomotor nuclear complex (third), which innervates the other four muscles. The action of the motoneurons innervating the eye muscles has been studied in considerable detail in alert animals (93, 188, 201).

An example of the activity of a neuron innervating the inferior rectus appears in Figure 15 and is shown here for the sake of providing a comparison with the eye-movement–related neurons of the superior colliculus, which will be dealt with later in this subsection. It can be seen that this neuron discharges proportionally with the degree of displacement of the eye in orbit. Quantitative data have shown a linear relationship between angular displacement in orbit and firing rate (93, 188, 201). In addition, this neuron discharges in association with saccades. Each downward saccade is accompanied by a high-frequency burst, the duration of which is an important determinant of saccade size. During upward saccades this unit is inhibited, and at this time high-frequency activity occurs in those neurons innervating the superior rectus muscle.

Eye movements can also be elicited by the vestibular system generating the vestibuloocular reflex, which keeps the eyes stable with respect to the world when the head or body is in motion. The two components to the vestibuloocular reflex, the slow phase and the fast phase, appear to be similar to the pursuit and saccadic types of eye movement. During the slow phase the eye is stabilized with respect to the world while the head and body are moving. The fast phase resets the eye rapidly to a new orbital position and immediately gives way to the slow phase again. Vestibular nystagmus is a special case of this sawtoothlike action and can be produced, for example, by putting cold water into the ear canal. A similar alternation of the fast and slow phases can be elicited by the so-called optokinetic nystagmus, which is produced by rotating a striped drum in front of an animal or human.

With these points in mind, let us return to the activity of neurons in the lower layers of the superior colliculus of the alert rhesus monkey. Many of the cells in the intermediate and deep collicular layers discharge in association with saccadic eye movements (203, 218, 274). These cells begin their discharge activity prior to the onset of the saccade; the discharge frequency increases rapidly until a saccade is generated, after which the firing terminates abruptly. Figure 16 shows the activity of a typical cell in the intermediate layers. Several traces are shown (Fig. 16A–C) to demonstrate that the response is selective; this cell fires only with small, left saccades. Rapid eye movements in other directions or of greater amplitude are not associated with unit activity. From long records of the sort shown in Figure 16A–C one can generate a map such as that shown in Figure 17. This figure demonstrates that the cell fires only when eye movements of a certain direction and size occur. The response area depicted in Figure 17 (filled circles) is referred to as the motor field. These fields tend to be small for cells in the anterior portion of the colliculus where the response is associated with small saccades. The motor fields of neurons in more posterior regions of the colliculus are associated with larger saccades and have larger motor fields. The responses of the cells, however, are not uniform throughout the motor field: the discharge is most vigorous when the eye movements are directed toward the center of the field.

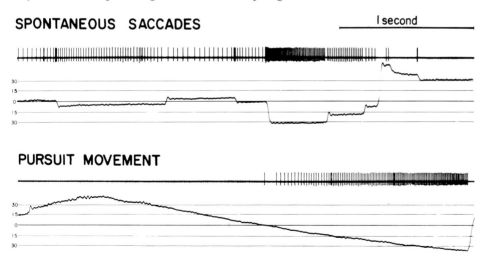

FIG. 15. Extracellular discharge characteristics of a single cell in oculomotor nucleus of monkey. This cell increases its firing rate in association with downward eye movement. *Upper row,* spontaneous saccadic eye movement with intervening periods of fixation. *Lower row,* unit activity during smooth pursuit brought about by moving the object in front of monkey. In each of the two rows: *upper trace,* unit activity; *lower trace,* vertical eye movement. *Horizontal lines* superimposed on eye movement record, coordinates in degrees of deviation from straight-ahead gaze; upward deflection, elevation of eye; downward deflection, depression of eye. [From Schiller (201).]

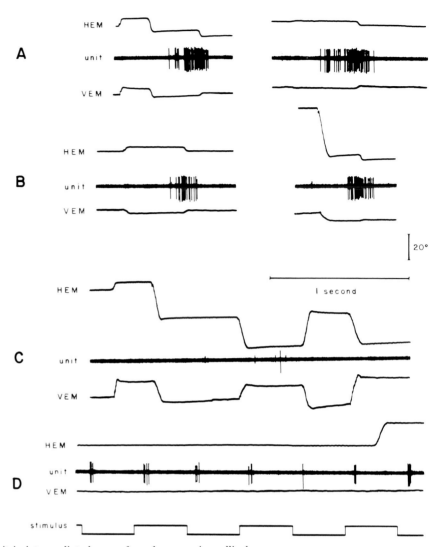

FIG. 16. Discharge characteristics of a unit in intermediate layers of monkey superior colliculus related to eye movement. Recordings obtained in an alert monkey with one eye surgically immobilized. *A*, *B*, *C*: unit discharge and eye movement in the light; moving eye unoccluded; cell discharges prior to small left and upward saccades. *D*: response to a 0.25° light spot moved back and forth with square wave motion within receptive field of immobilized eye; moving eye occluded. Marker, stimulus movement; HEM, horizontal eye movement record; VEM, vertical eye movement record. [From Schiller and Koerner (203).]

Systematic analysis, as performed in trained monkeys by Sparks and his collaborators (218, 220), has confirmed this. Their findings, shown in Figure 18, reveal a property associated with motor behavior that is similar to the motor behavior observed in those sensory systems where tuning curves have been generated—for example, for stimulus position in space, for orientation in visual cortex, or for frequency in the auditory system.

It is important to stress at this point that the activity of the collicular eye movement cells appears to reflect a retinotopic code: the discharge is specific for saccade size and direction and is basically independent of the position of the eye in the orbit. Thus a saccade of 10° leftward, for example, has the same discharge when the eye starts from straight ahead or from the far-right

position. The activity appears to have a function in moving the fovea to new target locations.

In the intermediate layers many of the collicular cells, in addition to their eye-movement–related activity, can also be activated by visual stimuli. Figure 16*D* shows this. These data were obtained in an animal with one eye immobilized (see *Methods*, p. 467). In Figure 16*D* the moving eye was occluded and the receptive field of the cell was stimulated with a small spot of light. The response was clear and consistent but was much weaker than what is seen when an eye movement occurs. The important question now is this: Where is the location of this receptive field? The answer is that it is in the same place on the map of sensory responses relative to the fovea as the location of the motor field is relative to the starting position of the eye. A motor response map is shown in Figure 17. The coordinate system of this map is similar to a map of sensory responses. To convert this motor response map to a sensory response map it is only necessary to name the central intersection the *foveal projection* and to change the labels to degrees of retinal eccentricity. If the receptive field were to be placed on this map in Figure 17, it would fall into the area where the black disks appear. Thus the sensory activation of the cell, when coupled with additional inputs, triggers a brisker rate of activity, resulting in a saccade and thereby bringing the fovea into that region of the visual field where the receptive field of the unit was located prior to the eye movement. The congruence between the sensory and motor characteristics of the colliculus has led several investigators to reaffirm the "hypothesis of visual grasp" proposed some years ago (94). Thus it has been suggested that one of the functions of the superior colliculus is foveation, a process that enables the organism to acquire, by the generation of saccadic eye movements, visual targets for foveal viewing (203, 206, 221).

The generation of visually guided saccades is by no means a simple process. The time course of events giving rise to a saccade raises several questions about the role of the superior colliculus in this process. The latency of a saccade triggered by a visual stimulus is about 150–250 ms. The response latency of single cells in the superficial layers of the superior colliculus,

however, is only about 50–75 ms, even at relatively low illumination levels. Electrical stimulation of the deep colliculus (see PHYSIOLOGY OF SUPERIOR COLLICULUS: STIMULATION STUDIES, p. 480) elicits a saccade in about 20–25 ms. This leaves unaccounted for a period of 100 ms, during which a great deal of computation is possible within the brain. Another complication is that visual stimulation is neither a sufficient nor a necessary signal for triggering collicular eye movement cells—not sufficient because, as seen in Figure 16D, the receptive field of eye movement cells can be activated without producing eye movement; not necessary because many collicular eye movement cells discharge in association with saccades in the absence of appropriate visual stimulation (153, 206, 207, 218, 274). Because of these factors it is not sensible to think of the superior colliculus as a simple switching device where sensory excitations are connected to motor signals. When a motor signal is generated by the colliculus, its emergence is the outcome of action in a number of brain structures.

In addition to the idea that the superior colliculus generates commands for the initiation of saccadic eye movements, several other hypotheses have also been advanced. Prominent among these, and based on work with rhesus monkeys, is one proposed by Wurtz and his collaborators (69, 274, 275, 277). They suggested that the superior colliculus is better suited to subserve a selective attentional mechanism rather than one that directly triggers specific eye movements. The issues centering around these hypotheses are by no means settled, and to help the reader evaluate them it may be useful to enumerate some of the details of single-unit function in relation to the following four questions.

1. How tightly coupled is the discharge activity of eye movement cells to saccadic eye movement? If the cells in the intermediate or deeper layers of the colliculus exercise a command function in the generation of saccades, one would expect this coupling to be very tight. Experiments by Sparks and his collaborators (220) have revealed that whereas the activity of some neurons is poorly correlated with saccade onset, others show extremely tight coupling upon initiation of this eye movement. Examples of this appear in Figure 19. These data were obtained in monkeys trained to perform repeated eye movements to a small target of light in the same point in the visual field. Spike burst latencies and saccade onset latencies are plotted against each other for two cells, generating a total of 88 points. The figure shows an extremely close correlation, as demonstrated by the narrow distribution along the 45° slope. This suggests then that at least some of the cells have the basic properties required of a command-type function.

2. Is the eye-movement–associated discharge of collicular cells triggered by visual stimuli? Several different types of eye movement cells have been discerned in the colliculus (153, 169). Some have a dual property;

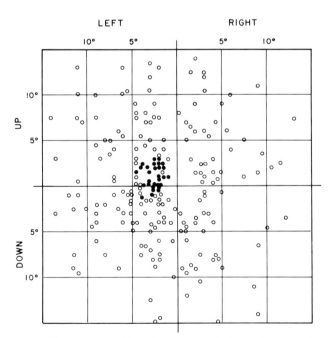

FIG. 17. Retinotopically coded motor field of a monkey superior colliculus unit. Each mark represents size and direction of a saccade. *Open circles*, saccades not associated with unit activity; *filled circles*, saccades preceded by a burst of spikes. Direction and size of saccade shown by quadrants designated left, right, up, down, and by degrees within these areas. Central crossing point, eye position prior to each saccade. Cell discharges only in association with small left saccades. [From Schiller and Koerner (203).]

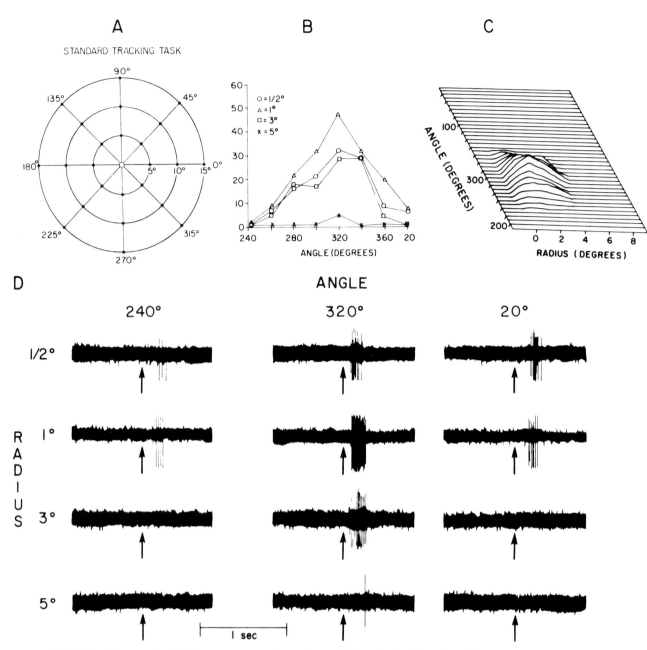

FIG. 18. Unit activity associated with eye movement in superior colliculus of trained monkeys. *A*: standard tracking task: if monkey fixated *center dot* for 2 s the target was moved to one of the 24 positions indicated by the *filled circles*. *B*: burst index as a function of angle of movement (difference between the number of spikes occurring during a 500-ms time sample for center target fixation and for a similar time period after eye movement to new target location): each point represents the median value of three observations. *C*: burst index as a function of angle and radius of eye movement. *D*: response of a superior colliculus unit to a series of saccades with a radius of 1° but varying in direction. Onset of target movement is indicated by *arrow* below each trace. [From Sparks (218).]

the response occurs not only in association with eye movement but also to visual stimuli. Other cells, typically in the deeper portions of the superior colliculus, do not have visual receptive fields. A further distinction has also been made: some cells discharge with appropriate saccades even. in the absence of visual stimuli (153, 206, 207, 218, 274). Thus in darkness spontaneous saccades, when of appropriate direction

and amplitude, are preceded by the typical burst of activity characteristic of these units. Such responses can also be elicited with vestibular nystagmus. This property has been seen in both subclasses noted above but may not be true for all the cells. Mohler and Wurtz (169) reported recently that neurons located near the border between the superficial and intermediate layers discharged only when the saccades were visually trig-

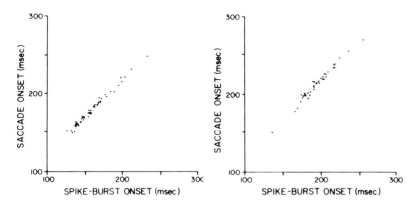

FIG. 19. Relation between spike burst latency and saccade latency for two neurons in monkey superior colliculus. Abscissa, interval between target onset and onset of spike pulse. Ordinate, saccade latency. [From Sparks and Pollack (221).]

gered. Thus it appears that some of the neurons in the colliculus form a selective link between the visual input and the saccade-associated activity, while others have a more general function and fire in relation to saccades in the absence of visual input. The source of saccade generation for these units is unknown. Saccades could be triggered as a result of input from other modalities or from higher centers coding spatial order in memory. Alternatively, of course, these units are possibly activated from a yet-unidentified brain structure that is involved in the generation of saccades, and this unidentified area may exercise a command function on the oculomotor centers.

3. What is known about the direction of information flow within the colliculus? The classic view has been that the flow in the colliculus is predominantly from the upper toward the lower layers. Recent anatomical work is largely in agreement with this, suggesting that the output of the superior colliculus to the brain stem emanates mostly from the deep layers. Current electrophysiological studies suggest that perhaps the deeper layers send projections to the superficial layers. Wurtz and Mohler (276) have argued, for example, that the cells in the upper layers of the superior colliculus, which show enhancement activity, acquire this property as a result of input from the deeper layers. Examination of the time course of eye-movement–associated discharges among neurons at different depths also suggests that the upper regions of the intermediate layers cannot provide the only input to the deep-layer cells. It is probable that there is information flow both from the upper to the lower layers and vice versa. The central question with respect to hypotheses of collicular function is not necessarily the direction of flow within this structure. Rather, the question is whether any of the cells in the colliculus associated with eye movement activity, in whatever layer they be, project downstream to regions closely affiliated with the final common path to the extraocular muscles. Current anatomical and electrophysiological data suggest that there are significant projections to areas intimately linked with the motor nuclei of the eye muscles (see *Outputs of Superior Colliculus*, p. 465, and BEHAVIORAL EFFECTS OF SUPERIOR COLLICULUS ABLATION, p. 492).

4. Can the eye movement units in the monkey colliculus be activated by movements of other parts of the body? To answer this question Robinson and Jarvis (194) assessed the activity of collicular cells in relation to both head and eye movements. The results have shown that these cells respond in association with the saccadic movement of the eyes, and that the cell response is not directly related to head movement.

It may be concluded on the basis of single-unit work that in the rhesus monkey the cells in intermediate and deep layers of the superior colliculus are closely linked to saccadic eye movement. The manner in which this structure is engaged in the generation of saccades in the monkey is discussed further in PHYSIOLOGY OF THE SUPERIOR COLLICULUS: STIMULATION STUDIES, p. 480.

The only other mammal in which eye-movement–related activity has been studied in single cells of the superior colliculus is the cat (251, 252, 254). The properties of cells that discharge prior to eye movement appear to be less specific than those found in the monkey, in that their discharge is generally independent of saccade amplitude. Some degree of specificity has been found, however, for the direction of eye movement. A few cells have been found whose activity relates directly to head movement rather than to eye movement. Another difference between these two species is that the eye movement cells in the cat are found in all the layers of the colliculus (252).

Summary

The visual receptive-field properties of single cells in the superficial laminae of the superior colliculus show considerable interspecies variation. In many birds and mammals directional selectivity is a prominent property: that is, neurons are excited by stimuli moving in specific directions across their receptive fields. The distribution of directional preferences varies among the species studied; in the cat the majority of these cells are most responsive to stimulus movement away from the vertical meridian; pigeons and hamsters, however, yield different kinds of distributions for directional preference. Surprisingly, in the rabbit, which has numerous direction-selective retinal ganglion cells, few direction-selective cells are found in the colliculus. Direction-selective neurons are also rare in the monkey. In cat and monkey, most cells without directional selectivity respond preferentially to stimuli subtending a small projection angle. Cells are not selective for shape or orientation of stimulus or sign of contrast. The responses are typically transient, and most cells in the binocular segment can be activated through either eye.

In the alert monkey 40% of the cells in the superficial laminae show an enhancement effect; cells respond more vigorously to stimuli in their receptive fields when a subsequent eye movement is made to that stimulus than when an eye movement is made to other parts of the visual field.

In the deeper laminae in a number of species there is evidence for sensory convergence. The auditory and somatosensory maps are arranged so that they are congruent with the visual map: thus, when the eyes are centered in the orbit, then visual, auditory, and somatosensory excitations from a particular region of space impinge on the same area within the colliculus. In paralyzed animals most cells in the deeper layers show a response decrement to repeated exposure of the same stimulus; the response recovers either with rest or when the stimulus is modified.

In alert, behaving monkeys it has been shown that eye movement cells predominate in the intermediate and deeper layers. These cells discharge prior to saccades. The motor fields are well defined. Some of the eye movement cells also have visual receptive fields that are congruent with the motor field: when the cells discharge, a saccade ensues that brings the fovea into the part of the visual field that contained the receptive field prior to the saccade. Many collicular eye movement cells, however, discharge in association with saccades in the absence of appropriate visual stimulation.

PHYSIOLOGY OF SUPERIOR COLLICULUS: STIMULATION STUDIES

Methods

Stimulation studies have relied most heavily on the method of passing current through fine wires or microelectrodes lowered into the superior colliculus. A notable exception to this approach is the classic study by Apter (13), who placed on the superior colliculus of cats small crystals of strychnine, which had the effect of sensitizing tissue, probably by removing inhibition. She then flashed diffuse light into the animal's eyes and observed an eye movement directed toward that part of the visual field represented by the tissue under the crystal. This remarkable observation paved the way for many other studies investigating the hypothesized motor commands originating from the superior colliculus. As a result, the colliculus was thought to be

an area involved in the generation of the visual-grasp reflex (2, 94).

Electrical stimulation also produces eye movements. Detracting from the significance of early studies was the observation that large regions of occipital cortex, areas of the frontal lobe, several subcortical regions, and the cerebellum, when electrically stimulated, also produce movements of the eye (18). Studies conducted in the last decade have shown, however, that there are substantial differences in the eye movements evoked by stimulating different brain regions and also in the mechanisms that mediate these responses (193, 196, 202, 206).

Fruitful examination of the consequences of electrical stimulation on eye movements requires the animal to be fully alert. Eye movement and orientation behavior are affected not only by anesthesia but also by the state of the animal. Sleep and drowsiness can significantly alter responsivity to electrical stimulation. Therefore it is necessary either to implant electrodes, so that they can be used after the animal recovers from surgery, or to employ the alert preparations described in *Methods*, p. 467. This latter technique makes it possible to continually adjust the location of the electrode tip and also to use microelectrodes that allow one to both record localized unit activity and stimulate the same region.

To gain an understanding of the effects of collicular stimulation, we shall look at results obtained in several brain structures. Stimulation studies of the monkey brain are dealt with most thoroughly.

Electrical Stimulation of Primate Superior Colliculus

Electrical stimulation of small regions of the monkey superior colliculus elicits saccadic eye movements. Trains of monophasic or biphasic pulses of 0.1–0.5-ms duration are adequate. The frequency must be somewhere between 60 and 500 Hz. The nature of the saccadic eye movements elicited in this fashion are easiest to understand when one compares the effects of stimulating two sites in an alert monkey whose head has been restrained: the abducens nucleus, in which the motoneurons innervating the lateral rectus muscle of the eye are located, and the superior colliculus. Two aspects of motoneuron discharges in the abducens and oculomotor nuclei control the amplitude of saccades: the firing frequency and the duration of the burst. In alert monkeys the frequency of abducens neuron discharges during saccades varies over a relatively small range, and for this reason it is the duration of the burst that has the more important role in defining saccade amplitude (188, 201).

When neuronal activity is mimicked by use of electrical stimulation of the abducens nucleus, the results obtained are as expected and are shown on the top row of Figure 20. As either the duration or frequency

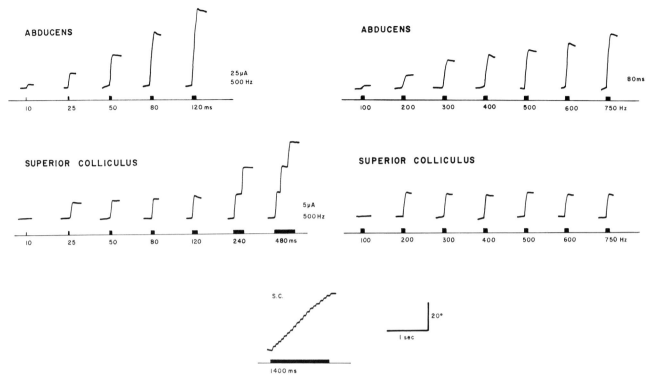

FIG. 20. Effects of electrical stimulation in abducens nucleus and superior colliculus of monkey as a function of burst duration and frequency. All eye movement records are horizontal, saccades going to the left. *Left*, stimulating frequency is constant and duration is varied; *right*, duration is constant and frequency is varied. Long staircase of saccades shown at bottom of figure was elicited by stimulating within the anterior tip of superior colliculus. [From Schiller and Stryker (206).]

of the burst is increased, the saccades become larger. This is a very straightforward result, and it gains significance only when it is compared with what happens when the superior colliculus is stimulated, as shown in the second row of Figure 20. The results are markedly different. Saccade size remains invariant as stimulus duration and frequency are varied over a wide range. Once a certain stimulation duration is exceeded, additional saccades occur with intervening fixations, but the size of each saccade remains much the same.

What then determines the size of the saccade in this situation? From the single-unit data already described, one might expect that it is determined by the particular site within the colliculus (189, 206). That expectation is confirmed: large saccades are elicited in the posterior region of the colliculus and small ones in the anterior part. In Figure 20, at the *bottom*, is shown a long staircase of small saccades that was produced by stimulating the anterior tip of the colliculus.

Prolonged electrical stimulation of the superior colliculus, even at low current levels, has a remarkable motor effect: the eyes traverse the orbit in a series of machinelike steps whenever current is passed. How might one interpret the staircase of saccades induced by prolonged stimulation? One conjecture is the following: the visuomotor system is equipped to sample

some events in the world in a discontinuous fashion; a sample is taken while the eye fixates, and this is followed by an eye movement and another sample. When the superior colliculus is stimulated for extended periods, the eye is ordered to acquire a visual target for foveal viewing, and a saccade takes place that ought to bring the imaginary target onto the fovea. The next sample discloses, however, that the target is still displaced by the same amount; thus another saccade occurs, and then another, until the stimulation ceases. It is not known whether the animal actually sees some sort of stimulus under these conditions. It is more likely that, because of the command nature of the event, the stimulation affects the motor channels directly. The animal appears largely helpless, and performs like an automaton. The events that are triggered, however, appear to be organized for the purpose of visual sampling.

The next question pertains to the position of the eye in orbit: Does the size of the stimulation-elicited saccade depend on the initial position of the eye in the orbit? The answer is mostly no. This is demonstrated in Figure 21A, where the amplitude and direction of the saccades evoked by repeated bursts of electrical stimulation are plotted (185). Saccades are much the same size, regardless of the initial position of the eye. It is true, however, that one can find slight nonuni-

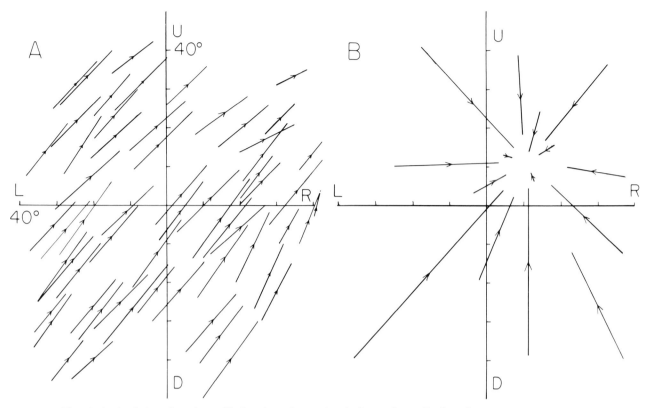

FIG. 21. Electrical stimulation of monkey colliculus: dependence of evoked saccade amplitude and direction on initial eye position. A saccade is represented as a directed line starting at initial eye position and ending at position to which saccade carried the eye. *A*: examples of colliculus-evoked saccades that did not depend on initial position. *B*: hypothetical example of way in which saccades would appear if they had been goal directed. [From Robinson (189).]

formities; in some cases the saccades become smaller as the eye is driven closer to the limits of its ocular motility. This does not detract significantly from the basic fact that the prime determinant of saccade size and direction is the site in the colliculus that is stimulated, and that the response elicited is independent of the position of the eye in orbit unless the limits of ocular motility are reached. Figure 21*B* shows what saccades would be like if the colliculus were a system that triggered goal-oriented saccades.

When a large number of sites are stimulated sequentially in the superior colliculus, at each of which the size and duration of single elicited saccades is assessed, one can compare the map of the motor responses thus generated with the map of sensory responses in the colliculus (189, 206). This kind of work has shown that these two maps are congruent: In the anterior region of the superior colliculus, where receptive fields are close to the fovea, elicited saccades are small. Medially the receptive fields are in the upper visual field, and saccades to electrical stimulation go upward. The same relationship is true for the lateral region, where fields and saccades are down.

The precision of this relationship between maps of sensory and motor responses was further demonstrated in an experiment where the following was

done: *1*) the discharge of a single cell was recorded with a microelectrode and the location of its visual receptive field was determined; *2*) the same area of the superior colliculus was electrically stimulated through the microelectrode and the size and direction of the saccade so triggered was recorded. Figure 22 shows the results of such an experiment for several sites within the superficial laminae. The receptive fields are the circular, hatched areas projected onto a map of the visual field. The arrows show the saccade elicited when each of the 14 sites was stimulated. The results show that the neural activity at each site produced by electrical stimulation brought the fovea into that region of the visual field in which the receptive fields of the stimulated area had been located (206).

These findings complement those obtained with single units in the middle and deeper regions of the superior colliculus. Both observations suggest that in the superior colliculus the maps of sensory and motor responses are congruent and that this structure may be involved in directing the eyes to selective regions of the visual field.

Let us now consider what happens as the depth of the stimulation site is varied in the colliculus. If the electrodes are lowered into the colliculus at right an-

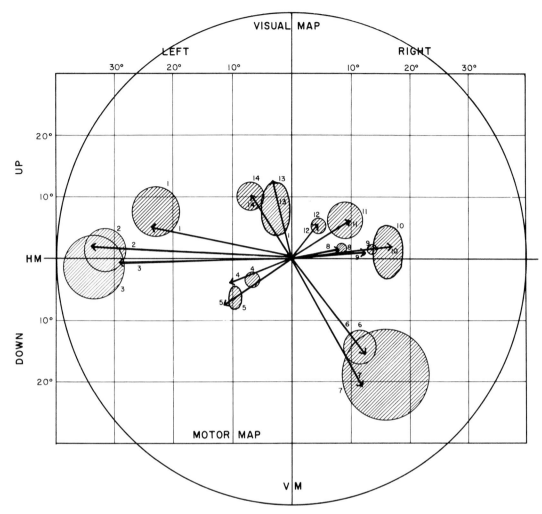

FIG. 22. Results of experiment that paired single-unit recordings and electrical stimulation at each of several sites in superficial layers of monkey superior colliculus. Map of visual field with receptive fields of 14 units is superimposed on map of motor responses, its *arrow* representing electrically elicited saccades at each of the 14 sites. Length of each *arrow* represents mean length of 8–14 stimulation-elicited saccades; direction of each *arrow* represents mean direction of saccades. HM, horizontal meridian; VM, vertical meridian; *hatched areas*, receptive fields of single neurons. Numerals correlate receptive fields and saccades. [From Schiller and Stryker (206).]

gles to its surface, the saccades elicited are similar at all depths. However, the amount of current required to produce the saccades is very different. If a microelectrode is used for the passing current, in the superficial layers 150–400 µA are required for activation; in the intermediate and deeper layers 1–9 µA are typically sufficient. For this level of activation so little current is passed that the responses of single cells, whose activity is monitored before and after stimulation, are not altered. Stoney et al. (248) have estimated that 3 µA of stimulation with duration pulses of 0.1 ms activates cells in an area 65 µm in diameter. This suggests that the region most directly concerned with the elicitation of saccadic eye movement is located in the intermediate and deep layers of the colliculus.

The amount of current for stimulation as noted here applies to fully alert animals. The situation is quite different when animals become drowsy or go to sleep. Under such conditions current levels that produced saccades consistently in the alert state are no longer effective. The current then has to be increased manyfold, until the animal is aroused, before a saccade is successfully elicited. This observation suggests that the intent to look is not generated within the superior colliculus itself.

The stimulation paradigm provides another interesting test. What happens when two sites in the superior colliculus are stimulated simultaneously? D. A. Robinson (189) has explored this question and has found that under such conditions "a single saccade occurred whose amplitude and direction was a weighted mean of the saccades that resulted when each site was stimulated by itself. The weighting factor was the relative intensity of the two stimulus currents." The effect is shown schematically in Figure 23. Suppose (Fig. 23, *left*) the two sites are the medial and lateral sides of the superior colliculus, which when stimulated individually produce 45° upward and 45° downward saccades. Stimulating them together generates a single saccade, which is horizontal. In this situation one can also manipulate the direction of the resultant saccade by varying the amount of current passed by each of the electrodes. Thus one can produce saccades of any direction within the boundaries of the two individually produced directions. The same also applies for saccade size, as shown in Figure 23, *right*. Here the anterior and posterior regions of the superior colliculus are stimulated on the horizontal meridian so that the direction is the same but the sizes are different. Paired stimulation produces saccades of in-between sizes and can be manipulated by current levels, just as above. There are some indications that these observations also apply where one electrode is placed in the left and the other in the right colliculus. The question is, What happens when mirror symmetric points are stimulated along the horizontal meridian? This is not yet known. One might expect no eye movement at all.

What does this paired stimulation paradigm reveal about collicular function? It shows that the output of

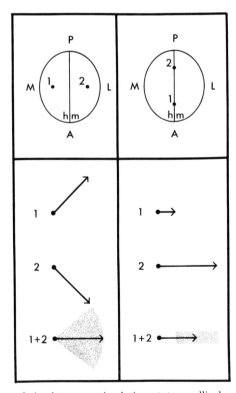

FIG. 23. Effects of simultaneous stimulation at two collicular sites in monkey superior colliculus. *Top*: schematic for two sets of stimulation sites in colliculus (1 and 2). *Bottom*: types of saccades elicited to single (1 or 2) or paired (1 and 2) stimulation. *Shaded areas*, range over which saccades can be elicited by varying amount of current delivered through the two electrodes. A, anterior; M, medial; L, lateral; P, posterior; hm, horizontal meridian.

the colliculus is somehow integrated. But the *where* and *how* questions remain unanswered. It is likely that the stimulation affects predominantly the motor end of the superior colliculus for this reason: if the stimulation were to elicit a visual impression (like a phosphene in cortex), it would be unlikely that the saccades would follow the vector rules. Humans and monkeys, when confronted with two simultaneous stimuli that appear in two different parts of the visual field, will generally not make a saccade halfway between these points. They will look at one stimulus or the other, or look at both successively.

It has already been noted that several other structures in the brain, when stimulated electrically, produce saccades similar to those obtained in the superior colliculus. In the monkey the frontal eye fields as well as visual cortex have this property (192, 202). Whereas the kinds of eye movements elicited in these three structures are the same, they differ in the amount of current needed to produce them. The deeper colliculus is most sensitive, for 1–9 μA of current triggers saccades. In the frontal eye fields more current is needed (35–150 μA) and in the visual cortex 500–2,000 μA are needed, sufficient to cause local tissue damage. Eye movements can also be elicited from the cerebellum. In this structure the direction of the saccade depends on the brain site stimulated, and the amplitude of the saccade appears to depend on the duration and frequency of the stimulus train used (196).

To compare these different brain structures some studies have paired ablation methods with stimulation (202). When the visual cortex is removed in the monkey, saccades elicited by stimulation in the superior colliculus and the frontal eye fields are unaffected. The same is true for the visual cortex and the superior colliculus after ablation of the frontal eye field. When the superior colliculus is removed, however, an interesting change occurs: stimulation of the visual cortex no longer produces saccades; stimulation of the frontal eye field, however, remains effective. This suggests that there are at least two pathways from the cortex affecting the triggering of retinotopically organized saccades. One of these passes to the brain stem via the superior colliculus. The other reaches the brain stem from the frontal eye fields without relaying in the superior colliculus.

In the experiments so far described the animal's head was restrained. What happens when the head is free to move? The results obtained with the head free are similar to those found with single-unit recordings. Stimulation has its primary effect on saccadic eye movement (255, 266). The head begins to move only after the eye has been driven in the orbit toward more extreme positions. A head movement is then initiated, which triggers the vestibuloocular reflex. As a result, normal compensatory eye movements occur driving the eye in the direction opposite to the movement of the head. These findings are in agreement with the already-noted single-unit study showing that collicular unit activity is not modified by head movement (194).

What bearing do these stimulation studies have on hypotheses of collicular function? The general observation that low-amplitude electrical stimulation of the colliculus elicits saccades, the directions and amplitudes of which depend on the site of stimulation, is consonant with the view that in the colliculus signals are generated for producing saccadic eye movements. The congruence of the sensory and motor maps, as observed with both recording and stimulation methods, has been interpreted to fit the foveation hypothesis. According to this view the colliculus generates a signal based on the error between the target that is to be acquired for foveal viewing and the current position of the fovea. Therefore, this is a retinocentric model; the position of the eye in orbit is not a factor. The only thing computed is target position on the retinal surface relative to the fovea.

This simple model has been drawn into question at the present time. It has been shown that saccadic eye movements are generated by taking into account not only the position of the target relative to the fovea (retinal error) but also the position of the eye in orbit. This appears to be true for both humans and monkeys. Hallett and Lightstone (84b, 84c) presented subjects with two successive spots of light in total darkness, each being flashed only briefly. While the subject's eye was in motion toward the initial target a second stimulus was flashed on. Upon completing the first saccade, subjects were instructed to make a second saccade to the second, already-extinguished stimulus.

The results were unequivocal; subjects made their second saccade to the actual physical location of the stimulus and not to a location where the stimulus was perceived relative to the fovea. The essential parts of this procedure are outlined in Figure 24A. The trial begins when the subject fixates point F. Next stimulus spot S_1 appears briefly. Shortly after the saccade to S_1 is initiated, stimulus S_2 is flashed on. This occurs in the diagram at the point marked by the × superimposed on the arrow designating the first saccade. After reaching position S_1 the subject makes a second saccade. If this one is straight up, as shown by the dashed line, only the retinal error signal is utilized, since target S_2 has appeared straight up from the fovea. If, on the other hand, the saccade the subject makes is to the physical position of S_2, information regarding eye position also has to be taken into account. Subjects in this situation always make their second saccade from S_1 to S_2. From this finding the inference was made that in the oculomotor system computations are based on both retinal error and on eye position.

To examine whether monkeys also utilize eye position information, Mays and Sparks have undertaken an ingenious experiment (152a). They trained animals to saccade to targets briefly flashed in total darkness. They then placed electrodes into the superior colliculus and electrically stimulated them after the target was extinguished but before the animal initiated his eye movement. Figure 24B gives an example of this procedure and the associated reasoning. Initially the

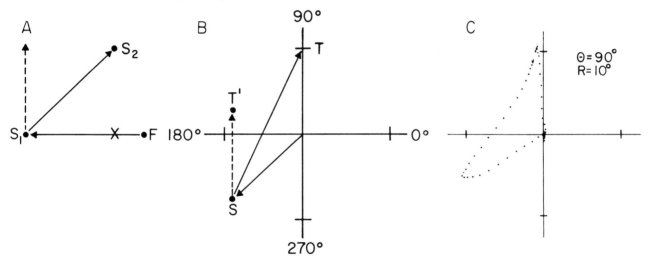

FIG. 24. Experimental procedures demonstrating that both retinal error and eye position information are used to compute size and direction of saccadic eye movements. *A*: human subject fixates in total darkness on fixation spot F, which is extinguished when stimulus S_1 is flashed. As subject initiates saccade toward S_1 (*horizontal arrow*) a second target, S_2, is flashed on at the time the eye is at position marked by ×, appearing straight up from fovea. Upon reaching position S_1 subject makes second saccade. If second saccade is straight up, only retinal error signal is computed. If second saccade is to S_2, both retinal error and eye position information are utilized. Subjects always saccade to S_2. *B*: schematic for experiment in which collicular stimulation in monkey is used to pull the eye to position S after brief appearance of target T to which animal has been trained to saccade. Utilization of retinal error signal alone should generate an eye movement to T′. Utilization of both retinal error and eye position signals should bring eye to T. For the first, going directly to T, target was flashed but colliculus was not stimulated. For the second, collicular stimulation displaced the eye toward S, but eye still ended up at T, suggesting utilization of both retinal error and eye position information. (*B, C*: courtesy of L. E. Mays and D. L. Sparks.)

eye fixates on the center of the large cross. The visual target flashes on at point T. Before the eye movement is initiated, the stimulation of the colliculus pulls the eye to position S. If the computation involves only the determination of where the target appears relative to the fovea, after stimulation the eye should move from S to T'. If, on the other hand, the computation also utilizes an eye position signal, the eye should move from S to T. Figure 24C shows what happens. Once again the results were unequivocal. After having been pulled to location S, the eyes move to location T. It appears, therefore, that the eye position signal is an integral part of the processing that is required for the performance of saccadic eye movements.

Where does this computation take place? The fact that the colliculus was stimulated in the experiment just described does not prove, of course, that the computation takes place in this structure. Stimulating the frontal eye field, for example, produces similar results. Further work is needed to determine how and where this computation is made, although Mays and Sparks have reported that some neurons in the superior colliculus are probably involved in coding the eye position error (153).

Electrical Stimulation of Cat and Rodent Superior Colliculi

Several current studies have explored the effects of electrical stimulation in the superior colliculus of the cat (9, 198–200, 236, 256). These studies are largely in agreement with earlier work, but they have also reported new effects that have triggered considerable controversy.

Collicular stimulation in the cat produces eye movements in most respects similar to that obtained in monkeys. The ocular motility of the cat is a visual angle of about 20° in any direction from straight-ahead gaze, compared with the monkey's angle of 70° or more. Cats show excellent small movements of the eye but seldom make large ones. They move their heads instead. They have a preference for keeping the eye roughly centered in the orbit.

These facts raise the question of neural organization in the part of the superior colliculus that represents the peripheral visual field. In the cat the superior colliculus has peripheral representation up to 90° from the area centralis. Since ocular motility in the horizontal plane is restricted to about 20° (a total excursion of 40°), for study of eye movement there would be no point in having a map of motor responses extend in congruence with the map of sensory responses to the limits of the visual-field representations. Several alternatives may be considered, therefore. One is that in the periphery the map of motor responses codes head and body movement rather than eye movement. This would enable the animal to orient rapidly toward peripheral targets by moving not only the eyes but also the rest of its body. Earlier work, for example, has

shown that long trains of stimulation pulses cause the animal to circle around and around (200).

An alternative hypothesis based on stimulation data has also emerged recently, and it is this hypothesis that has been the source of the controversy. Guitton, Roucoux and colleagues (84a, 198, 198a) claimed that in restrained animals stimulation of the posterior portions of the colliculus representing the peripheral field elicits goal-directed eye movements rather than the typical retinotopically coded ones observed in the anterior part of the colliculus. By goal-directed eye movements one means that the stimulation brings the eye to a particular region in orbit irrespective of its initial position (see Fig. 21B). This is an interesting and intriguing notion, not only because it ascribes a new kind of function to the superior colliculus but also because it breaks up the structure into two different kinds of organizational systems. The idea that the superior colliculus codes goal-directed eye movements has already been suggested by Straschill and Reiger (252, 253).

In contrast to this work, Stein and colleagues (236) as well as Harris (85a) failed to find any evidence for a region coding specific locations in orbit or in space. Resolution of this issue will require a considerable amount of additional research.

In rabbits and rodents with far more restricted eye movements than seen in primates and cats, collicular stimulation also produces orienting movements (200). Whereas ocular motility has not been measured in these studies, the head and body movements are similar to those already described: stimulation of any site in the superior colliculus elicits a movement that orients the animal toward the part of the visual field that the stimulated area represents. Prolonged stimulation induces repeated realignments and, hence, circling. Orienting behavior to electrical stimulation has also been demonstrated in fishes and amphibians (113).

Summary

Electrical stimulation of the superior colliculus produces saccadic eye movements in the rhesus monkey and the cat. In the monkey the direction and size of the saccades elicited depend on the site of stimulation in the colliculus and are independent of initial eye position. A burst of long duration produces a staircase of similar saccades. The motor response map of the superior colliculus obtained with a systematic sampling of many sites is congruent with the sensory-response map. In the cat the patterns of eye movements elicited by stimulating the superior colliculus are similar in the anterior colliculus, but in the posterior region the situation is less clear. In rodents, head and body orientations are most evident. Prolonged stimulation of one colliculus produces circling body movement in most species.

The results of stimulation studies in the monkey are in agreement with the recording studies: both support the idea that the colliculus is involved in the generation of saccadic eye movements. The manner in which this is accomplished is open to debate. Two hypotheses have been considered: according to the first, the colliculus computes only a retinal error signal; according to the second, eye movements are generated on the basis of both a retinal error and an eye position signal.

PHYSIOLOGICAL STUDIES OF INPUTS TO SUPERIOR COLLICULUS

Methods

In this section I am primarily concerned with two methods that have been used to study the inputs to the colliculus. The first of these examines the effect of selective disruption of inputs on the discharge characteristics of collicular cells. This can be accomplished by ablation of structures known to project to the colliculus. A more refined approach is to cool these brain areas, thus causing their temporary inactivation. This latter method has the advantage of reversibility; single cells can be studied before, during, and after a selected tectal input has been inactivated.

The second approach is one that examines the properties of cells that project to the colliculus from various other structures. To identify such cells the method of antidromic activation is typically used. Stimulating electrodes are placed in the colliculus, which can then backfire the cells projecting there. At the recording site antidromic activation can be determined unequivocally by relying on several tests, among which the collision method is the most reliable. Stimulation of the colliculus is initiated electronically when the cell from which the experimenter is recording fires spontaneously. This results in two pulses traveling in opposite directions along the axon. The outcome is a collision annihilating the action potentials. Therefore, failure of the experimenter to see the arrival of the antidromic spike at the recording site indicates to him that the cell projects to the colliculus.

Retinal Input

One of the remarkable features of the organization of the retina is that different populations of ganglion cells relay different types of information about a particular stimulus. These different classes of ganglion cells project selectively to the central nervous system and remain separated in some species through several relays. For details of this retinal organization the reader is referred to the chapter by Dowling and Dubin in this *Handbook*. The first investigators to note a functional specialization among retinal ganglion cells in mammals were Enroth-Cugell and Robson (48). They discerned in the cat two classes of retinal ganglion cells, which they labeled X- and Y-cells. Subsequently other investigators discerned one or two additional classes (32, 246, 247). Y-cells have rapidly conducting axons; the spatial summation within their

receptive fields is nonlinear, and they respond transiently to visual stimuli. The X-cells have slower conduction velocities, have linear spatial summation properties, and discharge in a sustained fashion. The remainder of the retinal ganglion cells, which Stone and Fukuda (246, 247) labeled W-cells, have slow conduction velocities. This group, which in general responds more sluggishly to visual stimuli, is more heterogeneous and consists of small cells, probably the oldest phylogenetically. The center-surround organization is less well defined; some cells are transient, others are sustained.

The superior colliculus of the cat receives input from both the Y- and W-type cells, but the W-cell input is more prominent than the Y-cell input (32, 62, 98, 147); X-cells do not project to the colliculus; their axons terminate mostly in the lateral geniculate nucleus.

Investigators have also differentiated several subclasses of retinal ganglion cells in the monkey retina (41, 75, 149, 204). The rhesus monkey, unlike the cat, has excellent color vision. One large group of retinal ganglion cells is color specific, and shows color-opponent responses. In most of these cells the color-opponent response is spatially distinct as well, the center being selective for one wavelength and the surround for another. These regions are arranged in an antagonistic fashion. If the center gives an on-response to one wavelength, the surround responds with an off-response to another wavelength. These cells respond in a sustained fashion, show linear summation properties, and conduct at medium velocities to the central nervous system (75, 149, 204). The second class of cells in the monkey retina are the broad-band cells, which are not color specific but show a distinct, antagonistic center-surround organization. These cells respond transiently and have rapid conduction velocities. Cells that do not fall into these two categories form a third, broad class of cells with slowly conducting axons that lack color selectivity and respond more sluggishly.

The similarity between cat and monkey retinal ganglion cells, for both receptive-field characteristics and projection sites, has led to the suggestion that the cat X-, Y-, and W-cells are analogous to the monkey color-opponent cells, the broad-band cells, and the third class of cells.

The superior colliculus in the monkey receives an extensive input from this third class and a sparse input from the broad-band cells. The color-opponent cells do not project to the colliculus (204).

In the cat and monkey the Y- (broad-band) cells are believed to represent only a small percentage of retinal ganglion cells (3%–10%). Similarly, it was initially believed that the W-cells were also a small group. Since the W-cells are very small, however, there is difficulty in recording from them, and so far anatomical methods have not yielded a way of discriminating them unequivocally. Estimates in the cat suggest that W-cells may actually exist in large numbers (62, 246, 264).

A selective projection has also been inferred in the ground squirrel, an animal with an all-cone retina. This animal is a protanope (dichromat), and Michael (164) has discerned three classes of retinal ganglion cells: contrast-sensitive broad-band cells, color-opponent cells, and direction-selective cells. The direction-selective cells appear to project to the superior colliculus, while the axons of the other two classes (the broad-band and color-opponent cells) terminate in the lateral geniculate nucleus. Michael estimated that the superior colliculus receives about half the optic nerve fibers. These findings stand in contrast to the rabbit, in which directional cells are abundant in the retina but are rare in the superior colliculus (16, 108, 152, 175).

In lower vertebrates, where the geniculostriate system is less developed, the percentage of fibers projecting to the superior colliculus is much higher. This also means that there is a less clear-cut separation of the central projections of ganglion cells. In many fishes, for example, there is evidence for excellent color vision. Single cells with color-opponent properties in these animals project to the colliculus.

In summary, the superior colliculus of higher mammals receives a selective projection from the retina. Most prominent are the phylogenetically old, W-type cells in this projection. In addition, there is evidence that Y-type or broad-band cells also project to the colliculus. The X-, or color-opponent, cells in mammals do not send their axons to the superior colliculus.

Cortical Input

Numerous cortical sites project to the superior colliculus (see ANATOMY OF SUPERIOR COLLICULUS, p. 457). Four different approaches are notable in assessing these projections:

1. A description of the anatomical properties of cells in the cortical areas known to project to the colliculus (66, 143).

2. A description of the effect of ablation or cooling of selected cortical sites on collicular function. The advantage of the cooling method, as already noted, is that collicular cells can be studied before, during, and after removal of a particular input.

3. A description of the properties of those cells in the cortex that project to the colliculus. In this case, cells are identified by activating them antidromically.

4. A description of the effect of electrical stimulation of the cortex on the response properties of superior colliculus cells.

Most of the work in categories 2, 3, and 4 has been restricted to visual cortex, and only four different species have been studied in detail: the monkey, the cat, the rabbit, and the ground squirrel. I first examine the effects of cooling or ablation of cortex on collicular cells.

In the rhesus monkey the results of cooling or ablating the striate cortex are straightforward: the activity of cells in stratum griseum superficiale and the upper part of stratum opticum are largely unaffected. Below this level cells stop responding to visual stimuli (207). An example of this appears in Figure 25. Recordings were made in the superior colliculus and a topographically corresponding area of cortex was cooled with a thermoelectric cooling device, which was attached to a silver plate overlying area 17. When the corticotectal pathways are disrupted by the inactivation of cells in area 17, cells in the deeper layers of the colliculus can no longer be driven with visual stimuli. Similar results can be obtained with ablation of the visual cortex; this method does not enable the investigator to compare the same collicular cell before and after the experiment. But sampling of the two superior colliculi in the same monkey in which the visual cortex has been removed on only one side shows that the single cells on the intact side can be visually activated in all collicular layers, whereas on the cortically ablated side visual activation is restricted to stratum griseum superficiale and parts of the stratum opticum (207). This effect is not a temporary one. When adult monkeys are studied 6 months after ablation of the visual cortex the effects are similar. These results suggest that in the monkey the visual cortex takes a central role in the control of information flow in the colliculus.

In the ground squirrel the results of cortical cooling are similar to the results in the monkey (164). Although the properties of collicular cells are different in several respects, cooling disrupts the visual activation of all cells in the deeper layers. Three notable differences may be seen between the receptive-field organization of collicular cells in the monkey and in the ground squirrel: 1) There are many direction-selective cells in the upper layers of the ground squirrel colliculus, and cooling visual cortex has no effect on them. In the monkey, direction selectivity in the colliculus is mostly absent. 2) Cells in the deeper layers of the ground squirrel have properties similar to those found in the visual cortex. Some are orientation selective and some have hypercomplex properties, as already noted. The deeper cells in the colliculus of the monkey lack these properties. Yet in both species, cooling and ablation disrupt the visually driven activity of these cells. This finding in the ground squirrel led Michael (164) to suggest that the deeper cells are driven by the cortex, and that this input determines the receptive-field characteristics of these collicular cells. This is an interesting hypothesis, for it implies that the superficial and deep layers in the superior colliculus do not interact extensively. Unfortunately, the crucial experiment, in which the retinotectal pathway is disrupted without damage to the corticotectal pathway, has not yet been done. This manipulation is probably not possible in most species, for the two pathways are very close to each other, and near the tectum they are intermingled. 3) The third characteristic differentiating the superior colliculus in the monkey and in the ground squirrel is that, in the former,

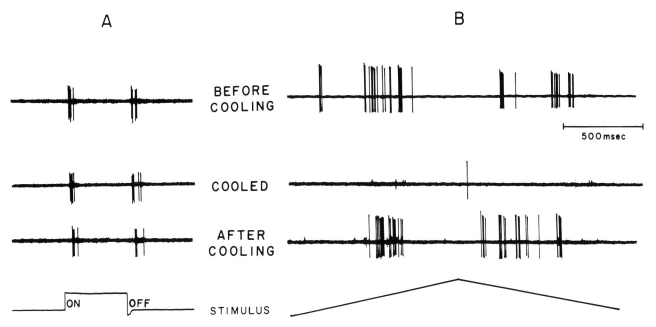

FIG. 25. Response characteristics of two units in superior colliculus of monkey before, during, and after cooling of visual cortex. *A*: unit 220 μm below surface of colliculus (stratum griseum superficiale). *Bottom trace*, time course of presentation of stimulus, a flashing spot centered in receptive field. *B*: unit 400 μm below surface of colliculus (stratum opticum); stimulus, a moving spot. *Bottom trace*, movement of stimulus. [From Schiller et al. (207).]

most cells have a binocular input. In the ground squirrel most cells are monocular. As determined by anatomical methods in the monkey, the axon projections from the retina to the superior colliculus and the lateral geniculate nucleus contain almost equal numbers of crossed and uncrossed fibers (see ANATOMY OF SUPERIOR COLLICULUS, p. 457); in the ground squirrel the retinal input is mostly from the contralateral eye.

The effects on collicular function of cooling or ablation of the visual cortex in the cat are somewhat more complicated. In this animal, as in the monkey and ground squirrel, disruption of the corticotectal pathway eliminates visually driven activity in the deeper layers of the colliculus (235). In addition, there is an effect on cells in the upper layers (21, 167, 197, 244, 267). When the cortical influence is eliminated, most cells lose their direction specificity, and also most cells can only be activated through the contralateral eye. In the cat then, these two qualities are determined mostly by the visual cortex. These results differ both from those in the monkey and from those in the ground squirrel. In the ground squirrel directional selectivity is already seen in the retinal ganglion cells and is transmitted directly to the superior colliculus. The cortex does not seem to affect this property. In the cat directional selectivity is first seen within the retinostriate system in the visual cortex and appears to be transmitted to the colliculus via the corticotectal pathway. In the monkey there are few directional cells in the colliculus and it is not known whether the corticotectal pathway defines this property in these few cells.

Ocular dominance in the monkey is not changed significantly when the corticotectal pathway is disrupted; this suggests that retinal ganglion cells from the two eyes converge extensively on single cells in the colliculus. In the cat, when cortical cooling results in a predominance of monocularly driven cells in the colliculus, the effect seems to follow from the anatomical facts of the retinal projections. Whereas in the optic tract about equal numbers of fibers project from the ipsilateral and contralateral eye to each lateral geniculate body, and in turn to the visual cortex of each hemisphere, the majority of retinotectal fibers to the superior colliculus arise from the contralateral eye [see Fig. 6; (242)]. Thus elimination of the visual input from the cortex leaves the colliculus with a much heavier input from the contralateral eye and therefore results in the observed shift in ocular dominance.

In the rabbit, the only other species studied so far, ablation of the visual cortex has been reported to have no discernible effects on the superior colliculus (152, 245).

What we find common among the mammalian species studied so far is that the visual input to the deeper superior colliculus is controlled by the cortex. The nature of this cortical control has not yet been fully established. One notion is that the deeper collicular layers attain all their receptive-field properties as a result of the cortical input (164). Another hypothesis is that the cortex exercises a gating function on the flow of information through the colliculus (207).

In addition to the visual cortex, the auditory cortex and the somatosensory cortex also project to the superior colliculus. In a recent study Stein (234) asked the following question: Are the somatosensory and auditory inputs of the cat mediated by the sensory cortex in the same manner as the visual input? To determine this he recorded from cells in the superior colliculus and cooled auditory, somatosensory, or visual cortices. Unit activity in the colliculus was altered only with respect to visual stimulation. Single cells activated by somatosensory or auditory input remained active throughout all cooling procedures. Assuming that all the essential cortical areas were adequately inactivated by the cooling, an effect that has not been proved unequivocally, these findings suggest a significant difference in the organization of the superior colliculus with respect to visual and other sensory inputs: the visual input is under cortical control, whereas other inputs can effectively drive collicular cells from subcortical areas without relying on the cortical input.

Input to the superior colliculus from the frontal eye fields has also been explored. This area of the cortex is complex and contains cells that respond both to light and in association with eye movement (24, 25, 168). The eye-movement–related cells, unlike those in the colliculus, do not discharge prior to saccades but rather discharge simultaneously with the rapid eye movements. There is a significant projection from the frontal eye fields to the deeper layers of the superior colliculus (14, 135). Ablation of the frontal eye fields produces temporary neglect for sensory stimuli and alters fixation patterns but does not seem to significantly affect saccadic and smooth-pursuit eye movements (139, 140).

The third approach to be discussed here regarding the cortical input to the superior colliculus is the one that examines the properties of those cortical cells known from antidromic identification to project to the colliculus. This work so far has only been done in area 17 of the cat and monkey (55, 177). The corticotectal cells in area 17 are located mostly in layer 5; they are all cells that can be classified as complex; they have relatively large receptive fields and respond to both light increment and light decrement throughout the field. Almost all of these cells can be activated from either eye. The responses are consistent (there is no evidence for habituation) and the spontaneous activity is typically high. Many of the cells are selective for the direction of motion and for the orientation of light bars presented in their receptive fields. In the monkey neither of these properties is transmitted to the collicular cells, whereas in the cat direction selectivity appears to be transmitted but orientation selectivity is not. How is this possible? If one assumes that cortical cells provide the deeper collicular cells with their receptive-field properties, it must also be assumed that in the monkey there is extensive convergence that cancels out both orientation and direction specificity. In the cat, convergence is such that the direction specificity is preserved but orientation is not.

Alternatively, it is possible that the cortex acts as a gate, and that the properties of deeper collicular cells result from the interaction of the cortical input and the retinal input through the superficial layers. Considerable additional work is needed to clarify the role of these inputs in the colliculus.

The fourth approach, which entails the examination of the effects of electrical stimulation in the cortex on the response properties of collicular cells, has yielded three notable findings: 1) The corticotectal cells in area 17 of the cat are driven selectively by the Y-cells of the retina (101, 260). Thus it appears that the X-cells reach the colliculus neither directly nor indirectly. Recent work on the monkey supports this view. In this species the corticotectal pathway from striate cortex is activated almost exclusively by the broadband system (205). 2) The initial effect of the corticotectal pathway on collicular cells is excitation followed by inhibition. This inhibition is believed to be produced within the colliculus, probably by interneurons (101). 3) The corticotectal projection is arranged topographically and is congruent with the visual-field representation of the retinotectal pathway (158).

Subcortical Input

I close the discussion of the inputs to the superior colliculus by considering the pathway from the caudal thalamus, which has not been studied in mammals but has been examined in frogs and toads (50, 51, 115). This pathway has been established as an important modulator of orienting and prey-catching behavior. Lesions involving the pretectal area produce a striking syndrome of disinhibition. The effect of the lesion is that the toad will persistently orient toward or attempt to approach any moving stimulus. This is the case even for a relatively large stimulus, which in intact animals generally produces avoidance behavior. Thus the effect of the lesion is that the animal is turned into an automaton; he is stimulus bound and will reach over and over again in the same manner toward the stimulus. The effect is so strong that moving a stimulus upward over the toad's body will cause the animal to orient toward it until gravity takes control and the toad falls over backward.

The action of the caudal thalamus on tectal neurons has also been examined by use of electrophysiological methods (115). In the tectum of intact frogs, cells habituate rapidly to repeated presentations of a visual stimulus. When the pathway is severed, cells no longer habituate. They respond, instead, in a consistent fashion to repeated stimulus presentation. The thalamotectal pathway therefore appears to have an important modulatory influence on the optic tectum; this must contribute to the selection of stimuli toward which or away from which the animal orients. These findings further support the observation that response dynamics observed in the colliculus are largely due to inputs for other areas.

Summary

Several distinct classes of retinal ganglion cells have been identified. In the cat these have commonly been grouped into X-, Y-, and W-types. In the monkey a similar threefold division has been proposed consisting of color-opponent (X-like), broad-band (Y-like), and W-like cells. The superior colliculus receives a large input from the slowly conducting W-cells and a lesser input from the rapidly conducting broad-band (Y-) cells. In fishes and amphibians the retinotectal projection is not as selective.

In most mammals studied disruption of the corticotectal pathway by ablation or by cooling of visual cortex renders the deeper collicular cells unresponsive to visual stimuli. The superficial layers in ground squirrel, rabbit, and monkey are unaffected by this manipulation. In the cat, however, directional selectivity and binocularity are severely reduced in these layers when the corticotectal pathway is blocked. The response properties of somatosensory and auditory units are not altered in the cat colliculus when cortical areas subserving hearing and touch sensation are disrupted by cooling.

In the striate cortex, cells that project to the colliculus reside in layer 5. They are complex cells with large receptive fields that have high spontaneous activity and appear to be driven selectively by the fast Y- (broad-band) pathway. In both cat and monkey some of these cells show orientation specificity, and many are directionally selective.

In frogs and toads the pathway projecting from the caudal thalamus to the superior colliculus has a significant role in the modulation of orienting behavior. When this pathway is sectioned, tectal cells no longer habituate and the animal becomes an automaton responding to stimuli in an invariant fashion.

PHYSIOLOGICAL STUDIES OF OUTPUTS
OF SUPERIOR COLLICULUS

Physiological studies that have been conducted with the aim of elucidating the tectofugal pathways have relied predominantly on combined stimulation-recording methods. Such methods can disclose not only the conduction direction of the pathways between two structures but can also determine whether the pathways are direct or indirect. Most of the research on the outflow of the colliculus is recent, and the work is limited to a few studies examining the brain stem projections (77, 131, 180, 182, 184). Investigators have addressed two major questions: *1*) Does the colliculus project to areas involved in the control of eye movement, and *2*) What are the properties of the collicular neurons projecting to brain stem areas?

Studies examining the connection between the superior colliculus and the abducens nucleus demonstrate a crossed excitatory and an uncrossed inhibitory pathway, which for the most part is disynaptic or multisynaptic (77, 182), although Grantyn and Grantyn (77) suggest that a small fraction of the excitatory pathway may be monosynaptic. These studies therefore demonstrate a close link between the superior colliculus and the motoneurons that form the final common path to the muscles.

Since for the most part there is at least one synapse between the superior colliculus and the motoneurons innervating the eye muscles, determination of the intervening sites becomes desirable. It has been shown that the pontine reticular formation is a major center for eye movement control (192). Several different kinds of cells have been identified here that discharge in relation to eye movement (131). Some cells fire in a tonic fashion proportional to fixation position of the eye. Others burst in association with saccades, and in yet another class the maintained firing rate is interrupted by pauses whenever saccades occur. Notable among the burst cells are the so-called long-lead burst neurons; because these neurons are quite similar in their properties to those collicular eye movement cells that, after a buildup, discharge in discrete bursts with saccades, they typically begin their gradually increasing discharge 50–80 ms prior to a saccade. There is one essential difference, however: the high-frequency burst duration of collicular neurons, as described earlier, is roughly the same for all neurons irrespective of the size of the saccade they code (131, 184). By contrast, the temporal discharge pattern of the long-lead burst cells in the pontine reticular formation varies as a function of saccade size and duration (131).

Grantyn and Grantyn (77) have shown in the anesthetized cat and Raybourn and Keller (184) in the alert monkey that reticular neurons receive a significant excitatory monosynaptic connection from the contralateral superior colliculus. In the monkey about one-third of the long-lead burst neurons were monosynaptically driven from the colliculus. Activation was effective from many regions of the superior colliculus that demonstrated a significant convergence. In addition to the reticular burst cells, most of the so-called pausers were also monosynaptically driven from the colliculus. Another class, however, the so-called medium-lead bursters, which begin their discharge just preceding the high-frequency activity of motoneurons, were not synaptically driven from the colliculus.

In a recent study Keller (131) placed stimulating electrodes in the pontine reticular formation and then recorded in the superior colliculus of alert monkeys. He found that all the discretely bursting collicular eye movement cells could be antidromically activated from the reticular area. Also important was the observation that such stimulation did not elicit any orthodromic activity in collicular eye movement cells. In agreement with the anatomical work discussed in ANATOMY OF SUPERIOR COLLICULUS, p. 457, these studies demonstrate convincingly that from the superior colliculus there is a significant monosynaptic pathway to the pontine reticular formation, an area immediately supranuclear to the oculomotor complex. That the medium-lead bursters do not form a part of this network suggests that there must be other significant inputs to the reticular formation leading to eye movement activity. Whether these other pathways also contribute to visually triggered eye movement activity remains to be determined.

BEHAVIORAL EFFECTS OF SUPERIOR
COLLICULUS ABLATION

Examination of collicular function by recording and stimulation methods suggests that this midbrain structure has an important role in vision and orientation. Visual pattern analysis is extensively handled by the colliculus in submammalian species. In mammals this function is increasingly relegated to the geniculostriate system. The colliculus appears to remain effective in contributing to orientation and to the control of saccadic eye movement. From these observations one might expect that ablation of the superior colliculus should have notable effects on the visual capacities of submammalian species and should show deficits in orientation and eye movement in higher mammals. These expectations are largely confirmed by experiments involving collicular ablation.

The naturalistic examination of orientation behavior has established several facets of this function. First of all, animals may orient themselves toward objects: prey-catching behavior is a good example. A frog, upon perceiving a fly, will orient its head and body toward it and will then lash out its tongue to catch the fly. Secondly, animals may exhibit escape behavior by turning away from objects. Frogs, for example, when they perceive a large moving object or what is assumed to be a predator, will jump away from the source of such a stimulus. Thirdly, animals have to orient themselves relative to other stimuli, which may form natural barriers in the pursuit of the first two modes of action. Thus frogs can move around or sidestep such obstacles in the pursuit of prey (113, 116, 117).

In the frog, removal of the optic tecti causes serious deficits in vision, although the animal does not become totally blind. Tectal ablation renders the animal insensitive to moving objects. This is true both for small objects that typically elicit prey-catching behavior and for large objects that in the normal animal produce avoidance behavior. Curiously, the ability to take obstacles into account is not affected. Thus if an animal is forced to move, as when it is pinched, it will direct its escape leap correctly, avoiding obstacles placed in its path (114, 117). In birds tectal lesions produce deficits in visual discrimination, localization, and reflex orientation (10, 33, 96, 121, 161). Some disagreement among investigators exists regarding the severity of this deficit, which may be due to differences in lesion size and in behavioral assessment methods (33, 96, 121, 161).

The orientation behavior of such mammals as the cat, hamster, rat, and tree shrew is also affected by collicular ablation (17, 30, 70, 71, 209, 230). In his classic study, Schneider (209, 210) has shown that the hamster, after removal of the superior colliculi, still possesses the ability to discriminate patterns but is severely impaired in his ability to orient toward them. These and related findings led to the perhaps simplistic view of the two visual systems, a proposal according to which the geniculostriate system is for telling *what* things are and the retinotectal system is for telling *where* they are.

Research on the tree shrew has shown deficits induced by ablation of the superior colliculus; in some respects these deficits are similar to those observed in the frog. Orientation toward objects of prey is severely affected, and Casagrande and Diamond (30) have captured this deficit on a remarkable film showing the tree shrew's behavior before and after colliculectomy. The normal animal is extremely quick and orients with its eye, head, and body with great agility. For example, a mealworm held with forceps and moved rapidly in front of a normal tree shrew will elicit movement of the head and eyes, and when the worm is placed close enough, the tree shrew will strike and consume it. After tectal removal, this behavior is totally absent; the animal stares vacantly into space and takes the mealworm only when the mouth is touched. In spite of this striking deficit, these animals can negotiate well through a maze having a series of partitions with small doors in them through which the animal has to progress to a food well. These findings are in some respects similar to what was observed in frogs.

The deficits noted for the tree shrew are found only when both the superficial and deep layers of the tectum are removed (30). When only the superficial layers (stratum griseum superficiale, stratum opticum) are ablated, the animal orients normally. These observations lend credence to the notion that the superficial and deep collicular layers are to some degree functionally separate. This distinction is anatomically notable among nonmammalian forms where the third ventricle intervenes between the superficial and deep tectal layers.

In the cat the deficits induced by tectal lesions also relate predominantly to orientation, although deficits in pattern perception have also been reported (20, 26, 56, 229–231, 233). For part of their work Sprague and his collaborators used a cleverly contrived apparatus to assess the animal's ability to orient. This is shown in Figure 26, as used by Sherman (212). The hungry cat, when released, will progress straight ahead to reach a food object. On some trials, as the animal initiates its motion, a second food object is lowered into its field of vision from above at various retinal eccentricities. Intact animals will invariably orient toward and take the second food object, since it is closer. When the superior colliculus is removed, animals no

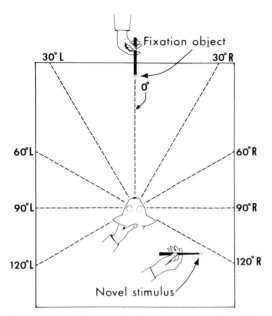

FIG. 26. Method for testing sensitivity in various parts of the visual field. Cat is restrained, its lateral canthi aligned along the 90° guidelines and its nose pointed along the 0° guideline to the fixation object (a piece of food in forceps). For tests of specific visual responses the novel stimulus (food in forceps or a painted ball at the end of a stiff wire) is introduced along one of the guidelines, after which the cat is freed from restraint and its behavior noted. For control tests of nonspecific responses the novel stimulus either is not introduced or is introduced laterally at approximately 120° (out of the cat's visual field) before the cat is freed. [From Sherman (216).]

longer orient toward the second piece of food. The deficit is transitory, however, and animals show significant postoperative recovery.

Use of this method disclosed another interesting finding about combined collicular and cortical function in the cat, first reported by Sprague in 1966 (228). He found that unilateral ablation of occipitotemporal cortex, as expected, results in hemianopia. Visually guided behavior was partially restored, however, when either the contralateral tectum was removed or the intertectal commissure was sectioned. Sherman (217) used the same behavioral technique shown in Figure 26 to replicate this effect with some modifications. After the initial training period, the occipitotemporal cortex was removed bilaterally and the animals were retested. Then, in a second operation, the intertectal commissure was severed and the animals were retested. The results showed the following: 1) normal animals orient accurately, and the vision of each eye extends 45° into the contralateral field; 2) after occipitotemporal lesions, animals no longer orient; 3) after tectal split, orientation behavior is reestablished; but 4) each eye can see only to the midline, not beyond it.

Sprague's initial results, as well as those just described, suggest that the colliculi receive facilitative input from the cortex and are mutually inhibitory on one another via the intertectal commissure (101, 228). Removal of the facilitative cortical input leaves each

colliculus with inhibition induced from the other colliculus. Tectal split removes this inhibition, rendering the colliculi functional again.

This finding has aroused considerable interest, since it suggested that some visual malfunction due to cortical dysfunction could be restored by sectioning of the intertectal commissure. Nevertheless, the Sprague effect does not appear to exist in the rhesus monkey for the control of saccadic eye movement (148).

Examination of deficits incurred by colliculectomy in monkey has produced results that are less clear cut than those observed in other species. Some investigators reported no discernible effects on such behaviors as visual discrimination, orientation, and attention (7, 178). In other work, in particular that of Denny-Brown (42), it has been noted that after complete removal of the superior colliculi, monkeys tend to have a vacant stare, move their eyes much less, and not react to stimuli as readily as before (129, 134, 146). The size of the collicular lesions was notably different in these studies, and so were the behavioral tasks used.

Studies that have included the recording of eye movements have shown that after colliculectomy monkeys tend to show some or all of the following deficits: 1) increased latency of saccade initiation; 2) increased number of corrective saccades to reach targets; 3) increased errors in correct target acquisition; 4) a decrease in the number and velocity of saccades (134, 148, 208, 275). The extent to which any of these deficits is manifested depends on the nature of the task and on the animal strategy. It should be emphasized that these deficits are not by any means devastating. The animal can still orient well, it can attend to stimuli even though it may not use its eyes as readily, and its perception of visual patterns is basically intact.

In contrast, the complete removal of the visual cortex in monkeys causes pronounced deficits in detailed pattern perception. The animal's ability to fixate, however, is still good, provided the stimuli used are either intense enough or large enough. When monkeys suffer combined cortical and collicular lesions they are seriously disabled and can neither orient toward visual targets nor discriminate them (170).

Another combined lesion study of interest here is one in which ablation of the superior colliculus is paired with removal of the frontal eye fields. When the latter structure is ablated bilaterally, only small, transient deficits in orientation and gaze are observed, and virtually no deficits in saccadic and smooth-pursuit movements (139, 140, 208) or discrimination are seen. When the colliculus is also removed, a notable deficit appears: monkeys become virtually unable to produce visually targeted eye movements (208). Thus in the primate both the superior colliculus and the frontal eye fields are significant in the guidance of visually triggered saccades.

To summarize: Deficits incurred by removal of the superior colliculus are less pronounced in higher mammals than in animals lower on the phylogenetic scale.

Except for exhibiting ballistic escape behavior, frogs become blind after tectal ablations. Tree shrews no longer orient toward targets, but they can move through space adequately. Hamsters after colliculectomy can still make pattern discriminations but can no longer assess where things are located in space. Cats become deficient in orientation behavior, but there is significant postoperative recovery. In monkeys only relatively subtle deficits are observed in eye movements. In the case of paired frontal cortex and colliculus lesions in the monkey, however, loss of function is as extensive as that observed in the tree shrew with colliculus removal alone. The findings of ablation studies are largely consistent with the results of electrophysiological research in ascribing orientation and eye movement control functions to the mammalian superior colliculus.

DEVELOPMENTAL STUDIES OF SUPERIOR COLLICULUS

Methods

Neurophysiological studies designed to examine the development of the superior colliculus have been undertaken mostly in paralyzed, anesthetized animals. By studying the receptive-field properties of collicular cells and the topography of this region in animals of different ages it is possible to provide a descriptive account of the course of normal development.

Surgical manipulations designed to selectively interfere with the growth pattern of the retinotectal fibers have been performed using several different paradigms. Most of these studies are concerned with the question of how the retinal fibers make their orderly, topographic connections onto the surface of the optic tectum. When the optic nerve is severed in amphibia, the retinal fibers regrow into the tectum in an orderly fashion. This procedure can be coupled with other manipulations such as eye rotation or partial removal of the optic tectum. The subsequent study of regrowth patterns by systematic recordings in the colliculus yields a new topography, which can be compared with the normal layout of this structure. Recent studies have shown that similar experiments are possible in the hamster and rabbit, provided the surgical manipulations are accomplished during the first few days after birth, when the optic fibers have not yet grown into the tectum.

Study of the effects of selective rearing on collicular function in mammals has been performed by depriving animals of normal binocular vision. This can be done by suturing one eyelid or by sectioning eye muscles to disrupt normal conjugate eye movements. Interference with normal motion perception has been accomplished by raising animals under stroboscopic illumination or exposing them to stimuli that are moved in only one direction in their environment. After such exposure single-unit recordings in the colliculus can demonstrate how these procedures affect the recep-

tive-field properties of collicular cells and to what extent observed changes are dependent on the age of the animal.

Development of Mammalian Superior Colliculus

Kittens are virtually blind when they first open their eyes, about one week after birth (173). Visually guided behavior develops over a period of several weeks (173, 237, 239). Visual and auditory orienting and following make their first appearance around the 10th postnatal day and are well established by day 25. By contrast, such visual behaviors as obstacle avoidance, visual placing, and depth discrimination appear not earlier than 25 days.

Examination of the receptive-field properties of collicular cells has shown that directionally selective cells are rarely found in kittens studied between the ages of 10 and 19 days. By 30 to 40 days, however, the percentage of such cells is similar to that found in adult cats. This is shown in Figure 27.

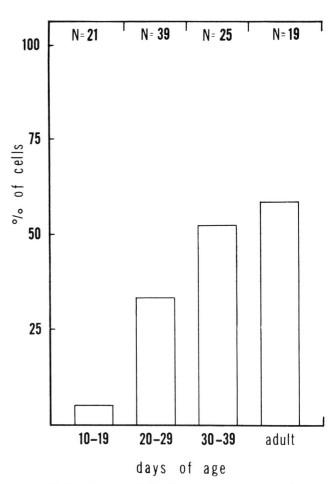

FIG. 27. Development of direction-selective responses with age in superior colliculus of kitten. Height of each *bar*, proportion of cells in each age group that gave direction-selective responses. N, number of cells. [From Norton (173).]

A similar sequence was reported by Norton (173) for ocular dominance. Initially only about 30% of the collicular cells can be binocularly activated. When the animals are 30–39 days old most cells become binocular and are similar in performance to collicular cells in the adult cat. These findings relate to what is observed in the adult cat after removal of the visual cortex leaves the colliculus with few direction-selective and mostly monocularly driven cells. The developmental changes may well reflect the maturation of the corticotectal pathway. Norton believes that the emergence of visually guided behavior parallels the development of the collicular receptive field properties.

Effect of Surgical Interference on Retinotectal Pathway

Research on surgical manipulation of parts of the brain has its roots in questions posed by philosophers centuries ago about the role of nature and of nurture on the developing organism. In particular, this research has been concerned with the question of how those parts of the brain develop that mediate perception, and how this development can be altered by experience. This is a large research area; here only that aspect is covered that relates closely to collicular function.

In fishes and amphibians the optic tectum is the main visual center; it is responsible for the analysis of visual information about the location of stimuli in space and about their spatial pattern. It is also the area that generates orienting and striking behavior (113, 116, 117). As has already been described, the visual field is represented in an orderly topographic fashion within the colliculus.

When the optic nerve is severed in fishes and amphibians it regrows into the tectum, recreating the same orderly distribution of fiber terminals. It was Sperry (222–225) who first realized that this phenomenon of regeneration offered an opportunity to examine the role of experience in the establishment of neural connections. To do this he rotated one eye of newts, anuran amphibians, and teleost fishes through 180° and coupled this with sectioning of the optic nerve. After regrowth of the optic nerve these animals were tested behaviorally. The results showed that the innervation was not adaptive. Fibers made connections to their original sites in the tectum, and these animals, when viewing the world through the rotated eye, did not orient correctly; for example, frogs struck to the left when a fly was presented on the right. Subsequent experiments by Gaze (65), using electrophysiological findings, confirmed these results. On the basis of this work Sperry (226, 227) formulated his neuronal specificity hypothesis, often referred to as the chemoaffinity theory, which proposed that retinal ganglion cells have unique cytochemical labels that enable them to find similarly labeled regions in the tectum. Later experiments have indicated, however, that if the eye is rotated during early embryonic stages,

a normal map of the visual field onto the tectum can be reestablished (111, 130).

Sperry's work has triggered a tremendous amount of research and, as is inevitable, a great deal of controversy. Current evidence suggests that a strict point-to-point specificity probably does not exist. It has been shown in some amphibian species, at least, that if half the tectum is ablated, the ingrowing retinal fibers will distribute in an orderly fashion over the remaining tissue, the entire visual field then being represented in half the tectum (130). Conversely, it has also been shown in some experiments that if half of the retina is ablated, the remaining retina will distribute over the entire tectum. These findings have produced other hypotheses about possible mechanisms of orderly neural growth that emphasize chemical sensitivity among retinal fibers and chemical gradients rather than a strict point-to-point chemoaffinity. Whereas there is considerable controversy about the exact mechanism of neural specificity, these kinds of studies clearly show that the retinotectal connections in fishes and amphibians are largely determined by genetic factors and are only modifiable by environmental influences during the earliest stages of development.

Recently it has been shown that surgical manipulations can induce significant modifications in the central connections of retinal fibers of hamsters and rabbits, provided the work is done in infant animals (31, 211–214). This is an important finding, for it extends to mammals some of the observations made in fishes and amphibians. If one superior colliculus is removed in the hamster, the fibers from the contralateral retina will make several abnormal innervations in such regions as the medial portion of the ipsilateral tectum and neighboring neural structures. Most dramatic are the connections that are made when both the tectum and one eye are removed on the same side. Under these conditions the retinal fibers, after failing to find the contralateral tectum, turn sharply and enter the uninnervated ipsilateral tectum, on which they make orderly, mirror-image connections. When tested behaviorally these animals make incorrect orientations in space; if a seed is shown in the right visual field the animal will orient to the left. Electrophysiological studies confirm the mirror-image innervations (54). These findings provide further evidence for the role of the superior colliculus in orienting behavior and also demonstrate that abnormal connections can occur under unusual conditions.

Effect of Selective Rearing on Collicular Functions

The results described so far suggest that in fishes, amphibians, and the hamster there is a strong tendency for connections to be made according to genetically programmed instructions; where manipulations put environmental and innate factors in conflict, the latter predominate.

In higher mammals recent work examined changes

in the superior colliculus produced by selective environmental deprivation. As described in *Methods*, p. 494, in these studies the visual input is modified either by interference with normal binocular vision or by exposing the animal to only a restricted set of visual stimuli.

It is known that when the normal operation and alignment of the two eyes are interfered with by unilateral eye suture, alternating occlusion, or eye-muscle section (induced strabismus), most of the cells in the visual cortex lose their binocularity and can be activated through only one eye (73, 74, 106, 107, 269, 270). If one eyelid is sutured, most cortical cells can be driven only through the normal eye. Induced strabismus or alternating occlusion also yields only monocularly driven cells, but the left and right eyes are equally represented in each area 17.

In the superior colliculus suturing has effects that are different from induced strabismus or alternating occlusion (73, 74). Study of collicular cells shows that they become almost exclusively monocularly driven if one eyelid has been sutured for the first 3 months of life; each colliculus can be activated only through the nondeprived eye. This, shown in Figure 28, is the same as in the visual cortex. Induced strabismus in the

cortex yields monocular cells, the left and right eyes being about equally well represented. By contrast, in the superior colliculus of strabismic animals the majority of cells remain binocular (also shown in Fig. 28). There is a pronounced difference, however, in the two colliculi: the ocular dominance distribution for the neuron population in the colliculus contralateral to the muscle-sectioned eye is only slightly different from that found in normal animals, while in the ipsilateral colliculus there is a greater representation for the normal eye. In animals raised with alternating occlusion the ocular dominance distribution of the superior colliculus is similar to that found in the strabismic kittens (74). If induced strabismus is paired with alternating occlusion, both colliculi remain mostly binocularly driven (73).

A normal corticotectal pathway is essential for the maintenance of binocularity in the cat colliculus. Disruption of this pathway results in mostly monocular cells. How is it possible, then, to have binocular cells in the colliculus after induced strabismus and alternating occlusion when cortical cells become monocular under these conditions? The most likely explanation is that monocular cells from the cortex converge upon collicular cells. Such convergence is only possible when

RIGHT EYE SUTURE

INDUCED STRABISMUS

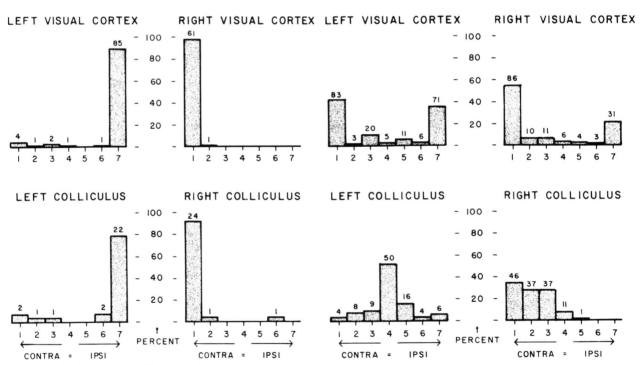

FIG. 28. Ocular dominance histograms for striate cortex and superior colliculus of cats raised either with eye suture or with induced strabismus. Cells in group 1 can be activated only through the contralateral eye; cells in group 4 are equally driven by either eye; and cells in group 7 are activated only by the ipsilateral eye. [Data from Wiesel and Hubel (106, 269, 270), Sterling and Wickelgren (243), and Gordon and Gummow (73).]

either of the two eyes can activate cortical cells, as is the case with induced strabismus and alternating occlusion. When one eyelid is sutured, only the normal eye retains representation in the cortex; hence the cortical input to the colliculus is from only one eye and yields only monocularly driven cells.

In addition to these effects another interesting finding has been reported in the cat: in the lateral geniculate nucleus deprivation of vision by suturing of the eyelid has a more devastating effect on Y-cells than on X-cells (100). This suggests that the visual cortex receives virtually no Y-cell input in such animals. Since in normal cats the input to the superior colliculus from the visual cortex is predominantly from the Y pathway (98), one would expect that in lid-sutured animals this input would be largely absent. Hoffmann and Sherman (100) examined this question and have confirmed this expectation: in lid-sutured kittens the Y pathway from the visual cortex was lost, but the direct retinotectal pathways remained normal.

The effect of various deprivation conditions on the directional properties of cat collicular cells has also been studied. Rearing in the dark or suturing of one eyelid virtually eliminates direction selectivity through the deprived eye (268). In animals in which strabismus was induced by medial and lateral rectus muscle sectioning there is a significant change in the distribution of preferred directions; a higher percentage of collicular cells are found that respond best to upward (vertical) stimulus movement (73). Animals deprived in this fashion have a significant decrement in horizontal eye movements.

Several studies have reported on kittens raised in environments that exposed them to unilaterally moving stimuli. These findings show little change as a result of such rearing conditions (39, 58). Kittens have also been reared in a stroboscopically illuminated environment; this environment eliminates the perception of continuous motion, and under these conditions, directional selectivity is virtually abolished in the col-

liculus (58, 59). None of these studies have succeeded in demonstrating a constructive environmentally induced change in collicular cells. Most of the noted effects can be attributed to a selective dropping out of those cells whose function is not maintained by appropriate stimuli. One recent study, however, has used an interesting method that allows one to determine whether or not constructive changes occur. To do this Cynader et al. (40) rotated one eye of kittens 90° shortly after birth and subsequently recorded in the contralateral superior colliculus, in which many binocularly driven, directionally selective cells were found. Most of the directional cells responded preferentially through either eye to the same direction of motion on the tangent screen. Had there been no adaptation, the preferred direction, as tested through the rotated eye, should have been perpendicular to that obtained through the normal eye. An example of such a cell appears in Figure 29. These data show a similar preference in the two eyes as mapped on the tangent screen. The results of this study provide the first demonstration of adaptive changes in the mammalian colliculus. Similar work (40) in the visual cortex of kittens with one eye rotated in infancy did not show adaptive changes in orientation selectivity of single cells. In these studies, however, only a few binocularly driven cells were encountered. Such cells are by definition the least modifiable, since their binocular connectivity remains normal despite a marked strabismus.

Summary

Research on the innervation of the optic tectum from the retina suggests that topographic order is genetically determined. Eye rotation and similar manipulations when performed early in life have little effect on the basic innervation pattern. The mechanisms responsible for this are not yet fully understood.

In cats the superior colliculus matures rapidly during the first month of life. The binocularity and direc-

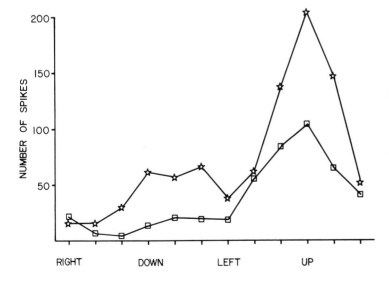

FIG. 29. Response characteristics of a cat superior colliculus cell as assessed through rotated (*squares*) and normal (*stars*) eye. Twelve directions of movement in 30° steps were presented eight times in a randomized order. Each eye was tested separately. Tuning curves in the two eyes are similar, indicating that this cell responded optimally to the same direction of stimulus movement in visual space through the two eyes despite the 90° rotation of one eye. Stimulus size, 3° square; stimulus velocity, 20°/s. [From Cynader et al. (40).]

tion selectivity of single cells appear later than other functions. This is attributable to the delayed development of the corticotectal pathway.

Deprivation studies have shown that the ocular dominance of collicular cells can be severely modified by rearing kittens with one eye sutured or by making them strabismic. Direction selectivity can be significantly reduced by raising the animals in strobe-lit environments. Most effects can be explained in terms of selective loss of certain functions. One recent study has indicated, however, that under certain conditions constructive changes can occur.

CONCLUDING REMARKS

I conclude this chapter by making 11 general statements about the superior colliculus and list the evidence justifying these statements.

1. The superior colliculus, or optic tectum, is a laminated midbrain structure that can be divided into a dorsal region, which is concerned with visual functions, and a ventral, integrative region, which is involved in the control of eye movement and orientation: *a*) The dorsal region of the colliculus receives inputs from visual structures and projects predominantly to other brain areas concerned with vision. *b*) Single cells in this region respond almost exclusively to visual stimuli. *c*) The deeper laminae receive projections from many nonvisual areas, among which the auditory and somatosensory inputs are prominent; the single cells of this region can be activated by visual, auditory, and somatosensory stimuli. *d*) The deeper laminae terminate extensively in brain stem areas involved in the regulation of eye movement and orientation. *e*) In alert monkeys the single cells of the deeper colliculus respond in association with eye movement. *f*) Electrical stimulation of the intermediate and deep layers of the colliculus elicits eye movements and orientation behavior at low thresholds. *g*) Ablation interferes with eye movement and orientation functions, although the extent of the deficit varies among species.

2. The midbrain visual area has undergone significant changes in the course of evolution. In fishes and amphibians it is the major visual center, while in higher mammals it is involved predominantly in orienting behavior: *a*) In fishes and amphibians ablation of the optic tectum causes significant deficits in visual pattern perception. In mammals the deficit is most pronounced for orienting behavior. *b*) Single cells in the colliculus show more specificity for patterns in fishes and amphibians than in higher mammals. *c*) There is a significant increase in the relative amount of brain tissue in the telencephalon devoted to vision as the phylogenetic scale is ascended. *d*) There is a significant decrease in the percentage of retinal ganglion cells that project to the superior colliculus as the phylogenetic scale is ascended.

3. In some mammals the superior colliculus appears to tell the animal *where* events occur in the visual world, while the geniculostriate system tells it *what* they are: *a*) In some lower mammals ablation of the superior colliculus interferes with spatial orientation; destruction of the visual cortex interferes with pattern perception. *b*) Electrical stimulation to the colliculus elicits orientating behaviors at low thresholds.

4. The spatial arrangement of the auditory and somatosensory inputs to the deeper laminae conform to the visual topography of the colliculus, suggesting that the colliculus is organized from the standpoint of visual response: *a*) Single cell studies show that the visual, auditory, and somatosensory modalities have similar spatial representation in the superior colliculus. *b*) The topography of the somatosensory inputs is determined by the way tactile body parts are seen from the eye. *c*) The nonvisual input does not conform to peripheral innervation density; the visual input for the most part does conform.

5. The visual projections to the superior colliculus in higher mammals are selective: *a*) The retinal ganglion cells projecting to the colliculus comprise two classes—the rapidly conducting Y-type (broad-band) cells and the slowly conducting W-type cells. The major direct retinal input is from the W-type cells. *b*) The indirect visual input to the superior colliculus via the geniculostriate system is driven exclusively by Y-type ganglion cells.

6. In primates the superior colliculus is one of the brain structures involved in the control of visually guided saccadic eye movement: *a*) In the intermediate and deeper layers of the monkey superior colliculus eye movement cells predominate. *b*) Electrical stimulation of the colliculus elicits saccadic eye movements. *c*) Ablation causes deficits in eye movement.

7. In higher mammals other structures in addition to the superior colliculus play a role in the generation of visually guided saccadic eye movement: *a*) Ablation of the superior colliculus causes only partial deficits in eye movement. *b*) Electrical stimulation of other brain structures such as the visual cortex, the frontal eye fields, the cerebellum, and the brain stem elicits eye movements. In the frontal eye fields stimulation-elicited saccades persist after ablation of the superior colliculus, while such responses are abolished from the visual cortex after collicular ablation. *c*) Paired ablations of the visual cortex and colliculus or paired ablations of the frontal eye field and colliculus are necessary to cause serious deficits in visually triggered eye movements in monkeys.

8. The superior colliculus of higher mammals is under cortical control. This control is most pronounced for visual functions: *a*) Disruption of the corticotectal pathway from the visual cortex eliminates visually driven activity in the deeper colliculus. *b*) Disruption of the corticotectal pathway from auditory and somatosensory areas does not affect single-cell activity in the colliculus.

9. Mechanisms involved in stimulus and response

selectivity (attention) leading to eye movements are not intrinsic to the colliculus but are relayed to this structure from other brain regions: *a*) The threshold for stimulation-elicited motor responses from the colliculus is dependent on the state of the animal; the threshold is much higher when the animal is drowsy or asleep. *b*) Sectioning of the pathway from the caudal thalamus to the colliculus in frogs eliminates decrement in response to repeated stimulation in collicular cells. Such animals respond in an invariant fashion to repeated stimulus presentation.

10. For the most part, the basic organization of the colliculus is genetically determined; the extent to which constructive organizational changes can be produced by selective rearing is limited: *a*) In amphibians and lower mammals the retinotectal pathway makes its connections in accordance with a basic genetic plan and not according to environmentally induced changes such as eye rotation. *b*) In higher mammals such as cats, restricted rearing during the critical period can cause deficits in certain visual functions. Recent reports suggest that some constructive changes might occur under certain conditions in the mammalian superior colliculus.

11. Several hypotheses of primate collicular function have been proposed. These include the foveation hypothesis, the target localization hypothesis, and the selective attention hypothesis. According to the foveation hypothesis only retinal error information is used to initiate saccades; the target localization hypothesis holds that both retinal error and eye position information are used; and by the selective attention hypothesis an altering function is performed by the colliculus.

Evidence for the foveation hypothesis includes the following: *a*) In the intermediate layers of the colliculus many cells have dual properties. First, they discharge prior to saccades of specific directions and amplitudes; and second, they have visual receptive fields. The ensuing saccade brings the fovea to the region of the visual field that contained the receptive field prior to the saccade. *b*) Electrical stimulation of the colliculus elicits saccades that bring the fovea into the area of the visual field in which the receptive fields of the stimulated cells were located. *c*) Ablation of the colliculus induces deficits in eye movements. *d*) In monkeys collicular ablation does not cause significant deficits in selective attention.

Several observations provide evidence for the target localization hypothesis that in the colliculus both retinal error and eye position information are utilized for initiating saccades: *a*) Many collicular cells discharge in association with saccades even in the absence of appropriate visual stimuli. *b*) Some eye movement cells in the colliculus continue to discharge prior to saccades after removal of visual cortex, which disrupts the processing of visual information in the intermediate and deeper layers of the colliculus. *c*) One class of collicular cells appears to reflect an eye position error signal. *d*) Saccadic localization is correct even when collicular stimulation is used to pull the eye to a new orbital position immediately after the visual stimulus has been extinguished.

Finally, the following observations may be included in the evidence for the selective attention hypothesis: *a*) In the upper layers of the colliculus cells respond more vigorously to visual stimuli when an eye movement ensues that targets the fovea on the stimulus. *b*) Some units in the intermediate layers initiate their eye-movement–related discharge later than cells in the deeper layers. *c*) Ablation of the colliculus causes deficits, notable among which is an increased latency in saccade initiation.

REFERENCES

1. ABPLANALP, P. The neuroanatomical organization of the visual system in the tree shrew. *Folia Primat.* 16: 1–34, 1971.
2. AKERT, K. Der Visuelle Greifreflex. *Helv. Physiol. Pharmacol. Acta* 7: 112–134, 1949.
3. ALBANO, J. E., A. L. HUMPHREY, AND T. T. NORTON. The laminar organization of receptive-field properties in the tree shrew superior colliculus. *J. Neurophysiol.* 41: 1140–1164, 1978.
4. ALTMAN, J. Some fiber projections in the superior colliculus in the cat. *J. Comp. Neurol.* 119: 77–95, 1962.
5. ALTMAN, J., AND M. B. CARPENTER. Fiber projections of the superior colliculus in the cat. *J. Comp. Neurol.* 116: 157–178, 1961.
6. ALTMAN, J., AND L. MALIS. An electrophysiological study of the superior colliculus and visual cortex. *Exp. Neurol.* 5: 233–249, 1962.
7. ANDERSON, K. V., AND D. SYMMES. The superior colliculus and higher visual functions in the monkey. *Brain Res.* 13: 37–52, 1969.
8. ANDERSON, K. V., AND M. R. WILLIAMSON. Visual pattern discrimination in cats after removal of the superior colliculus. *Psychon. Sci.* 24: 125–127, 1971.
9. ANDERSON, M. E., M. YOSHIDA, AND V. J. WILSON. Influence of superior colliculus on cat neck motoneurons. *J. Neurophysiol.* 34: 898–907, 1971.
10. ANDREW, R. J. Changes in visual responsiveness following intercollicular lesions and their effects on avoidance and attack. *Brain Behav. Evol.* 10: 400–424, 1974.
11. ANGAUT, P. The fastigio-tectal projections. An anatomical experimental study. *Brain Res.* 13: 186–189, 1969.
12. APTER, J. T. Projection of the retina on superior colliculus of cats. *J. Neurophysiol.* 8: 123–134, 1945.
13. APTER, J. T. Eye movements following strychninization of the superior colliculus of cats. *J. Neurophysiol.* 9: 73–86, 1946.
14. ASTRUC, J. Corticofugal connections of area 8 (frontal eye fields) in *Macaca mulatta. Brain Res.* 33: 241–256, 1971.
15. BAKER, R., M. GRESTY, AND A. BERTHOZ. Neuronal activity in the prepositus hypoglossi nucleus correlated with vertical and horizontal eye movements in the cat. *Brain Res.* 101: 366–371, 1976.
16. BARLOW, H. B., R. M. HILL, AND W. R. LEVICK. Retinal ganglion cells responding selectively to direction and speed of image motion in the rabbit. *J. Physiol. London* 173: 377–407, 1964.
17. BARNES, P. H., L. M. SMITH, AND R. M. LATTO. Orientation to

visual stimuli and the superior colliculus in the rat. *Q. J. Exp. Psychol.* 22: 239-247, 1970.

18. BENDER, M. B. (editor). *The Oculomotor System.* New York: Hoeber, 1964.

19. BENEVENTO, L. A., AND J. H. FALLON. The ascending projections of the superior colliculus in the rhesus monkey. *J. Comp. Neurol.* 169: 339-362, 1975.

20. BERLUCCHI, G., J. M. SPRAGUE, J. LEVY, AND A. C. DIBERARDINO. Pretectum and superior colliculus in visually guided behavior, and in flux and form discrimination in the cat. *J. Comp. Physiol. Psychol.* 78: 123-172, 1972.

21. BERMAN, N., AND M. CYNADER. Comparison of receptive-field organization of the superior colliculus in Siamese and normal cats. *J. Physiol. London* 224: 363-389, 1972.

22. BISTI, S., L. MAFFEI, AND M. PICCOLINO. Visuovestibular interactions in the cat superior colliculus. *J. Neurophysiol.* 37: 146-155, 1974.

23. BISTI, S., AND R. C. SIRETEANU. Sensitivity to spatial frequency and contrast of visual cells in the cat superior colliculus. *Vision Res.* 16: 247-251, 1976.

24. BIZZI, E. Discharge of frontal eye field neurons during saccadic and following eye movements in unanesthetized monkeys. *Exp. Brain Res.* 6: 69-80, 1968.

25. BIZZI, E., AND P. H. SCHILLER. Single unit activity in the frontal eye fields of unanesthetized monkeys during eye and head movement. *Exp. Brain Res.* 10: 151-158, 1970.

26. BLAKE, L. The effects of lesions of the superior colliculus on brightness and pattern discriminations in the cat. *J. Comp. Physiol. Psychol.* 52: 272-278, 1959.

27. BLUM, B., V. GODEL, S. GITTER, AND R. STEIN. Impulse propagation from photically discharged neurons in the visual system. *Pfluegers Arch.* 331: 38-43, 1972.

28. BOYCOTT, B. B., AND H. WÄSSLE. The morphological types of ganglion cells of the domestic cat's retina. *J. Physiol. London* 240: 397-419, 1974.

29. BURGI, S. Das Tectum opticum. Seine Verbindungen bei der Katze und seine Bedeutung beim Menschen. *Dtsch. Z. Nervenheilk.* 176: 701-729, 1957.

30. CASAGRANDE, V. A., AND I. DIAMOND. Ablation study of the superior colliculus in tree shrew (*Tupaia glis*). *J. Comp. Neurol.* 156: 207-238, 1974.

31. CHOW, K. L., H. M. LAWRENCE, AND P. D. SPEAR. Spreading of uncrossed retinal projection in superior colliculus of neonatally enucleated rabbits. *J. Comp. Neurol.* 151: 307-322, 1973.

32. CLELAND, B. G., AND W. R. LEVICK. Brisk and sluggish concentrically organized ganglion cells in the cat's retina. *J. Physiol. London* 240: 421-456, 1974.

33. COHEN, D. H. Visual intensity discrimination in pigeons following unilateral and bilateral tectal lesions. *J. Comp. Physiol. Psychol.* 63: 172-174, 1967.

34. COLLEWIJN, H. The optokinetic system of the rabbit. *Doc. Ophthalmol.* 30: 205-226, 1971.

35. COLLEWIJN, H. Direction-selective units in the rabbit's nucleus of the optic tract. *Brain Res.* 100: 489-508, 1975.

36. COLLEWIJN, H. Oculomotor areas in the rabbit's midbrain and pretectum. *J. Neurobiol.* 6: 3-22, 1975.

37. CRONLY-DILLON, J. R. Units sensitive to direction of movement in goldfish optic tectum. *Nature* 203: 214-215, 1964.

38. CYNADER, M., AND N. BERMAN. Receptive-field organization of monkey superior colliculus. *J. Neurophysiol.* 35: 187-201, 1972.

39. CYNADER, M., N. BERMAN, AND A. HEIN. Cats raised in a one-directional world: effects on receptive fields in visual cortex and superior colliculus. *Exp. Brain Res.* 22: 267-280, 1975.

40. CYNADER, M., C. BLAKEMORE, AND R. C. VAN SLUYTERS. Congruent binocular preferred directions in the superior colliculus of kittens reared with one eye rotated (Abstract). *Soc. Neurosci. Abstr.* 4: 623, 1978.

41. DeMONASTERIO, F. M., P. GOURAS, AND D. J. TOLHURST. Trichromatic colour opponency in ganglion cells of the rhesus monkey retina. *J. Physiol. London* 251: 197-216, 1975.

42. DENNY-BROWN, D. The midbrain and motor integration. *Proc. R. Soc. Med.* 55: 527-538, 1962.

43. DIXON, J., AND B. E. STEIN. Receptive field characteristics of visual cells in the superior colliculus of the golden hamster (Abstract). *Soc. Neurosci. Abstr.* 3: 558, 1977.

44. DRÄGER, U. C., AND D. H. HUBEL. Responses to visual stimulation and relationship between visual, auditory, and somatosensory inputs in mouse superior colliculus. *J. Neurophysiol.* 38: 690-713, 1975.

45. DRÄGER, U. C., AND D. H. HUBEL. Topography of visual and somatosensory projections to mouse superior colliculus. *J. Neurophysiol.* 39: 91-101, 1976.

46. EDWARDS, S. B. The commissural projection of the superior colliculus in the cat. *J. Comp. Neurol.* 173: 23-40, 1977.

47. EDWARDS, S. B., AND C. K. HENKEL. Superior colliculus connections with the extraocular motor nuclei in the cat. *J. Comp. Neurol.* 179: 451-468, 1978.

48. ENROTH-CUGELL, C., AND J. G. ROBSON. The contrast sensitivity of retinal ganglion cells of the cat. *J. Physiol. London* 187: 517-552, 1966.

49. EVARTS, E. V. Methods for recording individual neurons in moving animals. In: *Methods in Medical Research*, edited by R. F. Rushman. Chicago: Year Book Med., 1966, p. 241-250.

50. EWERT, J.-P. Der Einfluss von Zwischenhirndefekten auf die Visuomotorik im Beute- und Fluchtverhalten der Erdkröte (*Bufo bufo* L.). *Z. Vgl. Physiol.* 61: 41-70, 1968.

51. EWERT, J.-P. Neural mechanisms of prey-catching and avoidance behavior in the toad (*Bufo bufo* L.). *Brain Behav. Evol.* 3: 36-56, 1970.

52. EWERT, J.-P., AND H. W. BORCHERS. Reaktionscharakteristik von Neuronen aus dem Tectum opticum und Subtectum der Erdkröte (*Bufo bufo* L.). *Z. Vgl. Physiol.* 71: 165-189, 1970.

53. FELDON, S., P. FELDON, AND L. KRUGER. Topography of retinal projection upon the superior colliculus of the cat. *Vision Res.* 10: 135-143, 1970.

54. FINLAY, B. L. Neuronal Specificity and Plasticity in the Hamster Superior Colliculus: Electrophysiological Studies. Cambridge: Massachusetts Inst. of Technol., 1976. Ph.D. thesis.

55. FINLAY, B. L., P. H. SCHILLER, AND S. F. VOLMAN. Quantitative studies of single-cell properties in monkey striate cortex. IV. Corticotectal cells. *J. Neurophysiol.* 39: 1352-1361, 1976.

56. FISCHMAN, M. W., AND T. MEIKLE. Visual intensity discrimination in cats after serial tectal and cortical lesions. *J. Comp. Physiol. Psychol.* 59: 193-201, 1965.

57. FITE, K. V. Single-unit analysis of binocular neurons in the frog optic tectum. *Exp. Neurol.* 24: 475-486, 1969.

58. FLANDRIN, J. M., AND M. JEANNEROD. Developmental constraints of motion detection mechanisms in the kitten. *Perception* 6: 513-527, 1977.

59. FLANDRIN, J. M., H. KENNEDY, AND B. AMBLARD. Effects of stroboscopic rearing on the binocularity and directionality of cat superior colliculus neurons. *Brain Res.* 101: 576-581, 1976.

60. FROST, B. J., AND D. E. DiFRANCO. Motion characteristics of single units in the pigeon optic tectum. *Vision Res.* 16: 1229-1234, 1976.

61. FROST, B. J., AND S. C. P. WONG. The effect of relative motion on directionally specific pigeon tectal units (Abstract). *Soc. Neurosci. Abstr.* 3: 560, 1977.

62. FUKUDA, Y., AND J. STONE. Retinal distribution and central projections of Y-, X-, and W-cells of the cat's retina. *J. Neurophysiol.* 37: 749-772, 1974.

63. GAREY, L. J., E. G. JONES, AND T. P. S. POWELL. Interrelationship of striate and extrastriate cortex with the primary relay sites of the visual pathway. *J. Neurol. Neurosurg. Psychiatry* 31: 135-157, 1968.

64. GAREY, L. J., AND T. P. POWELL. The projection of the retina in the cat. *J. Anat.* 102: 189-222, 1968.

65. GAZE, R. M. Regeneration of the optic nerve in *Xenopus laevis*. *Q. J. Exp. Physiol. Cogn. Med. Sci.* 44: 290-308, 1959.

66. GILBERT, D. C., AND J. P. KELLY. The projections of cells in different layers of the cat's visual cortex. *J. Comp. Neurol.* 163: 81-106, 1975.

67. GLENDENNING, K. K., J. A. HALL, AND W. C. HALL. The connections of the pulvinar in a primate (*Galago senegalensis*) (Abstract). *Anat. Rec.* 172: 316, 1972.

68. GOLDBERG, M. E., AND R. H. WURTZ. Activity of superior colliculus in behaving monkey. I. Visual receptive fields of single neurons. *J. Neurophysiol.* 35: 542–559, 1972.

69. GOLDBERG, M. E., AND R. H. WURTZ. Activity of superior colliculus in behaving monkey. II. Effect of attention on neuronal responses. *J. Neurophysiol.* 35: 560–574, 1972.

70. GOODALE, M. A., N. P. FOREMAN, AND A. D. MILNER. Visual orientation in the rat: a dissociation of deficits following cortical and collicular lesions. *Exp. Brain Res.* 31: 445–457, 1978.

71. GOODALE, M. A., AND R. C. C. MURISON. The effects of lesions of the superior colliculus on locomotor orientation and the orienting reflex in the rat. *Brain Res.* 88: 243–261, 1975.

72. GORDON, B. Receptive fields in deep layers of cat superior colliculus. *J. Neurophysiol.* 36: 157–178, 1973.

73. GORDON, B., AND L. GUMMOW. Effects of extraocular muscle section on receptive fields in cat superior colliculus. *Vision Res.* 15: 1011–1019, 1975.

74. GORDON, B., AND J. PRESSON. Effects of alternating occlusion on receptive fields in cat superior colliculus. *J. Neurophysiol.* 40: 1406–1414, 1977.

75. GOURAS, P. Antidromic responses of orthodromically identified ganglion cells in the monkey retina. *J. Physiol. London* 204: 407–419, 1969.

75a. GRAFSTEIN B. Axonal transport: the intracellular traffic of the neuron. In: *Handbook of Physiology. The Nervous System*, edited by John M. Brookhart and Vernon B. Mountcastle. Bethesda, MD: Am. Physiol. Soc., 1977, sect. 1, vol I, pt. 1, chapt. 19, p. 691–717.

76. GRAHAM, J. An autoradiographic study of the efferent connections of the superior colliculus in the cat. *J. Comp. Neurol.* 173: 629–654, 1977.

77. GRANTYN, A. A., AND R. GRANTYN. Synaptic actions of tectofugal pathways on abducens motorneurons in the cat. *Brain Res.* 105: 269–285, 1976.

78. GRAYBIEL, A. M. Visuo-cerebellar and cerebello-visual connections involving the ventral lateral geniculate nucleus. *Exp. Brain Res.* 20: 303–306, 1974.

79. GRAYBIEL, A. M. Anatomical organization of retinotectal afferents in the cat: An autoradiographic study. *Brain Res.* 96: 1–23, 1975.

80. GRAYBIEL, A. M. Evidence for banding of the cat's ipsilateral retinotectal connection. *Brain Res.* 114: 318–327, 1976.

81. GRAYBIEL, A. M., AND E. A. HARTWIEG. Some afferent connections of the oculomotor complex in the cat: an experimental study with tracer techniques. *Brain Res.* 81: 543–551, 1974.

82. GRÜSSER-CORNEHLS, U. Response of movement-detecting neurons of the frog's retina to moving patterns under stroboscopic illumination. *Pfluegers Arch.* 303: 1–13, 1968.

83. GRÜSSER-CORNEHLS, U., O.-J. GRÜSSER, AND T. H. BULLOCK. Unit responses in the frog's tectum to moving and nonmoving visual stimuli. *Science* 141: 820–822, 1963.

84. GRÜSSER-CORNEHLS, U., AND W. HIMSTEDT. Responses of retinal and tectal neurons of the salamander. *Brain. Behav. Evol.* 7: 145–168, 1973.

84a. GUITTON, D., M. CROMMELINCK, AND A. ROUCOUX. Stimulation of the superior colliculus in the alert cat. I. Eye movements and neck EMG activity evoked when the head is restrained. *Exp. Brain Res.* 39: 63–73, 1980.

84b. HALLETT, P. E., AND A. D. LIGHTSTONE. Saccadic eye movements to flashed targets. *Vision Res.* 16: 107–114, 1976.

84c. HALLETT, P. E., AND A. D. LIGHTSTONE. Saccadic eye movements towards stimuli triggered by prior saccades. *Vision Res.* 16: 99–106, 1976.

85. HAMILTON, B. L. Projections of the nuclei of the periaqueductal gray matter in the cat. *J. Comp. Neurol.* 152: 45–58, 1973.

85a. HARRIS, L. R., The superior colliculus and movements of the head and eyes in cats. *J. Physiol. London* 300: 367–391, 1980.

86. HARTING, J. K. Descending pathways from the superior collic-

ulus: an autoradiographic analysis in the rhesus monkey. *J. Comp. Neurol.* 173: 583–612, 1977.

87. HARTING, J. K., AND R. W. GUILLERY. Organization of retinocollicular pathways in the cat. *J. Comp. Neurol.* 166: 133–143, 1976.

88. HARTING, J. K., W. C. HALL, I. T. DIAMOND, AND G. F. MARTIN. Anterograde degeneration study of the superior colliculus in *Tupaia glis*: evidence for a subdivision between superficial and deep layers. *J. Comp. Neurol.* 148: 361–386, 1973.

88a. HARTING, J. K., M. F. HUERTA, A. J. FRANKFURTER, N. L. STROMINGER, AND G. J. ROYCE. Ascending pathways from the monkey superior colliculus: an autoradiographic analysis. *J. Comp. Neurol.* 192: 853–882, 1980.

89. HARTLINE, P. H., M. S. LOOP, AND L. KASS. Merging of modalities in the optic tectum: infrared and visual integration in rattlesnakes (Abstract). *Soc. Neurosc. Abstr.* 3: 364, 1977.

90. HAYASHI, Y. Recurrent collateral inhibition of visual cortical cells projecting to superior colliculus in cats. *Vision Res.* 9: 1367–1380, 1969.

91. HAYASHI, Y., T. NAGATA, Y. TAMAKI, AND K. IWAMA. Binocular interaction in the superior colliculus of chronic cats. *Exp. Brain Res.* 18: 531–547, 1973.

92. HAYHOW, W. R., A. SEFTON, AND C. WEBB. Primary optic centers of the rat in relation to the terminal distribution of the crossed and uncrossed optic nerve fibers. *J. Comp. Neurol.* 118: 295–321, 1962.

93. HENN, V., AND B. COHEN. Quantitative analysis of activity in eye muscle motoneurons during saccadic eye movements and positions of fixation. *J. Neurophysiol.* 36: 115–126, 1973.

94. HESS, W. R., S. BURGI, AND V. BUCHER. Motorische Funktion des Tektal- und Tegmentalgebietes. *Monatsschr. Psychiatr. Neurol.* 112: 1–52, 1946.

95. HIGHSTEIN, S. M., K. MACKAWA, A. STEINACKER, AND B. COHEN. Synaptic input from the pontine reticular nuclei to abducens motoneurons and internuclear neurons in the cat. *Brain Res.* 112: 162–167, 1976.

96. HODOS, W., AND H. J. KARTEN. Visual intensity and pattern discrimination deficits after lesions of the optic lobe in pigeons. *Brain Behav. Evol.* 9: 165–194, 1974.

97. HOFFMANN, K.-P. The retinal input to the superior colliculus in the cat. *Invest. Ophthalmol.* 11: 467–473, 1972.

98. HOFFMANN, K.-P. Conduction velocity in pathways from retina to superior colliculus in the cat: a correlation with receptive-field properties. *J. Neurophysiol.* 36: 409–424, 1973.

99. HOFFMANN, K.-P., AND B. DREHER. The spatial organization of the excitatory region of receptive fields in the cat's superior colliculus. *Exp. Brain Res.* 16: 354–370, 1973.

100. HOFFMANN, K.-P., AND S. M. SHERMAN. Effects of early monocular deprivation on visual input to cat superior colliculus. *J. Neurophysiol.* 37: 1276–1286, 1974.

101. HOFFMANN, K.-P., AND M. STRASCHILL. Influences of corticotectal and intertectal connections on visual responses in the cat's superior colliculus. *Exp. Brain Res.* 12: 120–131, 1971.

102. HORN, G., AND R. M. HILL. Responsiveness to sensory stimulation of units in the superior colliculus and subjacent tectotegmental regions of the rabbit. *Exp. Neurol.* 14: 199–223, 1966.

103. HUBEL, D. H. Cortical unit responses to visual stimuli in nonanesthetized cats. *Am. J. Ophthalmol.* 46: 110–121, 1958.

104. HUBEL, D. H., S. LEVAY, AND T. N. WIESEL. Mode of termination of retinotectal fibers in macaque monkey: an autoradiographic study. *Brain Res.* 96: 25–40, 1975.

105. HUBEL, D. H., AND T. N. WIESEL. Receptive fields, binocular interaction and functional architecture in the cat's visual cortex. *J. Physiol. London* 160: 106–154, 1962.

106. HUBEL, D. H., AND T. N. WIESEL. Binocular interaction in striate cortex of kittens reared with artificial squint. *J. Neurophysiol.* 28: 1041–1059, 1965.

107. HUBEL, D. H., AND T. N. WIESEL. The period of susceptibility to the physiological effects of unilateral eye closure in kittens. *J. Physiol. London* 206: 419–436, 1970.

108. HUGHES, A. Topographical relationship between the anatomy

and physiology of the rabbit visual system. *Doc. Ophthalmol.* 30: 33–159, 1971.

109. HUMPHREY, N. K. The receptive fields of visual units in the superior colliculus of the rat. *J. Physiol. London* 189: 86P–88P, 1967.

110. HUMPHREY, N. K. Responses to visual stimuli of units in the superior colliculus of rats and monkeys. *Exp. Neurol.* 20: 312–340, 1968.

111. HUNT, R. K., AND M. JACOBSON. Neuronal specificity revisited. *Curr. Top. Dev. Biol.* 8: 203–259, 1974.

112. INGLE, D. Visual releasers of prey-catching behavior in frogs and toads. *Brain Behav. Evol.* 1: 500–518, 1968.

113. INGLE, D. Visuomotor functions of the frog optic tectum. *Brain Behav. Evol.* 3: 57–71, 1970.

114. INGLE, D. Prey-catching behavior of Anurans toward moving and stationary objects. *Vision Res.* 11 (*Suppl.* 3): 447–456, 1971.

115. INGLE, D. Disinhibition of tectal neurons by pretectal lesions in the frog. *Science* 180: 422–424, 1973.

116. INGLE, D. Evolutionary perspectives on the function of the optic tectum. *Brain Behav. Evol.* 8: 211–237, 1973.

117. INGLE, D., AND J. M. SPRAGUE. Sensorimotor function of the midbrain tectum. *Neurosci. Res. Program Bull.* 13: 169–288, 1975.

118. ITO, M., T. SHIDA, N. YAGI, AND M. YAMAMOTO. Visual influence on rabbit horizontal vestibulo-ocular reflex presumably effected via the cerebellar flocculus. *Brain Res.* 65: 170–174, 1974.

119. JACOBS, G. H., AND R. L. YOLTON. Visual sensitivity and color vision in ground squirrels. *Vision Res.* 11: 511–537, 1971.

120. JACOBSON, M., AND R. M. GAZE. Types of visual response from single units in optic tectum and optic nerve of goldfish. *Q. J. Exp. Physiol. Cogn. Med. Sci.* 49: 199–209, 1964.

121. JARVIS, C. D. Visual discrimination and spatial localization deficits after lesions of the tectofugal pathway in pigeons. *Brain Behav. Evol.* 9: 195–228, 1974.

122. JASSIK-GERSCHENFELD, D., AND J. GUICHARD. Visual receptive fields of single cells in pigeon's optic tectum. *Brain Res.* 40: 303–317, 1972.

123. KADOYA, S., L. R. WOLIN, AND L. C. MASSOPUST, JR. Collicular unit responses to monochromatic stimulation in squirrel monkey. *Brain Res.* 32: 251–254, 1971.

124. KADOYA, S., L. R. WOLIN, AND L. C. MASSOPUST, JR. Photically evoked unit activity in the tectum opticum of the squirrel monkey. *J. Comp. Neurol.* 142: 495–508, 1971.

125. KANASEKI, T., AND J. M. SPRAGUE. Anatomical organization of pretectal nuclei and tectal laminae in the cat. *J. Comp. Neurol.* 158: 319–337, 1974.

126. KAWAMURA, K., A. BRODAL, AND G. HODDEVIK. The projection of the superior colliculus onto the reticular formation of the brain stem. An experimental anatomical study in the cat. *Exp. Brain Res.* 19: 1–19, 1974.

127. KAWAMURA, S., AND E. KOBAYASHI. Identification of laminar origin of some tecto-thalamic fibers in the cat. *Brain Res.* 91: 281–285, 1975.

128. KAWAMURA, S., J. M. SPRAGUE, AND K. NIIMI. Corticofugal projections from the visual cortices to the thalamus, pretectum and superior colliculus in the cat. *J. Comp. Neurol.* 158: 339–362, 1974.

129. KEATING, E. G. Impaired orientation after primate tectal lesions. *Brain Res.* 67: 538–541, 1974.

130. KEATING, M. J. The formation of visual neuronal connections in an appraisal of the present status of the theory of "neuronal specificity". In: *Studies in the Development of Behavior and the Nervous System. Neural and Behavioral Specificity,* edited by G. Gottlieb. New York: Academic, 1976, vol. 3, p. 59–110.

131. KELLER, E. L. Colliculoreticular organization in the oculomotor system. In: *Progress in Brain Research. Reflex Control of Posture and Movement,* edited by R. Granit and O. Pompeiano. Amsterdam: Elsevier, 1979, vol. 50, p. 725–734.

132. KELLY, J. P., AND C. D. GILBERT. The projections of different

morphological types of ganglion cells in the cat retina. *J. Comp. Neurol.* 163: 65–80, 1975.

133. KRUGER, L. The topography of the visual projection to the mesencephalon: a comparative study. *Brain Behav. Evol.* 3: 169–177, 1970.

134. KURTZ, D., AND C. M. BUTTER. Impairments in visual discrimination performance and gaze shifts in monkeys with superior colliculus lesions. *Brain Res.* 196: 109–124, 1980.

135. KUYPERS, H. G. J. M., AND D. G. LAWRENCE. Cortical projections to the red nucleus and the brain stem in the rhesus monkey. *Brain Res.* 4: 151–188, 1967.

136. LANE, R. H., J. M. ALLMAN, J. H. KAAS, AND F. M. MIEZIN. The visuotopic organization of the superior colliculus of the owl monkey (*Aotus trivirgatus*) and the bush baby (*Galago senegalensis*) *Brain Res.* 60: 335–349, 1973.

137. LANGER, T. P., AND R. D. LUND. The upper layers of the superior colliculus of the rat: a Golgi study. *J. Comp. Neurol.* 158: 405–436, 1974.

138. LATIES, A. M., AND J. M. SPRAGUE. The projection of the optic fibers to the visual centers in the cat. *J. Comp. Neurol.* 127: 35–70, 1966.

139. LATTO, R., AND A. COWEY. Fixation changes after frontal eye-field lesions in monkeys. *Brain Res.* 30: 25–36, 1971.

140. LATTO, R., AND A. COWEY. Visual field defects after frontal eye-field lesions in monkeys. *Brain Res.* 30: 1–24, 1971.

141. LEE, K. J., AND T. A. WOOLSEY. A proportional relationship between peripheral innervation density and cortical neuron number in the somatosensory system of the mouse. *Brain Res.* 99: 349–353, 1975.

142. LeVAY, S., M. P. STRYKER, AND C. J. SHATZ. Postnatal development of ocular dominance columns in layer IV of the cat's visual cortex. *Soc. Neurosci. Abstr.* 3: 567, 1977.

143. LUND, J. S., R. D. LUND, A. E. HENDRICKSON, A. H. BUNT, AND A. F. FUCHS. The origin of efferent pathways from the primary visual cortex area 17 of the macaque monkey as shown by retrograde transport of horseradish peroxidase. *J. Comp. Neurol.* 164: 287–304, 1975.

144. LUND, R. D. Synaptic patterns of the superficial layers of the superior colliculus of the rat. *J. Comp. Neurol.* 135: 179–208, 1969.

145. LUND, R. D. Synaptic patterns in the superficial layers of the superior colliculus of the monkey, *Macaca mulatta. Exp. Brain Res.* 15: 194–211, 1972.

146. MacKINNON, D. A., C. G. GROSS, AND D. B. BENDER. A visual deficit after superior colliculus lesions in monkeys. *Acta Neurobiol. Exp.* 36: 169–180, 1976.

147. MAGALHAES-CASTRO, H. H., L. A. MURATA, AND B. MAGALHAES-CASTRO. Cat retinal ganglion cells projecting to superior colliculus as shown by horseradish peroxidase method. *Exp. Brain Res.* 25: 541–549, 1976.

148. MALPELI, J. G., AND P. H. SCHILLER. Visuo-motor function in monkeys with visual cortex ablation and with crossed corticotectal ablations (Abstract). *Soc. Neurosci. Abstr.* 1: 72, 1975.

149. MALPELI, J. G., AND P. H. SCHILLER. Lack of blue OFF-center cells in the visual system of the monkey. *Brain Res.* 141: 385–389, 1978.

150. MANDL, G. The influence of visual pattern combinations on responses of movement sensitive cells in cat's superior colliculus. *Brain Res.* 75: 215–240, 1974.

151. MARROCCO, R. T., AND R. H. LI. Monkey superior colliculus: properties of single cells and their afferent inputs. *J. Neurophysiol.* 40: 844–860, 1977.

152. MASLAND, R. H., K. L. CHOW, AND D. L. STEWART. Receptive-field characteristics of superior colliculus neurons in the rabbit. *J. Neurophysiol.* 34: 148–156, 1971.

152a. MAYS, L. W., AND D. L. SPARKS. Saccades are spatially, not retinocentrically, coded. *Science* 208: 1163–1165, 1980.

153. MAYS, L. E., AND D. L. SPARKS. Dissociation of visual and saccade-related responses in superior colliculus neurons. *J. Neurophysiol.* 43: 207–232, 1980.

154. McILWAIN, J. T. Retinotopic fidelity of striate cortex-superior

colliculus interactions in the cat. *J. Neurophysiol.* 36: 702–710, 1973.

155. McILWAIN, J. T. Topographic relations in projection from striate cortex to superior colliculus of the cat. *J. Neurophysiol.* 36: 690–701, 1973.

156. McILWAIN, J. T. Visual receptive fields and their images in superior colliculus of cat. *J. Neurophysiol.* 38: 219–230, 1975.

157. McILWAIN, J. T., AND P. BUSER. Receptive fields of single cells in cat's superior colliculus. *Exp. Brain Res.* 5: 314–325, 1968.

158. McILWAIN, J. T., AND H. L. FIELDS. Interactions of cortical and retinal projections on single neurons of the cat's superior colliculus. *J. Neurophysiol.* 34: 763–772, 1971.

159. MEHLER, W. R. Some neurological species differences—"A Posteriori." *Ann. NY Acad. Sci.* 167: 424–468, 1969. (*Comparative and Evolutionary Aspects of the Vertebrate Central Nervous System.* edited by J. N. Petras and C. R. Noback.)

160. MEIKLE, T. H., JR., AND J. M. SPRAGUE. The neural organization of the visual pathways in the cat. *Int. Rev. Neurobiol.* 6: 148–189, 1964.

161. MELLO, N. K. The effects of unilateral lesions of the optic tectum on interhemispheric transfer of monocularly trained color and pattern discriminations in the pigeon. *Physiol. Behav.* 3: 725–734, 1968.

162. MICHAEL, C. R. Integration of retinal and cortical information in the superior colliculus of the ground squirrel. *Brain Behav. Evol.* 3: 205–209, 1970.

163. MICHAEL, C. R. Visual response properties and functional organization of cells in the superior colliculus of the ground squirrel. *Vision Res.* 11 (*Suppl. 3*): 299–308, 1971.

164. MICHAEL, C. R. Functional organization of cells in superior colliculus of the ground squirrel. *J. Neurophysiol.* 35: 833–846, 1972.

165. MICHAEL, C. R. Visual receptive fields of single neurons in superior colliculus of the ground squirrel. *J. Neurophysiol.* 35: 815–832, 1972.

166. MILES, F. A., AND J. H. FULLER. Adaptive plasticity in the vestibulo-ocular responses of the rhesus monkey. *Brain Res.* 80: 512–516, 1974.

167. MIZE, R. R., AND E. H. MURPHY. Alterations in receptive field properties of superior colliculus cells produced by visual cortex ablation in infant and adult cats. *J. Comp. Neurol.* 168: 393–424, 1976.

168. MOHLER, C. W., M. E. GOLDBERG, AND R. H. WURTZ. Visual receptive fields of frontal eye field neurons. *Brain Res.* 61: 385–389, 1973.

169. MOHLER, C. W., AND R. H. WURTZ. Organization of monkey superior colliculus; intermediate layer cells discharging before eye movements. *J. Neurophysiol.* 39: 722–744, 1976.

170. MOHLER, C. W., AND R. H. WURTZ. Role of striate cortex and superior colliculus in visual guidance of saccadic eye movements in monkeys. *J. Neurophysiol.* 40: 74–94, 1977.

171. MOORE, R. Y., AND J. M. GOLDBERG. Ascending projections of the inferior colliculus in the cat. *J. Comp. Neurol.* 121: 109–136, 1963.

172. NAUTA, W. J. H., AND H. G. J. M. KUYPERS. Some ascending pathways in the brainstem reticular formation of the cat. In: *Reticular Formation of the Brain,* edited by H. H. Jasper, L. D. Proctor, R. S. Knighton, W. C. Noshay, and R. T. Costello. Boston: Little, Brown, 1958, p. 3–30.

173. NORTON, T. T. Receptive-field properties of superior colliculus cells and development of visual behavior in kittens. *J. Neurophysiol.* 37: 674–690, 1974.

174. OYSTER, C. W. The analysis of image motion by the rabbit retina. *J. Physiol. London* 199: 613–635, 1968.

175. OYSTER, C. W., AND H. B. BARLOW. Direction-selective units in rabbit retina: distribution of preferred directions. *Science* 155: 841–842, 1966.

176. OYSTER, C. W., E. TAKAHISHI, AND J. COLLEWIJN. Direction-selective retinal ganglion cells and control of optokinetic nystagmus in the rabbit. *Vision Res.* 12: 183–193, 1972.

177. PALMER, L. A., AND A. C. ROSENQUIST. Visual receptive fields of single striate cortical units projecting to the superior collic-

ulus in the cat. *Brain Res.* 67: 27–42, 1974.

178. PASIK, T., P. PASIK, AND M. B. BENDER. The superior colliculi and eye movements. *Arch. Neurol. Chicago* 15: 420–436, 1966.

179. PETERSON, B. W., M. E. ANDERSON, AND M. FILION. Responses of ponto-medullary reticular neurons to cortical, tectal and cutaneous stimuli. *Exp. Brain Res.* 21: 19–44, 1974.

180. PETERSON, B. W., M. E. ANDERSON, M. FILION, AND V. J. WILSON. Responses of reticulospinal neurons to stimulation of the superior colliculus. *Brain Res.* 33: 495–498, 1971.

181. POWELL, E. W., AND J. B. HATTON. Projections of the inferior colliculus in the cat. *J. Comp. Neurol.* 136: 183–192, 1969.

182. PRECHT, W., P. C. SCHWINDT, AND P. C. MAGHERINI. Tectal influences on cat ocular motoneurons. *Brain Res.* 82: 27–40, 1974.

183. RACZKOWSKI, D., AND I. T. DIAMOND. Cells of origin of several efferent pathways from the superior colliculus in *Galago senegalensis. Brain Res.* 146: 351–357, 1978.

184. RAYBOURN, M. S., AND E. L., KELLER. Colliculoreticular organization in primate oculomotor system. *J. Neurophysiol.* 40: 861–878, 1977.

185. RINVIK, E., I. GROFOVA, AND O. P. OTTERSEN. Demonstration of nigrotectal and nigroreticular projections in the cat by axonal transport of proteins. *Brain Res.* 112: 388–394, 1976.

186. RIOCH, D. McK. Studies on the diencephalon of carnivora. I. Nuclear configuration of the thalamus, epithalamus and hypothalamus of dog and cat. *J. Comp. Neurol.* 49: 1–120, 1929.

187. ROBINSON, D. A. A method of measuring eye movement using a scleral search coil in a magnetic field. *IEEE Trans. Bio-Med. Electron.* 10: 137–145, 1963.

188. ROBINSON, D. A. Oculomotor unit behavior in the monkey. *J. Neurophysiol.* 33: 393–404, 1970.

189. ROBINSON, D. A. Eye movements by collicular stimulation in the alert monkey. *Vision Res.* 12: 1795–1808, 1972.

190. ROBINSON, D. A. The effect of cerebellectomy on the cat's vestibulo-ocular integrator. *Brain Res.* 71: 195–207, 1974.

191. ROBINSON, D. A. Adaptive gain control of vestibulo-ocular reflex by the cerebellum. *J. Neurophysiol.* 39: 954–969, 1976.

192. ROBINSON, D. A., Control of eye movements. In: *Handbook of Physiology. The Nervous System,* edited by J. M. Brookhart and V. B. Mountcastle. Bethesda, MD: Am. Physiol. Soc., 1981, sect. 1, vol. II, chapt. 28, p. 1275–1320.

193. ROBINSON, D. A., AND A. F. FUCHS. Eye movements evoked by stimulation of frontal eye fields. *J. Neurophysiol.* 32: 637–648, 1969.

194. ROBINSON, D. L., AND C. D. JARVIS. Superior colliculus neurons studied during head and eye movements of the behaving monkey. *J. Neurophysiol.* 37: 533–540, 1974.

195. ROBSON, J. A., AND W. C. HALL. Projections from the superior colliculus to the dorsal lateral geniculate nucleus of the grey squirrel (*Sciurus carolinensis*). *Brain Res.* 113: 379–385, 1976.

196. RON, S., AND D. A. ROBINSON. Eye movements evoked by cerebellar stimulation in the alert monkey. *J. Neurophysiol.* 36: 1004–1022, 1973.

197. ROSENQUIST, A. C., AND L. A. PALMER. Visual receptive field properties of cells of superior colliculus after cortical lesions in the cat. *Exp. Neurol.* 33: 629–652, 1971.

198. ROUCOUX, A., AND M. CROMMELINCK. Eye movements evoked by superior colliculus stimulation in the alert cat. *Brain Res.* 106: 349–363, 1976.

198a.ROUCOUX, A., D. GUITTON AND M. CROMMELINCK. Stimulation of the superior colliculus in the alert cat. II. Eye and head movements evoked when the head is unrestrained. *Exp. Brain Res.* 39: 74–85, 1980.

199. SCHAEFER, K.-P. Mikroableitungen im Tectum opticum des frei beweglichen Kaninchens. Ein experimenteller Beitrag zum Problem des Bewegungssehens. *Arch. Psychiatr. Nervenkr.* 208: 120–146, 1966.

200. SCHAEFER, K.-P. Unit analysis and electrical stimulation in the optic tectum of rabbits and cats. *Brain Behav. Evol.* 3: 222–240, 1970.

201. SCHILLER, P. H. The discharge characteristics of single units in the oculomotor and abducens nuclei of the unanesthetized

monkey. *Exp. Brain Res.* 10: 347–362, 1970.

202. SCHILLER, P. H. The effect of superior colliculus ablation on saccades elicited by cortical stimulation. *Brain Res.* 122: 154–156, 1977.

203. SCHILLER, P. H., AND F. KOERNER. Discharge characteristics of single units in the superior colliculus of the alert rhesus monkey. *J. Neurophysiol.* 34: 920–936, 1971.

204. SCHILLER, P. H., AND J. MALPELI. Properties and tectal projections of monkey retinal ganglion cells. *J. Neurophysiol.* 40: 428–445, 1977.

205. SCHILLER, P. H., J. G. MALPELI, AND S. J. SCHEIN. Composition of the geniculostriate input to superior colliculus of the rhesus monkey. *J. Neurophysiol.* 42: 1124–1133, 1979.

206. SCHILLER, P. H., AND M. STRYKER. Single-unit recording and stimulation in superior colliculus of the alert rhesus monkey. *J. Neurophysiol.* 35: 915–924, 1972.

207. SCHILLER, P. H., M. STRYKER, M. CYNADER, AND N. BERMAN. Response characteristics of single cells in the monkey superior colliculus following ablation or cooling of visual cortex. *J. Neurophysiol.* 37: 181–194, 1974.

208. SCHILLER, P. H., S. TRUE, AND J. CONWAY. The effects of frontal eye field and superior colliculus ablations on visually triggered eye movements. *Science* 206: 590–592, 1979.

209. SCHNEIDER, G. E. Contrasting visuomotor functions of tectum and cortex in the golden hamster. *Psychol. Forsch.* 31: 52–62, 1967.

210. SCHNEIDER, G. E. Mechanisms of functional recovery following lesions of visual cortex or superior colliculus in neonate and adult hamsters. *Brain Behav. Evol.* 3: 295–323, 1970.

211. SCHNEIDER, G. E. Competition for terminal space in formation of abnormal retinotectal connections, and a functional consequence (Abstract). *Anat. Rec.* 169: 420, 1971.

212. SCHNEIDER, G. E. Development and regeneration in the mammalian visual system. *Neurosci. Res. Program Bull.* 10: 287–290, 1972. Also in: *Neurosciences Research Symposium Summaries*, edited by F. O. Schmitt. Cambridge, MA: MIT Press, 1973, vol. 7, p. 287–290.

213. SCHNEIDER, G. E. Early lesions of superior colliculus: factors affecting the formation of abnormal retinal projections. *Brain Behav. Evol.* 8: 73–109, 1973.

214. SCHNEIDER, G. E., AND W. J. H. NAUTA. Formation of anomalous retinal projections after removal of the optic tectum in the neonate hamster (Abstract). *Anat. Rec.* 163: 258, 1969.

215. SHERK, H. The Circuit Formed by the Cat's Parabigeminal Nucleus and Superior Colliculus. Cambridge: Massachusetts Inst. of Technol., 1978. Ph.D. thesis.

216. SHERMAN, S. M. Visual field defects in monocularly and binocularly deprived cats. *Brain Res.* 49: 25–45, 1973.

217. SHERMAN, S. M. Visual fields of cats with cortical and tectal lesions. *Science* 185: 355–357, 1974.

218. SPARKS, D. L. Response properties of eye-movement related neurons in monkey superior colliculus. *Brain Res.* 90: 147–152, 1975.

219. SPARKS, D. L. Functional properties of neurons in the monkey superior colliculus: coupling of neuronal activity and saccade onset. *Brain Res.* 156: 1–16, 1978.

220. SPARKS, D. L., R. HOLLAND, AND B. L. GUTHRIE. Size and distribution of movement fields in the monkey superior colliculus. *Brain Res.* 113: 21–34, 1976.

221. SPARKS, D. L., AND J. G. POLLACK. The neural control of saccadic eye movements: the role of the superior colliculus. In: *Eye Movements*, edited by F. J. Bajandas and B. A. Brooks. New York: Plenum, 1977, p. 179–219.

222. SPERRY, R. W. Reestablishment of visuomotor coordination by optic nerve regeneration (Abstract). *Anat. Rec.* 84: 470, 1942.

223. SPERRY, R. W. Visuomotor coordination in the newt (*Triturus viridescens*) after regeneration of the optic nerve. *J. Comp. Neurol.* 79: 33–55, 1943.

224. SPERRY, R. W. Optic nerve regeneration with return of vision in anurans. *J. Neurophysiol.* 7: 57–69, 1944.

225. SPERRY, R. W. Patterning of central synapses in regeneration

of the optic nerve in teleosts. *Physiol. Zoology* 21: 351–361, 1948.

226. SPERRY, R. W. Mechanisms of neural maturation. In: *Handbook of Experimental Psychology*, edited by S. S. Stevens. New York: Wiley, 1951, p. 236–280.

227. SPERRY, R. W. Chemoaffinity in the orderly growth of nerve fiber patterns and connections. *Proc. Natl. Acad. Sci. USA* 50: 703–710, 1963.

228. SPRAGUE, J. M. Interaction of cortex and superior colliculus in mediation of visually guided behavior in the cat. *Science* 153: 1544–1547, 1966.

229. SPRAGUE, J. M. The superior colliculus and pretectum in visual behavior. *Invest. Ophthalmol.* 11: 473–482, 1972.

230. SPRAGUE, J. M., G. BERLUCCHI, AND A. DIBERARDINO. The superior colliculus and pretectum in visually guided behavior and visual discrimination in the cat. *Brain Behav. Evol.* 3: 285–294, 1970.

231. SPRAGUE, J. M., G. BERLUCCHI, AND G. RIZZOLATTI. The role of the superior colliculus and pretectum in vision and visually guided behavior. In: *Handbook of Sensory Physiology. Central Processing of Vision Information. Visual Centers in the Brain*, edited by R. Jung. New York: Springer-Verlag, 1973, vol. 7, pt. 3B, p. 27–201.

232. SPRAGUE, J. M., M. LEVITT, K. ROBSON, C. M. LIU, E. STELLAR, AND W. W. CHAMBERS. A neuroanatomical and behavioral analysis of the syndromes resulting from midbrain lemniscal and reticular lesions in the cat. *Arch. Ital. Biol.* 101: 225–295, 1963.

233. SPRAGUE, J. M., AND T. MEIKLE. The role of the superior colliculus in visually guided behavior. *Exp. Neurol.* 11: 115–146, 1965.

234. STEIN, B. E. Nonequivalent visual, auditory, and somatic corticotectal influences in cat. *J. Neurophysiol.* 41: 55–64, 1978.

235. STEIN, B. E., AND M. O. ARIGBEDE. Unimodal and multimodal response properties of neurons in the cat's superior colliculus. *Exp. Neurol.* 36: 179–196, 1972.

236. STEIN, B. E., S. J. GOLDBERG, AND H. P. CLAMANN. The control of eye movements by the superior colliculus in the alert cat. *Brain Res.* 118: 469–474, 1976.

237. STEIN, B. E., E. LABOS, AND L. KRUGER. Determinants of response latency in neurons of superior colliculus in kittens. *J. Neurophysiol.* 36: 680–689, 1973.

238. STEIN, B. E., E. LABOS, AND L. KRUGER. Long-lasting discharge properties of neurons in kitten midbrain. *Vision Res.* 13: 2615–2619, 1973.

239. STEIN, B. E., E. LABOS, AND L. KRUGER. Sequence of changes in properties of neurons of superior colliculus of the kitten during maturation. *J. Neurophysiol.* 36: 667–679, 1973.

240. STEIN, B. E., B. MAGALHÃES-CASTRO, AND L. KRUGER. Relationship between visual and tactile representations in cat superior colliculus. *J. Neurophysiol.* 39: 401–419, 1976.

241. STERLING, P. Receptive fields and synaptic organization of the superficial gray layer of the cat superior colliculus. *Vision Res.* 11: (Suppl. 3) 309–328, 1971.

242. STERLING, P. Quantitative mapping with the electron microscope: retinal terminals in superior colliculus. *Brain Res.* 54: 347–354, 1973.

243. STERLING, P., AND B. G. WICKELGREN. Visual receptive fields in the superior colliculus of the cat. *J. Neurophysiol.* 32: 1–15, 1969.

244. STERLING, P., AND B. G. WICKELGREN. Function of the projection from the visual cortex to the superior colliculus. *Brain Behav. Evol.* 3: 210–218, 1970.

245. STEWART, D. L., D. BIRT, AND L. C. TOWNS. Visual receptive-field characteristics of superior colliculus neurons after cortical lesions in the rabbit. *Vision Res.* 13: 1965–1977, 1973.

246. STONE, J., AND Y. FUKUDA. The naso-temporal division of the cat's retina re-examined in terms of Y-, X- and W-cells. *J. Comp. Neurol.* 155: 377–394, 1974.

247. STONE, J., AND Y. FUKUDA. Properties of the cat retinal ganglion cells: a comparison of W-cells with X- and Y-cells. *J. Neurophysiol.* 37: 722–748, 1974.

248. STONEY, S. D., JR., W. D. THOMPSON, AND H. ASANUMA. Excitation of pyramidal tract cells by intracortical microstimulation: effective extent of stimulating current. *J. Neurophysiol.* 31: 659–669, 1968.

249. STRASCHILL, M., AND K.-P. HOFFMANN. Relationship between localization and functional properties of movement-sensitive neurons of the cat's tectum opticum. *Brain Res.* 8: 382–385, 1968.

250. STRASCHILL, M., AND K.-P. HOFFMANN. Functional aspects of localization in the cat's tectum opticum. *Brain Res.* 13: 274–283, 1969.

251. STRASCHILL, M., AND K.-P. HOFFMANN. Activity of movement sensitive neurons of the cat's tectum opticum during spontaneous eye movements. *Exp. Brain Res.* 11: 318–326, 1970.

252. STRASCHILL, M., AND P. REIGER. Optomotor integration in the colliculus of the cat. In: *Cerebral Control of Eye Movement and Motion Perception*, edited by J. Dichgans and E. Bizzi. Basel: Karger, 1972. p. 130–138.

253. STRASCHILL, M., AND P. REIGER. Eye movements evoked by local stimulation of the cat's superior colliculus. *Brain Res.* 59: 211–227, 1973.

254. STRASCHILL, M., AND F. SCHICK. Discharges of superior colliculus neurons during head and eye movements of the alert cat. *Exp. Brain Res.* 27: 131–141, 1977.

255. STRYKER, M. P., AND P. H. SCHILLER. Eye and head movements evoked by electrical stimulation of monkey superior colliculus. *Exp. Brain Res.* 23: 103–112, 1975.

256. SYKA, J., AND T. RADIL-WEISS. Electrical stimulation of the tectum in freely moving cats. *Brain Res.* 28: 567–572, 1971.

257. SZÉKELY, G., G. SÉTÁLÓ, AND G. LÁZÁR. Fine structure of the frog's optic tectum: optic fibre termination layers. *J. Hirnforsch* 14: 189–225, 1973.

258. TERASHIMA, S., AND R. C. GORIS. Tectal organization of pit viper infrared reception. *Brain Res.* 83: 490–494, 1975.

259. TIAO, Y.-C., AND C. BLAKEMORE. Functional organization in the superior colliculus of the golden hamster. *J. Comp. Neurol.* 168: 483–504, 1976.

260. TOYAMA, K., K. MATSUNAMI, AND T. OHNO. Antidromic identification of association, commissural and corticofugal efferent cells in cat visual cortex. *Brain Res.* 14: 513–517, 1969.

261. UPDYKE, B. V. Characteristics of unit responses in superior colliculus of the *Cebus* monkey. *J. Neurophysiol.* 37: 896–909, 1974.

262. VICTOROV, I. V. Neuronal structure of superior colliculus in the cat. *Arch. Anat.* 2: 45–55, 1968.

263. WARTZOK, D., AND W. B. MARKS. Directionally selective visual units recorded in optic tectum of the goldfish. *J. Neurophysiol.* 36: 588–604, 1973.

264. WÄSSLE, H., W. R. LEVICK, AND B. CLELAND. The distribution of the alpha type of ganglion cells in the cat's retina. *J. Comp. Neurol.* 159: 419–438, 1975.

265. WESTHEIMER, G. Mechanism of saccadic eye movements. *AMA Arch. Ophthalmol.* 52: 710–724, 1954.

266. WESTHEIMER, G., AND S. M. BLAIR. Synkinese der Augen- und Kopfbewegungen bei Hirnstammreizungen am wachen Macacus-Affen. *Exp. Brain Res.* 24: 89–95, 1975.

267. WICKELGREN, B. G., AND P. STERLING. Influence of visual cortex on receptive fields in superior colliculus of the cat. *J. Neurophysiol.* 32: 16–23, 1969.

268. WICKELGREN-GORDON, B. Some effects of visual deprivation on the cat superior colliculus. *Invest. Ophthalmol.* 11: 460–466, 1972.

269. WIESEL, T. N., AND D. H. HUBEL. Single-cell responses in striate cortex of kittens deprived of vision in one eye. *J. Neurophysiol.* 26: 1003–1017, 1963.

270. WIESEL, T. N., AND D. H. HUBEL. Comparison of the effects of unilateral and bilateral eye closure on cortical unit responses in kittens. *J. Neurophysiol.* 28: 1029–1040, 1965.

271. WILSON, M. E., AND M. J. TOYNE. Retino-tectal and cortico-tectal projections in *Macaca mulatta*. *Brain Res.* 24: 395–406, 1970.

272. WOLIN, L. R., P. MASSOPUST, JR., AND J. MEDER. Differential color responses from the superior colliculi of squirrel monkeys. *Vision Res.* 6: 637–644, 1966.

273. WURTZ, R. H. Visual receptive fields of striate cortex neurons in awake monkeys. *J. Neurophysiol.* 32: 727–742, 1969.

274. WURTZ, R. H., AND M. E. GOLDBERG. Activity of superior colliculus in behaving monkey. III. Cells discharging before eye movements. *J. Neurophysiol.* 35: 575–586, 1972.

275. WURTZ, R. H., AND M. E. GOLDBERG. Activity of superior colliculus in behaving monkey. IV. Effects of lesions on eye movement. *J. Neurophysiol.* 35: 587–596, 1972.

276. WURTZ, R. H., AND C. W. MOHLER. Enhancement of visual responses in monkey striate cortex and frontal eye fields. *J. Neurophysiol.* 39: 766–772, 1976.

277. WURTZ, R. H., AND C. W. MOHLER. Organization of monkey superior colliculus: enhanced visual response of superficial layer cells. *J. Neurophysiol.* 39: 745–765, 1976.

CHAPTER 12

Postnatal development of function in the mammalian visual system

DONALD E. MITCHELL | *Department of Psychology, Dalhousie University, Halifax, Nova Scotia, Canada*

BRIAN TIMNEY | *Department of Psychology, University of Western Ontario, London, Ontario, Canada*

CHAPTER CONTENTS

THE ROLE THAT EARLY VISUAL EXPERIENCE plays in determining various visual capacities has been debated in many forms for more than three centuries. John Locke was probably the first person to make the issue explicit. In his *An Essay Concerning Human Understanding* (1690) he considered a question posed in a letter from his friend William Molyneux, a Dublin lawyer. Molyneux had asked whether a blind man on recovering his sight would be able to distinguish a cube from a sphere by vision alone, without recourse to tactile information. Both Locke and Molyneux answered this query in the negative. This question was addressed repeatedly by philosophers in the eighteenth century who were divided into two camps, empiricists and nativists, with respect to their attempts to account for the origin of ideas and knowledge (258). The empiricists argued that all ideas are derived from sensory experience. The infant mind was to them "a tabula rasa, a blank plate of wax upon which the moving finger of experience wrote the entire eventual content of consciousness and memory" (ref. 408, p. 57). Nativists, on the other hand, held that certain ideas are innate. This debate gradually shifted to a discussion of the origins of visual perception from the same two extreme viewpoints.

Although the issue was argued vociferously (258, 287a, 408), there was little relevant empirical data available until quite recently. What data there were came from three sources; *1*) studies of the perceptual abilities of newborn infants, *2*) cases of restored sight (such as the hypothetical case described by Molyneux) or of early distorted visual input, and *3*) demonstrations of the adaptability of the adult visual system to rearranged visual input. The limited data available and a number of technical, methodological, and logical reasons (6, 177, 243) made it impossible to resolve the conflict.

The advent of electrophysiological methods for the study of the functional properties of individual visual cortical cells within the last 20 years has made it possible to reformulate many of the old issues, now in specific terms. In turn this has led to a clearer understanding of the roles of genetic and experiential factors in the functional development of the neural systems that form the substrate of visual perception. This insight has been gained by applying the same approaches as those used earlier in attempting to determine the role of environmental input in human perceptual development. Studies of the functional properties of visual neurons in neonatal animals parallel attempts to examine the perceptual abilities of newborn infants, and studies of clinical populations (including cases of restored sight) foreshadow modern experiments that examine the functional properties of neurons in the visual pathways of animals reared with abnormal visual input.

Additional data relevant to the nature-nurture controversy have been obtained by application of new methods that permit rapid evaluation of the perceptual capacities of infant humans and animals. Although data from these new sources have allowed resolution of some issues, they have also led to new problems in interpretation that have generated just as much controversy as that which surrounded the interpretation of the earlier material.

It is not possible within the space available here to provide an exhaustive survey of the field. That is unnecessary, however, because a number of good reviews have been published recently (7, 34, 96, 237, 263). Consequently we concentrate here on examining the relationship between functional neural and perceptual development, and emphasize data on the normal development of perceptual abilities in humans and other higher mammals and on the manner in which this development is influenced by anomalous visual experience. The parallel information provided by behavioral studies may help resolve disputes that have arisen over the interpretation of some physiological findings. The initial neurophysiological experiments have brought into focus a number of specific questions concerning the role of early visual stimulation in the normal functional development of the visual system. The key issue to emerge from these studies has been the degree to which the functional development of individual neurons in the visual system can be modified by early visual input.

This chapter begins with a description of normal perceptual development in humans and animals and of the effects of prolonged periods of total visual deprivation imposed from birth. This description is followed by a brief survey of normal visual neural development at various levels of the geniculostriate pathway of higher mammals and of the effects of binocular visual deprivation. Parallels between these two levels of analysis are explored further in the final section, which describes the effects of early selective visual deprivation both on perceptual development and on the development of functional properties of neurons at various levels of the visual pathway. This survey focuses on development of the geniculostriate pathway and excludes discussion of other visual pathways such as those involved in orientating and other

oculomotor reflexive responses. This omission is made easier, because the principles of development derived from studies of the geniculostriate pathway appear to apply to these other visual pathways as well (e.g., refs. 82, 89, 90, 178). We concentrate on studies of the cat and the monkey, because these species have received by far the greatest attention. Some aspects of the material presented here have been discussed briefly in other chapters in volume I of the *Handbook* section on the nervous system (152, 207). It is also assumed that the reader is familiar with the functional properties of neurons at various levels of the mammalian geniculostriate pathway of adult animals, material that has been covered in a number of recent reviews (e.g., refs. 225, 317, 354 and the chapters by Dowling and Dubin and by Bishop in this *Handbook*).

DEVELOPMENT OF VISUAL PERCEPTION

We describe here the normal development of two basic aspects of form perception: *1*) spatial resolution (visual acuity and contrast sensitivity), and *2*) binocular depth perception (stereopsis). A detailed description of the development of other possibly more fundamental visual functions such as wavelength discrimination, spectral sensitivity, and absolute visual thresholds are omitted, because they are principally determined by retinal mechanisms. Moreover, these functions develop quite early, so that visual experience exerts little influence on their development. Human infants 2–3 mo old possess essentially normal adult photopic (108, 259, 290, 363) and scotopic (304) spectral sensitivities, and their absolute visual thresholds (304) are within an order of magnitude of those of adults (164). Some infants as young as 1 mo can make certain wavelength discriminations in the absence of luminance cues that establish that they are at least dichromats (291, 363, 366, 410). The limited data available suggest that by 3 mo of age their color vision is more adultlike and possibly trichromatic (57, 159). Infant pig-tailed monkeys (*Macaca nemestrina*), on the other hand, are demonstrably trichromatic at 6–8 wk of age (55). Finally, the fact that a monkey reared in darkness from 2 wk to 3 mo of age is also trichromatic strongly implies that visual experience plays little or no role in the development of trichromatic color vision (55).

Methods of Study

Virtually all of the recent knowledge of human perceptual development has been acquired by study of visual evoked potentials, optokinetic nystagmus, or preferential-looking (PL) behavior. The latter was first described by Stirnimann (353) and was later employed by Fantz (122, 124), primarily for other purposes. This procedure relies on the fact that young infants initially tend to fixate on patterned stimuli rather than on adjacent stimuli that are homogeneous, and to fixate on them longer. This behavior is demonstrable from birth to 6 mo of age and has even been used to study infants through the first year (157). To derive measures of acuity or contrast sensitivity, a grating pattern of variable spatial frequency and contrast is paired with an adjacent homogeneous surface of the same mean luminance. An observer views the infant through a peephole located between the two stimuli. The most sensitive technique, devised by Teller et al. (362, 365), incorporates a forced choice psychophysical procedure, and requires the observer (who is ignorant of the position of the patterned stimulus) to guess which display contains the target on the basis of the way the infant directs its gaze. As the stripes are made finer or as the contrast is reduced, the infant's visual behavior toward the displays becomes less obvious, and the observer makes fewer correct guesses. Thresholds are obtained by constructing psychometric functions of the observer's percentage of correct guesses as a function of spatial frequency or contrast and by interpolating to some arbitrarily defined value, such as 75% correct. It is assumed that this threshold, at which preference for the grating diminishes, is a conservative estimate of the true sensory threshold of the infant. It has been recently noted (166), however, that visual preference may reverse near threshold, a fact that if not taken into account may lead to an underestimation of the threshold.

Somewhat different criteria have been employed to predict the location of the target, such as the direction of the first fixation (e.g., ref. 16), the duration of fixation (e.g., ref. 123), or a global impression of the infant's behavior (365). Despite these and other methodological differences (110) the results obtained in different laboratories have been fairly consistent.

Estimates of sensory thresholds of human infants obtained by use of either optokinetic nystagmus or visual evoked potentials, although obtained by objective measures, may be more difficult to interpret than those obtained by exploitation of PL behavior. For example, it has been shown that in the cat (178), monkey (287), and rabbit (72), optokinetic nystagmus is mediated by the pretectum and accessory optic system. Consequently it is probable that estimates of spatial resolution of human infants obtained using this particular measure provide information on the fidelity of these pathways rather than that of the geniculostriate system. A comparable problem of interpretation exists with the use of visual evoked potentials, because at certain stages of development or after certain deprivation regimens, it is possible that potentials measured from the scalp may be dominated by signals from structures whose activity is unavailable to the infant at a conscious level. In addition, steady-state evoked potentials may be contaminated by age-dependent changes in the dynamic response characteristics of the visual pathway of the infant (313, 350). Consequently, greater weight has been placed in this chapter on results obtained using PL behavior than on

those obtained using either optokinetic nystagmus or evoked potentials.

Although the PL procedure has been applied successfully on both human and monkey infants (56, 365, 367), it has not proved to be applicable to nonprimates. This difficulty has been overcome for kittens by the development of a simple behavioral technique that uses a modified Lashley jumping stand (248, 249, 251).

Development of Spatial Resolution

The ability to resolve spatial detail is a basic attribute of form vision, and its assessment is fundamental to any evaluation of the status of the visual system. The vast majority of measurements of spatial resolution have been limited to assessment of visual acuity, the ability to resolve fine detail. Measurements of contrast thresholds, which in addition test the ability of the visual system to resolve spatial details considerably larger than the resolution limit, are a comparatively recent development. Consequently more data are available on the development of visual acuity than on the development of other aspects of spatial resolution. Virtually all of these observations were made using grating stimuli, with the visual acuity specified in terms of the highest spatial frequency of a grating (defined in terms of the number of cycles of the grating per degree of visual angle) that can be resolved. In central (foveal) vision the resolution limit of human adults is between 50 and 60 cycles/deg (63, 181), which matches closely the spacing of foveal cones (150). Peripheral acuity, on the other hand, is much poorer than the retinal grain and is probably limited by the size of receptive fields of ganglion cells and their packing density (150). Although comparable data are not available for monkeys, it is likely that a similar situation is true for this species. In the cat, however, even in the area centralis, resolution is limited neither by the optics nor the separation of receptors, but by the size of the receptive fields of ganglion cells and their separation (121, 191).

Humans. A large number of reports are now available on the development of infant visual acuity, the majority of which have been gathered using variants of the PL procedure (e.g., refs. 9–11, 17–19, 102, 111, 124, 240, 303, 347, 365). Because of differences in criteria used to define threshold (110), as well as more fundamental reasons (J. Allen, personal communication), measurements of infant acuity obtained from visually evoked potentials are somewhat higher than data gathered using PL, particularly in older infants.

Measurements of visual acuity have been made on infants ranging from several weeks preterm (109, 123) to about 5 yr of age (12, 242, 242a). At birth and through the first months of postnatal life, acuity is quite poor. During this period visual acuity does not exceed 2.4 cycles/deg even by the highest estimate (18), and most estimates using PL place it at less than 1 cycle/deg. At birth and through the first 12 wk of postnatal life, the acuity of premature babies is significantly poorer than that of full-term infants of the same postnatal age (109). This discrepancy disappears, however, if the age of the preterm babies is measured from the due date, which suggests that visual acuity is more closely correlated with the age from conception than the age from the actual date of birth (109). After birth, acuity increases systematically toward adult levels. Gwiazda et al. (157) studied infants through the 1st yr of life using a standard PL task, and they found values of about 12 cycles/deg at that age. Figure 1 illustrates their data for vertical gratings. Although these data agree closely with estimates obtained by other investigators (9, 17, 18) using PL, they are somewhat lower than values obtained from evoked potentials, which approach 30 cycles/deg by 6 mo of age (160, 240, 303, 347). By means of an operant procedure, Mayer and Dobson (242, 242a) extended measurement of visual acuity to 5 yr, at which time acuity approaches adult levels as assessed by this technique. A similar conclusion was reached by another group (12) that used a modified alley-running procedure on children from 3 to 5 yr old.

A more complete picture of the ability of the infant to process spatial information is provided by measuring contrast thresholds for gratings of various spatial frequencies (19). These measurements collectively define the contrast sensitivity function. Figure 2 illustrates the major points evident in the data from two groups (10, 11, 17–19). First, the contrast sensitivities of the infants are lower than those of adults by a factor of as much as 100 at all spatial frequencies. Second, the peak of the sensitivity function shifts toward higher spatial frequencies with age. Finally, the lowered sensitivity shown by adults for gratings of very low spatial frequencies (assumed to occur through lateral inhibitory interactions) is apparent only in infants 2 mo of age or older but is not present during the 1st mo of life.

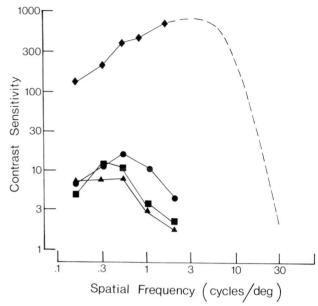

FIG. 2. Contrast sensitivity functions of human infants at 1, ▲; 2, ■; and 3, ● mo of age. Data gathered by PL procedure for large sine-wave gratings. Data for adults, ◆, were obtained on same apparatus. [Adapted from Banks and Salapatek (18). Copyright 1978 by The C. V. Mosby Company, St. Louis, MO.]

These changes indicate that the ability of the infant to process spatial information improves rapidly during the first few months of life, and is not complete at 3 mo of age. Although only limited data are available beyond this age, recent measurements suggest that contrast sensitivity continues to improve until 5 (12) or even 8 yr of age (57a). Evoked potential measurements of contrast sensitivity have been made on infants up to 12 mo (160, 303). They show that contrast thresholds determined from evoked potentials reach adult levels at about 1 yr. This is somewhat earlier than might be expected from behavioral measurements of the contrast sensitivity function.

The changes in the shape of the contrast sensitivity function with age suggest that maturation of different spatial frequency channels may occur at different rates. It is the high-frequency component of the contrast sensitivity function that develops latest, a significant point when considering the type of losses that occur after anomalous visual experience.

Monkeys. The earliest developmental studies of acuity in rhesus macaques (*M. mulatta*) (280–282) employed induced optokinetic nystagmus to measure acuity in the youngest animals and a more complex behavioral technique in older infants. On the day after birth seven of eight infants showed optokinetic nystagmus to stripes 18 min wide (equivalent to 3.3 cycles/deg), and by the end of the 1st mo they could discriminate 4-min stripes. One monkey reached an adult level of 30 cycles/deg by the 6th wk. More recently, acuity development has been studied in the pig-tailed macaque using PL, with similar results (221, 367). Acuities improved from 2.0 cycles/deg during the

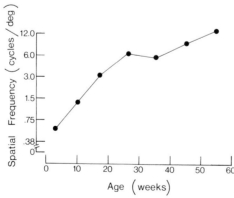

FIG. 1. Development of visual acuity in human infants. Data gathered using the preferential-looking (PL) procedure. Targets were high-contrast square-wave gratings matched with homogeneous gray fields of same space-averaged luminance. [Adapted from Gwiazda et al. (157). Copyright © 1982 American Academy of Optometry.]

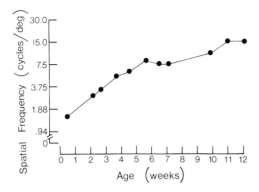

FIG. 3. Development of visual acuity for square-wave gratings for a single *Macaca nemestrina* monkey. Data obtained using PL procedure. [Adapted from Teller et al. (367). Copyright © 1978, with permission from Pergamon Press, Ltd.]

1st wk of life to 6 cycles/deg in the 5th wk. After 12 wk the mean acuity was slightly less than 7.5 cycles/deg. Figure 3 shows the results obtained in a single infant monkey studied longitudinally by Teller et al. (364). Comparison of these data with those of human infants indicates a rather similar function, but with a different time scale. The acuity of the monkey at birth is comparable to that of the 3-wk-old human infant, and thereafter develops about three times faster than the acuity of the human. Boothe (52) has suggested a simple mnemonic for specifying the absolute acuity values of these two species during development. For humans the acuity expressed in cycles per degree is equivalent to the age in months, whereas in the monkey it is approximately equal to the age expressed in weeks.

Longitudinal behavioral measurements on three infant monkeys (*M. nemestrina*), shown in Figure 4, indicate a similar pattern of development of contrast sensitivities to that of human infants, but with a different time scale (56). Sensitivity to spatial frequencies below 5 cycles/deg reach asymptotic levels first at 20 wk of age, but sensitivity to high spatial frequencies continues to develop for the first 28 wk or more. On the basis of the rule of thumb derived from acuity

data (J. Allen, personal communication; 367) relating the rates of visual development of human and monkey infants, these data suggest that the human contrast sensitivity function does not reach full adult levels until 28 mo of age (56). The limited data available at present, however, suggest that these levels are not achieved until much later (12, 57a).

Cats. Unlike the higher primates kittens suffer optical impediments to vision during the first few weeks of life. Their eyes do not open until some time during the 2nd wk, and because of the presence of the tunica vasculosa lentis (131, 369), a vascular net that covers the lens as it develops, image quality does not approach that of the adult until the 6th wk (51). Retinal image quality (51, 103), however, is considerably better than might be expected from ophthalmoscopic examination (see Fig. 8). Even at the youngest age at which behavioral assessments are possible (249), image quality would allow much better visual acuity than that observed. Figure 5 shows the acuities of a number of kittens measured on a jumping stand at different ages.

It is possible to obtain behavioral estimates of acuity in kittens from the age of about 4 wk (146, 249). Resolution improves gradually from approximately 0.75 cycles/deg at 30 days to approach adult values (5–7 cycles/deg) around the end of the 4th mo. The ability to make complex visual pattern discriminations has been demonstrated (423) by 6 wk of age, well before acuity has reached adult values.

Development of Depth Perception and Stereopsis

The ability to discriminate depth under natural viewing conditions depends on several cues, most of which are monocular but some are exclusively binocular. By far the most prominent binocular mechanism of depth perception is stereopsis, which relies on retinal disparity cues (414). The majority of early studies of depth perception in young animals were made in relatively natural situations with many cues available to determine whether infants could perceive depth

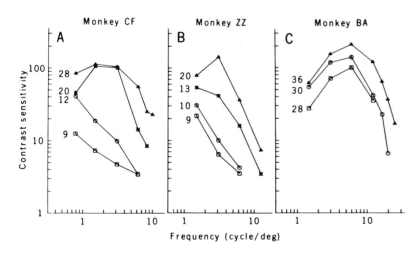

FIG. 4. Contrast sensitivity functions measured on 3 infant monkeys (*Macaca nemestrina*) at ages shown, in weeks, beside each curve. Data obtained by PL procedure. [From Boothe et al. (56). Copyright 1980 by the American Association for the Advancement of Science.]

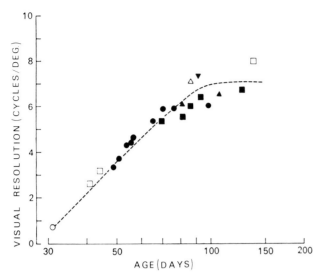

FIG. 5. Development of visual acuity for square-wave gratings in kittens obtained on jumping stand (248). Various symbols denote measurements made on different animals. [From Giffin and Mitchell (146).]

and react in a spatially appropriate manner. The visual cliff, developed by Walk and his colleagues (406, 407), is perhaps the best known of these, and it has proved valuable in demonstrating that infants of a number of species can discriminate large differences in depth at a very early age.

In this chapter it is important to focus attention on the development of stereopsis, a binocular mechanism of depth perception whose neural basis is recognized and one that is known to be disrupted by anomalous early visual input.

Humans. The majority of studies on infant stereopsis have attempted to determine the age at which infants are first able to detect retinal disparity. Using random-dot stereogram displays (205) and either a PL procedure or one involving habituation-dishabituation of a sucking response to repeatedly presented stimuli, Atkinson and Braddick (8) obtained evidence that some infants can make stereoscopic discriminations around 2 mo of age. However, the small sample size precluded a more general statement. More recently Fox et al. (129, 324) employed dynamic random-dot stereograms and a PL procedure on a number of infants, some of whom were followed longitudinally. The results indicated that stereopsis emerges at some time between 3.5 and 6 mo of age. A similar conclusion was reached by Held, Birch, and Gwiazda (28, 165), who also used PL behavior to a pattern of stripes containing bars, with a maximum disparity of 58 min presented as anaglyphs. They found that infants were capable of discriminating convergent (crossed) disparities at a mean age of 12 wk. Divergent (uncrossed) disparities were not detected until 17 wk, however. The difference between the time of onset of stereopsis for convergent versus divergent disparities was confirmed in a later study (28) that employed separate

samples of infants examined either cross sectionally or longitudinally. The results from the latter sample suggested that, although stereopsis developed later for divergent disparities, the subsequent improvement in stereoacuity occurred at the same rate as for convergent disparities. These differences between the stereoacuity for convergent and divergent disparities during development provide a compelling argument against the notion that the development of stereopsis simply depends on the onset of precise vergence eye movements.

In contrast to data on the development of visual acuity and contrast sensitivity, measurements of development of stereopsis obtained by PL show remarkable agreement with results obtained using electrophysiological methods. Evoked potentials to dynamic random-dot stereograms and correlograms can be observed in infants from 10 to 19 wk of age, several weeks after simple monocular evoked potentials to luminance patterns are first evident (292).

In addition to documenting the age of onset of stereopsis, Held, Birch, and Gwiazda (28, 165) also traced the subsequent development of stereoscopic acuity, which improved surprisingly rapidly. Within 3-4 wk of the onset of the ability to make stereoscopic discriminations, infants were able to detect disparities as small as 1 min, the smallest value tested. These data, illustrated in Figure 6, contrast rather sharply with the development of visual acuity, which develops far more slowly. Unfortunately Held et al. (165) were not able to take measurements to the limit of their infants' ability. Under optimum conditions adult ster-

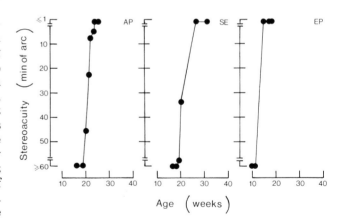

FIG. 6. Development of stereopsis in human infants. Data gathered using PL procedure. Infants sat 60 cm from 2 rear projection screens onto which 2 sets of stimuli were presented. Both sets of stimuli comprised 3 vertical bars 2° wide and spaced 2° apart. By means of polarizing filters in projectors and in lightweight goggles worn by infants, 1 set of stimuli was imaged with zero disparity and so appeared as 3 bars coplanar with screen, whereas on other screen the 2 outside bars were imaged with a known binocular disparity to appear (to a normal adult) as lying either in front of or behind central bar. Eight disparities ranging from 1 to 58 min of arc were tested. Data show smallest divergent disparities for which infants showed a preference on at least 80% of trials for 3 representative subjects of 16 examined. [Adapted from Held et al. (165).]

eoacuity is only a few seconds of arc, and it is of some interest to know how long this fine tuning of depth perception takes to develop.

Cats. Possibly because of a lack of suitable techniques very little is known about the development of stereopsis in species other than humans. Using a modified jumping stand (250) it is possible to determine the ability of kittens to discriminate small differences in depth between two surfaces. Although the depth present is real the number of cues available can be limited by appropriate masking of the edges of the surfaces to be discriminated. By comparing binocular with monocular performance it is possible to infer the presence of stereopsis on the assumption that superior binocular performance under otherwise identical viewing conditions represents the utilization of uniquely binocular depth cues, of which retinal disparity is the most potent.

When young kittens are tested under these conditions they show a marked binocular superiority by the age of 30–35 days, suggesting that they possess stereopsis. Figure 7 shows the development of binocular performance using a jumping stand for a group of kittens (371). Sensitivity to depth increased very rapidly between the 5th and 6th wk, with some animals exhibiting thresholds equivalent to a retinal disparity of 20 min. Thereafter depth thresholds improved more slowly, reaching adult levels (4 min) at about 70 days. It is particularly noteworthy that the period of rapid improvement in binocular depth perception coincides with the time course of fine tuning of binocular cells in the visual cortex to retinal disparity [see Fig. 11; (293)].

Overview

Adult humans achieve a foveal acuity for gratings that is closely matched to the retinal receptor mosaic (150, 191). There are even some acuity tasks such as vernier acuity and stereoacuity, collectively referred to as hyperacuities (411–413), which can be performed with a precision of the order of a few seconds of arc, less than one-tenth of a cone diameter. As Barlow (20) emphasizes, the high precision with which these tasks can be performed points to the existence of precisely ordered functional connections from the eye to the visual cortex. An even higher level of organization within the cortex is necessary to permit the determination of the position of contours with an accuracy compatible with the exquisite sensitivity characteristic of the hyperacuities.

The rather gradual development of acuity in all three species described above suggests at first sight that the neural connectivity underlying these tasks is not established innately, as is probably true for the chicken, which attains peak acuity within 48 hr of hatching (283). However, there are a number of peripheral factors that potentially could limit the acuity of cats, monkeys, and humans early in life even if

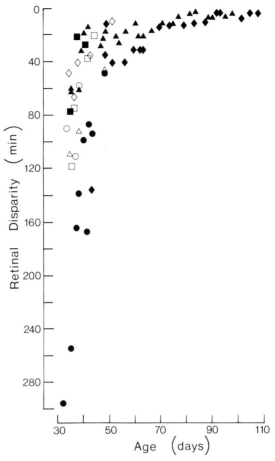

FIG. 7. Development of binocular depth perception in kittens measured using jumping stand (250). Data show threshold retinal disparity corresponding to smallest separation of target surfaces in depth that could be discriminated at various ages. Binocular disparity was calculated from knowledge of viewing distance and interocular separation. Each symbol represents data from different animal. [Adapted from Timney (371). Copyright 1981 by The C. V. Mosby Company, St. Louis, MO.]

neural connectivity were established at birth. A discussion follows of three prominent peripheral processes that could in principle contribute to the increase in spatial resolution observed in the immediate postnatal period.

Improvement in the optical transmission properties of the eye. The cloudy appearance of the optical media of kittens during the first few weeks of postnatal life suggests that optical image quality may serve as the major constraint on visual acuity during this period. As mentioned in *Cats*, p. 519, and illustrated in Figure 8, however, image quality is surprisingly good and considerably better than measured acuity. Thus it appears that optical factors do not impose a major constraint on acuity in the kitten. The optics of the eye of the monkey or the human are clear at birth on ophthalmoscopic examination. Although no quantitative measurements of line spread functions have been made in humans, recent measurements on the monkey

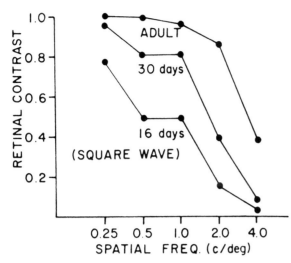

FIG. 8. Optical quality of kitten eye compared with eye of adult cat. Calculated retinal contrasts [$(I_{max} - I_{min})/(I_{max} + I_{min})$] of 100% contrast square-wave gratings imaged by eyes of 16- and 30-day-old kittens, and by eye of normal adult cat. Each data point represents contrast of retinal image computed from measurements of optical modulation transfer function at different ages. Latter functions derived from fundus photographs of retinal blood vessels. [From Bonds and Freeman (51). Copyright © 1978, with permission from Pergamon Press, Ltd.]

eye (424) reveal that optic quality is excellent 2 days after birth and by 13 wk is comparable with that of an adult. The optical changes are very small in comparison with the vast alterations in contrast sensitivity during this period and thus pose no limitation to the development of acuity. Similarly errors of accommodation are most unlikely to limit acuity development, because full adult accommodative responses are present by 4 wk of age (182).

Rescaling of the retinal map of visual space. Rescaling may be particularly relevant in the case of the kitten eye, the axial dimensions of which almost double from birth to 6 mo of age (369). If the linear spacing of receptors remained relatively constant during this time, the angular separation of the receptors would therefore decrease, with a consequent improvement in resolution. The presence of such rescaling would be revealed by changes with age in the angular separation of two retinal landmarks. Measurements of the angle between the visual axis and the axis projected from the center of the optic disk in kittens of different ages reveals that some rescaling occurs (278). From the time when behavioral acuity measurements are first possible (30 days) to the time at which acuity has stabilized (4–5 mo), however, this angle changes less than 30%. The improvement in acuity over this period is almost an order of magnitude (249). Thus, although some of the improvement in the acuity of the kitten may be attributed to growth of the eye itself, the extent of this contribution is not great. The contribution of growth of the eye to the development of acuity in monkeys is likely to be much less, because the changes in axial length are smaller. Between birth

and adulthood it is likely to be less than 25% (45), and between 4 and 20 wk of age the change in axial length increases retinal image size only about 14% (56). Changes in the axial length of the human eye are both larger and more protracted, because adult dimensions are not attained until 13 yr of age (348). Although the greatest increase occurs in the 1st yr (116), the magnitude of the change in axial length is proportionately much smaller than that of the kitten eye. Consequently it is likely that the changes in the dimensions of the human eye account for only a small proportion of the measured changes in visual acuity during the first 6 mo of life.

Changes in retinal receptor mosaic and/or neural organization. The anatomical organization of the retina of the cat (112, 202, 319, 355, 378), monkey (168, 321), and human (1, 116, 239) is incomplete at birth. This is especially true of the region of central specialization (the fovea or area centralis), which does not attain adult morphology for many weeks (1, 168, 239). A postnatal increase in central receptor density through migration of receptors and/or a decrease in receptor dimensions, both of which reduce the angular distance between receptors, would result in an increase in spatial resolution. Both of these processes occur in the monkey fovea and together result in a fourfold increase in the number of cones in the central fovea between birth and adulthood (168). Comparable changes of ganglion-cell density and size occur in the area centralis of kittens until about 8 wk of age (378). These changes in receptor and/or ganglion-cell density must contribute to the improvement in acuity observed after birth, but the magnitude of these changes is too small to account for much of the measured improvement in visual resolution.

Growth-related changes in the dimension of an individual eye could also limit stereoacuity. But more importantly stereoacuity is also influenced by the changes in interocular separation that occur with growth of the head. This has the effect of altering the depth value associated with a constant retinal disparity. The interpupillary distance of the kitten, for example, increases from about 2 cm at 4 wk of age to almost 4 cm in the adult. This means that the retinal disparity corresponding to a given separation between two targets increases by approximately a factor of two as the kitten grows. Even without improvement in neural tuning, discrimination of real separations in depth should improve by that amount. It is clear from the data presented here, however, that depth thresholds improve considerably more.

In summary, although each of the mentioned peripheral factors makes some contribution to the gradual improvement in visual performance observed in the first few months of postnatal life, the major source of the improvement must be attributed to changes in neural organization and/or connectivity central to the retina. Consequently we consider next the normal functional development of the visual pathway.

DEVELOPMENT OF VISUAL
NEURAL PROCESSES

Given the limited perceptual capabilities of very young mammals it is important to establish the extent to which these limits are determined by functional immaturity of neurons at different levels of the visual pathway. There have been few studies on the normal development of the retina and lateral geniculate nucleus and some uncertainty surrounds the developmental status of the neonatal cortex. Most of the data available were obtained on the cat, although there have been a few studies on the monkey.

Retina

Because of the anatomical immaturity of the retina at birth, some developmental changes might be expected in the functional properties of retinal ganglion cells in early postnatal life. Some attention has been directed toward the development of the functional properties of the major subclasses of retinal ganglion cells, the X- and Y-cells (see the chapter by Bishop in this *Handbook*, and refs. 225, 354). At any retinal eccentricity, X- and Y-cells can be distinguished functionally on the basis of three criteria in normal adult animals. Briefly, X-cells exhibit linear spatial summation, high spatial resolution, and have medium axonal conduction velocities. By contrast, Y-cells show nonlinear summation, poorer resolution than X-cells, but faster axonal conduction velocities. Anatomically they can be distinguished on the basis of differences in soma size and their decussation and projection patterns (354). Functionally kitten retinal ganglion cells are responsive from at least the age of 3 wk, which is the earliest they have been studied, although they do not acquire all their adult characteristics until several weeks later (158, 320). Classification as X- or Y-type (225) is difficult until the age of 4–5 wk. The most striking aspect of the receptive fields of young kitten ganglion cells is their relatively large angular size (320), with the implication that their spatial resolving power should be low. However, there is no direct evidence on this point.

Lateral Geniculate Nucleus

Daniels et al. (97) found that even in 6- to 13-day-old kittens, cells were segregated into laminae according to eye dominance and that the normal topographic representation of the visual field was already established. The response properties of the neurons, however, were grossly abnormal compared with the adult; a large proportion were visually unresponsive. In the youngest kittens lateral geniculate nucleus (LGN) cells had low spontaneous rates, long latencies to visual stimulation, and rapid adaptation to repeated stimulus presentations. The cells tended to have very large receptive fields and lacked both antagonistic surround responses and inhibition. Only a few cells in these

young animals could be classified as X- and Y-cells on the basis of a contrast reversal test. Most cells could be so classified by the 4th wk, but the Y-cells did not develop mature receptive fields until the 6th wk.

In the LGN of the newborn monkey, Blakemore and Vital-Durand (45) found no cells that were visually unresponsive; all could be classified as either X- or Y-cells on the basis of the contrast reversal test. Nevertheless they were clearly not adultlike, because responses to visual stimuli were comparatively weak.

Of greater pertinence to an understanding of the basis of the behaviorally observed improvement in visual acuity with age are measurements of the development of spatial resolution of LGN cells. These data exist for X-cells in both kittens and infant monkeys. Measurements have been made of the resolution of X-cells for gratings drifted across their receptive fields. In kittens the resolution of LGN cells (defined as the highest spatial frequency grating that could elicit a modulated discharge) in the vicinity of the area centralis is very low at 3 wk and slowly attains adult levels by 16 wk, with a time course comparable to the behavioral improvement of visual acuity (193). The spatial resolution of LGN X-cells with receptive fields in the central fovea improves sevenfold from birth to adulthood in monkeys (45). The spatial resolution of cells in the peripheral retina, 15° to 25° from the fovea, in newborn monkeys is comparable with that observed in adults. The time course of the average improvement in spatial resolution of X-cells with receptive field centers within 2° of the fovea is shown by the solid circles in Figure 9. Improvement continues until at least 5 mo of age, with some indication that adult performance may not be attained until after 7 mo. Although the resolution of the LGN cells was always higher, the general trend with age is comparable to the behavioral improvement of acuity with age (367).

The similarity of the improvement in resolution of LGN cells with age to the time course of the behavioral development of acuity suggests that the latter may be limited by the development of subcortical structures in the visual pathway. Because no measurements are available of the development of spatial resolution of retinal ganglion cells, however, it is unclear whether the development observed in the LGN changes in step with or lags behind retinal development.

Visual Cortex

The developmental status of the visually naive kitten cortex is uncertain, because several groups of investigators have drawn contradictory conclusions from apparently similar experiments. The uncertainties are difficult to resolve, because of differences in experimental procedures and differences among investigators in the criteria for classification of various receptive-field properties.

Hubel and Wiesel (185) examined the responsiveness of 17 neurons in two kittens, aged 8 and 16 days,

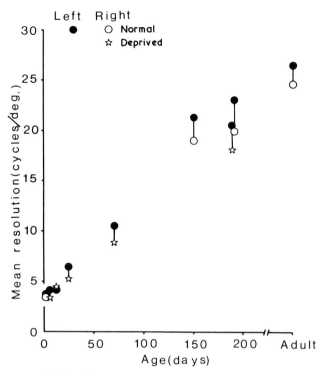

FIG. 9. Mean improvement in spatial resolution of foveal lateral geniculate nucleus (LGN) cells with age in normal and monocularly deprived monkeys. Each symbol depicts mean resolution of X-cells with receptive fields located within 2° of central fovea. Recordings made in right LGN ipsilateral to deprived eye of monocularly occluded monkeys (*stars*). *Filled circles* depict resolution of cells driven by left eye; *open circles* plot comparable data from right eye. Data points from both eyes of individual animals joined by *vertical line*. Monocular deprivation was from day of birth until time of recording. Note that monocular deprivation does not hinder improvement in resolution with age, and that even in normal animals LGN cells driven by ipsilateral (right) eye possess slightly lower acuity than cells driven by contralateral eye. [From Blakemore and Vital-Durand (45).]

neither of whom had any exposure to patterned visual stimuli. They reported that although cells tended to respond sluggishly and receptive fields were less precisely defined, most of the fundamental properties of adult neurons were present, including orientation selectivity, direction selectivity, and binocularity. They were also able to classify cells into simple and complex types. Barlow and Pettigrew (22), in a brief report, claimed that although there was evidence of direction selectivity and diffuse binocular connectivity in the cortex of visually inexperienced kittens, orientation and disparity selectivity were lacking.

Later studies provide partial support for both extreme positions. A more detailed account of this controversy can be found in recent reviews (34, 237, 263); here we summarize the emerging consensus. It is now accepted that a certain proportion of cells in very young, visually naive kitten cortex are orientation selective by the strictest criteria that may be applied. Blakemore and Van Sluyters (43) and Frégnac and Imbert (142) suggest that about 25% of neurons possess

this property in the absence of visual experience, at least through the first 4 wk of life. A much higher estimate is given by Sherk and Stryker (325), but these authors did not include in their analysis cells that did not respond reliably. There is some agreement that orientation-selective cells in the neonatal kitten cortex tend to be monocularly driven (43, 61, 142, 143), and some reports (142, 143, 231) suggest that their orientation preferences are clustered around the horizontal and vertical. Although some cells with high stimulus specificity are present in very young kittens, there is virtually universal agreement that a sizeable proportion either lack stimulus specificity or are unresponsive to visual stimuli.

With normal visual experience the vast majority of cortical neurons adopt adultlike properties by about 6 wk of age (43, 50, 61, 103, 105, 142, 293). This point is illustrated in Figure 10A, which shows the proportion of orientation-selective, orientation-biased, and nonoriented cells encountered by Bonds (50) in kittens of different ages. The average orientation selectivity (defined as the mean half width at half the maximum response) of those cells judged orientation selective is shown in Figure 10B as a function of age. There is a progressive increase in the proportion of selective cells at the expense of nonselective cells and at the same time a refinement of the tuning of orientation-selective cells. The orientation tuning achieves a value of 20° at between 5 and 6 wk of age, a value comparable to that of cortical cells in adults (169, 318). A somewhat similar developmental sequence occurs for directional selectivity (50). A recent study of the development of spatial resolution of cortical cells in kittens by Derrington and Fuchs (105) indicate a marked improvement between 2 and 6 wk of age, at which time spatial-frequency selectivity attains adult values. Nevertheless some other aspects of the response of cortical cells to gratings (such as the best spatial frequency) were still lower than adult levels.

One aspect of neonatal cortical organization on which there is a general consensus is the existence of binocularly excitable cells (185, 293, 419). It is apparent that the organization of the cortex into ocular dominance columns is not complete at birth, however, particularly in layer IV. Anatomical methods suggest that segregation of geniculate afferents in layer IV into discrete ocular dominance bands is not apparent at birth and only becomes evident several weeks later (190, 227, 228, 306). On the other hand physiological recordings in both kittens and neonatal monkeys reveal alternating regions of cortex dominated by first one eye and then the other (43, 419), suggesting that the development of ocular dominance columns is more advanced in cortical layers other than IV.

Although the proportion of binocular cells in the visual cortex of the kitten is high at birth, their tuning for retinal disparity is at first extremely poor. At 2 wk, binocular cells respond over a range of disparities of 6° or more, but by the 5th wk tuning has sharpened to

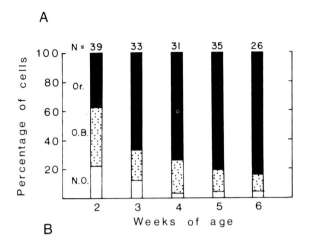

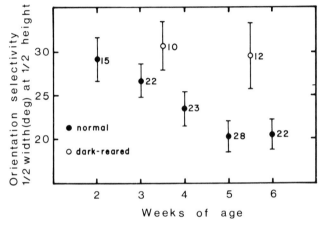

FIG. 10. *A*: proportion of types of orientation selectivity within a population of visually responsive cells recorded from normal kittens at ages shown. Or., orientation selective; O.B., orientation biased; N.O., nonoriented. Number of visually responsive cells recorded in each age group shown on *top*. *B*: orientation specificity of orientation-selective cells as function of age for both normal (*filled circles*) and dark-reared (*open circles*) kittens. Ordinate indicates half width of tuning curve at half of maximum response. *Bar* represents ± 1 SEM, and numbers beside each symbol indicate number of cells studied at each age. [From Bonds (50).]

nearly adult levels, responding only over a limited disparity range of about 1°. Disparity tuning curves obtained from animals of different ages are shown in Figure 11.

The immaturity of receptive-field properties of cortical cells in the newborn kitten and the refinement of these cells over the course of the next 6 wk occurs during a period of intense synaptogenesis in the cortex. Cragg (74, 75) reported that the number of synapses per neuron at the time of eye opening is only about 1% of the adult figure; thereafter the number increases dramatically to a maximum value at 7 wk of age that is approximately 30% higher than adult levels. Although it is unclear how these anatomical changes influence the physiological properties of cortical cells, there is qualitative agreement between the times during which both measures change most rapidly. On the

basis of changes in the number of dendritic spines, it is likely that the number of synapses per cortical cell in the monkey also undergoes a similar marked increase during the first 8 wk of postnatal life (236).

CONSEQUENCES OF BINOCULAR VISUAL DEPRIVATION

It is evident from the previous discussion that the visual system is not fully mature at birth and that quite extensive changes occur in the immediate postnatal period. The extent to which visual experience is necessary to promote and maintain the integrity of visual function may be assessed by studying animals deprived of vision from birth until the moment of testing. Clearly if the visual capacities of such an animal were at the level of a normally reared individual of the same age, it would have to be concluded that visual experience plays no role in the development

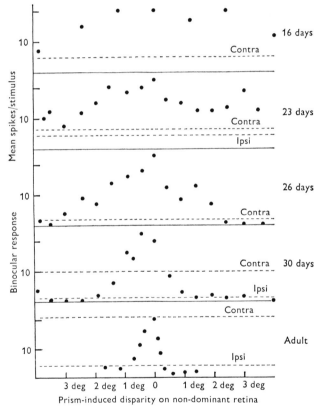

FIG. 11. Tuning of most selective binocular cortical cells to horizontal retinal disparity at various stages of development in kittens. Each *circle* indicates mean number of spikes (from 8–10 repetitions) elicited by movement of preferred stimulus over both receptive fields. Mean level of response elicited by monocular stimulation indicated by *dotted horizontal lines*. All cells were located within 5° of area centralis. Prior to 4th wk cells exhibited binocular facilitation that was relatively insensitive to changes in retinal disparity. Over course of next week zone of binocular facilitation became progressively narrower, and binocular response when receptive fields were not aligned fell below responses elicited monocularly. [From Pettigrew (293).]

of these abilities. On the other hand, if these visual skills are immature and only develop subsequently after considerable visual exposure, it must be concluded that visual experience influences the development of these particular visual functions. Hints as to the nature and extent of this influence may be obtained from experiments in which visual experience is modified in a selective way. In the following section we consider the consequences of binocular visual deprivation.

Forms of Binocular Deprivation

Binocular visual deprivation may be accomplished in two ways: by rearing animals from birth in total darkness, or by bilaterally suturing the lids. Early neurophysiological studies did not distinguish between these two procedures, and initial results suggested that they might be equivalent. More recent work, however, indicates that this may not be true (e.g., refs. 264, 266, 328).

The two deprivation conditions differ in several respects. Dark rearing eliminates all visual stimulation, whereas bilateral lid suture prevents pattern vision but only moderately reduces the amount of illumination reaching the retina (77, 235). The total amount of light reduction varies with skin pigmentation, and in some animals it may be different for each eye (219, 349). Jampolsky (200) has taken the position that disorganized or degraded input allows the system to develop, but abnormally, whereas total deprivation inhibits any development. On these grounds bilateral lid suture might be more deleterious than dark rearing. Contradictory to this position, however, are recent findings indicating that the degradation of pattern vision by lid suture may not be as great as previously thought because it is possible to plot receptive fields of cat cortical cells through closed eyelids (349). Furthermore Loop and Sherman (235) have even demonstrated that cats can make certain gross visual pattern discriminations through closed lids. Recent direct comparisons (264, 266) of the effects of the two deprivation conditions on the developing visual cortex indicate that the diffuse visual stimulation through closed eyelids results in partial specification of the visual cortex that cannot be modified by subsequent visual experience. Dark rearing, on the other hand, leaves the cortex in a nonspecified state that can be modified afterward. Thus concerning the question of whether perceptual skills develop normally in the absence of visual input, more emphasis should be placed on results obtained on animals reared in total darkness.

In humans such a severe form of visual deprivation rarely occurs. Conditions comparable to bilateral eyelid suture, however, do occur as a consequence of dense bilateral medial opacities such as cataracts. Because it has been possible for many years to restore a clear retinal image in these cases by removing the crystalline lens, there has been a long history of cases of restored sight (405). More recently, with the advent of corneal grafting, it has also been possible to restore visual input to patients who have suffered severe and long-standing corneal scarring.

Effects on Perception

SPATIAL RESOLUTION. *Humans.* Although there are a larger number of case histories of individuals bilaterally deprived of patterned visual input almost from birth with sight later restored by surgery, the lack of precise information about the time of onset and severity of the deprivation, as well as the frequent lack of quantitative measurements of visual function after restoration of clear visual input, make interpretation of much of the available material quite difficult. All that can be said with certainty is that visual recovery after restoration of visual input to patients who have suffered early and long-lasting peripheral impediments to vision is slow and incomplete, and often interrupted by periods of arrest or regression. The visual rehabilitation, which can take more than a year (382), is frequently accompanied by emotional depression (2, 151, 201, 382). Details of the length and extent of deprivation are not well documented, and some of the variability among patients with restored sight may be due in part to individual differences in the degree and duration of visual deprivation early in life. Visual rehabilitation is faster and more complete in patients who had visual experience prior to the period of blindness (201, 382). Because such peripheral impediments to vision as cataracts may develop slowly, some patients may have retained some patterned visual input for longer than supposed (243).

Monkeys. Some of the earliest studies of binocularly deprived primates employed only qualitative tests of visuomotor behavior (e.g., ref. 315). Although other studies of the time incorporated measurements of visual acuity, the results were conflicting, possibly because of gross differences in deprivation histories (67, 316). The most systematic study yet performed is that of Regal et al. (312), who reared monkeys in total darkness from 2 wk of age until either 3 or 6 mo. The monkeys deprived to 3 mo were impaired initially on most qualitative visuomotor tests, but they gave positive responses on all tests administered over the next few weeks. On the other hand, the two monkeys deprived to 6 mo showed a less extensive recovery. By contrast, quantitative measurements of visual acuity made using the PL procedure revealed surprisingly high visual acuities of between 2.5 and 7.5 cycles/deg (compared to 15 cycles/deg for normal controls). Most of these measurements were made within 1 mo after the animals were taken from the dark. There was no evidence of additional gain, however, when testing was repeated after a further 3 mo, although this may have been due in part to methodological limitations.

The available data on monkeys do not provide any

indication of the rate at which acuity develops following total deprivation, except to suggest that recovery is rapid. There are, however, data for the cat relating to this question.

Cats. The time course of development of visual acuity was measured systematically by Timney et al. (374) on animals reared in darkness from before eye opening until 4 or 6 mo of age. Representative results from these animals together with results from cats dark reared until either 8 or 10 mo (372) are shown in Figure 12. With increasing periods of deprivation the time taken for initial signs of vision to appear becomes progressively longer, from about 15 days in animals deprived to 4 mo to 66 days after 10 mo in the dark. Unpublished observations from our laboratories indicate that animals dark reared to 2 yr of age showed no signs of useful vision on the jumping stand even after more than 6 mo of normal visual experience. The degree of eventual visual recovery also becomes progressively less with increasing length of deprivation. Animals dark reared to 4 mo of age eventually recover normal visual acuity, but those deprived for progressively longer periods show only partial recovery. In contrast to the excellent recovery of dark-reared animals, cats deprived by binocular lid suture until 4 mo of age show only limited recovery (266, 342).

DEPTH PERCEPTION. Qualitative observations on dark-reared kittens (383), rats (361), and monkeys (427) have been made using the visual cliff (407), but

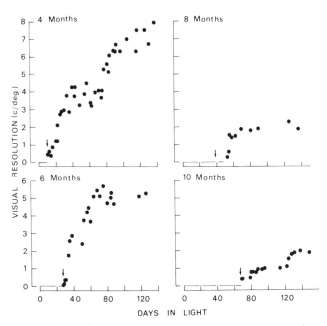

FIG. 12. Development of visual acuity for square-wave gratings for 4 cats that had been reared in total darkness from time of natural eye opening until either 4, 6, 8, or 10 mo of age indicated at *top* of graphs. During period indicated by *horizontal line*, animals were unable to perform pattern discriminations on jumping stand. *Arrows* indicate 1st day on which animals were able to discriminate an open from a closed door on jumping stand using visual cues alone.

systematic quantitative studies of depth perception have been attempted only on cats (211). By use of a jumping stand measurements were made of the ability of cats dark reared to between 100 and 136 days of age to discriminate depth both monocularly and binocularly (250). In contrast to normal cats, dark-reared animals performed as poorly binocularly as they did monocularly. This was true not only for dark-reared cats that developed a convergent eye alignment following exposure to light (83, 85) but also for those that maintained normal eye alignment (211). Thus dark-reared cats lack a uniquely binocular cue to depth and apparently they either do not possess stereopsis, or if they do, the stereoacuity is poor so that it provides no better depth information than can be obtained from monocular cues. Although this may be expected in animals that developed a convergent eye alignment on exposure to light, the absence of any evidence of stereopsis in the orthotropic animals is remarkable in view of both the proportion of cortical cells that are binocular (85, 211) and their recovery of normal visual acuity (374). Evidently the disparity selectivity of binocular cortical cells of dark-reared cats cannot recover to the same extent as the improvement of the spatial resolution of cortical cells with visual experience.

EFFECTS ON NEURAL FUNCTIONING. We have chosen to limit discussion to the changes that occur at the cortical level, because there is no evidence that retinal structures in cats and monkeys are adversely affected by binocular deprivation (65, 167, 330), although it should be noted that severe degeneration of retinal ganglion cells has been reported in chimpanzees kept in darkness for extremely long periods of time, from 16 to 33 mo (67). In addition the functional changes in the LGN appear to be modest (e.g., refs. 217, 265, 328, 415). On the other hand it is clear that cortical function in both cat and monkey is grossly disturbed in animals deprived of patterned visual input early in life.

The abnormality of cortical function in binocularly deprived animals was discovered by Wiesel and Hubel (417), who found that in cats deprived by bilateral lid suture from birth to at least 2.5 mo, about half the cortical cells encountered were either unresponsive to visual stimuli or else responded very poorly, and were quite unselective. They also noted that a significant proportion (41%) of neurons did respond normally. Subsequent investigators describe a higher proportion of abnormal cells (e.g., refs. 43, 86, 219, 231, 264, 336, 409). There is unanimous agreement that the cortex of binocularly deprived cats is characterized by reduced responsiveness to visual stimuli, and even those cells that do respond well adapt quickly. Recent work (264) indicates that the response properties of cells in animals deprived by lid suture are substantially different from those in dark-reared animals. The former procedure produces a much higher proportion of visually unresponsive cells and a low percentage of binocularly excitable cells. Dark-reared animals, on the other hand, exhibit a high proportion of visually responsive cells, but they tend to have nonspecific response properties. As with normally reared animals the majority of cells in dark-reared cats are binocular, so that the distribution of cortical ocular dominance is similar to that of normal cats. It appears that periods of binocular deprivation (dark-rearing) as brief as 3–6 days can diminish certain aspects of cortical responsivity in 4-wk-old kittens (136).

The limited data suggest that the effects of binocular deprivation on the cortex may be more severe in the monkey than in the cat (76, 419). Wiesel and Hubel (419) compared the responses of cortical cells in newborn monkeys with those of monkeys binocularly deprived by lid suture from near birth for 15 to 36 days. Whereas cells in neonatal monkeys appeared adultlike in responsiveness and orientation selectivity, from 10%–15% of cells in the monkeys deprived for only a few weeks exhibited abnormalities like those observed in cells of binocularly deprived kittens. Even more remarkable was the reduction in the proportion of binocularly activated cells. A similar result was obtained by Crawford et al. (76) on a single monkey binocularly deprived at 2 wk for a period of 8 wk and studied more than 3 yr later. Despite the long period of subsequent binocular visual input, half the cells studied were categorized as visually unresponsive. Very few of the visually responsive cells were binocular, and these tended to be unselective.

At least superficially the deprived cortex of cats resembles that of very young kittens, and it is useful to make a direct comparison between neonates and deprived animals. A number of investigators have done this, comparing the development of cortical responsiveness in normal and deprived kittens during the first few weeks of life (43, 50, 142, 293). During the first 2 wk there appear to be only small differences in the relative proportions of orientation-selective cells, although even at this stage visually experienced kittens are at a slight advantage. (cf. refs. 43, 142). Figure 13 shows a comparison of the proportion of various receptive-field characteristics in normal and dark-reared kittens at different ages. The receptive fields of normal and deprived kittens are clearly different beyond 3 wk of age. Even the tuning of the orientation-selective cells in the dark-reared kittens is worse than in normal animals of the same age. The open symbols of Figure 10 indicate that the tuning of orientation-selective cells, which attain adultlike performance in the normal kitten at 6 wk (50), is as broad in dark-reared kittens at 6 wk as it was at 2 wk. Both disparity-tuning (293) and spatial-frequency selectivity (104) apparently fail to improve in dark-reared kittens after 2–3 wk of age.

Thus it appears that experience promotes continued development from about 3 wk of age, and deprivation at best maintains the status quo and at worst leads to some atrophy of cortical function. At present the weight of evidence suggests that deprivation does more than just arrest or freeze cortical development.

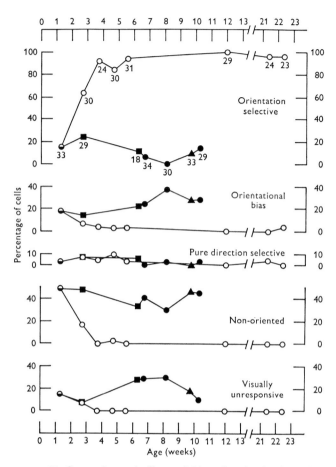

FIG. 13. Comparison of effects of binocular deprivation with those of normal visual experience on development of various receptive-field types in visual cortex of kittens. *Open circles* show percentages of each type of receptive field among sample of cells recorded from 7 normal kittens of different ages. *Filled symbols* show comparative data from 6 binocularly deprived kittens. In both cases *curves* originate from data from 9-day-old kitten recorded when eyelids were just beginning to part naturally. Data from animals deprived by bilateral lid suture are indicated by *filled circles*; those deprived by dark rearing are depicted by *filled squares*. *Filled triangles* show results from animals deprived by bilateral suture of nictitating membrane. Numbers beneath data points for *top set of curves* indicate total number of cells recorded in each animal. [From Blakemore and Van Sluyters (43).]

Some processes such as the anatomical segregation of ocular dominance columns may proceed normally in dark-reared animals, and synaptic development in the kitten cortex (74, 428) also proceeds, but at a reduced rate. However, there are a number of observations indicating that cortical functions actually deteriorate in animals dark reared beyond 6 wk of age (85, 92, 196). The limited data from monkeys also support the notion that extended periods of binocular deprivation result in a deterioration of cortical function rather than a simple arrest of development.

In view of the substantial recovery of vision of dark-reared cats after introduction to light (see Fig. 12), it might be expected that some of the abnormalities of cortical function observed initially are not permanent. Cynader et al. (85) described a substantial recovery of receptive-field properties in the visual cortex of cats visually deprived for as long as 15 mo. Just as with the behavioral recovery the rate and extent of cortical recovery is apparently less in animals initially deprived for longer periods. In animals deprived until 11–15 mo of age, about 50% of cortical cells regained orientation selectivity following 6- to 12-mo exposure to normally lighted surroundings (85). By contrast, in cats deprived to 4 mo, over 80% of cells were orientation selective after only 4 wk exposure to light (92). Together these behavioral and physiological findings suggest that the cortex of dark-reared animals retains a considerable capacity for change through visual experience, a point discussed further in *Extension of the sensitive period by binocular deprivation*, p. 534.

OVERVIEW. Both dark-reared cats and monkeys initially exhibit profound visual deficits when first exposed to light, but monkeys recover visual acuity at a faster rate than cats after comparable periods of deprivation. Although this may reflect a true species difference, it may be significant that the dark-reared monkeys (312) received 2 wk visual input prior to the period of visual deprivation. The rather protracted period of recovery of vision observed in cats deprived from birth for 6 mo or more is reminiscent of the slow recovery observed with humans in whom visual input had been restored after prolonged periods of blindness from birth (382). The recovery of spatial resolution of cortical cells that presumably is responsible for the improvement in visual acuity must occur at a much slower rate than the recovery of orientation selectivity, which in cats dark reared to 4 mo of age reaches an asymptotic level after only 8 wk exposure to light (268).

Although cats deprived of visual input to 4 mo of age develop normal visual acuity after 3–4 mo exposure to light (Fig. 12), they apparently do not recover stereopsis (211). This is surprising in view of the substantial proportion of cortical cells that are binocular. Evidently the tuning of the residual binocular cells for retinal disparity remains poor, even after many months of visual exposure.

The severe and permanent deficits in visual acuity and depth perception of dark-reared animals suggests that these particular perceptual capabilities do not mature or develop in the absence of visual input. A similar conclusion can be reached for most of the receptive-field properties of cortical cells. However, although the behavioral and physiological consequences of prolonged periods of binocular deprivation indicate that visual experience is required for both normal neural and perceptual functioning, the nature of the role that visual experience plays cannot be deduced from this class of experiment alone.

EFFECTS OF SELECTED VISUAL EXPERIENCE
ON NEURAL PROCESSES AND PERCEPTION

Gottlieb (149) has emphasized (in the context of the

development of imprinting behavior), as has Aslin (6), that there are several ways in which visual experience may influence neural and perceptual development. First, in a process referred to as maintenance by Aslin (6) and others, experience could serve a purely passive role by maintaining a preexisting or innate connectivity, which either remains at a certain level in the presence of visual experience or atrophies in its absence. With normal visual input, orientation selectivity and the sensitivity of visual cortical neurons are maintained but not refined beyond the state that existed at birth. On the other hand the visual environment could play a more active role in guiding neural development; for example, experience could serve to refine the degree of selectivity of a given neural characteristic around some innate bias, a process that Aslin (6) refers to as attunement, or to influence the rate at which this process occurs (facilitation). This could occur by a process of functional validation, (294) or strengthening by visual experience of a subset of an innately established set of neural connections. This model permits some refinement of selectivity to develop in the absence of visual input, but the degree or rate at which this occurs is enhanced or facilitated by experience. Alternatively, in the extreme case the development of a given neural response characteristic could be molded by experience to conform to some salient feature of the early visual environment of the animal, a process that Aslin refers to as induction. According to this scheme, cortical neurons at birth are like the philosophers tabula rasa on which virtually any stimulus preference may be imprinted. In the absence of visual input, development would be arrested at the level existing at birth.

Hints as to whether visual experience serves either a passive (maintenance) or a more active (facilitation, attunement, or induction) role during development can be obtained from examination of the neural visual response characteristics or the perceptual abilities of animals that have received selected visual exposure in early life. A strong prediction of any model that postulates an active role for visual experience in development is that it should be possible for neurons to develop visual response characteristics quite different from those innately specified in response to suitably biased early visual exposure. Conversely, models of development that allow experience only a passive role predict that neurons should either develop normally or fall short of normal development, but should never develop characteristics beyond those innately specified or different from those encountered in the cortex of normally reared animals. Advocates of this role for visual experience interpret the effects of selective visual deprivation in terms of a combination of normal development of connections that were adequately maintained by the biased early visual exposure and a loss or atrophy of other connections that were not adequately stimulated.

The most widely used exposure (or deprivation) conditions restrict visual input to one extreme of the range of stimulus preferences observed among cortical cells of normally reared animals. These include, for example, conditions in which vision is restricted to one eye (monocular deprivation), to a single contour orientation, or to stimuli moving in only one direction. These and other forms of early visual deprivation are considered in detail in CONDITIONS THAT INFLUENCE OCULAR DOMINANCE, this page.

Perhaps the ideal experimental approach to the elucidation of the role that visual experience plays in the development of neural function would be to record the changes that occur with time in the selectivity and tuning of a single cell in response to either a normal or a restricted visual input. Although this class of experiment has been attempted in acute preparations (297, 301), the results have been inconclusive. This is due in part to the small and temporary nature of the changes in selectivity reported, and also because of the possibility that the effects of repeated selective visual exposure may not be immediately manifested (297, but cf. 125). In addition, results of later experiments (134, 335a, 377) suggest that changes in the response characteristics of cortical cells can only be induced in acute paralyzed preparations if the eyes are made to move or if the mesencephalic reticular formation and/or the medial thalamic nuclei are activated. Thus it seems that this class of experiment may require recording from an individual cortical neuron for many hours in a nonparalyzed animal. Because of the difficulties associated with this experimental approach, the commonest strategy has been to examine the distribution of response characteristics of a sample of cortical cells from animals that received certain restricted visual exposure early in life. The effect of selective visual exposure on the development of cortical cells is inferred from the presence or absence of a bias in the distribution of various visual response characteristics among the sample population. The difficulty with this experimental approach is the need to obtain a random sample of cortical cells, a task made difficult by the columnar arrangement and other organizational aspects (27, 184, 189) of the visual cortex (4). Cells recorded near one another are likely to have similar properties. Other problems associated with this experimental strategy are discussed in detail by Lund (237) and Movshon and Van Sluyters (263). The most widely employed deprivation conditions are considered individually in the next section.

CONDITIONS THAT INFLUENCE OCULAR DOMINANCE

Monocular Deprivation

Many of the major concepts that guide the study of visual development have been derived from the study of the anatomical, physiological, and behavioral consequences of the restriction of vision through one eye for a period of time. Wiesel and Hubel (415) observed

that closure of one eye of kittens for 2.5 mo, beginning a few days after birth, led to a marked shrinkage in the size of cells in the LGN laminae that receive a projection from the deprived eye, although they did not observe any gross abnormalities in physiological responsiveness. In contrast, at the cortical level (416) there appeared to be no obvious anatomical deficits visible in Nissl-stained sections, but there were pronounced physiological effects; virtually all neurons encountered were driven exclusively by the nondeprived eye. This striking physiological effect was accompanied by an equally profound behavioral loss. On first being forced to employ their deprived eye the kittens appeared to be functionally blind (416).

Figure 14 shows some representative results from early experiments of Wiesel and Hubel in the form of ocular dominance histograms indicating the number of cells that fall into each of seven subjectively defined

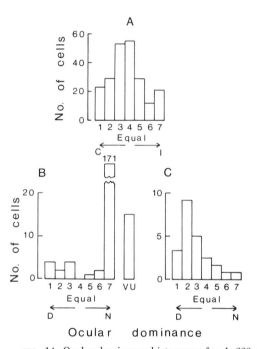

FIG. 14. Ocular dominance histograms for A: 223 cells recorded from visual cortex of a number of normal adult cats; B: 199 cells recorded from visual cortex of 5 kittens monocularly deprived by eyelid suture from time of natural eye opening until recording at between 8 and 14 wk of age; C: 26 cells recorded from single adult cat deprived by eyelid suture for 3 mo. In B and C, recordings were made from hemisphere contralateral to monocularly deprived eye. Cells are classified into 7 subjective ocular dominance groups according to relative influence of each of the 2 eyes. Cells classified as group 1 or 7 are excited exclusively by visual stimuli presented to eye contralateral or ipsilateral to recording electrode, respectively. Remaining groups are binocular; those classified as group 4 are influenced equally by the 2 eyes. Cells classified as belonging to groups 3 and 2 show progressively greater bias toward contralateral eye, whereas those classified as groups 5 and 6 exhibit increasing bias toward ipsilateral eye. Cells visually unresponsive denoted by letters VU (B). Letters C and I in A indicate groups dominated by contralateral and ipsilateral eye, respectively. Letters D and N in B and C beneath histograms denote ocular dominance group dominated by deprived and nondeprived eye, respectively. [Adapted from Hubel and Wiesel (186), and Wiesel and Hubel (416, 417).]

ocular dominance classes (see legend). The distribution of cortical ocular dominance in a pooled sample of cells drawn from a number of normal animals (Fig. 14A) is shown for comparison. The ocular dominance histograms shown in Figure 14B sum data from five kittens monocularly deprived from the time of eye opening until the age of recording at 8–14 wk. Only 13 of 199 cells (7%) could be excited by visual stimuli presented to the deprived eye (418). By contrast a similar period of monocular deprivation (3 mo) imposed on an adult animal (Fig. 14C) had no effect at all on the distribution of cortical ocular dominance, which suggests an early sensitive period for these effects.

During the first 4–6 wk after birth even very brief periods of monocular occlusion can produce changes in cortical ocular dominance as profound as those observed after several months deprivation. One wk to 10 days monocular occlusion during this period causes a complete shift of ocular dominance toward the nondeprived eye, in both cats (274) and monkeys (397). Even periods of monocular deprivation as short as 4–8 h imposed on kittens during the 5th wk can produce a clear functional disruption of binocular cortical connections (133, 138). This disruption occurs in animals reared normally until the brief period of deprivation; a few hours of occlusion is apparently sufficient to undo the accomplishments of 5 wk of normal visual experience (138, 274).

Since the initial report (416) the physiological consequences of monocular deprivation have been studied in various species, including rabbits (388), lambs (241), mice (113), owls (299), and hamsters (119). In monkeys the effects seem even more profound than in cats (15, 38, 46, 190, 229, 397). The severity of the visual loss observed in humans after even brief early monocular impediments to patterned visual input, a phenomenon referred to as deprivation amblyopia (392, 393), suggests that the underlying anatomical and physiological defects may be equally profound (e.g., refs. 13, 14, 171, 393).

The extent to which monocular deprivation disturbs the visual system and the extent to which subsequent recovery is possible depends on several factors, the most significant being the age at which occlusion is imposed and the duration of the deprivation period. Before discussing these topics in detail, however, we shall describe the effects of monocular deprivation on different levels of the geniculostriate pathway and discuss the mechanisms proposed to account for such effects.

VISUAL OPTICS. Monocular deprivation can result in prominent increases in the axial dimensions of the eyes of certain species. This was first observed in the monkey (420), and although the finding was initially disputed (396), it appears to occur in most animals (311, 329, 421). A similar phenomenon, but of smaller magnitude, has been observed in cats with the lids of one eye sutured shut (216, 425), although this also is not a consistent finding (147). The consequence of an increased axial length is myopia, unless compensatory changes occur in the cornea or lens. The refractive state of the monkey eye does become highly myopic (420), but there is evidence that in the cat the increased axial length may in part be compensated for by a reduction in the refractive power of the cornea (216).

Recent evidence suggests that myopia may also be induced in cats by optically imposed anisometropia (342). The magnitude of the refractive error induced [about 2 diopters (2 D)] is not great, and would be unlikely to influence behavioral measures of visual acuity. In monkeys, however, myopia induced by unilateral lid suture can be large (13 D) and could influence behavioral assessment of visual function of the deprived eye in those animals. There are indications that early monocular lid closure, such as that resulting from ptosis or hemangiomas, may produce similar changes in refractive state in humans (e.g., refs. 183, 273).

RETINA AND LATERAL GENICULATE NUCLEUS. There is no evidence that monocular deprivation produces changes in retinal anatomy or function (330). Even sensitive measurement of ganglion cell properties, such as spatial resolving power, reveal no abnormalities in resolution among the major classes of ganglion cell at any retinal eccentricity (70, 217).

At the level of the LGN, results are less certain. Although there are very obvious anatomical changes following monocular deprivation, there is uncertainty concerning the nature of any physiological deficit. A reduction by as much as 30% in the cross-sectional area of cells in the deprived layers of the LGN of the cat and monkey is one of the most consistent consequences of monocular occlusion. After Wiesel and Hubel's (415) original description in the cat, Guillery and Stelzner (158) indicated that cell shrinkage was limited to that part of the LGN subserving the binocular visual field, with no effect on the monocular segment. Later studies indicate that there is also some shrinkage in the monocular segment (173), although with considerable variability among animals (172) and within the segment itself (206). In general the differential effects of monocular occlusion in the binocular and monocular segments of the monkey LGN are not nearly so marked as in the cat (395, 401), and in animals deprived for long periods of time no differential effects are apparent (404).

Although these anatomical effects are well established, most of the other anatomical and physiological changes that have been described in the LGN are less so. The major dispute centers on the magnitude of the effects of monocular deprivation on X- and Y-cells. Sherman et al. (328) originally observed that monocular deprivation led to a marked reduction in the encounter rate of Y-cells within the deprived layers of the cat LGN, with no apparent loss of X-cells. Later studies suggested that X-cells were also affected. This was manifested as a reduction in spatial resolution by about a factor of two (223, 224, 338). Further suggestions of functional disturbance of LGN function in monocularly deprived cats have been derived from application of current source-density analysis (254, 255). Later reports (106, 322), however, have failed to confirm either the reduction in encounter rates of Y-cells or the resolution deficits in X-cells in cats. The latter reports agree with studies on monocularly deprived monkeys, for which there is no evidence of any enhanced effects on the magnocellular layers of the LGN (404), in which Y-cells are segregated (114), or of any effects on the spatial resolution of X-cells within the parvocellular layers (45). The star symbols of Figure 9 show mean spatial resolution of foveal LGN X-cells in the deprived eye of monkeys that were monocularly deprived from birth for between 4 days and 27 wk. Comparison of these data with those from normal animals (filled circles) indicates that monocular occlusion did not hinder the improvement in resolution with age. In view of the contradictory reports in cats and the absence of any reported effect on LGN cells in monkeys, it must be concluded that the effects of monocular deprivation on the functional properties of LGN cells are subtle in comparison to the clear effects on the visual cortex.

VISUAL CORTEX. *Layer IV.* One of the most significant additions to the early observations of Wiesel and Hubel (416) has been the finding that a substantial proportion of cells in layer IV of the visual cortex of monocularly deprived cats (323) and monkeys (46, 190) can be excited through the deprived eye. This finding was confirmed in the same preparations using anatomical methods that permit visualization of the geniculocortical afferents from each eye in layer IV of the cat and layer IVc of the monkey. In the normal adult cat or monkey the geniculocortical afferents from the two eyes are segregated into alternating bands at their terminations in layer IV (cat) or layer IVc (monkey) of the visual cortex. These bands provide the basis of the physiologically identified ocular dominance columns (184, 187) that extend vertically through the cortex (212). After early monocular deprivation the pattern of termination of geniculocortical afferents in layer IV of both cat (323) and monkey (190) is radically altered. The proportion of layer IV representing the deprived eye is diminished substantially, with a corresponding increase in the representation of the other eye. This finding is shown in Figure 15, which compares the ocular dominance banding pattern of a normal adult monkey, 15A, with that of a monocularly deprived animal, 15C. As illustrated in Figure 15B, the normal adult pattern of ocular dominance columns is achieved by 6 wk of age. In both the cat (323) and monkey (190) there is a convincing coincidence between the location of cells in layer IV that are dominated by the deprived eye and the anatomically visualized location of geniculocortical afferents from that eye.

Effects outside layer IV. Whereas a significant proportion (as much as 20%) of layer IVc remains controlled by the deprived eye in monkeys that were monocularly deprived in the first few days of postnatal life (229), virtually all cortical cells outside of this layer are strongly or completely dominated by the nondeprived eye (190, 323). This is just as apparent in cortical layers directly above or below the deprived eye columns in layer IV (38, 190). There have been no reports of silent cortex in any region of the visual cortex of monocularly deprived cats or monkeys. In addition, periods of monocular deprivation imposed after 10 wk of age and even as late as 1 yr can influence the distribution of cortical ocular dominance cells outside of layer IV without changing the relative sizes of ocular dominance bands within layer IV (38, 190, 229, 323). These observations imply that the changes observed outside of layer IV are brought about by a different mechanism from that responsible for alterations in layer IV. Such a mechanism probably involves changes in intracortical connectivity.

MINIMAL REQUIREMENTS FOR MONOCULAR DEPRIVATION. Monocular occlusion by lid suture both prevents pattern vision and attenuates the amount of light falling on the retina by several log units (77, 235, 425). But even relatively minor disturbances of the visual input of one eye can have far-reaching consequences. In their initial description of the phenomenon Wiesel and Hubel (415, 416) reported that suture of the nictitating membrane across the cornea, which reduces retinal illumination only by about 1 or 2 log units (77), produces cortical effects which are just as severe as those found with eye suture. Of the two consequences of eyelid suture, degradation of pattern vision and reduction of retinal illuminance, it is the former that is critical in the cat (32, 426). Simple unilateral reduction of retinal illuminance with a neutral density filter has only a very minor effect, whereas a translucent occluder in front of one eye and a neutral density filter over the other to equalize the retinal illuminance for the two eyes produces a complete shift of ocular dominance (32). A similar conclusion can be drawn for monkeys on the basis of results obtained on animals made unilaterally aphakic in the 1st mo of life. Although the effects on the cortex were not assessed, cell shrinkage in the appropriate recipient LGN laminae was as great as that observed after monocular lid suture (395). The implausible premise (200) that total unilateral deprivation (total absence of visual stimulation) may produce less deleterious effects on the visual cortex than an equivalent period of unilateral lid suture, which permits transmission of diffuse light, has been explored in monkeys (399). The effects on cortical ocular dominance and geniculate cell morphology that result from these two deprivation procedures appear to be identical.

Clinically there are a number of conditions that result in unilateral image degradation. At one extreme are severe medial opacities that severely degrade the retinal image. Much more common, however, are conditions in which one image is simply defocused due to the presence of uncorrected anisometropia. Because this is commonly associated with amblyopia (117, 392), attempts have been made to examine the effects of artificially induced anisometropia on the development of the visual pathways.

The cortical effects of anisometropia, induced by having kittens wear goggles containing a −8 D or −12 D lens in front of one eye, have been examined by Eggers and Blakemore (118). Although there was a reduction in the proportion of binocularly excited cells to 30%, the shift in ocular dominance toward the normal eye was not as marked as that following an equivalent period of monocular lid suture (32, 274). A similar finding was reported by Freeman (131) and Smith et al. (345) in kittens reared in a similar manner. Although the effects on cortical ocular dominance were not dramatic, Eggers and Blakemore noted a very obvious reduction in the spatial resolution of neurons excited through the deprived eye. Cells monocularly excited by the originally defocused eye tended to have lower cutoff spatial frequencies as well as lower contrast sensitivities compared to those excited by the normal eye. This difference was also observed in the remaining binocular cells. An indication of the consequences for vision can be obtained by superimposing the contrast sensitivity curves of every neuron for each eye and drawing the envelope of the highest contrast sensitivity among the curves over the full range of spatial frequencies. The results predict a greater deficit in performance at high than at low spatial frequencies in the originally defocused eye, a result consistent with the visual loss experienced in general by human anisometropes (170, 232).

Ikeda and Tremain (192) reported reduced resolution in LGN neurons of cats rendered anisometropic by daily instillation of atropine sulfate. This result should be accepted with caution, however, in view of results of other investigators in which no evidence was found for loss of spatial resolution following more severe deprivation such as lid suture (106, 322). It is also possible that the effects observed may be a consequence of some trophic effect of atropine on the retina itself. Although chronic unilateral atropinization produces only subtle effects on the visual cortex (192), it apparently causes the treated eye to become amblyopic (53, 345).

RECOVERY FROM THE EFFECTS OF MONOCULAR DEPRIVATION. Although the physiological effects of prolonged periods of early monocular visual deprivation on the kitten visual cortex are apparently permanent (e.g., refs. 179, 418), substantial recovery can occur if visual input to the deprived eye is restored sufficiently early. Behavioral (146, 245) and physiological (48, 245, 275) experiments have shown that significant cortical recovery can occur in monocularly deprived kittens following extended periods of binocular vision. However, the degree of recovery is substantially greater if

the animal is forced to use its formerly deprived eye by occluding the other eye, a procedure referred to as reverse occlusion (42, 48, 245, 275). The recovery of excitatory influence of the deprived eye is observed only if visual input is restored to this eye and does not occur spontaneously if the animal is placed in darkness after the initial period of monocular occlusion (275, 276). The rate of the recovery that can occur on restoration of normal visual input to the two eyes is illustrated by the fact that kittens subjected daily to a 4-h period of monocular occlusion showed normal cortical ocular dominance when allowed 18 h of normal binocular visual input between each daily period of monocular occlusion (276).

A similar recovery of the influence of the deprived eye on the cortex was observed in monkeys that were reverse sutured early in life (38, 46, 229, 360; see also SENSITIVE PERIODS, p. 530). In contrast to kittens, however, little or no recovery occurs on simple restoration of visual input to the deprived eye; forced usage of the deprived eye appears to be essential to recovery in the visual cortex of monocularly deprived monkeys (15, 46, 190, 229). The lack of recovery in the visual cortex of monocularly deprived monkeys that were subsequently allowed visual input to both eyes stands in striking contrast to the recovery of vision observed in similar circumstances in human infants that have suffered a brief period of monocular occlusion or deprivation (199).

BEHAVIORAL CONSEQUENCES OF MONOCULAR DEPRIVATION. Kittens monocularly deprived for an extended period from near birth appear to be completely blind when forced to use the deprived eye (e.g., refs. 146, 245, 416). The severity of the visual deficits thus parallels the magnitude of the changes observed in the visual cortex. In time, however, some recovery of visual function occurs, the rate and extent of which depend on the temporal parameters of the initial period of monocular deprivation (e.g., refs. 107, 145, 146, 422; and Fig. 16). The vision of the deprived eye is impaired in several respects, including the ability to mediate complex visuomotor behavior (e.g., ref. 107) and orienting responses (326), and the ability to learn complex visual pattern discriminations (144). However, the measure of visual loss that can be correlated with changes in cortical or geniculate physiology with the fewest assumptions is the deficit in spatial resolution.

After periods of monocular lid suture from birth to 6.5 wk of age, the temporal course of recovery of visual acuity in the deprived eye closely follows the rate of reversal of cortical ocular dominance (146, 260). However, the final acuity achieved in the deprived eye is better than might be predicted from the magnitude of the remaining cortical deficit expressed in terms of the proportion of cells dominated by the formerly deprived eye (245). This result serves to focus attention on the need for documentation of the properties of the cells dominated by the deprived eye, as well as knowledge

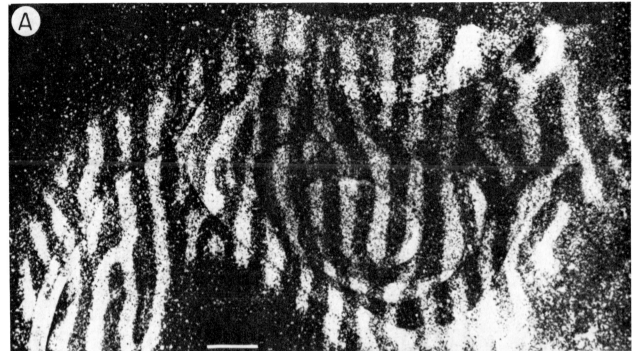

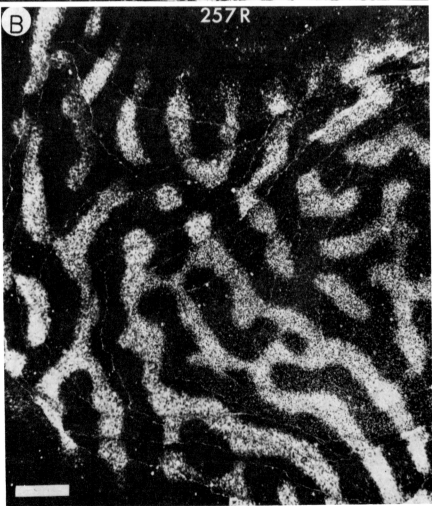

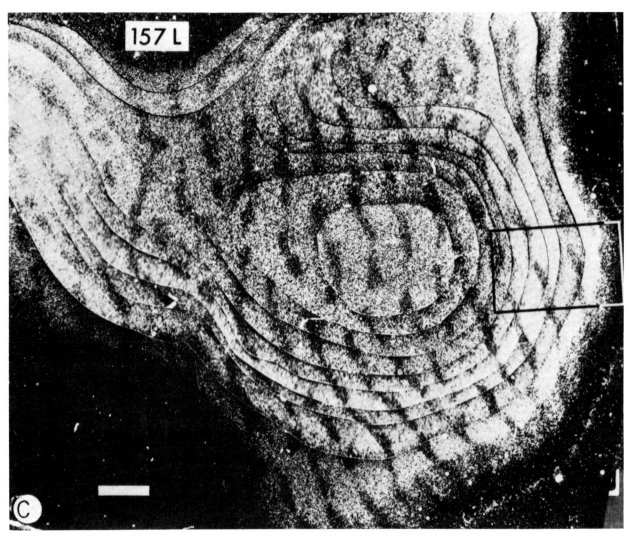

FIG. 15. Autoradiographic montages showing labeling pattern of ocular dominance columns of layer IVc of normal (*A* and *B*) and monocularly deprived (*C*) monkeys (*Macaca mulatta*). *A*: pattern of labeling in hemisphere contralateral to injected eye of normal adult monkey. *B*: labeling pattern from 6-wk-old normal monkey ipsilateral to injected eye. Labeled bands are as distinct as in adults. *C*: labeling pattern from monkey whose right eye was closed by eyelid suture at 2 wk of age. Left eye injected when animal was 18 mo old. Note expansion of labeled columns from open eye at expense of unlabeled columns for deprived eye. However, periodicity of columns, about 750 μm for a left-right pair, was identical to that of normal monkey. Unlabeled horizontal bars are 1 mm long. [From Hubel and Weisel (189) and LeVay et al. (229).]

of the relative number of such cells (36, 118, 146, 245). With increasing periods of deprivation the time taken for visual function mediated via the deprived eye to appear becomes progressively longer and the amount of vision eventually attained becomes smaller. This point is illustrated in Figure 16, which shows the time course of recovery of visual acuity of four cats monocularly deprived from birth to either 2, 4, 6, or 10 mo. Cats deprived for longer periods from birth recover only rudimentary form vision (203, 340).

Severe visual deficits comparable to those in kittens are observed in monkeys that have been monocularly deprived from near birth for 20 mo or more (15, 393, 403). Even after periods of recovery as long as 2 yr,

most animals recover only the ability to make brightness or color discriminations with their deprived eye, although some animals do recover rudimentary form vision (393). Periods of deprivation as brief as 2–4 wk imposed in the first 6 wk can lead to severe and permanent visual impairment (393). The amblyopia that follows brief periods of monocular lid suture in both cats (146) and monkeys (393) is far more profound than would be anticipated if the effect of monocular occlusion were simply to arrest the development of visual function in that eye at the level it had achieved at the time of lid suture.

Visual loss as severe as that observed in the deprived eye of cats and monkeys is also observed in humans

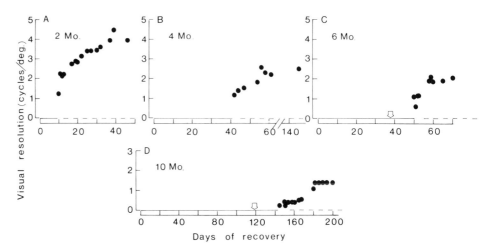

FIG. 16. Behavioral recovery of visual acuity (for square-wave gratings) of deprived eye of 4 cats monocularly deprived by eyelid suture from time of natural opening until ages indicated. After termination of period of monocular occlusion, visual input was allowed to both eyes. Measurement of visual acuity of formerly deprived eye was made with large opaque contact lens occluder covering nondeprived eye. During period indicated by *horizontal lines* animals were unable to make pattern discriminations on jumping stand. *Arrows* indicate days on which animals showed ability to discriminate a closed versus an open door on jumping stand using visual cues alone. [Data in *A* and *B* adapted from Giffin and Mitchell (146).]

with comparable early visual histories. Deprivation amblyopia is a well-recognized (392) clinical condition linked to a reversible peripheral obstruction to clear pattern vision in one eye during the first few years of life. A number of reports indicate that even brief periods of unilateral deprivation by cataracts or other conditions in early life can lead to severe visual deficits that remain despite rigorous attempts at treatment (13, 14, 196, 284, 392, 393). In some cases deprivation amblyopia secondary to a unilateral cataract is severe enough to lead to a complete loss of the capacity for resolving stationary or temporally modulated gratings. These subjects can detect the temporal attributes (flicker or movement) of the stimulus but cannot detect any pattern (171).

BINOCULAR COMPETITION. Wiesel and Hubel (417) observed that the effects of binocular deprivation on the visual cortex were much less extreme than the consequences of monocular occlusion. This is also reflected in the behavioral consequences of the two deprivation regimens (cf. Figs. 12 and 16). Although the initial behavioral deficits are similar, the rate and extent of visual recovery of dark-reared animals is substantially greater than that of the deprived eye of monocularly deprived animals. This difference is particularly obvious with primates. For example, infant monkeys dark reared to 3 or 6 mo recover very good visual acuity within a month (312), yet animals monocularly deprived for a similar period may never recover form vision in the deprived eye (393).

The vastly different effects of the two forms of deprivation on the visual cortex led Wiesel and Hubel (417) to propose that the functional integrity of the cortex depends not only on the total afferent activity

from the two eyes but also on a competitive interaction between the pathways from the two eyes. The effects in the visual cortex suggest that the afferent paths from the two eyes compete for control of cortical cells. According to this idea the open eye of a monocularly deprived animal is at a competitive advantage and gains functional control of target neurons in the cortex to the detriment of the deprived eye. Wiesel and Hubel suggested that the site of this competitive interaction was at the cortex; this idea is supported by the results of recent studies that employ a cylindrical lens in front of one eye. This lens clearly images only contours of a single orientation [Fig. 26; (91, 309)]. As a consequence binocular competition is possible only among cells (such as those in the visual cortex) that are orientation specific, but not among nonoriented cells. The actual mechanism of this binocular competition is still unknown, but the concept has proved extremely useful in accounting for various phenomena related to asymmetric binocular experience, including the effect of strabismus and alternating monocular deprivation (described in *Artificial Strabismus*, p. 535, and *Alternating Monocular Deprivation*, p. 537).

A process of binocular competition provides an explanation of the different physiological effects of monocular and binocular deprivation on the visual cortex, and is consistent with the accompanying morphological changes observed in the LGN. As Guillery and Stelzner (155) originally proposed, the differential shrinkage between the binocular and monocular segments strongly suggests a competitive interaction between the two eyes. Further support for a competitive mechanism was provided by the results of an experiment in which a small retinal lesion was produced in the nondeprived eye of a monocularly deprived cat to produce an artificial critical segment (153). Cells in the LGN laminae representing this same segment of the visual field for the deprived eye did not show any shrinkage (153). This result has been subsequently confirmed using behavioral and physiological measurements (327), and similar anatomical findings have been reported for the monkey (401).

The correlation between the magnitude and the time course of the morphological effects on the LGN and the relative sizes of left and right eye cortical ocular dominance columns (e.g., refs. 229, 262, 389) indicates that the effects observed in the LGN may be a secondary consequence of the binocular competition mechanism in the cortex responsible for the cortical effects of monocular deprivation. Thus the size of LGN neurons is related more to the size of axonal arborizations that they must sustain in the visual cortex (153, 226) than to specific changes in the LGN itself.

A mechanism involving binocular competition has been proposed by Hubel et al. (190) to account for both the normal postnatal segregation of ocular dominance columns in layer IV of the visual cortex of the cat and the monkey and the abnormal columnar organization observed in monocularly deprived animals. In both the cat (228) and the monkey (306), left eye and right eye afferents are intermingled in layer IV at birth. Although segregation into right and left columns for the monkey begins in utero, the process is not complete until 6 wk after birth (229, 306). In the cat the process of segregation is delayed until 3 wk after birth, but as in the monkey is completed at 6 wk of age (228). Hubel et al. (190) argue that the process of segregation into columns proceeds by retraction of both the left and right eye set of terminals through a process of binocular competition in areas occupied by both sets of terminals. Experiments performed on monkeys that had one eye enucleated in utero suggest that the process of binocular competition may even begin to exercise its influence before birth (307). In animals monocularly deprived from birth, in which one set of terminals has a competitive advantage, the same process of segregation takes place, with the exception that it is only the afferents from the deprived eye that retract. As a consequence afferents from the open eye retain territory they would normally relinquish, whereas afferents from the deprived eye abandon more territory than under normal conditions. In general it was suggested that as normal segregation proceeds the probability of binocular competition decreases, thereby decreasing the susceptibility of layer IV to the effects of monocular deprivation. This opinion receives some support from experiments performed on cats that either accentuate the process of separation of inputs from the two eyes by imposing an artificial strabismus (269) or reduce it by depriving both eyes of vision by dark rearing (359).

On the basis of this theory it should be possible only to alter the relative width of right and left eye columns in layer IVc of the monkey during the first 6 wk of life, the period in which segregation normally takes place. However, observations made on animals monocularly deprived at 5.5 wk or reverse sutured slightly later indicate that the period during which anatomical changes can be observed in layer IVc outlasts the period in life during which segregation normally takes place by several weeks (229).

SUPPRESSED SYNAPSES? A mechanism involving competition between afferents from the two eyes can account for most of the anatomical and physiological changes observed in layer IV of the cortex, but it is unclear whether the alterations of intracortical connections observed in other layers occur in the same manner. A number of observations suggest the operation of an alternative mechanism in which cortical cells retain inputs from the deprived eye that are suppressed by a tonic inhibitory influence from the nondeprived eye. Evidence for this possibility was first raised by reports that enucleation of the nondeprived eye in the long-term monocularly deprived cats results in an immediate increase in the proportion of cells that can be excited through the deprived eye (219, 343). This has been observed several times (80, 179, 385), although there have been some negative findings (39, 161, 163). The original physiological observation is supported by behavioral data that suggest significant improvement in the visual acuity of the deprived eye over that produced by simple reverse suture (340, 341) as a result of enucleation of the nondeprived eye. Again it should be noted that this behavioral finding is not consistent (203).

Further evidence of a suppression mechanism in the cortical effect of monocular deprivation has been provided by Singer (334), who, on the basis of a study of the potentials evoked by electrical stimulation of the optic nerve, reported that intracortical inhibitory pathways appear to be less affected by monocular deprivation than transmission in excitatory pathways. In addition Fiorentini and Maffei (127), by averaging hundreds of responses, found evidence of even weak excitatory inputs from the deprived eye onto cortical cells of monocularly deprived cats. Subthreshold input in response to visual stimulation of the deprived eye has recently been demonstrated (38a) during reversible pressure blinding of the nondeprived eye and also during iontophoretic administration of DL-homocysteic acid, which increases the excitability of cortical cells.

The most direct evidence for a suppressed input from the deprived eye in monocularly deprived cats, however, stems from studies of the effects of administration of bicuculline, an antagonist to the inhibitory neurotransmitter γ-aminobutyric acid (GABA). Several years ago Duffy et al. (115) reported a similar effect to that observed after enucleation with intravenous administration of bicuculline, an antagonist to GABA. The latter result has been explored subsequently in greater detail by Sillito and co-workers

(333) by iontophoretic application of bicuculline in the region immediately adjacent to individually recorded cortical cells in monocularly deprived cats (62, 332) and to cortical cells of extreme ocular dominance (group 1 or 7) in normal cats. Of 51 cells recorded from monocularly deprived cats that were all initially dominated exclusively by the nondeprived eye, 29% became responsive to visual stimulation of the deprived eye during application of bicuculline (332). However, this is significantly less than the proportion (approximately 50%) of monocularly dominated cells in normal cats that change ocular dominance in response to administration of bicuculline (333). In addition to the smaller proportion of cells that changed ocular dominance in monocularly deprived cats, the extent of the shift among those cells that did change was significantly less than that observed in normal animals. This suggests that GABA-mediated intracortical inhibitory processes exert a greater influence on ocular dominance in the normal visual cortex than in the cortex of monocularly deprived cats.

Together these results suggest the operation of a suppression mechanism in some of the cortical effects of monocular deprivation. The existence of such a mechanism could explain the rapid recovery observed in monocularly deprived kittens following restoration of visual input to the deprived eye. Although at present it appears that interocular suppression plays a secondary role to the redistribution of afferents within layer IV, it is possible that future investigations of the role of potential inhibitory neurotransmitters other than GABA may cause this conclusion to be revised.

SENSITIVE PERIODS. Detailed discussion of the evidence for sensitive periods in visual development together with speculations about their functional role are to be found in a number of recent reviews (6, 244, 294, 398).

Cats. The period of vulnerability of the kitten visual cortex to the effects of monocular deprivation was determined by Hubel and Wiesel (188) from examination of the physiological effects of periods of monocular occlusion imposed on different animals at various ages. Their data indicated that susceptibility to monocular occlusion "begins suddenly near the start of the fourth week, at about the time a kitten begins to use its eyes, and persists until some time between the sixth and eighth week; it then begins to decline, disappearing ultimately around the end of the third month" (ref. 188, p. 434). Unfortunately, because unequal periods of occlusion were employed at different ages, the results provide only a rough picture of the changing susceptibility of the cortex to monocular occlusion. This information can be obtained most accurately by subjecting each kitten to a fixed period of deprivation. Such a design was employed recently by Olson and Freeman (277) who imposed a constant 10-day period of monocular occlusion on 11 different kittens at progressively later ages. The distribution of

cortical ocular dominance from each kitten is displayed in Figure 17.

The picture of the changing cortical vulnerability to the effects of monocular deprivation that emerges from these data is illustrated in Figure 18. On the ordinate is plotted an index of the effect of the 10-day period of deprivation on cortical ocular dominance. This index, which is defined more precisely in the legend, was based on the proportion of cells dominated by the nondeprived eye. The index is defined in such a way that it has a mean value of zero for normal cats and a value of 1.0 in animals in which no cells were dominated by the deprived eye.

The data of Figures 17 and 18 suggest that the sensitive period begins earlier, at 2 wk of age, and that it persists longer, beyond 4 mo of age, than previously thought. Moreover the decline in vulnerability from 6 wk of age is apparently more gradual than estimates based on results obtained from reverse-sutured kittens (Fig. 18, open circles) by Blakemore and Van Sluyters

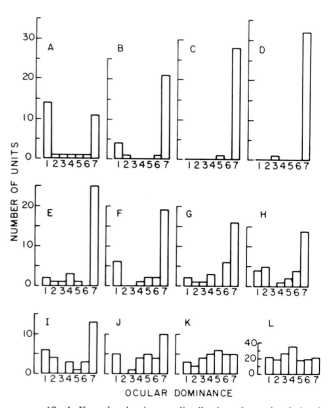

FIG. 17. *A–K*: ocular dominance distribution of sample of visual cortical neurons recorded in each of 11 kittens subjected to 10 and 12 days of monocular deprivation at progressively later ages. *L*: distribution of cortical ocular dominance of 4 normal kittens recorded at 45, 48, 55, or 135 days of age, respectively, is shown for comparison. Periods over which kittens (*A–K*) were monocularly deprived were: *A*, 8–19 days; *B*, 18–27 days; *C*, 28–37 days; *D*, 38–47 days; *E*, 48–57 days; *F*, 58–67 days; *G*, 69–79 days; *H*, 80–90 days; *I*, 91–100 days; *J*, 99–109 days; *K*, 109–120 days. Right eye was deprived by eyelid suture in every case, and recordings were made in left (contralateral) hemisphere. Ocular dominance groups are as defined in Fig. 14. [From Olson and Freeman (277).]

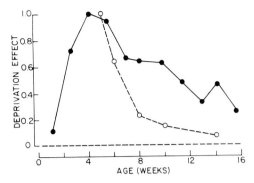

FIG. 18. Profile of sensitive period for monocular deprivation in kittens. *Filled circles* depict degree of functional disconnection resulting from 10–12 days of monocular deprivation imposed on various kittens at ages indicated. Effect of deprivation period expressed by index based on proportion of cells dominated by ipsilateral (nondeprived) eye [(percentage of cells in groups 5–7) − N]/[100% − N], where N was average percentage of cells in groups 5–7 (36%) in 4 normal kittens (see Fig. 17L). *Open circles* show data of Blakemore and Van Sluyters (32) obtained from kittens reverse sutured for 9 wk at ages indicated. Again, effect of period of reverse suture is expressed by index equal to proportion of cells dominated by originally deprived eye (percentage of cells in groups 5–7). [From Olson and Freeman (277).]

(42). The suggestion from the data of Olson and Freeman (277) that cortical susceptibility to monocular occlusion extends beyond 4 mo of age was verified by Cynader et al. (94) from examination of the effects of a 3-mo period of monocular eyelid closure imposed on different kittens at either 4, 5, 6, 7, or 8 mo of age. The distribution of ocular dominance among cortical cells recorded from animals reared under these conditions is shown in Figure 19. An obvious bias for cells to be dominated by the nondeprived eye is apparent in animals subjected to monocular deprivation at 4, 5, and 6 mo. Cortical cells in the animal deprived at 7 mo showed no tendency for either eye to dominate, whereas the sample recorded from the animal deprived at 8 mo exhibited the tendency observed in normally reared animals for cells to be dominated by the eye contralateral to the recording electrode. Together these data indicate that binocular cortical connections remain susceptible to disruption by monocular deprivation well beyond 6 mo of age.

Figure 17 indicates that an animal monocularly deprived between the 8th and 19th postnatal days suffers a disruption of cortical binocularity without any appreciable shift towards dominance by the open eye. A reduction in the proportion of binocular cells frequently precedes a shift toward control by the nondeprived eye (131, 188). In an earlier study (131) the rising phase of the sensitive period was studied on a larger group of kittens that were each deprived for 4 days at different ages. No effect on cortical ocular dominance was evident when deprivation began at 9 days, but kittens deprived at day 13 or later exhibited both a breakdown of binocularity and a shift of control toward the open eye. Thus it appears that susceptibility to monocular occlusion is present at 2 wk of age.

Although the rising phase of the sensitive period corresponds approximately to the time when the optical quality of the eye is improving, it is highly unlikely that it alone can account for the reduced susceptibility to monocular occlusion (51, 103).

An alternative approach to determining the time course is to examine the extent of recovery from the effects of a period of monocular occlusion that follows a period of reverse occlusion during which the animal is forced to use its deprived eye. This procedure was employed by Blakemore and Van Sluyters (42), who imposed a 9-wk period of reverse occlusion at progressively later ages during the 2nd and 3rd mo on five kittens monocularly deprived from birth. The extent of reversal of cortical ocular dominance, defined by a reversal index (the proportion of cells dominated by the initially deprived eye), is given by the open circles in Figure 18. Animals reverse sutured early, at 5 or 6 wk, showed almost complete reversal, which suggests that during the sensitive period the functional binocular connections can be both broken and reestablished. Both the extent and the rate (260) of cortical recovery, however, decline very rapidly after 6 wk of age, such that reversal at 14 wk results in almost no recapture of connections by the initially deprived eye (42). The rapid decline of the ability of cortical connections to become reestablished once broken (Fig. 18, open circles) appears to be far more precipitous than the very gradual reduction in the susceptibility of cortical connections to disruption by monocular occlusion. This difference may be attributed to the design of the reverse-suture experiment (42), in which the age of the animal at the time of reverse suture is confounded with the length of the initial period of deprivation; animals reverse sutured later also were subjected initially to a longer period of monocular occlusion.

The suggestion (94, 277) that binocular cortical connections in the cat remain susceptible to monocular occlusion beyond 4 mo of age is supported by behavioral findings indicating that the deprived eye recovers some vision even after periods of occlusion that extend to 1 yr of age (244, 340). It thus appears that binocular cortical connections may retain some residual susceptibility to disruption of visual input well into adolescence, a possibility that is considered further in *Functional Role of Visual Experience*, p. 544.

The mechanisms of control of the sensitive period are not known, but some possible biochemical mechanisms have been explored. Kasamatsu and Pettigrew (208–210) hypothesized that the presence of catecholamine neurohormones, particularly norepinephrine, originating in the locus ceruleus is necessary for the maintenance of cortical plasticity during the critical period. They showed that depletion of brain catecholamines by intraventricular injection or cortical microperfusion of 6-hydroxydopamine prevented disruption of binocular connections in monocularly deprived kittens (208–210, 298). However, they were able to restore susceptibility to monocular occlusion in catechola-

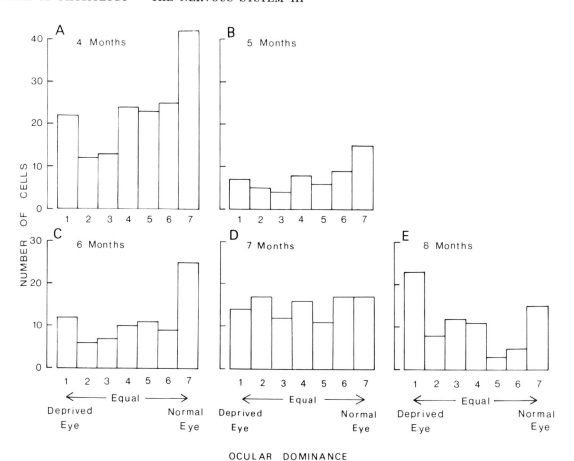

FIG. 19. Distribution of ocular dominance among samples of cells recorded from visual cortex of a number of cats monocularly deprived for 3 mo at ages indicated. In each case microelectrode was located in hemisphere contralateral to deprived eye. [From Cynader, Timney, and Mitchell (94).]

mine-depleted kittens by subsequent microperfusion of norepinephrine. They also were able to induce a limited degree of plasticity in adult cats by this same procedure (210).

Monkeys. Early behavioral experiments (393, 403) suggested that the sensitive period for the monkey may be quite short. Later physiological data (38, 190, 229, 398), however, indicate that cortical susceptibility to monocular deprivation extends beyond 1 yr of age, at least in cortical layers other than layer IVc.

The most extensive study is that of LeVay et al. (228), who combined cortical single-unit recording with autoradiographic visualization of ocular dominance columns in layer IVc of the visual cortex, and cross-sectional area measurements of cells in the LGN. From this set of measurements it was possible to obtain a picture of the different periods of vulnerability to the effects of monocular deprivation for both layer IVc and the other cortical layers. Representative cortical ocular dominance histograms from several animals in this series are shown in Figure 20. These include data only from cells outside layer IVc and thus provide information on the sensitive period for these other layers. Included for comparison is a pooled ocular dominance histogram based on recordings from

1,256 cells in area 17 of a number of normal adult and juvenile rhesus monkeys (419).

A normalized ocular dominance index was derived from each of the ocular-dominance histograms published by LeVay et al. (229). This index has a value of zero for normal monkeys and a value of 1 for a complete ocular dominance shift toward the nondeprived eye. Normalization was achieved by calculating the mean ocular dominance for normal monkeys, 4.3, based on results obtained earlier by Wiesel and Hubel (419). A normalized index was then calculated from the ocular dominance histogram for each monkey by using the formula (4.3 − mean ocular dominance)/3.3 for those animals in which recordings were made in the hemisphere (right) ipsilateral to the deprived eye, and (mean ocular dominance − 4.3)/2.7 for the others in which the electrode was located in the left hemisphere.

The filled symbols in Figure 21 depict values obtained in this manner for all animals, plotted as a function of the age at eyelid closure (log scale). The horizontal line to the right of each symbol represents the period of eyelid suture. The effect of deprivation on the relative areas of the left and right eye ocular dominance bands in layer IVc of the same animals are indicated by the open symbols and the ordinate at right. The effect of the period of deprivation is expressed by an index defined as the difference between the area occupied by the open-eye afferents, L, and that devoted to the deprived eye, R, as a function of the total area, L + R, of the reconstruction. An index was calculated for both hemispheres in those animals where column areas were measured on both sides of the brain. This index has a value of zero in normal animals where the left and right eye columns are equal in width (190) and a value of 1 where the columns of the deprived eye are completely eliminated.

Even short periods of deprivation in the 1st mo of postnatal life result in a dramatic shift in cortical ocular dominance and column area in layer IV. But thereafter the vulnerability of cortical layers other than IVc declines slowly. Even an animal deprived at 1 yr for a year showed an appreciable effect (see also Fig. 20). Although the index calculated from an adult animal deprived for 1.5 yr at 6 yr was still above zero, it should not be taken as an indication of the existence of some residual sensitivity to monocular eyelid clo-

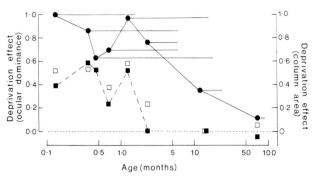

FIG. 21. Profile of sensitive period of visual cortex of monkeys to anatomical and physiological effects of monocular deprivation. *Filled circles* show effects of periods of monocular deprivation on cortical ocular dominance in cortical layers other than IVc (left ordinate), whereas *open* and *filled squares* depict concurrent effects on ocular dominance column area within layer IVc (right ordinate). Each *filled circle* depicts results from individual monkeys monocularly deprived at various ages for a duration indicated by length of *horizontal line* to right of each symbol. Physiological effects of period of monocular occlusion are expressed in form of normalized deprivation index calculated as follows: mean ocular dominance was first calculated from distribution of ocular dominance for sample of cortical cells recorded from each animal (such as those shown in Fig. 20). This was then normalized with respect to mean ocular dominance for normal animals (419) of 4.3 by using the formula (4.3 − mean ocular dominance)/3.3 for animals in which recordings were made in right hemisphere ipsilateral to deprived eye and the formula (mean ocular dominance − 4.3)/2.7 for animals in which recordings were made in left hemisphere. *Filled and open squares* show effects of monocular deprivation on ocular dominance column area in layer IVc expressed as ratio L − R/L + R, where L and R denote area in layer IVc devoted to left (nondeprived) and right (deprived) eye, respectively. *Filled symbols* indicate effects on column area in left hemisphere contralateral to deprived eye, and *open symbols* show effect in right hemisphere. [Adapted from LeVay et al. (229).]

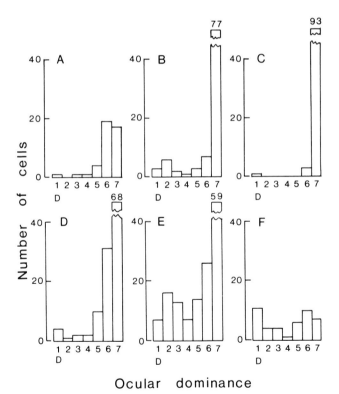

Ocular dominance

FIG. 20. Distribution of ocular dominance among sample of visual cortical cells recorded in each of 6 monkeys subjected to a period of monocular deprivation at progressively later ages. Periods of eyelid closure were from *A*, day 2 to day 24; *B*, day 21 to day 36; *C*, 5.5 wk to 16 mo; *D*, 10 wk to 16 mo; *E*, 1 yr to 2 yr; and *F*, 6 yr to 7.5 yr. Although effects of period of monocular deprivation were assessed only in right hemisphere of 3 monkeys (*C*, *D*, and *F*), results from these particular animals are depicted as if obtained from left hemisphere, contralateral to deprived eye. Ocular dominance groups are as defined for Fig. 14. Letter D indicates group completely dominated by the deprived eye. [Adapted from LeVay et al. (229).]

sure at that age, because the sample of cells studied in this animal was small. The sensitive period in layer IVc is obviously considerably shorter than that of the other cortical layers. The effects of monocular deprivation on layer IVc were extensive until 6 wk of age but thereafter became small or negligible. In layer IVc no effects were seen for any animal on which deprivation was imposed after 10 wk of age. Generally the effects observed on column area in layer IVc matched very closely the changes in cross-sectional cell area in the LGN (229).

Limited data from a number of monkeys reverse sutured at different ages (38, 229) provide additional support for the general picture of the sensitive period that emerges from Figure 21. As with the cat (Fig. 18), however, there are indications from reverse-sutured monkeys that the proportion of cells recovering connections with the initially deprived eye declines somewhat more precipitously than the fraction of neurons in normal animals that can become disconnected by a period of monocular deprivation. For example, whereas a normal monkey subjected to lid suture at 1 yr shows a definite shift in cortical ocular dominance, monkeys monocularly deprived from near birth and reverse sutured when 1 yr old (229), or even at 38.5 wk

(38), showed virtually no cortical recovery. Monkeys reverse sutured at 3 or at 6 wk (229) showed partial recovery in layer IVc, virtually all of which occurred in the lower sublamina, IVcβ, which receives afferents from the parvocellular layers of the LGN. These limited data add to the evidence that the period of sensitivity of layer IVc to monocular deprivation is much shorter than it is for the other cortical layers. The reasonably close match between the changes observed in the cortical layer IVc and cell shrinkage in the LGN help to explain a number of previously puzzling observations about the lack of correlation between changes observed in the LGN and the cortex as a whole (e.g., refs. 78, 397).

Humans. There have been a number of attempts to define the sensitive period in humans during which deprivation amblyopia can develop as a consequence of peripheral obstructions to pattern vision in one eye (e.g., refs. 14, 58, 95, 204, 381). There is general agreement that the period of vulnerability to monocular deprivation lasts much longer than in monkeys, to perhaps 7–10 yr of age. The presence of a number of uncontrolled factors in certain of these studies, however, makes interpretation of some of the results difficult. One example is the later development of a strabismus, which could itself result in amblyopia (243). A second complication is the frequent failure to adequately correct residual refractive errors after restoration of patterned visual input to the deprived eye. This is frequently the situation after removal of the crystalline lens in patients with traumatic or congenital cataract. Differences in the amount of the residual optical error (anisometropia) could partially account for the wide variation in the extent of recovery of such patients in a number of recent reports (e.g., refs. 23, 120, 257).

A new attempt to define the critical period for monocular deprivation of pattern vision in humans was made by Vaegan and Taylor (381) on the basis of data from subjects with unilateral cataracts. The cataracts were usually of traumatic origin, so the age of onset was known precisely. The duration of deprivation until the time of removal of the crystalline lens and the optical correction of the subsequent hypermetropia were also known. The effect of the period of unilateral visual deprivation was assessed in terms of visual acuity measured immediately on restoration of normal visual input and meticulous correction of the refractive error. The acuities for all 23 subjects measured immediately after termination of the period of deprivation are shown by horizontal lines in Figure 22. The left end of each line indicates the age of onset of the cataract, and the length of the line indicates the duration of the period of deprivation. The vertical position of the line indicates the visual acuity immediately on restoration of clear visual input and optical correction of the aphakia. Deprivation in the first 3 yr of life left only rudimentary vision. Patients afflicted progressively later suffered less visual loss. The two

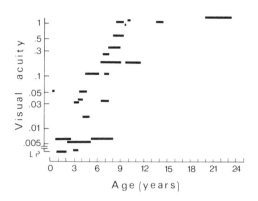

FIG. 22. Visual acuity of 23 human subjects with unilateral cataract (usually traumatic) immediately following restoration of normal visual input on removal of crystalline lens. Each subject is represented by a *horizontal bar*, whose length spans period of monocular deprivation and whose position with respect to ordinate defines first visual acuity score measured on careful optical correction following surgical removal of lens. Ordinate shows decimal acuity score where score of 1.0 represents an acuity of 6/6, and score of 0.1 is equivalent to 6/60. Subjects able to perceive only absence or presence of light (light perception) are designated by LP. [Adapted from Vaegan and Taylor (381).]

patients deprived after 10 yr of age showed no visual loss, which suggests that vulnerability to monocular visual deprivation has ceased by then. The heightened sensitivity of the visual system to the effects of deprivation in the first few years was reflected by a substantial improvement in vision in many of these same patients after restoration of normal visual input and suitable orthoptic treatment.

Extension of the sensitive period by binocular deprivation. It has been demonstrated that sensitive periods in behavioral development for phenomena such as imprinting and birdsong development depend not only on age but also to some extent on environmental factors. Animals reared in isolation, for example, remain susceptible to imprinting much longer than do animals reared communally (339). Similarly it is likely that the sensitive period to monocular deprivation does not depend only on the age of the animal but also on its experience.

As mentioned, animals reared in the dark for extended periods of time exhibit dramatic physiological and behavioral deficits on their first exposure to light. Nevertheless considerable recovery occurs with time, both physiologically (86) and behaviorally (373, 374). That this recovery can occur in animals well beyond the limits of the conventionally defined sensitive period raises the possibility that the period of binocular deprivation may delay the decline in vulnerability of the cortex to selected visual deprivation. Evidence of this was provided by Cynader and Mitchell (92), who monocularly deprived a number of dark-reared kittens immediately after they were brought into the light for 3 mo, beginning at either 6, 8, or 10 mo of age. The distribution of cortical ocular dominance for animals reared in this manner compared to light-reared control animals monocularly deprived for the same period at the same ages is shown in Figure 23. The effects of monocular occlusion on the dark-reared animals were quite dramatic and were considerably greater than the subtle or negligible effects observed in the normal animals. This finding has been confirmed in dark-reared animals in independent studies (264, 265). Surprisingly, however, a similar phenomenon was not observed in other animals binocularly deprived for comparable periods by bilateral lid suture. Evidently diffuse visual stimulation through the lids during development leaves the cortex in a state that cannot be modified by subsequent visual experience.

It is misleading to consider that the effect of dark rearing is to freeze the cortex in an immature state so that the age of the animal becomes irrelevant. Considerable differences exist in the capacity of animals reared in darkness for progressively longer times to recover, either behaviorally or physiologically, suggesting that both the age of the animal and its visual history are important in determining the response of the cortex to its visual input (86, 92).

Artificial Strabismus

This form of visual deprivation was introduced in the hope that it would provide a form of visual input with no possible effects on the visual pathway lower than the level of binocular combination (186). A divergent strabismus (exotropia) was produced in four newborn kittens by simple section of the medial rectus muscle of one eye. Subsequently cortical recording

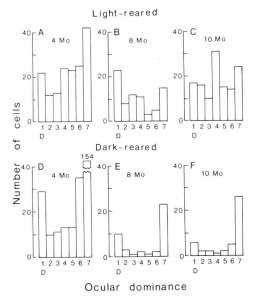

FIG. 23. Comparison of effects of 3-mo monocular deprivation on distribution of ocular dominance in visual cortex of light-reared or dark-reared animals of same age. Ocular dominance groups are as defined for Fig. 14. Letter D indicates ocular dominance group completely dominated by deprived eye. In every case the recording electrode was located in hemisphere contralateral to monocularly deprived eye. [Adapted from Cynader and Mitchell (92).]

revealed a marked decrease in the proportion of binocularly driven cells from the 80% found in normal cats to about 20%, with an approximately equal number of monocular cells controlled by each eye. Although the LGN of only one animal was studied in any detail, there did not appear to be any appreciable cell shrinkage. Hubel and Wiesel (186) concluded that the cortical effects of strabismus were a consequence of a lack of synchronous visual input due to the misaligned visual axes, a hypothesis supported by the cortical effects they observed of periods of alternating monocular occlusion.

Because strabismus is a widespread clinical disorder (117, 214) which comprises a complex syndrome of motor and sensory impairments, the finding of a decrease in the proportion of binocularly driven cells stimulated a large number of additional studies that attempted to locate the site(s) and mechanism(s) of the associated visual impairments, including strabismic amblyopia. The surgical technique employed by Hubel and Wiesel (186) produces a nonconcomitant strabismus (117), because it involves surgical intervention on the extraocular muscles. Nonconcomitant strabismus is less common clinically than concomitant strabismus, in which there is no peripheral motor abnormality. Partly for this reason a number of investigators have also examined the anatomical and physiological effects of artificial strabismus induced optically with prisms (24, 79, 344, 387). Although there is reasonable agreement about the nature of the effects of strabismus on the visual cortex, considerable uncertainty remains concerning the effects at lower levels of the visual pathway.

The original procedure used by Hubel and Wiesel (186) simply required section of one extraocular muscle. Although section of the medial rectus muscle reliably produces a stable divergent strabismus in kittens, the esotropia that follows section of the lateral rectus muscle is frequently not stable so that within a few weeks the eye reverts back to its original position. In monkeys simple section of one extraocular muscle is quite ineffective (402). Consequently production of a strabismus in monkeys frequently involves radical surgery on several muscles and for a time mechanically holding the eye with sutures in its new position (402). Other investigators have found it necessary to section several muscles so as to introduce a convergent strabismus in kittens (194). As a consequence of this radical surgery, the eye may have limited motility for some time after the operation. Thus, in addition to producing a misalignment of the visual axes, this surgical procedure may lead to another form of deprivation, namely immobilization of one eye. This may be of some importance, because it has been reported that immobilization of one eye in cats can lead to cell shrinkage in the LGN (125).

In the rhesus monkey convergent strabismus produced surgically results in a loss of vision in the deviating eye as severe as that produced by lid suture

(78, 393). The behavioral effects are accompanied in the cortex by a dramatic shift in ocular dominance of cortical cells toward the nondeviating eye and an almost complete elimination of binocular cells (15, 78). Cortical effects as dramatic as this can be produced within only 2 wk (78). The cortical changes are in turn accompanied by shrinkage of cells in LGN laminae that receive a projection from the deviating eye (393), which in short-term strabismus may be most marked in the parvocellular layers (78).

In contrast to the effects of a convergent deviation, Von Noorden (402, 404) found that surgically induced exotropia did not produce an amblyopia in the operated eye but did cause slight cell shrinkage in the parvocellular layers of the LGN. The changes in the ocular dominance of cortical cells were also less pronounced. As with esotropic animals there was a breakdown in binocularity, but the shift in ocular dominance toward the nonoperated eye was not so dramatic as that observed in esotropic monkeys (15, 404).

Investigations of the consequences of surgically induced strabismus in kittens have produced similar results, with a number of controversial or provocative claims. The deviating eye is usually amblyopic, especially in esotropia (69, 198). Exotropic kittens exhibit little (390) or no (ref. 186, and D. E. Mitchell and B. Timney, personal observations) amblyopia. Despite the frequent demonstrations of reduced vision in one eye, the shifts in cortical ocular dominance are far less dramatic than those observed in strabismic monkeys (26). Possibly the most controversial claim concerning the effects of strabismus is the report (194) of deficits in the spatial resolution of retinal ganglion cells in the vicinity of the area centralis of the deviating eye. This was observed only in esotropic cats made strabismic by removal of the body of one or usually two extraocular muscles from one eye, but not in animals that had the tendon of one muscle simply sectioned and that subsequently showed alternating fixation. The finding of ganglion cell deficits is surprising in view of the normal resolution of retinal ganglion cells in monocularly deprived cats and monkeys. Until further data are available it must be assumed that this finding is idiosyncratic to the particular surgical procedure employed or to the age of the cat when the strabismus was produced, because cats subjected to strabismus at 10 days of age by less radical means and that have demonstrated behavioral amblyopia in one eye show no deficits in retinal ganglion cell resolution in that eye (69). It is of importance that recent measurements of pattern electroretinograms reveal evidence of retinal abnormalities in many untreatable human amblyopes (4, 5).

A second controversial claim is the suggestion that cortical binocularity can be influenced in as yet some undefined way by asymmetries between the proprioceptive signals from the extraocular muscles of the two eyes. It has been claimed that a reduction in cortical binocularity occurs even in kittens subjected to surgical strabismus and reared in darkness (238).

Although subsequent studies on kittens reared with an optically induced strabismus do not entirely eliminate the possibility of some weak proprioceptive influence on cortical binocularity, the effects of anomalous proprioceptive signals are not nearly as effective in disrupting binocular cortical connectivity as nonsynchronous visual input (24, 387).

In both cats (24, 387) and monkeys (79) misalignment of the two retinal images achieved by prisms too powerful to permit fusion results in a breakdown of binocularity as severe as that produced by surgical strabismus [Fig. 24; (387)]. The other sequelae of optically induced strabismus, however, are not nearly as severe. Most significantly, in monkeys this form of strabismus is unaccompanied by changes in cell size in the LGN (79). Furthermore in both the cat and the monkey the loss of binocular cells is not accompanied by a shift in ocular dominance toward one eye (79); monocular neurons are equally divided between the two eyes, as observed originally by Hubel and Wiesel (186) in the cortex of kittens reared with a divergent surgical squint. This finding is consistent with the argument that the interference with ocular motility that occurs with surgical strabismus produces additional effects on the development of the visual pathway to those resulting only from a misalignment of the visual axes.

SENSITIVE PERIOD. Attempts to determine the sensi-

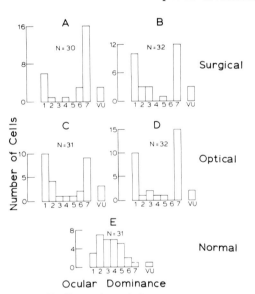

FIG. 24. Comparison of effects of optically and surgically induced strabismus on distribution of ocular dominance of cells in visual cortex. A, B: ocular dominance histograms from 2 kittens subjected to surgical (divergent) strabismus at 4 wk of age, then kept in darkness except for a period of visual exposure of 1 h each day until recording at 6 wk of age. C, D: histograms obtained from 2 kittens fitted with goggles that contained a total of 10$^\Delta$ of vertical prism (5$^\Delta$ base-up in front of right eye and 5$^\Delta$ base-down before left eye) at 4 wk of age. As with other pair of kittens, animals received 1 h of exposure each day; at all other times they were kept in total darkness until recording at 6 wk of age. E: control data from normal kitten allowed visual experience for only 1 h each day from 4 wk of age until date of recording at 6 wk of age. [From Van Sluyters and Levitt (387).]

tive period for the two major effects of surgical strabismus, namely the loss of binocular cortical connections and strabismic amblyopia, have been made for the cat but not for the monkey. Although the published reports are somewhat contradictory, there is general agreement that the period of vulnerability to disruption of cortical binocularity extends to 3 mo of age (26, 234, 429). One group (234), however, reports residual sensitivity at 5 mo and suggests that the sensitive period for the effects of strabismus may be similar to that for monocular deprivation. On the other hand Berman and Murphy (26) found that although the sensitive period for the loss of binocularity extends to only about 3 mo, the cortex remains susceptible to certain other sequelae of strabismus (such as changes in the size of receptive fields) for some time longer. A somewhat similar age dependence has been reported for the effects of strabismus on the spatial resolution of LGN neurons (195), a possible neural substrate for strabismic amblyopia.

Two estimates (16, 180) have been made of the sensitive period for the loss of binocularity in the human visual system due to strabismus. Each investigation employed the extent of interocular transfer of the tilt aftereffect as an indirect index of the state of binocularity (252, 261). This particular aftereffect refers to the temporary change in the apparent orientation of a line or grating after inspection of stimuli of slightly different orientation (252). In normal individuals this aftereffect shows partial interocular transfer; after monocular adaptation the magnitude of the aftereffect in the nonadapted eye is about 70% of that observed with the adapted eye. In marked contrast many subjects with an early strabismus or other early obstacle to concordant binocular vision exhibit no interocular transfer whatsoever of the tilt aftereffect (252), a finding consistent with a loss of binocular connectivity. The results of both studies that used this index of binocularity suggest that binocular connectivity in the human visual system is highly vulnerable in the first 18 mo of life, and that it remains susceptible until at least 7 yr of age (16, 180). Although attempts to determine the sensitive period for strabismic amblyopia have not been made, data from human infants with congenital esotropia indicate that visual acuity develops normally in both eyes until 4 mo of age, after which time the deviating eye becomes demonstrably amblyopic (256). A similar conclusion was reached for two pig-tailed monkeys reared with surgical esotropia (213). The onset of strabismic amblyopia coincides with the time at which stereopsis can first be demonstrated in human infants (165).

Alternating Monocular Deprivation

Another method of producing asynchronous visual input is to alternately occlude each eye for a discrete period. Such a procedure was first tried in kittens by Hubel and Wiesel (186), who showed that alternating 24-h periods of vision, first to one eye and then the other, resulted in an almost complete loss of binocularly driven cortical cells, with an equal number of monocular cells influenced by the two eyes. This result further specified the conditions required for disruption of binocular connections by demonstrating that the asynchronous input to the two eyes need not be present simultaneously, as in induced strabismus. Some of the temporal parameters involved in this phenomenon were studied by Blasdel and Pettigrew (49), who found that interocular intervals of at least 10 s were required to produce a significant disruption of binocularity. Preliminary experiments suggested that the duration of exclusive monocular stimulation was the crucial factor and that the duration of the blanking interval between exposure of the two eyes when neither eye receives visual input was less important. By using orthogonal gratings as stimuli for the two eyes, they were able to demonstrate that the effects of alternating exposure reflected neural processes that were intrinsic to the cortex.

In the original experiments on alternate occlusion of the eyes of kittens, the cortical representation of each eye was identical. A biased representation favoring one eye can be introduced, however, by exposing the two eyes alternately for unequal periods (370, 379, 380). Even a relatively small difference in duration (8 h vs. 4 h/day) can bias the cortical representation of the eye receiving the longer exposure (370). Evidently even a mild imbalance in the exposure of the two eyes may place one eye at a competitive advantage. Conversely the balance of cortical control by the two eyes does not appear to be influenced by the sequences of exposure (139) or by visuomotor restriction of one eye (132).

The severe disruption of binocular connections associated with alternating monocular deprivation might be expected to result in severe deficits in binocular visual functions such as stereopsis. A similar prediction could be made for strabismic cats. Even though strabismic kittens sometimes retain a higher proportion of cortical binocular cells, the binocular interactions of these cells are grossly abnormal (93). There is compelling evidence that kittens raised with alternating monocular occlusion lack stereopsis as adults (30, 285). Similarly humans with early strabismus are usually stereoblind (117) and in addition suffer a loss of some other binocular functions, such as the ability to transfer certain aftereffects interocularly (243, 252, 261).

The single attempt that has been made to determine the sensitive period for the effects of alternating monocular deprivation in kittens suggests that it may extend only to the end of the 3rd mo (305).

CONDITIONS THAT INFLUENCE OTHER RECEPTIVE-FIELD PROPERTIES

Orientation Selectivity

The question of whether or not it is possible to bias the distribution of orientation preference of visual cortical neurons has been discussed in a number of recent reviews (33, 34, 96, 263). We present here only a brief overview.

In 1970 two groups of investigators (35, 175, 176) reported that it is possible to bias the distribution of orientation preferences of cortical cells in young kittens by restricting the visual input of each eye to contours of a single orientation. Different procedures were employed to restrict the visual input, which may account in part for the differences in the findings of the two groups. Blakemore and Cooper (35) placed their otherwise dark-reared kittens for a few hours each day in large cylinders on which were painted vertical or horizontal stripes. Hirsch and Spinelli (176), on the other hand, used goggles to restrict the visual input of the kittens to bars that were vertical for one eye and horizontal for the other. The stimuli were placed at the focal plane of a strong convex lens mounted in the goggles close to the eyes. The kittens reared in cylinders could rotate their heads and thereby alter the orientation of the stripes on the retina and were also able to interact with their visual environment. By contrast, control of visual exposure was stricter for the kittens in the experiments of Hirsch and Spinelli, but at the cost of restriction of the visual field and, more importantly, interference with visuomotor integration. In their early experiments Blakemore and colleagues (31, 35, 40) reported dramatic biases in the distribution of orientation preferences of cortical cells toward the orientation of the contours in the cylinder in which the animals were reared. Hirsch and Spinelli, however, reported a high proportion of nonoriented cells, but those cells that were orientation specific were monocular and possessed orientation preferences similar to those of the contours presented to each eye during rearing (175, 176).

The biased distribution of orientation preferences observed in these experiments has been interpreted as arising from either of two processes. Cells with an innate bias for orientations not present during rearing could be either recruited or captured to match the orientation of the early environment; alternatively they could fail to develop further or even atrophy. The first process invokes an active role for visual experience, whereas the second merely requires that it serve a passive function. The reported absence of silent regions of cortex or nonspecific cells in the cortex of the kittens reared in cylinders (35) is consistent with the first process, whereas the presence of many nonoriented cells in the kittens that wore goggles provides support for the second. The original reports and others that followed (32, 40, 43, 230, 352) contained insufficient data to settle this issue. In fact the very existence of the phenomenon was doubted by Stryker and Sherk (357), who observed no orientation bias in kittens reared in cylinders, but did find a weak bias in the cortex of kittens wearing goggles, again with a high proportion of nonspecific cells. Stryker and Sherk

stressed the need for adequate sampling methods, blind recording procedures, and automated receptive field plotting. As a consequence later investigations have used more rigorous methods. Although these later studies have produced a wide variety of results, it is possible to detect an emerging consensus.

Much of the discrepancy among the results reported in various investigations can be attributed to variations in the degree of control of the early visual input. Further variability is introduced by the intrinsic columnar organization of the visual cortex, which makes adequate sampling of cells difficult. In addition to the difficulty of adequate sampling posed by the presence of orientation columns, recent evidence (27, 233) suggests a radial organization within the visual pathway. This raises the possibility of a systematic variation of the distribution of cortical orientation preferences within the visual cortex according to the location of receptive fields with respect to the area centralis.

There is universal agreement that when the visual input is restricted with goggles similar to those used by Hirsch and Spinelli, the distribution of orientation preferences of oriented cells is biased toward the orientation of the experienced contours (33, 147a, 148, 230, 352, 358). With two exceptions (33, 148) these investigations have also reported a higher proportion of nonoriented or nonspecific cells than reported in studies using other rearing procedures. There are indications that aspects of this particular rearing procedure, other than the orientation deprivation itself, contribute to the high proportion of abnormal cells (147a). Figure 25 shows results obtained by Blakemore (33) from two kittens reared monocularly and exposed either to vertical or horizontal stripes in goggles. The recording was performed blind; i.e., the nature of the early experience was unknown until the recording was completed. And in order to achieve absolute objectivity while still allowing hand plotting of receptive fields, a Dove prism was placed in front of the experienced eye and rotated an arbitrary (but known) amount between recording of each cell. The complicated conversion from the orientation preference of each cell measured on the tangent screen to that on the retina was performed on completion of the experiment. The polar plots of Figure 25 are corrected for the prism setting and display the true distribution of preferred orientations on the retina.

There is a much wider diversity of findings from kittens reared in cylinders, ranging from no orientation bias whatsoever (126, 357) to quite strong biases (e.g., refs. 32, 33, 41, 43, 47, 128). A similar variability of outcome has been observed among different animals within a single study (33). Substantially biased distributions have been reported (33, 49) for studies that have incorporated all the procedural modifications advocated by Stryker and Sherk (357). The greater variability associated with this particular rearing procedure can be attributed partly to the less strict control over the visual input arising from rotation of the head

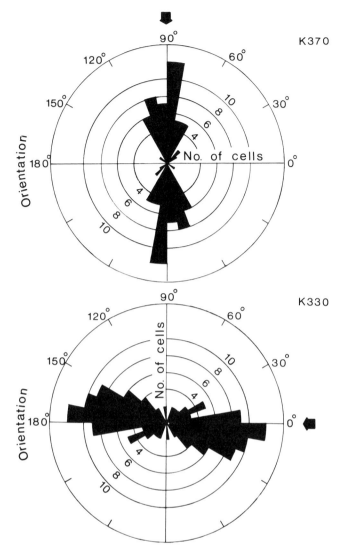

FIG. 25. Polar histograms of preferred orientations for samples of orientation-specific cortical cells recorded from 2 kittens reared with monocular visual exposure to contours of a single orientation, analyzed by method described in text. Receptive fields were plotted with a Dove prism before the eye that was rotated a variable, but known, angle between each cell. Preferred orientations plotted here are corrected for setting of prism. *Solid arrows* indicate contour orientation to which kittens were exposed, horizontal for K330 and vertical for K370. [Adapted from Blakemore (33).]

with respect to the stripes; another factor may be the relative orientation of the contours viewed by the two eyes during rearing. There are claims (148, 358) that, in situations in which the contours viewed by one eye are orthogonal to those seen by the other, much stronger cortical biases for the rearing orientation are observed than when they are identical for the two eyes, as was the usual situation for cylinder-reared cats.

A third rearing procedure that assures as constant an exposure as that achieved with the procedure of Hirsch and Spinelli uses strong cylindrical lenses to bias the visual input (see Fig. 26). This procedure has

the added feature of maintaining the viewing conditions closer to normal for the kittens and reduces the interference with visuomotor functions that occurs with the goggles of Hirsch and Spinelli. This rearing procedure also finds close parallels to naturally occurring astigmatism (246). The few studies that have used this procedure all report a strong bias of cortical orientation preferences with a much lower proportion of nonoriented cells than reported in the early goggles studies (91, 140, 309, 310).

In the most recent study employing cylindrical lenses (310), the effects of a wide variety of biased early visual inputs were examined, including situations comparable to those provided for the kittens in the earliest stripe-rearing studies. Strong cortical biases consistent with the rearing exposure were encountered in all cases, whether the visual input to the two eyes was identical or orthogonal. Although some cells were nonoriented or unresponsive, the proportion of such cells was insufficient to fully account for the orientation bias on the basis of atrophy of cells that had not received appropriate visual stimulation. This conclusion was reinforced by the results of careful reconstructions of electrode tracks. In virtually all conditions there was evidence that columns devoted to orientations experienced were expanded relative to the space committed to other orientations. Comparison with normal animals suggested that the columns devoted to experienced orientations may even have been expanded in absolute terms. On the basis of this careful quantitative analysis, Rauschecker and Singer (310) proposed that the biased orientation distributions observed in their kittens reflected both maintenance and instructive effects.

Only a few studies have been reported of the effects on monkeys of restricting the early visual input to contours of a single orientation. Von Noorden and Crawford (400) reported a normal distribution of cortical orientation preferences in monkeys exposed to vertical contours in a cylinder. And in contrast to kittens reared with artificial astigmatism induced with strong cylindrical lenses, Kiorpes et al. (215) observed no bias in the distribution of orientation preferences of cortical cells of monkeys reared in a similar manner. However, they did find a reduction in the spatial resolution of cortical cells responsive to the orientation that was blurred during rearing. Although such differences in the performance of cells of different preferred orientation may account for the behavioral resolution losses in monkeys (54) and humans, it should be mentioned that the monkeys of this study (54, 215) were reared with only 6D cylindrical lenses. It is possible that a more striking cortical effect, including a biased distribution of orientation preferences, would be observed in monkeys reared with stronger lenses or for longer periods.

BEHAVIORAL CORRELATES. Although there has been much discussion surrounding the results of studies of

FIG. 26. Effects of different degrees of astigmatism on appearance of a target, *A*, consisting of a radiating series of lines of different orientations. When axes of the astigmatism are horizontal and vertical, as shown, contours parallel to focal line imaged in film plane (vertical) are imaged clearly, whereas contours of other orientations become progressively more blurred toward horizontal.

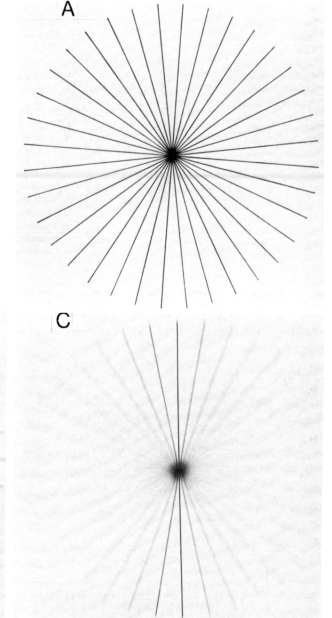

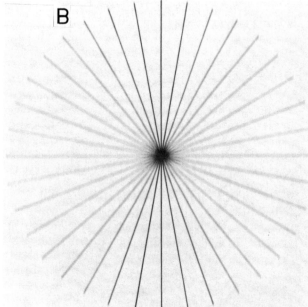

the effects of early exposure to contours of a single orientation, relatively little attention has been paid to behavioral evidence for orientation-specific perceptual deficits that appear to be experience dependent.

It was established quite early that kittens exposed to stripes in cylinders (47, 267) or by means of goggles (174) suffered only mild permanent impairments of vision. By contrast many humans with congenital astigmatism exhibit substantial deficits in acuity for contours orthogonal to those imaged clearly early in life, even after meticulous optical correction (139, 252). These orientational variations in resolution are of neural and not optical origin, because they are just as evident for interference fringes generated directly on the retina that bypass the optics of the eye (246, 253). Measurement of contrast sensitivity functions shows that the orientation-specific loss occurs over the whole spatial frequency spectrum. This point is illustrated in Figure 27, which shows the contrast sensitivity function for an astigmat for both horizontal and vertical gratings. Prior to optical correction at the age of 10 yr, the visual input of this subject was similar to that illustrated in Figure 26. Even with careful correction of the optical astigmatism, the contrast sensitivity was poorer for horizontal gratings than for vertical gratings, particularly at higher spatial frequencies. For comparison the results of a normal individual are also shown in Figure 27*A*. Normal individuals are equally

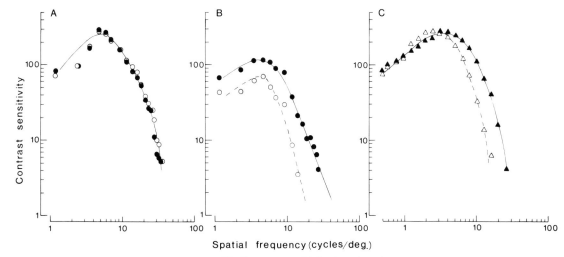

Spatial frequency (cycles/deg.)

FIG. 27. Contrast sensitivity functions for gratings of various orientations measured *A*: on normal adult human; *B*: on optically corrected adult astigmat with meridional amblyopia, whose early visual input was similar to that depicted in Fig. 26; and *C*: for left eye of a rhesus monkey (*Macaca mulatta*) with oblique axis astigmatism that was optically corrected for these measurements. In *A*, *filled* and *open symbols* indicate results obtained with vertical horizontal gratings, respectively. Similar symbols in *B* depict contrast sensitivities for gratings that were nearly vertical and horizontal (75° and 165°) close to axes of astigmatism. *Filled* and *open triangles* in *C* indicate contrast sensitivities for gratings oriented at 45° and 135°, respectively. In contrast to normal humans, *A*, astigmat in *B* resolved vertical gratings far better than horizontal gratings, even though optical astigmatism was fully corrected. Similarly, astigmatic monkey, *C*, exhibited equally large differences in resolution between gratings at 45° and 135°, again in marked contrast to results from normal monkeys (149), which resolve gratings of these two orientations equally well. Astigmatic errors were *B*: −0.25D spherical error; cylindrical error −4.50D axis 20°; *C*: L +1.25D spherical error; cylindrical error −1.00D axis 45°. [Adapted from Mitchell and Wilkinson (253) and Harwerth et al. (162).]

sensitive to vertical and horizontal gratings, but they show a slight reduction in performance with gratings that are obliquely oriented (64).

The orientation-specific resolution loss expected for many astigmats has been referred to as meridional amblyopia (246). There are a number of pieces of evidence that link meridional amblyopia to the orientation-specific changes observed in the visual cortex of stripe-reared animals. Meridional amblyopes, for example, show orientation-specific changes in visual evoked potentials recorded from the scalp (141). Monkeys raised with externally imposed astigmatism (54) or possessing natural astigmatism (162) show patterns of contrast sensitivity loss similar to those found in humans. A contrast-sensitivity function measured on a monkey with 2D natural astigmatism after optical correction of the refractive error is shown in Figure 27C. The reduction in sensitivity for gratings oriented at 45°, orthogonal to orientations imaged clearly when uncorrected, is comparable to that of the human observer shown in Figure 27B.

Although it is possible that some of the meridional variations in acuity experienced by astigmatic kittens, monkeys, or humans may reflect changes in the retina itself, recent examinations of the spatial resolution of retinal ganglion cells in astigmatic kittens (368) reveal neither a loss of grating resolution nor an abnormal pattern of orientation bias (cf. ref. 233). It must there-

fore be assumed that the meridional amblyopic deficit originates in the brain rather than the retina.

Measurements on young human infants with natural astigmatism reveal no evidence of meridional amblyopia during the 1st yr of life (256, 364), and preliminary data suggest that it may not develop until 3 yr of age (256). This relatively late emergence of meridional amblyopia adds further support to the view that links the deficit to the abnormal early visual input. Quite the opposite conclusion can be drawn, however, concerning the origin of the oblique effect, the much smaller orientational variation in acuity demonstrated by normal observers. This lowered acuity for oblique stimuli is apparent in human infants at 6 wk of age (222), which suggests that it reflects some fundamental organization of the visual pathways that is laid down under genetic instruction.

Movement and Direction Selectivity

Two strategies have been adopted in attempts to modify cortical direction selectivity by environmental manipulation. One approach has been to examine the effects of rearing animals in stroboscopic illumination, which allows patterned visual input but reduces or eliminates perception of motion. The alternative strategy has attempted to modify the distribution of cortical directional preferences by exposing kittens to visual stimuli that move in only a single direction.

The visual cortex of kittens reared in low-frequency (< 1 Hz) stroboscopic illumination closely resembles the cortex of dark-reared animals, with low proportions of either directional or oriented cells (84, 279). A few special cells have been reported that appear to respond selectively to strobe flashes (84). Increasing the flash frequency to 8 Hz has the effect of virtually abolishing direction selectivity while allowing orientation selectivity to develop normally (88).

Attempts to modify direction selectivity by exposing animals to unidirectional motion have been made by several investigators, with similar results (85, 101, 376). All found that a larger proportion of cells favored the direction to which the kittens had been exposed. Similar rearing conditions have not been attempted in the monkey, but Daw and Wyatt (100) report a failure to modify the directional properties of ganglion cells in the rabbit retina.

The period of susceptibility of the cortex to such directional deprivation may peak earlier and decline faster than that for monocular deprivation by 2–4 wk (25, 98, 99, 101). The most persuasive evidence for this was provided by Daw et al. (99), who simultaneously exposed kittens from near birth to monocular eyelid closure and unidirectional motion. Reversal of both deprivation conditions at 5 wk of age for several weeks resulted in a switch in ocular dominance to the initially deprived eye, but there was no such reversal of the cortical distribution of preferred directions, which was still strongly biased toward the direction of motion experienced first. This result raises the possibility that there may be a different sensitive period for influencing the development of each of the major response properties of cortical neurons.

Effects of Unusual Visual Input on Cortical Development

The rearing conditions described to this point were employed in order to determine if the stimulus preference of cortical neurons could be biased by early visual exposure restricted to one extreme of the range encountered in normal animals. The fact that this is possible indicates that visual experience plays an important role during development. It is difficult, however to learn the nature of that role during normal development from these experiments. A number of investigators have attempted to generate, by suitably restricting visual exposure, neurons with stimulus preferences outside the range normally encountered. The generation of such cellular properties would provide evidence of an inductive role for visual experience. A number of anecdotal descriptions of cells with unusual receptive fields encountered in the course of several studies suggest that such a process may exist (297, 337, 351, 352). Two groups (296, 386) restricted the visual input of kittens to either spots of light as in a planetarium or to small circular dots, in an attempt to determine if cortical cells would develop a preference

for spots of light rather than for elongated contours. Both reports suggested that this was true, but the results were not compelling. Not only was the sample size small, but the selectivity of the cells was not examined in sufficient detail to establish the maturity of the response characteristics of each cell.

Possibly the strongest evidence for an active role for visual experience can be found in the neural adaptations to surgical rotation of one or both eyes. Kittens reared from near the time of eye opening with one or both eyes rotated surgically show visuomotor, oculomotor, and sensory adaptation (81, 247, 288, 289, 375). Although initial attempts to locate a neural substrate for this behavioral recovery failed (44), later studies have uncovered some neural compensation both in the visual cortex (81) and in the superior colliculus (87). In one such experiment nine binocular cortical cells identified by physiological criteria (286) as lying in layer V had identical preferred directions for the two eyes in visual space (81). This represents precise compensation for the angle or rotation of the eye(s). The finding that all of the direction-selective cells that had adapted to the eye rotation were in layer V (the cells of which send a strong projection to the superior colliculus) complements rather nicely the compensation observed in this structure. Cynader et al. (87) report that the vast majority of binocular cells in the superior colliculus of kittens reared with one eye rotated 90° had preferred directions that were the same or similar for the two eyes in visual space. Because cells with either preferred orientation or directions 90° apart have not been reported in the cortex or superior colliculus of normal cats, it must be concluded that the stimulus preference of some cells must have changed to match the visual input. It must be emphasized, however, that in the cortex at least, the number of cells that showed this compensation was small.

GENETIC AND EXPERIENTIAL FACTORS IN VISUAL DEVELOPMENT

This chapter began with a survey of the development of various perceptual capacities in cats and monkeys as well as human infants. In none of these species was visual resolution or depth perception fully developed at birth; in fact, normal capacities were not attained for several months or even years (in the case of humans) later. [However, this is not true for other species such as the chicken, which attains adult levels of visual acuity within 48 h of hatching (283).] A somewhat similar statement summarizes neural development in the visual cortex. Although a fraction of cortical cells in the cat and monkey possess adultlike selectivity at or near birth, it is not until several weeks or months later that the proportion of orientation-selective cells (or the sensitivity of individual cells) approaches adult values. That visual experience plays a vital role in perceptual and cortical neural development is evident from the effects of total or selective early visual deprivation. At the same time there is general agreement that the effects of visual deprivation on the retina or LGN are at most minor, and that the major effects are observed in the cortex. Although there is no doubt that selective visual deprivation can produce effects on the distribution of stimulus preferences of cortical cells as well as on perception, the manner in which these effects are produced is uncertain.

Those who assign visual experience a passive role in visual development interpret the effects of total or partial visual deprivation in terms of maintenance or atrophy of innately specified connections through a process such as functional validation. Connections that are adequately stimulated remain, whereas those that are not are lost. Qualitatively at least, this model is consistent with the effects of binocular deprivation and with many of the reported effects of selected early visual exposure. It does not, however, account for the immature state of the cortex at birth and with the quantitative effects of restricted visual exposure (310), nor for some of the effects of selective deprivation, in which there is an obvious increase or expansion of territory of neurons tuned to the early visual input. This is shown by the effects of monocular deprivation, in which there is a takeover of cortical territory by the open eye (190, 229). Clearly the increase in cortical territory devoted to the nondeprived eye cannot always result from a simple atrophy of connections with the deprived eye. This argument is bolstered by behavioral observations of humans with early severe monocular cataract or extreme refractive errors, who as a result suffer severe deprivation or anisometropic amblyopia. It might be thought that any increase in cortical territory devoted to one eye above the amount controlled by either eye in normal individuals should be reflected by some improvement in the visual capabilities of that eye. This has, in fact, been demonstrated by measurement of vernier acuity, a hyperacuity that exceeds limitations set by the retinal grain and the optical modulation transfer function of the eye, factors that set a peripheral limit to grating resolution. With the remaining eye these subjects possess about the same vernier acuity as do normal subjects using both eyes but considerably better monocular acuity by a factor of about $\sqrt{2}$ (135).

A further argument against a simple maintenance model arises from its prediction that neurons should develop normally or that, as a consequence of deprivation, they should fail to achieve maturity. It should not be possible to produce cells with mature stimulus preferences that are different from those encountered in normal animals. But there is considerable evidence that some cells can acquire quite unusual characteristics as a consequence of selected early visual exposure. Perhaps the best examples are the neural adaptations of the visual cortex observed in layer V and in the superior colliculus in cats with one eye surgically

rotated 90° (81, 87). Binocular cells with matched directional preferences in visual space for which the preferred directions for the two eyes must differ 90° on retinal coordinates represent a class that has not been reported in normal animals. A related phenomenon is observed in reverse-sutured animals (260) and in cats reared viewing orthogonal patterns in the two eyes (230, 358), in which the preferred orientation of binocular cells can differ widely between the two eyes, and by much more than the largest difference, 15°, reported in normal animals (37, 270). Binocular cells with such discrepant preferred orientation in the two eyes have not been observed in reverse-sutured monkeys (38).

The observations outlined here can be accommodated by any model that permits visual experience to have an active or guiding role in development. The battleground on which most of the debate over the role of visual experience has been fought has been the experiments that attempt to restrict visual input to one or both eyes to contours of a single orientation. Many of the observations obtained with this rearing procedure, particularly those using goggles to restrict visual input (175, 358), provide evidence in favor of selective maintenance of innately specified connections. The evidence for a more active role for visual experience in producing the observed bias of orientation preferences is not widely accepted, because the information needed to support this view, such as detailed reconstructions of electrode tracks, is rarely presented. This criticism has been answered in the most recent study of this kind in which close analysis of electrode tracks combined with quantitative considerations of the proportion of unresponsive and nonoriented cells provided evidence of a guiding or instructional role for visual experience as well (310). The suggestion raised by the findings of this study that selective maintenance effects and instructional effects of visual experience may coexist, rather than be mutually exclusive, underscores the need to strike a balance between the two extreme views of the role of visual experience in neural development. At this state the broadest view is that postnatal visual neural development comprises many parallel and sequential processes that are influenced in various ways and at different times by visual experience. Just as with most of the prenatal development of the visual pathways, some of these processes proceed under genetic instruction and are virtually uninfluenced by the nature of the early visual input. The clearest examples of such a process (maturation) in postnatal neural development can be observed in the retina; beyond the retina and LGN it is difficult to identify such examples. Two examples could be the segregation of ocular dominance bands in layer IVc of the monkey cortex, which proceeds to the normal end point in the absence of visual input (229), and the development of orientation columns in layer IV of the cat visual cortex (335). It is likely, however, that only the example in the monkey is valid, since recent evidence (359) suggests that ocular dominance columns fail to segregate in kittens deprived of binocular visual input. Moreover it is obvious that even in the monkey the process of segregation of ocular dominance columns can be dramatically influenced by the nature of the early visual input, as attested to by the grossly abnormal columnar organization observed in monocularly deprived animals. Outside of layer IV the process of development of the stimulus preference of cortical cells for orientation, disparity, and movement is clearly influenced to different extents, either passively or actively, by visual experience.

Functional Role of Visual Experience

Although it is apparent that abnormal early visual experience can exert dramatic effects on visual neural development, these observations do not allow an understanding of the role that visual experience plays in normal development. One extreme hypothesis that has been raised from time to time (31, 237, 310) is that the developmental plasticity manifested by the visual system early in life allows fine tuning of cortical stimulus preferences to adapt individual animals to their own particular environments as closely as possible. This notion requires an active role for visual experience in development. Although this hypothesis has a certain appeal, however, it provides no ready explanation for the time course of the sensitive period, the limited plasticity in certain species such as rabbits, or the presence of considerable postnatal malleability in the cortex of precocial species such as the sheep, in which the stimulus preference and selectivity of cortical cells are comparable to those of adult cells at birth (308).

An alternative notion is that the cortical malleability in certain species early in life is linked to special requirements for stereoscopic depth localization (34, 42, 43, 293-295). Since the invention of the stereoscope by Wheatstone (414) it has been recognized that stereopsis depends on the detection of small horizontal disparities between the positions of images of objects on the two retinas. Humans can reliably detect disparities as small as 5 s of arc, (413) and even cats, which possess much poorer spatial resolution than humans, can discriminate disparities of 4 min of arc (30, 211, 250). It seems unlikely that the neural connections underlying a mechanism of such exquisite sensitivity could be laid down under genetic instruction with a high degree of specificity and at the same time accommodate the consequences of the change with age in interocular separation, or slight and unpredictable differences between the position of the two eyes or their oculomotor control that must arise during periods of rapid somatic growth. Conversely a mechanism that allows visual experience an active role during development could provide the necessary flexibility to accommodate such growth-related perturbations. More importantly visual experience could allow a matching of the stimulus preferences of binocular neurons in the two eyes, an essential requirement for proposed neural mechanisms of stereopsis (21, 271). This interpretation of the role of visual experience receives support from observations in kittens suggesting that correlated binocular visual experience is needed to match the preferred orientation of binocular cells in the two eyes. For example, in reverse-sutured cats that never receive simultaneous binocular vision, binocular cells can have widely different (as much as 90°) preferred orientations in the two eyes (42, 210). But in kittens allowed a period of normal binocular vision prior to monocular deprivation and subsequent reverse suture, the few cells that regain binocular connections have closely similar preferred orientations in the two eyes (385). Apparently the initial period of binocular vision is sufficient to allow matching of the inputs of binocular cells with sufficient strength to survive a temporary period of disruption. Other experiments on kittens reared wearing prisms that rotate the visual field of one eye with respect to the other indicate that there are limits to the extent to which the preferred orientation of binocular cells can be shifted relative to each other without any disruption of binocular connectivity. Whereas rotation of the visual inputs of the two eyes by 16° relative to each other by means of prisms can be so tolerated (59, 331), a relative rotation of 32° produces a massive disruption of binocular connections (197).

The limited available data on other more visually precocious species such as the monkey and sheep suggest that binocular visual experience may be less important for matching the preferred orientations of binocular cells in the two eyes. Not only is orientation selectivity more tightly tuned at birth (306, 419), but also the diversity of interocular differences in preferred orientation of binocular cells found after reverse suture in cats (260) is absent in monkeys that have undergone a similar deprivation regimen (38).

Possibly the most persuasive argument for linking early plasticity in the visual system to the special demands of stereoscopic vision emerges from comparative considerations. Species other than the cat and monkey with frontal eyes and with demonstrated binocular neural mechanisms for stereoscopic vision such as the sheep and owl (68, 300) also show a central neural vulnerability to visual deprivation in early life. Binocular connections in the visual cortex of the sheep (241) and in the homologous central visual area in the brain of the owl, the visual Wulst (299) appear as vulnerable to disruption by early monocular visual deprivation as those of the cat and monkey cortex. This point is illustrated in Figures 28 and 29. Figure 28 shows typical disparity tuning curves of three binocular neurons recorded in the visual Wulst of the barn own (*Tyto alba*). These cells were recorded with a reference technique; unit B8 was recorded from the right Wulst and held while unit A4 and then unit A10 were recorded in the left Wulst. Figure 29 shows ocular

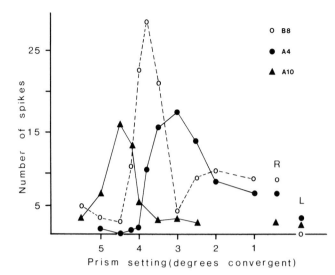

FIG. 28. Tuning of 3 binocular cells recorded in visual Wulst of an adult barn owl (*Tyto alba*) for horizontal retinal disparity. Recordings were made simultaneously from both right and left visual Wulst. Unit B8, recorded from right visual Wulst, served as a reference cell that was held for some time while first unit A4 and then A10 were investigated in left visual Wulst. *Connected symbols* show response of each cell to a vertical slit swept across 2 receptive fields. Data points to *right* indicate response of each cell to monocular presentations of stimulus (R, right eye; L, left eye). Connected symbols show response of each cell to binocular stimulation as a function of changes in horizontal retinal disparity produced by alterations of setting of a variable-power (Risley) prism mounted in front of left eye. Because visual axes are divergent under paralysis, each cell gives its best response with convergent setting of prism. Nevertheless each cell exhibits clear preference for a different retinal disparity. [From Pettigrew and Konishi (300). Copyright 1976 by the American Association for the Advancement of Science.]

dominance histograms obtained from the visual Wulst of six normal owls and two owlets that were monocularly deprived for 2–3 mo from either day 11 or day 29. Although binocular connections in the cortex of lambs and visual Wulst of owlets are highly susceptible to monocular deprivation, the existence of a critical period for these effects has not yet been demonstrated. Nevertheless the dramatic effects of monocular deprivation observed in these species with frontal eyes but with widely different evolutionary histories stand in striking contrast to the weak effects of similar deprivation imposed on animals with lateral eyes and with limited binocular overlap such as the rabbit (388) or hamster (119).

One of the most appealing features of the hypothesis that links the critical period to the demands of stereoscopic vision is that it provides an explanation for the time course of early neural plasticity. This insight has been provided by neurophysiological investigations of the system of binocular correspondence of certain species (73), a key component of which is a theoretical surface in visual space called the horopter. The horopter is defined as a surface passing through the point of fixation that is everywhere imaged on corresponding points of the two retinas (272). As such, it represents

the locus of points in space around which stereoscopic processing is possible. Recent neurophysiological determinations of the zero azimuthal meridian for the two eyes of the cat and of the burrowing owl (73) indicate that in life they are extorted with respect to each other in the same way as the corresponding meridians of the human retina. This means that the locus of points in space whose images fall simultaneously on these two meridians (referred to as the vertical horopter) is a line tilted in the midsagittal plane passing through the fixation point and which slopes away at the top. It has long been recognized that the vertical horopter of the human passes through the feet (71, 341), and it now appears as if a similar situation exists in the cat and owl (73). On the assumption that the vertical horopter must pass through the feet throughout development, then some plasticity of binocular connections is demanded throughout the time both height and interocular separation are changing. This situation requires that some plasticity be retained

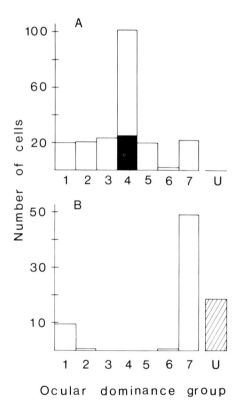

FIG. 29. Ocular dominance histograms for cells recorded from visual Wulst of A: normal barn owls (*Tyto alba*); and B: 2 owlets subjected to monocular deprivation by eyelid suture for 2–3 mo from postnatal day 11 or 29. In all cases microelectrode was located in left hemisphere, which for monocularly deprived owlets was contralateral to deprived eye. Ocular dominance groups are as for cats in Fig. 14. Group 4 cells in *filled portion* of histogram in A could be driven only by simultaneous presentation of stimuli to both eyes at a certain precise binocular disparity and could not be excited at all monocularly. Cells unresponsive to visual stimulation are indicated by U. [From Pettigrew and Konishi (299); reprinted by permission from *Nature* 264: 753–754, 1976. Copyright © 1976 Macmillan Journals Limited.]

into adolescence, a prediction that is supported by recent reexaminations of the sensitive period in cats (94, 244). Hänny and Von der Heydt (159a) recently provided evidence of changes in the mean interocular orientation preference of binocular cortical cells in cats in response to biased early visual exposure that had the effect of altering the slope of the vertical horopter by an amount consistent with the nature of the early visual input.

The need for a period of plasticity to accommodate the requirements of binocular vision provides an explanation of the so-called paradox of the critical period (294), with its potential for serious permanent visual handicap without an obvious compensating benefit. It is difficult to deny that the ability to accurately perceive the three-dimensional position of objects in space and to judge the trajectories of stimuli that move in depth (314) would convey an immense evolutionary advantage. This particular role for visual experience predicts that other species with demonstrated capabilities for binocular vision will also display a well-defined period of early neural plasticity in the visual pathway. We may confidently expect an increasing number of such comparative studies in the future (295).

Preparation of this chapter was assisted by grants from the Natural Sciences and Engineering Research Council (A7660 and A7062) and from the Medical Research Council of Canada (MA7125). We wish to express our gratitude to the secretaries who helped type early drafts of this paper, namely Linda Toenders, Carla Schneider, Dorothy Postma, Ann Baxter, and Carol McAulay. We particularly wish to thank Nancy Beattie, who typed several complete drafts, for her skill and patience.

REFERENCES

1. ABRAMOV, I., J. GORDON, A. HENDRICKSON, L. HAINLINE, V. DOBSON, AND E. LA BOSSIERE. The retina of the human newborn infant. *Science* 217: 265–267, 1982.
2. ACKROYD, C., N. K. HUMPHREY, AND E. K. WARRINGTON. Lasting effects of early blindness: a case study. *Q. J. Exp. Psychol.* 26: 114–124, 1974.
4. ARDEN, G. B., R. M. CARTER, C. R. HOGG, D. J. POWELL, AND VAEGAN. Reduced pattern electroretinograms suggest a preganglionic basis for non-treatable human amblyopia. *J. Physiol. London* 308: 82P–83P, 1980.
5. ARDEN, G. B., VAEGAN, C. R. HOGG, D. J. POWELL, AND R. M. CARTER. Pattern ERGs are abnormal in many amblyopes. *Trans. Ophthalmol. Soc. U. K.* 100: 453–460, 1980.
6. ASLIN, R. N. Experimental influences and sensitive periods in perceptual development: a unified model. In: *The Development of Perception: Psychobiological Perspectives, The Visual System*, edited by R. N. Aslin, J. R. Alberts, and M. R. Petersen. New York: Academic, 1981, vol. 2, p. 45–93.
7. ASLIN, R. N., J. R. ALBERTS, AND M. R. PETERSEN, (editors). *Development of Perception: Psychobiological Perspectives, The Visual System*, New York: Academic, 1981, vol. 2.
8. ATKINSON, J., AND O. BRADDICK. Stereoscopic discrimination in infants. *Perception* 5: 29–38, 1976.
9. ATKINSON, J., O. BRADDICK, AND F. BRADDICK. Acuity and contrast sensitivity of infant vision. *Nature London* 247: 403–404, 1974.
10. ATKINSON, J., O. BRADDICK, AND K. MOAR. Development of contrast sensitivity over the first 3 months of life in the human infant. *Vision Res.* 17: 1037–1044, 1977.
11. ATKINSON, J., O. BRADDICK, AND K. MOAR. Contrast sensitivity of the human infant for moving and static patterns. *Vision Res.* 17: 1045–1047, 1977.
12. ATKINSON, J., J. FRENCH, AND O. BRADDICK. Contrast sensitivity of preschool children. *Br. J. Ophthalmol.* 65: 525–529, 1981.
13. AWAYA, S., Y. MIYAKE, Y. IMAIZUMI, Y. SHIOSE, T. KANDU, AND K. KOMURO. Amblyopia in man, suggestive of stimulus deprivation amblyopia. *Jpn. J. Ophthalmol.* 17: 69–82, 1973.
14. AWAYA, S., M. SUGAWARA, AND S. MIYAKE. Observations in patients with occlusion amblyopia. *Trans. Ophthalmol. Soc. UK* 99: 447–454, 1979.
15. BAKER, F. H., P. GRIGG, AND G. K. VON NOORDEN. Effects of visual deprivation and strabismus on the responses of neurons in the visual cortex of the monkey, including studies on the striate and prestriate cortex in the normal animal. *Brain Res.* 66: 185–208, 1974.
16. BANKS, M. S., R. N. ASLIN, AND R. D. LETSON. Sensitive period for the development of human binocular vision. *Science* 190: 675–677, 1975.
17. BANKS, M. S., AND P. SALAPATEK. Contrast sensitivity function of the infant visual system. *Vision Res.* 16: 867–869, 1976.
18. BANKS, M. S., AND P. SALAPATEK. Acuity and contrast sensitivity in one-, two-, and three-month-old human infants. *Invest. Ophthalmol. Vis. Sci.* 17: 361–365, 1978.
19. BANKS, M. S., AND P. SALAPATEK. Infant pattern vision: a new approach based on the contrast sensitivity function. *J. Exp. Child Psychol.* 31: 1–45, 1981.
20. BARLOW, H. B. Visual experience and cortical development. *Nature London* 258: 199–204, 1975.
21. BARLOW, H. B., C. BLAKEMORE, AND J. D. PETTIGREW. The neural mechanism of binocular depth discrimination. *J. Physiol. London* 193: 327–342, 1967.
22. BARLOW, H. B., AND J. D. PETTIGREW. Lack of specificity of neurons in the visual cortex of young kittens. *J. Physiol. London* 218: 98P–101P, 1971.
23. BELLER, R., C. S. HOYT, E. MARG, AND J. V. ODOM. Good visual function after neonatal surgery for congenital monocular cataracts. *Am. J. Ophthalmol.* 91: 559–565, 1981.
24. BENNETT, M. J., E. L. SMITH III, R. S. HARWERTH, AND M. L. J. CRAWFORD. Ocular dominance, eye alignment and visual acuity in kittens reared with an optically induced squint. *Brain Res.* 193: 33–45, 1980.
25. BERMAN, N., AND N. W. DAW. Comparison of the critical periods for monocular and directional deprivation in cats. *J. Physiol. London* 265: 249–259, 1977.
26. BERMAN, N., AND H. MURPHY. The critical period for alteration in cortical binocularity resulting from divergent and convergent strabismus. *Dev. Brain Res.* 2: 181–202, 1982.
27. BERMAN, N., B. R. PAYNE, R. GARCIA-KENNEDY, AND E. H. MURPHY. Orientation anisotropy in cat visual cortex. *Invest. Ophthalmol. Vis. Sci. Suppl.* 20: 147, 1981.
28. BIRCH, E. E., J. GWIAZDA, AND R. HELD. Stereoacuity development for crossed and uncrossed disparities in human infants. *Vision Res.* 22: 507–513, 1982.
29. BLAKE, R., AND A. DIGIANFILIPPO. Spatial vision in cats with selective neural deficits. *J. Neurophysiol.* 43: 1197–1205, 1980.
30. BLAKE, R., AND H. V. B. HIRSCH. Deficits in binocular depth perception in cats after alternating monocular deprivation. *Science* 190: 1114–1116, 1975.
31. BLAKEMORE, C. Developmental factors in the formation of feature extracting neurons. In: *The Neurosciences Third Study Program*, edited by F. O. Schmitt and F. G. Worden. Cambridge, MA: MIT Press, 1974, p. 105–113.
32. BLAKEMORE, C. The conditions required for the maintenance of binocularity in the kitten's visual cortex. *J. Physiol. London* 261: 423–444, 1976.
33. BLAKEMORE, C. Genetic instructions and developmental plasticity in the kitten's visual cortex. *Philos. Trans. R. Soc.*

London Ser. B 278: 425–434, 1977.

34. BLAKEMORE, C. Maturation and modification in the developing visual system. In: *Handbook of Sensory Physiology. Perception*, edited by R. Held, H. Leibowitz, and H.-L. Teuber. New York: Springer-Verlag, 1978, vol. 8, p. 377–436.

35. BLAKEMORE, C., AND G. F. COOPER. Development of the brain depends on the visual environment. *Nature London* 228: 477–478, 1970.

36. BLAKEMORE, C., AND H. M. EGGERS. Animal models for human visual development. In: *Frontiers of Visual Science*, edited by S. J. Cool and E. L. Smith. New York: Springer-Verlag, 1978, p. 651–659.

37. BLAKEMORE, C., A. FIORENTINI, AND L. MAFFEI. A second neural mechanism of binocular depth discrimination. *J. Physiol. London* 226: 725–749, 1972.

38. BLAKEMORE, C., L. J. GAREY, AND F. VITAL-DURAND. The physiological effects of monocular deprivation and their reversal in the monkey's visual cortex. *J. Physiol. London* 283: 223–262, 1978.

38a.BLAKEMORE, C., M. J. HAWKEN, AND R. F. MARK. Brief monocular deprivation leaves subthreshold synaptic input on neurones of the cat's visual cortex. *J. Physiol. London* 327: 489–505, 1982.

39. BLAKEMORE, C., AND P. HILLMAN. An attempt to assess the effects of monocular deprivation an strabismus on synaptic efficiency in the kitten's visual cortex. *Exp. Brain Res.* 30: 187–202, 1977.

40. BLAKEMORE, C., AND D. E. MITCHELL. Environmental modifications of the visual cortex and the neural basis of learning and memory. *Nature London* 228: 467–468, 1973.

41. BLAKEMORE, C., J. A. MOVSHON, AND R. C. VAN SLUYTERS. Modification of the kitten's visual cortex by exposure to spatially periodic patterns. *Exp. Brain Res.* 31: 561–572, 1978.

42. BLAKEMORE, C., AND R. C. VAN SLUYTERS. Reversal of the physiological effects of monocular deprivation in kittens: further evidence for a sensitive period. *J. Physiol. London* 237: 195–216, 1971.

43. BLAKEMORE, C., AND R. C. VAN SLUYTERS. Innate and environmental factors in the development of the kitten's visual cortex. *J. Physiol. London* 248: 663–716, 1975.

44. BLAKEMORE, C., R. C. VAN SLUYTERS, C. K. PECK, AND A. HEIN. Development of the cat visual cortex following rotation of one eye. *Nature London* 257: 584–586, 1975.

45. BLAKEMORE, C., AND F. VITAL-DURAND. Development of the neural basis of visual acuity in monkeys: speculations on the origin of deprivation amblyopia. *Trans. Ophthalmol. Soc. UK* 99: 363–368, 1979.

46. BLAKEMORE, C., F. VITAL-DURAND, AND L. J. GAREY. Recovery from monocular deprivation in the monkey. I. Recovery of physiological effects in the visual cortex. *Proc. R. Soc. London Ser. B* 213: 399–423, 1981.

47. BLASDEL, G. G., D. E. MITCHELL, D. W. MUIR, AND J. D. PETTIGREW. A physiological and behavioural study in cats of the effect of early visual experience with contours of a single orientation. *J. Physiol. London* 265: 615–636, 1977.

48. BLASDEL, G. G., AND J. D. PETTIGREW. Effect of prior visual experience on cortical recovery from the effects of unilateral eyelid suture in kittens. *J. Physiol. London* 274: 601–619, 1978.

49. BLASDEL, G. G., AND J. D. PETTIGREW. Degree of interocular synchrony required for maintenance of binocularity in kitten's visual cortex. *J. Neurophysiol.* 42: 1692–1710, 1979.

50. BONDS, A. B. Development of orientation tuning in the visual cortex of kittens. In: *Developmental Neurobiology of Vision*, edited by R. D. Freeman. New York: Plenum, 1979, p. 31–41.

51. BONDS, A. B., AND R. D. FREEMAN. Development of optical quality in the kitten eye. *Vision Res.* 18: 391–398, 1978.

52. BOOTHE, R. G. Development of spatial vision in infant macaque monkeys under conditions of normal and abnormal visual experience. In: *Development of Perception: Psychobiological Perspectives, The Visual System*, edited by R. N. Aslin, J. R. Alberts, and M. R. Petersen. New York: Academic, 1981, vol. II, p. 217–242.

53. BOOTHE, R. G., L. KIORPES, AND A. HENDRICKSON. Anisome-

tropic amblyopia in *Macaca nemestrina* monkeys produced by atropinization of one eye during development. *Invest. Ophthalmol. Vis. Sci.* 22: 228–233, 1982.

54. BOOTHE, R. G., AND D. Y. TELLER. Meridional variations in acuity and CSFs in monkeys (*Macaca nemestrina*) reared with externally applied astigmatism. *Vision Res.* 22: 801–810, 1982.

55. BOOTHE, R., D. Y. TELLER, AND G. P. SACKETT. Trichromacy in normally-reared and light-deprived infant monkeys (*Macaca nemestrina*). *Vision Res.* 15: 1187–1191, 1975.

56. BOOTHE, R. G., R. A. WILLIAMS, L. KIORPES, AND D. Y. TELLER. Development of contrast sensitivity in infant *Macaca nemestrina* monkeys. *Science* 208: 1290–1291, 1980.

57. BORNSTEIN, M. H. Infants are trichromats. *J. Exp. Child Psychol.* 21: 424–445, 1976.

57a.BRADLEY, A., AND R. D. FREEMAN. Contrast sensitivity in children. *Vision Res.* 22: 953–959, 1982.

58. BRAENDSTRUP, P. *Amblyopia ex anopsia* in infantile cataract. *Acta Ophthalmol. Kbh.* 22: 52–71, 1944.

59. BRUCE, C. J., M. R. ISLEY, AND P. G. SHINKMAN. Visual experience and development of interocular orientation disparity in visual cortex. *J. Neurophysiol.* 46: 215–228, 1981.

60. BUISSERET, D., E. GARY-BOBO, AND M. IMBERT. Ocular motility and recovery of orientation properties of visual cortical neurones in dark-reared kittens. *Nature London* 272: 816–817, 1978.

61. BUISSERET, D., AND M. IMBERT. Visual cortical cells: their developmental properties in normal and dark-reared kittens. *J. Physiol. London* 255: 511–525, 1976.

62. BURCHFIEL, J. L., AND F. H. DUFFY. Role of intracortical inhibition in deprivation amblyopia: reversal by microionotophoretic bicuculline. *Brain Res.* 206: 479–484, 1981.

63. CAMPBELL, F. W., AND D. G. GREEN. Optical and retinal factors affecting visual resolution. *J. Physiol. London* 181: 576–593, 1965.

64. CAMPBELL, F. W., J. J. KULIKOWSKI, AND J. LEVINSON. The effect of orientation on the visual resolution of gratings. *J. Physiol. London* 187: 427–436, 1966.

65. CHOW, K. L. Failure to demonstrate changes in the visual system of monkeys kept in darkness or in colored lights. *J. Comp. Neurol.* 102: 597–606, 1955.

66. CHOW, K. L., A. H. RIESEN, AND F. W. NEWELL. Degeneration of retinal ganglion cells in infant chimpanzees reared in darkness. *J. Comp. Neurol.* 107: 27–42, 1957.

67. CHOW, K. L., AND D. L. STEWART. Reversal of structural and functional effects of long-term visual deprivation in cats. *Exp. Neurol.* 34: 409–433, 1972.

68. CLARKE, P. G. H., I. M. L. DONALDSON, AND D. WHITTERIDGE. Binocular visual mechanisms in cortical areas I and II of the sheep. *J. Physiol. London* 256: 509–526, 1976.

69. CLELAND, B., D. P. CREWTHER, S. GILLARD-CREWTHER, AND D. E. MITCHELL. Normality of spatial resolution of retinal ganglion cells in cats with strabismic amblyopia. *J. Physiol. London* 236: 235–249, 1982.

70. CLELAND, B. G., D. E. MITCHELL, S. G. CREWTHER, AND D. P. CREWTHER. Visual resolution of retinal ganglion cells in monocularly-deprived cats. *Brain Res.* 192: 261–266, 1980.

71. COGAN, A. I. The relationship between the apparent vertical and the vertical horopter. *Vision Res.* 19: 655–665, 1979.

72. COLLEWIJN, H. Oculomotor areas in the rabbit's midbrain and pretectum. *J. Neurobiol.* 6: 3–22, 1975.

73. COOPER, M. L., AND J. D. PETTIGREW. A neurophysiological determination of the vertical horopter in the cat and owl. *J. Comp. Neurol.* 184: 1–26, 1979.

74. CRAGG, B. The development of synapses in kitten visual cortex during visual deprivation. *Exp. Neurol.* 46: 445–451, 1975.

75. CRAGG, B. The development of synapses in the visual system of the cat. *J. Comp. Neurol.* 160: 147–166, 1975.

76. CRAWFORD, M. L. J., R. BLAKE, S. J. COOL, AND G. K. VON NOORDEN. Physiological consequences of unilateral and bilateral eye closure in macaque monkeys: some further observations. *Brain Res.* 84: 150–154, 1975.

77. CRAWFORD, M. L. J., AND R. E. MARC. Light transmission of cat and monkey eyelids. *Vision Res.* 16: 323–324, 1976.

78. CRAWFORD, M. L. J., AND G. K. VON NOORDEN. The effects of short-term experimental strabismus on the visual system in *Macaca mulatta*. *Invest. Ophthalmol. Vis. Sci.* 18: 496–505, 1979.

79. CRAWFORD, M. L. J., AND G. K. VON NOORDEN. Optically-induced concomitant strabismus in monkeys. *Invest. Ophthalmol. Vis. Sci.* 19: 1105–1109, 1980.

80. CREWTHER, D. P., S. G. CREWTHER, AND J. D. PETTIGREW. A role for extraocular afferents in post-critical period reversal of monocular deprivation. *J. Physiol. London* 282: 181–195, 1978.

81. CREWTHER, S. G., D. P. CREWTHER, C. K. PECK, AND J. D. PETTIGREW. Visual cortical effects of rearing cats with monocular or binocular cyclotorsion. *J. Neurophysiol.* 44: 97–118, 1980.

82. CYNADER, M. Competitive interaction in postnatal development. In: *Developmental Neurobiology of Vision*, edited by R. D. Freeman. New York: Plenum, 1979, p. 109–120.

83. CYNADER, M. Interocular alignment following visual deprivation in the cat. *Invest. Ophthalmol. Vis. Sci.* 18: 726–741, 1979.

84. CYNADER, M., N. BERMAN, AND A. HEIN. Cats reared in stroboscopic illumination: effects on receptive fields in visual cortex. *Proc. Natl. Acad. Sci. USA* 70: 1353–1354, 1973.

85. CYNADER, M., N. BERMAN, AND A. HEIN. Cats raised in a one-directional world: effects on receptive fields in visual cortex and superior colliculus. *Exp. Brain Res.* 22: 267–280, 1975.

86. CYNADER, M., N. BERMAN, AND A. HEIN. Recovery of function in cat visual cortex following prolonged deprivation. *Exp. Brain Res.* 25: 139–156, 1976.

87. CYNADER, M., C. BLAKEMORE, AND R. C. VAN SLUYTERS. Congruent binocular preferred directions in the superior colliculus of kittens reared with one eye rotated. *Soc. Neurosci. Abstr.* 4: 633, 1978.

88. CYNADER, M., AND G. CHERNENKO. Abolition of directional selectivity in the visual cortex of the cat. *Science* 193: 504–505, 1976.

89. CYNADER, M., AND K. P. HOFFMAN. Strabismus disrupts binocular convergence in cat nucleus of the optic tract. *Dev. Brain Res.* 1: 132–136, 1981.

90. CYNADER, M., F. LEPORÉ, AND J. P. GUILLEMOT. Interhemispheric competition during postnatal development. *Nature London* 290: 139–140, 1981.

91. CYNADER, M., AND D. E. MITCHELL. Monocular astigmatism effects on kitten visual cortex development. *Nature London* 270: 177–178, 1977.

92. CYNADER, M., AND D. E. MITCHELL. Prolonged sensitivity to monocular deprivation in dark-reared cats. *J. Neurophysiol.* 43: 1026–1040, 1980.

93. CYNADER, M., M. J. MUSTARI, AND J. C. GARDNER. Modification of cortical binocular connectivity. *Soc. Neurosci. Symp.* 4: 99–120, 1979.

94. CYNADER, M., B. N. TIMNEY, AND D. E. MITCHELL. Period of susceptibility of kitten visual cortex to the effects of monocular deprivation extends beyond six months of age. *Brain Res.* 191: 515–550, 1980.

95. DANIEL, R. An evaluation of contact lenses in unilateral post-traumatic aphakic children. *Contact Lens J.* 4 (6): 16–24, 1974.

96. DANIELS, J. D., AND J. D. PETTIGREW. Development of neuronal responses in the visual system of cats. In: *Neural and Behavioral Specificity: Studies on the Development of Behavior and the Nervous System*, edited by G. Gottlieb. New York: Academic, 1978, vol. 3, p. 195–232.

97. DANIELS, J. D., J. D. PETTIGREW, AND J. L. NORMAN. Development of single neuron responses in kitten's lateral geniculate nucleus. *J. Neurophysiol.* 41: 1373–1393, 1978.

98. DAW, N. W., AND M. ARIEL. Properties of monocular and directional deprivation. *J. Neurophysiol.* 44: 280–294, 1980.

99. DAW, N. W., N. E. J. BERMAN, AND M. ARIEL. Interaction of critical periods in the visual cortex of kittens. *Science* 199: 565–567, 1978.

100. DAW, N. W., AND H. J. WYATT. Raising rabbits in a moving visual environment: an attempt to modify direction sensitivity in the retina. *J. Physiol. London* 240: 309–330, 1974.

101. DAW, N. W., AND H. J. WYATT. Kittens reared in an undirectional environment: evidence for a critical period. *J. Physiol. London* 257: 155–170, 1976.

102. DAYTON, G. O., M. H. JONES, D. AIU, R. A. RAESON, B. STEELE, AND M. ROSE. Developmental study of coordinated eye movements in the human infant. I. Visual acuity in the newborn human: a study based on induced optokinetic nystagmus recorded by electro-oculograph. *Arch. Ophthalmol.* 71: 865–870, 1964.

103. DERRINGTON, A. M. Direct measurements of image quality in the kitten's eye. *J. Physiol. London* 300: 16P–17P, 1980.

104. DERRINGTON, A. M. Effect of visual deprivation on the development of spatial frequency selectivity in kitten striate cortex. *J. Physiol. London* 300: 62P, 1980.

105. DERRINGTON, A. M., AND A. F. FUCHS. The development of spatial-frequency selectivity in kitten striate cortex. *J. Physiol. London* 316: 1–10, 1981.

106. DERRINGTON, A. M., AND M. J. HAWKEN. Spatial and temporal properties of cat geniculate neurones after prolonged deprivation. *J. Physiol. London* 314: 107–120, 1981.

107. DEWS, P. B., AND T. N. WIESEL. Consequences of monocular deprivation on visual behaviour in kittens. *J. Physiol. London* 206: 437–455, 1970.

108. DOBSON, V. Spectral sensitivity of the 2-month-old infant as measured by the visually evoked cortical potential. *Vision Res.* 16: 367–374, 1976.

109. DOBSON, V., D. L. MAYER, AND C. P. LEE. Visual acuity screening of preterm infants. *Invest. Ophthalmol. Vis. Sci.* 19: 1498–1505, 1979.

110. DOBSON, V., AND D. Y. TELLER. Visual acuity in human infants: a review and comparison of behavioral and electrophysiological studies. *Vision Res.* 18: 1469–1483, 1978.

111. DOBSON, V., D. Y. TELLER, AND J. BELGUM. Visual acuity in human infants assessed with stationary stripes and phase-alternated checkerboards. *Vision Res.* 18: 1233–1238, 1978.

112. DONOVAN, A. The postnatal development of the cat's retina. *Exp. Eye Res.* 5: 249–254, 1966.

113. DRÄGER, U. C. Observations on monocular deprivation in mice. *J. Neurophysiol.* 41: 28–42, 1978.

114. DREHER, B., Y. FUKADA, AND R. W. RODIECK. Identification, classification and anatomical segregation of cells with X-like and Y-like properties in the lateral geniculate nucleus of old-world primates. *J. Physiol. London* 258: 433–452, 1976.

115. DUFFY, F. H., S. R. SNODGRASS, J. L. BURCHFIELD, AND J. L. CONWAY. Bicuculline reversal of deprivation amblyopia in the cat. *Nature London* 260: 256–257, 1976.

116. DUKE-ELDER, S. S., AND C. COOK. *System of Ophthalmology, Normal and Abnormal Development. Embryology*. London: Kimpton, 1963, vol. III, pt. 1.

117. DUKE-ELDER, S. S., AND K. WYBAR. *System of Ophthalmology, Ocular Motility and Strabismus*. London: Kimpton, 1973, vol. VI.

118. EGGERS, H. M., AND C. BLAKEMORE. Physiological basis of anisometropic amblyopia. *Science* 201: 264–267, 1978.

119. EMERSON, V. F., L. M. CHALUPA, I. D. THOMPSON, AND R. J. TALBOT. Behavioural, physiological, and anatomical consequences of monocular deprivation in the golden hamster (*Mesocricetus auratus*). *Exp. Brain Res.* 45: 168–178, 1982.

120. ENOCH, J. M., AND I. M. RABINOWICZ. Early surgery and visual correction of an infant born with unilateral lens opacity. *Doc. Ophthalmol.* 41: 371–382, 1976.

121. ENROTH-CUGELL, C., AND J. G. ROBSON. Direct measurement of image quality in the cat eye. *J. Physiol. London* 249: 30P–31P, 1974.

122. FANTZ, R. L. Pattern vision in young infants. *Psychol. Rec.* 8: 43–47, 1958.

123. FANTZ, R. L., J. F. FAGAN, AND S. R. MIRANDA. Early visual selectivity as a function of pattern variables, previous exposure, age from birth and conception, and expected cognitive deficit. In: *Infant Perception: From Sensation to Cognition. Basic Visual Processes*, edited by L. B. Cohen and P. Salapatek. New York: Academic, 1975, vol. 1, p. 249–345.

124. FANTZ, R. L., J. M. ORDY, AND M. S. UDELF. Maturation of pattern vision in infants during the first six months. *J. Comp. Physiol. Psychol.* 55: 907–917, 1962.

125. FIORENTINI, A., AND L. MAFFEI. Change of binocular properties of the simple cells of the cortex in adult cats following immobilization of one eye. *Vision Res.* 14: 217–218, 1974.

126. FIORENTINI, A., AND L. MAFFEI. Selective impairment of contrast sensitivity in kittens exposed to periodic gratings. *J. Physiol. London* 277: 455–466, 1978.

127. FIORENTINI, A., AND L. MAFFEI. Responses of cortical neurones of monocularly deprived kittens: a re-examination. *J. Physiol. London* 291: 35P, 1979.

128. FLOOD, D. G., AND P. D. COLEMAN. Demonstration of orientation columns with [^{14}C]2-deoxyglucose in a cat reared in a striped environment. *Brain Res.* 173: 538–542, 1979.

129. FOX, R., R. N. ASLIN, S. L. SHEA, AND S. T. DUMAIS. Stereopsis in human infants. *Science* 207: 323–324, 1980.

130. FREEMAN, R. D. Contrast sensitivity in meridional amblyopia. *Invest. Ophthalmol. Vis. Sci.* 14: 78–81, 1975.

131. FREEMAN, R. D. Some neural and non-neural factors in visual development of the kitten. *Arch. Ital. Biol.* 116: 338–351, 1978.

132. FREEMAN, R. D. Visuomotor restriction of one eye in kitten reared with alternate monocular deprivation. *Exp. Brain Res.* 33: 51–63, 1978.

133. FREEMAN, R. D. The consequences of a "consolidation" period following brief monocular deprivation in kittens. In: *Developmental Neurobiology of Vision*, edited by R. D. Freeman. New York: Plenum, 1979, p. 99–107.

134. FREEMAN, R. D., AND A. B. BONDS. Cortical plasticity in monocularly deprived immobilized kittens depends on eye movement. *Science* 206: 1093–1095, 1979.

135. FREEMAN, R. D., AND A. BRADLEY. Monocularly deprived humans: nondeprived eye has supernormal vernier acuity. *J. Neurophysiol.* 43: 1645–1653, 1980.

136. FREEMAN, R. D., R. MALLACH, AND S. HARTLEY. Responsivity of normal kitten visual cortex deteriorates after brief binocular deprivation. *J. Neurophysiol.* 45: 1074–1084, 1981.

137. FREEMAN, R. D., D. E. MITCHELL, AND M. MILLODOT. A neural effect of partial visual deprivation in humans. *Science* 175: 1384–1386, 1972.

138. FREEMAN, R. D., AND C. R. OLSON. Is there a "consolidation" effect for monocular deprivation? *Nature London* 282: 104–106, 1979.

139. FREEMAN, R. D., AND C. R. OLSON. Cortical effects of daily sequential stimulation of right and left eyes in the kitten. *Exp. Brain Res.* 39: 117–119, 1980.

140. FREEMAN, R. D., AND J. D. PETTIGREW. Alteration of visual cortex from environmental asymmetries. *Nature London* 246: 359–360, 1973.

141. FREEMAN, R. D., AND L. N. THIBOS. Visual evoked responses in humans with abnormal visual experience. *J. Physiol. London* 247: 711–724, 1975.

142. FRÉGNAC, Y., AND M. IMBERT. Early development of visual cortical cells in normal and dark-reared kittens: relationship between orientation selectivity and ocular dominance. *J. Physiol. London* 278: 27–44, 1978.

143. FRÉGNAC, Y., Y. TROTTER, E. BIONENSTOCK, P. BUISSERET, E. GARY-BOBO, AND M. IMBERT. Effect of neonatal unilateral enucleation on the development of orientation selectivity in the primary visual cortex of normally and dark-reared kittens. *Exp. Brain Res.* 42: 453–466, 1981.

144. GANZ, L. Sensory deprivation and visual discrimination. In: *Handbook of Sensory Physiology. Perception*, edited by R. Held, H. W. Leibowitz, and H. L. Teuber. Berlin: Springer-Verlag, 1978, vol. 8, p. 437–488.

145. GANZ, L., AND M. FITCH. The effect of visual deprivation on perceptual behavior. *Exp. Neurol.* 22: 638–660, 1968.

146. GIFFIN, F., AND D. E. MITCHELL. The rate of recovery of vision after early monocular deprivation in kittens. *J. Physiol. London* 274: 511–537, 1978.

147. GOLLENDER, M., F. THORN, AND P. ERICKSON. Development of axial ocular dimensions following eyelid suture in the cat.

Vision Res. 19: 221–223, 1979.

147a.GORDON, B., AND J. PRESSON. Orientation deprivation in cat: what produces the abnormal cells. *Exp. Brain Res.* 46: 144–146, 1982.

148. GORDON, B., J. PRESSON, J. PACKWOOD, AND R. SCHEER. Alteration of cortical orientation selectivity: importance of asymmetric input. *Science* 204: 1109–1111, 1979.

149. GOTTLIEB, G. The roles of experience in the development of behavior and the nervous system. In: *Neural and Behavioral Specificity*, edited by G. Gottlieb. New York: Academic, 1976, p. 25–54.

150. GREEN, D. G. Regional variations in the visual acuity for interference fringes on the retina. *J. Physiol. London* 207: 351–356, 1970.

151. GREGORY, R. L., AND J. G. WALLACE. Recovery from early blindness: a case study. *Experimental Psychology Society Monograph.* Cambridge, England: Heffer, 1963, no. 2.

152. GRINNELL, A. D. Specificity of neurons and their interconnections. In: *Handbook of Physiology. The Nervous System. Cellular Biology of Neurons*, edited by E. R. Kandel. Bethesda, MD: Am. Physiol. Soc., 1977, sect. 1, vol. I, pt. 2, chapt. 22, p. 803–853.

153. GUILLERY, R. W. Binocular competition in the control of geniculate cell growth. *J. Comp. Neurol.* 144: 117–130, 1972.

154. GUILLERY, R. W. The effect of lid suture upon the growth of cells in the dorsal lateral geniculate nucleus of kittens. *J. Comp. Neurol.* 148: 417–422, 1973.

155. GUILLERY, R. W., AND D. J. STELZNER. The differential effects of unilateral lid closure upon the monocular and binocular segments of the dorsal lateral geniculate nucleus in the cat. *J. Comp. Neurol.* 139: 413–422, 1970.

156. GWIAZDA, J., S. BRILL, I. MOHINDRA, AND R. HELD. Infant visual acuity and its meridional variation. *Vision Res.* 18: 1557–1564, 1978.

157. GWIAZDA, J., S. BRILL, I. MOHINDRA, AND R. HELD. Preferential looking acuity in infants from two to fifty-eight weeks of age. *Am. J. Optom. Physiol. Opt.* 57: 428–432, 1980.

158. HAMASAKI, D. I., AND V. G. SUTIJA. Development of X- and Y-cells in kittens. *Exp. Brain Res.* 35: 9–23, 1979.

159. HAMER, R. D., K. R. ALEXANDER, AND D. Y. TELLER. Rayleigh discriminations in young human infants. *Vision Res.* 22: 575–587, 1982.

159a.HÄRRY, P., AND R. VON DER HEYDT. The effect of horizontal-plane environment on the development of binocular receptive fields of cells in cat visual cortex. *J. Physiol. London* 329: 75–92, 1982.

160. HARRIS, L., J. ATKINSON, AND O. BRADDICK. Visual contrast sensitivity of a 6-month-old infant measured by the evoked potential. *Nature London* 264: 570–571, 1976.

161. HARRIS, W. A., AND M. P. STRYKER. Attempts to reverse the effects of monocular deprivation in the adult cat's visual cortex. *Soc. Neurosci. Abstr.* 3: 562, 1977.

162. HARWERTH, R. S., E. L. SMITH, AND R. L. BOLTZ. Meridional amblyopia in monkeys. *Exp. Brain Res.* 39: 351–356, 1980.

163. HAWKEN, M., R. MARK, AND C. BLAKEMORE. The effects of pressure blinding in monocularly deprived cats. *Arch. Ital. Biol.* 116: 448–451, 1978.

164. HECHT, S., S. SHLAER, AND M. H. PIRENNE. Energy, quanta and vision. *J. Gen. Physiol.* 25: 819–840, 1942.

165. HELD, R., E. E. BIRCH, AND J. GWIAZDA. Stereoacuity of human infants. *Proc. Natl. Acad. Sci. USA* 77: 5572–5576, 1980.

166. HELD, R., J. GWIAZDA, S. BRILL, I. MOHINDRA, AND J. WOLFE. Infant visual acuity is underestimated because near threshold gratings are not preferentially fixated. *Vision Res.* 19: 1377–1379, 1979.

167. HENDRICKSON, A., AND R. BOOTHE. Morphology of the retina and lateral geniculate nucleus in dark-reared monkeys (*Macaca nemestrina*). *Vision Res.* 16: 517–521, 1976.

168. HENDRICKSON, A., AND C. KUPFER. The histogenesis of the fovea in the macaque monkey. *Invest. Ophthalmol. Vis. Sci.* 15: 746–756, 1976.

169. HENRY, G. H., B. DREHER, AND P. O. BISHOP. Orientation specificity of cells in cat striate cortex. *J. Neurophysiol.* 37: 1394–1409, 1974.

170. HESS, R. F., F. W. CAMPBELL, AND R. ZIMMERN. Differences in the neural basis of human amblyopias: the effect of mean luminance. *Vision Res.* 20: 295–305, 1980.

171. HESS, R. F., T. FRANCE, AND U. TULUNAY-KEESEY. Residual vision in humans who have been monocularly deprived of pattern stimulation in early life. *Exp. Brain Res.* 44: 295–311, 1981.

172. HICKEY, T. L. Development of the dorsal lateral geniculate nucleus in normal and visually deprived cats. *J. Comp. Neurol.* 189: 467–481, 1980.

173. HICKEY, T. L., P. D. SPEAR, AND K. E. KRATZ. Quantitative studies of cell size in the cat's dorsal lateral geniculate nucleus following visual deprivation. *J. Comp. Neurol.* 172: 265–282, 1977.

174. HIRSCH, H. V. B. Visual perception in cats after environmental surgery. *Exp. Brain Res.* 15: 405–423, 1972.

175. HIRSCH, H. V. B., AND D. N. SPINELLI. Visual experience modifies distribution of horizontally and vertically oriented receptive fields in cats. *Science* 168: 869–871, 1970.

176. HIRSCH, H. V. B., AND D. N. SPINELLI. Modification of the distribution of receptive field orientation in cats by selective visual exposure during development. *Exp. Brain Res.* 13: 509–527, 1971.

177. HOCHBERG, J. Nativism and empiricism in perception. In: *Psychology in the Making*, edited by L. Postman. New York: Knopf, 1962, p. 255–330.

178. HOFFMANN, K.-P. Optokinetic nystagmus and single cell responses in the nucleus tractus opticus after early monocular deprivation in the cat. In: *Developmental Neurobiology of Vision*, edited by R. D. Freeman. New York: Plenum, 1979, p. 63–72.

179. HOFFMANN, K.-P., AND M. CYNADER. Functional aspects of plasticity in the visual system of adult cats after early monocular deprivation. *Philos. Trans. R. Soc. London Ser. B* 278: 411–424, 1977.

180. HOHMANN, A., AND O. D. CREUTZFELDT. Squint and the development of binocularity in humans. *Nature London* 254: 613–614, 1975.

181. HOWELL, E. R., AND R. F. HESS. The functional area for summation to threshold for sinusoidal gratings. *Vision Res.* 18: 369–374, 1978.

182. HOWLAND, H., R. G. BOOTHE, AND L. KIORPES. Accommodative defocus does not limit development of acuity in infant *Macaca nemestrina* monkeys. *Science* 215: 1409–1411, 1981.

183. HOYT, C. S., R. D. STONE, AND C. FROMER. Monocular axial myopia associated with neonatal eyelid closure in human infants. *Am. J. Ophthalmol.* 91: 197–200, 1981.

184. HUBEL, D. H., AND T. N. WIESEL. Receptive fields, binocular interaction and functional architecture in the cat's visual cortex. *J. Physiol. London* 160: 106–154, 1962.

185. HUBEL, D. H., AND T. N. WIESEL. Receptive fields of cells in striate cortex of very young, visually inexperienced kittens. *J. Neurophysiol.* 26: 994–1002, 1963.

186. HUBEL, D. H., AND T. N. WIESEL. Binocular interaction in striate cortex of kittens reared with artificial squint. *J. Neurophysiol.* 28: 1041–1059, 1965.

187. HUBEL, D. H., AND T. N. WIESEL. Receptive fields and functional architecture of monkey striate cortex. *J. Physiol. London* 195: 215–243, 1968.

188. HUBEL, D. H., AND T. N. WIESEL. The period of susceptibility to the physiological effects of unilateral eye closure in kittens. *J. Physiol. London* 206: 419–436, 1970.

189. HUBEL, D. H., AND T. N. WIESEL. Functional architecture of macaque monkey visual cortex. *Proc. R. Soc. London Ser. B* 198: 1–59, 1977.

190. HUBEL, D. H., T. N. WIESEL, AND S. LEVAY. Plasticity of ocular dominance columns in monkey striate cortex. *Philos. Trans. R. Soc. London Ser. B* 278: 377–409, 1977.

191. HUGHES, A. Cat retina and the sampling theorem: the relation of transient and sustained brisk-unit cut-off frequency to α and β-mode cell density. *Exp. Brain Res.* 42: 196–202, 1981.

192. IKEDA, H., AND K. E. TREMAIN. Amblyopia resulting from penalisation: neurophysiological studies of kittens reared with atropinisation of one or both eyes. *Br. J. Ophthalmol.* 62: 21–28, 1978.

193. IKEDA, H., AND K. E. TREMAIN. The development of spatial resolving power of lateral geniculate neurones in kittens. *Exp. Brain Res.* 31: 193–206, 1978.

194. IKEDA, H., AND K. E. TREMAIN. Amblyopia occurs in retinal ganglion cells in cats reared with convergent squint without alternating fixation. *Exp. Brain Res.* 35: 559–582, 1979.

195. IKEDA, H., K. E. TREMAIN, AND G. EINON. Loss of spatial resolution of lateral geniculate nucleus neurones in kittens raised with convergent squint produced at different stages in development. *Exp. Brain Res.* 31: 207–220, 1978.

196. IMBERT, M., AND P. BUISSERET. Receptive field characteristics and plastic properties of visual cortical cells in kittens reared with or without visual experience. *Exp. Brain Res.* 22: 25–36, 1975.

197. ISLEY, M. R., D. C. ROGERS, M. PODELL, AND P. G. SHINKMAN. Disruption of cortical binocularity due to early experience with 32° of rotational disparity between the left and right eyes' visual fields. *Soc. Neurosci. Abstr.* 6: 492, 1980.

198. JACOBSON, S. G., AND H. IKEDA. Behavioural studies of spatial vision in cats reared with convergent squint: is amblyopia due to arrest of development? *Exp. Brain Res.* 34: 11–26, 1979.

199. JACOBSON, S. G., I. MOHINDRA, AND R. HELD. Visual acuity in infants with ocular diseases. *Am. J. Ophthalmol.* 93: 198–209, 1982.

200. JAMPOLSKY, A. Unequal visual inputs and strabismus management: a comparison of human and animal strabismus. In: *Symposium on Strabismus. Transactions of the New Orleans Academy of Ophthalmology*. St. Louis, MO: Mosby, 1978, p. 358–492.

201. JEANNEROD, M., Déficit visuel persistant chez les aveugles-nés opérés données cliniques et experimentales. *Année Psychol.* 75: 169–196, 1975.

202. JOHNS, P. R., A. C. RUSOFF, AND M. W. DUBIN. Postnatal neurogenesis in the kitten retina. *J. Comp. Neurol.* 187: 545–556, 1979.

203. JONES, K. R., M. BERKLEY, P. SPEAR, AND L. TONG. Visual capacities of monocularly deprived cats after reverse lid suture and enucleation of the non-deprived eye. *Soc. Neurosci. Abstr.* 4: 1516, 1978.

204. JULER, F. Amblyopia from disuse. Visual acuity after traumatic cataract in children. *Trans. Ophthalmol Soc. UK* 41: 129–139, 1921.

205. JULESZ, B. *Foundations of Cyclopean Perception*. Chicago: Univ. of Chicago Press, 1971.

206. KALIL, R. A quantitative study of the effects of monocular enucleation and deprivation in the dorsal lateral geniculate nucleus of the cat. *J. Comp. Neurol.* 189: 483–524, 1980.

207. KANDEL, E. R. Neuronal plasticity and the modification of behavior. In: *Handbook of Physiology. The Nervous System. Cellular Biology of Neurons*, edited by E. R. Kandel. Bethesda, MD: Am. Physiol. Soc., 1977, sect. 1, vol. I, pt. 2, chapt. 29, p. 1137–1182.

208. KASAMATSU, T., AND J. D. PETTIGREW. Depletion of brain catecholamines: failure of ocular dominance shift after monocular occlusion in kittens. *Science* 194: 206–209, 1976.

209. KASAMATSU, T., AND J. D. PETTIGREW. Preservation of binocularity after monocular deprivation in the striate cortex of kittens treated with 6-hydroxydopamine. *J. Comp. Neurol.* 185: 139–162, 1979.

210. KASAMATSU, T., J. D. PETTIGREW, AND M. ARY. Restoration of visual cortical plasticity by local microperfusion of norepinephrine. *J. Comp. Neurol.* 185: 163–182, 1979.

211. KAYE, M., D. E. MITCHELL, AND M. CYNADER. Depth perception, eye alignment and cortical ocular dominance of dark-

reared cats. *Dev. Brain Res.* 2: 37–53, 1982.

212. KENNEDY, C., M. H. DES ROSIERS, O. SAKURDA, M. SHINO-HARA, M. REIVICH, H. W. JEBLE, AND L. SOKOLOFF. Metabolic mapping of the primary visual system of the monkey by means of the autoradiographic ^{14}C-deoxyglucose technique. *Proc. Natl. Acad. Sci. USA* 73: 4230–4234, 1976.

213. KIORPES, L., AND R. G. BOOTHE. The time course for the development of strabismic amblyopia in infant monkeys (*Macaca nemestrina*). *Invest. Ophthalmol. Vis. Sci.* 19: 841–845, 1980.

214. KIORPES, L., AND R. G. BOOTHE. Naturally occurring strabismus in monkeys (*Macaca nemestrina*). *Invest. Ophthalmol. Vis. Sci.* 20: 257–263, 1981.

215. KIORPES, L., L. THORELL, AND R. G. BOOTHE. Response properties of cortical cells in monkeys with experimentally produced meridional amblyopia. *Invest. Ophthalmol. Vis. Sci.* 18, Suppl.: 184, 1979.

216. KIRBY, A. W., L. SUTTON, AND H. WEISS. Elongation of cat eyes following neonatal lid suture. *Invest. Ophthalmol. Vis. Sci.* 22: 274–277, 1982.

217. KRATZ, K. E., S. C. MANGEL, S. LEHMKUHLE, AND S. M. SHERMAN. Retinal X- and Y-cells in monocularly lid-sutured cats: normality of spatial and temporal properties. *Brain Res.* 172: 545–551, 1979.

218. KRATZ, K. E., S. M. SHERMAN, AND R. KALIL. Lateral geniculate nucleus in dark-reared cats: loss of Y-cells without changes in cell size. *Science* 203: 1353–1355, 1979.

219. KRATZ, K. E., AND P. D. SPEAR. Effects of visual deprivation and alterations in binocular competition on responses of striate cortex neurons in the cat. *J. Comp. Neurol.* 170: 141–152, 1976.

220. KRATZ, K. E., P. D. SPEAR, AND D. C. SMITH. Postcritical-period reversal of effects of monocular deprivation on striate cortex cells in the cat. *J. Neurophysiol.* 39: 501–511, 1976.

221. LEE, C. P., AND R. G. BOOTHE. Visual acuity development in infant monkeys (*Macaca nemestrina*) having known gestational ages. *Vision Res.* 21: 805–809, 1981.

222. LEEHEY, S. C., A. MOSKOWITZ-COOK, S. BRILL, AND R. HELD. Orientational anisotropy in infant vision. *Science* 190: 900–902, 1975.

223. LEHMKUHLE, S. W., K. E. KRATZ, S. C. MANGEL, AND S. M. SHERMAN. An effect of early monocular lid suture upon the development of X-cells in the cat's lateral geniculate nucleus. *Brain Res.* 157: 346–350, 1978.

224. LEHMKULE, S., K. E. KRATZ, S. C. MANGEL, AND S. M. SHERMAN. Spatial and temporal sensitivity of X- and Y-cells in dorsal lateral geniculate nucleus of the cat. *J. Neurophysiol.* 43: 520–541, 1980.

225. LENNIE, P. Parallel visual pathways: a review. *Vision Res.* 20: 561–594, 1980.

226. LEVAY, S., AND D. FERSTER. Relay cell classes in the lateral geniculate nucleus of the cat and the effects of visual deprivation. *J. Comp. Neurol.* 172: 563–584, 1977.

227. LEVAY, S., AND M. P. STRYKER. The development of ocular dominance columns in the cat. *Soc. Neurosci. Symp.* 4: 83–98, 1979.

228. LEVAY, S., M. P. STRYKER, AND C. J. SHATZ. Ocular dominance columns and their development in layer IV of the cat's visual cortex: a quantitative study. *J. Comp. Neurol.* 179: 223–244, 1978.

229. LEVAY, S., T. N. WIESEL, AND D. H. HUBEL. The development of ocular dominance columns in normal and visually deprived monkeys. *J. Comp. Neurol.* 191: 1–51, 1980.

230. LEVENTHAL, A. G., AND H. V. B. HIRSCH. Cortical effect of early selective exposure to diagonal lines. *Science* 190: 902–904, 1975.

231. LEVENTHAL, A. G., AND H. V. B. HIRSCH. Effects of early experience upon the orientation sensitivity and the binocularity of neurons in the cat's visual cortex. *Proc. Natl. Acad. Sci. USA* 74: 1272–1276, 1977.

232. LEVI, D. M., AND R. S. HARWERTH. Spatio-temporal interactions in anisometropic and strabismic amblyopia. *Invest.*

233. LEVICK, W. R., AND L. N. THIBOS. Orientation bias of cat retinal ganglion cells. *Nature London* 286: 389–390, 1980.

234. LEVITT, F. B., AND R. C. VAN SLUYTERS. The sensitive period for strabismus in the kitten. *Dev. Brain Res.* 3: 323–327, 1982.

235. LOOP, M. S., AND S. M. SHERMAN. Visual discriminations during eyelid closure in the cat. *Brain Res.* 128: 329–339, 1977.

236. LUND, J. S., R. G. BOOTHE, AND R. D. LUND. Development of neurons in the visual cortex (area 17) of the monkey (*Macaca nemestrina*): a Golgi study from fetal day 127 to postnatal maturity. *J. Comp. Neurol.* 176: 149–188, 1977.

237. LUND, R. *Development and Plasticity of the Brain.* New York: Oxford Univ. Press, 1978, p. 253–284.

238. MAFFEI, L., AND S. BISTI. Binocular interaction in strabismic kittens deprived of vision. *Science* 191: 579–580, 1976.

239. MANN, I. *The Development of the Human Eye.* New York: Grune and Stratton, 1964, p. 110–117.

240. MARG, E., D. N. FREEMAN, D. PELTZMAN, AND P. J. GOLD-STEIN. Visual acuity development in human infants: evoked potential measurements. *Invest. Ophthalmol. Vis. Sci.* 15: 150–153, 1976.

241. MARTIN, K. A. C., V. S. RAMACHANDRAN, V. M. RAO, AND D. WHITTERIDGE. Changes in ocular dominance induced in monocularly deprived lambs by stimulation with rotating gratings. *Nature London* 277: 391–393, 1979.

242. MAYER, L., AND V. DOBSON. Assessment of vision in young children: a new operant approach yields estimates of acuity. *Invest. Ophthalmol. Vis. Sci.* 19: 566–570, 1980.

242a. MAYER, D. L., AND V. DOBSON. Visual acuity development in infants and young children, as assessed by operant preferential looking. *Vision Res.* 22: 1141–1151, 1982.

243. MITCHELL, D. E. Effect of early visual experience on the development of certain visual capacities in animals and man. In: *Perception and Experience*, edited by R. D. Walk and H. L. Pick, Jr. New York: Plenum, 1978, p. 37–75.

244. MITCHELL, D. E. Sensitive periods in visual development. In: *The Development of Perception: Psychobiological Perspectives*, edited by R. N. Aslin, J. R. Alberts, and M. R. Petersen. New York: Academic, 1981, vol. 2, p. 3–43.

245. MITCHELL, D. E., M. CYNADER, AND J. A. MOVSHON. Recovery from the effects of monocular deprivation in kittens. *J. Comp. Neurol.* 176: 53–64, 1977.

246. MITCHELL, D. E., R. D. FREEMAN, M. MILLODOT, AND G. HAEGERSTROM. Meridional amblyopia: evidence for modification of the human visual system by early visual experience. *Vision Res.* 13: 535–558, 1973.

247. MITCHELL, D. E., F. GIFFIN, D. MUIR, C. BLAKEMORE, AND R. C. VAN SLUYTERS. Behavioural compensation of cats after early rotation of one eye. *Exp. Brain Res.* 25: 109–113, 1976.

248. MITCHELL, D. E., F. GIFFIN, AND B. TIMNEY. A behavioural technique for the rapid assessment of the visual capabilities of kittens. *Perception* 6: 181–193, 1977.

249. MITCHELL, D. E., F. GIFFIN, F. WILKINSON, P. ANDERSON, AND M. L. SMITH. Visual resolution in young kittens. *Vision Res.* 16: 363–366, 1976.

250. MITCHELL, D. E., M. KAYE, AND B. TIMNEY. Assessment of depth perception in cats. *Perception* 8: 389–396, 1979.

251. MITCHELL, D. E., AND B. TIMNEY. Behavioral measurement of normal and abnormal development of vision in kittens. In: *Analysis of Visual Behavior*, edited by D. J. Ingle, M. A. Goodale, and R. J. Mansfield. Cambridge: MIT Press, 1981, p. 483–523.

252. MITCHELL, D. E., AND C. WARE. Interocular transfer of a visual aftereffect in normal and stereoblind humans. *J. Physiol. London* 236: 707–721, 1974.

253. MITCHELL, D. E., AND F. E. WILKINSON. The effect of early astigmatism on the visual resolution of gratings. *J. Physiol. London* 243: 739–756, 1974.

254. MITZDORF, U., AND G. NEUMANN. Effects of monocular deprivation in the lateral geniculate nucleus of the cat: an analysis of evoked potentials. *J. Physiol. London* 304: 221–230, 1980.

255. MITZDORF, U., AND W. SINGER. Monocular activation of visual cortex in normal and monocularly deprived cats: an analysis of evoked potentials. *J. Physiol. London* 304: 203–220, 1980.

256. MOHINDRA, I., S. G. JACOBSON, J. THOMAS, AND R. HELD. Development of amblyopia in infants. *Trans. Ophthalmol. Soc. UK* 99: 344–346, 1980.

257. MORAN, J., AND B. GORDON. Long term visual deprivation in a human. *Vision Res.* 22: 27–36, 1982.

258. MORGAN, M. J. *Molyneux's Question.* Cambridge, England: Cambridge Univ. Press, 1977.

259. MOSKOWITZ-COOK, A. The development of photopic spectral sensitivity in human infants. *Vision Res.* 19: 1133–1142, 1979.

260. MOVSHON, J. A. Reversal of the physiological effects of monocular deprivation in the kitten's visual cortex. *J. Physiol. London* 261: 125–174, 1976.

261. MOVSHON, J. A., B. E. I. CHAMBERS, AND C. BLAKEMORE. Interocular transfer of normal humans and those who lack stereopsis. *Perception* 1: 483–490, 1972.

262. MOVSHON, J. A., AND M. R. DÜRSTELER. Effects of brief periods of unilateral eye closure on the kitten's visual system. *J. Neurophysiol.* 40: 1255–1265, 1977.

263. MOVSHON, J. A., AND R. C. VAN SLUYTERS. Visual neuronal development. *Annu. Rev. Psychol.* 32: 477–522, 1981.

264. MOWER, G. D., D. BERRY, J. L. BURCHFIEL, AND F. H. DUFFY. Comparison of the effects of dark-rearing and binocular suture on development and plasticity of cat visual cortex. *Brain Res.* 220: 255–267, 1981.

265. MOWER, G. D., J. L. BURCHFIEL, AND F. H. DUFFY. The effects of dark-rearing on the development and plasticity of the lateral geniculate nucleus. *Dev. Brain Res.* 1: 418–424, 1981.

266. MOWER, G. D., C. J. CAPLAN, AND G. LETSOU. Behavioral recovery from binocular deprivation in the cat. *Behav. Brain Res.* 4: 209–215, 1982.

267. MUIR, D. W., AND D. E. MITCHELL. Behavioral deficits in cats following early selected visual exposure to contours of a single orientation. *Brain Res.* 85: 459–477, 1975.

268. MUSTARI, M. J., AND M. CYNADER. Rapid recovery from visual deprivation in neurons of cat parastriate cortex. *Soc. Neurosci. Abstr.* 4: 638, 1978.

269. MUSTARI, M. J., AND M. CYNADER. Prior strabismus protects kitten cortical neurons from the effects of monocular deprivation. *Brain Res.* 211: 165–170, 1981.

270. NELSON, J. I., H. KATO, AND P. O. BISHOP. Discrimination of orientation and position disparities by binocularly activated neurons in cat striate cortex. *J. Neurophysiol.* 40: 260–283, 1977.

271. NIKARA, T., P. O. BISHOP, AND J. D. PETTIGREW. Analysis of retinal correspondence by studying receptive fields of binocular single units in cat striate cortex. *Exp. Brain Res.* 6: 353–372, 1968.

272. OGLE, K. N. *Researches in Binocular Vision.* New York: Hafner, 1964, p. 10–49.

273. O'LEARY, D. J., AND M. MILLODOT. Eyelid closure causes myopia in humans. *Experientia* 35: 1478–1479, 1979.

274. OLSON, C. R., AND R. D. FREEMAN. Progressive changes in kitten striate cortex during monocular vision. *J. Neurophysiol.* 38: 26–32, 1975.

275. OLSON, C. R., AND R. D. FREEMAN. Monocular deprivation and recovery during sensitive period in kittens. *J. Neurophysiol.* 41: 65–74, 1978.

276. OLSON, C. R., AND R. D. FREEMAN. Cumulative effect of brief daily periods of monocular vision on kittens striate cortex. *Exp. Brain Res.* 38: 53–56, 1980.

277. OLSON, C. R., AND R. D. FREEMAN. Profile of the sensitive period for monocular deprivation in kittens. *Exp. Brain Res.* 39: 17–21, 1980.

278. OLSON, C. R., AND R. D. FREEMAN. Rescaling of the retinal map of visual space during growth of the kitten's eye. *Brain Res.* 186: 55–65, 1980.

279. OLSON, C. R., AND J. D. PETTIGREW. Single units in visual cortex of kittens reared in stroboscopic illumination. *Brain Res.* 70: 189–204, 1974.

280. ORDY, J. M., A. LATANICK, T. SAMORAJSKI, AND L. C. MASSOPUST, JR. Visual acuity in newborn primate infants. *Proc. Soc. Exp. Biol. Med.* 115: 677–680, 1964.

281. ORDY, J. M., L. C. MASSOPUST, JR., AND L. R. WOLIN. Postnatal development of the retina, electroretinogram and acuity in the rhesus monkey. *Exp. Neurol.* 5: 364–382, 1962.

282. ORDY, J. M., T. SAMORAJSKI, R. L. COLLINS, AND M. S. NAGY. Postnatal development of vision in a subhuman primate (*Macaca mulatta*). *Arch. Ophthalmol.* 73: 674–686, 1965.

283. OVER, R., AND D. MOORE. Spatial acuity of the chicken. *Brain Res.* 211: 424–426, 1981.

284. OWEN, W. C., AND W. F. HUGHES. Results of surgical treatment of congenital cataract. *A.M.A. Arch. Ophthalmol.* 39: 339–350, 1948.

285. PACKWOOD, J., AND B. GORDON. Stereopsis in normal domestic cat, Siamese cat, and cat raised with alternating monocular occlusion. *J. Neurophysiol.* 38: 1485–1499, 1975.

286. PALMER, L. A., AND A. C. ROSENQUIST. Visual receptive fields of single striate cortical units projecting to superior colliculus in cat. *Brain Res.* 67: 27–42, 1974.

287. PASIK, P., AND T. PASIK. Oculomotor function in monkeys with lesions of the cerebrum and the superior colliculi. In: *The Oculomotor System,* edited by M. B. Bender. New York: Hoever, 1964, p. 40–80.

287a.PASTORE, N. *Selective History of Theories of Visual Perception: 1650–1950.* New York: Oxford Univ. Press, 1971.

288. PECK, C. K., AND S. CREWTHER. Perceptual effects of surgical rotation of the eye in kittens. *Brain Res.* 99: 213–219, 1975.

289. PECK, C. K., S. G. CREWTHER, G. BARBER, AND C. J. JOHANNSEN. Pattern discrimination and visuomotor behavior following rotation of one or both eyes in kittens and in adult cats. *Exp. Brain Res.* 34: 401–418, 1979.

290. PEEPLES, D. R., AND D. Y. TELLER. White-adapted photopic spectral sensitivity in human infants. *Vision Res.* 18: 49–53, 1978.

291. PEEPLES, D. R., AND D. Y. TELLER. Color vision and brightness discrimination in two-month-old infants. *Science* 189: 1102–1103, 1975.

292. PETRIG, B., B. JULESZ, W. KROPFL, G. BAUMGARTNER, AND M. ANLIKER. Development of stereopsis and cortical binocularity in human infants: electrophysiological evidence. *Science* 213: 1402–1405, 1981.

293. PETTIGREW, J. D. The effect of visual experience on the development of stimulus specificity by kitten cortical neurones. *J. Physiol. London* 237: 49–74, 1974.

294. PETTIGREW, J. D. The paradox of the critical period for striate cortex. In: *Neuronal Plasticity,* edited by C. W. Cotman. New York: Raven, 1978, p. 311–330.

295. PETTIGREW, J. D. Comparative physiology of binocular vision. *Aust. J. Optom.* 63: 204–210, 1980.

296. PETTIGREW, J. D., AND R. D. FREEMAN. Visual experience without lines: effect on developing cortical neurons. *Science* 182: 599–601, 1973.

297. PETTIGREW, J. D., AND L. J. GAREY. Selective modification of single neuron properties in the visual cortex of kittens. *Brain Res.* 66: 160–164, 1974.

298. PETTIGREW, J. D., AND T. KASAMATSU. Local perfusion of noradrenaline maintains visual cortical plasticity. *Nature London* 271: 761–763, 1978.

299. PETTIGREW, J. D., AND M. KONISHI. Effects of monocular deprivation on binocular neurons in the owl's visual Wulst. *Nature London* 264: 753–754, 1976.

300. PETTIGREW, J. D., AND M. KONISHI. Neurons selective for orientation and binocular disparity in the visual Wulst of the barn owl (*Tyto alba*). *Science* 193: 675–678, 1976.

301. PETTIGREW, J. D., C. OLSON, AND H. B. BARLOW. Kitten visual cortex: short-term, stimulus-induced changes in connectivity. *Science* 180: 1202–1203, 1973.

302. PETTIGREW, J. D., C. OLSON, AND H. V. R. HIRSCH. Cortical effect of selective visual experience degeneration or reorganization? *Brain Res.* 51: 345–351, 1973.

303. PIRCHIO, M., D. SPINELLI, A. FIORENTINI, AND L. MAFFEI.

Infant contrast sensitivity evaluated by evoked potentials. *Brain Res.* 141: 179–184, 1978.

304. POWERS, M. K., M. SCHNECK, AND D. Y. TELLER. Spectral sensitivity of human infants at absolute threshold. *Vision Res.* 21: 1005–1016, 1981.

305. PRESSON, J., AND B. GORDON. Critical period and minimum exposure required for the effects of alternating monocular occlusion in cat visual cortex. *Vision Res.* 19: 807–811, 1979.

306. RAKIC, P. Prenatal development of the visual system in rhesus monkey. *Philos. Trans. R. Soc. London Ser. B* 278: 245–260, 1977.

307. RAKIC, P. Development of visual centers in the primate brain depends on binocular competition before birth. *Science* 214: 928–931, 1981.

308. RAMACHANDRAN, V. S., P. G. H. CLARKE, AND D. WHITERIDGE. Cells selective to binocular disparity in the cortex of newborn lambs. *Nature London* 268: 333–335, 1977.

309. RAUSCHECKER, J. P., AND W. SINGER. Changes in the circuitry of the kitten visual cortex are gated by postsynaptic activity. *Nature London* 280: 58–60, 1979.

310. RAUSCHECKER, J. P., AND W. SINGER. The effects of early visual experience on the cat's visual cortex and their possible explanation by Hebb synapses. *J. Physiol. London* 310: 215–239, 1981.

311. RAVIOLA, E., AND T. N. WIESEL. Effects of dark-rearing on experimental myopia in monkeys. *Invest. Ophthalmol. Vis. Sci.* 17: 485–489, 1978.

312. REGAL, D. M., R. BOOTHE, D. Y. TELLER, AND G. B. SACKETT. Visual acuity and visual responsiveness in dark-reared monkeys (*Macaca nemestrina*). *Vision Res.* 16: 523–530, 1976.

313. REGAN, D. Assessment of visual acuity by evoked potential recording: ambiguity caused by temporal dependence of spatial frequency selectivity. *Vision Res.* 18: 439–443, 1978.

314. REGAN, D., K. I. BEVERLEY, AND M. CYNADER. Stereoscopic subsystems for position in depth and for motion in depth. *Proc. R. Soc. London Ser. B* 204: 485–501, 1979.

315. RIESEN, A. H., K. L. CHOW, J. SEMMES, AND H. NISSEN. Chimpanzee vision after four conditions of light deprivation. *Am. Psychol.* 6: 282, 1951.

316. RIESEN, A. H., R. RAMSEY, AND P. D. WILSON. Development of visual acuity in rhesus monkeys deprived of patterned light during early infancy. *Psychon. Sci.* 1: 33–34, 1964.

317. RODIECK, R. W. Visual pathways. *Ann. Rev. Neurosci.* 2: 193–225, 1979.

318. ROSE, D., AND C. BLAKEMORE. An analysis of orientation selectivity in the cat's visual cortex. *Exp. Brain Res.* 20: 1–17, 1974.

319. RUSOFF, A. C. Development of ganglion cells in the retina of the cat. In: *Developmental Neurobiology of Vision*, edited by R. D. Freeman. New York: Plenum, 1979, p. 19–30.

320. RUSOFF, A. C., AND M. W. DUBIN. Development of receptive-field properties of retinal ganglion cells in kittens. *J. Neurophysiol.* 40: 1188–1198, 1977.

321. SAMORAJSKI, T., J. R. KEEFE, AND J. M. ORDY. Morphogenesis of photoreceptor and retinal ultrastructure in a sub-human primate. *Vision Res.* 5: 639–648, 1965.

322. SHAPLEY, R. M., AND Y. T. SO. Is there an effect of monocular deprivation on the proportion of X and Y cells in the cat lateral geniculate nucleus? *Exp. Brain Res.* 39: 41–48, 1980.

323. SHATZ, C. J., AND M. P. STRYKER. Ocular dominance in layer IV of the cat's visual cortex and the effects of monocular deprivation. *J. Physiol. London* 281: 267–283, 1978.

324. SHEA, S. L., R. FOX, R. N. ASLIN, AND S. T. DUMAIS. Assessment of stereopsis in human infants. *Invest. Ophthalmol. Vis. Sci.* 19: 1400–1404, 1980.

325. SHERK, H., AND M. P. STRYKER. Quantitative study of cortical orientation selectivity in visually inexperienced kitten. *J. Neurophysiol.* 39: 63–70, 1976.

326. SHERMAN, S. M. Visual field defects in monocularly and binocularly deprived cats. *Brain Res.* 49: 25–45, 1973.

327. SHERMAN, S. M., R. W. GUILLERY, J. H. KAAS, AND K. J. SANDERSON. Behavioral, electrophysiological and morphological studies of binocular competition in the development of the geniculo-cortical pathways of cats. *J. Comp. Neurol.* 158: 1–18, 1974.

328. SHERMAN, S. M., K. P. HOFFMAN, AND J. STONE. Loss of specific cell type from dorsal lateral geniculate nucleus in visually deprived cats. *J. Neurophysiol.* 35: 532–541, 1972.

329. SHERMAN, S. M., T. T. NORTON, AND V. A. CASAGRANDE. Myopia in the lid-sutured tree shrew (*Tupaia glis*). *Brain Res.* 124: 154–157, 1977.

330. SHERMAN, S. M., AND J. STONE. Physiological normality of the retina in visually deprived cats. *Brain Res.* 60: 224–230, 1973.

331. SHINKMAN, P. G., AND C. J. BRUCE. Binocular differences in cortical receptive fields of kittens after rotationally disparate binocular experience. *Science* 197: 285–287, 1977.

332. SILLITO, A. M., J. A. KEMP, AND C. BLAKEMORE. The role of GABAergic inhibition in the cortical effects of monocular deprivation. *Nature London* 291: 318–320, 1981.

333. SILLITO, A. M., J. A. KEMP, AND H. PATEL. Inhibitor interactions contributing to the ocular dominance of monocularly dominated cells in the normal cat striate cortex. *Exp. Brain Res.* 41: 1–10, 1980.

334. SINGER, W. Effects of monocular deprivation on excitatory and inhibitory pathways in cat striate cortex. *Exp. Brain Res.* 30: 25–41, 1977.

335. SINGER, W., B. FREEMAN, AND J. RAUSCHECKER. Development and organization of orientation columns in cat visual cortex. *Exp. Brain Res.* 41: A 15, 1981.

335a. SINGER, W., AND J. P. RAUSCHECKER. Central core control of developmental plasticity in the kitten visual cortex. II. Electrical activation of mesencephalic and diencephalic projections. *Exp. Brain Res.* 47: 223–233, 1982.

336. SINGER, W., AND F. TRETTER. Receptive-field properties and neuronal connectivity in striate and parastriate cortex of contour-deprived cats. *J. Neurophysiol.* 39: 613–630, 1976.

337. SINGER, W., AND F. TRETTER. Unusually large receptive fields in cats with restricted visual experience. *Exp. Brain Res.* 26: 171–184, 1976.

338. SIRETEANU, R., AND K. P. HOFFMAN. Relative frequency and visual resolution of X- and Y-cells in the LGN of normal and monocularly deprived cats: interlaminar differences. *Exp. Brain Res.* 34: 591–603, 1979.

339. SLUCKIN, W. *Early Learning in Man and Animals* (2nd ed.). London: Allen & Unwin, 1972.

340. SMITH, D. C. Developmental alterations in binocular competitive interactions and visual acuity in visually deprived cats. *J. Comp. Neurol.* 198: 667–676, 1981.

341. SMITH, D. C. Functional restoration of vision in the cat after long-term visual deprivation. *Science* 213: 1137–1139, 1981.

342. SMITH, D. C., R. LORBER, L. R. STANFORD, AND M. S. LOOP. Visual acuity following binocular deprivation in the cat. *Brain Res.* 183: 1–11, 1980.

343. SMITH, D. C., P. D. SPEAR, AND K. E. KRATZ. Role of visual experience in postcritical-period reversal of effects of monocular deprivation in cat striate cortex. *J. Comp. Neurol.* 178: 313–328, 1978.

344. SMITH, E. L., M. J. BENNET, R. S. HARWERTH, AND M. L. J. CRAWFORD. Binocularity in kittens reared with optically-induced squint. *Science* 204: 875–877, 1979.

345. SMITH, E. L., G. W. MAGUIRE, AND R. S. HARWERTH. Some effects of anisometropia on the kitten's visual system. *Invest. Ophthalmol. Vis. Sci. Suppl.* 19: 209–210, 1980.

346. SMITH, E. L. III, G. W. MAGUIRE, AND J. T. WATSON. Axial lengths and refractive errors in kittens reared with an optically-induced anisometropia. *Invest. Opthalmol Vis. Sci.* 19: 1250–1255, 1980.

347. SOKOL, S. Measurement of infant visual acuity from pattern reversal evoked potentials. *Vision Res.* 18: 33–39, 1978.

348. SORSBY, A., B. BENJAMIN, M. SHERIDAN, J. STONE, AND G. A. LEARY. Refraction and its components during the growth of the eye from the age of three. *Med. Res. Coun. G. B. Spec. Rep. Ser. 301.* London: HMSO, 1961.

349. SPEAR, P. D., L. TONG, AND A. LANGSETMO. Striate cortex

neurons of binocularly deprived kittens respond to visual stimuli through the closed eyelids. *Brain Res.* 155: 141–146, 1978.

350. SPEKREIJSE, H. Maturation of contrast EPs and development of visual resolution. *Arch. Ital. Biol.* 116: 358–369, 1978.

351. SPINELLI, D. N. Neural correlates of visual experience in single units of cat's visual and somatosensory cortex. In: *Frontiers of Visual Science*, edited by S. J. Cool and E. L. Smith III. New York: Springer-Verlag, 1978, p. 674–688.

352. SPINELLI, D. N., H. V. B. HIRSCH, J. PHELPS, AND J. METZLER. Visual experience as a determinant of the response characteristics of cortical receptive fields in cats. *Exp. Brain Res.* 15: 289–304, 1972.

353. STIRNIMANN, F. Ueber das farbenempfinden neugeborener. *Annal. Paediatr.* 163: 1–44, 1944.

354. STONE, J., B. DREHER, AND A. LEVENTHAL. Hierarchical and parallel mechanisms in the organization of the visual cortex. *Brain Res.* 1: 345–394, 1979.

355. STONE, J., D. H. RAPAPORT, R. W. WILLIAMS, AND L. CHALUPA. Uniformity of cell distribution in the ganglion cell layer of prenatal cat retina: implications for mechanisms of retinal development. *Dev. Brain Res.* 2: 231–242, 1982.

356. STRYKER, M. P. Late segregation of geniculate afferents to the cat's visual cortex after recovery from binocular impulse blockade. *Soc. Neurosci. Abstr.* 7: 842, 1981.

357. STRYKER, M. P., AND H. SHERK. Modification of cortical orientation selectivity in the cat by restricted visual experience: a reexamination. *Science* 190: 904–906, 1975.

358. STRYKER, M. P., H. SHERK, A. G. LEVENTHAL, AND H. V. B. HIRSCH. Physiological consequences for the cat's visual cortex of effectively restricting early visual experience with oriented contours. *J. Neurophysiol.* 41: 896–909, 1978.

359. SWINDALE, N. V. Absence of ocular dominance patches in dark-reared cats. *Nature London* 290: 332–333, 1981.

360. SWINDALE, N. V., F. VITAL-DURAND, AND C. BLAKEMORE. Recovery from monocular deprivation in the monkey. III. Reversal of anatomical effects in the visual cortex. *Proc. R. Soc. London Ser. B* 213: 435–450, 1981.

361. TEES, R. C. Perceptual development in mammals. In: *Neural and Behavioral Specificity*, edited by G. Gottlieb. New York: Academic, 1976, p. 281–326.

362. TELLER, D. Y. The forced choice preferential looking procedure: a psychophysical technique for use with human infants. *Infant Behav. Dev.* 2: 135–153, 1979.

363. TELLER, D. Y. Color vision in infants. In: *Development of Perception. Psychobiological Perspectives. The Visual System*, edited by R. N. Aslin, J. R. Alberts, and M. R. Petersen. New York: Academic, 1981, vol. 2, p. 297–311.

364. TELLER, D. Y., J. L. ALLEN, D. M. REGAL, AND D. L. MAYER. Astigmatism and acuity in two primate infants. *Invest. Ophthalmol. Vis. Sci.* 17: 344–349, 1978.

365. TELLER, D. Y., R. MORSE, R. BORTON, AND D. REGAL. Visual acuity for vertical and diagonal gratings in human infants. *Vision Res.* 14: 1433–1439, 1974.

366. TELLER, D. Y., D. R. PEEPLES, AND M. SEKEL. Discrimination of chromatic from white light by 2-month-old human infants. *Vision Res.* 18: 41–48, 1978.

367. TELLER, D. Y., D. M. REGAL, T. O. VIDEEN, AND E. PULOS. Development of visual acuity in infant monkeys (*Macaca nemestrina*) during the early postnatal weeks. *Vision Res.* 18: 561–566, 1978.

368. THIBOS, L. N., AND W. R. LEVICK. Astigmatic visual deprivation in cat: behavioral, optical and retinophysiological consequences. *Vision Res.* 22: 43–53, 1982.

369. THORN, F., M. GOLLENDER, AND P. ERICKSON. The development of the kitten's visual optics. *Vision Res.* 16: 1145–1149, 1976.

370. TIEMAN, D. G., M. A. McCALL, AND H. V. B. HIRSCH. Physiological effect of unequal alternating monocular deprivation. *Soc. Neurosci. Abstr.* 5: 810, 1979.

371. TIMNEY, B. The development of binocular depth perception in kittens. *Invest. Ophthalmol. Vis. Sci.* 21: 493–496, 1981.

372. TIMNEY, B., AND D. E. MITCHELL. Behavioural recovery from visual deprivation: comments on the critical period. In: *Developmental Neurobiology of Vision*, edited by R. D. Freeman. New York: Plenum, 1979, p. 149–160.

373. TIMNEY, B., D. E. MITCHELL, AND M. CYNADER. Behavioral evidence for prolonged sensitivity to effects of monocular deprivation in dark-reared cats. *J. Neurophysiol.* 43: 1041–1054, 1980.

374. TIMNEY, B., D. E. MITCHELL, AND F. GIFFIN. The development of vision in cats after extended periods of dark-rearing. *Exp. Brain Res.* 31: 547–560, 1978.

375. TIMNEY, B., AND C. K. PECK. Visual acuity in cats following surgically induced cyclotropia. *Behav. Brain Res.* 3: 289–302, 1981.

376. TRETTER, F., M. CYNADER, AND W. SINGER. Modification of direction selectivity of neurons in the visual cortex of kittens. *Brain Res.* 84: 143–149, 1975.

377. TSUMOTO, T., AND R. D. FREEMAN. Ocular dominance in kitten cortex: induced changes of single cells while they are recorded. *Exp. Brain Res.* 44: 347–351, 1981.

378. TUCKER, G. S. Light microscopic analysis of the kitten retina: postnatal development in the area centralis. *J. Comp. Neurol.* 180: 489–500, 1978.

379. TUMOSA, N., S. B. TIEMAN, AND H. V. B. HIRSCH. Anatomical effect of unequal alternate monocular deprivation. *Invest. Ophthalmol. Vis. Sci. Suppl.* 19: 59, 1980.

380. TUMOSA, N., S. B. TIEMAN, AND H. V. B. HIRSCH. Unequal alternating monocular deprivation causes asymmetric visual fields in cats. *Science* 208: 421–423, 1980.

381. VAEGAN AND D. TAYLOR. Critical period for deprivation amblyopia in children. *Trans. Ophthalmol. Soc. UK* 99: 432–439, 1980.

382. VALVO, A. Behavior patterns and visual rehabilitation after early and long-lasting blindness. *Am. J. Ophthalmol.* 65: 19–24, 1968.

383. VAN HOF-VAN DUIN, J. Development of visuomotor behavior in normal and dark-reared cats. *Brain Res.* 104: 233–241, 1976.

384. VAN HOF-VAN DUIN, J. Early and permanent effects of monocular pattern discrimination and visuomotor behavior in cats. *Brain Res.* 111: 261–276, 1976.

385. VAN SLUYTERS, R. C. Reversal of the physiological effects of brief periods of monocular deprivation in the kitten. *J. Physiol. London* 284: 1–17, 1978.

386. VAN SLUYTERS, R. C., AND C. BLAKEMORE. Experimental creation of unusual properties in visual cortex of kittens. *Nature London* 246: 506–508, 1973.

387. VAN SLUYTERS, R. C., AND F. LEVITT. Experimental strabismus in the kitten. *J. Neurophysiol.* 43: 686–699, 1980.

388. VAN SLUYTERS, R. C., AND D. L. STEWART. Binocular neurons of the rabbit's visual cortex: effects of monocular sensory deprivation. *Exp. Brain Res.* 19: 196–204, 1974.

389. VITAL-DURAND, F., L. J. GAREY, AND C. BLAKEMORE. Monocular and binocular deprivation in the monkey: morphological effects and reversibility. *Brain Res.* 158: 45–64, 1978.

390. VON GRUNAU, M. W., AND W. SINGER. Functional amblyopia in kittens with unilateral exotropia. II. Correspondence between behavioral and electrophysiological assessment. *Exp. Brain Res.* 40: 305–310, 1980.

391. VON HELMHOLTZ, H. *Treatise on Physiological Optics Vol. III*, (transl. of the 3rd German ed.), edited by J. P. C. Southall. New York: Opt. Soc. Am., 1925.

392. VON NOORDEN, G. K. Classification of amblyopia. *Am. J. Ophthalmol.* 63: 238–244, 1967.

393. VON NOORDEN, G. K. Experimental amblyopia in monkeys. Further behavioral observations and clinical correlations. *Invest. Ophthalmol. Vis. Sci.* 12: 721–726, 1973.

394. VON NOORDEN, G. K. New clinical aspects of stimulus deprivation amblyopia. *Am. J. Ophthalmol.* 92: 416–421, 1981.

395. VON NOORDEN, G. K., AND M. L. J. CRAWFORD. Form deprivation without light deprivation produces the visual deprivation syndrome in *Macaca mulatta*. *Brain Res.* 129: 37–44,

1977.

396. VON NOORDEN, G. K., AND M. L. J. CRAWFORD. Lid closure and refractive error in macaque monkeys. *Nature London* 272: 53-54, 1978.

397. VON NOORDEN, G. K., AND M. L. J. CRAWFORD. Morphological and physiological changes in the monkey visual system after short-term lid suture. *Invest. Ophthalmol. Vis. Sci.* 17: 762-768, 1978.

398. VON NOORDEN, G. K., AND M. L. J. CRAWFORD. The sensitive period. *Trans. Ophthalmol. Soc. UK* 99: 442-446, 1979.

399. VON NOORDEN, G. K., AND M. L. J. CRAWFORD. The effects of total unilateral occlusion vs. lid suture on the visual system of infant monkeys. *Invest. Ophthalmol. Vis. Sci.* 20: 142-146, 1981.

400. VON NOORDEN, G. K., AND M. L. J. CRAWFORD. Failure to preserve cortical binocularity in strabismic monkeys raised in a unidirectional visual environment. *Invest. Ophthalmol. Vis. Sci.* 20: 665-670, 1981.

401. VON NOORDEN, G. K., M. L. J. CRAWFORD, AND P. R. MIDDLEDITCH. The effects of monocular visual deprivation: disuse or binocular interaction. *Brain Res.* 111: 277-285, 1976.

402. VON NOORDEN, G. K., AND J. E. DOWLING. Experimental amblyopia in monkeys. II. Behavioral studies in strabismic amblyopia. *Arch. Ophthalmol.* 84: 215-220, 1970.

403. VON NOORDEN, G. K., J. E. DOWLING, AND D. C. FERGUSON. Experimental amblyopia in monkeys. I. Behavioral studies of stimulus deprivation amblyopia. *Arch. Ophthalmol.* 84: 206-214, 1970.

404. VON NOORDEN, G. K., AND P. R. MIDDLEDITCH. Histology of the monkey lateral geniculate nucleus after unilateral lid closure and experimental strabismus: further observations. *Invest. Ophthalmol. Vis. Sci.* 14: 674-683, 1975.

405. VON SENDEN, M. *Space and Sight* (transl. by P. Heath). London: Methuen, 1960.

406. WALK, R. D. The development of depth perception in animals and human infants. *Monogr. Soc. Res. Child Dev.* 31: 82-108, 1966.

407. WALK, R. D., AND E. J. GIBSON. A comparative and analytical study of visual depth perception. *Psychol. Monogr. Gen. Appl.* 75: 1-44, 1961.

408. WALLS, G. L. The problem of visual direction. I. The history to 1900. *Am. J. Optom. Physiol. Opt.* 28: 55-83, 1951.

409. WATKINS, D. W., J. R. WILSON, AND S. M. SHERMAN. Receptive-field properties of neurons in binocular and monocular segments of striate cortex in cats raised with binocular lid suture. *J. Neurophysiol.* 41: 322-337, 1978.

410. WERNER, J. S., AND B. R. WOOTEN. Human infant color vision and color perception. *Infant Behav. Dev.* 2: 241-274, 1979.

411. WESTHEIMER, G. Visual acuity and hyperacuity. *Invest. Ophthalmol. Vis. Sci.* 14: 570-572, 1975.

412. WESTHEIMER, G. The spatial sense of the eye. *Invest. Ophthalmol. Vis. Sci.* 18: 813-912, 1979.

413. WESTHEIMER, G., AND S. P. MCKEE. Integration regions for visual hyperacuity. *Vision Res.* 17· 89-93, 1977.

414. WHEATSTONE, C. Contributions to the physiology of vision. I. On some remarkable and hitherto unobserved phenomena of binocular vision. *Philos. Trans. R. Soc. London* 1838, p. 371-394.

415. WIESEL, T. N., AND D. H. HUBEL. Effects of visual deprivation on morphology and physiology of cells in the cat's lateral geniculate body. *J. Neurophysiol.* 26: 978-993, 1963.

416. WIESEL, T. N., AND D. H. HUBEL. Single-cell responses in striate cortex of kittens deprived of vision in one eye. *J. Neurophysiol.* 26: 1003-1017, 1963.

417. WIESEL, T. N., AND D. H. HUBEL. Comparison of the effects of unilateral and bilateral eye closure on cortical unit responses in kittens. *J. Neurophysiol.* 28: 1029-1040, 1965.

418. WIESEL, T. N., AND D. H. HUBEL. Extent of recovery from the effects of visual deprivation in the kitten. *J. Neurophysiol.* 28: 1060-1072, 1965.

419. WIESEL, T. N., AND D. H. HUBEL. Ordered arrangement of orientation columns in monkeys lacking visual experience. *J. Comp. Neurol.* 158: 307-318, 1974.

420. WIESEL, T. N., AND E. RAVIOLA. Myopia and eye enlargement after neonatal lid fusion in monkeys. *Nature London* 266: 66-68, 1977.

421. WIESEL, T. N., AND E. RAVIOLA. Increase in axial length of the macaque monkey eye after corneal opacification. *Invest. Ophthalmol. Vis. Sci.* 18: 1232-1236, 1979.

422. WILKINSON, F. E. Reversal of the behavioral effects of monocular deprivation as a function of age in the kitten. *Behav. Brain Res.* 1: 101-123, 1980.

423. WILKINSON, F. E., AND P. C. DODWELL. Young kittens can learn complex pattern discriminations. *Nature London* 284: 258-259, 1980.

424. WILLIAMS, R. A., AND R. G. BOOTHE. Development of optical quality in the infant monkey (*Macaca nemestrina*) eye. *Invest. Ophthalmol. Vis. Sci.* 20: 728-736, 1981.

425. WILSON, J. R., AND S. M. SHERMAN. Differential effects of early monocular deprivation on binocular and monocular segments of cat striate cortex. *J. Neurophysiol.* 40: 891-903, 1977.

426. WILSON, J. R., S. V. WEBB, AND S. M. SHERMAN. Conditions for dominance of one eye during competitive development of central connections in visually deprived cats. *Brain Res.* 136: 277-287, 1977.

427. WILSON, P. D., AND A. H. RIESEN. Visual development in rhesus monkeys neonatally deprived of patterned light. *J. Comp. Physiol. Psychol.* 61: 87-95, 1966.

428. WINFIELD, D. A. The postnatal development of synapses in the visual cortex of the cat and the effects of eyelid closure. *Brain Res.* 206: 166-171, 1981.

429. YINON, U. Age dependence of the effect of squint on cells in kitten's visual cortex. *Exp. Brain Res.* 26: 151-157, 1976.

INDEX

Index

PART 1: pages 1–556; PART 2: pages 557–1190